# INSTRUCTOR'S SOLUTIONS MANUAL

DAVID ATWOOD
*Rochester Community and Technical College*

TERRY KRIEGER
*Rochester Community and Technical College*

*with*

THOMAS KRIEGER

# COLLEGE ALGEBRA WITH MODELING AND VISUALIZATION

## FOURTH EDITION

Gary Rockswold
*Minnesota State University, Mankato*

Addison-Wesley
is an imprint of

Reproduced by Pearson Addison-Wesley from electronic files supplied by the author.


Publishing as Pearson Addison-Wesley, 75 Arlington Street, Boston, MA 02116.



ISBN-13: 978-0-321-57697-2
ISBN-10: 0-321-57697-7

1 2 3 4 5 6 CRS 12 11 10 09 08

**Addison-Wesley**
is an imprint of

www.pearsonhighered.com

# Preface

This is a comprehensive manual written for both instructors and teaching assistants. It contains all solutions to the exercises in the text *College Algebra with Modeling and Visualization 4/e* by Gary Rockswold. It also includes solutions for Checking Basic Concepts exercises as well as Extended and Discovery exercises.

In addition to providing solutions to exercises, it is the author's intent that this quality manual serve many roles. First, this manual can save time for instruction. It contains comprehensive solutions written in a clear format with hundreds of graphs and tables. It frequently includes not only symbolic solutions but also graphical and numerical solutions, thereby freeing the instructor from generating solutions, graphs and tables. Secondly, this manual can be helpful when selecting assignments for students. By merely browsing the solutions, an instructor can observe both the variety of exercises and the large number of application exercises available. The exercises have varying levels of difficulty. Instructors can quickly select both appropriate and meaningful exercises for their students. Thirdly, this manual provides direction and guidance for explaining solutions to students in the classroom. Many of the applications included are real-data exercises that are unique to this text. This manual is consistent with the text and gives solutions that are accessible to most college algebra students.

It is the authors' hope that you will find this manual helpful when teaching from the text *College Algebra with Modeling and Visualization 4/e*. Please feel free to send comments to either of the email addresses below. Your opinion is important. Best wishes for an enjoyable and successful college algebra course.

Terry Krieger

terry.krieger@roch.edu

David Atwood

david.atwood@roch.edu

# Table of Contents

# Chapter 1: Introduction to Functions and Graphs

## 1.1: Numbers, Data, and Problem Solving

1. $\frac{21}{24}$ is a real and rational number.

2. 20,082 is a real number, rational number, integer, and natural number.

3. 7.5 is a real and rational number.

4. 25.8 is a real and rational number.

5. $90\sqrt{2}$ is a real number.

6. $-71$ is an integer, real number, and rational number.

7. Natural number: $\sqrt{9} = 3$; integers: $-3$, $\sqrt{9}$; rational numbers: $-3, \frac{2}{9}, \sqrt{9}, 1.\overline{3}$; irrational numbers: $\pi, -\sqrt{2}$

8. Natural numbers: $\frac{3}{1} = 3$, $5.6 \times 10^3 = 5600$; integers: $\frac{3}{1}, 0, 5.6 \times 10^3$;

   rational numbers: $\frac{3}{1}, -\frac{5}{8}, 0.\overline{45}, 0, 5.6 \times 10^3$; irrational number: $\sqrt{7}$

9. Natural number: None; integer: $-\sqrt{4} = -2$; rational numbers: $\frac{1}{3}, 5.1 \times 10^{-6}, -2.33, 0.\overline{7}, -\sqrt{4}$;

   irrational number: $\sqrt{13}$

10. Natural numbers: $\sqrt{100} = 10$; integers:

    $-103, \sqrt{100}$; rational numbers: $-103, \frac{21}{25}, \sqrt{100}, -\frac{5.7}{10}, \frac{2}{9}, -1.457$;

    irrational number: $\sqrt{3}$

11. Shoe sizes are normally measured to within half sizes. Rational numbers are most appropriate.

12. Population is measured using natural numbers.

13. Gasoline is usually measured to a fraction of a gallon using rational numbers.

14. Speed limit is measured using natural numbers.

15. Temperature is typically measured to the nearest degree in a weather forecast. Since temperature can include negative numbers, the integers would be most appropriate.

16. Compact disc sales could be measured in natural numbers, since fractions of a disc are not allowed.

17. $|5 - 8 \cdot 7| = |5 - 56| = |-51| = 51$

18. $-2(16 - 3 \cdot 5) \div 2 = -2(16 - 15) \div 2 = -2(1) \div 2 = -2 \div 2 = -1$

19. $-6^2 - 3(2 - 4)^4 = -6^2 - 3(-2)^4 = -36 - 3(16) = -36 - 48 = -84$

20. $(4 - 5)^2 - 3^2 - 3\sqrt{9} = (-1)^2 - 9 - 3(3) = 1 - 9 - 9 = -17$

21. $\sqrt{9 - 5} - \frac{8 - 4}{4 - 2} = \sqrt{4} - \frac{4}{2} = 2 - 2 = 0$

22. $\frac{6 - 4^2 \div 2^3}{3 - 4} = \frac{6 - 16 \div 8}{-1} = \frac{6 - 2}{-1} = -4$

23. $\sqrt{13^2 - 12^2} = \sqrt{169 - 144} = \sqrt{25} = 5$

24. $\dfrac{13 - \sqrt{9 + 16}}{|5 - 7|^2} = \dfrac{13 - \sqrt{25}}{|-2|^2} = \dfrac{13 - 5}{4} = \dfrac{8}{4} = 2$

25. $\dfrac{4 + 9}{2 + 3} - \dfrac{-3^2 \cdot 3}{5} = \dfrac{13}{5} - \dfrac{-27}{5} = \dfrac{40}{5} = 8$

26. $10 \div 2 \div \dfrac{5 + 10}{5} = 10 \div 2 \div \dfrac{15}{5} = 10 \div 2 \div 3 = 5 \div 3 = \dfrac{5}{3}$

27. $-5^2 - 20 \div 4 - 2 = -25 - 5 - 2 = -32$

28. $5 - (-4)^3 - 4^3 = 5 - (-64) - 64 = 5 + 64 - 64 = 5$

29. $184{,}800 = 1.848 \times 10^5$

30. $29{,}285{,}000 = 2.9285 \times 10^7$

31. $0.04361 = 4.361 \times 10^{-2}$

32. $0.62 = 6.2 \times 10^{-1}$

33. $2450 = 2.45 \times 10^3$

34. $105.6 = 1.056 \times 10^2$

35. $0.56 = 5.6 \times 10^{-1}$

36. $-0.00456 = -4.56 \times 10^{-3}$

37. $-0.0087 = -8.7 \times 10^{-3}$

38. $1{,}250{,}000 = 1.25 \times 10^6$

39. $206.8 = 2.068 \times 10^2$

40. $0.00007 = 7 \times 10^{-5}$

41. $10^{-6} = 0.000001$

42. $9.11 \times 10^{-31} = 0.000000000000000000000000000000911$

There are 30 zeros between the decimal point and the digits 911.

43. $2 \times 10^8 = 200{,}000{,}000$

44. $9 \times 10^{12} = 9{,}000{,}000{,}000{,}000$

45. $1.567 \times 10^2 = 156.7$

46. $-5.68 \times 10^{-1} = -0.568$

47. $5 \times 10^5 = 500{,}000$

48. $3.5 \times 10^3 = 3500$

49. $0.045 \times 10^5 = 4500$

50. $-5.4 \times 10^{-5} = -0.000054$

51. $67 \times 10^3 = 67{,}000$

52. $0.0032 \times 10^{-1} = 0.00032$

53. $(4 \times 10^3)(2 \times 10^5) = 4 \cdot 2 \times 10^{3+5} = 8 \times 10^8$; 800,000,000

54. $(3 \times 10^1)(3 \times 10^4) = 3 \cdot 3 \times 10^{1+4} = 9 \times 10^5$; 900,000

55. $(5 \times 10^2)(7 \times 10^{-4}) = 5 \cdot 7 \times 10^{2-4} = 35 \times 10^{-2} = 3.5 \times 10^{-1}$; 0.35

56. $(8 \times 10^{-3})(7 \times 10^{1}) = 8 \cdot 7 \times 10^{-3+1} = 56 \times 10^{-2} = 5.6 \times 10^{-1}$; 0.56

57. $\dfrac{6.3 \times 10^{-2}}{3 \times 10^{1}} = \dfrac{6.3}{3} \times 10^{-2-1} = 2.1 \times 10^{-3}$; 0.0021

58. $\dfrac{8.2 \times 10^{2}}{2 \times 10^{-2}} = \dfrac{8.2}{2} \times 10^{2-(-2)} = 4.1 \times 10^{4}$; 41,000

59. $\dfrac{4 \times 10^{-3}}{8 \times 10^{-1}} = \dfrac{4}{8} \times 10^{-3-(-1)} = 0.5 \times 10^{-2} = 5 \times 10^{-3}$; 0.005

60. $\dfrac{2.4 \times 10^{-5}}{4.8 \times 10^{-7}} = \dfrac{2.4}{4.8} \times 10^{-5-(-7)} = 0.5 \times 10^{2} = 5 \times 10^{1}$; 50

61. $\dfrac{8.947 \times 10^{7}}{0.00095}(4.5 \times 10^{8}) \approx 42381 \times 10^{15} = 4.2381 \times 10^{19} \approx 4.24 \times 10^{19}$

62. $(9.87 \times 10^{6})(34 \times 10^{11}) = 335.58 \times 10^{17} = 3.3558 \times 10^{19} \approx 3.36 \times 10^{19}$

63. $\left(\dfrac{101 + 23}{0.42}\right)^{2} + \sqrt{3.4 \times 10^{-2}} \approx 87166 + 0.2 \approx 87166.2 \approx 8.72 \times 10^{4}$

64. $\sqrt[3]{(2.5 \times 10^{-8})} + 10^{-7} \approx 0.005 = 5.0 \times 10^{-3}$

65. $(8.5 \times 10^{-5})(-9.5 \times 10^{7})^{2} = (8.5 \times 10^{-5})(9.025 \times 10^{15}) \approx 76.7 \times 10^{10} = 7.67 \times 10^{11}$

66. $\sqrt{\pi(4.56 \times 10^{4}) + (3.1 \times 10^{-2})} \approx 378.5 \approx 3.78 \times 10^{2}$

67. $\sqrt[3]{192} \approx 5.769$

68. $\sqrt{(32 + \pi^{3})} \approx 7.938$

69. $|\pi - 3.2| \approx 0.058$

70. $\dfrac{1.72 - 5.98}{35.6 + 1.02} \approx -0.116$

71. $\dfrac{0.3 + 1.5}{5.5 - 1.2} \approx 0.419$

72. $3.2(1.1)^{2} - 4(1.1) + 2 = 1.472$

73. $\dfrac{1.5^{3}}{\sqrt{2 + \pi} - 5} \approx \dfrac{3.375}{-2.732} \approx -1.235$

74. $4.3^{2} - \dfrac{5}{17} \approx 18.49 - 0.294 = 18.196$

75. $15 + \dfrac{4 + \sqrt{3}}{7} \approx 15.819$

76. $\dfrac{5 + \sqrt{5}}{2} \approx 3.618$

77. $\dfrac{13 - 8}{8} \times 100 = \dfrac{5}{8} \times 100 = 62.5$; 62.5%

78. $\dfrac{13.47 - 0.90}{0.9} \times 100 = \dfrac{12.57}{0.9} \times 100 \approx 1396.7$; 1396.7%

79. $\dfrac{0.85 - 1.4}{1.4} \times 100 = \dfrac{-0.55}{1.4} \times 100 \approx -39.3$; −39.3%

80. $\dfrac{1195 - 1256}{1250} \times 100 = \dfrac{-61}{1256} \times 100 \approx -4.9$; −4.9%

81. $\frac{B - 100}{100} \times 100 = 6 \Rightarrow B - 100 = 6 \Rightarrow B = \$106;$

$\frac{B - 106}{106} \times 100 = -6 \Rightarrow (B - 106)\left(\frac{50}{53}\right) = -6 \Rightarrow B - 106 = -6.36 \Rightarrow B = \$99.64$

82. $\frac{5132 - 433}{433} \times 100 \approx 1085.2$; From 1976 to 2004 tuition and fees increased by 1085.2%.

83. $0.14 = 1.4 \times 10^{-1}$ watt

84. The movement of the Pacific plate in one year is $7.1 \times 10^{-5}$ kilometers per year. In one million years, the Pacific plate will move $(7.1 \times 10^{-5}) \cdot (1 \times 10^{6}) = 7.1 \times 10^{1} = 71$ km.

85. The distance Mars travels around the sun is $2\pi r = 2\pi(141{,}000{,}000) \approx 885{,}929{,}128$ miles. The number of hours in 1.88 years is $365 \times 1.88 \times 24 \approx 16{,}469$ hours. So Mars' speed is $\frac{885{,}929{,}128}{16{,}469} \approx 53{,}794$ miles per hour.

86. In one year light travels $186{,}000 \times 60 \times 60 \times 24 \times 365 \approx 5.87 \times 10^{12}$ miles. It takes $\frac{6 \times 10^{17}}{5.87 \times 10^{12}} \approx 102{,}000$ years for light to cross the Milky Way.

87. (a) $\frac{3.7 \times 10^{11}}{2.03 \times 10^{8}} \approx \$1{,}820$ per person

(b) $\frac{5.54 \times 10^{12}}{2.81 \times 10^{8}} \approx \$19{,}715$ per person

88. One cubic mile is equal to $5280 \times 5280 \times 5280 \approx 1.47 \times 10^{11}$ cubic feet. In one day, the Amazon River discharges $(4.2 \times 10^{6}) \times 60 \times 60 \times 24 \approx 3.6 \times 10^{11}$ cubic feet, which is approximately 2.5 cubic miles.

89. The area of the film is $\pi r^2$ or $\pi(11.5)^2 \approx 415.5\text{ cm}^2$ and the volume of the drop is $0.12\text{ cm}^3$. The thickness of the film is equal to the volume divided by the area. $\frac{0.12}{415.5} \approx 2.9 \times 10^{-4}$ cm.

90. Since one cubic centimeter of gold has a mass of 19.3 grams, the gold foil must have a volume of $\frac{23.16}{19.3} = 1.2\text{ cm}^3$. The sheet has an area of $20 \times 30 = 600\text{ cm}^2$. Using this hint, the thickness is $\frac{1.2}{600} = 0.002$ cm.

91. (a) It would take $\frac{5.54 \times 10^{12}}{100} \approx 5.54 \times 10^{10}$ or 55.4 billion \$100-dollar bills to equal the federal debt. The height of the stacked bills would be $\frac{5.54 \times 10^{10}}{250} \approx 2.216 \times 10^{8}$ inches or $\frac{2.216 \times 10^{8}}{12} \approx 18{,}466{,}667$ feet.

(b) There are 5280 feet in one mile, so the stacked bills would span $\frac{18{,}466{,}667}{5280} \approx 3497$ miles. It would reach farther than the distance between Los Angles and New York.

92. $V = \frac{1}{3}\pi r^2 h \Rightarrow V = \frac{1}{3}\pi(4)^2(12) \Rightarrow V = \frac{1}{3}(\pi)(16)(12) \Rightarrow V = 201.06\text{ in}^3$

93. (a) $V = \pi r^2 h \Rightarrow V = \pi(1.3)^2(4.4) \Rightarrow V = 7.436\pi \approx 23.4\text{ in}^3$

(b) $1\text{ in}^3 = 0.55$ fluid ounce $\Rightarrow 23.4 \cdot 0.55 = 12.87$ fluid ounces; Yes, it can hold 12 fluid ounces.

94. $V = \frac{4}{3}\pi r^3 = \frac{4}{3}\pi(3)^3 = 36\pi\text{ ft}^3 \approx 113.1\text{ ft}^3$

95. $V = l \cdot w \cdot h \Rightarrow 125 = (100)(5)h \Rightarrow h = 0.25$ ft or 3 in.

96. Volume of the lake $=$ (area $\times$ depth) $\Rightarrow 7.5 \times 10^8 = (2.5 \times 10^7)$(depth) $\Rightarrow$ depth $= 3 \times 10^1 = 30$ ft.

## 1.2: Visualizing and Graphing Data

1. (a) −6 −4 −2 0 2 4 6 8

   (b) Maximum: 6; minimum: $-2$

   (c) $\dfrac{3 + (-2) + 5 + 0 + 6 + (-1)}{6} = \dfrac{11}{6} = 1.8\overline{3}$

2. (a) −6 −4 −2 0 2 4 6 8

   (b) Maximum: 6; minimum: $-3$

   (c) $\dfrac{5 + (-3) + 4 + (-2) + 1 + 6}{6} = \dfrac{11}{6} = 1.8\overline{3}$

3. (a) −30 −20 −10 0 10 20 30 40

   (b) Maximum: 30; minimum: $-20$

   (c) $\dfrac{-10 + 20 + 30 + (-20) + 0 + 10}{6} = 5$

4. (a) −3 −2 −1 0 1 2 3 4

   (b) Maximum: 4.5; minimum: $-3.5$

   (c) $\dfrac{0.5 + (-1.5) + 2.0 + 4.5 + (-3.5) + (-1.0)}{6} = \dfrac{1}{6} = 0.1\overline{6}$

5.

| −30 | −30 | −10 | 5 | 15 | 25 | 45 | 55 | 61 |
|---|---|---|---|---|---|---|---|---|

   (a) The maximum is 61 and the minimum is –30.

   (b) The mean is $\dfrac{-30 - 30 - 10 + 5 + 15 + 25 + 45 + 55 + 61}{9} \approx 15.11$ and the median is 15.

6.

| −3.5 | −1.25 | 1.5 | 1.5 | 2.5 | 4.75 | 4.75 |
|---|---|---|---|---|---|---|

   (a) The maximum is 4.75 and the minimum is –3.5.

   (b) The mean is $\dfrac{-3.5 - 1.25 + 1.5 + 1.5 + 2.5 + 4.75 + 4.75}{7} \approx 1.46$ and the median is 1.5.

7. $\sqrt{15} \approx 3.87$, $2^{2.3} \approx 4.92$, $\sqrt[3]{69} \approx 4.102$, $\pi^2 \approx 9.87$, $2^\pi \approx 8.82$, 4.1

| $\sqrt{15}$ | 4.1 | $\sqrt[3]{69}$ | $2^{2.3}$ | $2^\pi$ | $\pi^2$ |
|---|---|---|---|---|---|

   (a) The maximum is $\pi^2$ and the minimum is $\sqrt{15}$.

   (b) The mean is $\dfrac{\sqrt{15} + 4.1 + \sqrt[3]{69} + 2^{2.3} + 2^\pi + \pi^2}{6} \approx 5.95$ and the median is $\dfrac{\sqrt[3]{69} + 2^{2.3}}{2} \approx 4.51$.

8. $\dfrac{22}{7} \approx 3.1429, 3.14, \sqrt[3]{28} \approx 3.04, \sqrt{9.4} \approx 3.07, 4^{0.9} \approx 3.48, 3^{1.2} \approx 3.74$

| $\sqrt[3]{28}$ | $\sqrt{9.4}$ | 3.14 | $\frac{22}{7}$ | $4^{0.9}$ | $3^{1.2}$ |
|---|---|---|---|---|---|

(a) The maximum is $3^{1.2}$ and the minimum is $\sqrt[3]{28}$.

(b) The mean is $\dfrac{\sqrt[3]{28} + \sqrt{9.4} + 3.14 + \frac{22}{7} + 4^{0.9} + 3^{1.2}}{6} \approx 3.27$ and the median is $\dfrac{3.14 + \frac{22}{7}}{2} \approx 3.14$.

9. (a) 4 8 12 16 20 24 28 32

(b) Mean $= \dfrac{31.7 + 22.3 + 12.3 + 26.8 + 24.9 + 23.0}{6} = 23.5$; Median $= \dfrac{23.0 + 24.9}{2} = 23.95$. The average area of the six largest freshwater lakes is 23,500 square miles. Half of the lakes have areas larger than 23,950 square miles and half have less. The largest difference in area between any two lakes is 19,400 square miles.

(c) The freshwater lake with the largest area is Lake Superior.

10. (a) 4 8 12 16 20 24 28 32

(b) Mean $= \dfrac{19.3 + 18.5 + 29.0 + 7.31 + 16.1 + 22.8 + 20.3}{7} \approx 19.0$; Median $= 19.3$.

The average maximum elevation of the seven continents is about 19,000 feet. About half of these continents have maximum elevations below 19,300 feet and about half are above. The largest difference between these elevations is about 21,700 feet.

(c) The mountain with the highest elevation is Mount Everest in Asia.

11. *Answers may vary.* 16, 18, 26; No

12. *Answers may vary.* 3, 5, 9, 15, 18; No

13. $d = \sqrt{(5-2)^2 + (2-(-2))^2} = \sqrt{3^2 + 4^2} = \sqrt{25} = 5$

14. $d = \sqrt{(12-0)^2 + (-8-(-3))^2} = \sqrt{12^2 + (-5)^2} = \sqrt{169} = 13$

15. $d = \sqrt{(9-7)^2 + (1-(-4))^2} = \sqrt{2^2 + 5^2} = \sqrt{29} \approx 5.39$

16. $d = \sqrt{(-8-(-1))^2 + (-5-(-6))^2} = \sqrt{(-7)^2 + 1^2} = \sqrt{50} \approx 7.07$

17. $d = \sqrt{(-2.1-3.6)^2 + (8.7-5.7)^2} = \sqrt{(-5.7)^2 + 3^2} = \sqrt{41.49} \approx 6.44$

18. $d = \sqrt{(3.6-(-6.5))^2 + (-2.9-2.7)^2} = \sqrt{10.1^2 + (-5.6)^2} = \sqrt{133.37} \approx 11.55$

19. $d = \sqrt{(-3-(-3))^2 + (10-2)^2} = \sqrt{0^2 + 8^2} = \sqrt{64} = 8$

20. $d = \sqrt{(-1-7)^2 + (9-9)^2} = \sqrt{(-8)^2 + 0^2} = \sqrt{64} = 8$

21. $d = \sqrt{\left(\frac{3}{4} - \frac{1}{2}\right)^2 + \left(\frac{1}{2} - \left(-\frac{1}{2}\right)\right)^2} = \sqrt{\left(\frac{1}{4}\right)^2 + 1^2} = \sqrt{\frac{1}{16} + 1} = \sqrt{\frac{17}{16}} = \frac{\sqrt{17}}{4} \approx 1.03$

22. $d = \sqrt{\left(\frac{1}{3} - \left(-\frac{1}{3}\right)\right)^2 + \left(-\frac{4}{3} - \frac{2}{3}\right)^2} = \sqrt{\left(\frac{2}{3}\right)^2 + (-2)^2} = \sqrt{\frac{4}{9} + 4} = \sqrt{\frac{40}{9}} = \frac{\sqrt{40}}{3} \approx 2.11$

23. $d = \sqrt{\left(-\frac{1}{10} - \frac{2}{5}\right)^2 + \left(\frac{4}{5} - \frac{3}{10}\right)^2} = \sqrt{\left(-\frac{1}{2}\right)^2 + \left(\frac{1}{2}\right)^2} = \sqrt{\frac{1}{4} + \frac{1}{4}} = \sqrt{\frac{1}{2}} = \frac{\sqrt{2}}{2} = 0.71$

24. $d = \sqrt{\left(\frac{1}{3} - \left(-\frac{1}{2}\right)\right)^2 + \left(-\frac{5}{2} - \frac{2}{3}\right)^2} = \sqrt{\left(\frac{5}{6}\right)^2 + \left(-\frac{19}{6}\right)^2} = \sqrt{\frac{25}{36} + \frac{361}{36}} = \sqrt{\frac{386}{36}} = \frac{\sqrt{386}}{6} = 3.27$

25. $d = \sqrt{(-30 - 20)^2 + (-90 - 30)^2} = \sqrt{(-50)^2 + (-120)^2} = \sqrt{2500 + 14,400} = \sqrt{16,900} = 130$

26. $d = \sqrt{(-20 - 40)^2 + (17 - 6)^2} = \sqrt{(-60)^2 + (11)^2} = \sqrt{3600 + 121} = \sqrt{3721} = 61$

27. $d = \sqrt{(0 - a)^2 + (-b - 0)^2} = \sqrt{(-a)^2 + (-b)^2} = \sqrt{a^2 + b^2}$

28. $d = \sqrt{(x - 1)^2 + (y - 2)^2}$

29. $d = \sqrt{(3 - 0)^2 + (4 - 0)^2} = \sqrt{3^2 + 4^2} = \sqrt{9 + 16} = \sqrt{25} = 5$

$d = \sqrt{(7 - 3)^2 + (1 - 4)^2} = \sqrt{4^2 + (-3)^2} = \sqrt{16 + 9} = \sqrt{25} = 5$

The side between (0,0) and (3,4) and the side between (3,4) and (7,1) have equal length, so the triangle is isosceles.

30. $d = \sqrt{(2 - (-1))^2 + (3 - (-1))^2} = \sqrt{3^2 + 4^2} = \sqrt{9 + 16} = \sqrt{25} = 5$

$d = \sqrt{(-4 - 2)^2 + (3 - 3)^2} = \sqrt{(-6)^2 + 0^2} = \sqrt{36} = 6$

Since two of the sides have different lengths, the triangle cannot be an equilateral triangle.

31. (a) See Figure 31.

(b) $d = \sqrt{(0 - (-40))^2 + (50 - 0)^2} = \sqrt{40^2 + 50^2} = \sqrt{1600 + 2500} = \sqrt{4100} \approx 64.0$ miles.

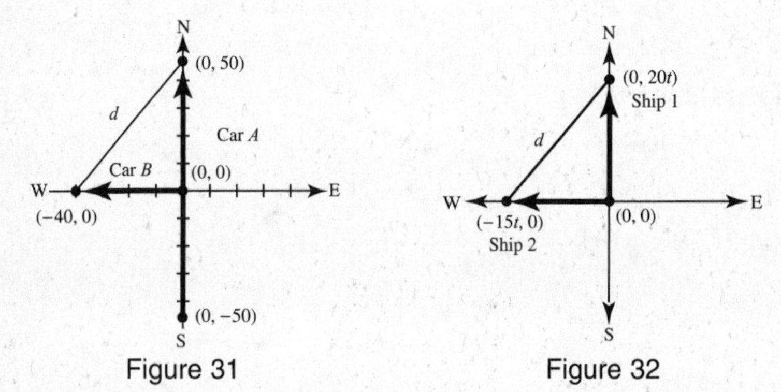


Figure 31 Figure 32

32. $d = \sqrt{(0 - (-15t))^2 + (20t - 0)^2} = \sqrt{(15t)^2 + (20t)^2} = \sqrt{225t^2 + 400t^2} = \sqrt{625t^2} = 25t$

See Figure 32.

33. Use the midpoint formula: $M = \left(\frac{1980 + 2000}{2}, \frac{77.4 + 79.5}{2}\right) = (1990, 78.45)$. According to the midpoint estimate the life expectancy was 78.45 years. This compares favorably to the actual life expectancy of 78.8 years.

34. Use the midpoint formula: $M = \left(\frac{1990 + 2000}{2}, \frac{773,919 + 1,391,892}{2}\right) = (1995, 1,082,905)$. This midpoint estimate of 1,082,905, is over 40,000 below the actual inmate population in 1995.

35. Assuming the distance of 0 meters requires 0 seconds to run, the midpoint between the data points (0, 0) and (200, 20) is equal to $M = \left(\frac{0 + 200}{2}, \frac{0 + 20}{2}\right) = (100, 10)$. According to the midpoint estimate the time required to run 100 meters is 10 seconds or half the time required to run 200 meters.

36. Use the midpoint formula to compute the value of $\frac{a + b}{2}$.

37. $M = \left(\frac{1 + 5}{2}, \frac{2 + (-3)}{2}\right) = (3, -0.5)$

38. $M = \left(\frac{-6 + 9}{2}, \frac{7 + (-4)}{2}\right) = (1.5, 1.5)$

39. $M = \left(\frac{-30 + 50}{2}, \frac{50 + (-30)}{2}\right) = (10, 10)$

40. $M = \left(\frac{28 + 52}{2}, \frac{-33 + 38}{2}\right) = (40, 2.5)$

41. $M = \left(\frac{1.5 + (-5.7)}{2}, \frac{2.9 + (-3.6)}{2}\right) = (-2.1, -0.35)$

42. $M = \left(\frac{9.4 + (-7.7)}{2}, \frac{-4.5 + 9.5}{2}\right) = (0.85, 2.5)$

43. $M = \left(\frac{\sqrt{2} + \sqrt{2}}{2}, \frac{\sqrt{5} + (-\sqrt{5})}{2}\right) = (\sqrt{2}, 0)$

44. $M = \left(\frac{\sqrt{7} + (-\sqrt{7})}{2}, \frac{3\sqrt{3} + (-\sqrt{3})}{2}\right) = (0, \sqrt{3})$

45. $M = \left(\frac{a + (-a)}{2}, \frac{b + 3b}{2}\right) = (0, 2b)$

46. $M = \left(\frac{-a + 3a}{2}, \frac{b + b}{2}\right) = (a, b)$

47. (a) $S = \{(-1, 5), (2, 2), (3, -1), (5, -4), (9, -5)\}$

(b) $D = \{-1, 2, 3, 5, 9\}$

$R = \{-5, -4, -1, 2, 5\}$

48. (a) $S = \{(-2, -4), (0, -2), (2, -1), (4, 0), (6, 4)\}$

(b) $D = \{-2, 0, 2, 4, 6\}$

$R = \{-4, -2, -1, 0, 4\}$

49. (a) $S = \{(1, 5), (4, 5), (5, 6), (4, 6), (1, 5)\}$

(b) $D = \{1, 4, 5\}$

$R = \{5, 6\}$

50. (a) $S = \left\{\left(-1, \frac{1}{2}\right), (0, 1), \left(3, \frac{3}{4}\right), (-1, 3), \left(-2, -\frac{5}{6}\right)\right\}$

(b) $D = \{-2, -1, 0, 3\}$

$R = \left\{-\frac{5}{6}, \frac{1}{2}, \frac{3}{4}, 1, 3\right\}$

51. (a) The domain is $D = \{0, -3, -2, 7\}$ and the range is $R = \{5, 4, -5, -3, 0\}$.

(b) The minimum $x$-value is –3, and the maximum $x$-value is 7. The minimum $y$-value is –5, and the maximum $y$-value is 5.

(c) The axes must include at least $-3 \le x \le 7$ and $-5 \le y \le 5$. It would be appropriate to extend the axes slightly beyond these intervals and let each tick mark represent 2 units. Plot the points $(0, 5)$, $(-3, 4)$, $(-2, -5)$, $(7, -3)$, and $(0, 0)$.

(d) See Figure 51.

52. (a) The domain is $D = \{1, 3, -5, 8, 0\}$ and the range is $R = \{1, 0, -5, -2, 3\}$.

(b) The minimum $x$-value is –5, and the maximum $x$-value is 8. The minimum $y$-value is –5, and the maximum $y$-value is 3.

(c) The axes must include at least $-5 \leq x \leq 8$ and $-5 \leq y \leq 3$. Extend each axis slightly beyond these intervals and let each tick mark represent 2 units. Plot the points $(1, 1)$, $(3, 0)$, $(-5, -5)$, $(8, -2)$, and $(0, 3)$.

(d) See Figure 52.

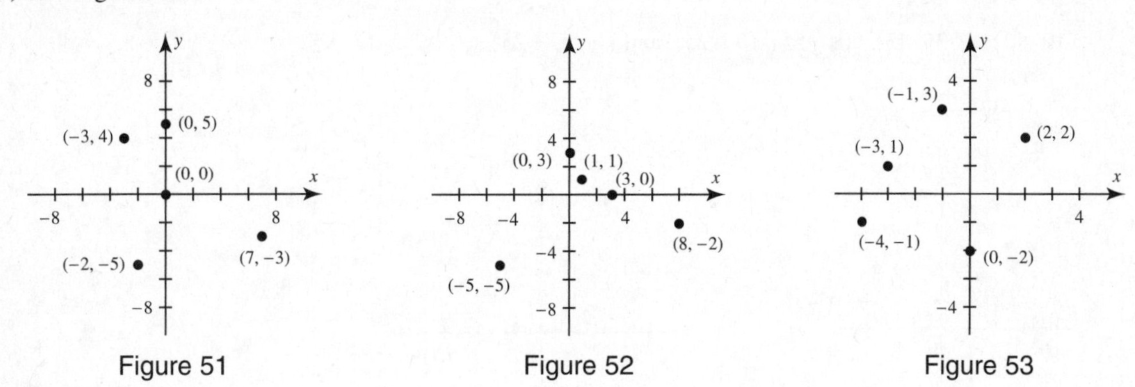


Figure 51 Figure 52 Figure 53

53. (a) The domain is $D = \{2, -3, -4, -1, 0\}$ and the range is $R = \{2, 1, -1, 3, -2\}$.

(b) The minimum $x$-value is $-4$, and the maximum $x$-value is 2. The minimum $y$-value is $-2$, and the maximum $y$-value is 3.

(c) The axes must include at least $-4 \leq x \leq 2$ and $-2 \leq y \leq 3$. Extend each axis slightly beyond these intervals and let each tick mark represent 1 unit. Plot the points $(2, 2)$, $(-3, 1)$, $(-4, -1)$, $(-1, 3)$, and $(0, -2)$.

(d) See Figure 53.

54. (a) The domain is $D = \{1, 2, -1\}$ and the range is $R = \{1, -3, -1, 2, 0\}$.

(b) The minimum $x$-value is $-1$, and the maximum $x$-value is 2. The minimum $y$-value is $-3$, and the maximum $y$-value is 2.

(c) The axes must include at least $-1 \leq x \leq 2$ and $-3 \leq y \leq 2$. Extend each axis slightly beyond these intervals and let each tick mark represent 1 unit. Plot the points $(1, 1)$, $(2, -3)$, $(-1, -1)$, $(-1, 2)$, and $(-1, 0)$.

(d) See Figure 54.

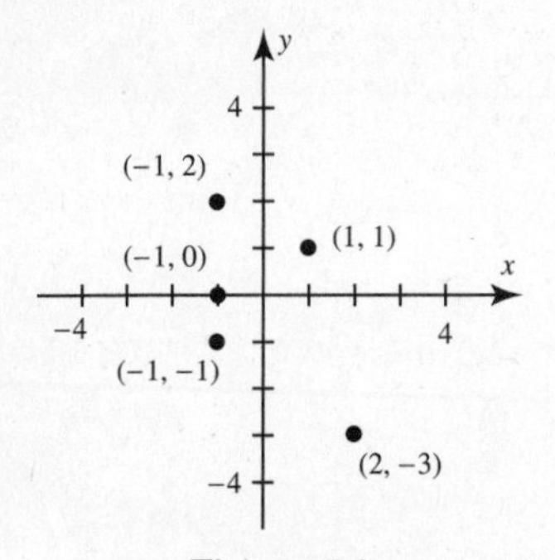


Figure 54

55. (a) The domain is $D = \{10, -35, 0, 75, -25\}$ and the range is $R = \{50, 45, -55, 25, -25\}$

(b) The minimum $x$-value is $-35$, and the maximum $x$-value is 75. The minimum $y$-value is $-55$, and the maximum $y$-value is 50.

(c) The axes must include at least $-35 \leq x \leq 75$ and $-55 \leq y \leq 50$, and let each tick mark represent 25 units. It would be appropriate to extend the axes slightly beyond these intervals. Plot the points $(10, 50)$, $(-35, 45)$, $(0, -55)$, $(75, 25)$, and $(-25, -25)$.

(d) See Figure 55.

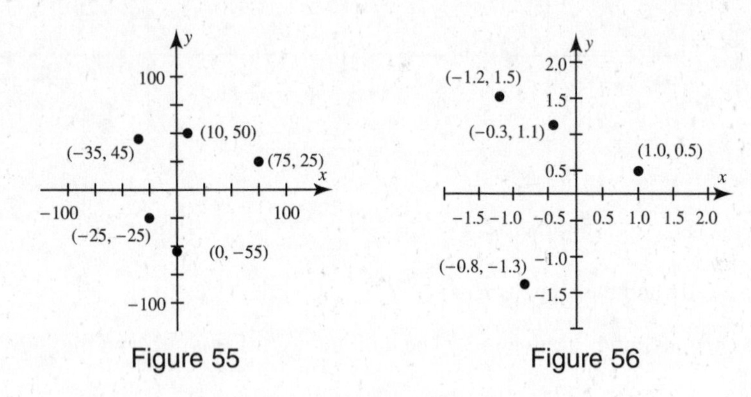


Figure 55 Figure 56

56. (a) The domain is $D = \{-1.2, 1.0, -0.3, -0.8\}$ and the range is $R = \{1.5, 0.5, 1.1, -1.3\}$

(b) The minimum $x$-value is $-1.2$, and the maximum $x$-value is 1.0. The minimum $y$-value is $-1.3$, and the maximum $y$-value is 1.5.

(c) The axes must include at least $-1.2 \leq x \leq 1.0$ and $-1.3 \leq y \leq 1.5$ beyond these intervals and let each tick mark represent 0.5 unit. It would be appropriate to extend the axes slightly beyond these intervals. Plot the points $(-1.2, 1.5)$, $(1.0, 0.5)$, $(-0.3, 1.1)$, and $(-0.8, -1.3)$.

(d) See Figure 56.

57. $(1990, 5)$, $(1995, 34)$, $(2000, 109)$, $(2005, 208)$. See Figures 57a & 57b.

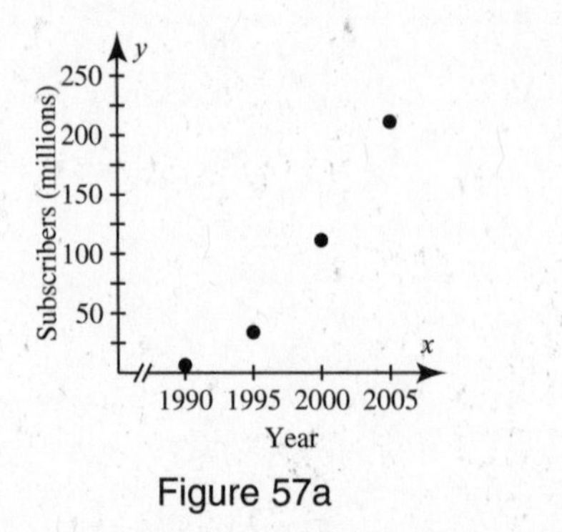


Figure 57a

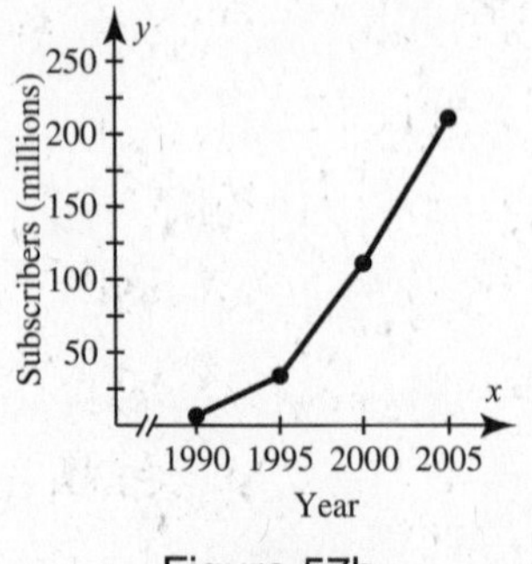


Figure 57b

58. (1958, 315), (1958, 315), (1975, 335), (1990, 355), (2005, 380). See Figures 58a & 58b.

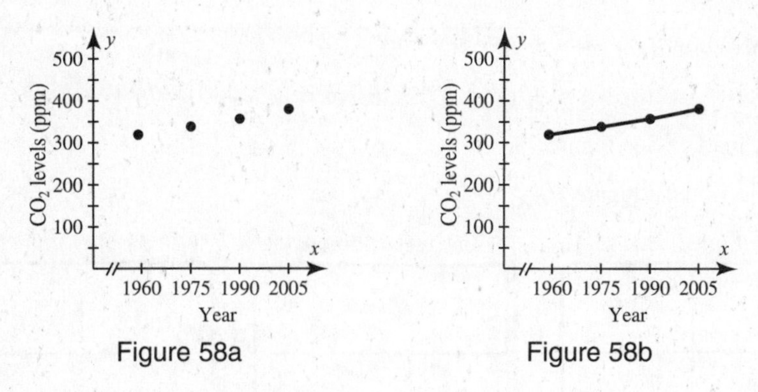


Figure 58a Figure 58b

59. $x^2 + y^2 = 25 \Rightarrow (x - 0)^2 + (y - 0)^2 = 5^2 \Rightarrow$ Center: $(0, 0)$; Radius: 5

60. $x^2 + y^2 = 100 \Rightarrow (x - 0)^2 + (y - 0)^2 = 10^2 \Rightarrow$ Center: $(0, 0)$; Radius: 10

61. $x^2 + y^2 = 7 \Rightarrow (x - 0)^2 + (y - 0)^2 = (\sqrt{7})^2 \Rightarrow$ Center: $(0, 0)$; Radius: $\sqrt{7}$

62. $x^2 + y^2 = 20 \Rightarrow (x - 0)^2 + (y - 0)^2 = (\sqrt{20})^2 \Rightarrow$ Center: $(0, 0)$; Radius: $\sqrt{20} = 2\sqrt{5}$

63. $(x - 2)^2 + (y + 3)^2 = 9 \Rightarrow (x - 2)^2 + (y - (-3))^2 = 3^2 \Rightarrow$ Center: $(2, -3)$; Radius: 3

64. $(x + 1)^2 + (y - 1)^2 = 16 \Rightarrow (x - (-1))^2 + (y - 1)^2 = 4^2 \Rightarrow$ Center: $(-1, 1)$; Radius: 4

65. $x^2 + (y + 1)^2 = 100 \Rightarrow (x - 0)^2 + (y - (-1))^2 = 10^2 \Rightarrow$ Center: $(0, -1)$; Radius: 10

66. $(x - 5)^2 + y^2 = 19 \Rightarrow (x - 5)^2 + (y - 0)^2 = (\sqrt{19})^2 \Rightarrow$ Center: $(5, 0)$; Radius: $\sqrt{19}$

67. Since the center is (1, –2) and the radius is 1, the equation is $(x - 1)^2 + (y + 2)^2 = 1$.

68. Since the center is (0, 0) and the radius is 3, the equation is $x^2 + y^2 = 9$.

69. Since the center is (–2, 1) and the radius is 2, the equation is $(x + 2)^2 + (y - 1)^2 = 4$.

70. Since the center is (–2, 0) and the radius is 4, the equation is $(x + 2)^2 + y^2 = 16$.

71. $(x - 3)^2 + (y - (-5))^2 = 8^2 \Rightarrow (x - 3)^2 + (y + 5)^2 = 64$

72. $(x - (-1))^2 + (y - 4)^2 = 5^2 \Rightarrow (x + 1)^2 + (y - 4)^2 = 25$

73. $(x - 3)^2 + (y - 0)^2 = 7^2 \Rightarrow (x - 3)^2 + y^2 = 49$

74. $(x - 0)^2 + (y - 0)^2 = 1^2 \Rightarrow x^2 + y^2 = 1$

75. First find the radius using the distance formula: $r = \sqrt{(-3 - 0)^2 + (-1 - 0)^2} = \sqrt{10}$.

$(x - 0)^2 + (y - 0)^2 = (\sqrt{10})^2 \Rightarrow x^2 + y^2 = 10$

76. First find the radius using the distance formula: $r = \sqrt{(4 - 3)^2 + (2 - (-5))^2} = \sqrt{50}$.

$(x - 3)^2 + (y - (-5))^2 = (\sqrt{50})^2 \Rightarrow (x - 3)^2 + (y + 5)^2 = 50$

77. First find the center using the midpoint formula: $C = \left(\frac{-5 + 1}{2}, \frac{-7 + 1}{2}\right) = (-2, -3)$.

Then find the radius using the distance formula: $r = \sqrt{(-2 - 1)^2 + (-3 - 1)^2} = \sqrt{25} = 5$.

$(x - (-2))^2 + (y - (-3))^2 = 5^2 \Rightarrow (x + 2)^2 + (y + 3)^2 = 25$

78. First find the center using the midpoint formula: $C = \left(\frac{-3+1}{2}, \frac{-2+(-4)}{2}\right) = (-1, -3)$.

Then find the radius using the distance formula: $r = \sqrt{(-1-1)^2 + (-3-(-4))^2} = \sqrt{5}$.

$(x-(-1))^2 + (y-(-3))^2 = (\sqrt{5})^2 \Rightarrow (x+1)^2 + (y+3)^2 = 5$

79. $x$-axis: 10 tick marks; $y$-axis: 10 tick marks. See Figure 79.

80. $x$-axis: 4 tick marks; $y$-axis: 3 tick marks. See Figure 80.

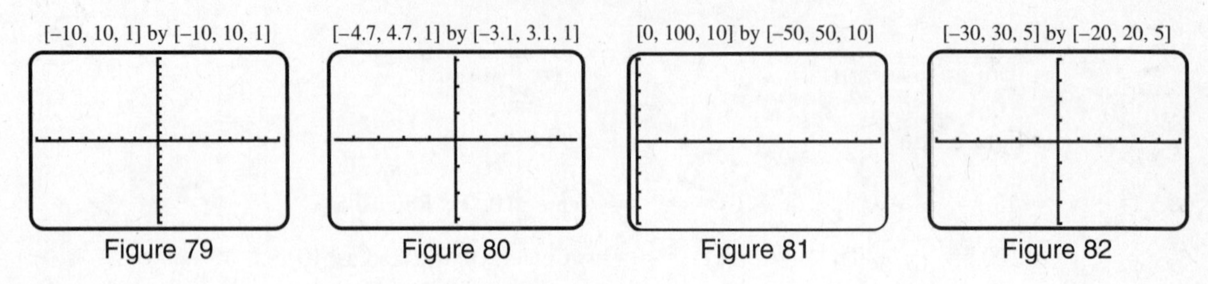

Figure 79 Figure 80 Figure 81 Figure 82

81. $x$-axis: 10 tick marks; $y$-axis: 5 tick marks. See Figure 81.

82. $x$-axis: 6 tick marks; $y$-axis: 4 tick marks. See Figure 82.

83. $x$-axis: 16 tick marks; $y$-axis: 5 tick marks. See Figure 83.

84. $x$-axis: 11 tick marks; $y$-axis: 4 tick marks. See Figure 84.

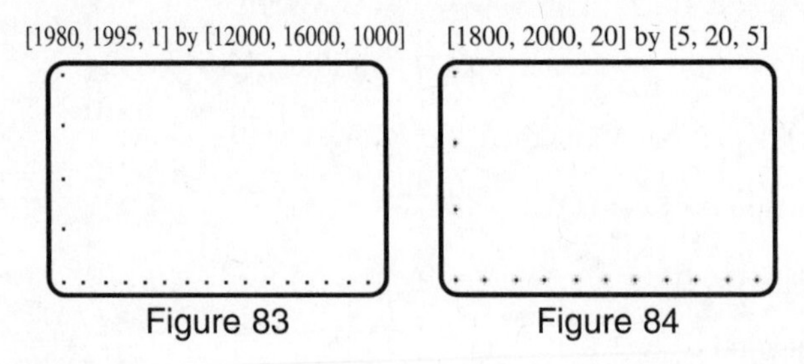

Figure 83 Figure 84

85. Graph b

86. Graph d

87. Graph a

88. Graph c

89. Plot the points $(1, 3)$, $(-2, 2)$, $(-4, 1)$, $(-2, -4)$ and $(0, 2)$ in $[-5, 5, 1]$ by $[-5, 5, 1]$. See Figure 89.

90. Plot the points $(6, 8)$, $(-4, -10)$, $(-2, -6)$, and $(2, -5)$ in $[-7, 7, 1]$ by $[-11, 11, 1]$. See Figure 90.

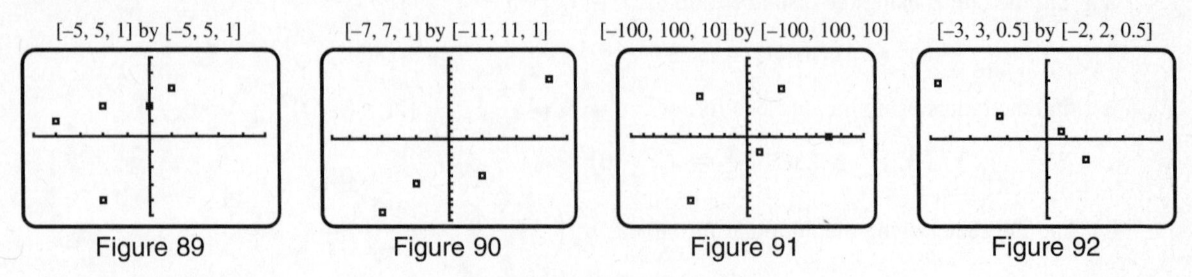

Figure 89 Figure 90 Figure 91 Figure 92

91. Plot the points $(10, -20)$, $(-40, 50)$, $(30, 60)$, $(-50, -80)$, and $(70, 0)$ in $[-100, 100, 10]$ by $[-100, 100, 10]$. See Figure 91.

92. Plot the points $(-1.2, 0.6)$, $(1.0, -0.5)$, $(0.4, 0.2)$, and $(-2.8, 1.4)$ in $[-3, 3, 0.5]$ by $[-2, 2, 0.5]$, See Figure 92.

93. (a) $x$-min: 2005; $x$-max: 2008; $y$-min: 19.7; $y$-max: 25.0

    (b) $[2003, 2010, 1]$ by $[15, 30, 5]$. *Answers may vary.*

    (c) See Figure 93c.

    (d) See Figure 93d.

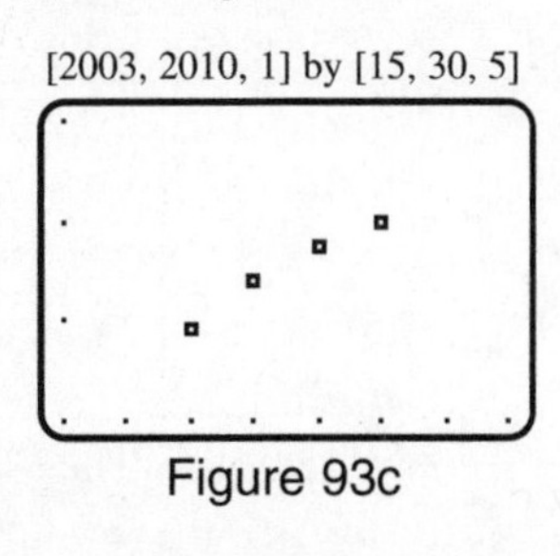

Figure 93c

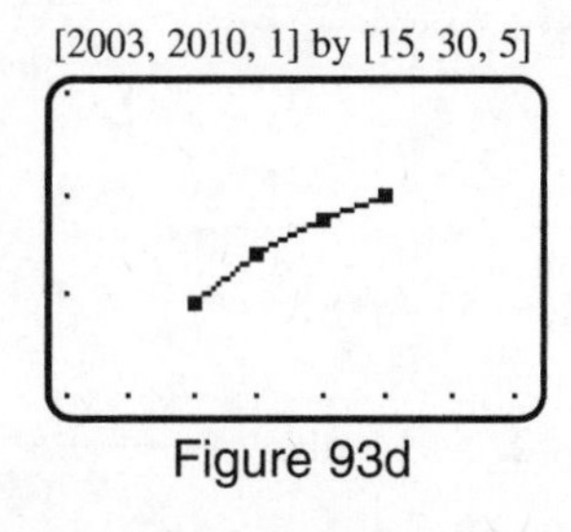

Figure 93d

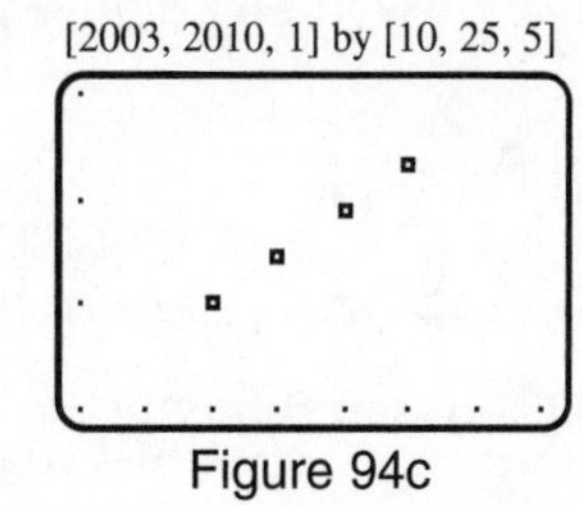

Figure 94c

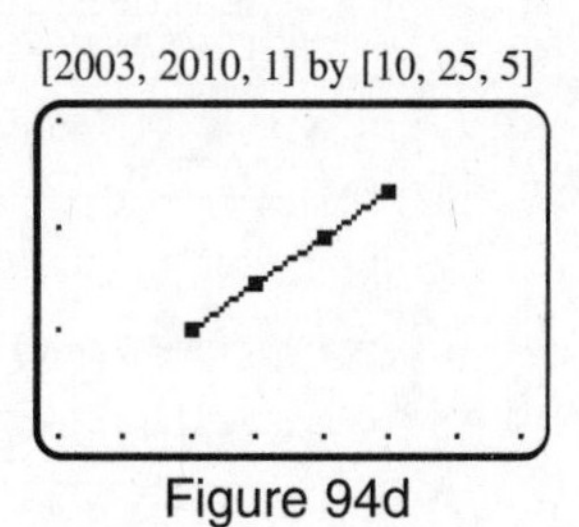

Figure 94d

94. (a) $x$-min: 2005; $x$-max: 2008; $y$-min: 15.1; $y$-max: 21.7

    (b) $[2003, 2010, 1]$ by $[10, 25, 5]$ *Answers may vary.*

    (c) See Figure 94c.

    (d) See Figure 94d.

95. (a) $x$-min: 1950; $x$-max: 2000; $y$-min: 1.7; $y$-max: 5.5

    (b) $[1940, 2010, 10]$ by $[0, 7, 1]$ *Answers may vary.*

    (c) See Figure 95c.

    (d) See Figure 95d.

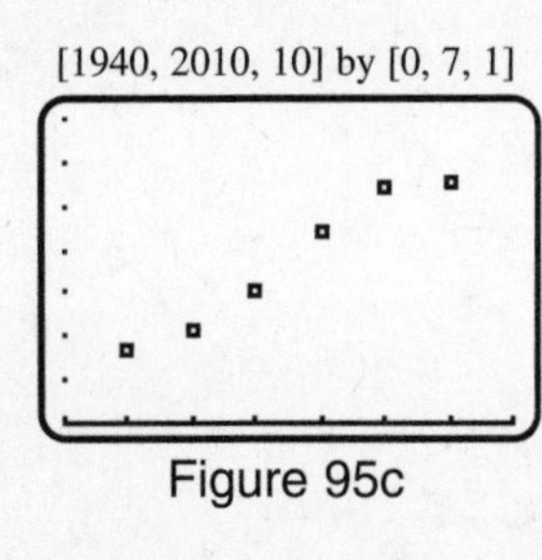

Figure 95c

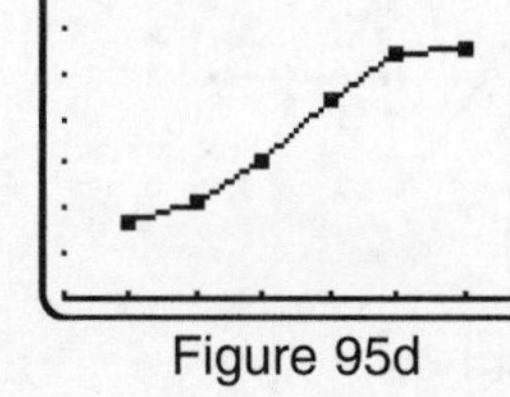

Figure 95d

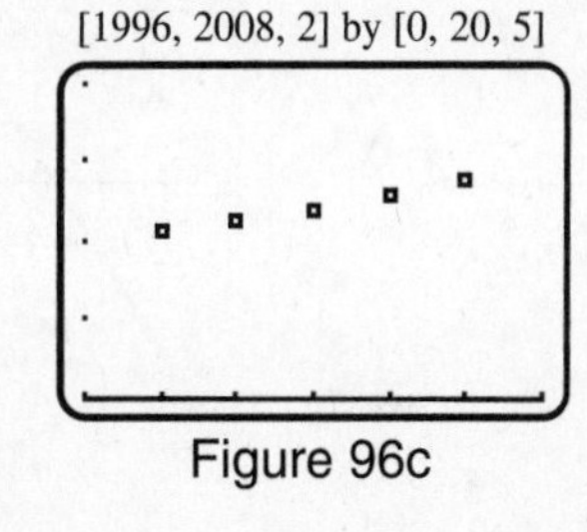

Figure 96c

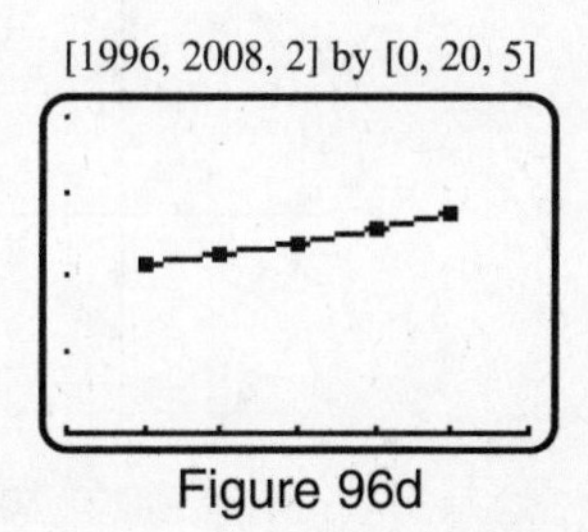

Figure 96d

96. (a) $x$-min: 1998; $x$-max: 2006; $y$-min: 10.5; $y$-max: 14.0

    (b) $[1996, 2008, 2]$ by $[0, 20, 5]$ *Answers may vary.*

    (c) See Figure 96c.

    (d) See Figure 96d.

## Checking Basic Concepts for Sections 1.1 and 1.2

1. (a) $\sqrt{4.2(23.1 + 0.5^3)} \approx 9.88$

   (b) $\dfrac{23 + 44}{85.1 - 32.9} \approx 1.28$

2. (a) $5 - (-4)^2 \cdot 3 = 5 - 16 \cdot 3 = 5 - 48 = -43$

   (b) $5 \div 5\sqrt{2 + 2} = 5 \div 5\sqrt{4} = 5 \div (5)(2) = 1 \cdot 2 = 2$

3. (a) $348{,}500{,}000 = 3.485 \times 10^8$

   (b) $-1237.4 = -1.2374 \times 10^3$

   (c) $0.00198 = 1.98 \times 10^{-3}$

4. $d = \sqrt{(3 - (-3))^2 + (-5 - 1)^2} = \sqrt{6^2 + (-6)^2} = \sqrt{36 + 36} = \sqrt{36 \times 2} = 6\sqrt{2} \approx 8.49$

5. $M = \left(\frac{-2 + 4}{2}, \frac{3 + 2}{2}\right) = \left(1, \frac{5}{2}\right)$

6. $(x - h)^2 + (y - k)^2 = r^2 \Rightarrow (x - (-4))^2 + (y - 5)^2 = 8^2 \Rightarrow (x + 4)^2 + (y - 5)^2 = 64$

7. Mean $= \frac{13{,}215 + 12{,}881 + 13{,}002 + 3953}{4} = 10{,}762.75$; Median $= \frac{12{,}881 + 13{,}002}{2} = 12{,}941.5$. The mean average depth of the four oceans is 10,762.75 feet. Half of the oceans have average depths of more than 12,941.5 feet and half have average depths of less than 12.941.5 feet. The largest difference in average depths between any two oceans is 9262 feet.

8. $(-5, -4)$: Quad. III; $(-1, 2)$: Quad. II; $(2, -2)$: Quad. IV; $(3, 6)$: Quad. I

   See Figures 8a and 8b.

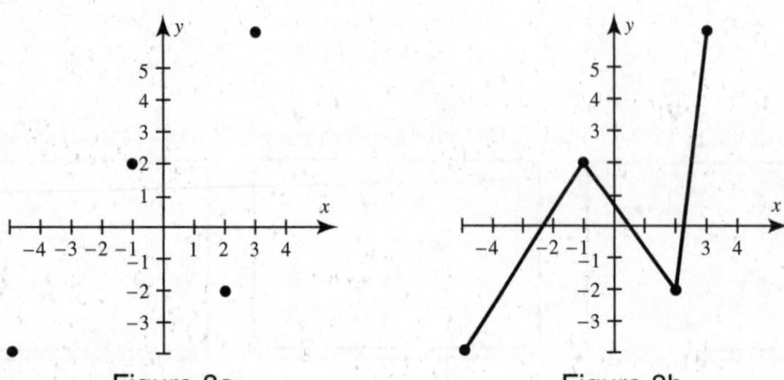

Figure 8a    Figure 8b

## 1.3: Functions and Their Representations

1. If $f(-2) = 3$, then the point (–2, 3) is on the graph of $f$.
2. If $f(3) = -9.7$, then the point (3, –9.7) is on the graph of $f$.
3. If (7, 8) is on the graph of $f$, then $f(7) = 8$.
4. If (–3, 2) is on the graph of $f$, then $f(-3) = 2$.
5. See Figure 5.
6. See Figure 6.

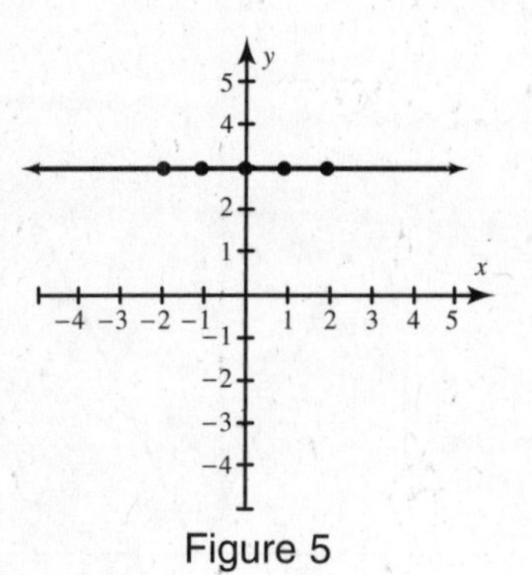


Figure 5

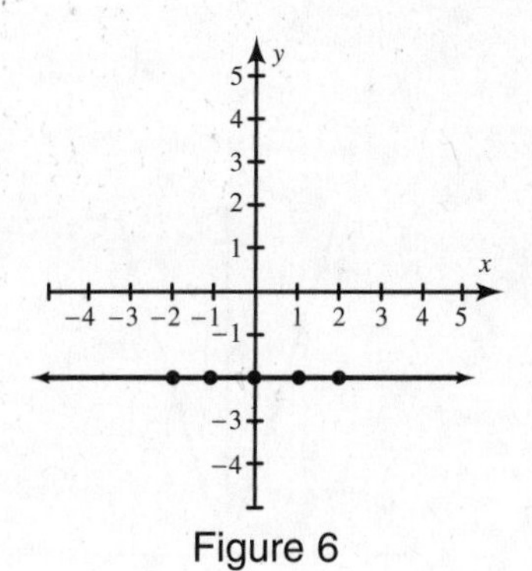


Figure 6

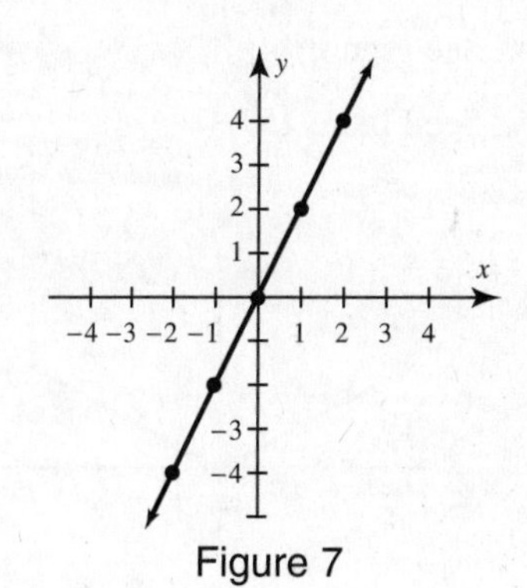


Figure 7

7. See Figure 7.

8. See Figure 8.

9. See Figure 9.

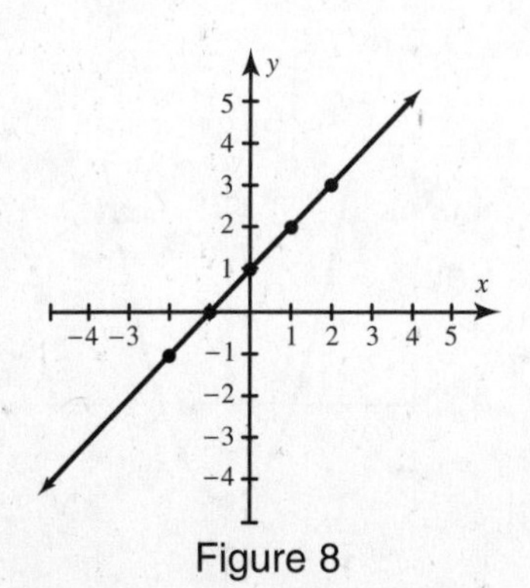


Figure 8

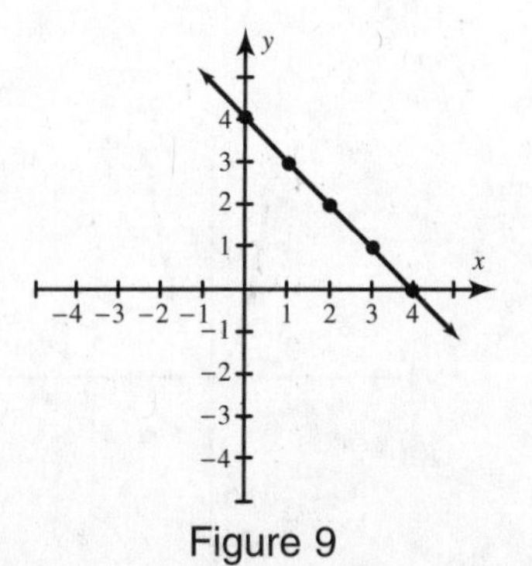


Figure 9

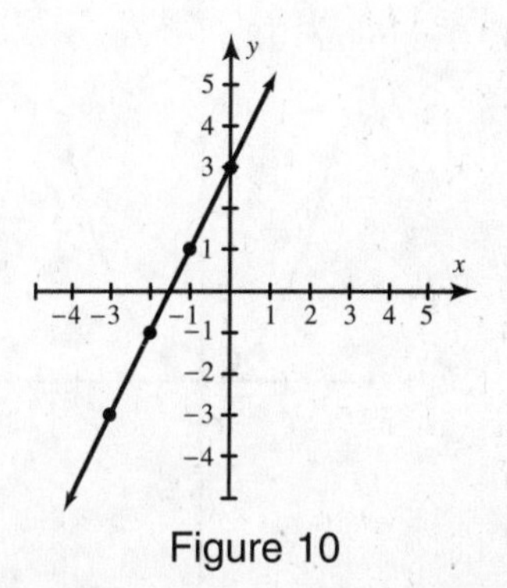


Figure 10

10. See Figure 10.

11. See Figure 11.

12. See Figure 12.

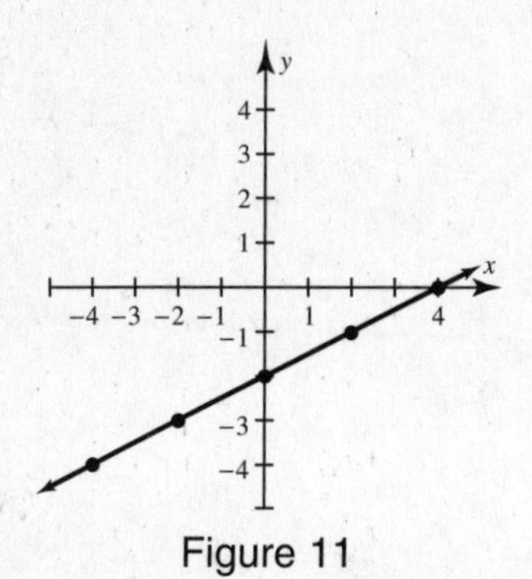


Figure 11

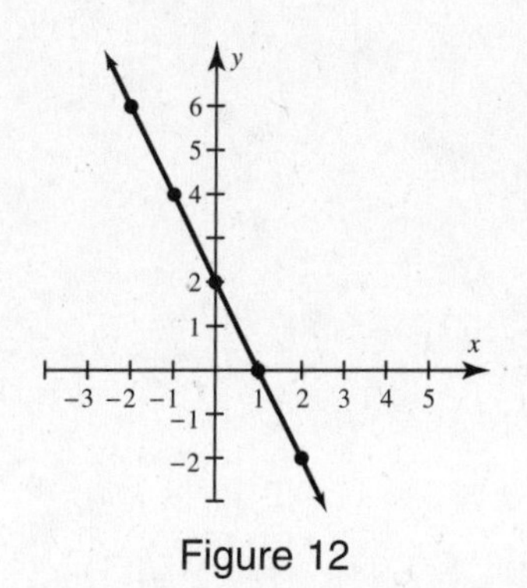


Figure 12

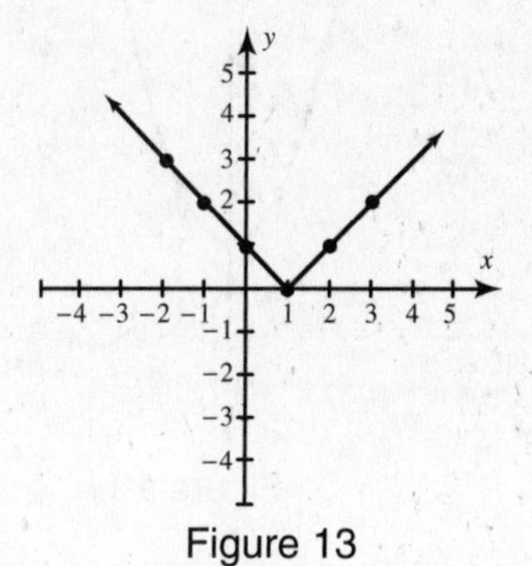


Figure 13

13. See Figure 13.

14. See Figure 14.

15. See Figure 15.

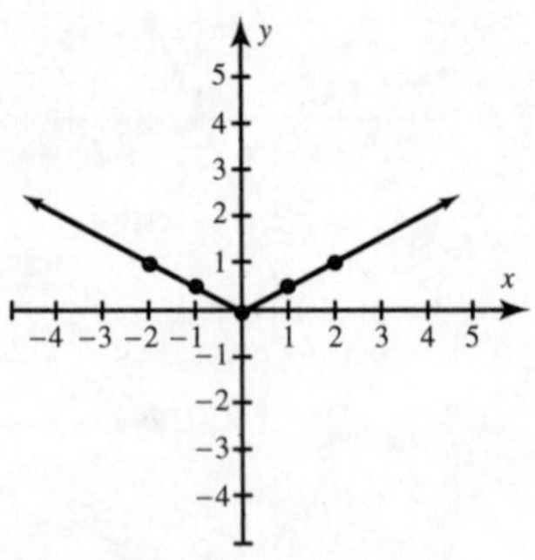

Figure 14

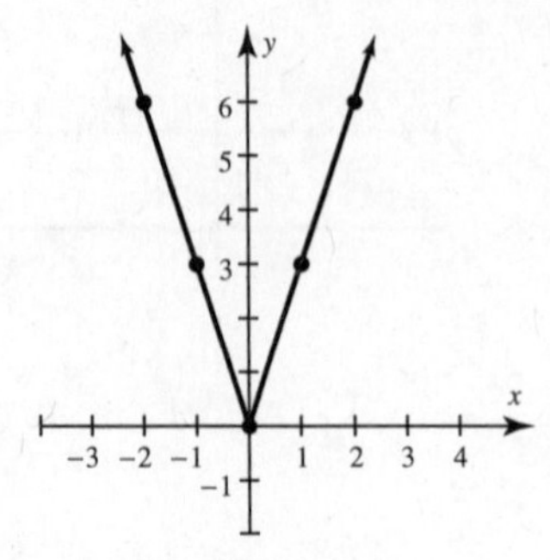

Figure 15

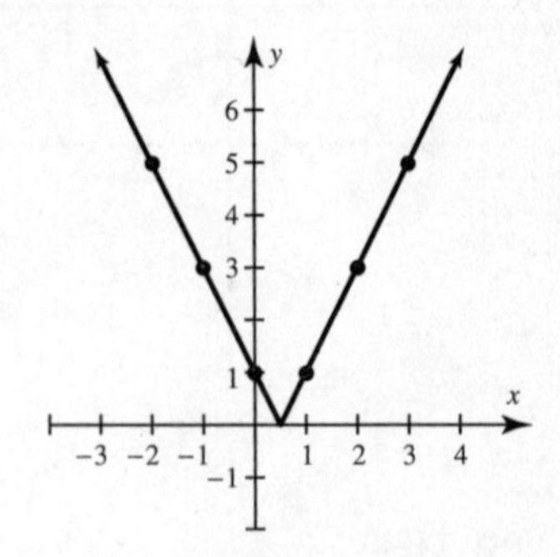

Figure 16

16. See Figure 16.

17. See Figure 17.

18. See Figure 18.

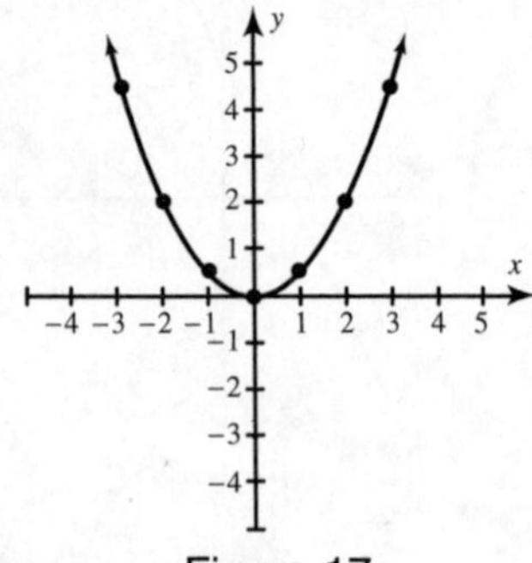

Figure 17

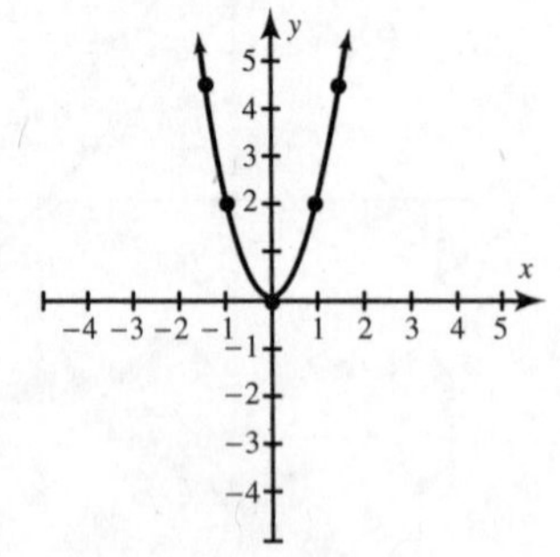

Figure 18

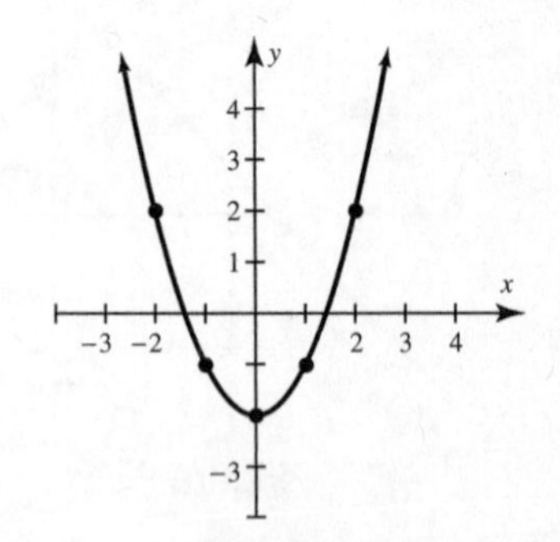

Figure 19

19. See Figure 19.

20. See Figure 20.

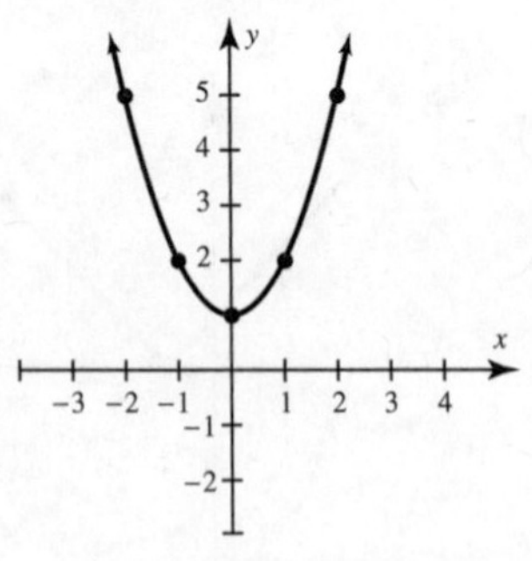

Figure 20

21. (a) $f(x) = x^3 \Rightarrow f(-2) = (-2)^3 = -8$ and $f(5) = 5^3 = 125$.

    (b) All real numbers.

22. (a) $f(x) = 2x - 1 \Rightarrow f(8) = 2(8) - 1 = 15$ and $f(-1) = 2(-1) - 1 = -3$.

    (b) All real numbers.

23. (a) $f(x) = \sqrt{x} \Rightarrow f(-1) = \sqrt{-1}$ which is not a real number, and $f(a+1) = \sqrt{a+1}$.

    (b) All non-negative real numbers.

24. (a) $f(x) = \sqrt{1-x} \Rightarrow f(-2) = \sqrt{1-(-2)} = \sqrt{3}$ and $f(a+2) = \sqrt{1-(a+2)} = \sqrt{-1-a}$.

    (b) All real numbers less than or equal to 1 ($x \leq 1$).

25. (a) $f(x) = 6 - 3x \Rightarrow f(-1) = 6 - 3(-1) = 6 + 3 = 9$ and

    $f(a+1) = 6 - 3(a+1) = 6 - 3a - 3 = 3 - 3a$

    (b) All real numbers.

26. (a) $f(x) = \dfrac{3x-5}{x+5} \Rightarrow f(-1) = \dfrac{3(-1)-5}{-1+5} = -\dfrac{8}{4} = -2$ and $f(a) = \dfrac{3a-5}{a+5}$.

    (b) All real numbers not equal to –5 ($x \neq -5$).

27. (a) $f(x) = -7 \Rightarrow f(6) = -7$ and $f(a-1) = -7$. ($f$ is a constant function.)

    (b) All real numbers.

28. (a) $f(x) = x^2 - x + 1 \Rightarrow f(1) = 1^2 - 1 + 1 = 1$ and $f(-2) = (-2)^2 - (-2) + 1 = 7$.

    (b) All real numbers.

29. (a) $f(x) = \dfrac{1}{x^2} \Rightarrow f(4) = \dfrac{1}{4^2} = \dfrac{1}{16}$ and $f(-7) = \dfrac{1}{(-7)^2} = \dfrac{1}{49}$.

    (b) All real numbers not equal to 0 ($x \neq 0$).

30. (a) $f(x) = \sqrt{x-3} \Rightarrow f(4) = \sqrt{4-3} = \sqrt{1} = 1$ and $f(a+4) = \sqrt{(a+4)-3} = \sqrt{a+1}$.

    (b) All real numbers greater than or equal to 3 ($x \geq 3$).

31. (a) $f(x) = \dfrac{1}{x^2-9} \Rightarrow f(4) = \dfrac{1}{4^2-9} = \dfrac{1}{16-9} = \dfrac{1}{7}$ and

    $f(a-5) = \dfrac{1}{(a-5)^2-9} = \dfrac{1}{a^2-10a+25-9} = \dfrac{1}{a^2-10a+16}$.

    (b) All real numbers not equal to 3 or –3 ($x \neq 3, x \neq -3$).

32. (a) $f(x) = \dfrac{1}{x^2+4} \Rightarrow f(-2) = \dfrac{1}{(-2)^2+4} = \dfrac{1}{4+4} = \dfrac{1}{8}$ and $f(a+4) = \dfrac{1}{(a+4)^2+4} =$

    $\dfrac{1}{(a^2+8a+16)+4} = \dfrac{1}{a^2+8a+20}$

    (b) All real numbers.

33. (a) $f(x) = \dfrac{1}{\sqrt{2-x}} \Rightarrow f(1) = \dfrac{1}{\sqrt{2-1}} = \dfrac{1}{\sqrt{1}} = \dfrac{1}{1} = 1$ and $f(a+2) = \dfrac{1}{\sqrt{2-(a+2)}} = \dfrac{1}{\sqrt{-a}}$

    (b) $2 - x > 0 \Rightarrow -x > -2 \Rightarrow x < 2$

34. (a) $f(x) = \dfrac{1}{\sqrt{x-1}} \Rightarrow f(0) = \dfrac{1}{\sqrt{0-1}} = \dfrac{1}{\sqrt{-1}}$ which is not a real number, and

    $f(a^2-a+1) = \dfrac{1}{\sqrt{a^2-a+1-1}} = \dfrac{1}{\sqrt{a^2-a}}$

    (b) The domain of $f$ includes all real numbers greater than 1 ($x > 1$).

35. (a) All real numbers.

    (b) $g(x) = 2x - 1 \Rightarrow g(-1) = 2(-1) - 1 = -3$ and $g(2) = 2(2) - 1 = 3$

    (c) $g(-1) = -3$ and $g(2) = 3$

36. (a) All real numbers.

(b) $g(x) = -\frac{1}{2}x - 1 \Rightarrow g(-1) = -\frac{1}{2}(-1) - 1 = -\frac{1}{2}$ and $g(2) = -\frac{1}{2}(2) - 1 = -2$

(c) $g(-1) = -\frac{1}{2}$ and $g(2) = -2$

37. (a) All real numbers.

(b) $g(x) = 2 - x^2 \Rightarrow g(-1) = 2 - (-1)^2 = 2 - 1 = 1$ and $g(2) = 2 - (2)^2 = 2 - 4 = -2$

(c) $g(-1) = 1$ and $g(2) = -2$

38. (a) All real numbers.

(b) $g(x) = 3 - 2|x| \Rightarrow g(-1) = 3 - 2|-1| = 3 - 2 = 1$ and $g(2) = 3 - 2|2| = 3 - 4 = -1$

(c) $g(-1) = 1$ and $g(2) = -1$

39. (a) $-2 \le x \le 2$

(b) $g(x) = x^2 - 3 \Rightarrow g(-1) = (-1)^2 - 3 = 1 - 3 = -2$ and $g(2) = (2)^2 - 3 = 4 - 3 = 1$

(c) $g(-1) = -2$ and $g(2) = 1$

40. (a) $-2 \le x \le 2$

(b) $g(x) = x^3 - 4x \Rightarrow g(-1) = (-1)^3 - 4(-1) = -1 + 4 = 3$ and $g(2) = (2)^3 - 4(2) = 8 - 8 = 0$

(c) $g(-1) = 3$ and $g(2) = 0$

41. $D = \{x \mid -3 \le x \le 3\}$

$R = \{y \mid 0 \le y \le 3\}$

$f(0) = 3.$

42. $D = \{x \mid -2 \le x \le 2\}$

$R = \{y \mid -3 \le y \le 3\}$

$f(0) = 0$

43. $D = \{\text{all real numbers}\}$

$R = \{y \mid y \le 2\}$

$f(0) = 2$

44. $D = \{\text{all real numbers}\}$

$R = \{\text{all real numbers}\}$

$f(0) = 0$

45. $D = \{x \mid x \ge -1\}$

$R = \{y \mid y \le 2\}$

$f(0) = 0$

46. $D = \{x \mid x \le 2\}$

$R = \{y \mid y \le 3\}$

$f(0) = 3$

47. (a) $f(2) = 7$

(b) $f = \{(1, 7), (2, 7), (3, 8)\}$

(c) $D = \{1, 2, 3\}$; $R = \{7, 8\}$

48. (a) $f(2) = 5$

(b) $f = \{(0, 1), (2, 5), (4, 3)\}$

(c) $D = \{0, 2, 4\}$; $R = \{1, 3, 5\}$

49. Graph $f(x) = 0.25x^2$ in $[-4.7, 4.7, 1]$ by $[-3.1, 3.1, 1]$ by letting $Y_1 = 0.25X\wedge2$. See Figure 49.

(a) From the graph, it appears that $f(2) = 1$.

(b) $f(2) = 0.25(2)^2 = 0.25(4) = 1$

(c) See Figure 49c.

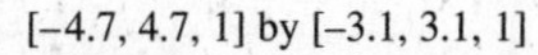
[-4.7, 4.7, 1] by [-3.1, 3.1, 1]

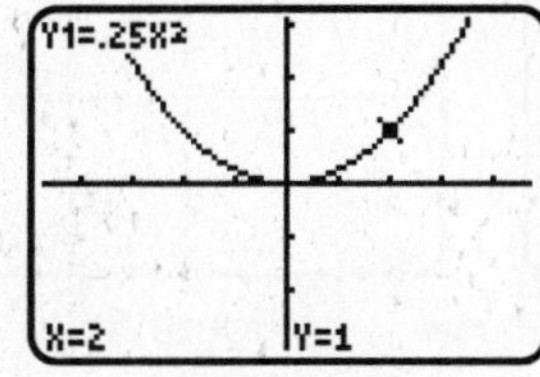

Figure 49

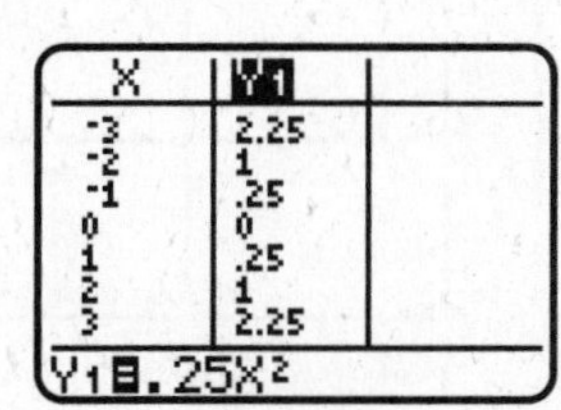

Figure 49c

[-4.7, 4.7, 1] by [-3.1, 3.1, 1]

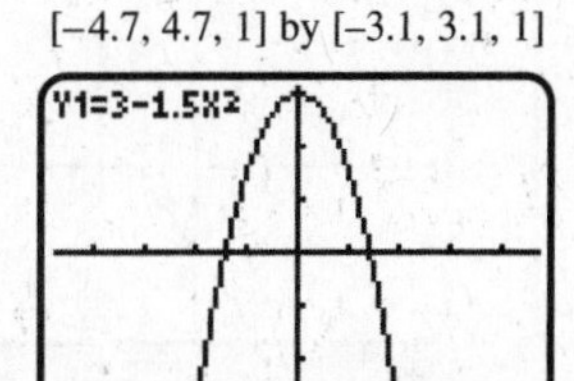

Figure 50

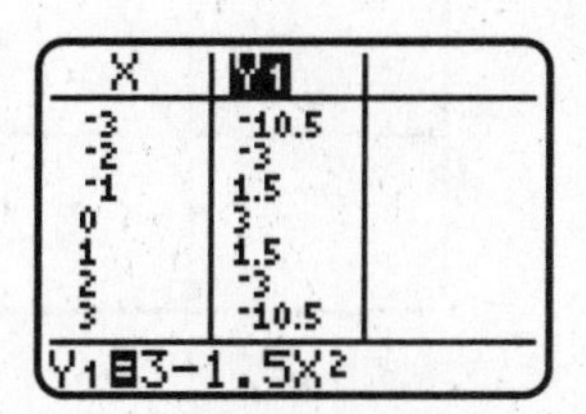

Figure 50c

50. Graph $f(x) = 3 - 1.5x^2$ in $[-4.7, 4.7, 1]$ by $[-3.1, 3.1, 1]$ by letting $Y_1 = 3 - 1.5X\wedge2$. See Figure 50.

(a) From the graph, it appears that $f(2) = -3$.

(b) $f(2) = 3 - 1.5(2)^2 = 3 - 1.5(4) = 3 - 6 = -3$

(c) See Figure 50c.

51. Graph $f(x) = \sqrt{x + 2}$ in $[-4.7, 4.7, 1]$ by $[-3.1, 3.1, 1]$ by letting $Y_1 = \sqrt{}(X + 2)$. See Figure 51.

(a) From the graph, it appears that $f(2) = 2$.

(b) $f(2) = \sqrt{2 + 2} = \sqrt{4} = 2$

(c) See Figure 51c.

[-4.7, 4.7, 1] by [-3.1, 3.1, 1]

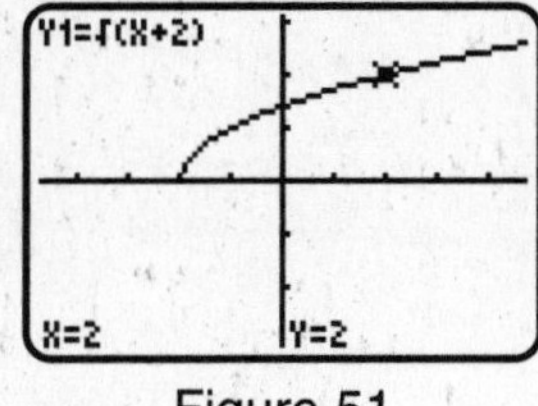

Figure 51

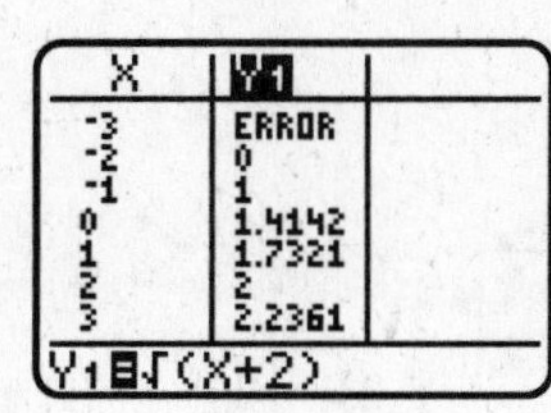

Figure 51c

[-4.7, 4.7, 1] by [-3.1, 3.1, 1]

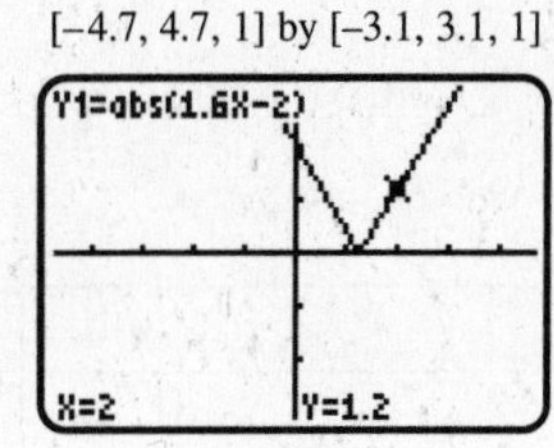

Figure 52

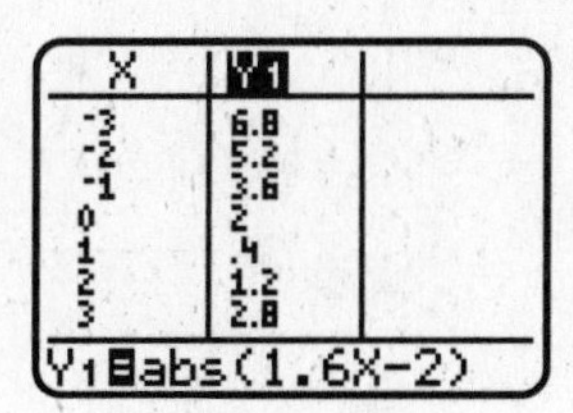

Figure 52c

52. Graph $f(x) = |1.6x - 2|$ in $[-4.7, 4.7, 1]$ by $[-3.1, 3.1, 1]$ by letting $Y_1 = \text{abs}(1.6X - 2)$. See Figure 52.

(a) From the graph, it appears that $f(2) = 1.2$.

(b) $f(2) = |1.6(2) - 2| = |3.2 - 2| = |1.2| = 1.2$

(c) See Figure 52c.

53. Verbal: Square the input $x$.

Graphical: Graph $Y_1 = X^2$. See Figure 53.

Numerical:

| $x$ | −2 | −1 | 0 | 1 | 2 |
|---|---|---|---|---|---|
| $y$ | 4 | 1 | 0 | 1 | 4 |

$f(2) = 4$

54. Verbal: Multiply the input $x$ by 2 and subtract 5 from the result.

Graphical: Graph $Y_1 = 2X - 5$. See Figure 54.

Numerical:

| $x$ | −2 | −1 | 0 | 1 | 2 |
|---|---|---|---|---|---|
| $y$ | −9 | −7 | −5 | −3 | −1 |

$f(2) = -1$

[−10, 10, 1] by [−10, 10, 1]

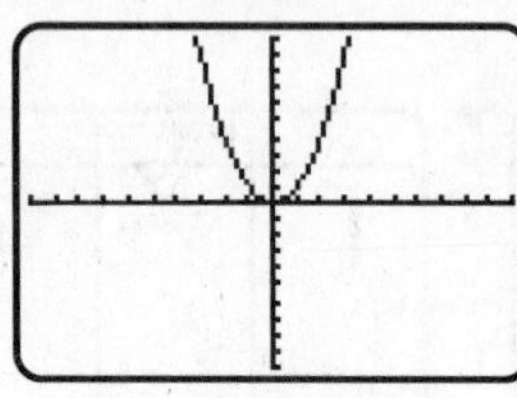

Figure 53

[−10, 10, 1] by [−10, 10, 1]

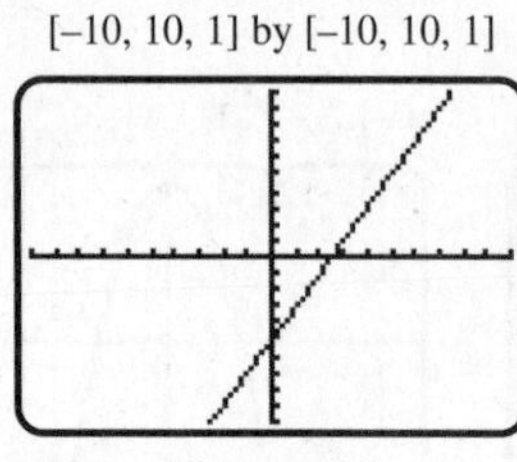

Figure 54

[−6, 6, 1] by [−4, 4, 1]

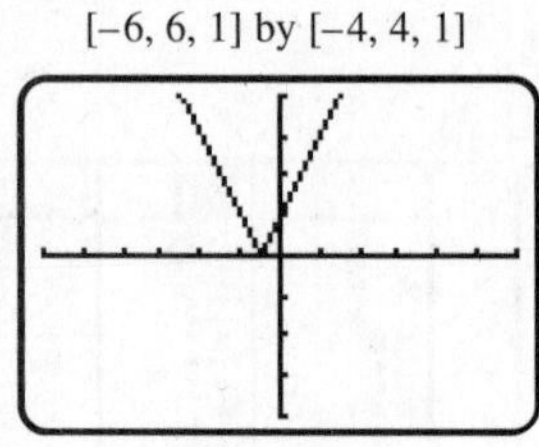

Figure 55

[−10, 10, 1] by [−10, 10, 1]

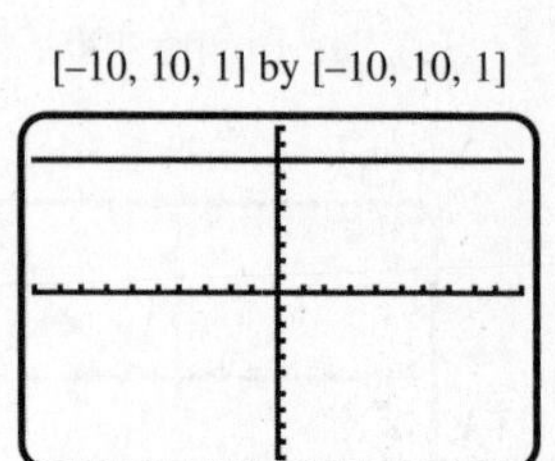

Figure 56

55. Verbal: Multiply the input $x$ by 2, add 1, and then take the absolute value.

Graphical: Graph $Y_1 = \text{abs}(2X + 1)$. See Figure 55.

Numerical:

| $x$ | −2 | −1 | 0 | 1 | 2 |
|---|---|---|---|---|---|
| $y$ | 3 | 1 | 1 | 3 | 5 |

$f(2) = 5$

56. Verbal: Regardless of the input $x$, outputalways has a value of 8.

Graphical: $Y_1 = 8$. See Figure 56.

Numerical:

| $x$ | −2 | −1 | 0 | 1 | 2 |
|---|---|---|---|---|---|
| $y$ | 8 | 8 | 8 | 8 | 8 |

$f(2) = 8$

57. Verbal: Subtract the input $x$ from 5.

Graphical: $Y_1 = 5 - X$. See Figure 57.

Numerical:

| $x$ | −2 | −1 | 0 | 1 | 2 |
|---|---|---|---|---|---|
| $y$ | 7 | 6 | 5 | 4 | 3 |

$f(2) = 3$

58. Verbal: Compute the absolute value of the input $x$.

Graphical: Graph $Y_1 = \text{abs}(X)$. See Figure 58.

Numerical:

| $x$ | −2 | −1 | 0 | 1 | 2 |
|---|---|---|---|---|---|
| $y$ | 2 | 1 | 0 | 1 | 2 |

$f(2) = 2$

[−10, 10, 1] by [−10, 10, 1]

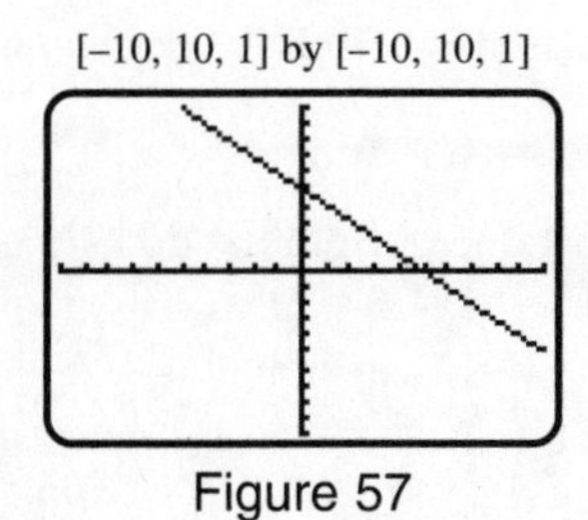

Figure 57

[−6, 6, 1] by [−4, 4, 1]

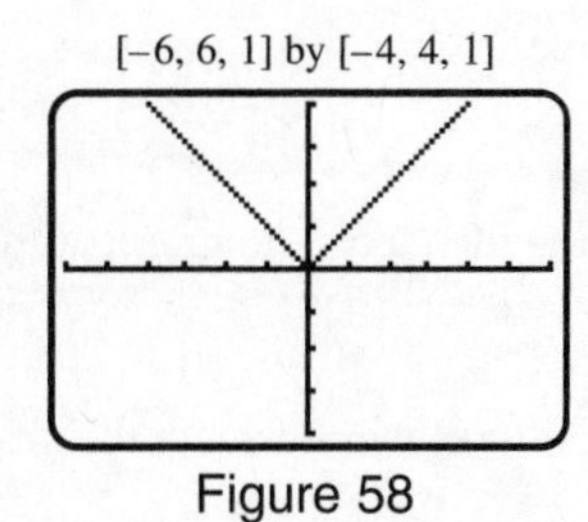

Figure 58

[−6, 6, 1] by [−4, 4, 1]

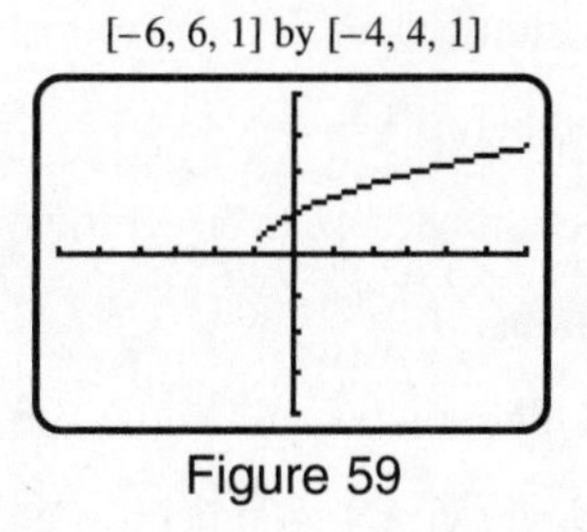

Figure 59

[−10, 10, 1] by [−10, 10, 1]

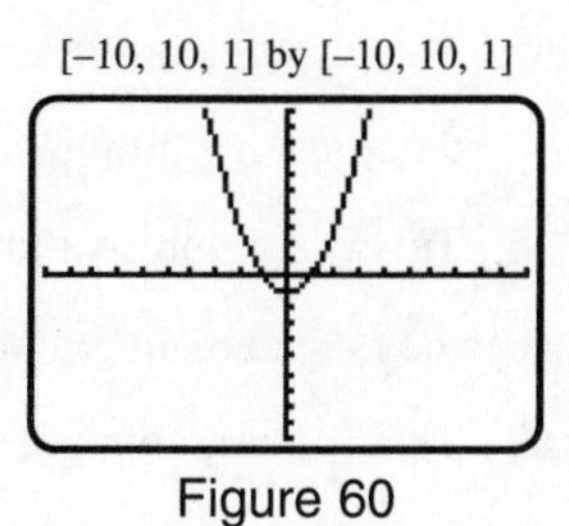

Figure 60

59. Verbal: Add 1 to the input $x$ and then take the square root of the result.

Graphical: Graph $Y_1 = \sqrt{(X + 1)}$ See Figure 59.

Numerical:

| $x$ | −2 | −1 | 0 | 1 | 2 |
|---|---|---|---|---|---|
| $y$ | — | 0 | 1 | $\sqrt{2}$ | $\sqrt{3}$ |

$f(2) = \sqrt{3}$

60. Verbal: Square the input $x$ and then subtract 1 from the result.

Graphical: $Y_1 = X^2 - 1$. See Figure 60.

Numerical:

| $x$ | −2 | −1 | 0 | 1 | 2 |
|---|---|---|---|---|---|
| $y$ | 3 | 0 | −1 | 0 | 3 |

$f(2) = 3$

61. (a) $g = \{(-1, 2), (0, 4), (1, -3), (2, 2)\}$

(b) $D = \{-1, 0, 1, 2\}$; $R = \{-3, 2, 4\}$

62. (a) $g = \{(-4, 5), (0, -5), (4, 5), (8, 0)\}$

(b) $D = \{-4, 0, 4, 8\}$; $R = \{-5, 0, 5\}$

63. It costs about \$0.50 per mile.

Symbolic: $f(x) = 0.50x$.

Graphical: See Figure 63a.

Numerical: See Figure 63b.

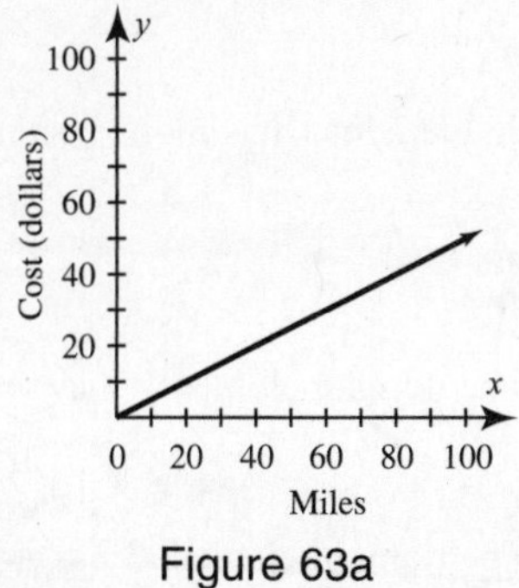


Figure 63a

| Miles | 1 | 2 | 3 | 4 | 5 | 6 |
|---|---|---|---|---|---|---|
| Cost | 0.50 | 1.00 | 1.50 | 2.00 | 2.50 | 3.00 |

Figure 63b

64.

| Bills (millions) | 0 | 1 | 2 | 3 | 4 | 5 | 6 |
|---|---|---|---|---|---|---|---|
| Counterfeit Bills | 0 | 9 | 18 | 27 | 36 | 45 | 54 |

65. This is a graph of a function because every vertical line intersects the graph at most once. Both the domain and the range are all real numbers.

66. This is a graph of a function because every vertical line intersects the graph at most once. Both the domain and the range are all real numbers.

67. This is not a graph of a function because some vertical lines can intersect the graph twice. Because a vertical line can intersect the graph twice, two functions are necessary to create this graph.

68. This is a graph of a function because every vertical line intersects the graph at most once. The domain is $\{x \mid -5 \le x \le 5\}$. The range is $\{y \mid -1 \le y \le 1\}$.

69. This is a graph of a function because every vertical line intersects the graph at most once. The domain is $\{x \mid -4 \le x \le 4\}$. The range is $\{y \mid 0 \le y \le 4\}$.

70. This is not a graph of a function because it is possible for a vertical line to intersect the graph four times. Four functions would be necessary to create this graph.

71. Yes. The calculation of the cube root requires the input of a real number. It produces a single output. A number has only one cube root.

72. Yes. A person can only have one age for a given date.

73. No. On most English exams, more than one person passes. Therefore, for a given English exam as input, there is more than one output.

74. No. The domain for most relations will contain more than one $x$-value.

75. Yes, because the IDs are unique.

76. No, because two students could have the same height.

77. No. The ordered pairs (1, 2) and (1, 3) belong to the set $S$. The domain element 1 has more than one range element associated with it.

78. Yes. Each element in its domain is associated with exactly one range element.

79. Yes. Each element in its domain is associated with exactly one range element.

80. No. The ordered pairs $(a, 2)$ and $(a, 3)$ belong to the set $S$. The domain element $a$ has more than one range element associated with it.

81. No. The ordered pairs (1, 10.5) and (1, –0.5) belong to the set $S$. The domain element 1 has more than one range element associated with it.

82. Yes. Each element in its domain is associated with exactly one range element.

83. No, for example, the ordered pairs (1, –1) and (1, 1) belong to the relation. The domain element 1 has more than one range element associated with it.

84. No, for example, the ordered pairs (3, 2) and (3, –2) belong to the relation. The domain element 3 has more than one range element associated with it.

85. Yes. Each element in the domain of $f$ is associated with exactly one range element.

86. Yes. Each element in the domain of $f$ is associated with exactly one range element.

87. No, for example, the ordered pairs $(0, \sqrt{70})$ and $(0, -\sqrt{70})$ belong to the relation. The domain element 0 has more than one range element associated with it.

88. No, for example, the ordered pairs $(1, 1)$ and $(1, -1)$ belong to the relation. The domain element 1 has more than one range element associated with it.

89. Yes. Each element in the domain of $f$ is associated with exactly one range element.

90. Yes. Each element in the domain of $f$ is associated with exactly one range element.

91. $g(x) = 12x \Rightarrow g(10) = 12(10) = 120$; there are 120 inches in 10 feet.

92. $g(x) = 4x \Rightarrow g(10) = 4(10) = 40$; there are 40 quarts in 10 gallons.

93. $g(x) = 0.25x \Rightarrow g(10) = 0.25(10) = 2.50$; there are 2.5 dollars in 10 quarters.

94. $g(x) = 4x \Rightarrow g(10) = 4(10) = 40$; there are 40 quarters in 10 dollars.

95. $g(x) = 60 \cdot 60 \cdot 24 \cdot x \Rightarrow g(x) = 86{,}400x \Rightarrow g(10) = 86{,}400(10) = 864{,}000$; there are 864,000 seconds in 10 days.

96. $g(x) = 5280x \Rightarrow g(10) = 5280(10) = 52{,}800$; there are 52,800 feet in 10 miles.

97. (a) $I = \{(N, 19162), (H, 26029), (B, 41681), (M, 51316)\}$

(b) $D = \{N, H, B, M\}$; $R = \{19162, 26029, 41681, 51316\}$

98. (a) $P = \{(2002, 0.5\%), (2003, 1.3\%), (2004, 2.9\%), (2005, 5.7\%), (2006, 9.4\%)\}$

(b) $D = \{2002, 2003, 2004, 2005, 2006\}$; $R = \{0.5\%, 1.3\%, 2.9\%, 5.7\%, 9.4\%\}$

99. $N(x) = 2200x$; $N(3) = 2200(3) = 6600$; in 3 years the average person uses 6600 napkins.

100. $W(x) = 40x$; $W(30) = 40(30) = 1200$; 30 loads of clothes use 1200 gallons of water.

101. Verbal: Multiply the input $x$ by –5.8 to obtain the change in temperature.

Symbolic: $f(x) = -5.8x$.

Graphical: $Y_1 = -5.8X$. See Figure 101a.

Numerical: Table $Y_1 = -5.8X$. See Figure 101b.

[0, 3, 1] by [–20, 20, 5]

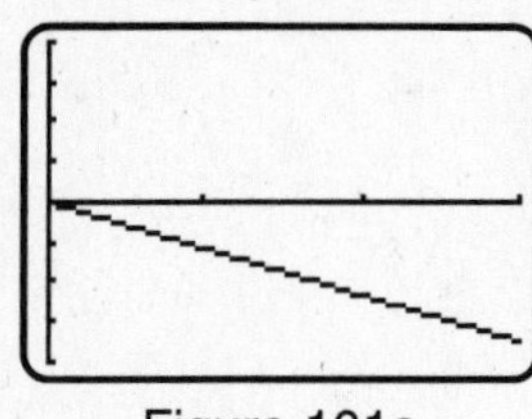

Figure 101a

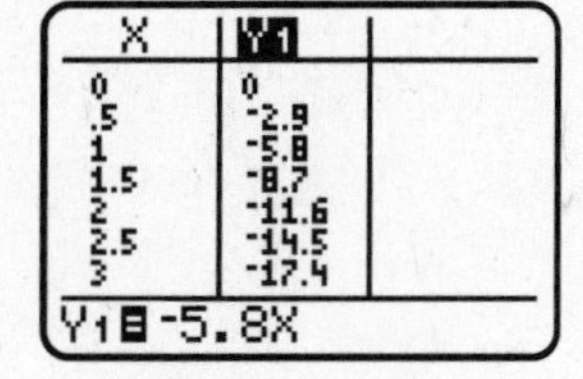


Figure 101b

102. Since 6 ft. 3 in. = 75 in. and $f(x) = 0.72x + 2$, $f(75) = 0.72(75) + 2 = 56$ in.;

$f(x + 1) - f(x) = 0.72(x + 1) + 2 - [0.72x + 2] = 0.72x + 0.72 + 2 - 0.72x - 2 = 0.72$; for each 1-inch increase in a person's height, the recommended crutch length increases by 0.72 in.

103. Let $x$ = time in seconds that elapsed for the observer to hear the thunder from the lightning bolt. The distance is found by multiplying the speed by the time. Since 5280 ft. = 1 mi., the distance in miles is given by $f(x) = \frac{1150}{5280}x = \frac{115}{528}x$; $f(15) = \frac{115}{528}(15) \approx 3.3$; with a 15-second delay, the lightning bolt was about 3.3 miles away.

104. A reasonable domain is $0 < x \le 20$. For this domain, the range is $0 < y \le 4.4$. See Figure 104.

*Answers may vary.*

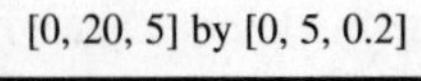


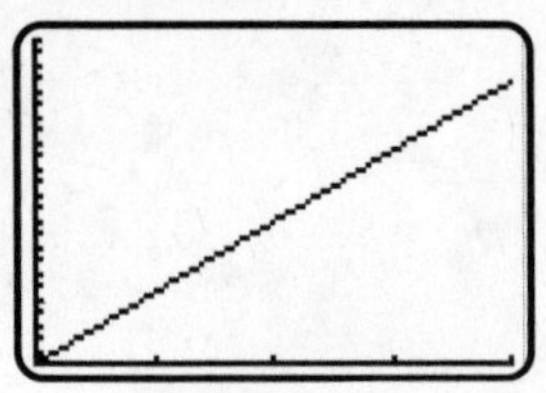

Figure 104

## 1.4: Types of Functions

1. $f(x) = 5 - 2x \Rightarrow f(x) = -2x + 5;\ a = -2, b = 5$

2. $f(x) = 3 - 4x \Rightarrow f(x) = -4x + 3;\ a = -4, b = 3$

3. $f(x) = -8x \Rightarrow f(x) = -8x + 0;\ a = -8, b = 0$

4. $f(x) = 10x \Rightarrow f(x) = 10x + 0;\ a = 10, b = 0$

5. $f(x) = 7 \Rightarrow f(x) = 0x + 7;\ a = 0, b = 7$

6. $f(x) = -6 \Rightarrow f(x) = 0x - 6;\ a = 0, b = -6$

7. $m = \dfrac{5 - 6}{2 - 4} = \dfrac{-1}{-2} = \dfrac{1}{2} = 0.5$

8. $m = \dfrac{-7 - 5}{-3 - (-8)} = \dfrac{-12}{5} = -2.4$

9. $m = \dfrac{-2 - 4}{5 - (-1)} = \dfrac{-6}{6} = -1$

10. $m = \dfrac{7 - (-4)}{-15 - 10} = \dfrac{11}{-25} = -0.44$

11. $m = \dfrac{-8 - (-8)}{7 - 12} = \dfrac{0}{-5} = 0$

12. $m = \dfrac{2 - (-5)}{8 - 8} = \dfrac{7}{0}$, undefined slope

13. $m = \dfrac{0.4 - (-0.1)}{-0.3 - 0.2} = \dfrac{0.5}{-0.5} = -1$

14. $m = \dfrac{1.1 - 0.6}{-0.2 - (-0.3)} = \dfrac{0.5}{0.1} = 5$

15. $m = \dfrac{7.6 - 9.2}{-0.3 - (-0.5)} = \dfrac{-1.6}{0.2} = -8$

16. $m = \dfrac{5 - 12}{1.6 - 1.6} = \dfrac{-7}{0} =$ undefined

17. $m = \dfrac{7.9 - 5.6}{1994 - 1997} = -\dfrac{23}{30} \approx -0.7667$

18. $m = \dfrac{380 - 108}{1900 - 1824} = \dfrac{272}{76} = \dfrac{68}{19} \approx 3.5789$

19. $m = \dfrac{8 - 6}{-5 - (-5)} = \dfrac{2}{0} = \text{undefined}$

20. $m = \dfrac{7 - 7}{19 - 17} = \dfrac{0}{2} = 0$

21. $m = \dfrac{\frac{7}{10} - \left(-\frac{3}{5}\right)}{-\frac{5}{6} - \frac{1}{3}} = \dfrac{\frac{13}{10}}{-\frac{7}{6}} = \dfrac{13}{10} \cdot \left(-\dfrac{6}{7}\right) = -\dfrac{39}{35} \approx -1.143$

22. $m = \dfrac{\frac{3}{16} - \left(-\frac{7}{8}\right)}{\frac{1}{10} - \left(-\frac{13}{15}\right)} = \dfrac{\frac{17}{16}}{\frac{29}{30}} = \dfrac{17}{16} \cdot \dfrac{30}{29} = \dfrac{255}{232} \approx 1.0991$

23. Slope $= 2$; the graph rises 2 units for every unit increase in $x$.

24. Slope $= -1$; the graph falls 1 unit for every unit increase in $x$.

25. Slope $= -\dfrac{3}{4}$ ; the graph falls $\dfrac{3}{4}$ unit for every unit increase in $x$, or equivalently, the graph falls 3 units for every 4-unit increase in $x$.

26. Slope $= \dfrac{2}{3}$ ; the graph rises $\dfrac{2}{3}$ unit for every unit increase in $x$, or equivalently, the graph rises 2 units for every 3-unit increase in $x$.

27. Slope $= 0$; the graph neither falls nor rises since the $y$-value is always –5.

28. Slope $= 1$; the graph rises 1 unit for every unit increase in $x$.

29. Slope $= -1$; the graph falls 1 unit for every unit increase in $x$.

30. Slope $= 0$; the graph neither falls nor rises since the $y$-value is always 23.

31. (a) Buying no carpet should and does cost \$0.

    (b) Slope $= \dfrac{100}{5} = 20$

    (c) The carpet costs \$20 per square yard.

32. (a) Zero tons of rock would cost \$0.

    (b) Slope $= \dfrac{25}{1} = 25$

    (c) The rock costs \$25 per ton.

33. (a) $P(x) = 19.4x \Rightarrow P(20) = 19.4(20) = 388$. Burning 20 gallons of gas produces 388 lbs. of $CO_2$.

    (b) Slope equals 19.4; 19.4 lbs. of $CO_2$ are produced for every gallon of gas that is burned.

34. (a) $D(x) = 150 - 20x \Rightarrow D(5) = 150 - 20(5) = 50$. After 5 hours the train is 50 miles from the station.

    (b) Slope equals –20. The train is traveling toward the station at 20 mph.

35. (a) $D(2) = 75(2) = 150$ miles

    (b) Slope $= 75$; the car is traveling away from the rest stop at 75 miles per hour.

36. (a) To find the median ages in 1980 and 2000, we must evaluate $A(1980)$ and $A(2000)$.

    $A(1980) = 0.243(1980) - 450.8 = 30.34$ and $A(2000) = 0.243(2000) - 450.8 = 35.2$

    In 1980, the median age was 30.34 years and in 2000, it increased to 35.2 years.

    (b) Since $A(t) = 0.243t - 450.8$, the slope of its graph is $m = 0.243$. The value of 0.243 means that the median age in the United States is increasing by approximately 0.243 each year from 1970 to 2010.

37. If the distance is constant, the car is not moving. The car's velocity is zero.

38. If the car's distance is described by a linear function $f$, its velocity is equal to the slope of the graph of $f$. In this exercise the car's velocity is equal to $a$, where the sign of $a$ indicates the direction traveled by the car.

39. $f(x) = -2x + 5$ is a linear function, but not a constant function, with a slope of $m = -2$. See Figure 39.

40. $f(x) = 3x - 2$ is a linear function, but not a constant function. See Figure 40.

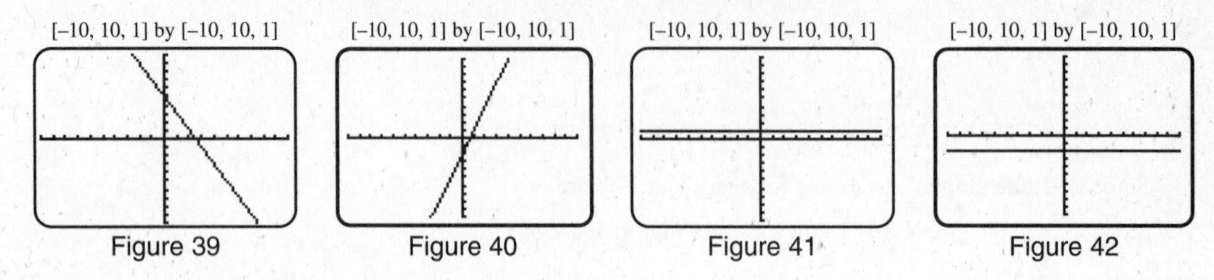

Figure 39 Figure 40 Figure 41 Figure 42

41. $f(x) = 1$ is a constant (and linear) function. See Figure 41.

42. $f(x) = -2$ is a constant (and linear) function. See Figure 42.

43. From its graph, we see that $f(x) = |x + 1|$ represents a nonlinear function. See Figure 43.

44. From its graph, we see that $f(x) = |2x - 1|$ represents a nonlinear function. See Figure 44.

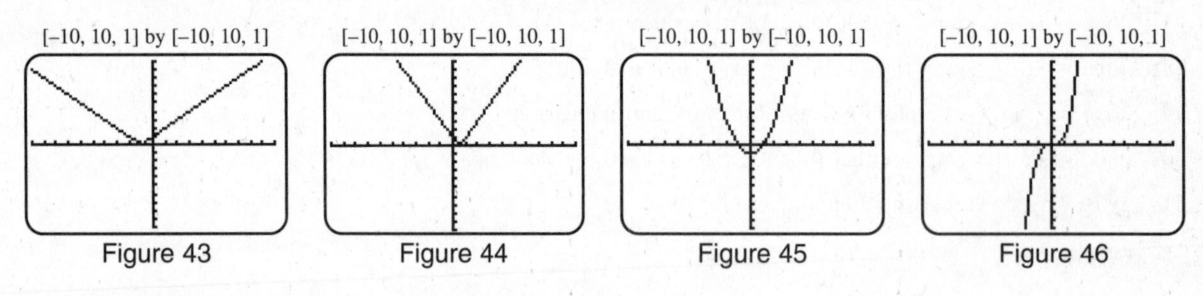

Figure 43 Figure 44 Figure 45 Figure 46

45. From its graph, we see that $f(x) = x^2 - 1$ represents a nonlinear function. See Figure 45.

46. From its graph, we see that $f(x) = x^3$ represents a nonlinear function. See Figure 46.

47. From its graph, we see that $f(x) = 2\sqrt{x}$ is a nonlinear function. See Figure 47.

48. From its graph, we see that $f(x) = \sqrt{x - 1}$ is a nonlinear function. See Figure 48.

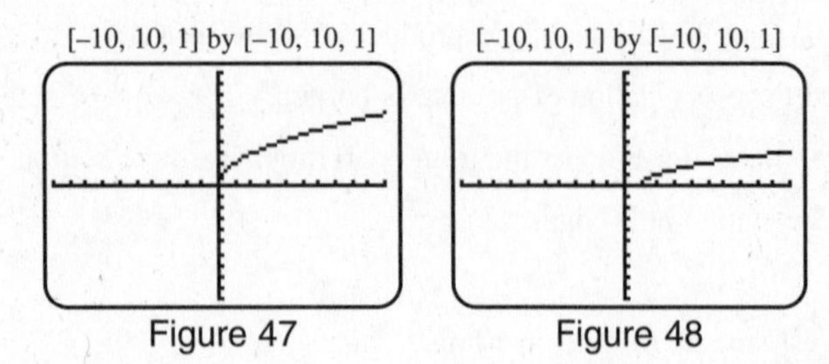

Figure 47 Figure 48

49. Between each pair of points, the $y$-values increase 4 units for each unit increase in $x$. Therefore, the data is linear. The slope of the line passing through the data points is 4.

50. The $y$-values decrease 1.5 units for every 2-unit increase in $x$. Therefore, the data is linear. The slope of the line passing through the data points is $-\frac{1.5}{2} = -0.75$.

51. The $y$-values do not increase by a constant amount for each 2-unit increase in $x$. The data is nonlinear.

52. The data is linear. The slope of the line passing through the data points is 0.

53. The $y$-values decrease 0.5 unit for each unit increase in $x$, therefore, the data is linear. The slope of the line passing through the data points is $-0.5$.

54. The $y$-values do not increase by a constant amount for each 5-unit increase in $x$. The data is nonlinear.

55. (a) See Figure 55.

(b) The function is linear since the slopes of the line segments are all equal.

56. (a) See Figure 56.

(b) From the line graph it can be seen that $f$ is linear. The slopes of the line segments are all equal.

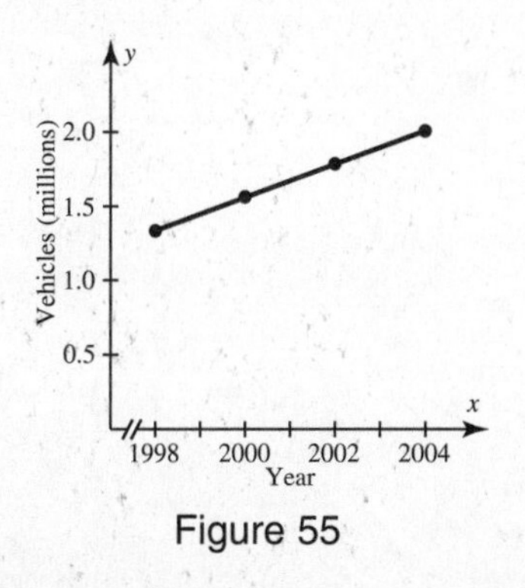

Figure 55

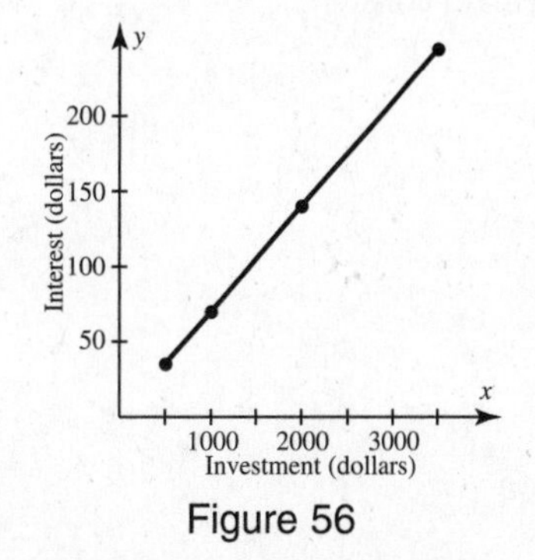

Figure 56

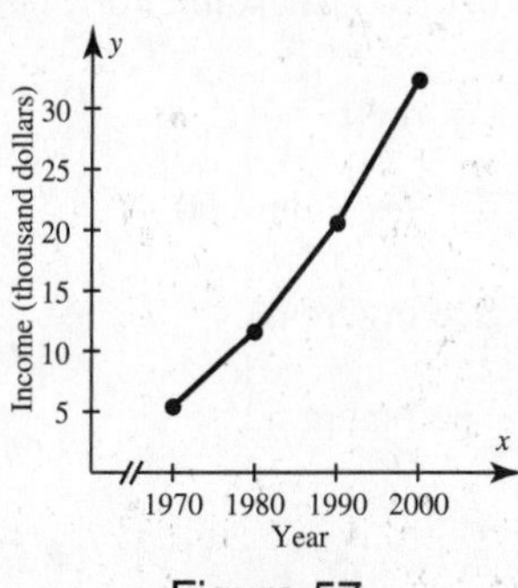

Figure 57

57. (a) See Figure 57.

(b) From the line graph it can be seen that the data is not linear. The function $f$ is nonlinear.

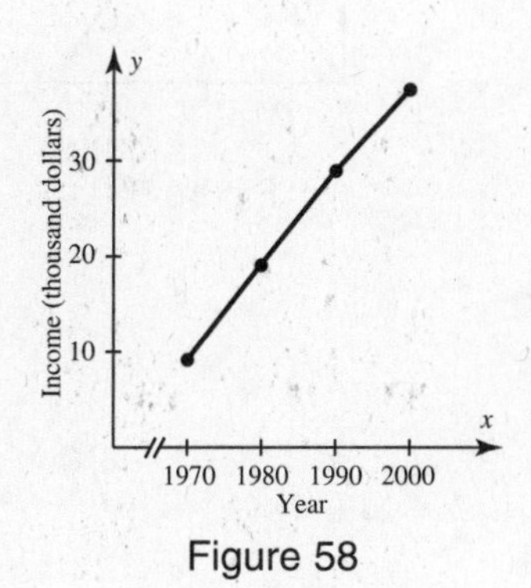

Figure 58

58. (a) See Figure 58.

(b) The function $f$ is a nonlinear function, although the graph looks nearly linear.

59. (a) Since the wind speed is not constant, it cannot be represented exactly by a constant function.

    (b) The average of the twelve wind speeds is 7 miles per hour. It would be reasonable to approximate the wind speed at Myrtle Beach by $f(x) = 7$.

    (c) A scatterplot of the data and the function $f(x) = 7$ are shown in Figure 59.

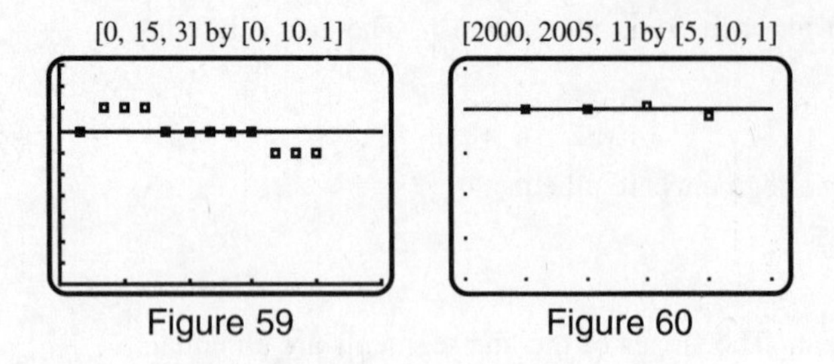

Figure 59 Figure 60

60. (a) No. The value for $y$ does not remain constant.

    (b) $f(x) = 9$

    (c) See Figure 60.

61. See Figure 61.

62. See Figure 62.

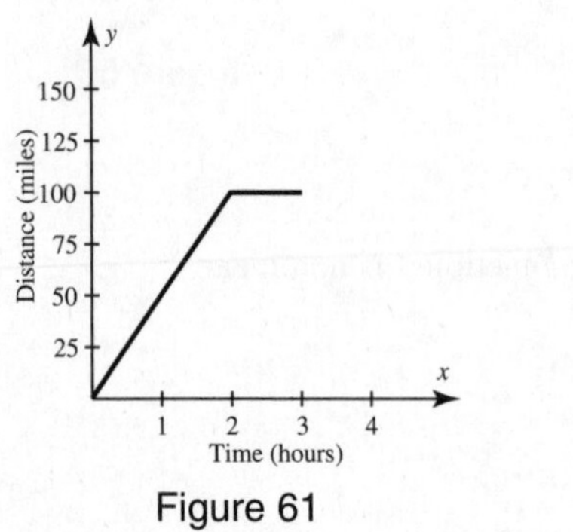

Figure 61

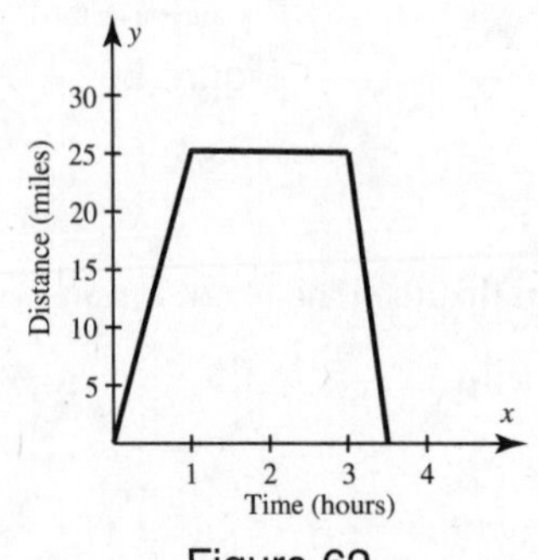

Figure 62

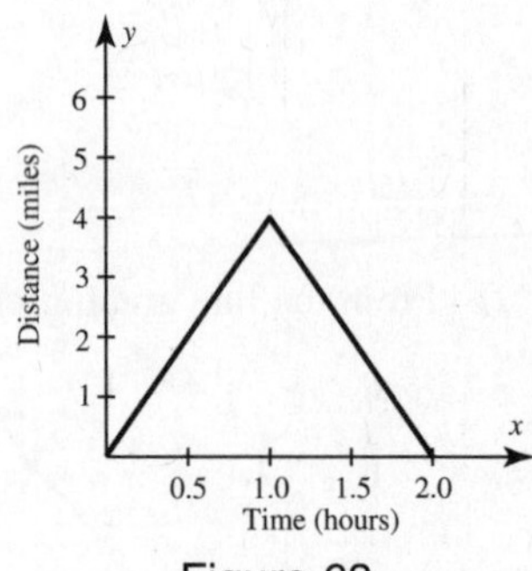

Figure 63

63. See Figure 63.

64. See Figure 64.

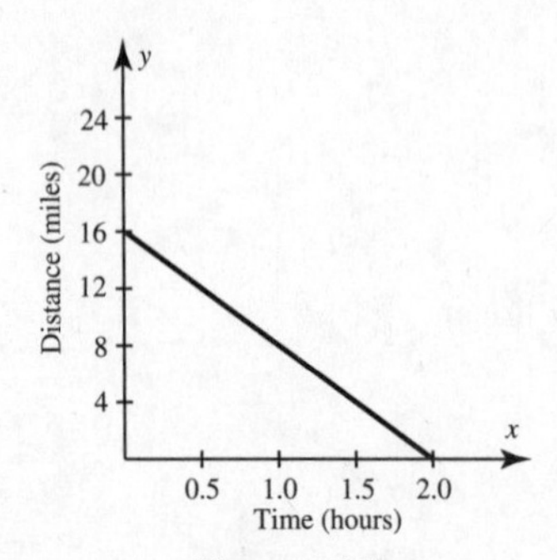

Figure 64

## Extended and Discovery Exercises for Section 1.4

1. (a) $C(r) = 2\pi r \Rightarrow C(r+1) = 2\pi(r+1) = 2\pi r + 2\pi$; for every 1 inch increase in the radius, the circumference increases by $2\pi$ inches. So the circumference increases at a constant rate of $2\pi$ inches per second.

   (b) No, because the area function, $A(r) = \pi r^2$, depends on the radius squared. The area function is not linear and thus does not increase at a constant rate.

## Checking Basic Concepts for Sections 1.3 and 1.4

1. Symbolic: $f(x) = 5280x$

   Numerical: Use a table $f$ starting at $x = 1$, incrementing by 1. See Figure 1a.

   Graphical: Graph $Y_1 = 5280X$ as shown in Figure 1b.

| $x$ | 1 | 2 | 3 | 4 | 5 |
|---|---|---|---|---|---|
| $f(x)$ | 5280 | 10,560 | 15,840 | 21,120 | 26,400 |

Figure 1a

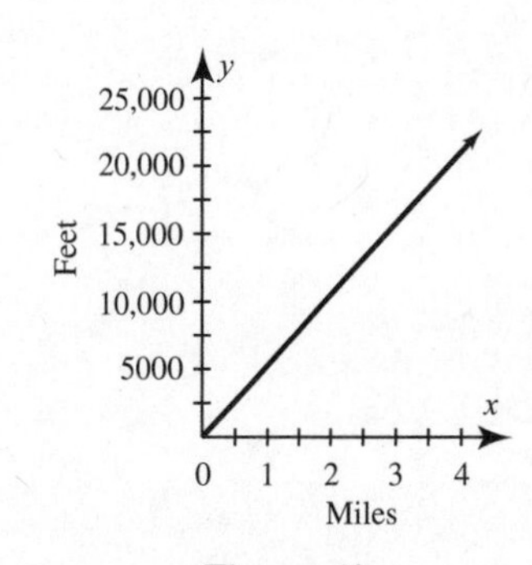


Figure 1b

2. (a) $f(2) = \dfrac{2(2)}{2-4} = \dfrac{4}{-2} = -2$; $f(a+4) = \dfrac{2(a+4)}{(a+4)-4} = \dfrac{2a+8}{a}$

   (b) The function is undefined when the denominator $x - 4 = 0$. This happens when $x = 4$; therefore, $D = \{x \mid x \neq 4\}$.

3. See Figure 3. $D =$ all real numbers; $R = \{y \mid y \geq -2\}$

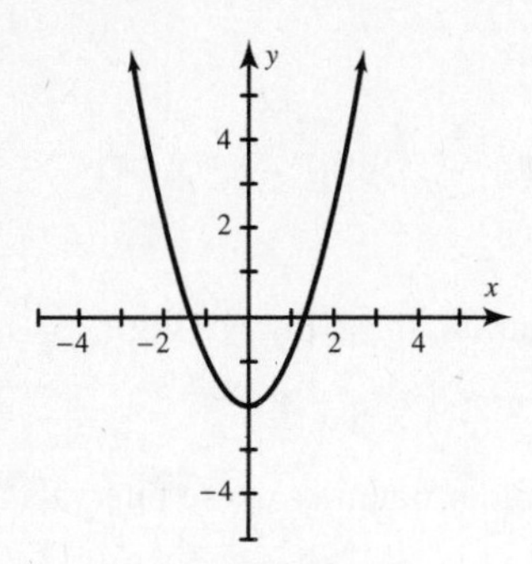


Figure 3

4. The slope is calculated as follows: $m = \dfrac{-5-4}{4-(-2)} = -\dfrac{9}{6} = -\dfrac{3}{2}$

   If the graph of the linear function $f(x) = ax + b$, passes through the points (–2, 4) and (4, –5), its slope must be equal to $-\dfrac{3}{2}$; therefore, $a = -\dfrac{3}{2}$.

5. (a) $f(x) = -1.4x + 5.1$ represents a linear function.

   (b) $f(x) = 25$ represents a constant (and linear) function.

   (c) $f(x) = 2x^2 - 5$ represents a nonlinear function.

## 1.5: Functions and Their Rates of Change

1. $[5, \infty)$
2. $(-\infty, 100)$
3. $[4, 19)$
4. $(-4, -1)$
5. $(-\infty, -37]$
6. $(-\infty, -3]$
7. $[-1, \infty)$
8. $[-3, 17)$
9. $(-\infty, 1) \cup [3, \infty)$
10. $(-\infty, -2] \cup [0, \infty)$
11. $(-3, 5]$
12. $[2, \infty)$
13. $(-\infty, -2)$
14. $[-4, 4]$
15. $(-\infty, -2) \cup [1, \infty)$
16. $(-\infty, -1] \cup [1, \infty)$
17. $f$ is decreasing on $(-\infty, \infty)$. In set-builder notation, the interval is $\{x \mid -\infty < x < \infty\}$.
18. $f$ is decreasing on $[0, \infty)$. In set-builder notation, the interval is $\{x \mid x \geq 0\}$.
19. $f$ is increasing on $[2, \infty)$ and decreasing on $(-\infty, 2]$. In set-builder notation, these intervals are $\{x \mid x \geq 2\}$ and $\{x \mid x \leq 2\}$ respectively.
20. $f$ is increasing on $(-\infty, -1]$ and decreasing on $[-1, \infty)$. In set-builder notation, these intervals are $\{x \mid x \leq -1\}$ and $\{x \mid x \geq -1\}$ respectively.
21. $f$ is increasing on $(-\infty, -2] \cup [1, \infty)$ and decreasing on $[-2, 1]$. In set-builder notation, these intervals are $\{x \mid x \leq 2 \text{ or } x \geq 1\}$ and $\{x \mid -2 \leq x \leq 1\}$ respectively.
22. $f$ is increasing on $(-\infty, -2] \cup [0, 1]$ and decreasing on $[-2, 0] \cup [1, \infty)$. In set-builder notation, these intervals are $\{x \mid x \leq -2 \text{ or } 0 \leq x \leq 1\}$ and $\{x \mid -2 \leq x \leq 0 \text{ or } x \geq 1\}$ respectively.
23. $f$ is increasing on $[-8, 0] \cup [8, \infty)$ and decreasing on $(-\infty, -8] \cup [0, 8]$. In set-builder notation, these intervals are $\{x \mid -8 \leq x \leq 0 \text{ or } x \geq 8\}$ and $\{x \mid x \leq -8 \text{ or } 0 \leq x \leq 8\}$ respectively.

24. $f$ is increasing on $(-\infty, 0]$ and decreasing on $[0, \infty)$. In set builder notation, these intervals are $\{x \mid x \leq 0\}$ and $\{x \mid x \geq 0\}$ respectively.

25. When $x$ increases, $f(x)$ remains constant at $(-3)$ $\Rightarrow$ the function is neither increasing or decreasing.

26. When $x$ increases, $f(x)$ remains constant at 5 $\Rightarrow$ the function is neither increasing or decreasing.

27. The graph of this equation is linear with a slope of 2 $\Rightarrow$ it is increasing: $(-\infty, \infty)$ and decreasing: never. In set builder notation, the interval is $\{x \mid -\infty < x < \infty\}$.

28. The graph of this equation is linear with a slope of $-1$ $\Rightarrow$ it is increasing: never and decreasing: $(-\infty, \infty)$. In set builder notation, the interval is $\{x \mid -\infty < x < \infty\}$.

29. The graph of this equation is a parabola with a vertex $(0, -2)$ $\Rightarrow$ it is increasing: $[0, \infty)$ and decreasing: $(-\infty, 0)$. In set builder notation, these intervals are $\{x \mid x \geq 0\}$ and $\{x \mid x \leq 0\}$ respectively.

30. The graph of this equation is a parabola with a vertex (0, 0), because of the negative coefficient it opens downward $\Rightarrow$ it is increasing: $(-\infty, 0]$ and decreasing: $[0, \infty)$. In set builder notation, these intervals are $\{x \mid x \leq 0\}$ and $\{x \mid x \geq 0\}$ respectively.

31. The graph of this equation is a parabola with a vertex (1, 1), because of the negative coefficient before $x^2$ it opens downward $\Rightarrow$ it is increasing: $(-\infty, 1]$ and decreasing: $[1, \infty)$. In set builder notation, these intervals are $\{x \mid x \leq 1\}$ and $\{x \mid x \geq 1\}$ respectively.

32. The graph of this equation is a parabola with a vertex $(2, -4)$ $\Rightarrow$ it is increasing: $[2, \infty)$ and decreasing: $(-\infty, 2]$. In set builder notation, these intervals are $\{x \mid x \geq 2\}$ and $\{x \mid x \leq 2\}$ respectively.

33. The square root equation graph has a starting point $(1, 0)$, all $x$-values less than 1 are undefined $\Rightarrow$ it is increasing: $[1, \infty)$ and decreasing: never. In set builder notation, the interval is $\{x \mid x \geq 1\}$.

34. The square root equation graph has a starting point $(-1, 0)$, because of the negative coefficient before $\sqrt{x+1}$ the graph opens down to the right $\Rightarrow$ it is increasing: never and decreasing: $[-1, \infty)$. In set builder notation, the interval is $\{x \mid x \geq -1\}$.

35. The absolute value graph has a vertex $(-3, 0)$ $\Rightarrow$ it is increasing: $[-3, \infty)$ and decreasing: $(-\infty, -3]$. In set builder notation, these intervals are $\{x \mid x \geq -3\}$ and $\{x \mid x \leq -3\}$ respectively.

36. The absolute value graph has a vertex $(1, 0)$ $\Rightarrow$ it is increasing: $[1, \infty)$ and decreasing: $(-\infty, 1]$. In set builder notation, these intervals are $\{x \mid x \geq 1\}$ and $\{x \mid x \leq 1\}$ respectively.

37. The basic $x^3$ function is always increasing $\Rightarrow$ it is increaing: $(-\infty, \infty)$ and decreasing: never. In set builder notation, the interval is $\{x \mid -\infty < x < \infty\}$.

38. The basic $\sqrt[3]{x}$ function is always increasing $\Rightarrow$ it is increaing: $(-\infty, \infty)$ and decreasing: never. In set builder notation, the interval is $\{x \mid -\infty < x < \infty\}$.

39. The graph of this cubic equation has turning points $\left(-2, \frac{16}{3}\right)$ and $\left(2, \frac{-16}{3}\right)$ $\Rightarrow$ it is increasing: $(-\infty, -2]$ or $[2, \infty)$; and decreasing: $[-2, 2]$. In set builder notation, these intervals are $\{x \mid x \leq -2 \text{ or } x \geq 2\}$ and $\{x \mid -2 \leq x \leq 2\}$ respectively.

40. The graph of this cubic equation has turning points $(-1, 2)$ and $(1, -2) \Rightarrow$ it is increasing: $(-\infty, -1]$ or $[1, \infty)$; and decreasing: $[-1, 1]$. In set builder notation, these intervals are $\{x \mid x \le -1 \text{ or } x \ge 1\}$ and $\{x \mid -1 \le x \le 1\}$ respectively.

41. The graph of this cubic equation has turning points $(-2, 20)$ and $(1, -7) \Rightarrow$ it is increasing: $(-\infty, -2]$ or $[1, \infty)$; and decreasing: $[-2, 1]$. In set builder notation, these intervals are $\{x \mid x \le -2 \text{ or } x \ge 1\}$ and $\{x \mid -2 \le x \le 1\}$ respectively.

42. The graph of this cubic equation has a negative lead coefficient therefore is reflected through the $x$-axis has turning points $(-1, -15)$ and $(3, 17) \Rightarrow$ it is increasing: $[-1, 3]$; and decreasing: $(-\infty, -1]$ or $[3, \infty)$. In set builder notation, these intervals are $\{x \mid -1 \le x \le 3\}$ and $\{x \mid x \le -1 \text{ or } x \ge 3\}$ respectively.

43. The graph of this $x^4$ graph has a negative lead coefficient therefore is reflected through the $x$-axis has turning points $\left(-1, \frac{5}{12}\right)$, $(0, 0)$ and $\left(2, \frac{8}{3}\right) \Rightarrow$ it is increasing: $(-\infty, -1]$ or $[0, 2]$; and decreasing: $[-1, 0]$ or $[2, \infty)$. In set builder notation, these intervals are $\{x \mid x \le -1 \text{ or } 0 \le x \le 2\}$ and $\{x \mid -1 \le x \le 0 \text{ or } x \ge 2\}$ respectively.

44. The graph of this $x^4$ graph has turning points $(-2, -4)$, $(0, 0)$ and $(2, -4) \Rightarrow$ it is increasing: $[-2, 0]$ or $[2, \infty)$; and decreasing: $(-\infty, -2]$ or $[0, 2]$. In set builder notation, these intervals are $\{x \mid -2 \le x \le 0 \text{ or } x \ge 2\}$ and $\{x \mid x \le -2 \text{ or } 0 \le x \le 2\}$ respectively.

45. According to the graph the water levels are increasing on the time intervals $[0, 2.4]$, $[8.7, 14.7]$ and $[21, 27]$. In set builder notation, these intervals are $\{x \mid 0 \le x \le 2.4 \text{ or } 8.7 \le x \le 14.7 \text{ or } 21 \le x \le 27\}$.

46. According to the graph the water levels are decreasing on the time intervals $[2.4, 8.7]$ and $[14.7, 21]$. In set builder notation, these intervals are $\{x \mid 2.4 \le x \le 8.7 \text{ or } 14.7 \le x \le 21\}$.

47. The average rate of change from –3 to –1 is $\dfrac{f(-1) - f(-3)}{-1 - (-3)} = \dfrac{4 - 4}{2} = 0$.

The average rate of change from 1 to 3 is $\dfrac{f(3) - f(1)}{3 - 1} = \dfrac{4 - 4}{2} = 0$.

48. The average rate of change from –3 to –1 is $\dfrac{f(-1) - f(-3)}{-1 - (-3)} = \dfrac{-3 - (-7)}{2} = 2$.

The average rate of change from 1 to 3 is $\dfrac{f(3) - f(1)}{3 - 1} = \dfrac{5 - 1}{2} = 2$.

49. The average rate of change from –3 to –1 is $\dfrac{f(-1) - f(-3)}{-1 - (-3)} = \dfrac{3.7 - 1.3}{2} = \dfrac{2.4}{2} = 1.2$.

The average rate of change from 1 to 3 is $\dfrac{f(3) - f(1)}{3 - 1} = \dfrac{1.3 - 3.7}{2} = -\dfrac{2.4}{2} = -1.2$.

50. The average rate of change from –3 to –1 is $\dfrac{f(-1) - f(-3)}{-1 - (-3)} = \dfrac{-3.7 - (-1.3)}{2} = -\dfrac{2.4}{2} = -1.2$.

The average rate of change from 1 to 3 is $\dfrac{f(3) - f(1)}{3 - 1} = \dfrac{-1.3 - (-3.7)}{2} = \dfrac{2.4}{2} = 1.2$.

51. (a) $f(x) = x^2 \Rightarrow f(1) = 1^2 = 1$ and $f(2) = 2^2 = 4 \Rightarrow (1, 1), (2, 4)$; using the slope formula for rate of change we get $\dfrac{4-1}{2-1} = \dfrac{3}{1} = 3.$

(b) See Figure 51.

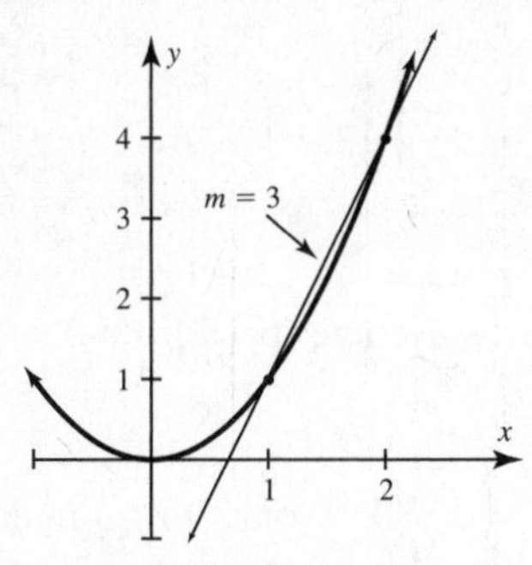


Figure 51

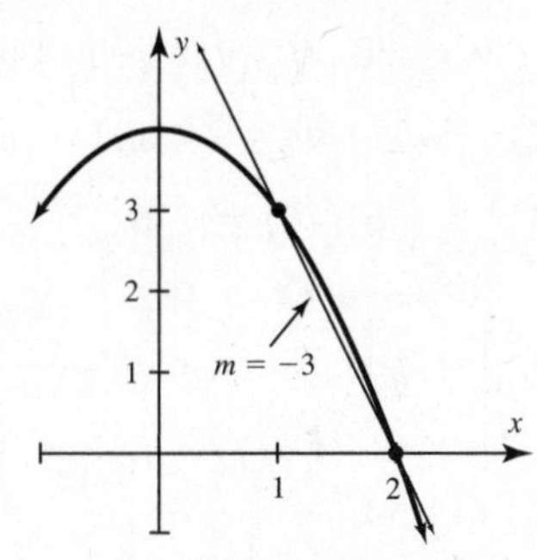


Figure 52

52. (a) $f(x) = 4 - x^2 \Rightarrow f(1) = 4 - (1)^2 = 4 - 1 = 3$ and $f(2) = 4 - (2)^2 = 4 - 4 = 0 \Rightarrow$ $(1, 3), (2, 0)$; using the slope formula for rate of change we get $\dfrac{0-3}{2-1} = \dfrac{-3}{1} = -3.$

(b) See Figure 52.

53. If $f(x) = 7x - 2$ then $\dfrac{f(4) - f(1)}{4 - 1} = 7$. The slope of the graph is 7.

54. If $f(x) = -8x + 5$ then $\dfrac{f(0) - f(-2)}{0 - (-2)} = -8$. The slope of the graph is $-8$.

55. If $f(x) = x^3 - 2x$ then $\dfrac{f(4) - f(2)}{4 - 2} = \dfrac{56 - 4}{2} = 26$. The slope of the line passing through the points $(2, f(2))$ and $(4, f(4))$ is 26.

56. If $f(x) = 0.5x^2 - 5$ then $\dfrac{f(4) - f(-1)}{4 - (-1)} = \dfrac{3 - (-4.5)}{5} = \dfrac{7.5}{5} = 1.5$. The slope of the line passing through the points $(-1, f(-1))$ and $(4, f(4))$ is 1.5.

57. If $f(x) = \sqrt{2x - 1}$ then $\dfrac{f(3) - f(1)}{3 - 1} \approx 0.62$. The slope of the line passing through the points $(1, f(1))$ and $(3, f(3))$ is approximately 0.62.

58. If $f(x) = \sqrt[3]{x + 1}$ then $\dfrac{f(26) - f(7)}{26 - 7} = \dfrac{3 - 2}{19} = \dfrac{1}{19} = 0.05$. The slope of the line passing through the points $(7, f(7))$ and $(26, f(26))$ is 0.05.

59. (a) The average rate of change from 1900 to 1940 is calculated as $\dfrac{182 - 3}{1940 - 1900} = \dfrac{179}{40} = 4.475$; from 1940 to 1980: $\dfrac{632 - 182}{1980 - 1940} = \dfrac{450}{40} = 11.25$; from 1980 to 2006: $\dfrac{371 - 632}{2006 - 1980} = \dfrac{-261}{26} \approx -10.04$.

(b) The average rates of change in cigarette consumption in the time periods 1900 to 1940, 1940 to 1980, and 1980 to 2006 were 4.475, 11.25, and –10.04, respectively.

60. (a) The average rate of change from 1940 to 1960 is calculated as $\frac{2.07 - 1.56}{1960 - 1940} = \frac{0.51}{20} = 0.0255$; from 1960 to 1980: $\frac{2.76 - 2.07}{1980 - 1960} = \frac{0.69}{20} = 0.0345$; from 1980 to 2000: $\frac{2.18 - 2.76}{2000 - 1980} = \frac{-0.58}{20} = -0.029$.

(b) The average rates of change in alcohol consumption during the time periods 1940 to 1960, 1960 to 1980, and 1980 to 2000 were 0.0255, 0.0345, and –0.029 respectively.

61. (a) $D(t) = 16t^2 \Rightarrow D(2) = (16)(2)^2 = (16)(4) = 64$ and
$D(t) = 16t^2 \Rightarrow D(4) = (16)(4)^2 = (16)(16) = 256$.

(b) Average rate of change from 2 to 4 is $\frac{256 - 64}{4 - 2} = \frac{192}{2} = 96$. The object's average speed from 2 to 4 seconds is 96 ft/sec.

62. (a) The a verage rate of change from 1 to 1.5 is $\frac{A(1.5) - A(1)}{1.5 - 1} = \frac{49 - 64}{0.5} = -30$. From 1 to 1.5 minutes water is leaving the tank at a rate of 30 gallons per minute, on average. From 2 to 2.5, the average rate of change is $\frac{A(2.5) - A(2)}{2.5 - 2} = \frac{25 - 36}{0.5} = -22$. From 2 to 2.5 minutes water is leaving the tank at a rate of 22 gallons per minute, on average.

(b) The average rates of change are different because water drains faster when the tank is fuller.

63. See Figure 63. *Answers may vary.*

64. See Figure 64. *Answers may vary.*

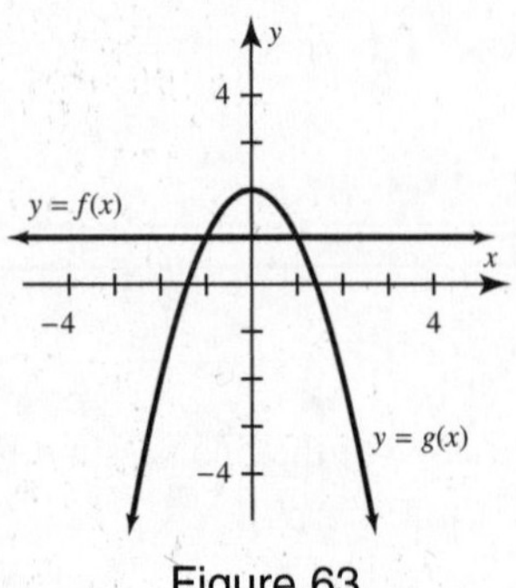

Figure 63

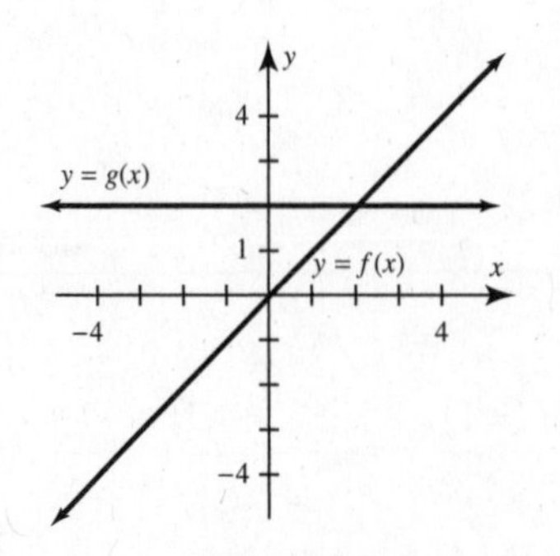

Figure 64

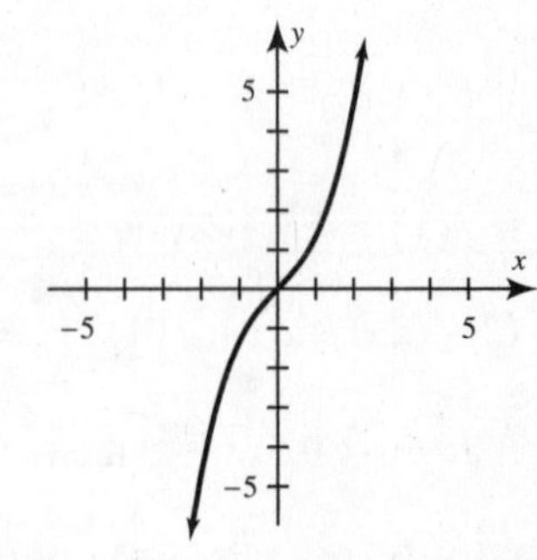

Figure 65

65. See Figure 65. *Answers may vary.*

66. See Figure 66. *Answers may vary.*

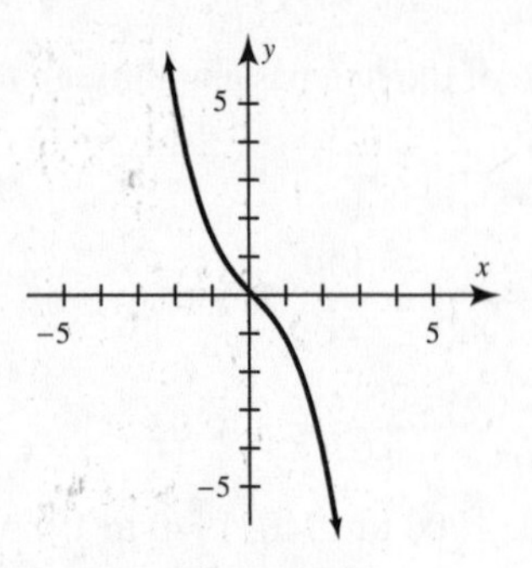

Figure 66

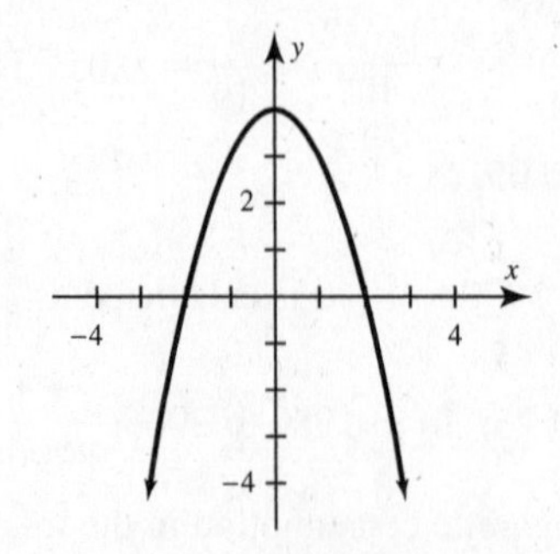

Figure 67

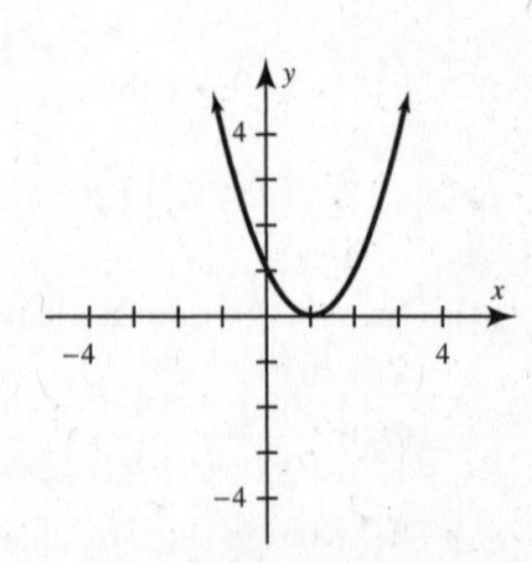

Figure 68

67. See Figure 67. *Answers may vary.*

68. See Figure 68. *Answers may vary.*

69. (a) $f(x + h) = 3$

(b) $\dfrac{f(x + h) - f(x)}{h} = \dfrac{3 - 3}{h} = \dfrac{0}{h} = 0$

70. (a) $f(x + h) = -5$

(b) $\dfrac{f(x + h) - f(x)}{h} = \dfrac{-5 - (-5)}{h} = \dfrac{0}{h} = 0$

71. (a) $f(x + h) = -2(x + h) = -2x - 2h$

(b) $\dfrac{f(x + h) - f(x)}{h} = \dfrac{-2x - 2h - (-2x)}{h} = \dfrac{-2h}{h} = -2$

72. (a) $f(x + h) = 10(x + h) = 10x + 10h$

(b) $\dfrac{f(x + h) - f(x)}{h} = \dfrac{10x + 10h - 10x}{h} = \dfrac{10h}{h} = 10$

73. (a) $f(x + h) = 2(x + h) + 1 = 2x + 2h + 1$

(b) $\dfrac{f(x + h) - f(x)}{h} = \dfrac{2x + 2h + 1 - (2x + 1)}{h} = \dfrac{2h}{h} = 2$

74. (a) $f(x + h) = -3(x + h) + 4 = -3x - 3h + 4$

(b) $\dfrac{f(x + h) - f(x)}{h} = \dfrac{-3x - 3h + 4 - (-3x + 4)}{h} = \dfrac{-3h}{h} = -3$

75. (a) $f(x + h) = 3(x + h)^2 + 1 = 3(x^2 + 2xh + h^2) + 1 = 3x^2 + 6xh + 3h^2 + 1$

(b) $\dfrac{f(x + h) - f(x)}{h} = \dfrac{3x^2 + 6xh + 3h^2 + 1 - (3x^2 + 1)}{h} = \dfrac{6xh + 3h^2}{h} = 6x + 3h$

76. (a) $f(x + h) = (x + h)^2 - 2 = x^2 + 2xh + h^2 - 2$

(b) $\dfrac{f(x + h) - f(x)}{h} = \dfrac{x^2 + 2xh + h^2 - 2 - (x^2 - 2)}{h} = \dfrac{2xh + h^2}{h} = 2x + h$

77. (a) $f(x + h) = -(x + h)^2 + 2(x + h) = -(x^2 + 2xh + h^2) + 2x + 2h = -x^2 - 2xh - h^2 + 2x + 2h$

(b) $\dfrac{f(x + h) - f(x)}{h} = \dfrac{-x^2 - 2xh - h^2 + 2x + 2h - (-x^2 + 2x)}{h} = \dfrac{-2xh - h^2 + 2h}{h} =$

$-2x - h + 2$

78. (a) $f(x + h) = -4(x + h)^2 + 1 = -4(x^2 + 2xh + h^2) + 1 = -4x^2 - 8xh - 4h^2 + 1$

(b) $\dfrac{f(x + h) - f(x)}{h} = \dfrac{-4x^2 - 8xh - 4h^2 + 1 - (-4x^2 + 1)}{h} = \dfrac{-8xh - 4h^2}{h} = -8x - 4h$

79. (a) $f(x + h) = 2(x + h)^2 - (x + h) + 1 = 2(x^2 + 2xh + h^2) - (x + h) + 1 =$

$2x^2 + 4xh + 2h^2 - x - h + 1$

(b) $\dfrac{f(x + h) - f(x)}{h} = \dfrac{2x^2 + 4xh + 2h^2 - x - h + 1 - (2x^2 - x + 1)}{h} = \dfrac{4xh + 2h^2 - h}{h} =$

$4x + 2h - 1$

80. (a) $f(x + h) = (x + h)^2 + 3(x + h) - 2 = x^2 + 2xh + h^2 + 3x + 3h - 2$

(b) $\frac{f(x + h) - f(x)}{h} = \frac{x^2 + 2xh + h^2 + 3x + 3h - 2 - (x^2 + 3x - 2)}{h} = \frac{2xh + h^2 + 3h}{h} =$

$2x + h + 3$

81. (a) $f(x + h) = (x + h)^3 = x^3 + 3hx^2 + 3h^2x + h^3$

(b) $\frac{f(x + h) - f(x)}{h} = \frac{x^3 + 3hx^2 + 3h^2x + h^3 - (x^3)}{h} = \frac{3hx^2 + 3h^2x + h^3}{h} = 3x^2 + 3hx + h^2$

82. (a) $f(x + h) = 1 - (x + h)^3 = 1 - x^3 - 3hx^2 - 3h^2x - h^3$

(b) $\frac{f(x + h) - f(x)}{h} = \frac{1 - x^3 - 3hx^2 - 3h^2x - h^3 - (1 - x^3)}{h} = \frac{-3hx^2 - 3h^2x - h^3}{h} =$

$-3x^2 - 3hx - h^2$

83. (a) $d(t + h) = 8(t + h)^2 = 8(t^2 + 2th + h^2) = 8t^2 + 16th + 8h^2$

(b) $\frac{d(t + h) - d(t)}{h} = \frac{8t^2 + 16th + 8h^2 - (8t^2)}{h} = \frac{16th + 8h^2}{h} = 16t + 8h$

(c) If $t = 4$ and $h = 0.05$, the difference quotient becomes $16t + 8h = 16(4) + 8(0.05) =$ $64 + 0.4 = 64.4$. The average speed of the car during the time interval from 4 to 4.05 seconds is 64.4 feet per second.

84. (a) $G(t + h) = 4000 - 100(t + h) = 4000 - 100t - 100h$

(b) $\frac{G(t + h) - G(t)}{h} = \frac{4000 - 100t - 100h - (4000 - 100t)}{h} = \frac{-100h}{h} = -100$; the pool is being emptied at a constant rate of 100 gallons per hour.

## Extended and Discovery Exercises for Section 1.5

1. Difference quotient $= 4t + 2h$. Let $t = 7$ and $h = 0 \Rightarrow 4(7) + 2(0) = 28$ ft/s is the velocity of the racehorse at exactly 7 seconds.

## Checking Basic Concepts for Section 1.5

1. (a) $(-\infty, 5]$

   (b) $[1, 6)$

2. The graph of $f$ is a parabola opening up with vertex $(0, -2) \Rightarrow$ it is increasing on $[0, \infty)$ and decreasing on $(-\infty, 0]$.

3. $\frac{f(-1) - f(-3)}{-1 - (-3)} = \frac{4 - 18}{2} = -7$

4. $\frac{f(x + h) - f(x)}{h} = \frac{4(x + h)^2 - 4x^2}{h} = \frac{4(x^2 + 2xh + h^2) - 4x^2}{h} =$

   $\frac{4x^2 + 8xh + 4h^2 - 4x^2}{h} = \frac{8xh + 4h^2}{h} = 8x + 4h$

# Chapter 1 Review Exercises

1. $-2$ is an integer, rational number, and real number. $\frac{1}{2}$ is both a rational and a real number. 0 is an integer, rational number, and real number. 1.23 is both a rational and a real number. $\sqrt{7}$ is a real number. $\sqrt{16} = 4$ is a natural number, integer, rational number, and real number.

2. 55 is a natural number, integer, rational number, and real number. 1.5 is both a rational and a real number. $\frac{104}{17}$ is both a rational and a real number. $2^3 = 8$ is a natural number, integer, rational number, and real number. $\sqrt{3}$ is a real number. $-1000$ is an integer, rational number, and real number.

3. $1{,}891{,}000 = 1.891 \times 10^6$

4. $0.0001001 = 1.001 \times 10^{-4}$

5. $1.52 \times 10^4 = 15{,}200$

6. $-7.2 \times 10^{-3} = -0.0072$

7. (a) $\sqrt[3]{1.2} + \pi^3 \approx 32.07$

   (b) $\frac{3.2 + 5.7}{7.9 - 4.5} \approx 2.62$

   (c) $\sqrt{5^2 + 2.1} \approx 5.21$

   (d) $1.2(6.3)^2 + \frac{3.2}{\pi - 1} \approx 49.12$

8. (a) $(4 \times 10^3)(5 \times 10^{-5}) = (4)(5) \times 10^{3-5} = 20 \times 10^{-2} = 2 \times 10^{-1}$; 0.2

   (b) The scientific notation is $\frac{3 \times 10^{-5}}{6 \times 10^{-2}} = \frac{3}{6} \times \frac{10^{-5}}{10^{-2}} = 0.5 \times 10^{-5-(-2)} = 0.5 \times 10^{-3} = 5 \times 10^{-4}$.

   This is equivalent to 0.0005 in standard form.

9. $4 - 3^2 \cdot 5 = 4 - 9 \cdot 5 = 4 - 45 = -41$

10. $3 \cdot 3^2 \div \frac{3 - 5}{6 + 2} = 3 \cdot 9 \div \frac{-2}{8} = 27 \div \left(-\frac{1}{4}\right) = 27(-4) = -108$

11.

| −23 | −5 | 8 | 19 | 24 |
|---|---|---|---|---|

   (a) Maximum = 24; Minimum = −23

   (b) Mean $= \frac{-23 + (-5) + 8 + 19 + 24}{5} = 4.6$; Median = 8

12.

| −3.8 | −1.2 | 0.8 | 1.7 | 1.7 | 8.9 |
|---|---|---|---|---|---|

   (a) Maximum = 8.9; Minimum = −3.8

   (b) Mean $= \frac{-3.8 + (-1.2) + 0.8 + 1.7 + 1.7 + 8.9}{6} = 1.35$; Median $= \frac{0.8 + 1.7}{2} = 1.25$

13. (a) $S = \{(-15, -3), (-10, -1), (0, 1), (5, 3), (20, 5)\}$

    (b) $D = \{-15, -10, 0, 5, 20\}$ and $R = \{-3, -1, 1, 3, 5\}$

14. (a) $S = \{(-0.6, 10), (-0.2, 20), (0.1, 25), (0.5, 30), (1.2, 80)\}$

(b) $D = \{-0.6, -0.2, 0.1, 0.5, 1.2\}$ and $R = \{10, 20, 25, 30, 80\}$

15. The relation $\{(10, 13), (-12, 40), (-30, -23), (25, -22), (10, 20)\}$ is plotted in Figure 15. It is not a function since both (10, 13) and (10, 20) are contained in the set. Notice that these points are lined up vertically.

[−50, 50, 10] by [−50, 50, 10]

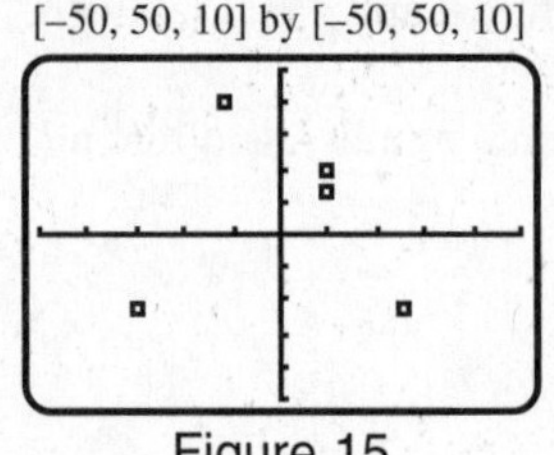

Figure 15

[−4, 4, 1] by [−4, 4, 1]

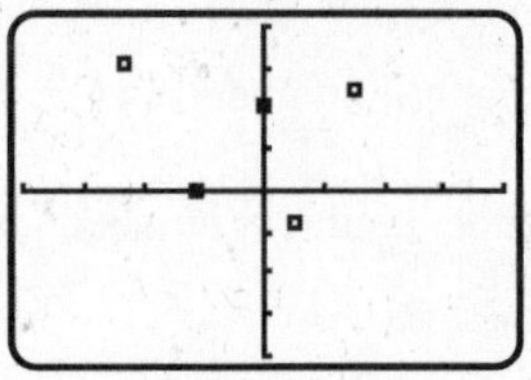

Figure 16

16. The relation $\{(1.5, 2.5), (0, 2.1), (-2.3, 3.1), (0.5, -0.8), (-1.1, 0)\}$ is plotted in Figure 16. It is a function.

17. $d = \sqrt{(2-(-4))^2 + (-3-5)^2} = \sqrt{6^2 + (-8)^2} = \sqrt{36+64} = \sqrt{100} = 10$

18. $d = \sqrt{(0.2-1.2)^2 + (6-(-4))^2} = \sqrt{(-1)^2 + 10^2} = \sqrt{101}$

19. $M = \left(\frac{24+(-20)}{2}, \frac{-16+13}{2}\right) = \left(\frac{4}{2}, \frac{-3}{2}\right) = \left(2, \frac{-3}{2}\right)$

20. $M = \left(\frac{\frac{1}{2}+\frac{1}{2}}{2}, \frac{\frac{5}{4}+\left(\frac{-5}{2}\right)}{2}\right) = \left(\frac{1}{2}, \frac{-5}{8}\right)$

21. Use the distance formula to find the side lengths:

$d_1 = \sqrt{(1-(-3))^2 + (2-5)^2} = \sqrt{4^2 + (-3)^2} = \sqrt{16+9} = \sqrt{25} = 5$

$d_2 = \sqrt{((-3)-0)^2 + (5-9)^2} = \sqrt{(-3)^2 + (-4)^2} = \sqrt{9+16} = \sqrt{25} = 5$

$d_3 = \sqrt{(1-0)^2 + (2-9)^2} = \sqrt{1^2 + (-7)^2} = \sqrt{1+49} = \sqrt{50} = 7.07$

Two sides are 5 units long and the other side is 7.07 units long, therefore, the triangle is isosceles.

22. The equation is $(x+5)^2 + (y-3)^2 = 81$.

23. First calculate the midpoint of the diameter: $x = \frac{6+(-2)}{2} = \frac{4}{2} = 2$ and $y = \frac{6+4}{2} = \frac{10}{2} = 5 \Rightarrow$ the center is (2, 5). Then calculate the length of the radius using points (2, 5) and (6, 6):

$d = \sqrt{(6-2)^2 + (6-5)^2} = \sqrt{4^2 + 1^2} = \sqrt{17}$. The equation is $(x-2)^2 + (y-5)^2 = 17$.

24. (a) $D = \{x \mid -2 \le x \le 2\}$ and $R = \{y \mid -2 \le y \le 0\}$; $f(-2) = 0$

(b) $D =$ all real numbers and $R = \{y \mid y \le 2\}$; $f(-2) = 2$

25. See Figure 25.

26. See Figure 26.

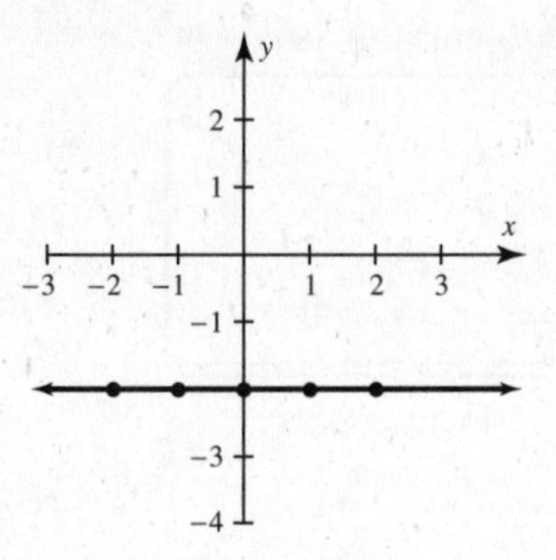

Figure 25

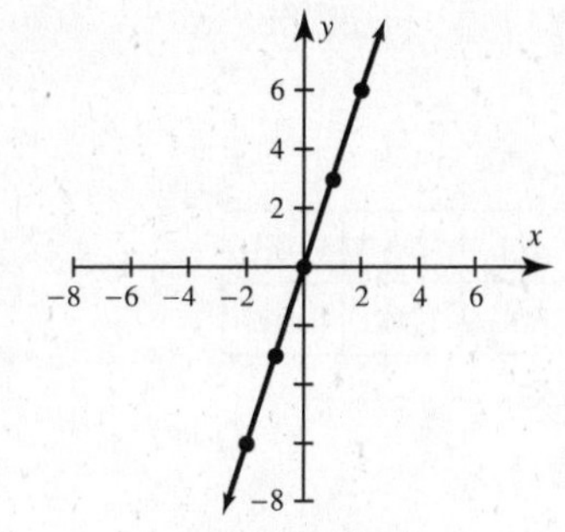

Figure 26

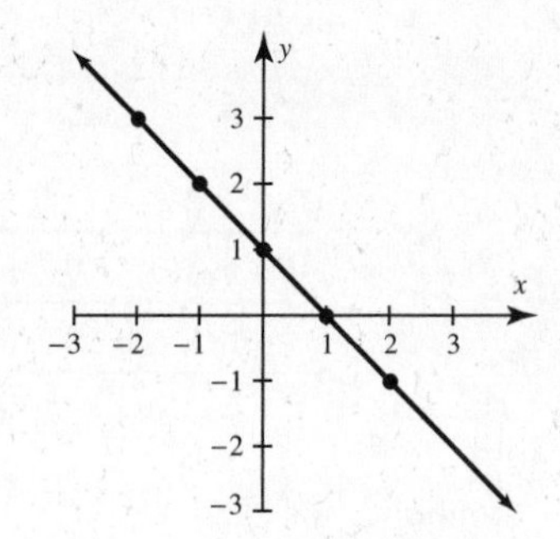

Figure 27

27. See Figure 27.

28. See Figure 28.

29. See Figure 29.

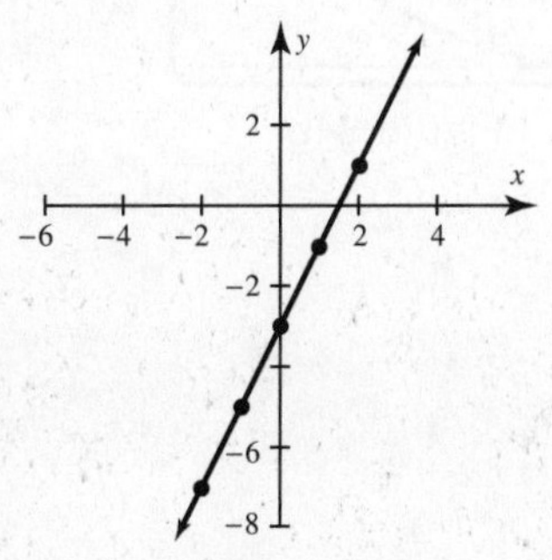

Figure 28

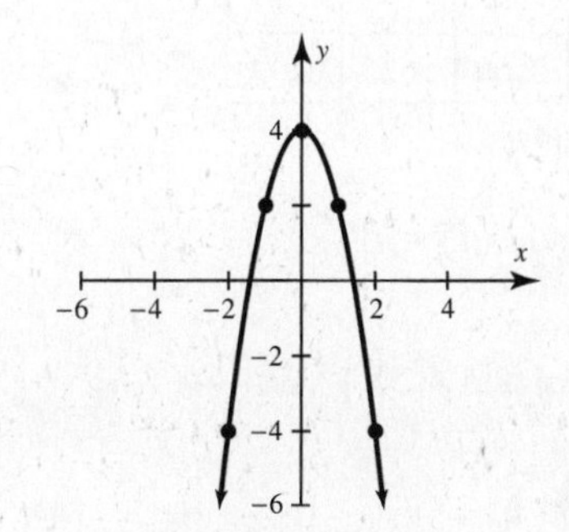

Figure 29

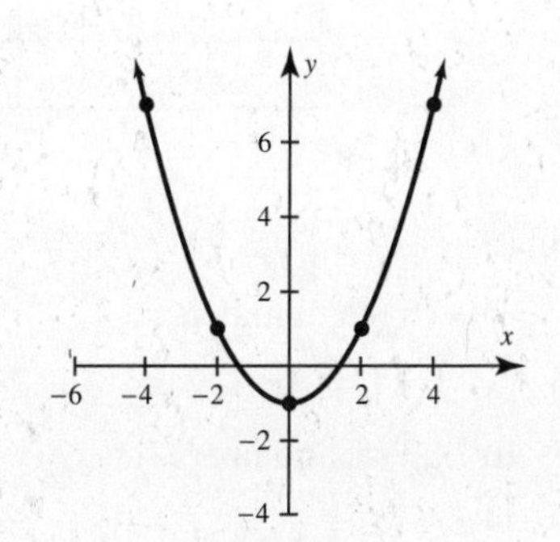

Figure 30

30. See Figure 30.

31. See Figure 31.

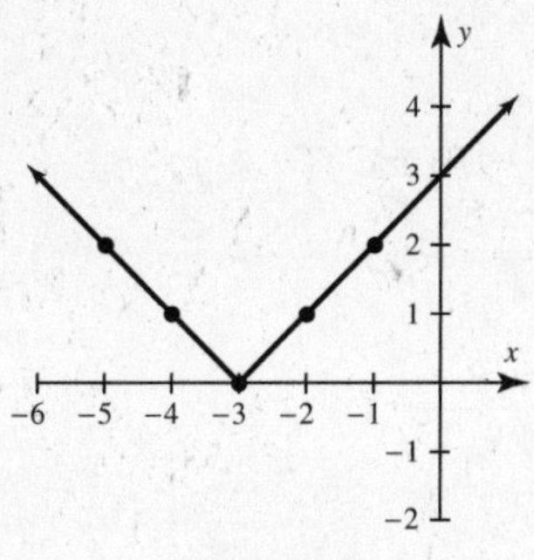

Figure 31

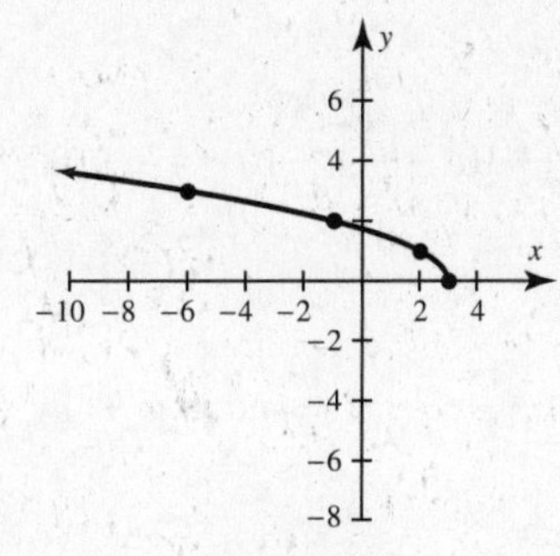

Figure 32

32. See Figure 32.

33. Symbolic: $f(x) = 16x$.

Numerical: Table $f$ starting at $x = 0$, incrementing by 25. See Figure 33a.

Graphical: Graph $Y_1 = 16X$ in [0, 100, 10] by [0, 1800, 300]. See Figure 33b.

| $x$ | 0 | 25 | 50 | 75 | 100 |
|---|---|---|---|---|---|
| $f(x)$ | 0 | 400 | 800 | 1200 | 1600 |

Figure 33a

[0, 100, 10] by [0, 1800, 300]

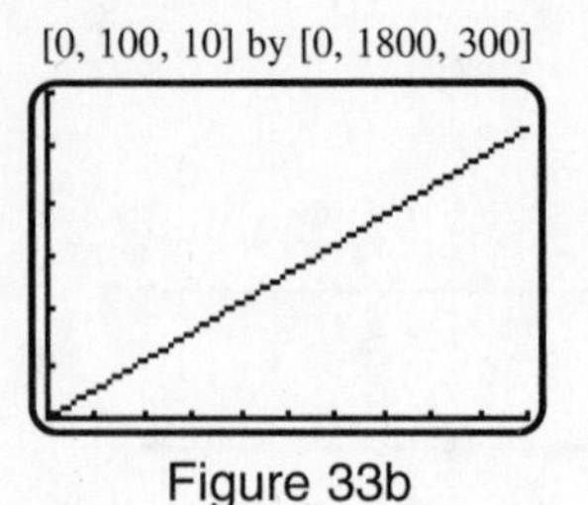

Figure 33b

34. Symbolic: $f(x) = x^2$.

Numerical: Table $f$ starting at $x = 0$, incrementing by 25. See Figure 34a.

Graphical: Graph $Y_1 = X^2$ in [0, 100, 10] by [0, 12000, 1000]. See Figure 34b.

| $x$ | 0 | 25 | 50 | 75 | 100 |
|---|---|---|---|---|---|
| $f(x)$ | 0 | 625 | 2500 | 5625 | 10,000 |

Figure 34a

[0, 100, 10] by [0, 12000, 1000]

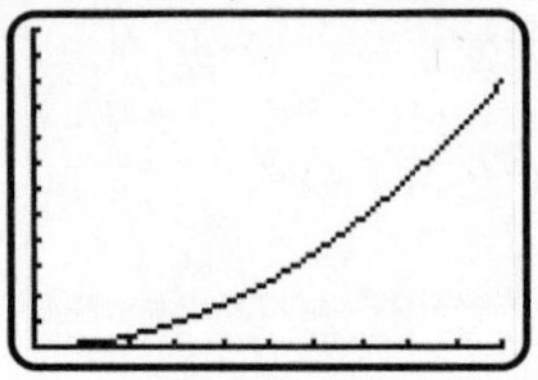

Figure 34b

35. (a) $f(x) = \sqrt[3]{x} \Rightarrow f(-8) = -2$ and $f(1) = 1$

(b) All real numbers

36. (a) $f(x) = 3x + 2 \Rightarrow f(-2) = -4$ and $f(5) = 17$

(b) All real numbers

37. (a) $f(x) = 5 \Rightarrow f(-3) = 5$ and $f(1.5) = 5$

(b) All real numbers

38. (a) $f(x) = 4 - 5x \Rightarrow f(-5) = 4 - 5(-5) = 29$ and $f(6) = 4 - 5(6) = -26$

(b) All real numbers

39. (a) $f(x) = x^2 - 3 \Rightarrow f(-10) = (-10)^2 - 3 = 97$ and $f(a + 2) = (a + 2)^2 - 3 =$
$a^2 + 4a + 4 - 3 = a^2 + 4a + 1$

(b) All real numbers

40. (a) $f(x) = x^3 - 3x \Rightarrow f(-10) = (-10)^3 - 3(-10) = -1000 + 30 = -970$ and $f(a + 1) =$
$(a + 1)^3 - 3(a + 1) = a^3 + 3a^2 + 3a + 1 - 3a - 3 = a^3 + 3a^2 - 2$

(b) All real numbers

41. (a) $f(x) = \dfrac{1}{x^2 - 4} \Rightarrow f(-3) = \dfrac{1}{(-3)^2 - 4} = \dfrac{1}{5}$ and $f(a + 1) = \dfrac{1}{(a + 1)^2 - 4} =$
$\dfrac{1}{(a^2 + 2a + 1) - 4} = \dfrac{1}{a^2 + 2a - 3}$

(b) $D = \{x \mid x \neq \pm 2\}$

42. (a) $f(x) = \sqrt{x + 3} \Rightarrow f(1) = \sqrt{1 + 3} = \sqrt{4} = 2$ and $f(a - 3) = \sqrt{(a - 3) + 3} = \sqrt{a}$

(b) $D = \{x \mid x \geq -3\}$

43. No, for example, an input $x = 6$ produces outputs of $y = \pm 1$.

44. $[5, 10)$

45. Since any vertical line intersects the graph of $f$ at most once, it is a function.

46. Some vertical lines will intersect the graph of $f$ twice, so it is not a function.

47. Yes, it is a function. Each input produces a single output.

48. No, it is not a function. The input $x = -1$ produces two outputs, 3 and 7.

49. $a = 0$, so the slope $= 0$.

50. $a = \frac{1}{3}$, so the slope $= \frac{1}{3}$.

51. $m = \dfrac{4 - 7}{3 - (-1)} = -\dfrac{3}{4}$

52. $m = \dfrac{10 - (-4)}{2 - 1} = \dfrac{14}{1} = 14$

53. $m = \dfrac{4 - 4}{-2 - 8} = \dfrac{0}{-10} = 0$

54. $m = \dfrac{-\frac{5}{6} - \frac{2}{3}}{-\frac{1}{3} - (-\frac{1}{3})} = \dfrac{\frac{-3}{2}}{0}$ is undefined

55. $f(x) = 8 - 3x$ represents a linear function.

56. $f(x) = 2x^2 - 3x - 8$ represents a nonlinear function.

57. $f(x) = |x + 2|$ represents a nonlinear function.

58. $f(x) = 6$ represents a constant (and linear) function.

59. See Figure 59.

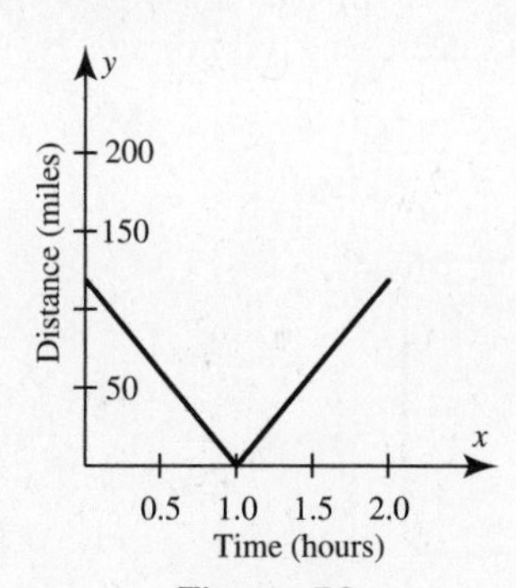


Figure 59

60. $f(x) = |x - 3|$ is an absolute value function opening up with vertex at $(3, 0) \Rightarrow f$ is increasing on $[3, \infty)$ and decreasing on $(-\infty, 3]$. In set-builder notation, these intervals are $\{x \mid x \geq 3\}$ and $\{x \mid x \leq 3\}$ respectively.

61. The best model is linear, but not constant, since the $y$-values decrease 8 units for every 2-unit increase in $x$.

62. For $f(x) = x^2 - x + 1$, the average rate of change from 1 to 3 is $\dfrac{f(3) - f(1)}{3 - 1} = \dfrac{7 - 1}{2} = 3$.

63. $f(x + h) = 5(x + h) + 1 = 5x + 5h + 1$

$$\frac{f(x + h) - f(x)}{h} = \frac{5x + 5h + 1 - (5x + 1)}{h} = \frac{5h}{h} = 5$$

64. $f(x+h) = 3(x+h)^2 - 2 = 3(x^2 + 2xh + h^2) - 2 = 3x^2 + 6xh + 3h^2 - 2$

$$\frac{f(x+h) - f(x)}{h} = \frac{3x^2 + 6xh + 3h^2 - 2 - (3x^2 - 2)}{h} = \frac{6xh + 3h^2}{h} = 6x + 3h$$

65. $\dfrac{2.28 \times 10^8}{3 \times 10^5} = 760$ seconds $= 12\dfrac{2}{3}$ minutes

66. The paint on the circular piece of plastic can be thought of as a thin cylinder.

The volume of a cylinder is given by $V = \pi r^2 h$. Substitute 0.25 in$^3$ for $V$ and 10 in. for $r$:

$0.25 = \pi(10)^2 h \Rightarrow 0.25 = 100\pi h \Rightarrow h = \dfrac{0.25}{100\pi} \approx 7.96 \times 10^{-4}$

The thickness of the plastic is about 0.000796 inches.

67. (a) Sketching a diagram of the pool and sidewalk (Not Shown) gives the following dimensions:

$l = 62$ ft. and $w = 37$ ft. Thus, $P = 2(62) + 2(37) = 198$ ft.

(b) The area of the sidewalk would consist of the area of four $6 \times 6$ squares, two $50 \times 6$ rectangles, and two $25 \times 6$ rectangles. $A = 4(6 \cdot 6) + 2(50 \cdot 6) + 2(25 \cdot 6) = 4(36) + 2(300) + 2(150) = 1044$ ft$^2$

68. (a) $D(2) = 280 - 70(2) = 280 - 140 = 140$ miles

(b) $D(1) = 280 - 70(1) = 280 - 70 = 210$. Now using the slope formula for (1, 210) and (2, 140) we get

$\dfrac{140 - 210}{2 - 1} = \dfrac{-70}{1} = -70$; the driver is moving toward the rest stop at 70 miles per hour.

69. (a) Plot the points (0, 100), (1, 10), (2, 6), (3, 3), and (4, 2) and make a line graph. See Figure 69. The survival rates decrease rapidly at first. This means that a large number of eggs never develop into mature adults.

(b) Since any vertical line could intersect the graph at most once, this graph could represent a function.

(c) From 0 to 1, $\dfrac{10 - 100}{1 - 0} = -90$; from 1 to 2, $\dfrac{6 - 10}{2 - 1} = -4$; from 2 to 3, $\dfrac{3 - 6}{3 - 2} = -3$;

from 3 to 4, $\dfrac{2 - 3}{4 - 3} = -1$; during the first year, the population of sparrows decreased, on average, by 90 birds. The other average rates of change can be interpreted similarly.

[-1, 5, 1] by [0, 110, 10]

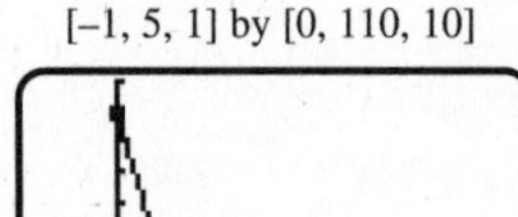

Figure 69

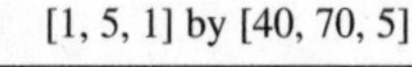

[1, 5, 1] by [40, 70, 5]

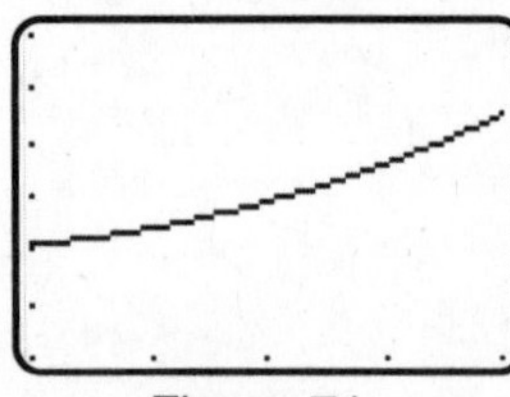

Figure 71a

[1, 5, 1] by [50, 63, 1]

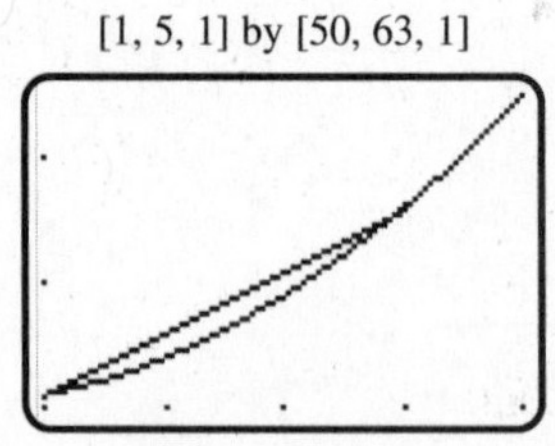

Figure 71c

70. (a) Taking zero credits would cost \$0.

(b) $\dfrac{100 - 0}{1 - 0} = 100$

(c) The cost per credit is \$100.

71. (a) See Figure 71a. $f$ is nonlinear.

(b) $f(x) = 0.5x^2 + 50 \Rightarrow \dfrac{f(4) - f(1)}{4 - 1} = \dfrac{58 - 50.5}{3} = 2.5$

(c) The average rate of change in outside temperature from 1 P.M. to 4 P.M. was 2.5° F per hour. The slope of the line segment from (1, 50.5) to (4, 58) is 2.5. See Figure 71c.

72. Using the Pythagorean theorem to solve for the distance, we have one leg $20 + 30\left(\frac{3}{4}\right) = 42.5$ and the other leg $50\left(\frac{3}{4}\right) = 37.5 \Rightarrow$ Approximating $42.5^2 + 37.5^2 = c^2 \Rightarrow 3212.5 = c^2 \Rightarrow c \approx 57.$

## Extended and Discovery Exercises for Chapter 1

1. For (–3, 1.8) and (–1.5, 0.45): $d = \sqrt{(-1.5+3)^2 + (0.45-1.8)^2} \approx 2.018$

   For (–1.5, 0.45) and (0, 0): $d = \sqrt{(1.5)^2 + (-0.45)^2} \approx 1.566$

   For (0, 0) and (1.5, 0.45): $d = \sqrt{(1.5)^2 + (0.45)^2} \approx 1.566$

   For (1.5, 0.45) and (3, 1.8): $d = \sqrt{(3-1.5)^2 + (1.8-0.45)^2} \approx 2.018$

   Curve length $\approx 2(2.018) + 2(1.566) \approx 7.17$ km.

2. For (–1, 1) and (0, 0): $d = \sqrt{(0+1)^2 + (0-1)^2} = \sqrt{2}$

   For (0, 0) and (1, 1): $d = \sqrt{(1-0)^2 + (1-0)^2} = \sqrt{2}$

   For (1, 1) and (2, 4): $d = \sqrt{(2-1)^2 + (4-1)^2} = \sqrt{10}$

   Curve length $\approx 2\sqrt{2} + \sqrt{10} \approx 5.991$. See Figure 2.

3. For (–1, –1) and (0, 0): $d = \sqrt{(0+1)^2 + (0+1)^2} = \sqrt{2}$

   For (0, 0) and (1, 1): $d = \sqrt{(1-0)^2 + (1-0)^2} = \sqrt{2}$

   For (1, 1) and (2, $\sqrt[3]{2}$): $d = \sqrt{(2-1)^2 + \sqrt[3]{2} - 1)^2} \approx 1.033$

   Curve length $\approx 2\sqrt{2} + 1.033 \approx 3.862$. See Figure 3.

[–4.5, 4.5, 1] by [–1, 5, 1]

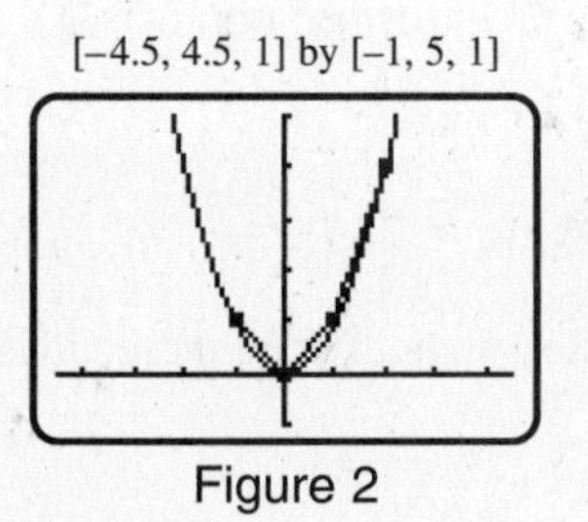

Figure 2

[–3, 3, 1] by [–2, 2, 1]

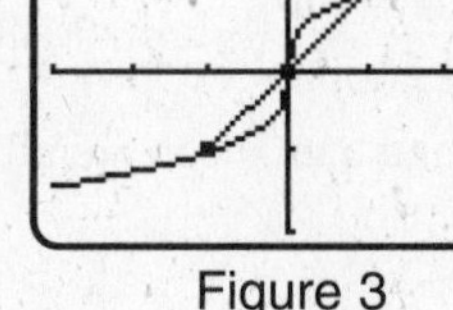

Figure 3

[–4.5, 4.5, 1] by [0, 6, 1]

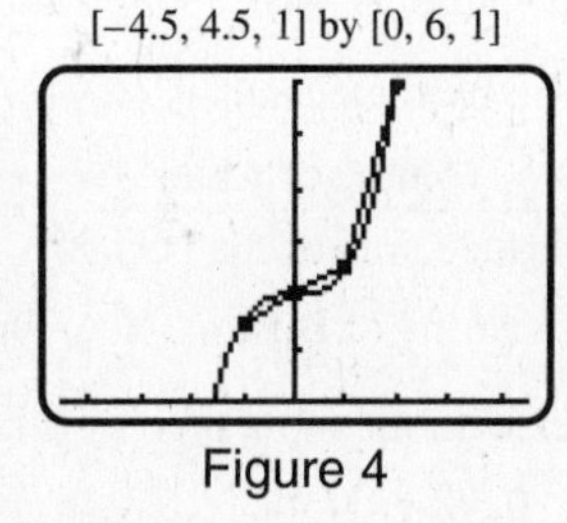

Figure 4

[–3, 3, 1] by [–1, 3, 1]

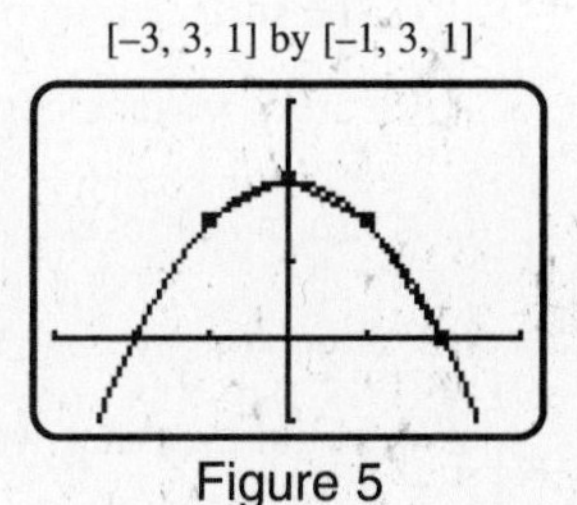

Figure 5

4. For (–1, 1.5) and (0, 2): $d = \sqrt{(0+1)^2 + (2-1.5)^2} \approx 1.118$

   For (0, 2) and (1, 2.5): $d = \sqrt{(1-0)^2 + (2.5-2)^2} \approx 1.118$

   For (1, 2.5) and (2, 6): $d = \sqrt{(2-1)^2 + (6-2.5)^2} \approx 3.640$

   Curve length $\approx 2(1.118) + 3.640 \approx 5.876$. See Figure 4.

5. For (–1, 1.5) and (0, 2): $d = \sqrt{(0+1)^2 + (2-1.5)^2} \approx 1.118$

   For (0, 2) and (1, 1.5): $d = \sqrt{(1-0)^2 + (1.5-2)^2} \approx 1.118$

   For (1, 1.5) and (2, 0): $d = \sqrt{(2-1)^2 + (0-1.5)^2} \approx 1.803$

   Curve length $\approx 2(1.118) + 1.803 \approx 4.039$. See Figure 5.

6. The graph of $y = 9 - x^2$ has the same shape as the graph of $y = x^2$ except that it has been reflected across the $x$-axis and shifted up 9 units. Note that if the point (0, 0) is reflected across the $x$-axis and shifted up 9 units it becomes the point (0, 9). Similarly, the point (3, 9), when reflected across the $x$-axis and shifted up 9 units, becomes the point (3, 0). Therefore the distances are identical. The distance from (0, 9) to (3, 0) along the curve $y = 9 - x^2$ is also approximately 9.747.

7. The graph of $y = \sqrt{x}$ is nearly linear from (1, 1) to (4, 2). It would be reasonable to estimate the distance along the curve by finding the linear distance from (1, 1) to (4, 2).
$d = \sqrt{(4-1)^2 + (2-1)^2} = \sqrt{(3)^2 + (1)^2} = \sqrt{10} \approx 3.162$

8. (a) See Figure 8a.
(b) Choosing (0, 3697) and (19, 1127), we get the average rate of change $= \dfrac{1127 - 3697}{19 - 0} \approx -135.$
Since 3697 is the initial value, the function $f(x) = 3697 - 135x$ models the data approximately.
(c) See Figure 8c.
(d) For 1987, $x = 7 \Rightarrow f(7) \approx 2752$; for 2003, $x = 23 \Rightarrow f(23) \approx 592.$

[0, 20, 5] by [1000, 3800, 200]

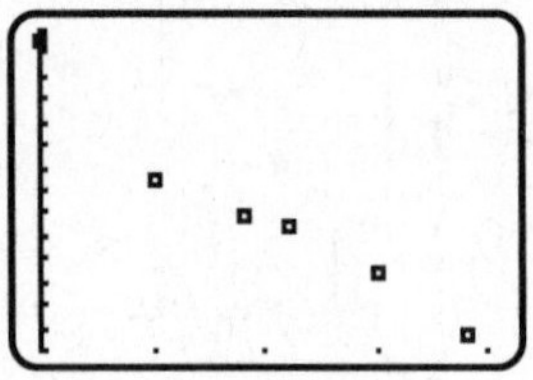

Figure 8a

[0, 20, 5] by [1000, 3800, 200]

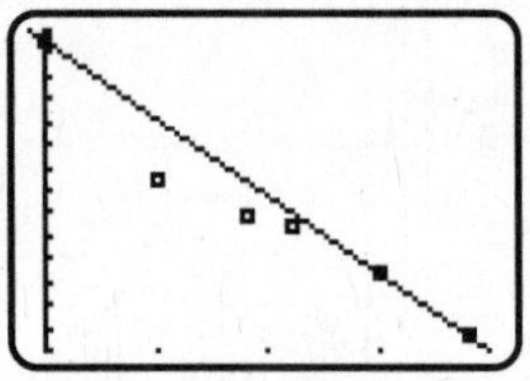

Figure 8c

9. (a) Determine the number of square miles of the Earth's surface that are covered by the oceans. Then divide the total volume of water from the ice caps by the surface area of the oceans to get the rise in sea level.
(b) The surface area of a sphere is $4\pi r^2$, so the surface area of Earth is $4\pi(3960)^2 \approx 197{,}061{,}000$ sq. mi.;
Part of surface covered by the oceans is $(0.71)(197{,}061{,}000) \approx 139{,}913{,}000$ sq. mi.;
rise in sea level $= \dfrac{\text{volume of water}}{\text{surface area of the oceans}} = \dfrac{680{,}000 \text{ mi.}^3}{139{,}913{,}000 \text{ mi.}^2} \approx 0.00486 \text{ mi.} \approx 25.7 \text{ ft.}$
(c) Since the average elevations of Boston, New Orleans, and San Diego are all less than 25 feet, these cities would be under water without some type of dike system.
(d) Rise in sea level $= \dfrac{6{,}300{,}000 \text{ mi.}^3}{139{,}913{,}000 \text{ mi.}^2} \approx 0.04503 \text{ mi.} \approx 238 \text{ ft.}$

10. Begin by assuming that $\sqrt{2}$ is rational. Then $\sqrt{2} = \dfrac{a}{b}$ for some integers $a$ and $b$, where $a$ and $b$ have no common factors. Squaring both sides of this equation gives $2 = \dfrac{a^2}{b^2}$ and so $a^2 = 2b^2$. That is, $a^2$ is even, which implies that $a$ itself must be even. If $a$ is even, $a = 2c$ for some integer $c$. Substituting $2c$ for $a$ in $a^2 = 2b^2$ results in $4c^2 = 2b^2$ or $2c^2 = b^2$; Thus, $b^2$ is even which implies that $b$ itself must be even. Now, both $a$ and $b$ are even which is a contradiction since $a$ and $b$ have no common factors. We conclude that $\sqrt{2}$ is irrational.

# Chapter 2: Linear Functions and Equations

## 2.1: Linear Functions and Models

1. (a) $V(t) = -0.2t + 12.8 \Rightarrow V(0) = -0.2(0) + 12.8 = 12.8,\ V(4) = -0.2(4) + 12.8 = 12.0$

   (b) $V(t) = -0.2t + 12.8 \Rightarrow V(2) = -0.2(2) + 12.8 = 12.4$ million vehicles, estimate involves interpolation;

   $V(6) = -0.2(6) + 12.8 = 11.6$, estimate involves extrapolation.

   (c) The interpolation is more accurate.

2. (a) $A(t) = 13.5t + 237 \Rightarrow A(0) = 13.5(0) + 237 = 237,\ A(2) = 13.5(2) + 237 = 264$

   (b) $A(t) = 13.5t + 237 \Rightarrow A(-2) = 13.5(-2) + 237 = \$210$ billion, estimate involves extrapolation;

   $A(1) = 13.5(1) + 237 = \$250.5$ billion, estimate involves interpolation.

   (c) The interpolation is more accurate.

3. Evaluating $f$ for $x = 1, 2, 3, 4$ we get: $f(1) = 5(1) - 2 = 3$, value agrees with table;

   $f(2) = 5(2) - 2 = 8$, value agrees with table; $f(3) = 5(3) - 2 = 13$, value agrees with table;

   $f(4) = 5(4) - 2 = 18$, value agrees with table. Since all agree, $f$ models the data exactly.

4. Evaluating $f$ for $x = 5, 10, 15, 20$ we get: $f(5) = 1 - 0.2(5) = 0$, value agrees with table;

   $f(10) = 1 - 0.2(10) = -1$, value agrees with table; $f(15) = 1 - 0.2(15) = -2$, value agrees with table;

   $f(20) = 1 - 0.2(20) = -3$, value does not agree with table. Since $f(20)$ does not agree (but is close) and the others agree, $f$ models the data approximately.

5. Evaluating $f$ for $x = -6, 0, 1$ we get: $f(-6) = 3.7 - 1.5(-6) = 12.7$, value agrees with table;

   $f(0) = 3.7 - 1.5(0) = 3.7$, value agrees with table; $f(1) = 3.7 - 1.5(1) = 2.2$, value does not agree with table. Since $f(1)$ does not agree (but is close) and the others agree, $f$ models the data approximately.

6. Evaluating $f$ for $x = 1, 2, 5$ we get: $f(1) = 13.3(1) - 6.1 = 7.2$, value agrees with table;

   $f(2) = 13.3(2) - 6.1 = 20.5$; value agrees with table. $f(5) = 13.3(5) - 6.1 = 60.4$, value agrees with table. Since all agree, $f$ models the data exactly.

7. slope $= \dfrac{\text{rise}}{\text{run}} = \dfrac{-1}{2} = -\dfrac{1}{2}$; $y$-intercept: $3 \Rightarrow y = mx + b \Rightarrow y = -\dfrac{1}{2}x + 3 \Rightarrow f(x) = -\dfrac{1}{2}x + 3$

8. slope $= \dfrac{\text{rise}}{\text{run}} = \dfrac{4}{6} = \dfrac{2}{3}$; $y$-intercept: $-1 \Rightarrow y = mx + b \Rightarrow y = \dfrac{2}{3}x - 1 \Rightarrow f(x) = \dfrac{2}{3}x - 1$

9. slope $= \dfrac{\text{rise}}{\text{run}} = \dfrac{2}{1} = 2$; $y = mx + b \Rightarrow y = 2x + b$

   Use $(1, 7)$ to find $b$: $7 = 2(1) + b \Rightarrow b = 5 \Rightarrow y = 2x + 5 \Rightarrow f(x) = 2x + 5$

10. slope $= \dfrac{\text{rise}}{\text{run}} = \dfrac{-10}{15} = -\dfrac{2}{3}$; $y = mx + b \Rightarrow y = -\dfrac{2}{3}x + b$

    Use $(15, 40)$ to find $b$: $40 = -\dfrac{2}{3}(15) + b \Rightarrow b = 50 \Rightarrow y = -\dfrac{2}{3}x + 50 \Rightarrow f(x) = -\dfrac{2}{3}x + 50$

11. (a) $f(x) = \frac{x}{16}$

(b) $f(x) = 10x$

(c) $f(x) = 0.06x + 6.50$

(d) $f(x) = 500$

12. (a) $f(x) = 50x$ (miles)

(b) $f(x) = 24$

(c) $f(x) = 6x + 1$

(d) The radius of the tire is 1 ft., so the distance traveled by the tire after 1 rotation is $2\pi r = 2\pi$ ft. If the tire rotates 14 times per second, the speed of the car is $f(x) = 28\pi$ feet per second.

13. (a) Slope $= \frac{\text{rise}}{\text{run}} = \frac{2}{1} = 2$; $y$-intercept: –1; $x$-intercept: 0.5

(b) $f(x) = ax + b \Rightarrow f(x) = 2x - 1$

(c) 0.5

(d) increasing

14. (a) Slope $= \frac{\text{rise}}{\text{run}} = \frac{-2}{1} = -2$; $y$-intercept: 1; $x$-intercept: 0.5

(b) $f(x) = ax + b \Rightarrow f(x) = -2x + 1$

(c) 0.5

(d) decreasing

15. (a) Slope $= \frac{\text{rise}}{\text{run}} = \frac{-1}{3} = -\frac{1}{3}$; $y$-intercept: 2; $x$-intercept: 6

(b) $f(x) = ax + b \Rightarrow f(x) = -\frac{1}{3}x + 2$

(c) 6

(d) decreasing

16. (a) Slope $= \frac{\text{rise}}{\text{run}} = \frac{3}{4}$; $y$-intercept: –3; $x$-intercept: 4

(b) $f(x) = ax + b \Rightarrow f(x) = \frac{3}{4}x - 3$

(c) 4

(d) increasing

17. (a) Slope $= \frac{\text{rise}}{\text{run}} = \frac{100}{5} = 20$; $y$-intercept: –50; $x$-intercept: 2.5

(b) $f(x) = ax + b \Rightarrow f(x) = 20x - 50$

(c) 2.5

(d) increasing

18. (a) Slope $= \frac{\text{rise}}{\text{run}} = \frac{-200}{1} = -200$; $y$-intercept: 300; $x$-intercept: 1.5

(b) $f(x) = ax + b \Rightarrow f(x) = -200x + 300$

(c) 1.5

(d) decreasing

19. $f(x) = 3x + 2$; $m = 3$; $y$-intercept $= 2$. See Figure 19.

20. $f(x) = -\frac{3}{2}x$; $m = -\frac{3}{2}$; $y$-intercept $= 0$. See Figure 20.

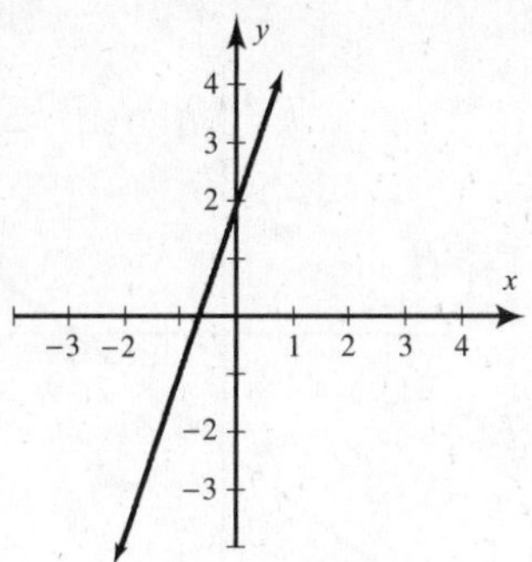


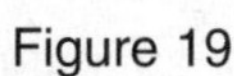
Figure 19

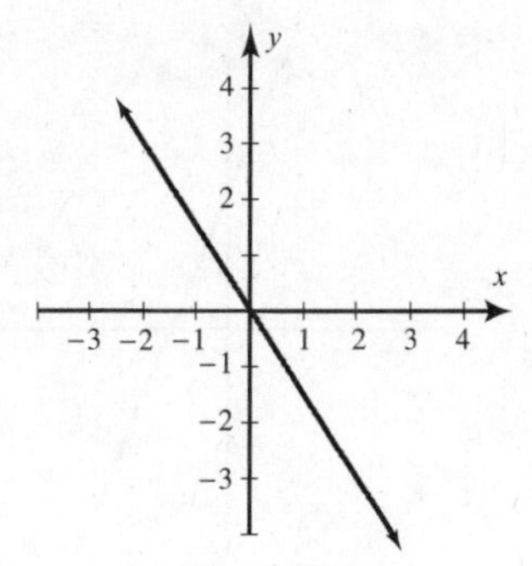

Figure 20

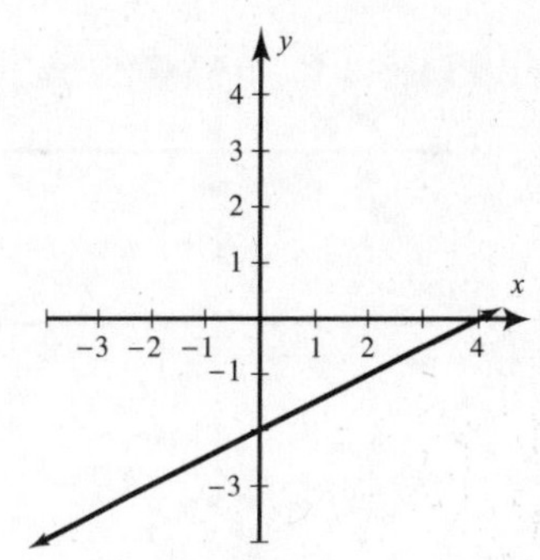

Figure 21

21. $f(x) = \frac{1}{2}x - 2$; $m = \frac{1}{2}$; $y$-intercept $= -2$. See Figure 21.

22. $f(x) = 3 - x$; $m = -1$; $y$-intercept $= 3$. See Figure 22.

23. $g(x) = -2$; $m = 0$; $y$-intercept $= -2$. See Figure 23.

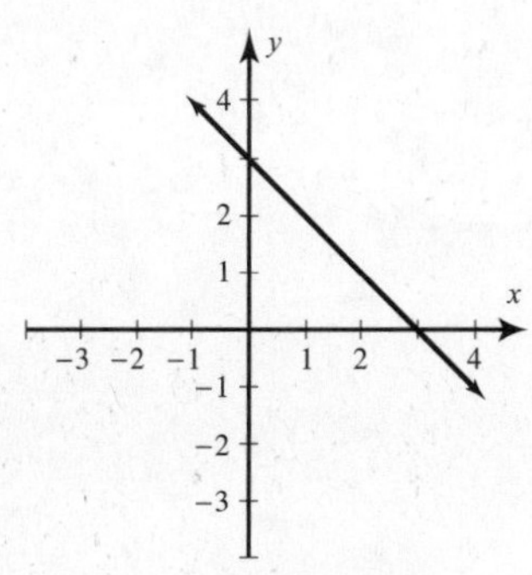

Figure 22

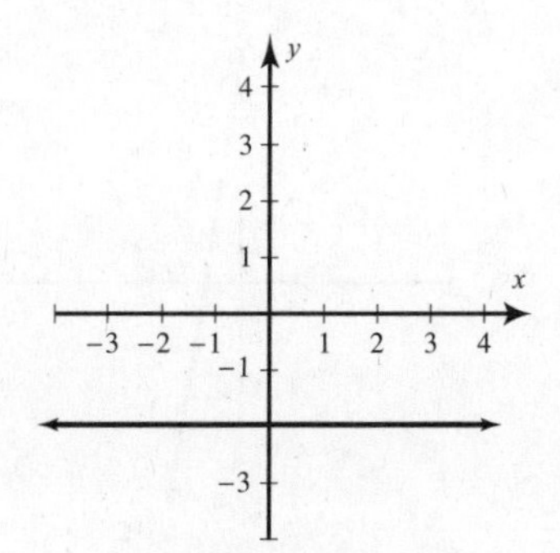

Figure 23

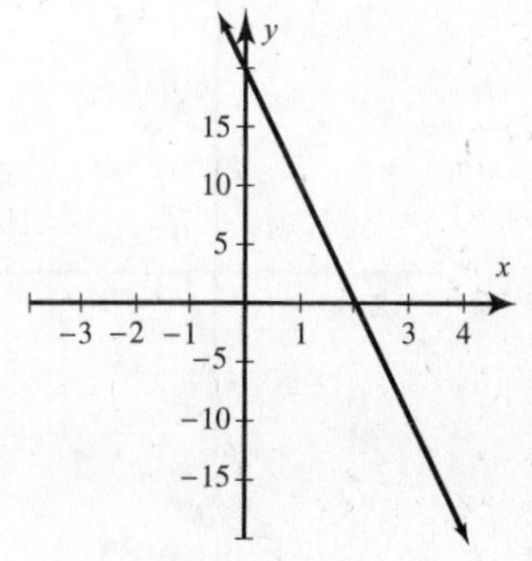

Figure 24

24. $g(x) = 20 - 10x$; $m = -10$; $y$-intercept $= 20$. See Figure 24.

25. $f(x) = 4 - \frac{1}{2}x$; Slope $= -\frac{1}{2}$; $y$-intercept $= 4$. See Figure 25.

26. $f(x) = 2x - 3$; Slope $= 2$; $y$-intercept $= -3$. See Figure 26.

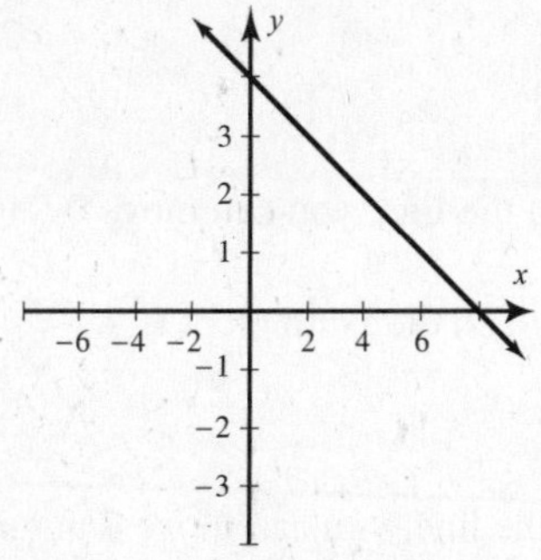

Figure 25

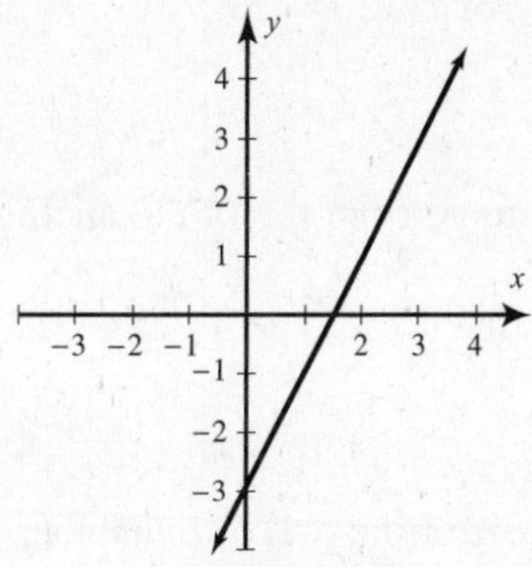

Figure 26

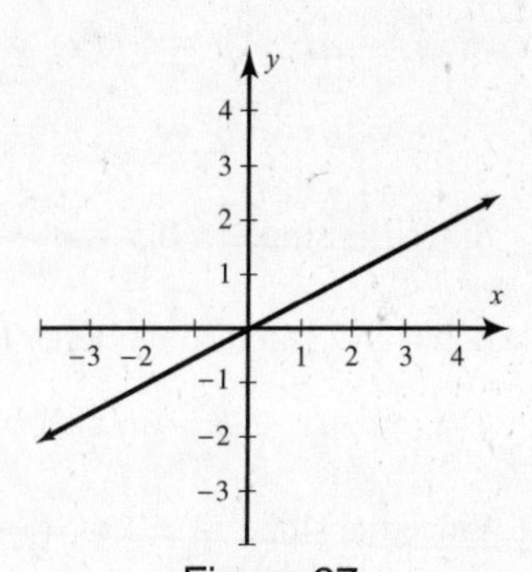

Figure 27

27. $g(x) = \frac{1}{2}x$; Slope $= \frac{1}{2}$; $y$-intercept $= 0$. See Figure 27.

28. $g(x) = 3$; Slope $= 0$; $y$-intercept $= 3$. See Figure 28.

29. $g(x) = 5 - 5x$; Slope $= -5$; $y$-intercept $= 5$. See Figiure 29.

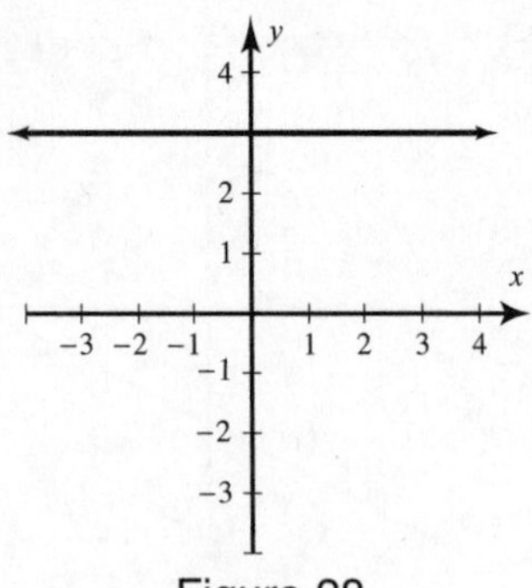


Figure 28

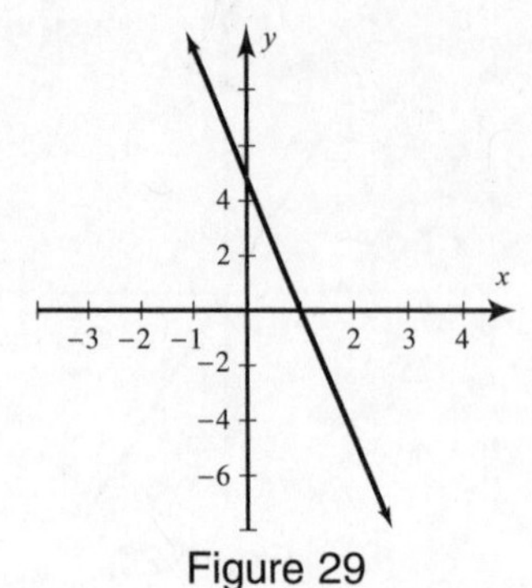


Figure 29

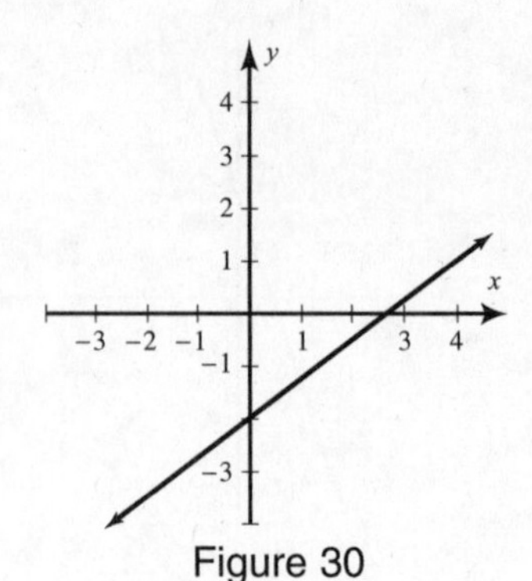


Figure 30

30. $g(x) = \frac{3}{4}x - 2$; Slope $= \frac{3}{4}$; $y$-intercept $= -2$. See Figure 30.

31. $f(x) = 20x - 10$; Slope $= 20$; $y$-intercept $= -10$. See Figure 31.

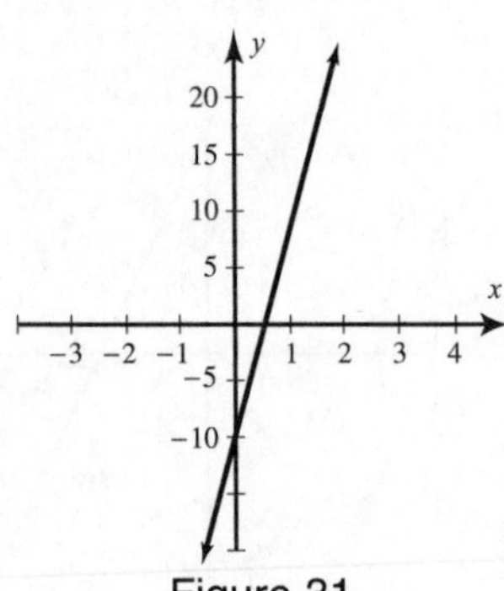


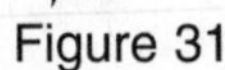

Figure 31

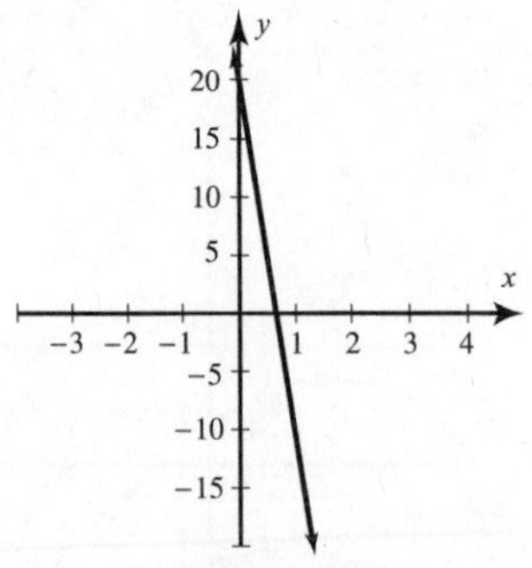


Figure 32

32. $g(x) = -30x + 20$; Slope $= -30$; $y$-intercept $= 20$. See Figure 32.

33. $f(x) = ax + b \Rightarrow f(x) = -\frac{3}{4}x + \frac{1}{3}$

34. $f(x) = ax + b \Rightarrow f(x) = -122x + 805$

35. $f(x) = ax + b \Rightarrow f(x) = 15x + 0$, or $f(x) = 15x$

36. $f(x) = ax + b \Rightarrow f(x) = 1.68x + 1.23$

37. Since the slope $= 0.5 = \frac{0.5}{1} = \frac{-0.5}{-1}$, to go from (1, 4.5) to another point on the line, you can move 0.5 unit down and 1 unit to the left. This gives the point $(1 - 1, 4.5 - 0.5) = (0, 4)$, so the $y$-intercept is 4.

 $f(x) = mx + b \Rightarrow f(x) = 0.5x + 4$

38. Since the slope $= -2 = \frac{-2}{1} = \frac{2}{-1}$, to go from (–1, 5) to another point on the line, you can move 2 units down and 1 unit to the right. This gives the point $(-1 + 1, 5 - 2) = (0, 3)$, so the $y$-intercept is 3.

 $f(x) = mx + b \Rightarrow f(x) = -2x + 3$

39. $f(-2) = 10$ and $f(2) = 10 \Rightarrow$ we have points $(-2, 10)$ and $(2, 10)$; the slope of this line is $m = \dfrac{10 - 10}{2 - (-2)} = \dfrac{0}{4} = 0$. The average rate of change is 0. For two distinct real numbers $a$ and $b$ the points are $(a, 10)$ and $(b, 10)$; the slope of this line is $m = \dfrac{10 - 10}{b - a} = \dfrac{0}{b - a} = 0$. The average rate of change is 0.

40. $f(-2) = -5$ and $f(2) = -5 \Rightarrow$ we have points $(-2, -5)$ and $(2, -5)$; the slope of this line is $m = \dfrac{(-5) - (-5)}{2 - (-2)} = \dfrac{0}{4} = 0$. The average rate of change is 0. For two distinct real numbers $a$ and $b$ the points are $(a, -5)$ and $(b, -5)$; the slope of this line is $m = \dfrac{-5 - (-5)}{b - a} = \dfrac{0}{b - a} = 0$. The average rate of change is 0.

41. $f(-2) = -\dfrac{1}{4}(-2) = \dfrac{1}{2}$ and $f(2) = -\dfrac{1}{4}(2) = -\dfrac{1}{2} \Rightarrow$ we have points $\left(-2, \dfrac{1}{2}\right)$ and $\left(2, -\dfrac{1}{2}\right)$; the slope of this line is $m = \dfrac{-\frac{1}{2} - \frac{1}{2}}{2 - (-2)} = \dfrac{-1}{4} = -\dfrac{1}{4}$. The average rate of change is $-\dfrac{1}{4}$. For two distinct real numbers $a$ and $b$ the points are given by $f(b) = -\dfrac{1}{4}b$ or $\left(a, -\dfrac{1}{4}a\right)$ and $\left(b, -\dfrac{1}{4}b\right)$; the slope of this line is $m = \dfrac{-\frac{1}{4}b - (-\frac{1}{4}a)}{b - a} = \dfrac{-\frac{1}{4}(b - a)}{b - a} = -\dfrac{1}{4}$. The average rate of change is $-\dfrac{1}{4}$.

42. $f(-2) = \dfrac{5}{3}(-2) = -\dfrac{10}{3}$ and $f(2) = \dfrac{5}{3}(2) = \dfrac{10}{3} \Rightarrow$ we have points $\left(-2, -\dfrac{10}{3}\right)$ and $\left(2, \dfrac{10}{3}\right)$; the slope of this line is $m = \dfrac{\frac{10}{3} - (-\frac{10}{3})}{2 - (-2)} = \dfrac{\frac{20}{3}}{4} = \dfrac{5}{3}$. The average rate of change is $\dfrac{5}{3}$. For two distinct real numbers $a$ and $b$ the points are given by $f(a) = \dfrac{5}{3}a$ and $f(b) = \dfrac{5}{3}b$ or $\left(a, \dfrac{5}{3}a\right)$ and $\left(b, \dfrac{5}{3}b\right)$; the slope of this line is $m = \dfrac{\frac{5}{3}b - \frac{5}{3}a}{b - a} = \dfrac{\frac{5}{3}(b - a)}{b - a} = \dfrac{\frac{5}{3}}{1} = \dfrac{5}{3}$. The average rate of change is $\dfrac{5}{3}$.

43. $f(-2) = 4 - 3(-2) = 4 + 6 = 10$ and $f(2) = 4 - 3(2) = 4 - 6 = -2 \Rightarrow$ we have points $(-2, 10)$ and $(2, -2)$; the slope of this line is $m = \dfrac{-2 - 10}{2 - (-2)} = \dfrac{-12}{4} = -3$. The average rate of change is $-3$. For two distinct real numbers $a$ and $b$ the points are given by $f(a) = 4 - 3a$ and $f(b) = 4 - 3b$ or $(a, 4 - 3a)$ and $(b, 4 - 3b)$; the slope of this line is $m = \dfrac{(4 - 3b) - (4 - 3a)}{b - a} = \dfrac{-3b + 3a}{b - a} = \dfrac{-3(b - a)}{b - a} = \dfrac{-3}{1} = -3$. The average rate of change is $-3$.

44. $f(-2) = 5(-2) + 1 = -9$ and $f(2) = 5(2) + 1 = 11 \Rightarrow$ we have points $(-2, -9)$ and $(2, 11)$; the slope of this line is $m = \dfrac{11 - (-9)}{2 - (-2)} = \dfrac{20}{4} = 5$. The average rate of change is 5. For two distinct real numbers $a$ and $b$ the points are given by $f(a) = 5a + 1$ and $f(b) = 5b + 1$ or $(a, 5a + 1)$ and $(b, 5b + 1)$; the slope of this line is $m = \dfrac{(5b + 1) - (5a + 1)}{b - a} = \dfrac{5b - 5a}{b - a} = \dfrac{5(b - a)}{b - a} = \dfrac{5}{1} = 5$. The average rate of change is 5.

45. The height of the Empire State Building is constant; the graph that has no rate of change is d.

46. The price of a car in 1980 is above \$0 and then climbs through 2000; the graph that has positive $y$ and positive slope is b.

47. As time increases the distance to the finish line decreases; the graph that shows this decline in distance as time increases is c.

48. Working zero hours merits \$0 pay and as time increases, pay increases; the graph that represents this is a.

49. $I(t) = 1.5t + 68$; $t$ represents years after 2006; $D = \{t \mid 0 \le t \le 4\}$.

50. $C(t) = 20t + 208$; $t$ represents years after 2005; $D = \{t \mid 0 \le t \le 3\}$.

51. $V(t) = 32t$; $t$ represents time in seconds; $D = \{t \mid 0 \le t \le 3\}$

52. $S(t) = 30 - \frac{3}{2}t$; $t$ represents time in seconds; $D = \{t \mid 0 \le t \le 20\}$

53. $P(t) = 21.5 + 0.581t$; $t$ represents years after 1900; $D = \{t \mid 0 \le t \le 100\}$

54. $I(t) = 8.3 - 0.32t$; $t$ represents years after 1992; $D = \{t \mid 0 \le t \le 9\}$

55. (a) $W(t) = -10t + 300$

(b) $W(7) = -10(7) + 300 = 230$ gallons

(c) See Figure 55. $x$-intercept: 30, after 30 minutes the tank is empty; $y$-intercept: 300, the tank initially contains 300 gallons of water.

(d) $D = \{t \mid 0 \le t \le 30\}$

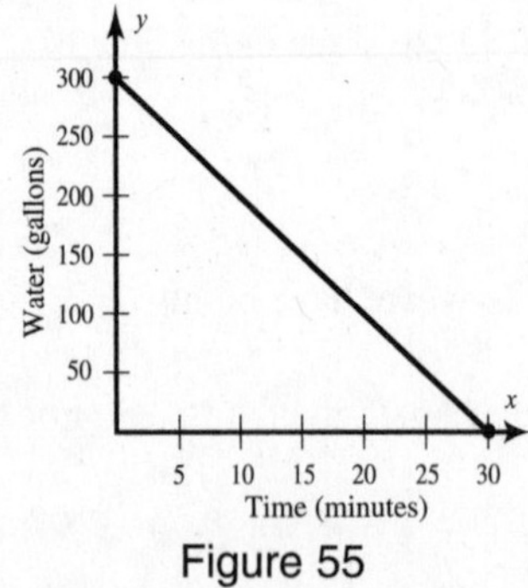

Figure 55

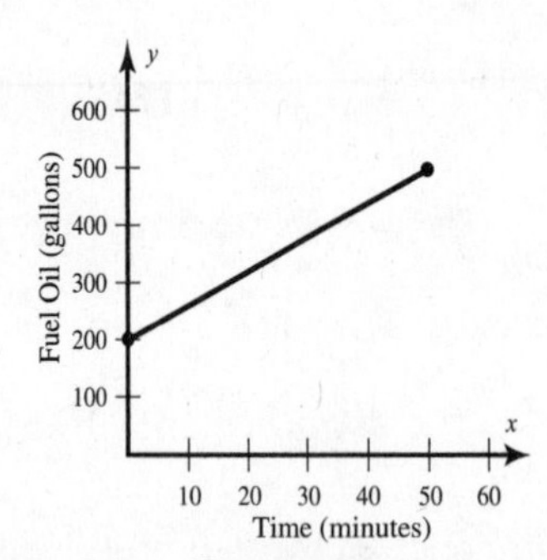

Figure 56

56. (a) $f(x) = 6x + 200$

(b) See Figure 56. $D = \{x \mid 0 \le x \le 50\}$

(c) The $y$-intercept is 200, which indicates that the tank initially contains 200 gallons of fuel oil.

(d) No, the $x$-intercept of $-\frac{100}{3}$ is not in the domain.

57. (a) $f(x) = 4.3x + 40$

(b) Since 2006 corresponds to $x = 0$, 2012 corresponds to $x = 6$; $f(6) = 4.3(6) + 40 = 65.8$, which means that about 65,800,000 may be infected by 2012.

58. (a) $f(x) = 16.7 - 0.21x$

(b) Since 1990 corresponds to $x = 0$, 2003 corresponds to $x = 13$; $f(13) = 16.7 - 0.21(13) = 13.97$, which means that in 2003 there were about 13.97 births per 1000 people in the United States. This value is close to the actual value of 14.

59. (a) $f(x) = 0.25x + 0.5$

(b) $f(2.5) = 0.25(2.5) + 0.5 = 1.125$ inches

60. (a) $V = \pi r^2 h = \pi(240)^2(1) = 57{,}600\pi \approx 180{,}956$ cubic inches

(b) $g(x) = (180{,}956 \text{ cu. in.})\left(\dfrac{1 \text{ gal.}}{231 \text{ cu. in.}}\right)x = \dfrac{180{,}956}{231}x$, where $x$ is the number of hours.

(c) $g(2.5) = \dfrac{180{,}956}{231}(2.5) \approx 1958$ gallons

(d) No; 1958 gallons in 2.5 hours means 783.2 gallons of water land on the roof in 1 hour. Since $\dfrac{783.2}{400} = 1.958$, there should be 2 drain spouts.

61. (a) $(5, 84), (10, 169) \Rightarrow \text{slope} = \dfrac{169 - 84}{10 - 5} = 17$

$(10, 169), (15, 255) \Rightarrow \text{slope} = \dfrac{255 - 169}{15 - 10} = 17.2$

$(15, 255), (20, 338) \Rightarrow \text{slope} = \dfrac{338 - 255}{20 - 15} = 16.6$

(b) $f(x) = 17x$

(c) See Figure 61. The slope indicates that the number of miles traveled per gallon is 17.

(d) $f(30) = 17(30) = 510$ miles. This indicates that the vehicle traveled 510 miles on 30 gallons of gasoline.

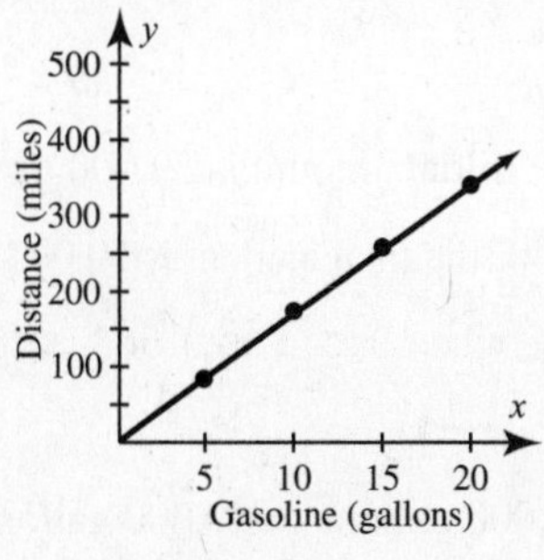

Figure 61

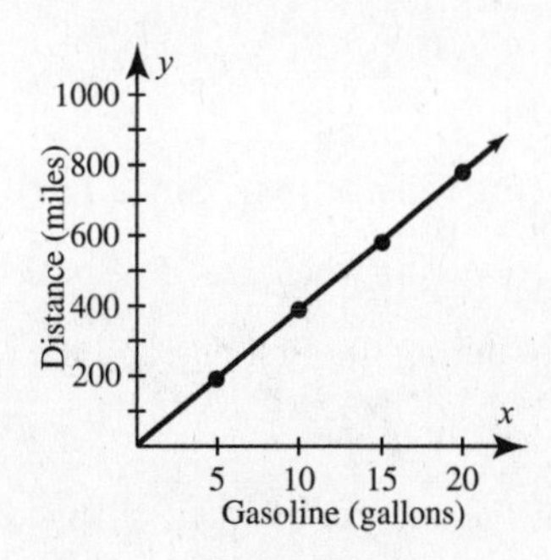

Figure 62

62. (a) $(5, 194), (10, 392) \Rightarrow \text{slope} = \dfrac{392 - 194}{10 - 5} = 39.6$

$(10, 392), (15, 580) \Rightarrow \text{slope} = \dfrac{580 - 392}{15 - 10} = 37.6$

$(15, 580), (20, 781) \Rightarrow \text{slope} = \dfrac{781 - 580}{20 - 15} = 40.2$

(b) $f(x) = 39x$

(c) See Figure 62. The slope indicates that the number of miles traveled per gallon is 39.

(d) $f(30) = 39(30) = 1170$ miles. This indicates that the vehicle traveled 1170 miles on 30 gallons of gasoline.

63. (a) The maximum speed limit is 55 mph and the minimum is 30 mph.

(b) The speed limit is 55 for $0 \le x < 4$, $8 \le x < 12$, and $16 \le x < 20$. This is $4 + 4 + 4 = 12$ miles.

(c) $f(4) = 40$, $f(12) = 30$, and $f(18) = 55$.

(d) The graph is discontinuous when $x = 4, 6, 8, 12$, and 16. The speed limit changes at each discontinuity.

64. (a) The initial amount in the cash machine occurred when $x = 0$ and was \$1000. The final amount occurred when $x = 60$ and was \$600.

(b) Using the graph, $f(10) = 900$ and $f(50) = 600$. $f$ is not continuous.

(c) Since the amount of money in the machine decreased 3 times, there were 3 withdrawals.

(d) The largest withdrawal of \$300 occurred after 15 minutes.

(e) The amount deposited was \$200.

65. (a) $P(1.5) = 0.97$; it costs \$0.97 to mail 1.5 ounces. $P(3) = 1.14$; it costs \$1.14 to mail 3 ounces.

(b) See Figure 65. $D = \{x \mid 0 < x \le 5\}$

(c) $x = 1, 2, 3, 4$

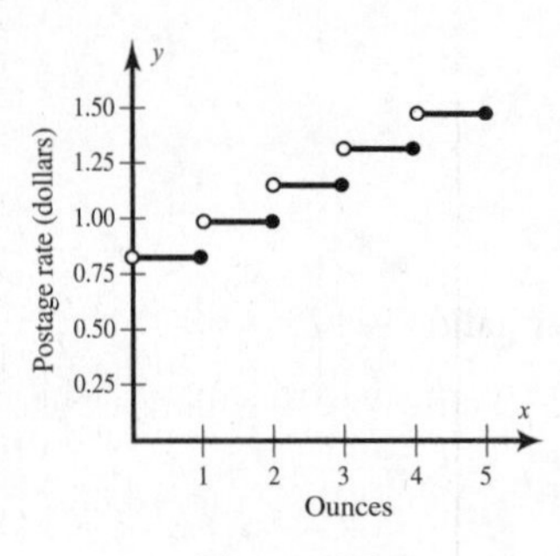


Figure 65

66. (a) The initial amount in the pool occurs when $x = 0$. Since $f(0) = 50$, the initial amount is 50,000 gallons. The final amount of water in the pool occurs when $x = 5$. Since, $f(5) = 30$, the final amount is 30,000 gallons.

(b) The water level remained constant during the first day and the fourth day, when $0 \le x \le 1$ or $3 \le x \le 4$.

(c) $f(2) = 45$ thousand and $f(4) = 40$ thousand

(d) During the second and third days, the amount of water changed from 50,000 gallons to 40,000 gallons. This represents 10,000 gallons in 2 days or 5000 gallons per day were being pumped out of the pool.

67. (a) $f(1.5) = 30$; $f(4) = 10$

(b) $m_1 = 20$ indicates that the car is moving away from home at 20 mph; $m_2 = -30$ indicates that the car is moving toward home at 30 mph; $m_3 = 0$ indicates that the car is not moving; $m_4 = -10$ indicates that the car is moving toward home at 10 mph.

(c) The driver starts at home and drives away from home at 20 mph for 2 hours. The driver then travels toward home at 30 mph for 1 hour. Then the car does not move for 1 hour. Finally, the driver returns home in 1 hour at 10 mph.

(d) Increasing: $0 \le x \le 2$; Decreasing: $2 \le x \le 3$ or $4 \le x \le 5$; Constant: $3 \le x \le 4$

68. (a) $f(1.5) = 50$; $f(4) = 100$

(b) $m_1 = -75$ indicates that the car is moving toward home at 75 mph; $m_2 = 0$ indicates that the car is not moving; $m_3 = 50$ indicates that the car is moving away from home at 50 mph.

(c) The driver starts 125 miles from home and drives toward home at 75 mph for 1 hour. Then the car does not move for 2 hours. Finally, the driver travels away from home at 50 mph for 1 hour.

(d) Increasing: $3 \le x \le 4$; Decreasing: $0 \le x \le 1$; Constant: $1 \le x \le 3$

69. (a) $D = \{x \mid -5 \le x \le 5\}$

(b) $f(-2) = 2, f(0) = 0 + 3 = 3, f(3) = 3 + 3 = 6$

(c) See Figure 69.

(d) $f$ is continuous.

70. (a) $D = \{x \mid -3 \le x \le 3\}$

(b) $f(-2) = 2(-2) + 1 = -3, f(0) = 0 - 1 = -1, f(3) = 3 - 1 = 2$

(c) See Figure 70.

(d) $f$ is not continuous.

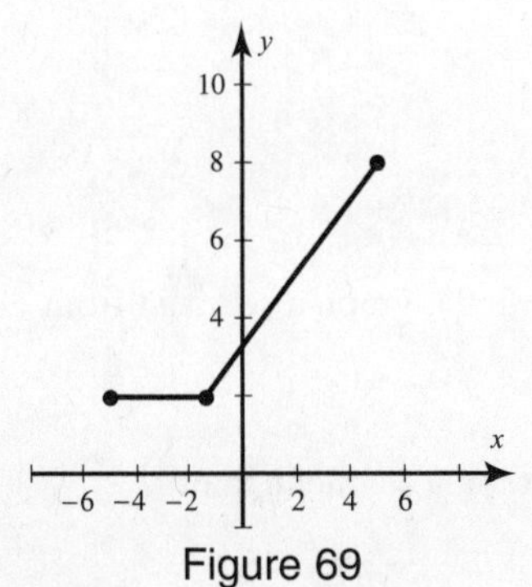

Figure 69

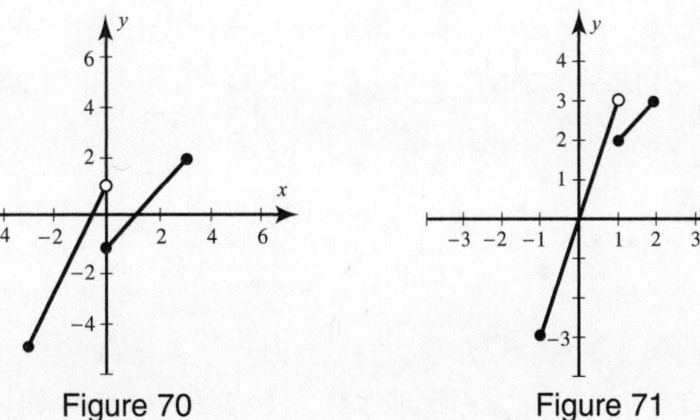

Figure 70

Figure 71

71. (a) $D = \{x \mid -1 \le x \le 2\}$

(b) $f(-2)$ is undefined, $f(0) = 3(0) = 0$, $f(3)$ is undefined

(c) See Figure 71.

(d) $f$ is not continuous.

72. (a) $D = \{x | -6 \leq x \leq 4\}$

(b) $f(-2) = 0, f(0) = 3(0) = 0, f(3) = 3(3) = 9$

(c) See Figure 72.

(d) $f$ is not continuous.

73. (a) $D = \{x | -3 \leq x \leq 3\}$

(b) $f(-2) = -2, f(0) = 1, f(3) = 2 - 3 = -1$

(c) See Figure 73.

(d) $f$ is not continuous.

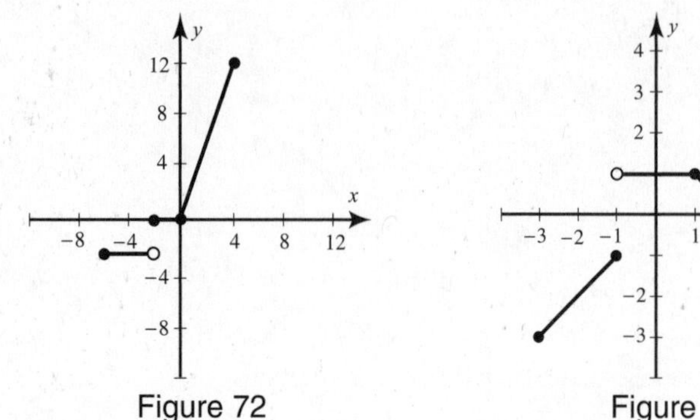


Figure 72 Figure 73

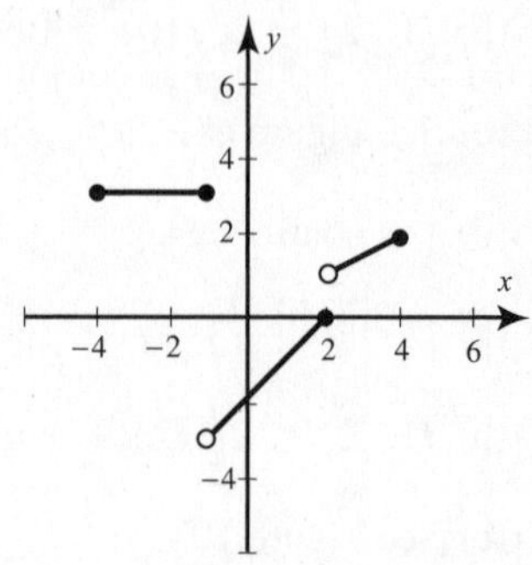


Figure 74

74. (a) $D = \{x | -4 \leq x \leq 4\}$

(b) $f(-2) = 3, f(0) = 0 - 2 = -2, f(3) = 0.5(3) = 1.5$

(c) See Figure 74.

(d) $f$ is not continuous.

75. $f(-4) = -\frac{1}{2}(-4) + 1 = 3, (-4, 3)$; $f(-2) = -\frac{1}{2}(-2) + 1 = 2, (-2, 2)$; graph a segment from $(-4, 3)$ to $(-2, 2)$, use a closed dot for each point. See Figure 75.

$f(-2) = 1 - 2(-2) = 5, (-2, 5)$; $f(1) = 1 - 2(1) = -1, (1, -1)$; graph a segment from $(-2, 5)$ to $(1, -1)$, use an open dot at $(-2, 5)$ and a closed dot for $(1, -1)$. See Figure 75.

$f(1) = \frac{2}{3}(1) + \frac{4}{3} = 2, (1, 2)$; $f(4) = \frac{2}{3}(4) + \frac{4}{3} = 4, (4, 4)$; graph a segment from $(1, 2)$ to $(4, 4)$, use an open dot at $(1, 2)$ and a closed dot for $(4, 4)$. See Figure 75.

76. $f(-3) = \frac{3}{2} - \frac{1}{2}(-3) = 3, (-3, 3)$; $f(-1) = \frac{3}{2} - \frac{1}{2}(-1) = 2, (-1, 2)$; graph a segment from $(-3, 3)$ to $(-1, 2)$, use a closed dot at $(-3, 3)$ and an open dot at $(-1, 2)$. See Figure 76.

$f(-1) = -2(-1) = 2, (-1, 2)$; $f(2) = -2(2) = -4, (2, -4)$; graph a segment from $(-1, 2)$ to $(2, -4)$, use a closed dot at each point. See Figure 76.

$f(2) = \frac{1}{2}(2) - 5 = -4, (2, -4)$; $f(3) = \frac{1}{2}(3) - 5 = -\frac{7}{2}, \left(3, -\frac{7}{2}\right)$; graph a segment from $(2, -4)$ to $\left(3, -\frac{7}{2}\right)$, use an open dot at $(2, -4)$ and a closed dot for $\left(3, -\frac{7}{2}\right)$. See Figure 76.

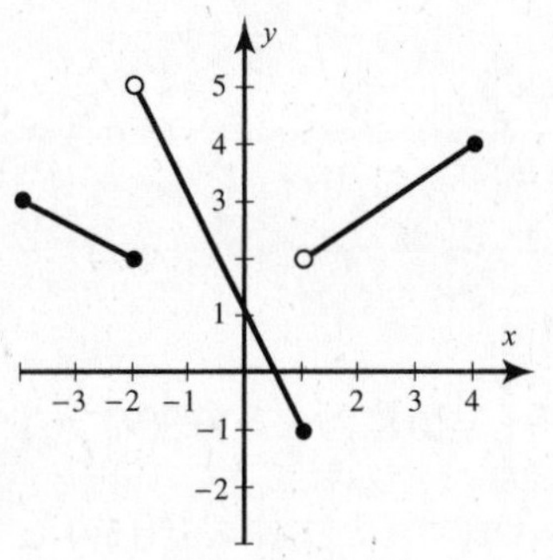

Figure 75

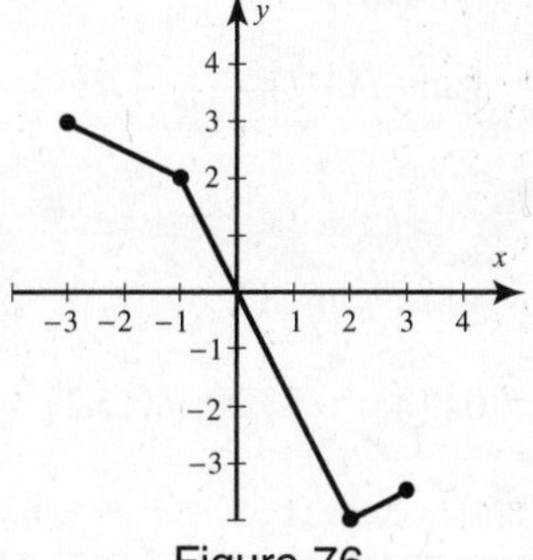

Figure 76

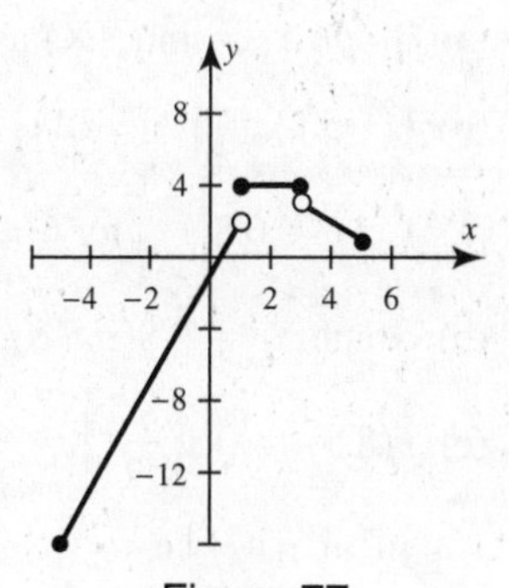

Figure 77

77. (a) $f(-3) = 3(-3) - 1 = -10, f(1) = 4, f(2) = 4$, and $f(5) = 6 - 5 = 1$

(b) The function $f$ is constant with a value of 4 on the interval [1, 3].

(c) See Figure 77. $f$ is not continuous.

78. (a) $g(-8) = -2(-8) - 6 = 10; g(-2) = -2(-2) - 6 = -2; g(2) = 0.5(2) + 1 = 2;$

$g(8) = 0.5(8) + 1 = 5$

(b) The slope is equal to 1 for $-2 < x < 2$ and 0.5 for $2 \leq x \leq 8$. That is, $g$ is increasing for $-2 < x \leq 8$.

(c) See Figure 78. $g$ is continuous.

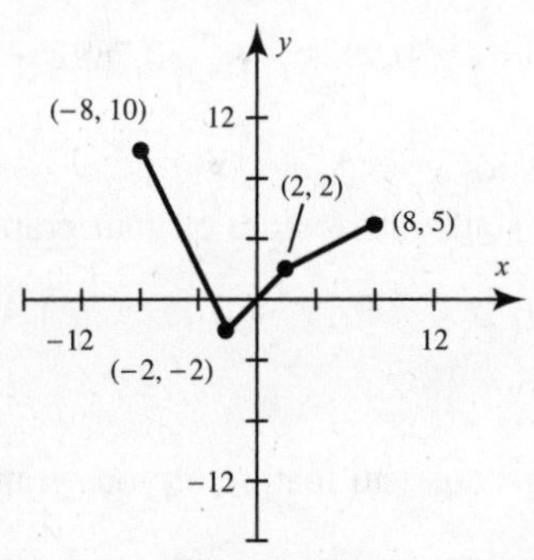

Figure 78

79. (a) Graph $Y_1 = \text{int}(2X - 1)$ as shown in Figure 79.

(b) $f(-3.1) = \llbracket 2(-3.1) - 1 \rrbracket = \llbracket -7.2 \rrbracket = -8$ and $f(1.7) = \llbracket 2(1.7) - 1 \rrbracket = \llbracket 2.4 \rrbracket = 2$

80. (a) Graph $Y_1 = \text{int}(X + 1)$ as shown in Figure 80.

(b) $f(-3.1) = \llbracket -3.1 + 1 \rrbracket = \llbracket -2.1 \rrbracket = -3$ and $f(1.7) = \llbracket 1.7 + 1 \rrbracket = \llbracket 2.7 \rrbracket = 2$

[−10, 10, 1] by [−10, 10, 1]

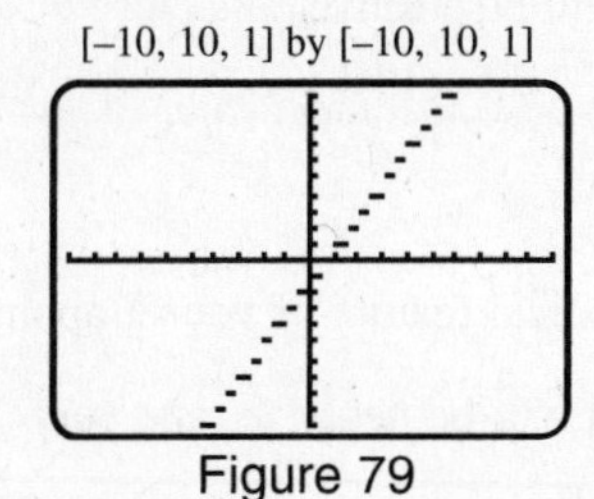
Figure 79

[−10, 10, 1] by [−10, 10, 1]

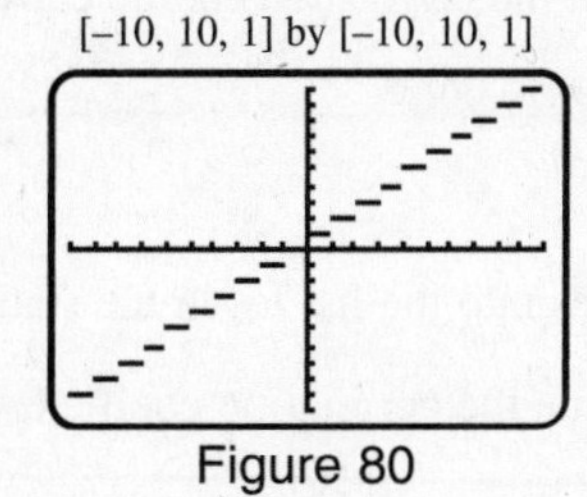
Figure 80

[−10, 10, 1] by [−10, 10, 1]

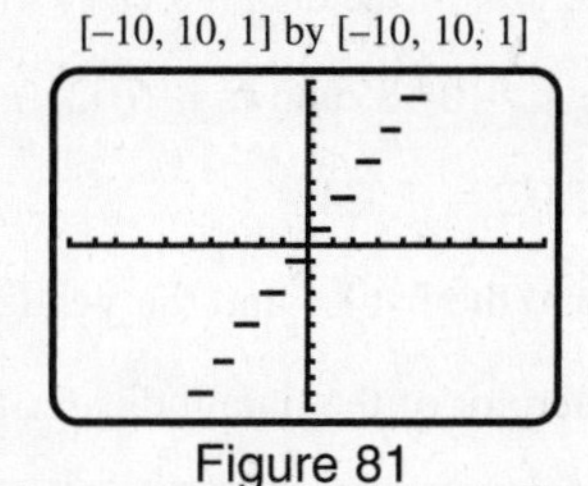
Figure 81

81. (a) Graph $Y_1 = 2(\text{int}(X)) + 1$ as shown in Figure 81.

(b) $f(-3.1) = 2\llbracket -3.1 \rrbracket + 1 = 2(-4) + 1 = -7$ and $f(1.7) = 2\llbracket 1.7 \rrbracket + 1 = 2(1) + 1 = 3$

82. (a) Graph $Y_1 = \text{int}(-X)$ as shown in Figure 82.

(b) $f(-3.1) = [\![-(-3.1)]\!] = [\![3.1]\!] = 3$ and $f(1.7) = [\![-1.7]\!] = -2$

83. (a) $f(x) = 0.8\left[\!\!\left[\frac{x}{2}\right]\!\!\right]$ for $6 \le x \le 18$

(b) Graph $Y_1 = 0.8(\text{int}(X/2))$ as shown in Figure 83.

(c) $f(8.5) = 0.8\left[\!\!\left[\frac{8.5}{2}\right]\!\!\right] = 0.8[\![4.25]\!] = 0.8(4) = \$3.20$; $f(15.2) = 0.8\left[\!\!\left[\frac{15.2}{2}\right]\!\!\right] = 0.8[\![7.6]\!] = 0.8(7) = \$5.60$

[-10, 10, 1] by [-10, 10, 1]

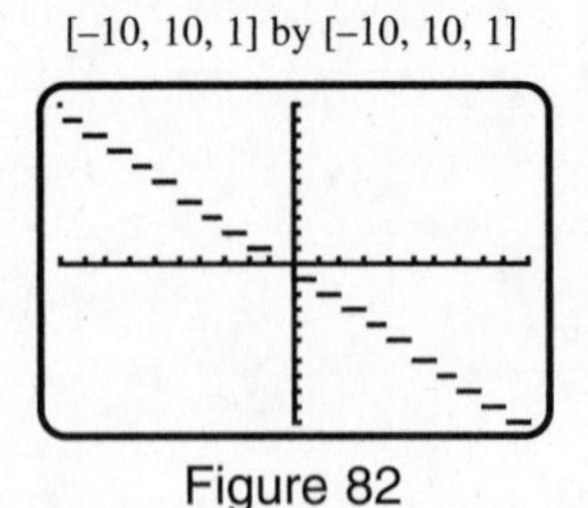

Figure 82

[6, 18, 1] by [0, 8, 1]

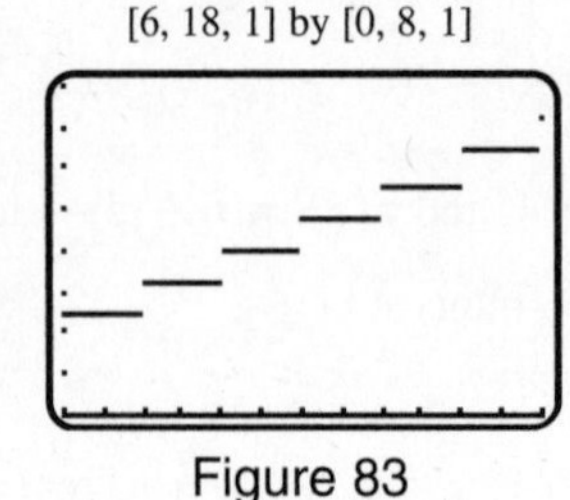

Figure 83

[-3, 4, 1] by [-3, 3, 1]

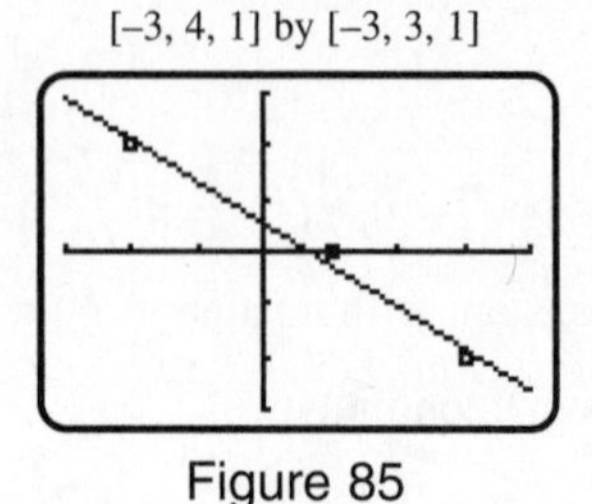

Figure 85

[-2, 3, 1] by [-2, 7, 1]

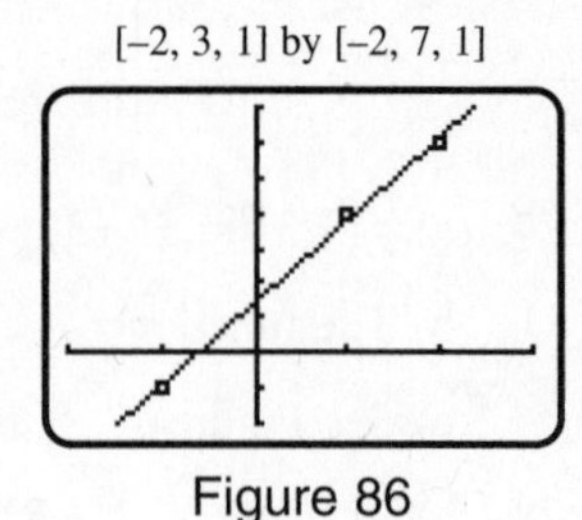

Figure 86

84. (a) Total cost = \$36/ft(9 ft) = \$324

(b) $P(x) = 36[\![x]\!]$

85. Enter the $x$-values into the list $L_1$ and the $y$-values into the list $L_2$. Use the statistical feature of your graphing calculator to find the correlation coefficient $r$ and the regression equation. $r \approx -0.993$; $y \approx -0.789x + 0.526$

See Figure 85.

86. Enter the $x$-values into the list $L_1$ and the $y$-values into the list $L_2$. Use the statistical feature of your graphing calculator to find the correlation coefficient $r$ and the regression equation. $r \approx 0.999$; $y \approx 2.357x + 1.429$

See Figure 86.

87. (a) Enter the $x$-values into the list $L_1$ and the $y$-values into the list $L_2$ in the statistical feature of your graphing calculator; the scatterplot of the data indicates that the correlation coefficient will be positive (and very close to 1).

(b) $y = ax + b$, where $a \approx 3.25$ and $b \approx -2.45$; $r \approx 0.9994$

(c) $y \approx 3.25(2.4) - 2.45 = 5.35$

88. (a) Enter the $x$-values into the list $L_1$ and the $y$-values into the list $L_2$ in the statistical feature of your graphing calculator; the scatterplot of the data indicates that the correlation coefficient will be positive (and close to 1).

(b) $y = ax + b$, where $a = 0.985$ and $b = 5.02$; $r \approx 0.9967$

(c) $y \approx 0.985(2.4) + 5.02 = 7.384$

89. (a) Enter the $x$-values into the list $L_1$ and the $y$-values into the list $L_2$ in the statistical feature of your graphing calculator; the scatterplot of the data indicates that the correlation coefficient will be negative (and very close to –1).

(b) $y = ax + b$, where $a \approx -3.8857$ and $b \approx 9.3254$; $r \approx -0.9996$

(c) $y \approx -3.8857(2.4) + 9.3254 = -0.00028$. *Due to rounding answers may very slightly.*

90. (a) Enter the $x$-values into the list $L_1$ and the $y$-values into the list $L_2$ in the statistical feature of your graphing calculator; the scatterplot of the data indicates that the correlation coefficient will be negative (and very close to –1).

(b) $y = ax + b$, where $a \approx -2.9867$ and $b = 24.92$; $r \approx -0.9995$

(c) $y \approx -2.9867(2.4) + 24.92 \approx 17.752$

91. (a) The data points (50, 990), (650, 9300), (950, 15000) and (1700, 25000) are plotted in Figure 91. The data appears to have a linear relationship.

(b) Use the linear regression feature on your graphing calculator to find the values of $a$ and $b$ in the equation $y = ax + b$. In this instance, $a \approx 14.680$ and $b \approx 277.82$.

(c) We must find the $x$-value when $y = 37{,}000$. This can be done by solving the equation $37{,}000 = 14.680x + 277.82 \Rightarrow 14.680x = 36{,}722.18 \Rightarrow x \approx 2500$ light years away. One could also solve the equation graphically to obtain the same approximation.

[-100, 1800, 100] by [-1000, 28000, 1000]

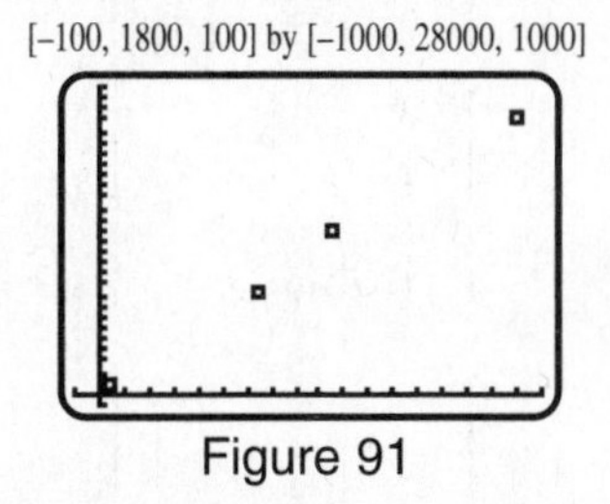

Figure 91

[–10, 110, 10] by [0, 5, 1]

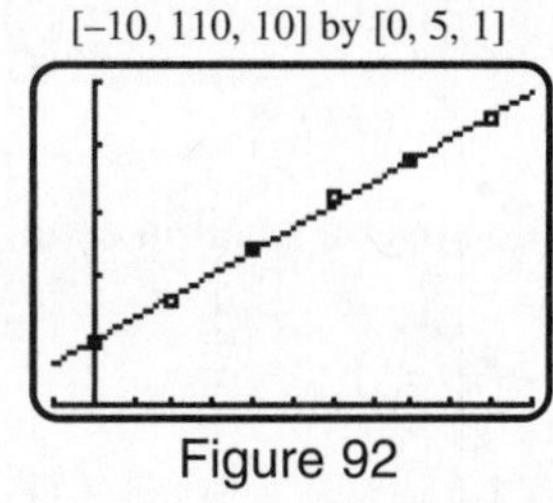

Figure 92

[–5, 40, 5] by [0, 6, 1]

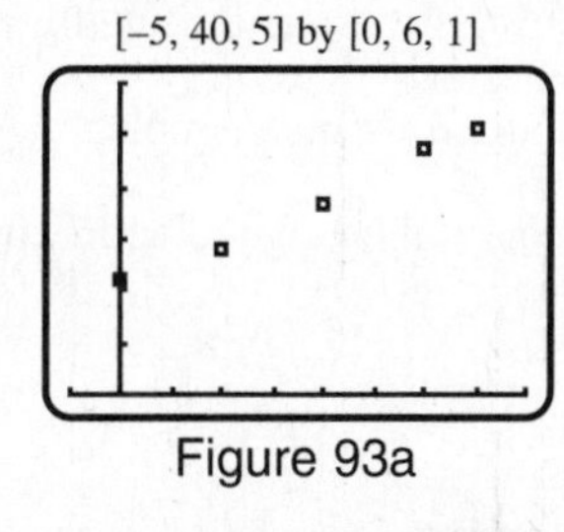

Figure 93a

[–5, 40, 5] by [0, 6, 1]

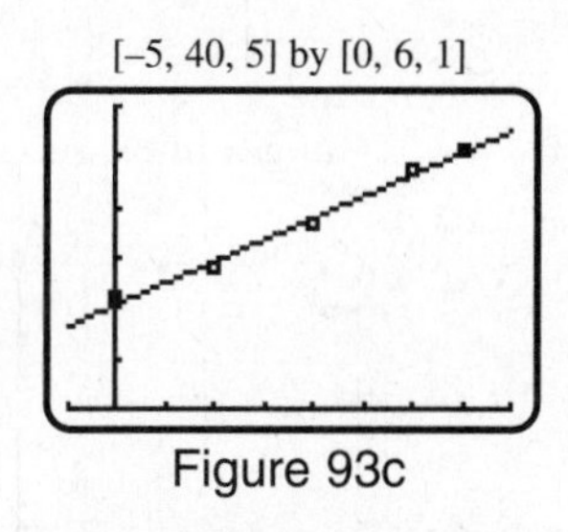

Figure 93c

92. (a) Use the linear regression feature on your graphing calculator to find the values of $a$ and $b$ in the equation $y = ax + b$. In this instance, $a \approx 0.0349$ and $b \approx 0.9905$. See Figure 92.

(b) If $P = 50$, then $D \approx 0.0349(50) + 0.9905 \approx 2.74$ minutes.

93. (a) Positive. See Figure 93a.

(b) Enter the $x$-values into the list $L_1$ and the $y$-values into the list $L_2$ in the statistical feature of your graphing calculator. $f(x) \approx 0.0854x + 2.078$

(c) See Figure 93c. The slope indicates the number of miles traveled by passengers per year.

(d) Year 2010 $\Rightarrow x = 40$; $f(40) \approx 0.0854(40) + 2.078 \approx 5.5$; 5.5 trillion miles

94. (a) Enter the $x$-values into the list $L_1$ and the $y$-values into the list $L_2$ in the statistical feature of your graphing calculator. $f(x) \approx 0.233x + 13.552$

(b) See Figure 94. The slope indicates the increase in the number of high school students enrolled per year.

(c) Year 2002 $\Rightarrow x = 2$; $f(2) \approx 0.233(2) + 13.552 = 14.018$ million. The result is slightly lower than the actual 14.1 million.

[-100, 1800, 100] by [-1000, 28,000, 1000]

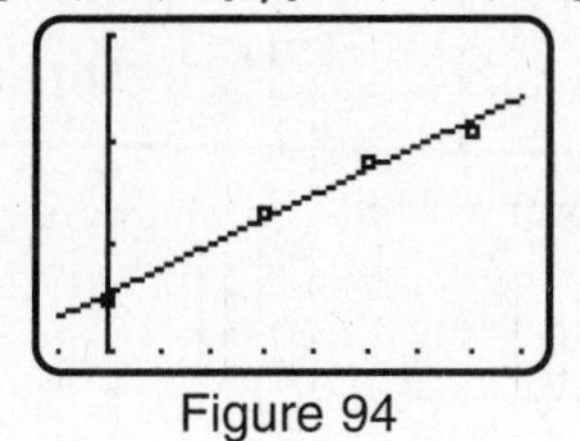

Figure 94

## Extended and Discovery Exercises for Section 2.1

1. *Answers may vary.*

2. (a) Graph $Y_1 = 4X - X^3$. If one repeatedly zooms in on any portion of the graph, it begins to look like a straight line. See Figure 2 for an example.

   (b) A linear approximation will be a good approximation over a small interval.

[−0.625, 0.625, 0.1] by [−0.625, 0.625, 0.1]

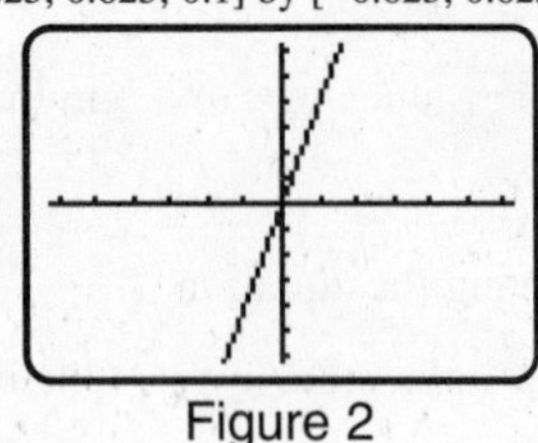

Figure 2

[1.580, 1.584, 0.001] by [−6.252, −6.248, 0.001]

Figure 3

3. (a) Graph $Y_1 = X^4 - 5X^2$. If one repeatedly zooms in on any portion of the graph, it begins to look like a straight line. See Figure 3 for an example.

   (b) A linear approximation will be a good approximation over a small interval.

## 2.2: Equations of Lines

1. Find slope: $m = \frac{-2 - 2}{3 - 1} = \frac{-4}{2} = -2$. Using $(x_1, y_1) = (1, 2)$ and point-slope form $y = m(x - x_1) + y_1$, we get $y = -2(x - 1) + 2$. See Figure 1.

2. Find slope: $m = \frac{0 - 3}{1 - (-2)} = \frac{-3}{3} = -1$. Using $(x_1, y_1) = (-2, 3)$ and point-slope form $y = m(x - x_1) + y_1$, we get $y = -(x + 2) + 3$. See Figure 2.

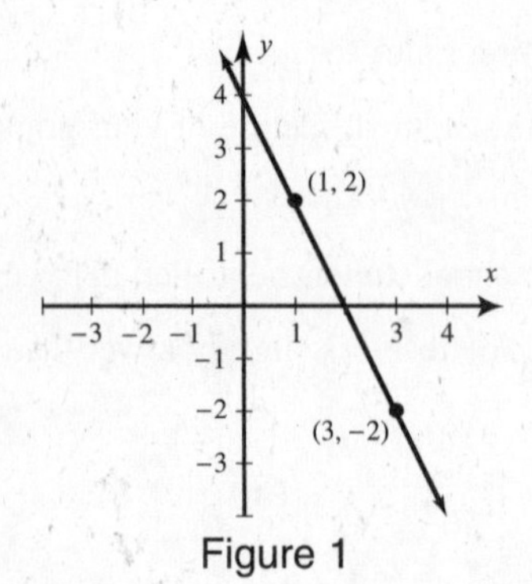


Figure 1

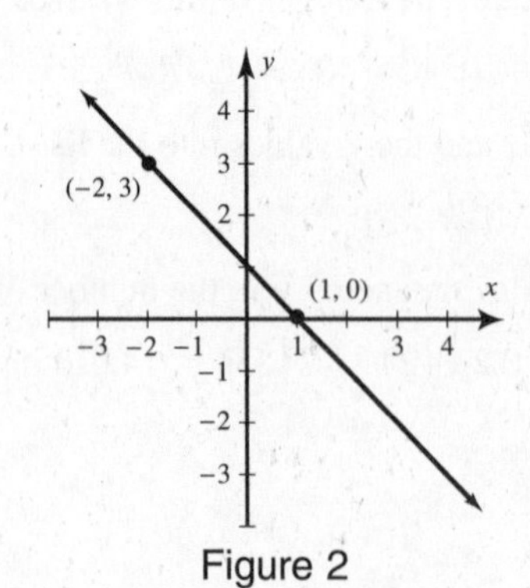


Figure 2

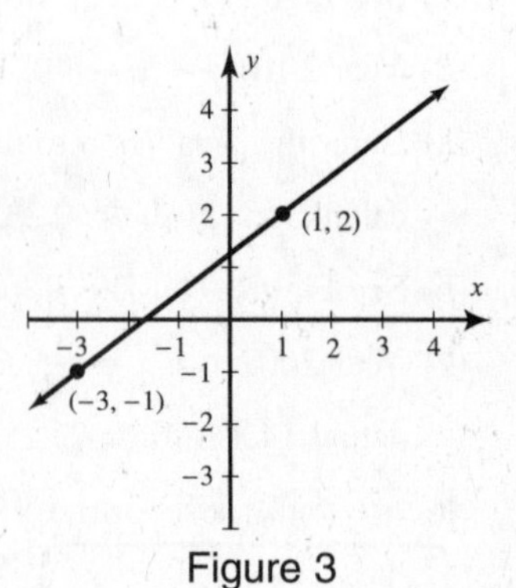


Figure 3

3. Find slope: $m = \frac{2 - (-1)}{1 - (-3)} = \frac{3}{4}$. Using $(x_1, y_1) = (-3, -1)$ and point-slope form $y = m(x - x_1) + y_1$, we get $y = \frac{3}{4}(x + 3) - 1$. See Figure 3.

4. Find slope: $m = \dfrac{(-3) - 2}{(-2) - (-1)} = \dfrac{-5}{-1} = 5$. Using $(x_1, y_1) = (-1, 2)$ and point-slope form $y = m(x - x_1) + y_1$, we get $y = 5(x + 1) + 2$. See Figure 4.

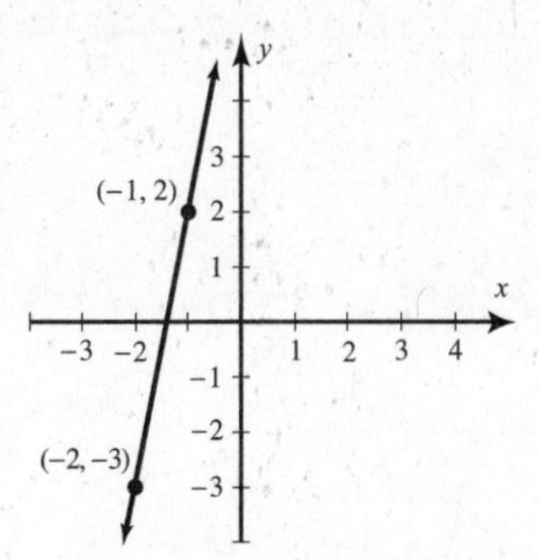


Figure 4

5. The point-slope form is given by $y = m(x - x_1) + y_1$. Thus, $m = -2.4$ and $(x_1, y_1) = (4, 5) \Rightarrow$ $y = -2.4(x - 4) + 5 \Rightarrow y = -2.4x + 9.6 + 5 \Rightarrow y = -2.4x + 14.6$.

6. The point-slope form is given by $y = m(x - x_1) + y_1$. Thus, $m = 1.7$ and $(x_1, y_1) = (-8, 10) \Rightarrow$ $y = 1.7(x + 8) + 10 \Rightarrow y = 1.7x + 13.6 + 10 \Rightarrow y = 1.7x + 23.6$.

7. First find the slope between the points (1, –2) and (–9, 3): $m = \dfrac{3 - (-2)}{-9 - 1} = -\dfrac{1}{2}$.
$y = -\dfrac{1}{2}(x - 1) - 2 \Rightarrow y = -\dfrac{1}{2}x + \dfrac{1}{2} - 2 \Rightarrow y = -\dfrac{1}{2}x - \dfrac{3}{2}$.

8. $m = \dfrac{-12 - 10}{5 - (-6)} = -\dfrac{22}{11} = -2$; thus, $y = -2(x + 6) + 10 \Rightarrow y = -2x - 12 + 10 \Rightarrow$ $y = -2x - 2$.

9. $(4, 0), (0, -3)$; $m = \dfrac{-3 - 0}{0 - 4} = \dfrac{3}{4}$. Thus, $y = \dfrac{3}{4}(x - 4) + 0$ or $y = \dfrac{3}{4}x - 3$.

10. $(-2, 0), (0, 5)$; $m = \dfrac{5 - 0}{0 - (-2)} = \dfrac{5}{2}$. Thus, $y = \dfrac{5}{2}(x + 2) + 0$ or $y = \dfrac{5}{2}x + 5$.

11. Using the points (0, –1) and (3, 1), we get $m = \dfrac{1 - (-1)}{3 - 0} = \dfrac{2}{3}$ and $b = -1$; $y = mx + b \Rightarrow y = \dfrac{2}{3}x - 1$.

12. Using the points (0, 50) and (100, 0), we get $m = \dfrac{0 - 50}{100 - 0} = \dfrac{-50}{100} = -\dfrac{1}{2}$ and $b = 50$; $y = mx + b \Rightarrow y = -\dfrac{1}{2}x + 50$.

13. Using the points (–2, 1.8) and (1, 0), we get $m = \dfrac{0 - 1.8}{1 - (-2)} = \dfrac{-1.8}{3} = -\dfrac{18}{30} = -\dfrac{3}{5}$; to find $b$, we use (1, 0) in $y = mx + b$ and solve for $b$: $0 = -\dfrac{3}{5}(1) + b \Rightarrow b = \dfrac{3}{5}$; $y = -\dfrac{3}{5}x + \dfrac{3}{5}$.

14. Using the points (–4, –2) and (3, 1), we get $m = \dfrac{1 - (-2)}{3 - (-4)} = \dfrac{3}{7}$; to find $b$, we use (3, 1) in $y = mx + b$ and solve for $b$: $1 = \dfrac{3}{7}(3) + b \Rightarrow b = -\dfrac{2}{7}$; $y = \dfrac{3}{7}x - \dfrac{2}{7}$.

15. c

16. f

17. b

18. a

19. e

20. d

21. $m = \dfrac{2 - (-4)}{1 - (-1)} = 3;\ y = 3(x + 1) - 4 = 3x + 3 - 4 = 3x - 1$

22. $m = \dfrac{-3 - 6}{2 - (-1)} = -3;\ y = -3(x + 1) + 6 = -3x - 3 + 6 = -3x + 3$

23. $m = \dfrac{-3 - 5}{1 - 4} = \dfrac{8}{3};\ y = \dfrac{8}{3}(x - 4) + 5 = \dfrac{8}{3}x - \dfrac{32}{3} + 5 = \dfrac{8}{3}x - \dfrac{17}{3}$

24. $m = \dfrac{-3 - (-2)}{-2 - 8} = -\dfrac{1}{2};\ y = -\dfrac{1}{2}(x - 8) - 2 = -\dfrac{1}{2}x + 4 - 2 = -\dfrac{1}{2}x + 2$

25. $b = 5$ and $m = -7.8 \Rightarrow y = -7.8x + 5.$

26. $b = -155$ and $m = 5.6 \Rightarrow y = 5.6x - 155.$

27. The line passes through the points (0, 45) and (90, 0).

$m = \dfrac{0 - 45}{90 - 0} = -\dfrac{1}{2};\ b = 45$ and $m = -\dfrac{1}{2} \Rightarrow y = -\dfrac{1}{2}x + 45$

28. The line passes through the points (–6, 0) and (0, –8).

$m = \dfrac{-8 - 0}{0 - (-6)} = -\dfrac{4}{3};\ b = -8$ and $m = -\dfrac{4}{3} \Rightarrow y = -\dfrac{4}{3}x - 8$

29. $m = -3$ and $b = 5 \Rightarrow y = -3x + 5$

30. Using the point-slope form with

$m = \dfrac{1}{3}$ and $(x_1, y_1) = \left(\dfrac{1}{2}, -2\right)$, we get $y = \dfrac{1}{3}\left(x - \dfrac{1}{2}\right) - 2 = \dfrac{1}{3}x - \dfrac{1}{6} - 2 = \dfrac{1}{3}x - \dfrac{13}{6}.$

31. $m = \dfrac{0 - (-6)}{4 - 0} = \dfrac{6}{4} = \dfrac{3}{2}$ and $b = -6;\ y = mx + b \Rightarrow y = \dfrac{3}{2}x - 6$

32. $m = \dfrac{\frac{7}{4} - (-\frac{1}{4})}{\frac{5}{4} - \frac{3}{4}} = \dfrac{\frac{8}{4}}{\frac{2}{4}} = 4;$ using the point-slope form with $m = 4$ and $\left(\dfrac{3}{4}, -\dfrac{1}{4}\right)$, we get

$y = 4\left(x - \dfrac{3}{4}\right) - \dfrac{1}{4} = 4x - 3 - \dfrac{1}{4} = 4x - \dfrac{13}{4}.$

33. $m = \dfrac{\frac{2}{3} - \frac{3}{4}}{\frac{1}{5} - \frac{1}{2}} = \dfrac{-\frac{1}{12}}{-\frac{3}{10}} = \dfrac{5}{18};$ using the point-slope form with $m = \dfrac{5}{18}$ and $\left(\dfrac{1}{2}, \dfrac{3}{4}\right)$, we get

$y = \dfrac{5}{18}\left(x - \dfrac{1}{2}\right) + \dfrac{3}{4} \Rightarrow y = \dfrac{5}{18}x - \dfrac{5}{36} + \dfrac{3}{4} \Rightarrow y = \dfrac{5}{18}x + \dfrac{11}{18}.$

34. $m = \dfrac{-\frac{7}{6} - \frac{5}{3}}{\frac{5}{6} - (-\frac{7}{3})} = \dfrac{-\frac{17}{6}}{\frac{19}{6}} = -\dfrac{17}{19};$ using the point-slope form with $m = -\dfrac{17}{19}$ and $\left(-\dfrac{7}{3}, \dfrac{5}{3}\right)$, we get

$y = -\dfrac{17}{19}\left(x + \dfrac{7}{3}\right) + \dfrac{5}{3} \Rightarrow y = -\dfrac{17}{19}x - \dfrac{119}{57} + \dfrac{5}{3} \Rightarrow y = -\dfrac{17}{19}x - \dfrac{24}{57} \Rightarrow y = -\dfrac{17}{19}x - \dfrac{8}{19}.$

35. The line has a slope of 4 and passes through the point (–4, –7); $y = 4(x + 4) - 7 \Rightarrow y = 4x + 9.$

36. The line has a slope of $-\frac{3}{4}$ and passes through the point (1, 3);

$y = -\frac{3}{4}(x - 1) + 3 \Rightarrow y = -\frac{3}{4}x + \frac{3}{4} + 3 = -\frac{3}{4}x + \frac{15}{4}$

37. The slope of the perpendicular line is equal to $\frac{3}{2}$ and the line passes through the point (1980, 10);

$y = \frac{3}{2}(x - 1980) + 10 \Rightarrow y = \frac{3}{2}x - 2960$

38. The slope of the perpendicular lineis equal to $-\frac{1}{6}$ and the line passes through the point (15, –7);

$y = -\frac{1}{6}(x - 15) - 7 \Rightarrow y = -\frac{1}{6}x - \frac{27}{6} = -\frac{1}{6}x - \frac{9}{2}$

39. $y = \frac{2}{3}x + 3 \Rightarrow m = \frac{2}{3}$; the parallel line has slope $\frac{2}{3}$; since it passes through (0, –2.1), the $y$-intercept $= -2.1$; $y = mx + b \Rightarrow y = \frac{2}{3}x - 2.1$.

40. $y = -4x - \frac{1}{4} \Rightarrow m = -4$; the parallel line has slope $-4$; since it passes through (2, –5), the equation is $y = -4(x - 2) - 5 = -4x + 8 - 5 = -4x + 3$.

41. $y = -2x \Rightarrow m = -2$; the perpendicular line has slope $\frac{1}{2}$; since it passes through (–2, 5), the equation is $y = \frac{1}{2}(x + 2) + 5 = \frac{1}{2}x + 1 + 5 = \frac{1}{2}x + 6$.

42. $y = -\frac{6}{7}x + \frac{3}{7} \Rightarrow m = -\frac{6}{7}$; the perpendicular line has slope $\frac{7}{6}$; since it passes through (3, 8), the equation is $y = \frac{7}{6}(x - 3) + 8 = \frac{7}{6}x - \frac{7}{2} + 8 = \frac{7}{6}x + \frac{9}{2}$.

43. $y = -x + 4 \Rightarrow m = -1$; the perpendicular line has slope 1; since it passes through (15, –5), the equation is $y = 1(x - 15) - 5 = x - 15 - 5 = x - 20$.

44. $y = \frac{2}{3}x + 2 \Rightarrow m = \frac{2}{3}$; the parallel line has slope $\frac{2}{3}$; since it passes through (4, –9), the equation is $y = \frac{2}{3}(x - 4) - 9 = \frac{2}{3}x - \frac{8}{3} - 9 = \frac{2}{3}x - \frac{35}{3}$.

45. $m = \frac{1 - 3}{-3 - 1} = \frac{-2}{-4} = \frac{1}{2}$; a line parallel to this line also has slope $m = \frac{1}{2}$. Using $(x_1, y_1) = (5, 7)$, $m = \frac{1}{2}$, and point-slope form $y = m(x - x_1) + y_1$, we get $y = \frac{1}{2}(x - 5) + 7 \Rightarrow$ $y = \frac{1}{2}x + \frac{9}{2}$.

46. $m = \frac{8 - 3}{2000 - 1980} = \frac{5}{20} = \frac{1}{4}$; a line parallel to this line also has slope $m = \frac{1}{4}$. Using $(x_1, y_1) = (1990, 4)$, $m = \frac{1}{4}$, and point-slope form $y = m(x - x_1) + y_1$, we get $y = \frac{1}{4}(x - 1990) + 4 \Rightarrow$ $y = \frac{1}{4}x - \frac{1990}{4} + 4 \Rightarrow y = \frac{1}{4}x - \frac{987}{2}$.

47. $m = \frac{\frac{2}{3} - \frac{1}{2}}{-3 - (-5)} = \frac{\frac{1}{6}}{2} = \frac{1}{12}$; a line perpendicular to this line has slope $m = -\frac{12}{1} = -12$. Using $(x_1, y_1) = (-2, 4)$, $m = -12$, and point-slope form $y = m(x - x_1) + y_1$, we get $y = -12(x + 2) + 4 \Rightarrow y = -12x - 24 + 4 \Rightarrow y = -12x - 20$.

48. $m = \dfrac{0-(-5)}{-4-(-3)} = \dfrac{5}{-1} = -5$. A line perpendicular to this line will have slope $m = \dfrac{1}{5}$. Using $(x_1, y_1) = \left(\dfrac{3}{4}, \dfrac{1}{4}\right)$, $m = \dfrac{1}{5}$, and point-slope form $y = m(x - x_1) + y_1$, we get $y = \dfrac{1}{5}\left(x - \dfrac{3}{4}\right) + \dfrac{1}{4} \Rightarrow$ $y = \dfrac{1}{5}x - \dfrac{3}{20} + \dfrac{1}{4} \Rightarrow y = \dfrac{1}{5}x + \dfrac{2}{20} \Rightarrow y = \dfrac{1}{5}x + \dfrac{1}{10}$.

49. $x = -5$

50. $x = 1.95$

51. $y = 6$

52. $y = 10.7$

53. Since the line $y = 15$ is horizontal, the perpendicular line through $(4, -9)$ is vertical and has equation $x = 4$.

54. Since the line $x = 15$ is vertical, the perpendicular line through $(1.6, 7.5)$ is horizontal and has equation $y = -9.5$.

55. The line through $(19, 5.5)$ and parallel to $x = 4.5$ is also vertical and has equation $x = 19$.

56. Since the line $y = -2.5$ is horizontal, the parallel line through (1985, 67) is also horizontal with equation $y = 67$.

57. Let $4x - 5y = 20$.

$x$-intercept: Substitute $y = 0$ and solve for $x$. $4x - 5(0) = 20 \Rightarrow 4x = 20 \Rightarrow x = 5$; $x$-intercept: 5

$y$-intercept: Substitute $x = 0$ and solve for $y$. $4(0) - 5y = 20 \Rightarrow -5y = 20 \Rightarrow y = -4$; $y$-intercept: $-4$

See Figure 57.

58. Let $-3x - 5y = 15$.

$x$-intercept: Substitute $y = 0$ and solve for $x$. $-3x - 5(0) = 15 \Rightarrow -3x = 15 \Rightarrow x = -5$; $x$-intercept: $-5$

$y$-intercept: Substitute $x = 0$ and solve for $y$. $-3(0) - 5y = 15 \Rightarrow -5y = 15 \Rightarrow y = -3$; $y$-intercept: $-3$

See Figure 58.

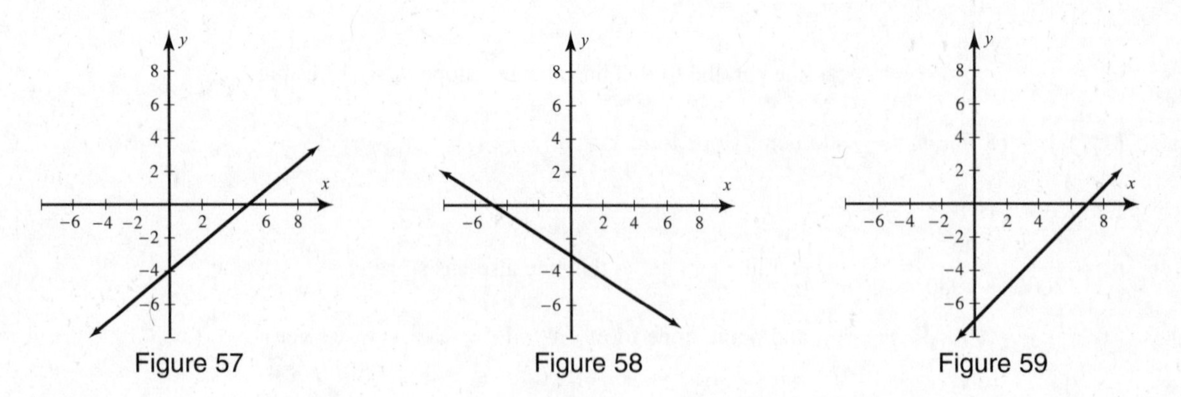


Figure 57 Figure 58 Figure 59

59. Let $x - y = 7$.

$x$-intercept: Substitute $y = 0$ and solve for $x$. $x - 0 = 7 \Rightarrow x = 7$; $x$-intercept: 7

$y$-intercept: Substitute $x = 0$ and solve for $y$. $0 - y = 7 \Rightarrow -y = 7 \Rightarrow y = -7$; $y$-intercept: $-7$

See Figure 59.

60. Let $15x - y = 30$.

$x$-intercept: Substitute $y = 0$ and solve for $x$. $15x - 0 = 30 \Rightarrow 15x = 30 \Rightarrow x = 2$; $x$-intercept: 2

$y$-intercept: Substitute $x = 0$ and solve for $y$. $15(0) - y = 30 \Rightarrow -y = 30 \Rightarrow y = -30$; $y$-intercept: $-30$

See Figure 60.

61. Let $6x - 7y = -42$.

$x$-intercept: Substitute $y = 0$ and solve for $x$. $6x - 7(0) = -42 \Rightarrow 6x = -42 \Rightarrow x = -7$; $x$-intercept: $-7$

$y$-intercept: Substitute $x = 0$ and solve for $y$. $6(0) - 7y = -42 \Rightarrow -7y = -42 \Rightarrow y = 6$; $y$-intercept: 6

See Figure 61.

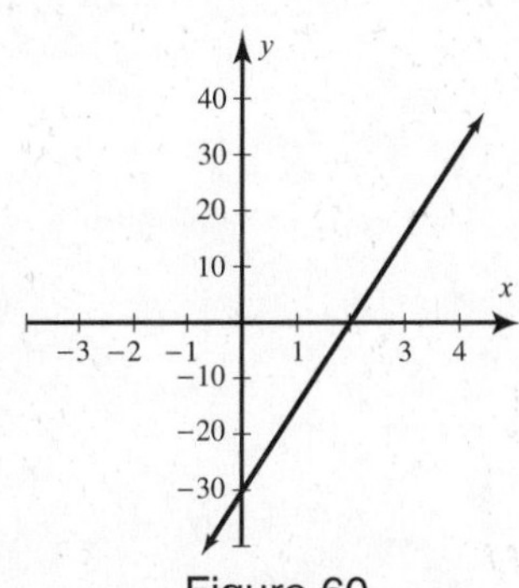

Figure 60

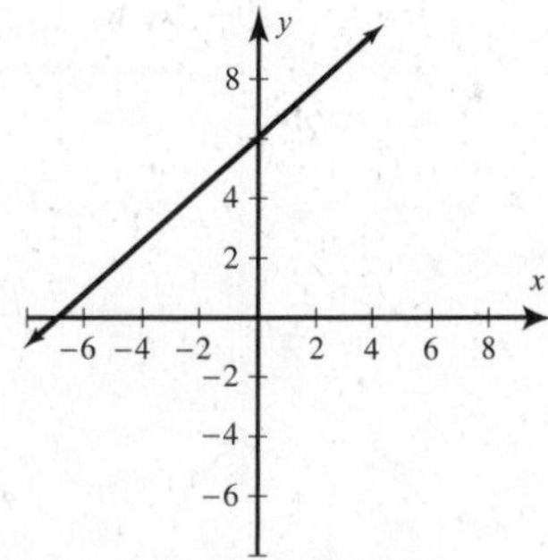

Figure 61

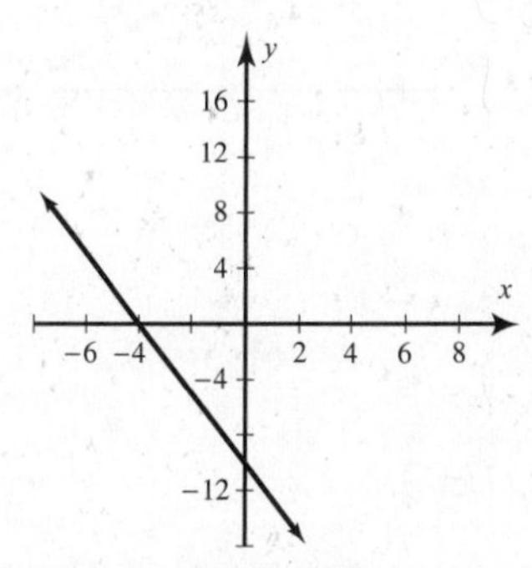

Figure 62

62. Let $5x + 2y = -20$.

$x$-intercept: Substitute $y = 0$ and solve for $x$. $5x + 2(0) = -20 \Rightarrow 5x = -20 \Rightarrow x = -4$; $x$-intercept: $-4$

$y$-intercept: Substitute $x = 0$ and solve for $y$. $5(0) + 2y = -20 \Rightarrow 2y = -20 \Rightarrow y = -10$; $y$-intercept: $-10$

See Figure 62.

63. Let $y - 3x = 7$.

$x$-intercept: Substitute $y = 0$ and solve for $x$. $0 - 3x = 7 \Rightarrow -3x = 7 \Rightarrow x = -\frac{7}{3}$; $x$-intercept: $-\frac{7}{3}$

$y$-intercept: Substitute $x = 0$ and solve for $y$. $y - 3(0) = 7 \Rightarrow y - 0 = 7 \Rightarrow y = 7$; $y$-intercept: 7

See Figure 63.

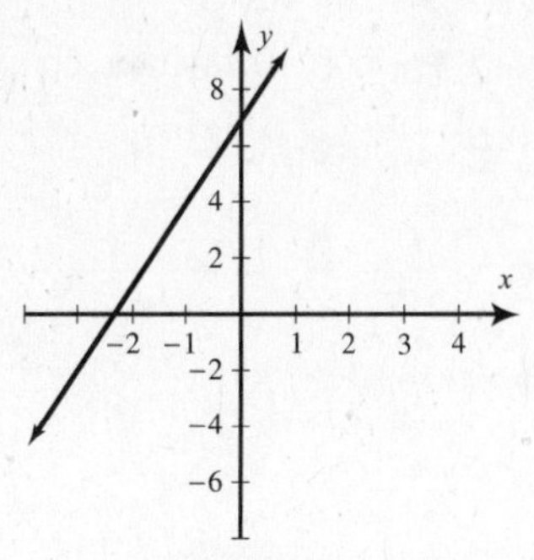

Figure 63

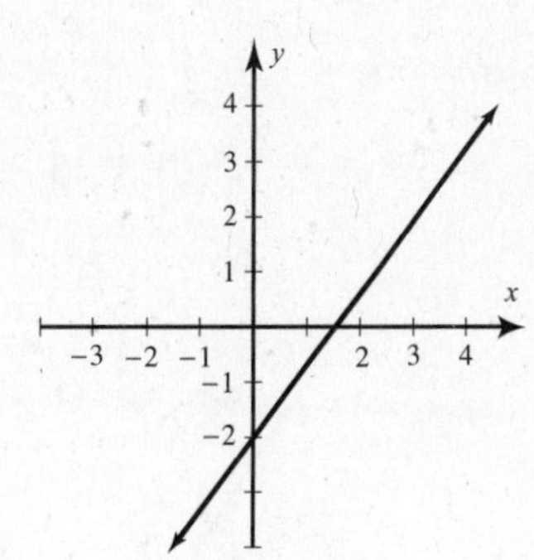

Figure 64

64. Let $4x - 3y = 6$.

$x$-intercept: Substitute $y = 0$ and solve for $x$. $4x - 3(0) = 6 \Rightarrow 4x = 6 \Rightarrow x = \frac{3}{2}$; $x$-intercept: $\frac{3}{2}$

$y$-intercept: Substitute $x = 0$ and solve for $y$. $4(0) - 3y = 6 \Rightarrow -3y = 6 \Rightarrow y = -2$; $y$-intercept: $-2$

See Figure 64.

65. Let $0.2x + 0.4y = 0.8$.

$x$-intercept: Substitute $y = 0$ and solve for $x$. $0.2x + 0.4(0) = 0.8 \Rightarrow 0.2x = 0.8 \Rightarrow x = 4$; $x$-intercept: 4

$y$-intercept: Substitute $x = 0$ and solve for $y$. $0.2(0) + 0.4y = 0.8 \Rightarrow 0.4y = 0.8 \Rightarrow y = 2$; $y$-intercept: 2

See Figure 65.

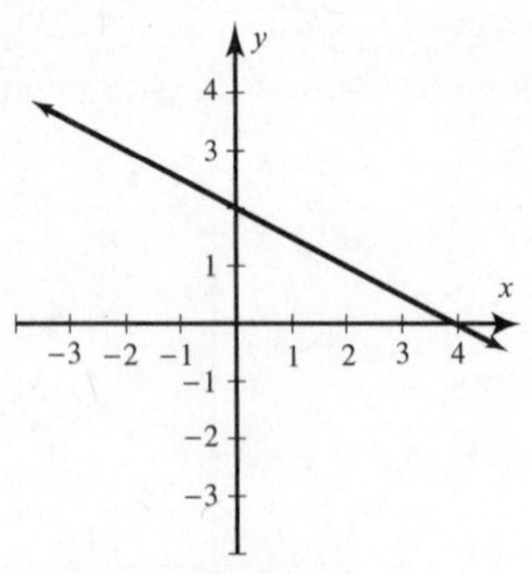

Figure 65

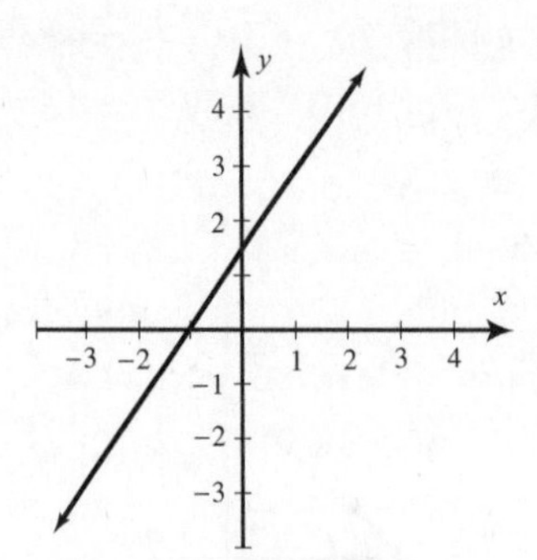

Figure 66

66. Let $\frac{2}{3}y - x = 1$.

$x$-intercept: Substitute $y = 0$ and solve for $x$. $\frac{2}{3}(0) - x = 1 \Rightarrow x = -1$; $x$-intercept: $-1$

$y$-intercept: Substitute $x = 0$ and solve for $y$. $\frac{2}{3}y - 0 = 1 \Rightarrow \frac{2}{3}y = 1 \Rightarrow y = \frac{3}{2}$; $y$-intercept: $\frac{3}{2}$

See Figure 66.

67. Let $y = 8x - 5$.

$x$-intercept: Substitute $y = 0$ and solve for $x$. $0 = 8x - 5 \Rightarrow 5 = 8x \Rightarrow x = \frac{5}{8}$; $x$-intercept: $\frac{5}{8}$

$y$-intercept: Substitute $x = 0$ and solve for $y$. $y = 8(0) - 5 \Rightarrow y = -5$; $y$-intercept: $-5$

See Figure 67.

68. Let $y = -1.5x + 15$.

$x$-intercept: Substitute $y = 0$ and solve for $x$. $0 = -1.5x + 15 \Rightarrow 1.5x = 15 \Rightarrow x = 10$; $y$-intercept: 10

$y$-intercept: Substitute $x = 0$ and solve for $y$. $y = -1.5(0) + 15 \Rightarrow y = 15$; $y$-intercept: 15

See Figure 68.

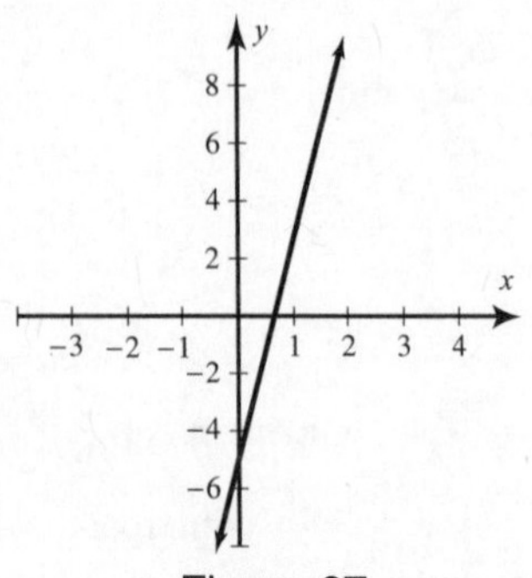

Figure 67

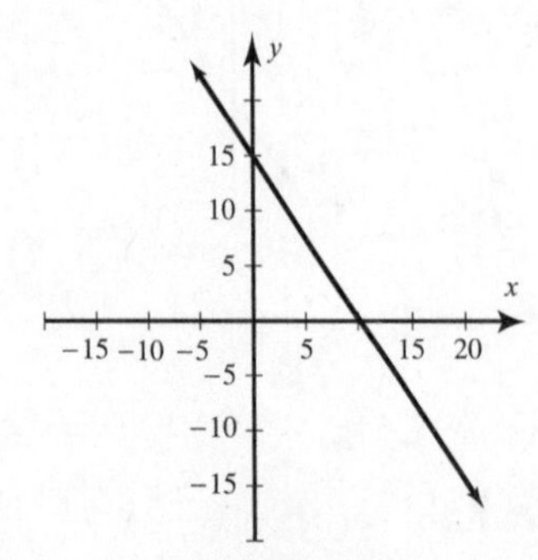

Figure 68

69. Let $\frac{x}{5} + \frac{y}{7} = 1$.

$x$-intercept: Substitute $y = 0$ and solve for $x$. $\frac{x}{5} + \frac{0}{7} = 1 \Rightarrow \frac{x}{5} = 1 \Rightarrow x = 5$; $x$-intercept: 5

$y$-intercept: Substitute $x = 0$ and solve for $y$. $\frac{0}{5} + \frac{y}{7} = 1 \Rightarrow \frac{y}{7} = 1 \Rightarrow y = 7$; $y$-intercept: 7

$a$ and $b$ represent the $x$- and $y$-intercepts, respectively.

70. Let $\frac{x}{2} + \frac{y}{3} = 1$.

$x$-intercept: Substitute $y = 0$ and solve for $x$. $\frac{x}{2} + \frac{0}{3} = 1 \Rightarrow \frac{x}{2} = 1 \Rightarrow x = 2$; $x$-intercept: 2

$y$-intercept: Substitute $x = 0$ and solve for $y$. $\frac{0}{2} + \frac{y}{3} = 1 \Rightarrow \frac{y}{3} = 1 \Rightarrow y = 3$; $y$-intercept: 3

$a$ and $b$ represent the $x$- and $y$-intercepts, respectively.

71. Let $\frac{2x}{3} + \frac{4y}{5} = 1$.

$x$-intercept: Substitute $y = 0$ and solve for $x$. $\frac{2x}{3} + \frac{4(0)}{5} = 1 \Rightarrow \frac{2x}{3} = 1 \Rightarrow x = \frac{3}{2}$; $x$-intercept: $\frac{3}{2}$

$y$-intercept: Substitute $x = 0$ and solve for $y$. $\frac{2(0)}{3} + \frac{4y}{5} = 1 \Rightarrow \frac{4y}{5} = 1 \Rightarrow y = \frac{5}{4}$; $y$-intercept: $\frac{5}{4}$

$a$ and $b$ represent the $x$- and $y$-intercepts, respectively.

72. Let $\frac{5x}{6} - \frac{y}{2} = 1$.

$x$-intercept: Substitute $y = 0$ and solve for $x$. $\frac{5x}{6} - \frac{0}{2} = 1 \Rightarrow \frac{5x}{6} = 1 \Rightarrow x = \frac{6}{5}$; $x$-intercept: $\frac{6}{5}$

$y$-intercept: Substitute $x = 0$ and solve for $y$. $\frac{5(0)}{6} - \frac{y}{2} = 1 \Rightarrow -\frac{y}{2} = 1 \Rightarrow y = -2$; $y$-intercept: $-2$

$a$ and $b$ represent the $x$- and $y$-intercepts, respectively.

73. $\frac{x}{a} + \frac{y}{b} = 1$; $x$-intercept: $5 \Rightarrow a = 5$, $y$-intercept: $9 \Rightarrow b = 9$; $\frac{x}{5} + \frac{y}{9} = 1$

74. $\frac{x}{a} + \frac{y}{b} = 1$; $x$-intercept: $\frac{2}{3} \Rightarrow a = \frac{2}{3}$, $y$-intercept: $-\frac{5}{4} \Rightarrow b = -\frac{5}{4}$; $\frac{x}{\frac{2}{3}} + \frac{y}{-\frac{5}{4}} = 1 \Rightarrow \frac{3x}{2} - \frac{4y}{5} = 1$

75. (a) Since the point $(0, -3.2)$ is on the graph, the $y$-intercept is $-3.2$. The data is exactly linear, so one can use any two points to determine the slope. Using the points $(0, -3.2)$ and $(1, -1.7)$, $m = \frac{-1.7 - (-3.2)}{1 - 0} = 1.5$. The slope-intercept form of the line is $y = 1.5x - 3.2$.

(b) When $x = -2.7$, $y = 1.5(-2.7) - 3.2 = -7.25$. This calculation involves interpolation.

When $x = 6.3$, $y = 1.5(6.3) - 3.2 = 6.25$. This calculation involves extrapolation.

76. (a) Since the point $(0, 6.8)$ is on the graph, the $y$-intercept is $6.8$. The data is exactly linear, so one can use any two points to determine the slope. Using the points $(0, 6.8)$ and $(1, 5.1)$, $m = \frac{5.1 - 6.8}{1 - 0} = -1.7$. The slope-intercept form of the line is $y = -1.7x + 6.8$.

(b) When $x = -2.7$, $y = -1.7(-2.7) + 6.8 = 11.39$. This calculation involves extrapolation.

When $x = 6.3$, $y = -1.7(6.3) + 6.8 = -3.91$. This calculation involves extrapolation.

77. (a) Since the data is exactly linear, one can use any two points to determine the slope. Using the points (5, 94.7) and (23, 56.9), $m = \dfrac{56.9 - 94.7}{23 - 5} = -2.1$. The point-slope form of the line is $y = -2.1(x - 5) + 94.7$ and the slope-intercept form of the line is $y = -2.1x + 105.2$.

(b) When $x = -2.7$, $y = -2.1(-2.7) + 105.2 = 110.87$. This calculation involves extrapolation.

When $x = 6.3$, $y = -2.1(6.3) + 105.2 = 91.97$. This calculation involves interpolation.

78. (a) Since the data is exactly linear, one can use any two points to determine the slope. Using the points (–3, –0.9) and (2, 8.6), $m = \dfrac{8.6 - (-0.9)}{2 - (-3)} = 1.9$. The point-slope form of the line is $y = 1.9(x - 2) + 8.6$ and the slope-intercept form of the line is $y = 1.9x + 4.8$.

(b) When $x = -2.7$, $y = 1.9(-2.7) + 4.8 = -0.33$. This calculation involves interpolation.

When $x = 6.3$, $y = 1.9(6.3) + 4.8 = 16.77$. This calculation involves extrapolation.

79. (a) The slope between (1998, 3305) and (1999, 3185) is –120, and the slope between (1999, 3185) and (2000, 3089) is –96. Using the average of –120 and –96, we will let $m = -108$.

$f(x) = -108(x - 1998) + 3305$, or $f(x) = -108x + 219{,}089$ approximately models the data.

*Answers may vary.*

(b) $f(2005) = -108(2005) + 219{,}089 = 2549$; this estimated value is too low (compared to the actual value of 3450); this estimate involved extrapolation.

(c) Numbers were decreasing but increased after 911.

80. (a) The slope between (1998, 43) and (1999, 26) is –17, and the slope between (1999, 26) and (2000, 9) is –17; letting $m = -17$, $f(x) = -17(x - 1998) + 43$, or $f(x) = -17x + 34{,}009$ exactly models the data.

(b) $f(2003) = -17(2003) + 34{,}009 = -42$; this estimated value is not possible. Extrapolation.

(c) *Answers may vary.*

81. (a) Find the slope: $m = \dfrac{37{,}000 - 25{,}000}{2010 - 2003} = \dfrac{12{,}000}{7}$. Using the first point (2003, 25000) for $(x_1, y_1)$ and $m = \dfrac{12{,}000}{7}$, we get $y = \dfrac{12{,}000}{7}(x - 2003) + 25{,}000$. The cost of attending a private college or university is increasing by $\dfrac{12{,}000}{7} \approx \$1714$ per year on average.

(b) $y = \dfrac{12{,}000}{7}(2007 - 2003) + 25{,}000 \Rightarrow y = \dfrac{12{,}000}{7}(4) + 25{,}000 \Rightarrow y \approx 6857 + 25{,}000 \Rightarrow$ $y \approx \$31{,}857$; interpolation

(c) $y = \dfrac{12{,}000}{7}(x - 2003) + 25{,}000 \Rightarrow y \approx \dfrac{12{,}000}{7}x - 3{,}433{,}714 + 25{,}000 \Rightarrow$ $y \approx 1714x - 3{,}408{,}714$ (approximate)

82. (a) The average rate of change $= \dfrac{161 - 128}{4 - 1} = \dfrac{33}{3} = 11 \Rightarrow$ the biker is traveling 11 mile per hour.

(b) Using $m = 11$ and the point (1, 128), we get $y = 11(x - 1) + 128 = 11x - 11 + 128 \Rightarrow$ $y = 11x + 117$.

(c) Find the $y$-intercept in $y = 11x + 117 \Rightarrow b = 117$; the biker is initially 117 miles from the interstate highway.

(d) 1 hour and 15 minutes = 1.25 hours; $y = 11(1.25) + 117 = 13.75 + 117 = 130.75$; the biker is 130.75 miles from the interstate highway after 1 hour and 15 minutes.

83. (a) Find the slope: $m = \frac{3.6 - 1.6}{2005 - 2002} = \frac{2}{3}$. Using the first point (2002, 1.6) for $(x_1, y_1)$ and $m = \frac{2}{3}$, we get

$y = \frac{2}{3}(x - 2002) + 1.6$; online music sales increased by $\frac{2}{3}$ billion dollars $\approx$ \$0.67 billion per year on average.

(b) $y = \frac{2}{3}(2008 - 2002) + 1.6 \Rightarrow y = \frac{2}{3}(6) + 1.6 \Rightarrow y = 4 + 1.6 \Rightarrow y = 5.6$ or \$5.6 billion; extrapolation

(c) $y = \frac{2}{3}(x - 2002) + 1.6 \Rightarrow y = \frac{2}{3}x - \frac{4004}{3} + \frac{8}{5} \Rightarrow y = \frac{2}{3}x - \frac{19{,}996}{15}$

84. (a) Water is leaving the tank because the amount of water in the tank is decreasing. After 3 minutes there are approximately 70 gallons of water in the tank.

(b) The $x$-intercept is 10. This means that after 10 minutes the tank is empty. The $y$-intercept is 100. This means that initially there are 100 gallons of water in the tank.

(c) To determine the equation of the line, we can use 2 points. The points (0, 100) and (10, 0) lie on the line. The slope of this line is $m = \frac{0 - 100}{10 - 0} = -10$. This slope means the water is being drained at a rate of 10 gallons per minute. Since the $y$-intercept is 100, the slope-intercept form of this line is given by $y = -10x + 100$.

(d) From the graph, when $y = 50$ the $x$-value appears to be 5. Symbolically, when $y = 50$ then $-10x + 100 = 50 \Rightarrow -10x = -50 \Rightarrow x = 5$. The $x$-coordinate is 5.

85. (a) See Figure 85.

(b) Use the first and last points to find slope $m = \frac{8.8 - 1.0}{2004 - 1999} = \frac{7.8}{5} = 1.56$. Now using the first point (1999, 1.0) for $(x_1, y_1)$ and $m = 1.56$, we get $y = 1.56(x - 1999) + 1.0$. The daily worldwide spam message numbers increased 1.56 billion per year on average. *Answers may vary.*

(c) $y = 1.56(2007 - 1999) + 1.0 \Rightarrow y = 1.56(8) + 1.0 \Rightarrow y = 12.48 + 1 \Rightarrow y \approx 13.5$ billion. *Answers may vary.*

86. (a) See Figure 86.

(b) Using the second and fourth points, $f(x) = 149.3(x - 1985) + 1318$; The average cost of tuition and fees at public four-year colleges has increased by about \$149 per year.

(c) In 1992, the average cost of tuition and fees was $f(1992) = 149(1992 - 1985) + 1318 \Rightarrow f(1992) = 149.3(7) + 1318 \Rightarrow f(1992) \approx \$2361$. This is fairly close to the actual of \$2334.

(d) The 2005 value; it is too large.

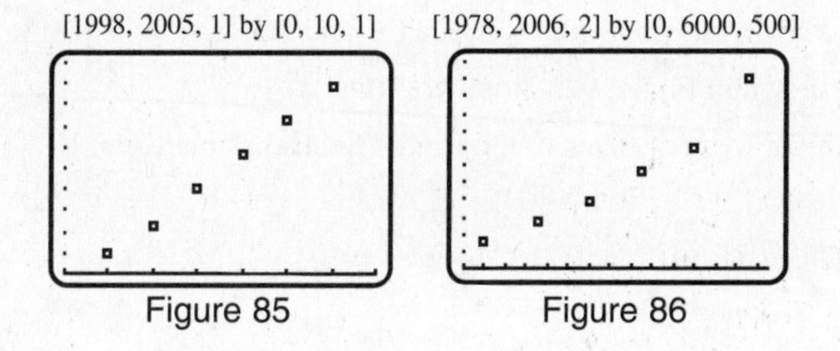


Figure 85 Figure 86

87. (a) See Figure 87.

(b) Use the first and last points to find slope $m = \dfrac{2 - 1.4}{2004 - 1998} = \dfrac{0.6}{6} = 0.1$. Now using the first point and slope $m = 0.1$, we get $y = 0.1(x - 1998) + 1.4$. U.S. sales of Toyota vehicles has increased by 0.1 million per year.

(c) $f(x)$ is an exact model for the listed data.

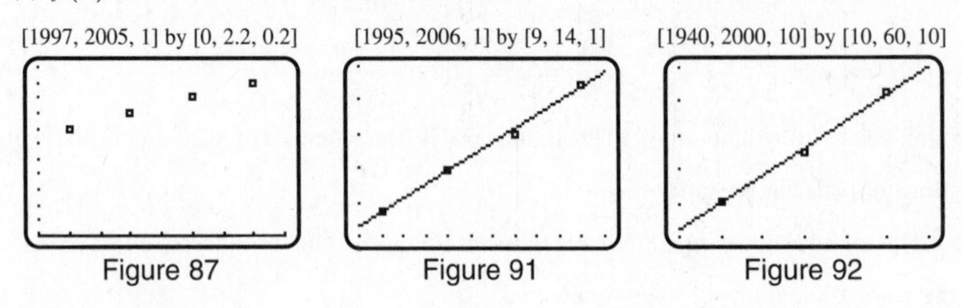


Figure 87 Figure 91 Figure 92

88. (a) $m = 280$ and $(1988, 4000)$ is a data point; $y = 280(x - 1988) + 4000$.

(b) Let $x = 1975 \Rightarrow y = 280(1975 - 1988) + 4000 = 360$; the number of incidents in 1975 was 360.

89. (a) The annual fixed cost would be $350 \times 12 = \$4200$. The variable cost of driving $x$ miles is $0.29x$. Thus, $f(x) = 0.29x + 4200$.

(b) The $y$-intercept is 4200, which represents the annual fixed costs. This means that even if the car is not driven, it will still cost \$4200 each year to own it.

90. (a) The line passes through the points (1970, 8.46) and (2005, 8.18). The slope of this line is $m = \dfrac{8.18 - 8.46}{2005 - 1970} = \dfrac{0.28}{-35} = -0.008$. A point-slope form for the equation of the line is $y = -0.008(x - 1970) + 8.46$.

(b) Wages have decreased by about \$0.008 per year.

(c) When $x = 2000$, $y = -0.008(2000 - 1970) + 8.46 = \$8.22$. This is more than the actual value.

91. (a) Scatterplot the data in the table.

(b) Start by picking a data point for the line to pass through. If we choose (1996, 9.7), $f$ is represented by $f(x) = m(x - 1996) + 9.7$. Using trial and error, the slope m is between 0 and 1. Let $m = 0.42$. The graph of $f$ together with the scatterplot is shown in Figure 91. *Answers may vary.*

(c) A slope of $m \approx 0.42$ means that Asian-American population is predicted to increase by approximately 0.42 million (420,000) people each year.

(d) To predict the population in the year 2008, evaluate $f(2008) = 0.4167(2008 - 1996) + 9.7 \approx 14.7$ million people.

92. (a) Scatterplot the data in the table.

(b) Start by picking a data point for the line to pass through. If we choose (1950, 20.2), $f$ is represented by $f(x) = m(x - 1950) + 20.2$. Using trial and error, the slope $m$ is between 0.5 and 1.5. Let $m = 0.815$. The graph of $f$ together with the scatterplot is shown in Figure 92. *Answers may vary.*

(c) A slope of $m \approx 0.815$ means that population in the western states of the United States has increased by approximately 0.82 million people each year.

(d) To predict the population in the year 2010, evaluate $f(2010) = 0.815(2010 - 1950) + 20.2 = 69.1$ million people.

93. (a) Graph $Y_1 = X/1024 + 1$ in $[0, 3, 1]$ by $[-2, 2, 1]$ as in Figure 93. The line appears to be horizontal in this viewing rectangle, however, we know that the graph of the line is not horizontal because its slope is $\frac{1}{1024} \neq 0$.

(b) The resolution of most graphing calculator screens is not good enough to show the slight increase in the $y$-values. Since the $x$-axis is 3 units long, this increase in $y$-values amounts to only $\frac{1}{1024} \times 3 \approx 0.003$ units, which does not show up on the screen.

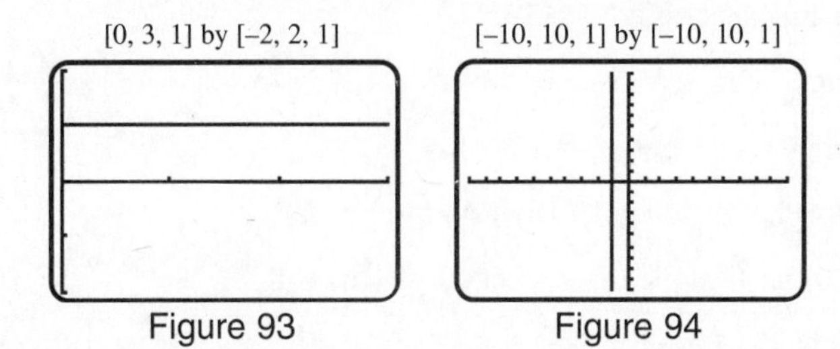


Figure 93 Figure 94

94. (a) The graph appears to be the vertical line $x = -1$. However, the line actually is not vertical, since it has slope of 1000, which is defined. See Figure 94.

(b) The resolution of most graphing calculator screens is not good enough to show that the line is slightly non-vertical on the interval [–10, 10].

95. (a) From Figure 95a, one can see that the lines do not appear to be perpendicular.

(b) The lines are graphed in the specified viewing rectangles and shown in Figures 95b-d, respectively. In the windows [–15, 15, 1] by [–10, 10, 1] and [–3, 3, 1] by [–2, 2, 1] the lines appear to be perpendicular.

(c) The lines appear perpendicular when the distance shown along the $x$-axis is approximately 1.5 times the distance along the $y$-axis. For example, in window [–12, 12,1] by [–8, 8, 1], the lines will appear perpendicular. The distance along the $x$-axis is 24 while the distance along the y-axis is 16. Notice that $1.5 \times 16 = 24$. This is called a "square window" and can be set automatically on some graphing calculators.

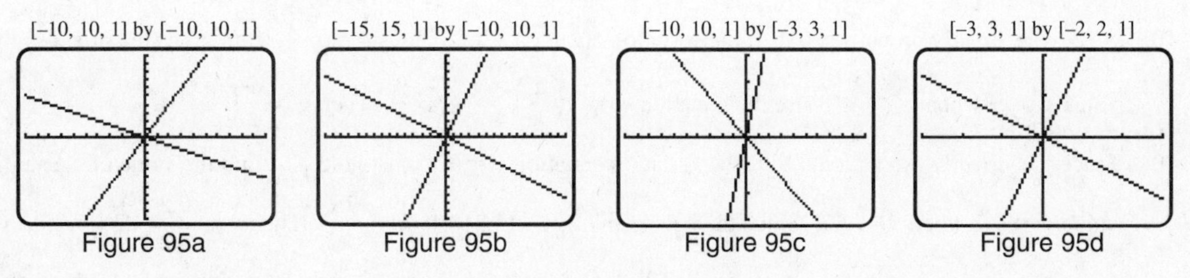


Figure 95a Figure 95b Figure 95c Figure 95d

96. The circle will appear to be a circle rather than an ellipse for the window [–9, 9, 1] by [–6, 6, 1], since the distance along the $x$-axis is 18, which is 1.5 times the distance along the $y$-axis, 12. Similarly, a circle will result in the viewing window [–18, 18, 1] by [–12, 12, 1]. The results are shown in Figures 96a-d.

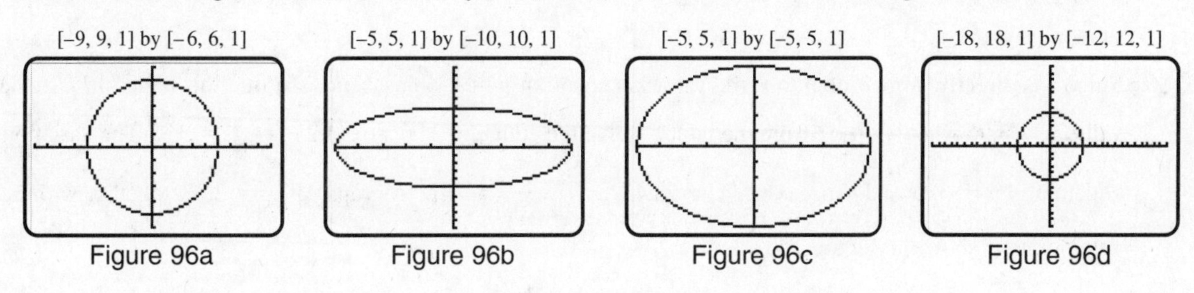


Figure 96a Figure 96b Figure 96c Figure 96d

97. (i) The slope of the line connecting (0, 0) and (2, 2) is 1. Let $y_1 = x$.
(ii) A second line passing through (0, 0) has a slope of $-1$. Let $y_2 = -x$.
(iii) A third line passing through (1, 3) has a slope of 1. Let $y_3 = (x - 1) + 3 = x + 2$.
(iv) A fourth line passing through (2, 2) has a slope of $-1$. Let $y_4 = -(x - 2) + 2 = -x + 4$.

98. (i) The slope of the line connecting (1, 1) and (5, 1) is 0. Let $y_1 = 1$.
(ii) A second line passing through (1, 1) is vertical. Its equation is $x = 1$.
(iii) A third line passing through (5, 1) is vertical. Its equation is $x = 5$.
(iv) A fourth line passing through (5, 5) is horizontal. Let $y_4 = 5$.

99. (i) The slope of the line connecting $(-4, 0)$ and $(0, 4)$ is 1. Let $y_1 = x + 4$.
(ii) A second line passing through $(4, 0)$ and $(0, -4)$ has a slope of 1. Let $y_2 = x - 4$.
(iii) A third line passing through $(0, -4)$ and $(-4, 0)$ has a slope of $-1$. Let $y_3 = -x - 4$.
(iv) A fourth line passing through (0, 4) and (4, 0) is $-1$. Let $y_4 = -x + 4$.

100. (i) The slope of the line connecting (1, 1) and (2, 3) is 2. Let $y_1 = 2(x - 1) + 1$.
(ii) The second line is perpendicular to $y_1$ and passes through (1, 1). Let $y_2 = -\frac{1}{2}(x - 1) + 1$.
(iii) The third line is perpendicular to $y_1$ and passes through (2, 3). Let $y_3 = -\frac{1}{2}(x - 2) + 3$.
(iv) The fourth line is parallel to $y_1$ and passes through (3.5, 1). Let $y_4 = 2(x - 3.5) + 1$.

101. Since $y$ is directly proportional to $x$, the variation equation $y = kx$ must hold. To find the value of $k$, use the value $y = 7$ when $x = 14$. Solve the equation $7 = k(14) \Rightarrow k = \frac{1}{2}$. Then $y = \frac{1}{2}(5) = \frac{5}{2} = 2.5$.

102. Since $y$ is directly proportional to $x$, the variation equation $y = kx$ must hold. To find the value of $k$, use the value $y = 13$ when $x = 10$. Solve the equation $13 = k(10) \Rightarrow k = \frac{13}{10}$. Then $y = \frac{13}{10}(2.5) = 3.25$.

103. Since $y$ is directly proportional to $x$, the variation equation $y = kx$ must hold. To find the value of $k$, use the value $y = \frac{3}{2}$ when $x = \frac{2}{3}$. Solve the equation $\frac{3}{2} = k\left(\frac{2}{3}\right) \Rightarrow k = \frac{9}{4}$. Then $y = \frac{9}{4}\left(\frac{1}{2}\right) = \frac{9}{8}$.

104. Since $y$ is directly proportional to $x$, the variation equation $y = kx$ must hold. To find the value of $k$, use the value $y = 7.2$ when $x = 5.2$. Solve the equation $7.2 = k(5.2) \Rightarrow k = \frac{7.2}{5.2}$. Then $y = \frac{7.2}{5.2}(1.3) = 1.8$.

105. Since $y$ is directly proportional to $x$, the variation equation $y = kx$ must hold. To find the value of $k$ use the value $y = 7.5$ when $x = 3$ from the table. Solve the equation $7.5 = k(3) \Rightarrow k = 2.5$. The variation equation is $y = 2.5x$ and hence $y = 2.5(8) = 20$ when $x = 8$. A graph of $Y_1 = 2.5X$ together with the data points is shown in Figure 105.

106. Since $y$ is directly proportional to $x$, the variation equation $y = kx$ must hold. To find the value of $k$ use the value $y = 3.96$ when $x = 1.2$ from the table. Solve the equation $3.96 = k(1.2) \Rightarrow k = 3.3$. The variation equation is $y = 3.3x$ and hence when $y = 23.43$, $x = \frac{23.43}{3.3} = 7.1$. A graph of $Y_1 = 3.3X$ together with the data points is shown in Figure 106.

[0, 10, 1] by [0, 24, 2] [0, 10, 1] by [0, 30, 2] [0, 100, 10] by [0, 6, 1] [0, 6, 1] by [0, 80, 10]

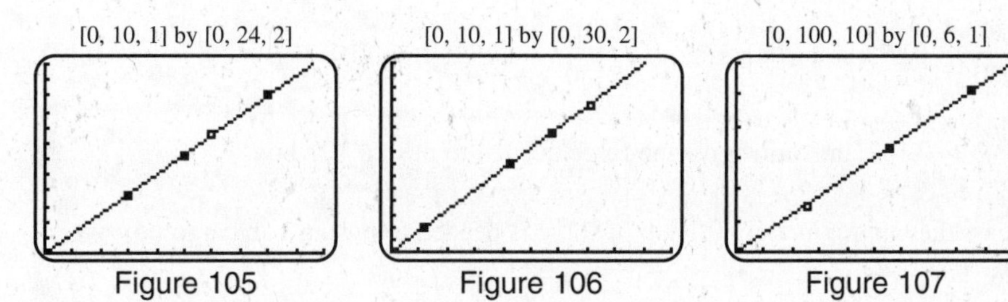

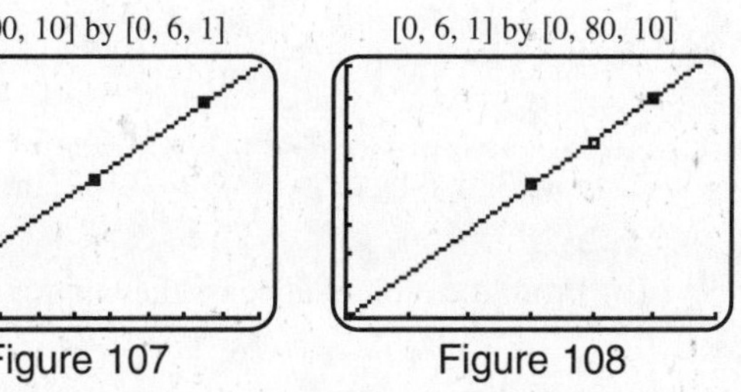

Figure 105 Figure 106 Figure 107 Figure 108

107. Since $y$ is directly proportional to $x$, the variation equation $y = kx$ must hold. To find the value of $k$ use the value $y = 1.50$ when $x = 25$ from the table. Solve the equation $1.50 = k(25) \Rightarrow k = 0.06$. The variation equation is $y = 0.06x$ and hence when $y = 5.10$, $x = \dfrac{5.1}{0.06} = 85$. A graph of $Y_1 = 0.06X$ together with the data points is shown in Figure 107.

108. Since $y$ is directly proportional to $x$, the variation equation $y = kx$ must hold. To find the value of $k$ use the value $y = 41.97$ when $x = 3$ from the table. Solve the equation $41.97 = k(3) \Rightarrow k = 13.99$. The variation equation is $y = 13.99x$ and hence $y = 13.99(5) = 69.95$ when $x = 5$. A graph of $Y_1 = 13.99X$ together with the data points is shown in Figure 108.

109. Let $y$ represent the cost of tuition and $x$ represent the number of credits taken. Since the cost of tuition is directly proportional to the number of credits taken, the variation equation $y = kx$ must hold. If cost $y = \$720.50$ when the number of credits $x = 11$, we find the constant of proportionality $k$ by solving $720.50 = k(11) \Rightarrow k = 65.50$. The variation equation is $y = 65.50x$. Therefore, the cost of taking 16 credits is $y = 65.50(16) = \$1048$.

110. Let $y$ represent the maximum load and $x$ represent the beam width. Since the maximum load is directly proportional to the beam width, the variation equation $y = kx$ must hold. If the maximum load is $y = 250$ pounds when the beam width $x = 1.5$ inches, we find the constant of proportionality $k$ by solving $250 = k(1.5) \Rightarrow k = 166\frac{2}{3}$. The variation equation is $y = 166\frac{2}{3}x$. Therefore, a 3.5 inch beam can support a maximum load of $y = 166\frac{2}{3}(3.5) = 583\frac{1}{3}$ pounds.

111. (a) Since the points (0, 0) and (300, 3) lie on the graph of $y = kx$, the slope of the graph is $\dfrac{3-0}{300-0} = 0.01$ and $y = 0.01x$, so $k = 0.01$.

     (b) $y = 0.01(110) = 1.1$ millimeters.

112. $25 = 10k \Rightarrow k = 2.5$; then $195 = 2.5x \Rightarrow 78$.

113. (a) Using $F = kx \Rightarrow 15 = k(8) \Rightarrow k = \dfrac{15}{8}$

     (b) The variation equation is $y = \dfrac{15}{8}x$; $25 = \dfrac{15}{8}(x) \Rightarrow x = 13\frac{1}{3}$ inches.

114. Using $F = kx \Rightarrow 80 = k(3) \Rightarrow k = \dfrac{80}{3}$; then $x = 7 \Rightarrow F = \dfrac{80}{3}(7) = 186.\overline{6}$.

115. (a) For (150, 26), $\frac{F}{x} = \frac{26}{150} \approx 0.173$; for (180, 31), $\frac{F}{x} = \frac{31}{180} \approx 0.172$; for (210, 36), $\frac{F}{x} = \frac{36}{210} \approx 0.171$;

for (320, 54), $\frac{F}{x} = \frac{54}{320} \approx 0.169$; the ratios give the force needed to push a 1 lb box.

(b) From the table it appears that approximately 0.17 lb of force is needed to push a 1 lb cargo box $\Rightarrow$ $k = 0.17$.

(c) See Figure 115.

(d) $F \approx 0.17(275) \Rightarrow F = 46.75$ lbs of force.

[125, 350, 25] by [0, 75, 5]

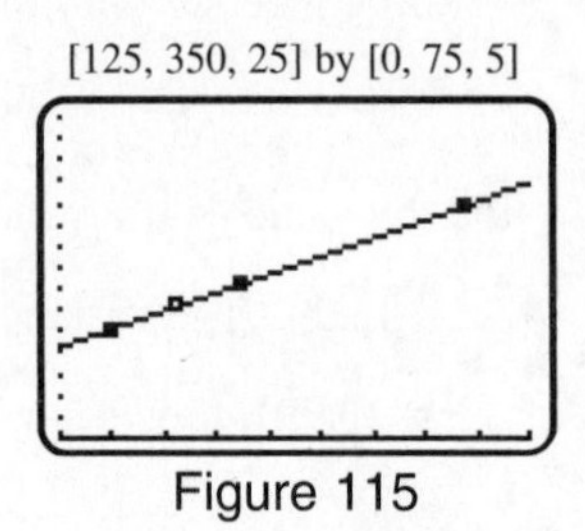

Figure 115

116. Let $y$ represent the resistance and $x$ represent the wire length. Since the resistance is directly proportional to the length, the variation equation $y = kx$ must hold. If the resistance $y = 1.2$ ohms when the length $x = 255$ feet, we find the constant of proportionality $k$ by solving $1.2 = k(255) \Rightarrow k \approx 0.0047059$. The variation equation is $y \approx 0.0047059x$. A 135-foot wire will have a resistance of $y \approx 0.0047059(135) \approx 0.6353$ ohm. The constant of proportionality represents the resistance of the wire in ohms per foot.

## Extended and Discovery Exercises for Section 2.2

1. Let $x =$ number of fish in the sample and $y =$ number of tagged fish. Then $y = kx$, where $k$ represents the proportion of fish tagged. From the data point (94, 13), get $13 = k(94) \Rightarrow k \approx 0.138298$. Letting the sample represent the entire number of fish, we get $y = 0.138298x \Rightarrow 85 = 0.138298x \Rightarrow x \approx 615$.

2. Let $x =$ number of black birds in the sample and $y =$ number of tagged blackbirds. Then $y = kx$, where $k$ represents the proportion of blackbirds tagged. From the data point (32, 8), we get $8 = k(32) \Rightarrow k = 0.25$. Letting the sample represent the entire blackbird population, we get $y = 0.25x \Rightarrow 63 = 0.25x \Rightarrow x = 252$. There are about 252 blackbirds in the area.

## Checking Basic Concepts for Sections 2.1 and 2.2

1. $f(x) = 4 - 2x$. See Figure 1. Slope: –2; $y$-intercept: 4; $x$-intercept: 2

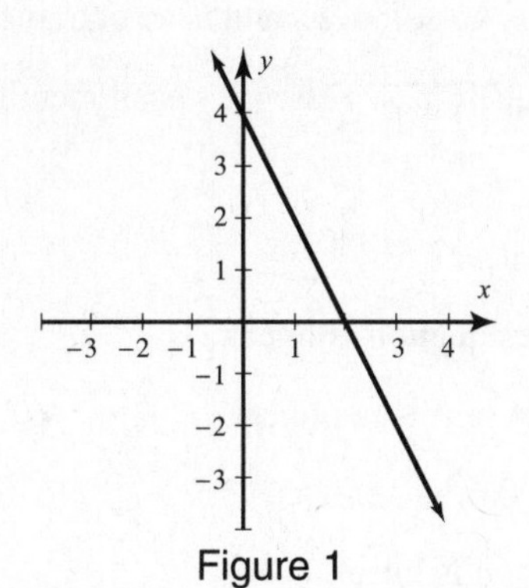


Figure 1

2. (a) The rate of change is 2.7 per 100,000 people, or 27 per 1,000,000 $\Rightarrow m = 27$; $f(x) = 27x$, where $x$ is in millions.

   (b) $f(39) = 27(39) = 1053$; the number of people 15 to 24 years old who die from heart disease is 1053.

3. Since the car is initially 50 miles south of home and driving south at 60 mph, the $y$-intercept is 50 and $m = 60$; $f(t) = 60t + 50$, where $t$ is in hours.

4. The slope of the line passing through (–3, 4) and (5, –2) is $m = \frac{-2 - 4}{5 - (-3)} = -\frac{3}{4}$. Using the point-slope form of a line results in $y = -\frac{3}{4}(x + 3) + 4$ or $y = -\frac{3}{4}x + \frac{7}{4}$. The line $y = -\frac{3}{4}x$ is parallel to $y = -\frac{3}{4}x + \frac{7}{4}$ and $y = \frac{4}{3}x$ is perpendicular. *Answers may vary.*

5. $y = 7$ is the equation of the horizontal line passing through (–4, 7) and $x = -4$ is the vertical line passing through this point.

6. Since the line passes through $(-1, 2)$ and $(1, -1)$, the slope is $m = \frac{2 - (-1)}{-1 - 1} = -\frac{3}{2}$. The $y$-intercept is $\frac{1}{2} \Rightarrow y = -\frac{3}{2}x + \frac{1}{2}$.

7. Let $-3x + 2y = -18$.

   $x$-intercept: Substitute $y = 0$ and solve for $x$. $-3x + 2(0) = -18 \Rightarrow -3x = -18 \Rightarrow x = 6$; $x$-intercept: 6

   $y$-intercept: Substitute $x = 0$ and solve for $y$. $-3(0) + 2y = -18 \Rightarrow 2y = -18 \Rightarrow y = -9$; $x$-intercept: $-9$

## 2.3: Linear Equations

1. $ax + b = 0 \Rightarrow ax = -b \Rightarrow x = \frac{-b}{a}$. This shows that the equation $ax + b = 0$ has only one solution.

2. Since the graph of $y = ax + b$ is a linear equation, the graph will intersect the $x$-axis at one point.

3. $4 - (5 - 4x) = 4 - 5 + 4x = -1 + 4x = 4x - 1$

4. $15x = 5 \Rightarrow \frac{1}{15}(15x) = \frac{1}{15}(5) \Rightarrow x = \frac{1}{3}$. This shows the multiplication property of equality.

5. The zero of f and the $x$-intercept of the graph of $f$ are equal. The zero of $f$ and the $x$-intercept of the graph of $f$ are both found by finding the value of $x$ when $y = 0$.

6. A contradiction has no solutions. For example, the equation $x + 2 = x$ has no solutions and is a contradiction. In an identity, every value of the variable is a solution. For example, the equation $x + x = 2x$ is an identity because every value for $x$ makes the equation true.

7. $3x - 1.5 = 7 \Rightarrow 3x - 1.5 - 7 = 0 \Rightarrow 3x - 8.5 = 0$; the equation is linear.

8. $100 - 23x = 20x \Rightarrow 100 - 23x - 20x = 0 \Rightarrow -43x + 100 = 0$; the equation is linear.

9. $2\sqrt{x} + 2 = 1$; since the equation cannot be written in the form $ax + b = 0$, it is nonlinear.

10. $4x^3 - 7 = 0$; since the equation cannot be written in the form $ax + b = 0$, it is nonlinear.

11. $7x - 5 = 3(x - 8) \Rightarrow 7x - 5 = 3x - 24 \Rightarrow 4x + 19 = 0$; the equation is linear.

12. $2(x - 3) = 4 - 5x \Rightarrow 2x - 6 = 4 - 5x \Rightarrow 7x - 10 = 0$; it is linear.

13. $2x - 8 = 0 \Rightarrow 2x = 8 \Rightarrow x = 4$ Check: $2(4) - 8 = 0 \Rightarrow 8 - 8 = 0 \Rightarrow 0 = 0$

14. $4x - 8 = 0 \Rightarrow 4x = 8 \Rightarrow x = 2$ Check: $4(2) - 8 = 0 \Rightarrow 8 - 8 = 0 \Rightarrow 0 = 0$

15. $-5x + 3 = 23 \Rightarrow -5x = 20 \Rightarrow x = -4$ Check: $-5(-4) + 3 = 23 \Rightarrow 20 + 3 = 23 \Rightarrow 23 = 23$

16. $-9x - 3 = 24 \Rightarrow -9x = 27 \Rightarrow x = -3$ Check: $-9(-3) - 3 = 24 \Rightarrow 27 - 3 = 24 \Rightarrow 24 = 24$

17. $4(z - 8) = z \Rightarrow 4z - 32 = z \Rightarrow 3z = 32 \Rightarrow z = \frac{32}{3}$ Check: $4\left(\frac{32}{3} - 8\right) = \frac{32}{3} \Rightarrow 4\left(\frac{8}{3}\right) = \frac{32}{3} \Rightarrow \frac{32}{32} = \frac{32}{32}$

18. $-3(2z - 1) = 2z \Rightarrow -6z + 3 = 2z \Rightarrow -8z = -3 \Rightarrow z = \frac{3}{8}$ Check: $-3\left(2\left(\frac{3}{8}\right) - 1\right) = 2\left(\frac{3}{8}\right) \Rightarrow -3\left(-\frac{1}{4}\right) = \frac{3}{4} \Rightarrow \frac{3}{4} = \frac{3}{4}$

19. $-5(3 - 4t) = 65 \Rightarrow -15 + 20t = 65 \Rightarrow 20t = 80 \Rightarrow t = 4$ Check: $-5[3 - 4(4)] = 65 \Rightarrow -5(3 - 16) = 65 \Rightarrow -5(-13) = 65 \Rightarrow 65 = 65$

20. $6(5 - 3t) = 66 \Rightarrow 30 - 18t = 66 \Rightarrow -18t = 36 \Rightarrow t = -2$ Check: $6[5 - 3(-2)] = 66 \Rightarrow 6(11) = 66 \Rightarrow 66 = 66$

21. $k + 8 = 5k - 4 \Rightarrow -4k = -12 \Rightarrow k = 3$ Check: $3 + 8 = 5(3) - 4 \Rightarrow 11 = 15 - 4 \Rightarrow 11 = 11$

22. $2k - 3 = k + 3 \Rightarrow k = 6$ Check: $2(6) - 3 = 6 + 3 \Rightarrow 12 - 3 = 9 \Rightarrow 9 = 9$

23. $2(1 - 3x) + 1 = 3x \Rightarrow 2 - 6x + 1 = 3x \Rightarrow -6x + 3 = 3x \Rightarrow -9x = -3 \Rightarrow x = \frac{1}{3}$

Check: $2\left[1 - 3\left(\frac{1}{3}\right)\right] + 1 = 3\left(\frac{1}{3}\right) \Rightarrow 2(1 - 1) + 1 = 1 \Rightarrow 0 + 1 = 1 \Rightarrow 1 = 1$

24. $5(x - 2) = -2(1 - x) \Rightarrow 5x - 10 = -2 + 2x \Rightarrow 3x = 8 \Rightarrow x = \frac{8}{3}$

Check: $5\left(\frac{8}{3} - 2\right) = -2\left(1 - \frac{8}{3}\right) \Rightarrow 5\left(\frac{2}{3}\right) = -2\left(-\frac{5}{3}\right) \Rightarrow \frac{10}{3} = \frac{10}{3}$

25. $-5(3-2x)-(1-x)=4(x-3) \Rightarrow -15+10x-1+x=4x-12 \Rightarrow 11x-16=4x-12 \Rightarrow$
$7x=4 \Rightarrow x=\frac{4}{7}$ Check: $-5\left[3-2\left(\frac{4}{7}\right)\right]-\left(1-\frac{4}{7}\right)=4\left(\frac{4}{7}-3\right) \Rightarrow$
$-5\left(\frac{13}{7}\right)-\frac{3}{7}=4\left(-\frac{17}{7}\right) \Rightarrow -\frac{65}{7}-\frac{3}{7}=-\frac{68}{7} \Rightarrow -\frac{68}{7}=-\frac{68}{7}$

26. $-3(5-x)-(x-2)=7x-2 \Rightarrow -15+3x-x+2=7x-2 \Rightarrow 2x-13=7x-2 \Rightarrow$
$-5x=11 \Rightarrow x=-\frac{11}{5}$ Check: $-3\left[5-\left(-\frac{11}{5}\right)\right]-\left(-\frac{11}{5}-2\right)=7\left(-\frac{11}{5}\right)-2 \Rightarrow$
$-3\left(\frac{36}{5}\right)-\left(-\frac{21}{5}\right)=-\frac{77}{5}-2 \Rightarrow -\frac{108}{5}+\frac{21}{5}=-\frac{87}{5} \Rightarrow -\frac{87}{5}=-\frac{87}{5}$

27. $-4(5x-1)=8-(x+2) \Rightarrow -20x+4=8-x-2 \Rightarrow -20x+4=6-x \Rightarrow -19x=2 \Rightarrow$
$x=-\frac{2}{19}$ Check: $-4\left[5\left(-\frac{2}{19}\right)-1\right]=8-\left(-\frac{2}{19}+2\right) \Rightarrow -4\left(-\frac{10}{19}-1\right)=8+\frac{2}{19}-2 \Rightarrow$
$\frac{40}{19}+4=6+\frac{2}{19} \Rightarrow \frac{116}{19}=\frac{116}{19}$

28. $6(3-2x)=1-(2x-1) \Rightarrow 18-12x=1-2x+1 \Rightarrow 18-12x=2-2x \Rightarrow 16=10x \Rightarrow$
$x=\frac{16}{10}=\frac{8}{5}$ Check: $6\left[3-2\left(\frac{8}{5}\right)\right]=1-\left[2\left(\frac{8}{5}\right)-1\right] \Rightarrow 6\left(3-\frac{16}{5}\right)=1-\left(\frac{16}{5}-1\right) \Rightarrow$
$6\left(-\frac{1}{5}\right)=1-\left(\frac{11}{5}\right) \Rightarrow -\frac{6}{5}=-\frac{6}{5}$

29. $\frac{2}{7}n+\frac{1}{5}=\frac{4}{7} \Rightarrow \frac{2}{7}n=\frac{13}{35} \Rightarrow n=\frac{13}{10}$ Check: $\frac{2}{7}\left(\frac{13}{10}\right)+\frac{1}{5}=\frac{4}{7} \Rightarrow \frac{26}{70}+\frac{1}{5}=\frac{4}{7} \Rightarrow \frac{40}{70}=\frac{4}{7} \Rightarrow$
$\frac{4}{7}=\frac{4}{7}$

30. $\frac{6}{11}-\frac{2}{33}n=\frac{5}{11}n \Rightarrow -\frac{17}{33}n=-\frac{6}{11} \Rightarrow n=\frac{18}{17}$ Check: $\frac{6}{11}-\frac{2}{33}\left(\frac{18}{17}\right)=\frac{5}{11}\left(\frac{18}{17}\right) \Rightarrow$
$\frac{6}{11}-\frac{36}{561}=\frac{90}{187} \Rightarrow \frac{270}{561}=\frac{90}{187} \Rightarrow \frac{90}{187}=\frac{90}{187}$

31. $\frac{1}{2}(d-3)-\frac{2}{3}(2d-5)=\frac{5}{12} \Rightarrow \frac{1}{2}d-\frac{3}{2}-\frac{4}{3}d+\frac{10}{3}=\frac{5}{12} \Rightarrow -\frac{5}{6}d+\frac{11}{6}=\frac{5}{12} \Rightarrow$
$-\frac{5}{6}d=-\frac{17}{12} \Rightarrow d=\frac{17}{10}$
Check: $\frac{1}{2}\left(\frac{17}{10}-3\right)-\frac{2}{3}\left[2\left(\frac{17}{10}\right)-5\right]=\frac{5}{12} \Rightarrow \frac{1}{2}\left(-\frac{13}{10}\right)-\frac{2}{3}\left(\frac{34}{10}-5\right)=\frac{5}{12} \Rightarrow$
$\frac{1}{2}\left(-\frac{13}{10}\right)-\frac{2}{3}\left(-\frac{16}{10}\right)=\frac{5}{12} \Rightarrow -\frac{13}{20}+\frac{32}{30}=\frac{5}{12} \Rightarrow \frac{25}{60}=\frac{5}{12} \Rightarrow \frac{5}{12}=\frac{5}{12}$

32. $\frac{7}{3}(2d-1)-\frac{2}{5}(4-3d)=\frac{1}{5}d \Rightarrow \frac{14}{3}d-\frac{7}{3}-\frac{8}{5}+\frac{6}{5}d=\frac{1}{5}d \Rightarrow \frac{88}{15}d-\frac{59}{15}=\frac{1}{5}d \Rightarrow \frac{85}{15}d=\frac{59}{15} \Rightarrow$
$d=\frac{59}{85}$ Check: $\frac{7}{3}\left[2\left(\frac{59}{85}\right)-1\right]-\frac{2}{5}\left[4-3\left(\frac{59}{85}\right)\right]=\frac{1}{5}\left(\frac{59}{85}\right) \Rightarrow$
$\frac{7}{3}\left(\frac{118}{85}-1\right)-\frac{2}{5}\left(4-\frac{177}{85}\right)=\frac{59}{425} \Rightarrow \frac{7}{3}\left(\frac{33}{85}\right)-\frac{2}{5}\left(\frac{163}{85}\right)=\frac{59}{425} \Rightarrow \frac{59}{425}=\frac{59}{125}$

33. $\frac{x-5}{3}+\frac{3-2x}{2}=\frac{5}{4} \Rightarrow 12\left(\frac{x-5}{3}+\frac{3-2x}{2}\right)=12\left(\frac{5}{4}\right) \Rightarrow 4x-20+18-12x=15 \Rightarrow$

$-8x-2=15 \Rightarrow -8x=17 \Rightarrow x=-\frac{17}{8}$ Check: $\frac{-\frac{17}{8}-5}{3}+\frac{3-2(-\frac{17}{8})}{2}=\frac{5}{4} \Rightarrow$

$\frac{-\frac{57}{8}}{3}+\frac{3+\frac{34}{8}}{2}=\frac{5}{4} \Rightarrow -\frac{19}{8}+\frac{\frac{58}{8}}{2}=\frac{5}{4} \Rightarrow -\frac{19}{8}+\frac{29}{8}=\frac{5}{4} \Rightarrow \frac{10}{8}=\frac{5}{4} \Rightarrow \frac{5}{4}=\frac{5}{4}$

34. $\frac{3x-1}{5}-2=\frac{2-x}{3} \Rightarrow 15\left(\frac{3x-1}{5}-2\right)=15\left(\frac{2-x}{3}\right) \Rightarrow 9x-3-30=10-5x \Rightarrow 14x=43 \Rightarrow$

$x=\frac{43}{14}$ Check: $\frac{3(\frac{43}{14})-1}{5}-2=\frac{2-\frac{43}{14}}{3} \Rightarrow \frac{\frac{129}{14}-1}{5}-2=\frac{2-\frac{43}{14}}{3} \Rightarrow \frac{\frac{115}{14}}{5}-2=\frac{-\frac{15}{14}}{3} \Rightarrow$

$\frac{23}{14}-\frac{28}{14}=\frac{-5}{14} \Rightarrow \frac{-5}{14}=\frac{-5}{14}$

35. $0.1z-0.05=-0.07z \Rightarrow 0.17z=0.05 \Rightarrow z=\frac{0.05}{0.17} \Rightarrow z=\frac{5}{17}$ Check:

$0.1\left(\frac{5}{17}\right)-0.05=-0.07\left(\frac{5}{17}\right) \Rightarrow \frac{5}{170}-\frac{5}{100}=-\frac{35}{1700} \Rightarrow \frac{50}{1700}-\frac{85}{1700}=-\frac{35}{1700} \Rightarrow$

$-\frac{35}{1700}=-\frac{35}{1700}$

36. $1.1z-2.5=0.3(z-2) \Rightarrow 1.1z-2.5=0.3z-0.6 \Rightarrow 0.8z=1.9 \Rightarrow z=\frac{1.9}{0.8} \Rightarrow z=\frac{19}{8}$

Check: $1.1\left(\frac{19}{8}\right)-2.5=0.3\left(\frac{19}{8}-2\right) \Rightarrow \frac{209}{80}-\frac{5}{2}=\frac{3}{10}\left(\frac{3}{8}\right) \Rightarrow \frac{209}{80}-\frac{200}{80}=\frac{9}{80} \Rightarrow \frac{9}{80}=\frac{9}{80}$

37. $0.15t+0.85(100-t)=0.45(100) \Rightarrow 0.15t+85-0.85t=45 \Rightarrow -0.7t=-40 \Rightarrow t=\frac{40}{0.7} \Rightarrow$

$t=\frac{400}{7}$ Check: $0.15\left(\frac{400}{7}\right)+0.85\left(100-\frac{400}{7}\right)=0.45(100) \Rightarrow \frac{6000}{700}+85-\frac{34{,}000}{700}=45 \Rightarrow$

$\frac{60}{7}+85-\frac{340}{7}=45 \Rightarrow 85-\frac{280}{7}=45 \Rightarrow 85-40=45 \Rightarrow 45=45$

38. $0.35t+0.65(10-t)=0.55(10) \Rightarrow 0.35t+6.5-0.65t=5.5 \Rightarrow -0.3t=-1 \Rightarrow t=\frac{1}{0.3} \Rightarrow t=\frac{10}{3}$

Check: $0.35\left(\frac{10}{3}\right)+0.65\left(10-\frac{10}{3}\right)=0.55(10) \Rightarrow \frac{350}{300}+0.65\left(\frac{20}{3}\right)=\frac{550}{100} \Rightarrow$

$\frac{350}{300}+\frac{1300}{300}=\frac{550}{100} \Rightarrow \frac{350}{300}+\frac{1300}{300}=\frac{1650}{300} \Rightarrow \frac{1650}{300}=\frac{1650}{300}$

39. (a) $5x-1=5x+4 \Rightarrow -1=4 \Rightarrow$ there is no solution.

(b) Since no $x$-value satisfies the equation, it is contradiction.

40. (a) $7-9z=2(3-4z)-z \Rightarrow 7-9z=6-8z-z \Rightarrow 7=6 \Rightarrow$ there is no solution.

(b) Since no $x$-value satisfies the equation, it is a contradiction.

41. (a) $3(x-1)=5 \Rightarrow 3x-3=5 \Rightarrow 3x=8 \Rightarrow x=\frac{8}{3}$

(b) Since one $x$-value is a solution and other $x$-values are not, the equation is conditional.

42. (a) $22=-2(2x+1.4) \Rightarrow 22=-4x-2.8 \Rightarrow 24.8=-4x \Rightarrow x=\frac{24.8}{-4}=-6.2$

(b) Since one $x$-value is a solution and other $x$-values are not, the equation is conditional.

43. (a) $0.5(x - 2) + 5 = 0.5x + 4 \Rightarrow 0.5x - 1 + 5 = 0.5x + 4 \Rightarrow 0.5x + 4 = 0.5x + 4 \Rightarrow$ every $x$-value satisfies this equation.

(b) Since every $x$-value satisfies the equation, it is an identity.

44. (a) $\frac{1}{2}x - 2(x - 1) = -\frac{3}{2}x + 2 \Rightarrow \frac{1}{2}x - 2x + 2 = -\frac{3}{2}x + 2 \Rightarrow 2 = 2 \Rightarrow$ every $x$-value satisfies this equation.

(b) Since every $x$-value satisfies the equation, it is an identity.

45. (a) $\frac{t + 1}{2} = \frac{3t - 2}{6} \Rightarrow 6\left(\frac{t + 1}{2} = \frac{3t - 2}{6}\right) \Rightarrow 3t + 3 = 3t - 2 \Rightarrow 3 = -2 \Rightarrow$ there is no solution.

(b) Since no $x$-value satisfies the equation, it is contradiction.

46. (a) $\frac{2x + 1}{3} = \frac{2x - 1}{3} \Rightarrow 3(2x + 1) = 3(2x - 1) \Rightarrow 6x + 3 = 6x - 3 \Rightarrow 3 = -3 \Rightarrow$ there is no solution.

(b) Since no $x$-value satisfies the equation, it is contradiction.

47. (a) $\frac{1 - 2x}{4} = \frac{3x - 1.5}{-6} \Rightarrow -6(1 - 2x) = 4(3x - 1.5) \Rightarrow -6 + 12x = 12x - 6 \Rightarrow 0 = 0 \Rightarrow$ every $x$-value satisfies this equation.

(b) Since every $x$-value satisfies the equation, it is an identity.

48. (a) $0.5(3x - 1) + 0.5x = 2x - 0.5 \Rightarrow 1.5x - 0.5 + 0.5x = 2x - 0.5 \Rightarrow 2x - 0.5 = 2x - 0.5 \Rightarrow$ every $x$-value satisfies this equation.

(b) Since every $x$-value satisfies the equation, it is an identity.

49. In the graph, the lines intersect at $(3, -1)$. The solution is the $x$-value, 3.

50. In the graph, the lines intersect at $(-5, 6)$. The solution is the $x$-value, $-5$.

51. (a) From the graph, when $f(x)$ or $y = -1$, $x = 4$; the solution is the $x$-value, 4.

(b) From the graph, when $f(x)$ or $y = 0$, $x = 2$; the solution is the $x$-value, 2.

(c) From the graph, when $f(x)$ or $y = 2$, $x = -2$; the solution is the $x$-value, $-2$.

52. (a) From the graph, when $f(x)$ or $y = -1$, $x = 0$; the solution is the $x$-value, 0.

(b) From the graph, when $f(x)$ or $y = 0$, $x = 1$; the solution is the $x$-value, 1.

(c) From the graph, when $f(x)$ or $y = 2$, $x = 3$; the solution is the $x$-value, 3.

53. Graph $Y_1 = X + 4$ and $Y_2 = 1 - 2X$. See Figure 53. The lines intersect at $x = -1$.

$x + 4 = 1 - 2x \Rightarrow 3 = -3x \Rightarrow x = -1$

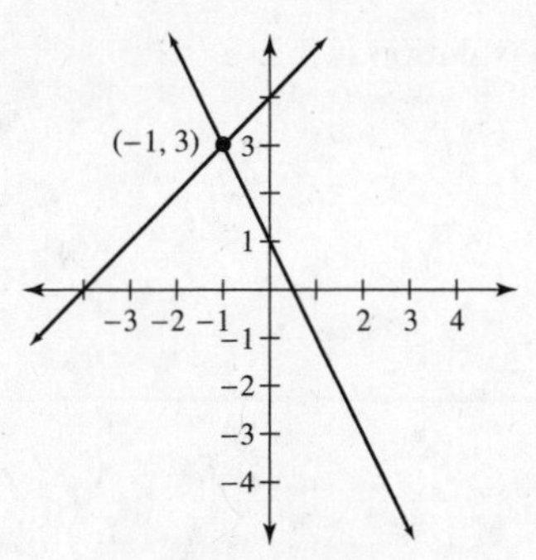


Figure 53

54. Graph $Y_1 = 2X$ and $Y_2 = 3X - 1$. See Figure 54. The lines intersect at $x = 1$.

$2x = 3x - 1 \Rightarrow -x = -1 \Rightarrow x = 1$

55. Graph $Y_1 = -X + 4$ and $Y_2 = 3X$. See Figure 55. The lines intersect at $x = 1$.

$-x + 4 = 3x \Rightarrow 4 = 4x \Rightarrow x = 1$

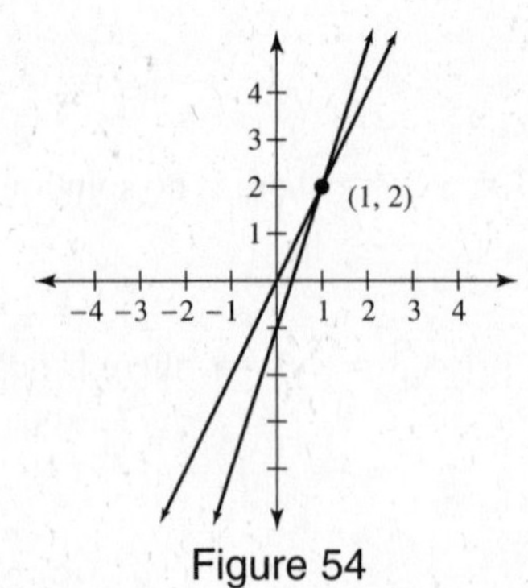


Figure 54

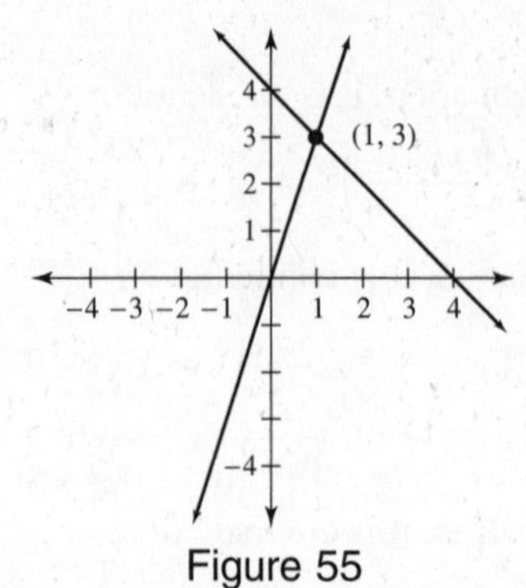


Figure 55

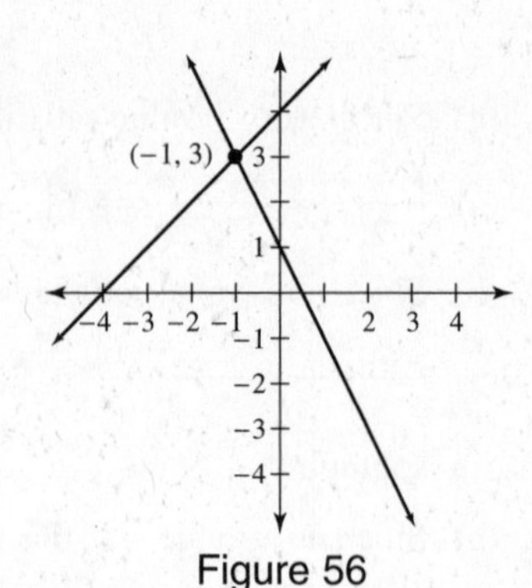


Figure 56

56. Graph $Y_1 = 1 - 2X$ and $Y_2 = X + 4$. See Figure 56. The lines intersect at $x = -1$.

$1 - 2x = x + 4 \Rightarrow -3x = 3 \Rightarrow x = -1$

57. Graph $Y_1 = 2(X - 1) - 2$ and $Y_2 = X$. See Figure 57. The lines intersect at $x = 4$.

$2(x - 1) - 2 = x \Rightarrow 2x - 2 - 2 = x \Rightarrow 2x - 4 = x \Rightarrow -4 = -x \Rightarrow x = 4$

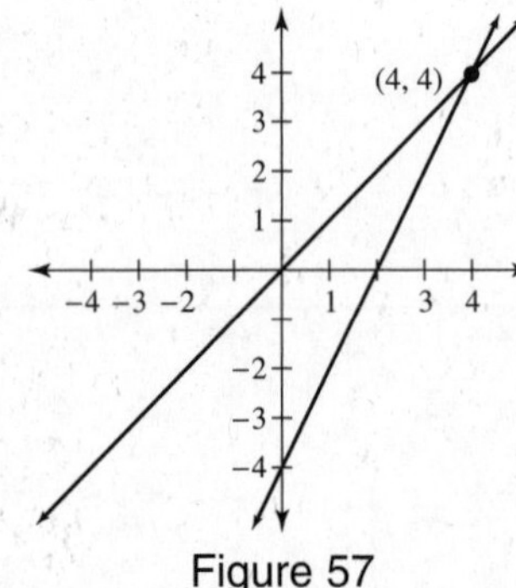


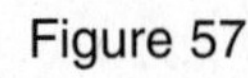

Figure 57

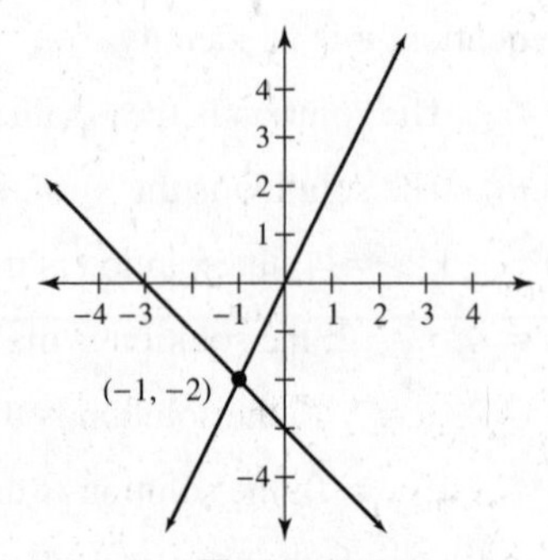


Figure 58

58. Graph $Y_1 = -(X + 1) - 2$ and $Y_2 = 2X$. The lines intersect at $x = -1$. See Figure 58.

$-(x + 1) - 2 = 2x \Rightarrow -x - 1 - 2 = 2x \Rightarrow -x - 3 = 2x \Rightarrow -3 = 3x \Rightarrow x = -1$

59. Graph $Y_1 = 5X - 1.5$ and $Y_2 = 5$. Their graphs intersect at (1.3, 5). The solution is 1.3. See Figure 59.

60. Graph $Y_1 = 8 - 2X$ and $Y_2 = 1.6$. Their graphs intersect at (3.2, 1.6). The solution is 3.2.

See Figure 60.

[−10, 10, 1] by [−10, 10, 1]

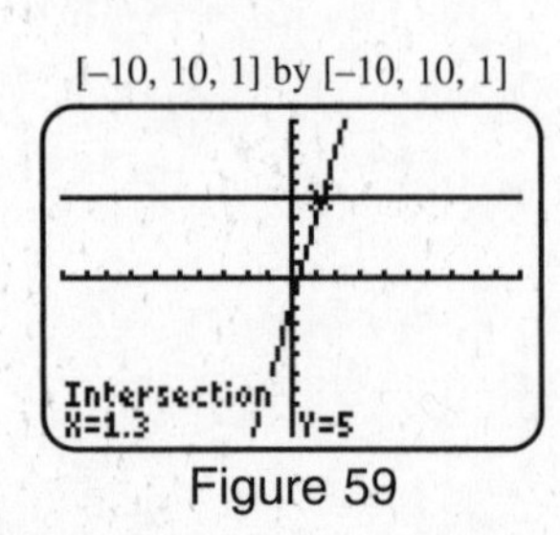


Figure 59

[−10, 10, 1] by [−10, 10, 1]

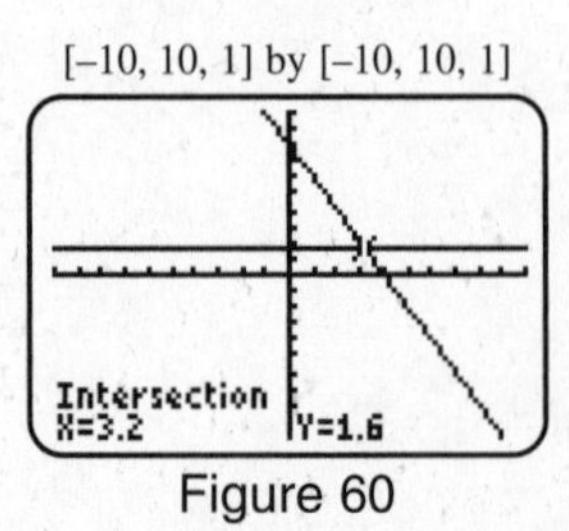


Figure 60

61. Graph $Y_1 = 3X - 1.7$ and $Y_2 = 1 - X$. Their graphs intersect at (0.675, 0.325). The solution is 0.675. See Figure 61.

[−10, 10, 1] by [−10, 10, 10]

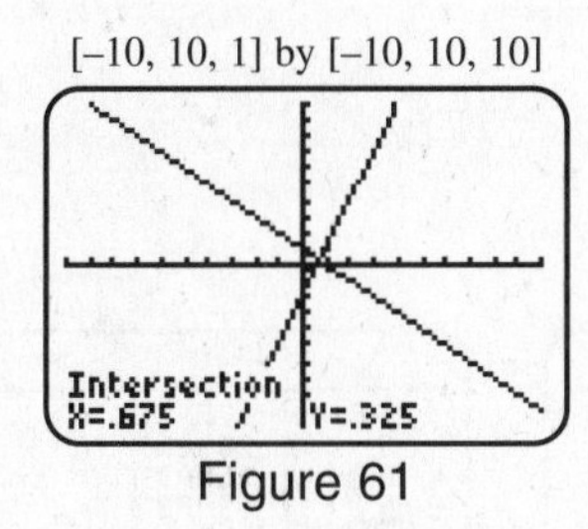


Figure 61

[−10, 10, 1] by [−10, 10, 10]

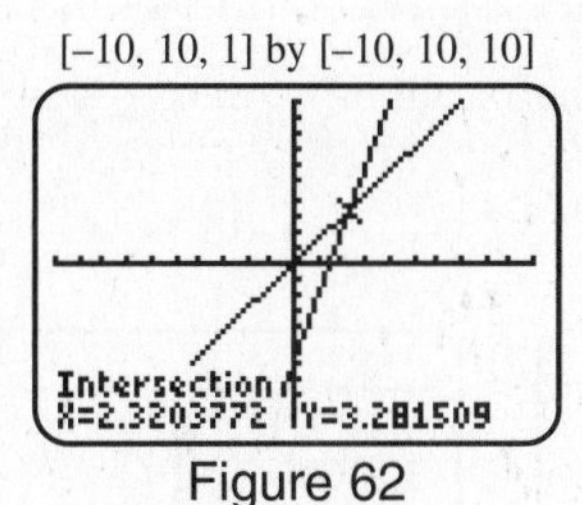


Figure 62

62. Graph $Y_1 = \sqrt{(2)}X$ and $Y_2 = 4X - 6$. Their graphs intersect near (2.320, 3.282). The solution is approximately 2.320. See Figure 62.

63. Graph $Y_1 = 3.1(X - 5)$ and $Y_2 = X/5 - 5$. Their graphs intersect near (3.621, −4.276). The solution is approximately 3.621. See Figure 63.

64. Graph $Y_1 = 65$ and $Y_2 = 8(X - 6) - 5.5$. Their graphs intersect at (14.813, 65). The solution is 14.813. See Figure 64.

[−10, 10, 1] by [−10, 10, 10]

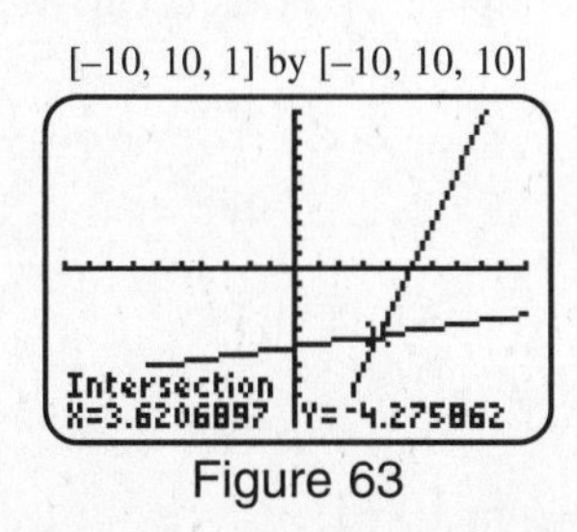


Figure 63

[−100, 100, 10] by [−100, 100, 10]

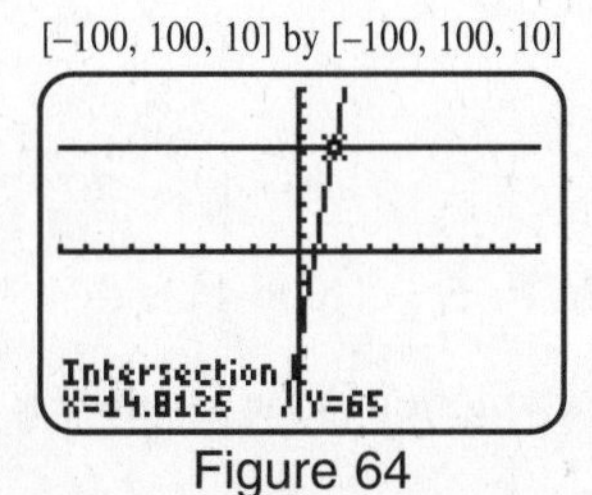


Figure 64

[−10, 10, 1] by [−10, 10, 1]

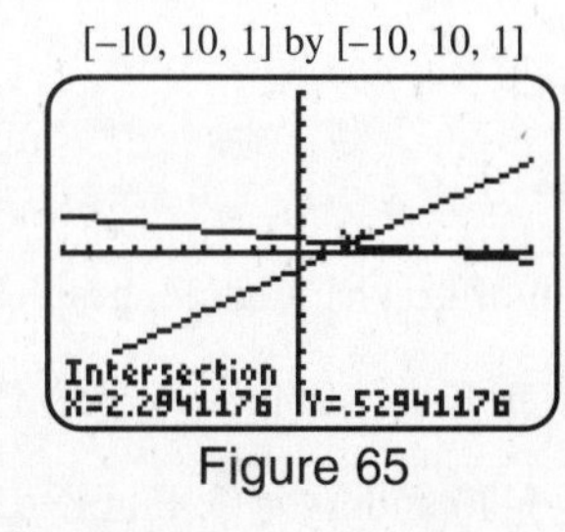


Figure 65

[−10, 10, 1] by [−10, 10, 1]

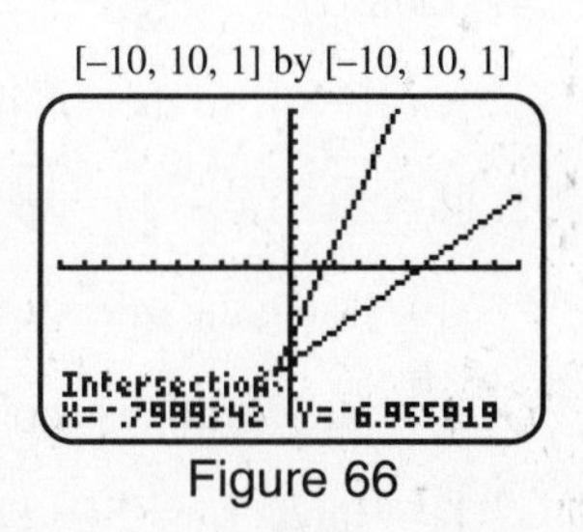


Figure 66

65. Graph $Y_1 = (6 - X)/7$ and $Y_2 = (2X - 3)/3$. Their graphs intersect near (2.294, 0.529). The solution is approximately 2.294. See Figure 65.

66. Graph $Y_1 = \pi(X - \sqrt{(2)})$ and $Y_2 = 1.07X - 6.1$. Their graphs intersect near (−0.800, −6.956). The solution is approximately −0.800. See Figure 66.

67. One way to solve this equation is to table $Y_1 = 2X - 7$ and determine the $x$-value where $Y_1 = -1$. See Figure 67. This occurs when $x = 3$, so the solution is 3.

68. Table $Y_1 = 1 - 6X$ and determine the $x$-value where $Y_1 = 7$. See Figure 68. This occurs when $x = -1$, so the solution is −1.

| X | Y1 |
|---|---|
| 0 | -7 |
| 1 | -5 |
| 2 | -3 |
| 3 | -1 |
| 4 | 1 |
| 5 | 3 |
| 6 | 5 |

X=3

Figure 67

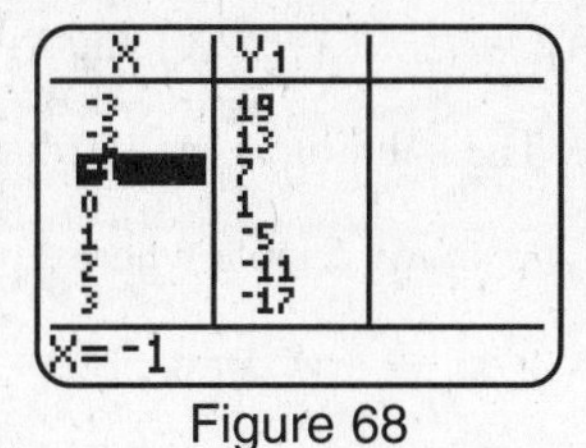


Figure 68

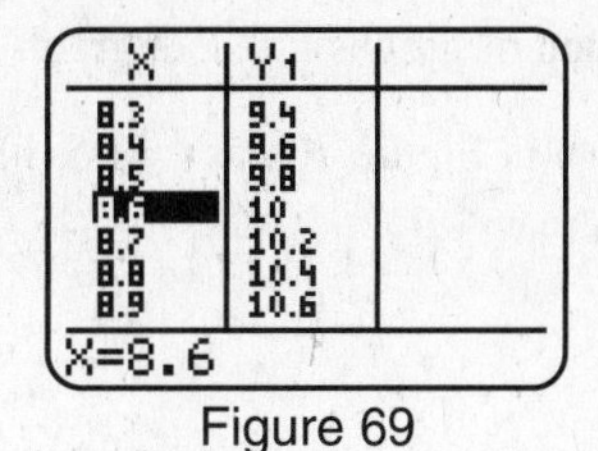


Figure 69

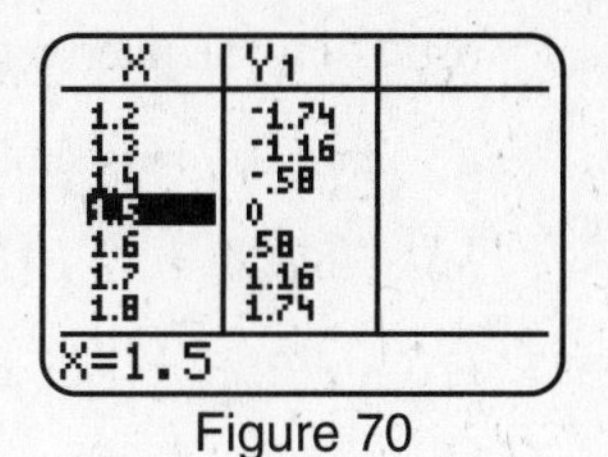


Figure 70

69. Table $Y_1 = 2X - 7.2$ and determine the $x$-value where $Y_1 = 10$. See Figure 69. This occurs when $x = 8.6$, so the solution is 8.6.

70. Table $Y_1 = 5.8X - 8.7$ and determine the $x$-value where $Y_1 = 0$. See Figure 70. This occurs when $x = 1.5$, so the solution is 1.5.

71. Table $Y_1 = \sqrt{(2)}(4X - 1) + \pi X$ and determine the $x$-value where $Y_1 = 0$. See Figure 71. This occurs when $x \approx 0.2$, so the solution is 0.2.

72. Table $Y_1 = \pi(0.3X - 2) + \sqrt{2}(X)$ and determine the $x$-value where $Y_1 = 0$. See Figure 72. This occurs when $x \approx 2.7$, so the solution is 2.7.

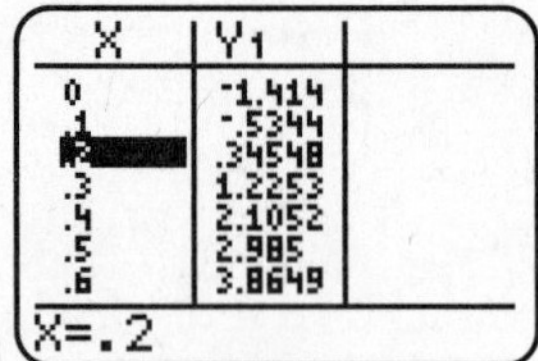

Figure 71

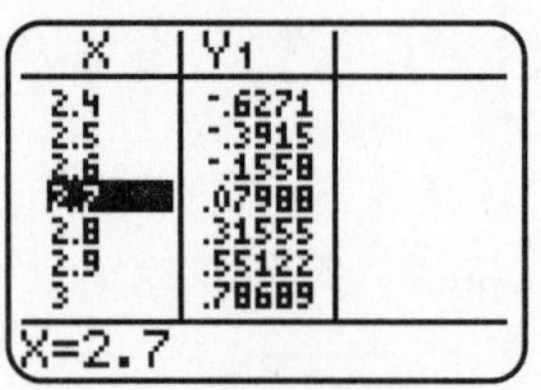

Figure 72

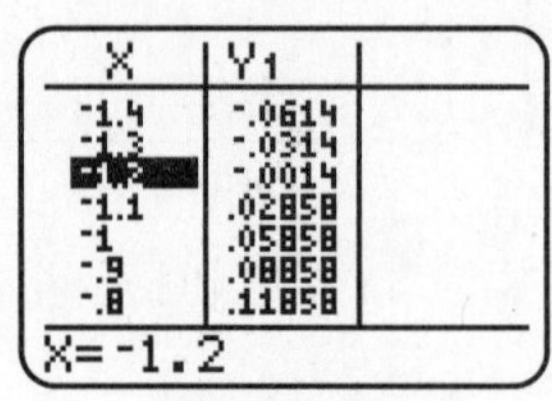

Figure 73

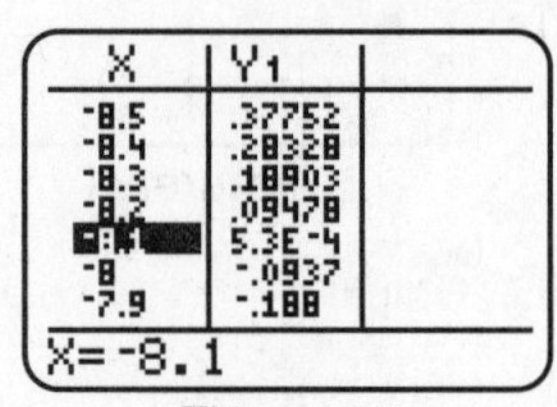

Figure 74

73. Table $Y_1 = 0.5 - 0.1(\sqrt{(2)} - 3X)$ and determine the $x$-value where $Y_1 = 0$. See Figure 73. This occurs when $x \approx -1.2$, so the solution is $-1.2$.

74. Table $Y_1 = \sqrt{(5)} - \pi(\pi + 0.3X)$ and determine the $x$-value where $Y_1 = 0$. See Figure 74. This occurs when $x \approx -8.1$, so the solution is $-8.1$.

75. (a) $5 - (x + 1) = 3 \Rightarrow 5 - x - 1 = 3 \Rightarrow 4 - x = 3 \Rightarrow x = 1$

(b) Using the intersection of graphs method, graph $Y_1 = 5 - (X + 1)$ and $Y_2 = 3$. Their point of intersection is shown in Figure 75b as (1, 3). The solution is the $x$-value, 1.

(c) Table $Y_1 = 5 - (X + 1)$ and $Y_2 = 3$. Figure 75c shows a table where $Y_1 = Y_2$ at $x = 1$.

[−10, 10, 1] by [−10, 10, 1]

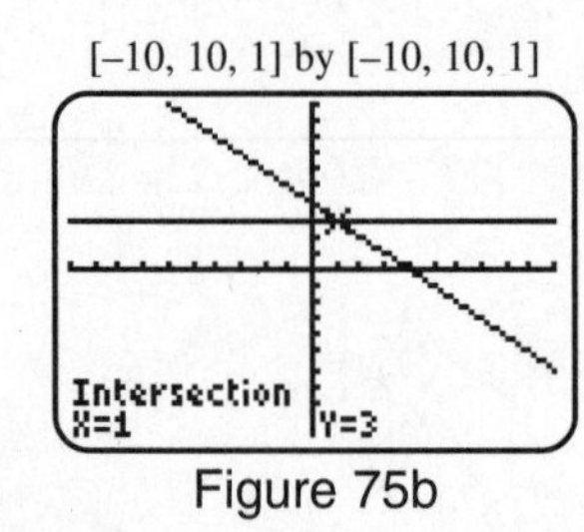

Figure 75b

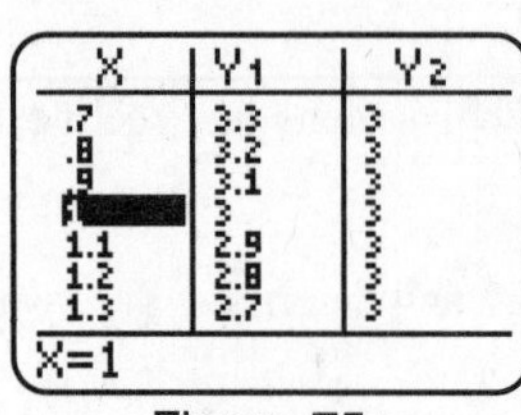

Figure 75c

[−10, 10, 1] by [−10, 10, 1]

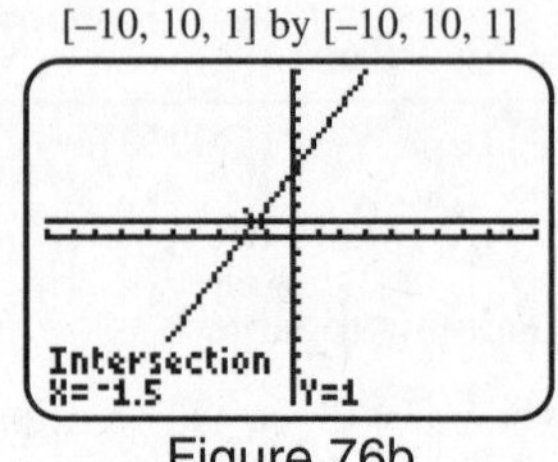

Figure 76b

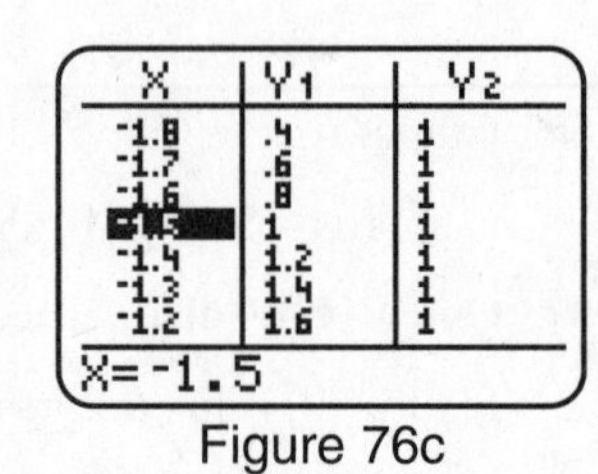

Figure 76c

76. (a) $7 - (3 - 2x) = 1 \Rightarrow 7 - 3 + 2x = 1 \Rightarrow 4 + 2x = 1 \Rightarrow x = -1.5$

(b) Using the intersection of graphs method, graph $Y_1 = 7 - (3 - 2X)$ and $Y_2 = 1$. Their point of intersection is shown in Figure 76b as $(-1.5, 1)$. The solution is the $x$-value, $-1.5$.

(c) Table $Y_1 = 7 - (3 - 2X)$ and $Y_2 = 1$. Figure 76c shows a table where $Y_1 = Y_2$ at $x = -1.5$.

77. (a) $\sqrt{3}(2 - \pi x) + x = 0 \Rightarrow 2\sqrt{3} - \sqrt{3}\pi x + x = 0 \Rightarrow -\sqrt{3}\pi x + x = -2\sqrt{3} \Rightarrow$

$$x(-\sqrt{3}\pi + 1) = -2\sqrt{3} \Rightarrow x = \frac{-2\sqrt{3}}{(-\sqrt{3}\pi + 1)} \approx 0.8.$$

(b) Using the intersection of graphs method, graph $Y_1 = \sqrt{(3)}(2 - \pi X) + X$ and $Y_2 = 0$. Their point of intersection is shown in Figure 77b as approximately (0.8, 0). The solution is the $x$-value, 0.8.

(c) Table $Y_1 = \sqrt{(3)}(2 - \pi X) + X$ and $Y_2 = 0$. Figure 77c shows a table where $Y_1 = Y_2$ at $x \approx 0.8$.

[–10, 10, 1] by [–10, 10, 1]

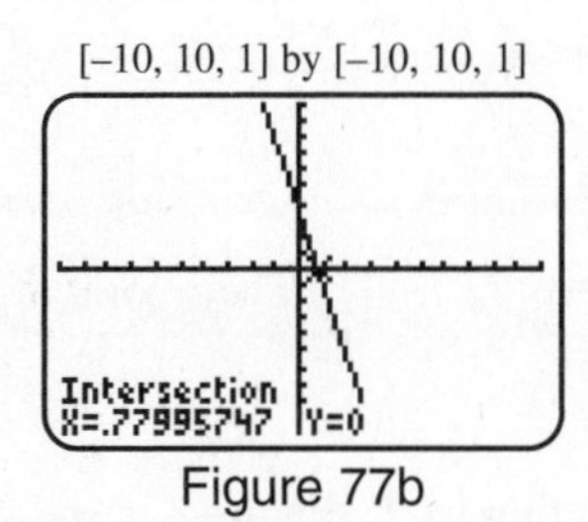


Figure 77b

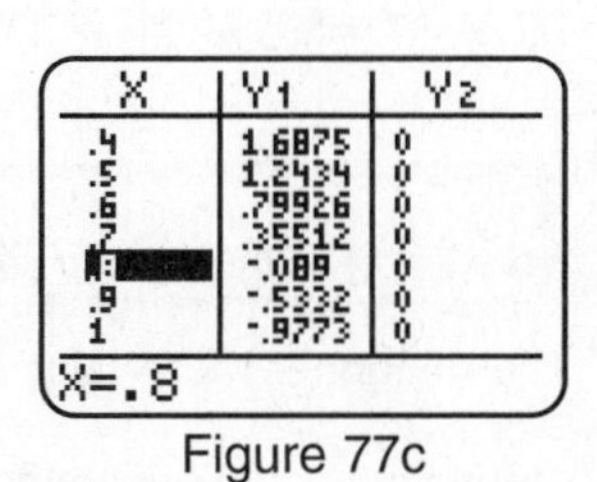


Figure 77c

[–10, 10, 1] by [–10, 10, 1]

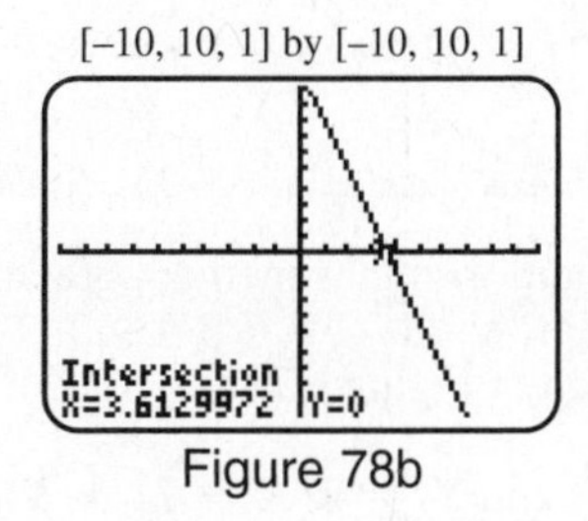


Figure 78b

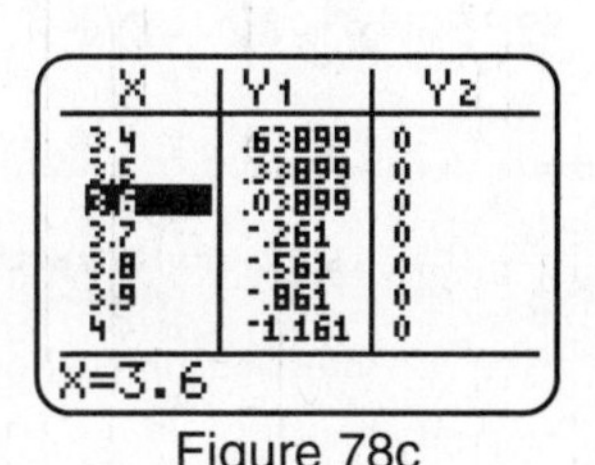


Figure 78c

78. (a) $3(\pi - x) + \sqrt{2} = 0 \Rightarrow 3\pi - 3x + \sqrt{2} = 0 \Rightarrow 3\pi + \sqrt{2} = 3x \Rightarrow x = \pi + \frac{\sqrt{2}}{3} \approx 3.6$

(b) Using the intersection of graphs method, graph $Y_1 = 3(\pi - X) + \sqrt{(2)}$ and $Y_2 = 0$. Their point of intersection is shown in Figure 78b as approximately $(3.6, 0)$. The approximate solution is the $x$-value, 3.6.

(c) Table $Y_1 = 3(\pi - X) + \sqrt{(2)}$ and $Y_2 = 0$. Figure 78c shows a table where $Y_1 = Y_2$ at $x \approx 3.6$.

79. (a) $x - 3 = 2x + 1 \Rightarrow -x = 4 \Rightarrow x = -4$

(b) Using the intersection-of-graphs method, graph $Y_1 = X - 3$ and $Y_2 = 2X + 1$. Their point of intersection is shown in Figure 79b as $(-4, -7)$. The solution is the $x$-value, $-4$.

(c) Table $Y_1 = X - 3$ and $Y_2 = 2X + 1$, starting at $x = -7$, incrementing by 1. Figure 79c shows a table where $Y_1 = Y_2$ at $x = -4$.

[–12, 8, 1] by [–12, 8, 1]

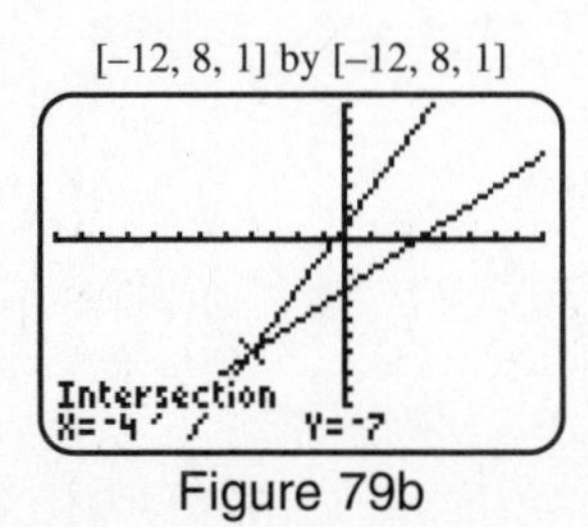


Figure 79b

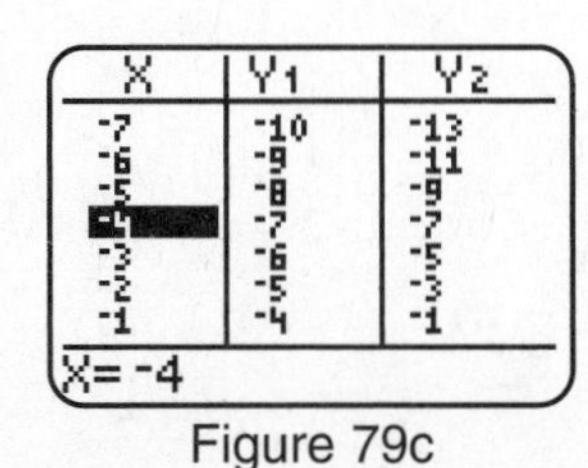


Figure 79c

[–10, 10, 1] by [–10, 10, 10]

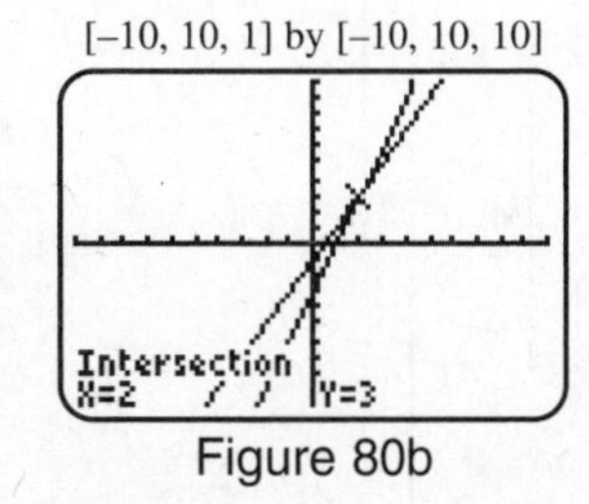


Figure 80b

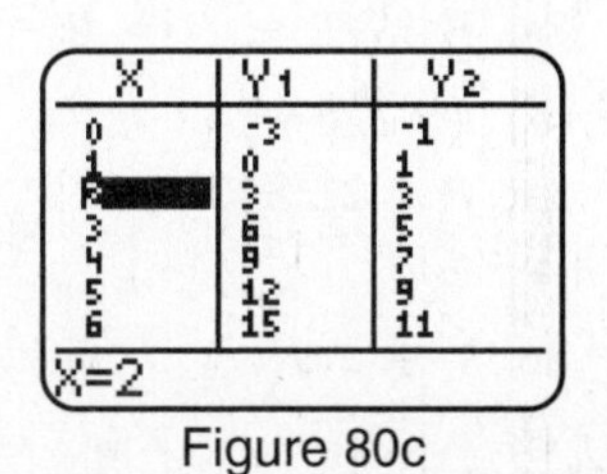


Figure 80c

80. (a) $3(x - 1) = 2x - 1 \Rightarrow 3x - 3 = 2x - 1 \Rightarrow x = 2$

(b) Using the intersection-of-graphs method, graph $Y_1 = 3(X - 1)$ and $Y_2 = 2X - 1$. Their point of intersection is shown in Figure 80b as $(2, 3)$. The solution is the $x$-value, 2.

(c) Table $Y_1 = 3(X - 1)$ and $Y_2 = 2X - 1$, starting at $x = 0$, incrementing by 1. Figure 80c shows a table where $Y_1 = Y_2$ at $x = 2$.

81. (a) $6x - 8 = -7x + 18 \Rightarrow 13x = 26 \Rightarrow x = 2$

(b) Using the intersection-of-graphs method, graph $Y_1 = 6X - 8$ and $Y_2 = -7X + 18$. Their point of intersection is shown in Figure 81b as (2, 4). The solution is the $x$-value, 2.

(c) Table $Y_1 = 6X - 8$ and $Y_2 = -7X + 18$, starting at $x = 0$, incrementing by 1. Figure 81c shows a table where $Y_1 = Y_2$ at $x = 2$.

[–10, 10, 1] by [–10, 10, 1]

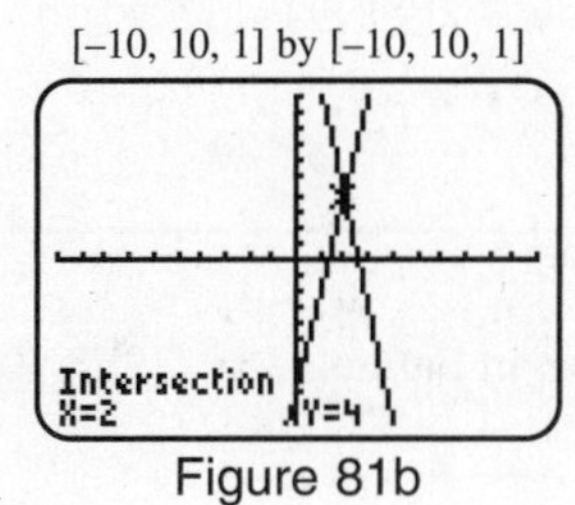


Figure 81b

| X | $Y_1$ | $Y_2$ |
|---|---|---|
| 0 | -8 | 18 |
| 1 | -2 | 11 |
| 2 | 4 | 4 |
| 3 | 10 | -3 |
| 4 | 16 | -10 |
| 5 | 22 | -17 |
| 6 | 28 | -24 |

X=2

Figure 81c

82. (a) $5 - 8x = 3(x - 7) + 37 \Rightarrow 5 - 8x = 3x - 21 + 37 \Rightarrow 5 + 21 - 37 = 3x + 8x \Rightarrow$

$-11 = 11x \Rightarrow x = -1$

(b) Using the intersection-of-graphs method, graph $Y_1 = 5 - 8X$ and $Y_2 = 3(X - 7) + 37$. Their point of intersection is shown in Figure 82b as (–1, 13). The solution is the $x$-value of $x = -1$.

(c) Table $Y_1 = 5 - 8X$ and $Y_2 = 3(X - 7) + 37$, starting at $x = -3$, incrementing by 1. Figure 82c shows a table where $Y_1 = Y_2$ at $x = -1$.

[–10, 10, 1] by [–10, 10, 1]

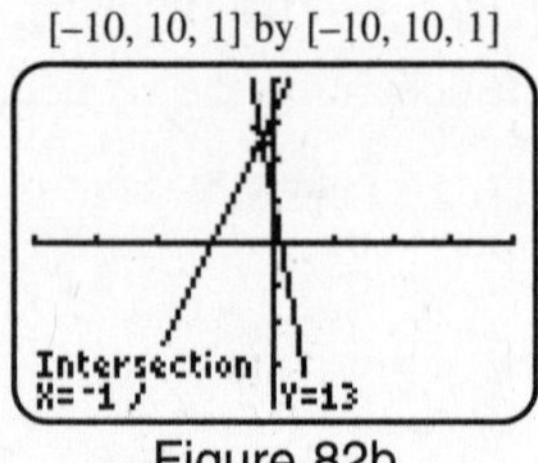

Figure 82b

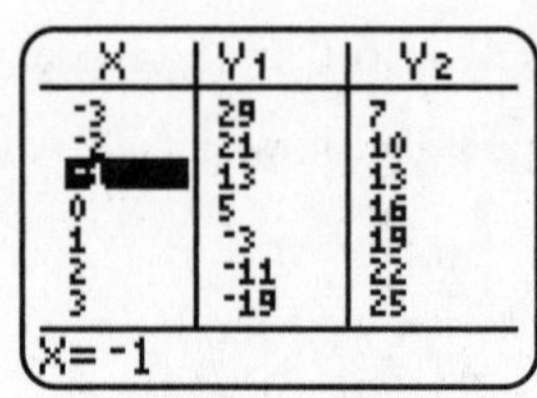

| X | Y1 | Y2 |
|---|---|---|
| -3 | 29 | 7 |
| -2 | 21 | 10 |
| -1 | 13 | 13 |
| 0 | 5 | 16 |
| 1 | -3 | 19 |
| 2 | -11 | 22 |
| 3 | -19 | 25 |

X=-1

Figure 82c

[1980, 1990, 2] by [0, 200, 20]

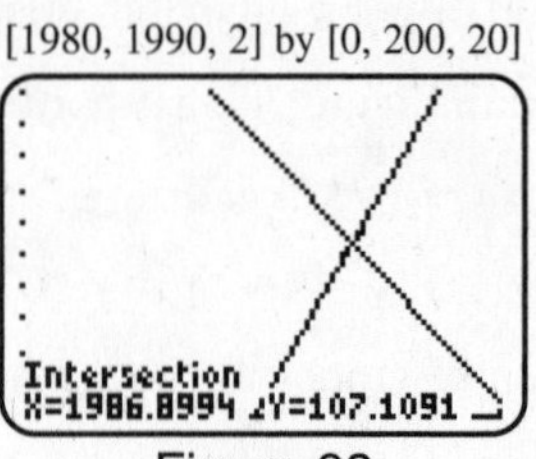

Figure 93

83. $A = LW \Rightarrow W = \dfrac{A}{L}$

84. $E = IR + 2 \Rightarrow E - 2 = IR \Rightarrow R = \dfrac{E - 2}{I}$

85. $P = 2L + 2W \Rightarrow P - 2W = 2L \Rightarrow L = \dfrac{P - 2W}{2} \Rightarrow L = \dfrac{1}{2}P - W$

86. $V = 2\pi rh + \pi r^2 \Rightarrow V - \pi r^2 = 2\pi rh \Rightarrow h = \dfrac{V - \pi r^2}{2\pi r}$

87. $3x + 2y = 8 \Rightarrow 2y = 8 - 3x \Rightarrow y = 4 - \dfrac{3}{2}x$

88. $5x - 4y = 20 \Rightarrow -4y = 20 - 5x \Rightarrow y = \dfrac{5}{4}x - 5$

89. $y = 3(x - 2) + x \Rightarrow y = 3x - 6 + x \Rightarrow y = 4x - 6 \Rightarrow 4x = y + 6 \Rightarrow x = \dfrac{1}{4}y + \dfrac{3}{2}$

90. $y = 4 - (8 - 2x) \Rightarrow y = 4 - 8 + 2x \Rightarrow y = -4 + 2x \Rightarrow 2x = y + 4 \Rightarrow x = \dfrac{1}{2}y + 2$

91. $f(x) = 19{,}000$ and $f(x) = 1000(x - 1980) + 10{,}000 \Rightarrow 1000(x - 1980) + 10{,}000 = 19{,}000 \Rightarrow$

$1000(x - 1980) = 9000 \Rightarrow x - 1980 = 9 \Rightarrow x = 1989$. The per capita income was \$19,000 in 1989.

92. $f(x) = 13{,}700$ and $f(x) = 630.8(x - 1980) + 3617 \Rightarrow 630.8(x - 1980) + 3617 = 13{,}700 \Rightarrow$

$630.8(x - 1980) = 10{,}083 \Rightarrow x - 1980 = \dfrac{10{,}083}{630.8} \Rightarrow x = 1980 + \dfrac{10{,}083}{630.8} \Rightarrow x \approx 1995.984464.$

The tuition and fees were \$13,700 in about 1996.

93. Using the intersection of graphs method, graph $Y_1 = 51.6(X - 1985) + 9.1$ and

$Y_2 = -31.9(X - 1985) + 167.7$. Their approximate point of intersection is shown in Figure 93 as (1987, 107).

In approximately 1987 the sales of LP records and compact discs were equal.

94. $A(x) = 37$ and $A(x) = 0.07(x - 2000) + 35.3 \Rightarrow 0.07(x - 2000) + 35.3 = 37 \Rightarrow$
$0.07(x - 2000) = 1.7 \Rightarrow x - 2000 = \frac{1.7}{0.07} \Rightarrow x = 2000 - \frac{1.7}{0.07} \Rightarrow x \approx 2024$. The mediam age will reach 37 years of age in about 2024.

95. The graph of $f$ must pass through the points (1980, 64) and (2000, 80). Its slope is $m = \frac{80 - 64}{2000 - 1980} = 0.8$.
Thus, $f(x) = 0.8(x - 2000) + 80$. Find $x$ when $f(x) = 87 \Rightarrow 87 = 0.8(x - 2000) + 80 \Rightarrow$
$7 = 0.8(x - 2000) \Rightarrow (x - 2000) = 8.75 \Rightarrow x = 2008.75$. The US population density reached 87 people per square mile in about 2009.

96. (a) The graph of $V$ must pass through the points (1999, 180,000) and (2009, 245,000). Its slope is
$m = \frac{245{,}000 - 180{,}000}{2009 - 1999} = 6500$. Thus, $V(x) = 6500(x - 2009) + 245{,}000 \Rightarrow$
$V(x) = 6500x - 12{,}813{,}500$.

(b) The slope 6500 represents an increase in value of the house of \$6500 per year, on average.

(c) $219{,}900 = 6500x - 12{,}813{,}500 \Rightarrow 6500x = 13{,}033{,}400 \Rightarrow x \approx 2005.14$; the approximate year was 2005.

97. To calculate the sale price subtract 25% of the regular price from the regular price.
$f(x) = x - 0.25x \Rightarrow f(x) = 0.75x$. An item which normally costs \$56.24 will be on sale for
$f(56.24) = 0.75(56.24) = \$42.18$.

98. To calculate the regular price of an item that is on sale for \$19.62, solve the equation $0.75x = 19.62$.
$0.75x = 19.62 \Rightarrow x = \frac{19.62}{0.75} \Rightarrow x = \$26.16$.

99. (a) The number of skin cancer cases can is given by $0.045x$.

(b) There were 65,000 cases of skin cancer diagnosed in 2007. So, $65{,}000 = 0.045x \Rightarrow x = \frac{65{,}000}{0.045} \Rightarrow$
$x = 1{,}444{,}000$. There were about 1,444,000 cancer cases in 2007.

100. Let $x$ be the final score on the exam. The maximum number of points possible is 500. To obtain 90% of 500 points, the following equation must be satisfied: $\frac{82 + 88 + 91 + x}{500} = 0.90 \Rightarrow$
$82 + 88 + 91 + x = 450 \Rightarrow x = 189$. The student must obtain a minimum score of 189 on the final exam.

101. (a) It would take a little less time than the faster gardener, who can rake the lawn alone in 3 hours. It would take both gardeners about 2 hours working together. *Answers may vary.*

(b) Let $x$ = time to rake the lawn working together. In 1 hour thge first gardener can rake $\frac{1}{3}$ of the lawn, whereas the second gardener can rake $\frac{1}{5}$ of the lawn; in $x$ hours both gardeners working together can rake $\frac{x}{3} + \frac{x}{5}$ of the lawn; $\frac{x}{3} + \frac{x}{5} = 1 \Rightarrow 5x + 3x = 15 \Rightarrow 8x = 15 \Rightarrow x = \frac{15}{8} = 1.875$ hours.

102. Let $x$ = time that both pumps can empty the pool together; in 1 hour the first pump can empty $\frac{1}{50}$ of the pool and the second pump can empty $\frac{1}{80}$ of the pool; in $x$ hours both pumps working together can empty $\frac{x}{50} + \frac{x}{80}$ of the pool; $\frac{x}{50} + \frac{x}{80} = 1 \Rightarrow 8x + 5x = 400 \Rightarrow 13x = 400 \Rightarrow x \approx 30.77$ hours.

103. Let $t$ = time spent traveling at 55 mph and $6 - t$ = time spent traveling at 70 mph. Using $d = rt$, we get $d = 55t + 70(6 - t) \Rightarrow 372 = 55t + 420 - 70t \Rightarrow -48 = -15t \Rightarrow t = 3.2$ and $6 - t = 2.8$; the car traveled 3.2 hours at 55 mph and 2.8 hours at 70 mph.

104. Let $x$ = amount of the \$2.50 per pound candy and $5 - x$ = amount of the \$4.00 per pound candy; we get the equation $2.50x + 4.00(5 - x) = 17.60 \Rightarrow 250x + 400(5 - x) = 1760 \Rightarrow$ $250x + 2000 - 400x = 1760 \Rightarrow -150x = -240 \Rightarrow x = 1.6$ and $5 - x = 3.4$; add 1.6 pounds of \$2.50 candy to 3.4 pounds of \$4.00 candy.

105. Let $t$ = time traveled by car at 55 mph and $t + \frac{1}{2}$ = time traveled by runner at 10 mph; since $d = rt$ and the distance is the same for both runner and driver, we get $55t = 10\left(t + \frac{1}{2}\right) \Rightarrow 55t = 10t + 5 \Rightarrow 45t = 5 \Rightarrow$ $t = \frac{1}{9}$; it takes the driver $\frac{1}{9}$ hour or $6\frac{2}{3}$ minutes to catch the runner.

106. Let $x$ = amount invested at 5% and $5000 - x$ = amount invested at 7%; $0.05x + 0.07(5000 - x) = 325 \Rightarrow 5x + 7(5000 - x) = 32{,}500 \Rightarrow 5x + 35{,}000 - 7x = 32{,}500 \Rightarrow$ $-2x = -2500 \Rightarrow x = 1250$ and $5000 - x = 3750$; \$1250 is invested at 5% and \$3750 is invested at 7%.

107. The follow sketch illustrates the situation, where $x$ = height of streetlight. See Figure 107. Using similar triangles, we get $\frac{x}{15 + 7} = \frac{5.5}{7} \Rightarrow x = \frac{(5.5)(22)}{7} \Rightarrow x \approx 17.29$. The streetlight is about 17.29 feet high.

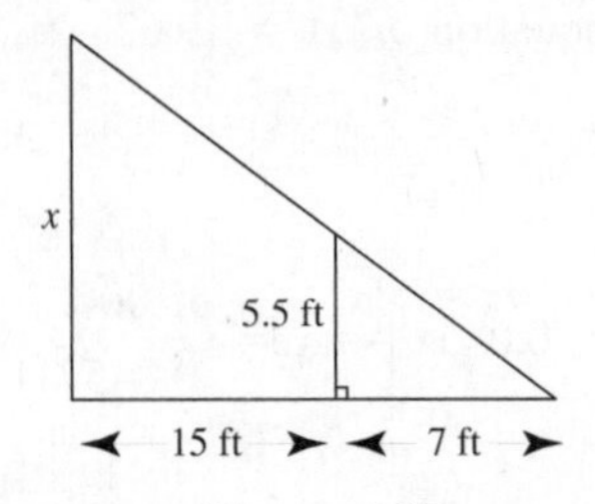


Figure 107

108. This problem can be solved using similar triangles or a proportion. Let $x$ be the height of the tree; then, $\frac{5}{4} = \frac{x}{33} \Rightarrow x = \frac{5 \times 33}{4} = 41.25$. The height of the tree is 41.25 feet.

109. Use similar triangles to find the radius of the cone when the water is 7 feet deep: $\frac{r}{3.5} = \frac{7}{11} \Rightarrow r \approx \frac{49}{22}$ ft. Use $V = \frac{1}{3}\pi r^2 h$ to find the volume of the water in the cone at $h = 7$ ft.: $V = \frac{1}{3}\pi\left(\frac{49}{22}\right)^2(7) \approx 36.4\ \text{ft}^3$.

110. $V = \frac{1}{3}\pi r^2 h \Rightarrow 100 = \frac{1}{3}\pi(3)^2 \cdot h \Rightarrow 100 = 3\pi h \Rightarrow \frac{100}{3\pi} = h \Rightarrow h \approx 10.6$ ft.

111. Let $x$ = amount of pure water to be added and $x + 5$ = final amount of the 15% solution. Since pure water is 0% sulfuric acid, we get $0\%x + 40\%(5) = 15\%(x + 5) \Rightarrow 0.40(5) = 0.15(x + 5) \Rightarrow$ $40(5) = 15(x + 5) \Rightarrow 200 = 15x + 75 \Rightarrow 15x = 125 \Rightarrow x = \frac{125}{15} \approx 8.333$; about 8.33 liters of pure water should be added.

112. Let $x$ = gallons of 15% solution removed and amount of 65% antifreeze added. Then $0.15(5) - 0.15x + 0.65x = 0.40(5) \Rightarrow 0.75 + 0.50x = 2 \Rightarrow 0.5x = 1.25 \Rightarrow x = 2.5$ gallons.

113. $P = 2w + 2l \Rightarrow 180 = 2w + 2(w + 18) \Rightarrow 180 = 4w + 36 \Rightarrow 4w = 144 \Rightarrow w = 36$ and $w + 18 = 54$; the window is 36 inches by 54 inches.

114. (a) The linear function $S$ must fit the coordinates (2003, 17) and (2006, 26).

$$m = \frac{26 - 17}{2006 - 2003} = 3;\ S(x) = 3(x - 2003) + 17 \Rightarrow S(x) = 3x - 5992.$$

(b) The slope shows that sales increased, on average, by \$3 billion per year.

(c) Let $S(x) = 41$ and solve for $x$. $41 = 3x - 5992 \Rightarrow 6033 = 3x \Rightarrow x = 2011$

115. (a) Using (2002, 75) and (2006, 45), find slope: $m = \frac{45 - 75}{2006 - 2002} \Rightarrow \frac{-30}{4} \Rightarrow -7.5$; therefore, $C(x) = -7.5(x - 2002) + 75 \Rightarrow C(x) = -7.5x + 15{,}090$. Now using (2002, 29) and (2006, 88), find slope: $m = \frac{88 - 29}{2006 - 2002} = \frac{59}{4} = 14.75$. Therefore, $L(x) = 14.75(x - 2002) + 29 \Rightarrow$ $L(x) = 14.75x - 29{,}500.5$.

(b) Sales of CRT monitors decreased by 7.5 million per year, on average. Sales of LCD monitors increased by 14.75 million monitors per year, on average.

(c) Graph $C(x) = -7.5x + 15{,}090$ and $L(x) = 14.75x - 29{,}500$. See Figure 115c. The lines of the functions intersect at $x = 2004$ or year 2004.

(d) Set $L(x) = C(x)$ and solve: $14.75x - 29{,}500 = -7.5x + 15{,}090 \Rightarrow 22.25x = 44{,}590 \Rightarrow x \approx 2004$

(e) Table $Y_1 = -7.5X + 15{,}090$ and $Y_2 = 14.75X - 29{,}500$, starting at 2000, incrementing by 1. Figure 115e shows a table where $Y_1 = Y_2$ and $x = 2004$.

[2000, 2008, 1] by [0, 80, 10]

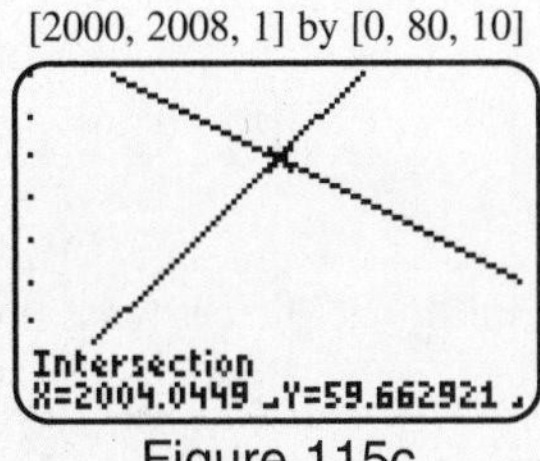

Figure 115c

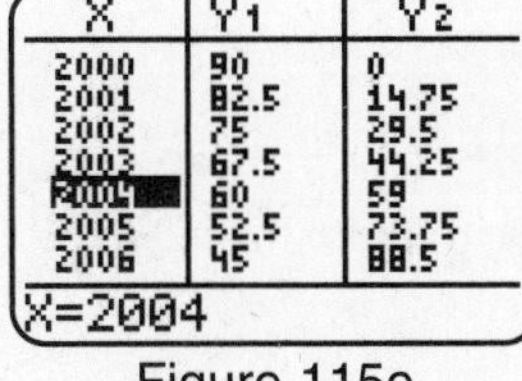

| X | Y1 | Y2 |
|---|---|---|
| 2000 | 90 | 0 |
| 2001 | 82.5 | 14.75 |
| 2002 | 75 | 29.5 |
| 2003 | 67.5 | 44.25 |
| 2004 | 60 | 59 |
| 2005 | 52.5 | 73.75 |
| 2006 | 45 | 88.5 |

X=2004

Figure 115e

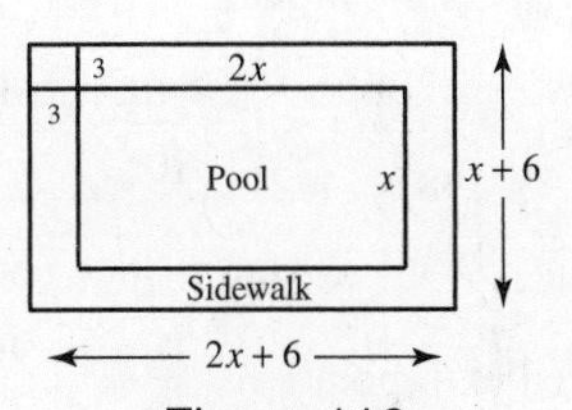

Figure 116

116. $2(x + 6) + 2(2x + 6) = 174 \Rightarrow 2x + 12 + 4x + 12 = 174 \Rightarrow 6x + 24 = 174 \Rightarrow 6x = 150 \Rightarrow$ $x = 25 \Rightarrow 2x = 50$. The swimming pool is 25 ft by 50 ft. See Figure 116.

117. $C = \frac{5}{9}(F - 32)$ and $F = C \Rightarrow F = \frac{5}{9}(F - 32) \Rightarrow F = \frac{5}{9}F - \frac{160}{9} \Rightarrow \frac{4}{9}F = -\frac{160}{9} \Rightarrow F = -40$; $-40°\ F$ is equivalent to $-40°\ C$.

118. Let $x =$ number of copies made; the cost of producing the compact discs is given by $C(x) = 2000 + 0.45x$; $2990 = 2000 + 0.45x \Rightarrow 990 = 0.45x \Rightarrow x = 2200$; the company manufactured 2200 copies and the master disc.

119. (a) It is reasonable to expect that $f$ is linear because if the number of gallons of gas doubles so should the amount of oil. Five gallons of gasoline requires five times the oil that one gallon of gasoline would. The increase in oil is always equal to 0.16 pint for each additional gallon of gasoline. Oil is mixed at a constant rate, so a linear function describes this amount.

(b) $f(3) = 0.16(3) = 0.48$; 0.48 pint of oil should be added to 3 gallons of gasoline to get the correct mixture.

(c) $0.16x = 2 \Rightarrow x = 12.5$; 12.5 gallons of gasoline should be mixed with 2 pints of oil.

120. $P = 2w + 2l \Rightarrow 25 = 2(2x) + 2(5x - 1) \Rightarrow 25 = 4x + 10x - 2 \Rightarrow 27 = 14x \Rightarrow x = \frac{27}{14}$ ft.;

$5x - 1 = 5\left(\frac{27}{14}\right) - 1 = \frac{121}{14} \approx 8.6$ ft.

121. Linear regression gives the model:

$y = 0.36x - 0.21$. $y = 2.99 \Rightarrow 2.99 = 0.36x - 0.21 \Rightarrow 3.2 = 0.36x \Rightarrow x \approx 8.89$

122. Linear regression gives the model:

$y = 3.72x - 5.38$. $y = 2.99 \Rightarrow 2.99 = 3.72x - 5.38 \Rightarrow 8.37 = 3.72x \Rightarrow x = 2.25$

123. (a) Linear regression gives the model:

$S(x) \approx 3.974x - 14{,}479$. *Answers may vary.*

(b) $S(x) = 6 \Rightarrow 6 = 3.974x - 14.479 \Rightarrow 20.479 = 3.974x \Rightarrow x \approx 5.15$; The circumference of a finger with ring size 6 is approximately 5.15 cm.

124. (a) Linear regression gives the model:

$S(x) \approx 0.3218x - 0.0402$. *Answers may vary.*

(b) $S(x) = 7.5 \Rightarrow 7.5 = 0.3218x - 0.0402 \Rightarrow 7.5402 = 0.3218x \Rightarrow x \approx 23.4$; The circumference of a head with hat size 7.5 is approximately 23.4 in.

125. (a) Linear regression gives the model:

$f(x) \approx 0.10677x - 211.69$. *Answers may vary.*

(b) $f(1987) = 0.10677(1987) - 211.69 \Rightarrow f(1987) \approx 0.462$.

The cost of a 30-scond Super Bowl ad in 1987 was approximated to be \$0.5 million. The estimate that was found involved extrapolation.

(c) $f(x) = 3.2 \Rightarrow 3.2 = 0.10677x - 211.69 \Rightarrow 214.89 = 0.10677x \Rightarrow x \approx 2012.644$.

Thus, the cost for a 30-second Super Bowl ad could reach \$3.2 million in 2013.

126. (a) Linear regression gives the model:

$P(x) \approx 0.19573x - 369.44$. *Answers may vary.*

(b) Using $P(x) \approx 0.19573x - 369.44$, let $x = 2003$. $P(2003) = 0.19573(2003) - 369.44 \Rightarrow$ $f(2003) \approx 22.6\%$. The percentage of women in 2003 was approximated to be 22.4%. The estimate found involved interpolation.

(c) $P(x) = 25 \Rightarrow 25 = 0.19573x - 369.44 \Rightarrow 394.44 = 0.19573x \Rightarrow x \approx 2015.22$.

Thus, the percentage could reach 25% in 2015.

## Extended and Discovery Exercises for Section 2.3

1. (a) Yes; since multiplication distributes over addition, doubling the lengths gives double the sum of the lengths.

   (b) No; If the length and width are doubled, the product of the length and width is multiplied by 4.

2. If each side of a figure is doubled, then the perimeter of the larger figure is twice the perimeter of the original figure, and the area of the larger figure will be four times the area of the original figure; if the radius of a circle is doubled, then the larger circle will have twice the circumference and four times the area of the original circle.

3. (a) $(100 \text{ ft}^2)(140\ \mu\text{g}/\text{ft}^2) = 14{,}000\ \mu\text{g}$; $f(x) = 14{,}000x$.

   (b) $(800 \text{ ft}^3)(33\mu\text{g}/\text{ft}^3) = 26{,}400\ \mu\text{g}$; $f(x) = 14{,}000x \Rightarrow 26{,}400 = 14{,}000x \Rightarrow x \approx 1.9$; it takes about 1.9 hours for the concentrations to reach $33\ \mu\text{g}/\text{ft}^3$.

4. (a) See Figure 4.

   (b) Using the data points (0, 30) and (25, 32.7), we get $m = \dfrac{32.7 - 30}{25 - 0} = \dfrac{2.7}{25} = 0.108$; the point $(0, 30) \Rightarrow b = 30$; $f(x) = mx + b \Rightarrow f(x) = 0.108x + 30$.

   (c) $f(65) = 0.108(65) + 30 = 37.02$; when the temperature is 65°C, the volume of the gas is $37.02 \text{ in}^3$.

   (d) Let $f(x) = 25$, then $25 = 0.108x + 30 \Rightarrow -5 = 0.108x \Rightarrow x \approx -46.3$. The answer was found using extrapolation. The answer is accurate because of the ideal gas laws. ***Answers may vary.***

[-5, 125, 25] by [0, 50, 10]

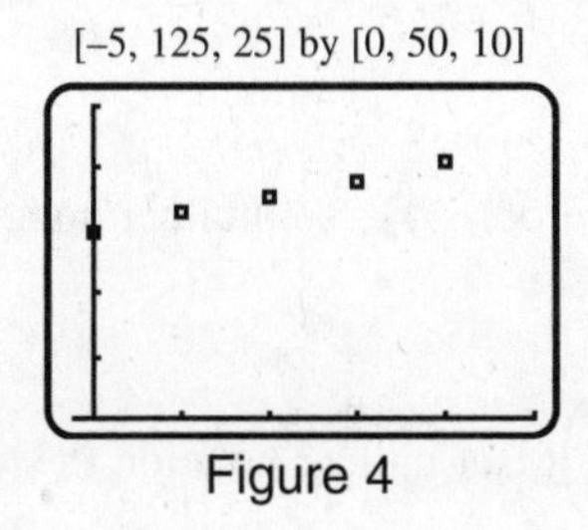

Figure 4

## 2.4: Linear Inequalities

1. $(-\infty, 2)$
2. $(-3, \infty)$
3. $[-1, \infty)$
4. $[\infty, 7]$
5. $[1, 8)$
6. $(-2, 4]$
7. $(-\infty, 1]$
8. $(5, \infty)$
9. $2x + 6 \geq 10 \Rightarrow 2x \geq 4 \Rightarrow x \geq 2$; $[2, \infty)$; set-builder notation the interval is $\{x \mid x \geq 2\}$.
10. $-4x - 3 < 5 \Rightarrow -4x < 8 \Rightarrow x > -2$; $(-2, \infty)$; set-builder notation the interval is $\{x \mid x > -2\}$.
11. $-2(x - 10) + 1 > 0 \Rightarrow -2x + 21 > 0 \Rightarrow -2x > -21 \Rightarrow x < 10.5$; $(-\infty, 10.5)$; set-builder notation the interval is $\{x \mid x < 10.5\}$.

12. $3(x + 5) \le 0 \Rightarrow x + 5 \le 0 \Rightarrow x \le -5$; $(-\infty, -5]$; set-builder notation the interval is $\{x \mid x \le -5\}$.

13. $\frac{t + 2}{3} \ge 5 \Rightarrow t + 2 \ge 15 \Rightarrow t \ge 13$; $[13, \infty)$; set-builder notation the interval is $\{t \mid t \ge 13\}$.

14. $\frac{2 - t}{6} < 0 \Rightarrow 2 - t < 0 \Rightarrow 2 < t$; $(2, \infty)$; set-builder notation the interval is $\{t \mid t > 2\}$.

15. $4x - 1 < \frac{3 - x}{-3} = 7 \Rightarrow -12x + 3 > 3 - x \Rightarrow -11x > 0 \Rightarrow x < 0$; $(-\infty, 0)$; set-builder notation the interval is $\{x \mid x < 0\}$.

16. $\frac{x + 5}{-10} > 2x + 3 \Rightarrow x + 5 < -20x - 30 \Rightarrow 21x < -35 \Rightarrow x < -\frac{5}{3}$; $\left(-\infty, -\frac{5}{3}\right)$; set-builder notation the interval is $\left\{x \mid x < -\frac{5}{3}\right\}$.

17. $-3(z - 4) \ge 2(1 - 2z) \Rightarrow -3z + 12 \ge 2 - 4z \Rightarrow z \ge -10$; $[-10, \infty)$; set-builder notation the interval is $\{z \mid z \ge -10\}$.

18. $-\frac{1}{4}(2z - 6) + z \ge 5 \Rightarrow -\frac{1}{2}z + \frac{3}{2} + z \ge 5 \Rightarrow \frac{1}{2}z \ge \frac{7}{2} \Rightarrow z \ge 7$; $[7, \infty)$; set-builder notation the interval is $\{z \mid z \ge 7\}$.

19. $\frac{1 - x}{4} < \frac{2x - 2}{3} \Rightarrow 3(1 - x) < 4(2x - 2) \Rightarrow 3 - 3x < 8x - 8 \Rightarrow -11x < -11 \Rightarrow x > 1$; $(1, \infty)$; set-builder notation the interval is $\{x \mid x > 1\}$.

20. $\frac{3x}{4} < x - \frac{x + 2}{2} \Rightarrow 3x < 4x - 2(x + 2) \Rightarrow 3x < 2x - 4 \Rightarrow x < -4$; $(-\infty, -4)$; set-builder notation the interval is $\{x \mid x < -4\}$.

21. $2x - 3 > \frac{1}{2}(x + 1) \Rightarrow 2x - 3 > \frac{1}{2}x + \frac{1}{2} \Rightarrow \frac{3}{2}x > \frac{7}{2} \Rightarrow x > \frac{7}{3}$; $\left(\frac{7}{3}, \infty\right)$; set-builder notation the interval is $\left\{x \mid x > \frac{7}{3}\right\}$.

22. $5 - (2 - 3x) \le -5x \Rightarrow 5 - 2 + 3x \le -5x \Rightarrow 8x \le -3 \Rightarrow x \le -\frac{3}{8}$; $\left(-\infty, -\frac{3}{8}\right]$; set-builder notation the interval is $\left\{x \mid x \le -\frac{3}{8}\right\}$.

23. $5 < 4t - 1 \le 11 \Rightarrow 6 < 4t \le 12 \Rightarrow \frac{3}{2} < t \le 3$; $\left(\frac{3}{2}, 3\right]$; set-builder notation the interval is $\left\{t \mid \frac{3}{2} < t \le 3\right\}$.

24. $-1 \le 2t \le 4 \Rightarrow -\frac{1}{2} \le t \le 2$; $\left[-\frac{1}{2}, 2\right]$; set-builder notation the interval is $\left\{t \mid -\frac{1}{2} \le t \le 2\right\}$.

25. $3 \le 4 - x \le 20 \Rightarrow -1 \le -x \le 16 \Rightarrow 1 \ge x \ge -16$; $[-16, 1]$; set-builder notation the interval is $\{x \mid -16 \le x \le 1\}$.

26. $-5 < 1 - 2x < 40 \Rightarrow -6 < -2x < 39 \Rightarrow 3 > x > -19.5$; $(-19.5, 3)$; set-builder notation the interval is $\{x \mid -19.5 < x < 3\}$.

27. $-7 \le \frac{1-4x}{7} < 12 \Rightarrow -49 \le 1 - 4x < 84 \Rightarrow -50 \le -4x < 83 \Rightarrow 12.5 \ge x > -20.75;$

$(-20.75, 12.5]$; set-builder notation the interval is $\{x \mid -20.75 < x \le 12.5\}$.

28. $0 < \frac{7x-5}{3} \le 4 \Rightarrow 0 < 7x - 5 \le 12 \Rightarrow 5 < 7x \le 17 \Rightarrow \frac{5}{7} < x \le \frac{17}{7}; \left(\frac{5}{7}, \frac{17}{7}\right]$; set-builder notation the interval is $\left\{x \mid \frac{5}{7} < x \le \frac{17}{7}\right\}$.

29. $5 > 2(x+4) - 5 > -5 \Rightarrow 5 > 2x + 8 - 5 > -5 \Rightarrow 2 > 2x > -8 \Rightarrow 1 > x > -4; (-4, 1)$;

set-builder notation the interval is $\{x \mid -4 < x < 1\}$.

30. $\frac{8}{3} \ge \frac{4}{3} - (x+3) \ge \frac{2}{3} \Rightarrow 8 \ge 4 - 3(x+3) \ge 2 \Rightarrow 8 \ge 4 - 3x - 9 \ge 2 \Rightarrow 13 \ge -3x \ge 7 \Rightarrow$

$-\frac{13}{3} \le x \le -\frac{7}{3}; \left[-\frac{13}{3}, -\frac{7}{3}\right]$; set-builder notation the interval is $\left\{x \mid -\frac{13}{3} \le x \le -\frac{7}{3}\right\}$.

31. $3 \le \frac{1}{2}x + \frac{3}{4} \le 6 \Rightarrow 12 \le 2x + 3 \le 24 \Rightarrow 9 \le 2x \le 21 \Rightarrow \frac{9}{2} \le x \le \frac{21}{2}; \left[\frac{9}{2}, \frac{21}{2}\right]$; set-builder notation the interval is $\left\{x \mid \frac{9}{2} \le x \le \frac{21}{2}\right\}$.

32. $-4 \le 5 - \frac{4}{5}x < 6 \Rightarrow -20 \le 25 - 4x < 30 \Rightarrow -45 \le -4x < 5 \Rightarrow \frac{45}{4} \ge x > -\frac{5}{4}; (-1.25, 11.25]$;

set-builder notation the interval is $\{x \mid -1.25 < x \le 11.25\}$.

33. $5x - 2(x+3) \ge 4 - 3x \Rightarrow 5x - 2x - 6 \ge 4 - 3x \Rightarrow 6x \ge 10 \Rightarrow x \ge \frac{5}{3}; \left[\frac{5}{3}, \infty\right)$; set-builder notation the interval is $\left\{x \mid x \ge \frac{5}{3}\right\}$.

34. $3x - 1 < 2(x-3) + 1 \Rightarrow 3x - 1 < 2x - 6 + 1 \Rightarrow x < -4; (-\infty, -4)$; set-builder notation the interval is $\{x \mid x < -4\}$.

35. $\frac{1}{2} \le \frac{1-2t}{3} < \frac{2}{3} \Rightarrow \frac{3}{2} \le 1 - 2t < 2 \Rightarrow \frac{1}{2} \le -2t < 1 \Rightarrow -\frac{1}{4} \ge t > -\frac{1}{2} \Rightarrow -\frac{1}{2} < t \le -\frac{1}{4};$

$\left(-\frac{1}{2}, -\frac{1}{4}\right]$; set-builder notation the interval is $\left\{t \mid -\frac{1}{2} < t \le -\frac{1}{4}\right\}$.

36. $-\frac{3}{4} < \frac{2-t}{5} < \frac{3}{4} \Rightarrow -\frac{15}{4} < 2 - t < \frac{15}{4} \Rightarrow -\frac{23}{4} < -t < \frac{7}{4} \Rightarrow \frac{23}{4} > t > -\frac{7}{4} \Rightarrow -\frac{7}{4} < t < \frac{23}{4};$

$\left(-\frac{7}{4}, \frac{23}{4}\right)$; set-builder notation the interval is $\left\{t \mid -\frac{7}{4} < t < \frac{23}{4}\right\}$.

37. $\frac{1}{2}z + \frac{2}{3}(3 - z) - \frac{5}{4}z \ge \frac{3}{4}(z - 2) + z \Rightarrow \frac{1}{2}z + 2 - \frac{2}{3}z - \frac{5}{4}z \ge \frac{3}{4}z - \frac{3}{2} + z \Rightarrow$

$-\frac{17}{12}z + 2 \ge \frac{7}{4}z - \frac{3}{2} \Rightarrow -\frac{38}{12}z \ge -\frac{7}{2} \Rightarrow z \le \frac{21}{19}; \left(-\infty, \frac{21}{19}\right]$; set-builder notation the interval is

$\left\{z \mid z \le \frac{21}{19}\right\}$.

38. $\frac{2}{3}(1 - 2z) - \frac{3}{2}z + \frac{5}{6}z \geq \frac{2z - 1}{3} + 1 \Rightarrow \frac{2}{3} - \frac{4}{3}z - \frac{3}{2}z + \frac{5}{6}z \geq \frac{2z - 1}{3} + 1 \Rightarrow$

$2 - 4z - \frac{9}{2}z + \frac{5}{2}z \geq 2z - 1 + 3 \Rightarrow -6z + 2 \geq 2z + 2 \Rightarrow 0 \geq 8z \Rightarrow z \leq 0$; $(-\infty, 0)$; set-builder notation the interval is $\{x \mid x \leq 0\}$.

39. Graph $y_1 = x + 2$ and $y_2 = 2x$. See Figure 39. $y_1 \geq y_2$ when the graph of $y_1$ is above the graph of $y_2$, which is left of the intersection point $(2, 4)$ and includes point $(2, 4) \Rightarrow \{x \mid x \leq 2\}$.

40. Graph $y_1 = 2x - 1$ and $y_2 = x$. See Figure 40. $y_1 \leq y_2$ when the graph of $y_1$ is below the graph of $y_2$, which is left of the intersection point $(1, 1)$ and includes point $(1, 1) \Rightarrow \{x \mid x \leq 1\}$.

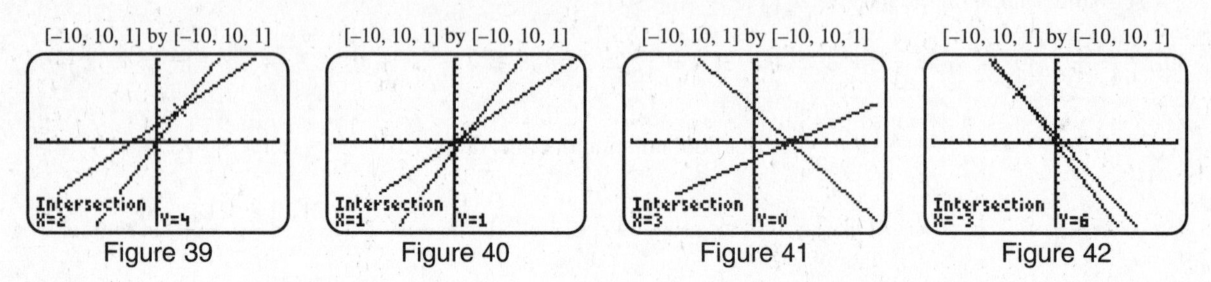

Figure 39 Figure 40 Figure 41 Figure 42

41. Graph $y_1 = \frac{2}{3}x - 2$ and $y_2 = -\frac{4}{3}x + 4$. See Figure 41. $y_1 > y_2$ when the graph of $y_1$ is above the graph of $y_2$, which is right of the intersection point $(3, 0)$ and does not include point $(3, 0) \Rightarrow \{x \mid x > 3\}$.

42. Graph $y_1 = -2x$ and $y_2 = -\frac{5}{3}x + 1$. See Figure 42. $y_1 \geq y_2$ when the graph of $y_1$ is above the graph of $y_2$, which is left of the intersection point $(-3, 6)$ and includes point $(-3, 6) \Rightarrow \{x \mid x \leq -3\}$.

43. Graph $y_1 = -1$, $y_2 = 2x - 1$, and $y_3 = 3$. See Figure 43. $y_1 \leq y_2 \leq y_3$ when the graph of $y_2$ is in between the graphs of $y_1$ and $y_3$, which is in between the intersection points $(0, -1)$ and $(2, 3)$ and it does include each point $\Rightarrow \{x \mid 0 \leq x \leq 2\}$.

44. Graph $y_1 = -2$, $y_2 = 1 - x$, and $y_3 = 2$. See Figure 44. $y_1 < y_2 < y_3$ when the graph of $y_2$ is in between the graphs of $y_1$ and $y_3$, which is in between the intersection points $(-1, 2)$ and $(3, -2)$ and it does not include each point $\Rightarrow \{x \mid -1 < x < 3\}$.

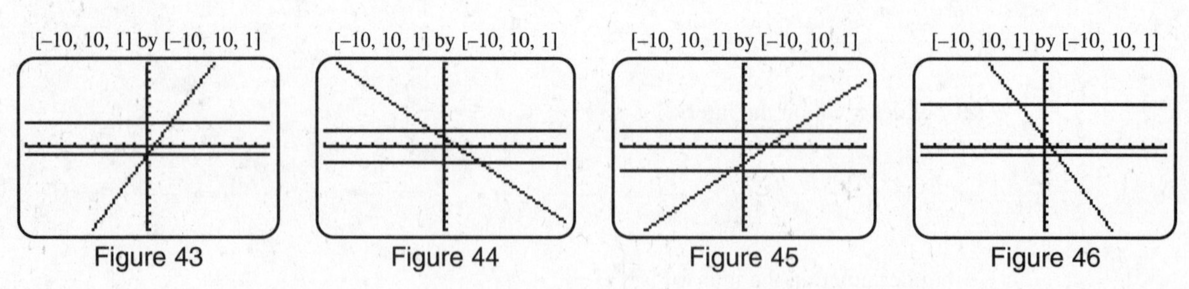

Figure 43 Figure 44 Figure 45 Figure 46

45. Graph $y_1 = -3$, $y_2 = x - 2$, and $y_3 = 2$. See Figure 45. $y_1 < y_2 \leq y_3$ when the graph of $y_2$ is in between the graphs of $y_1$ and $y_3$, which is in between the intersection points $(-1, -3)$ and $(4, 2)$ and it does not include the point $(-1, -3)$ but does include $(4, 2) \Rightarrow \{x \mid -1 < x \leq 4\}$.

46. Graph $y_1 = -1$, $y_2 = 1 - 2x$, and $y_3 = 5$. See Figure 46. $y_1 \leq y_2 < y_3$ when the graph of $y_2$ is in between the graphs of $y_1$ and $y_3$, which is in between the intersection points $(-2, 5)$ and $(1, -1)$ and it does not include $(-2, 5)$ and does include $(1, -1) \Rightarrow \{x \mid -2 < x \leq 1\}$.

47. (a) $y = \frac{3}{2}x - 3$, then $ax + b = 0$ gives us $\frac{3}{2}x - 3 = 0 \Rightarrow \frac{3}{2}x = 3 \Rightarrow x = 2$

(b) $ax + b < 0$ gives us $\frac{3}{2}x - 3 < 0 \Rightarrow x < 2 \Rightarrow (-\infty, 2)$ or in set builder notation, $\{x | x < 2\}$.

(c) $ax + b \geq 0$ gives us $\frac{3}{2}x - 3 \geq 0 \Rightarrow x \geq 2 \Rightarrow [2, \infty)$ or in set builder notation, $\{x | x \geq 2\}$.

48. (a) $y = -x + 1$, then $ax + b = 0$ gives us $-x + 1 = 0 \Rightarrow -x = -1 \Rightarrow x = 1$

(b) $ax + b < 0$ gives us $-x + 1 < 0 \Rightarrow x > 1 \Rightarrow (1, \infty)$ or in set builder notation, $\{x | x > 1\}$.

(c) $ax + b \geq 0$ gives us $-x + 1 \geq 0 \Rightarrow x \leq 1 \Rightarrow (-\infty, 1]$ or in set builder notation, $\{x | x \leq 1\}$.

49. (a) $y = -x - 2$, then $ax + b = 0$ gives us $-x - 2 = 0 \Rightarrow -x = 2 \Rightarrow x = -2$

(b) $ax + b < 0$ gives us $-x - 2 < 0 \Rightarrow x > -2 \Rightarrow (-2, \infty)$ or in set builder notation, $\{x | x > -2\}$.

(c) $ax + b \geq 0$ gives us $-x - 2 \geq 0 \Rightarrow x \leq -2 \Rightarrow (-\infty, -2]$ or in set builder notation, $\{x | x \leq -2\}$.

50. (a) $y = 3x + 3$, then $ax + b = 0$ gives us $3x + 3 = 0 \Rightarrow 3x = -3 \Rightarrow x = -1$

(b) $ax + b < 0$ gives us $3x + 3 < 0 \Rightarrow x < -1 \Rightarrow (-\infty, -1)$ or in set builder notation, $\{x | x < -1\}$.

(c) $ax + b \geq 0$ gives us $3x + 3 \geq 0 \Rightarrow x \geq -1 \Rightarrow [-1, \infty)$ or in set builder notation, $\{x | x \geq -1\}$.

51. $x - 3 \leq \frac{1}{2}x - 2 \Rightarrow x - 3 - \frac{1}{2}x + 2 \leq 0 \Rightarrow \frac{1}{2}x - 1 \leq 0$. Figure 51 shows the graph of $y_1 = \frac{1}{2}x - 1$. The solution set for $y_1 \leq 0$ occurs when the graph is on or below the $x$-axis, or when $x \leq 2$. The solution set is $(-\infty, 2]$. Solving symbolically, $x - 3 \leq \frac{1}{2}x - 2 \Rightarrow \frac{1}{2}x \leq 1 \Rightarrow x \leq 2 \Rightarrow$ $(-\infty, 2]$. In set-builder notation the interval is $\{x | x \leq 2\}$.

52. $x - 2 \leq \frac{1}{3}x \Rightarrow x - 2 - \frac{1}{3}x \leq 0 \Rightarrow \frac{2}{3}x - 2 \leq 0$. Figure 52 shows the graph of $y_1 = \frac{2}{3}x - 2$. The solution set for $y_1 \leq 0$ occurs when the graph is on or below the $x$-axis, or when $x \leq 3$. The solution set is $(-\infty, 3]$. Solving symbolically, $x - 2 \leq \frac{1}{3}x \Rightarrow \frac{2}{3}x \leq 2 \Rightarrow x \leq 3 \Rightarrow (-\infty, 3]$. In set-builder notation the interval is $\{x | x \leq 3\}$.

[-10, 10, 1] by [-10, 10, 1]

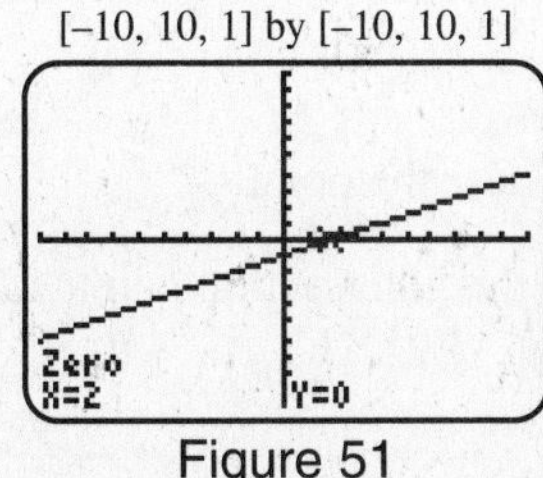


Figure 51

[-10, 10, 1] by [-10, 10, 1]

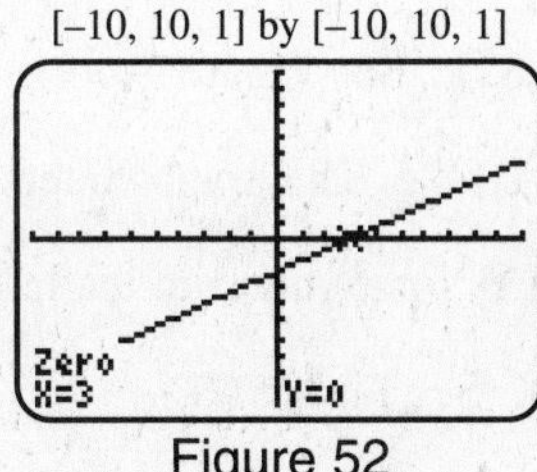


Figure 52

[-10, 10, 1] by [-10, 10, 1]

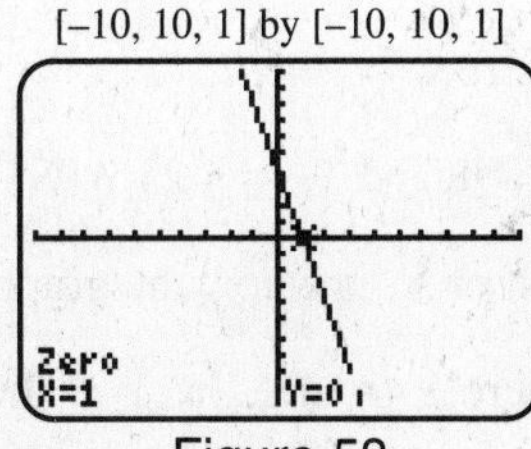


Figure 53

[-10, 10, 1] by [-10, 10, 1]

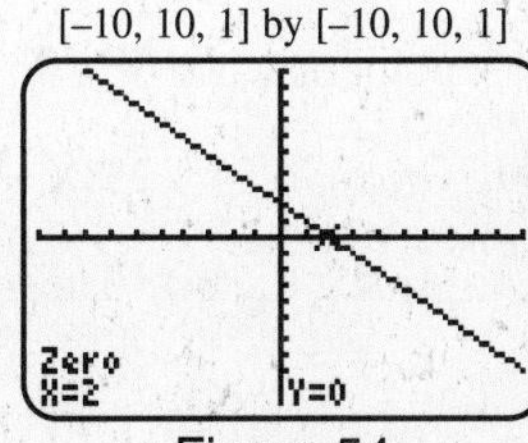


Figure 54

53. $2 - x < 3x - 2 \Rightarrow 2 - x - 2x + 2 < 0 \Rightarrow -4x + 4 < 0$. Figure 53 shows the graph of $y_1 = -4x + 4$. The solution set for $y_1 < 0$ occurs when the graph is below the $x$-axis, or when $x > 1$. The solution set is $(1, \infty)$. Solving symbolically, $2 - x < 3x - 2 \Rightarrow -4x < -4 \Rightarrow x > 1 \Rightarrow (1, \infty)$. In set-builder notation the interval is $\{x | x > 1\}$.

54. $\frac{1}{2}x + 1 > \frac{3}{2}x - 1 \Rightarrow \frac{1}{2}x + 1 - \frac{3}{2}x + 1 > 0 \Rightarrow -x + 2 > 0$. Figure 54 shows the graph of $y_1 = -x + 2$. The solution set for $y_1 > 0$ occurs when the graph is above the $x$-axis, or when $x < 2$. The solution set is $(-\infty, 2)$. Solving symbolically, $\frac{1}{2}x + 1 > \frac{3}{2}x - 1 \Rightarrow -x > -2 \Rightarrow x < 2 \Rightarrow (-\infty, 2)$. In set-builder notation the interval is $\{x | x \leq 2\}$.

55. Graph $Y_1 = 5X - 4$ and $Y_2 = 10$. The graphs intersect at the point (2.8, 10). The graph of $Y_1$ is above the graph of $Y_2$ for $x$-values to the right of this intersection point or where $x > 2.8$, $\{x \mid x > 2.8\}$. See Figure 55.

56. Graph $Y_1 = -3X + 6$ and $Y_2 = 9$. The graphs intersect at the point (–1, 9). The graph of $Y_1$ is below the graph of $Y_2$ for $x$-values to the right of this intersection point, so $y_1 \leq y_2$ when $x \geq -1$, $\{x \mid x \geq -1\}$. See Figure 56.

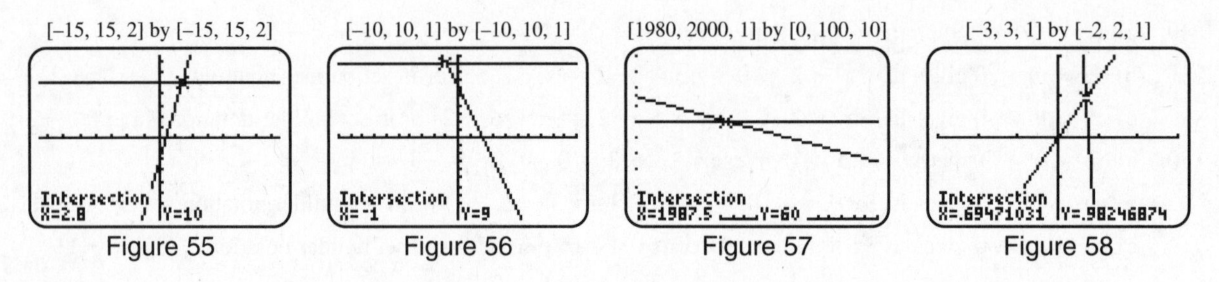

Figure 55 Figure 56 Figure 57 Figure 58

57. Graph $Y_1 = -2(X - 1990) + 55$ and $Y_2 = 60$. The graphs intersect at the point (1987.5, 60). The graph of $Y_1$ is above the graph of $Y_2$ for $x$-values to the left of this intersection point, so $y_1 \geq y_2$ when $x \leq 1987.5$, $\{x \mid x \leq 1987.5\}$. See Figure 57.

58. Graph $Y_1 = \sqrt{(2)}X$ and $Y_2 = 10.5 - 13.7X$. The graphs intersect near the point (0.6947, 0.9825). The graph of $Y_1$ is above the graph of $Y_2$ for $x$-values to the right of this intersection point or when $x > k$, where $k \approx 0.69$, $\{x \mid x > 0.69\}$. See Figure 58.

59. Graph $Y_1 = \sqrt{(5)}(X - 1.2) - \sqrt{(3)}X$ and $Y_2 = 5(X + 1.1)$. The graphs intersect near the point (–1.820, –3.601). The graph of $Y_1$ is below the graph of $Y_2$ for $x$-values to the right of this intersection point or when $x > k$, where $k \approx -1.82$, $\{x \mid x > -1.82\}$. See Figure 59.

60. Graph $Y_1 = 1.238X + 0.998$ and $Y_2 = 1.23(3.987 - 2.1X)$. The graphs intersect near the point (1.022, 2.264). The graph of $Y_1$ is below the graph of $Y_2$ for $x$-values to the left of this intersection point, so $y_1 \leq y_2$ when $x \leq k$, where $k \approx 1.02$, $\{x \mid x \leq 1.02\}$. See Figure 60.

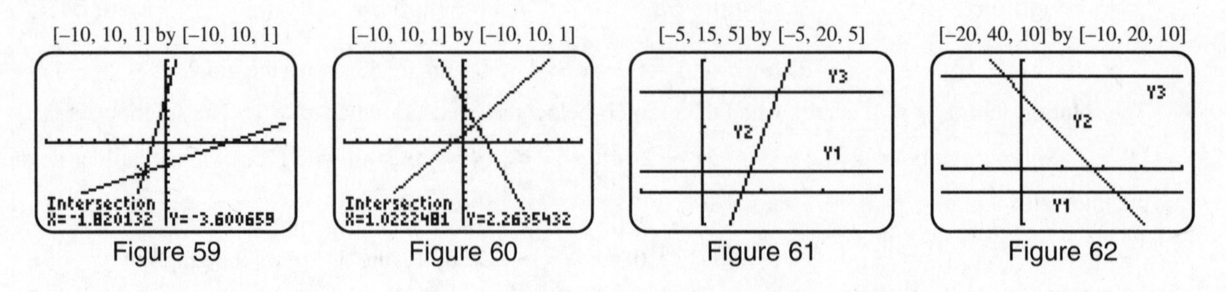

Figure 59 Figure 60 Figure 61 Figure 62

61. Graph $Y_1 = 3$, $Y_2 = 5X - 17$ and $Y_3 = 15$, as shown in Figure 61. The graphs intersect at the points (4, 3) and (6.4, 15). The solutions to $Y_1 \leq Y_2 < Y_3$ are the $x$-values between 4 and 6.4, including $4 \Rightarrow [4, 6.4)$. In set-builder notation the interval is $\{x \mid 4 \leq x < 6.4\}$.

62. Graph $Y_1 = -4$, $Y_2 = (55 - 3.1X)/4$ and $Y_3 = 17$, as shown in Figure 62. The graphs intersect near the points $(22.9, -4)$ and $(-4.2, 17)$. The solutions to $Y_1 < Y_2 < Y_3$ are the $x$-values between $-4.2$ and $22.9$ or $-4.2 < x < 22.9 \Rightarrow (-4.2, 22.9)$ (approximate). In set-builder notation the interval is $\{x \mid -4.2 < x < 22.9\}$.

63. Graph $Y_1 = 1.5$, $Y_2 = 9.1 - 0.5X$ and $Y_3 = 6.8$, as shown in Figure 63. The graphs intersect at the points $(4.6, 6.8)$ and $(15.2, 1.5)$. The solutions to $Y_1 \leq Y_2 \leq Y_3$ are the $x$-values between 4.6 and 15.2 (inclusive) or $4.6 \leq x \leq 15.2 \Rightarrow [4.6, 15.2]$. In set builder notation the interval is $\{x \mid 4.6 \leq x \leq 15.2\}$.

64. Graph $Y_1 = 0.2X$, $Y_2 = (2X - 5)/3$ and $Y_3 = 8$, as shown in Figure 64. The graph of $y_2$ intersects the graphs of $y_1$ and $y_3$ near $(3.571, 0.7143)$ and at $(14.5, 8)$. The solutions to $Y_1 < Y_2 < Y_3$ are the $x$-values between 3.6 and 14.5 or $3.6 < x < 14.5 \Rightarrow (3.6, 14.5)$ (approximate). In set-builder notation the interval is $\{x \mid 3.6 < x < 4.5\}$.

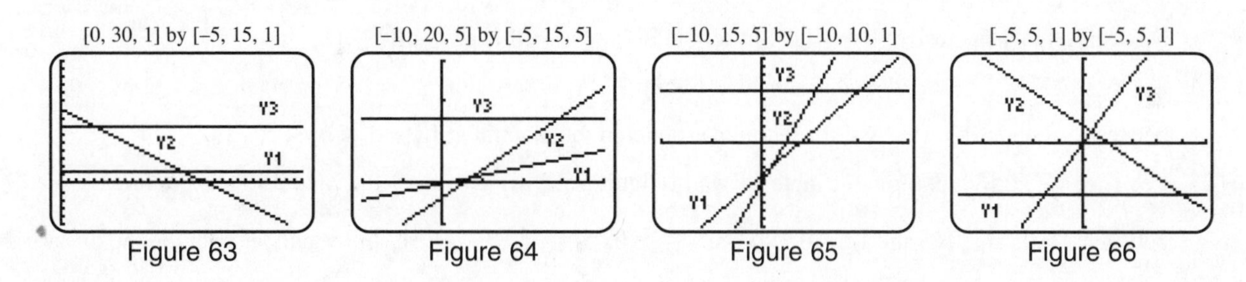

Figure 63 Figure 64 Figure 65 Figure 66

65. Graph $Y_1 = X - 4$, $Y_2 = 2X - 5$ and $Y_3 = 6$, as shown in Figure 65. The graph of $y_2$ intersects the graphs of $y_1$ and $y_3$ at $(1, -3)$ and $(5.5, 6)$. The solutions to $Y_1 < Y_2 < Y_3$ are the $x$-values between 1 and 5.5 or $1 < x < 5.5 \Rightarrow (1, 5.5)$. In set-builder notation the interval is $\{x \mid 1 < x < 5.5\}$.

66. Graph $Y_1 = -3$, $Y_2 = 1 - X$ and $Y_3 = 2X$, as shown in Figure 66. The graph of $y_2$ intersects the graphs of $y_1$ and $y_3$ near $(0.3333, 0.6667)$ and at $(4, -3)$. The solutions to $Y_1 \leq Y_2 \leq Y_3$ are the $x$-values between 0.33 and 4 (inclusive) or $0.33 \leq x \leq 4 \Rightarrow [0.33, 4]$ (approximate). In set-builder notation the interval is $\{x \mid 0.33 \leq x \leq 4\}$.

67. (a) The graphs intersect at the point $(8, 7)$. Therefore, $g(x) = f(x)$ is satisfied when $x = 8$. The solution is 8.
    (b) $g(x) > f(x)$ whenever the $y$-values on the graph of $g$ are above the $y$-values on the graph of $f$. This occurs to the left of the point of intersection. Therefore the $x$-values that satisfy this inequality are $x < 8$. In set-builder notation the interval is $\{x \mid x < 8\}$.

68. (a) $f(x) = g(x)$ when $x = 4$ since their graphs intersect at $(4, 200)$. The solution is 4.
    (b) $g(x) = h(x)$ when $x = 2$ since their graphs intersect at $(2, 400)$. The solution is 2.
    (c) $f(x) < g(x) < h(x)$ when $2 < x < 4$. In set-builder notation the interval is $\{x \mid 2 < x < 4\}$.
    (d) $g(x) > h(x)$ when $0 \leq x < 2$. In set-builder notation the interval is $\{x \mid 0 \leq x < 2\}$.

69. From the table,
    $Y_1 = 0$ when $x = 4$. $Y_1 > 0$ when $x < 4 \Rightarrow \{x \mid x < 4\}$; $Y_1 \leq 0$ when $x \geq 4 \Rightarrow \{x \mid x \geq 4\}$.

70. From the table, $Y_1 = 0$ when $x = -3$. $Y_1 < 0$ when $x < -3$ and $Y_1 \geq 0$ when $x \geq -3 \Rightarrow$ $\{x \mid x < -3\}$; $\{x \mid x \geq -3\}$.

71. Let $Y_1 = -4X - 6$. From the table shown in Figure 71, $Y_1 = 0$ when $x = -1.5$ or $-\frac{3}{2}$. $Y_1 > 0$ when $x < -\frac{3}{2}$.

In set-builder notation the interval is $\left\{x \mid x < -\frac{3}{2}\right\}$.

72. Let $Y_1 = 1 - 2X$. From the table shown in Figure 72, $Y_1 = 9$ when $x = -4$. $Y_1 \geq 9$ when $x \leq -4 \Rightarrow$ $(-\infty, -4]$. In set builder notation the interval is $\{x \mid x \leq -4\}$.

Figure 71

Figure 72

Figure 73

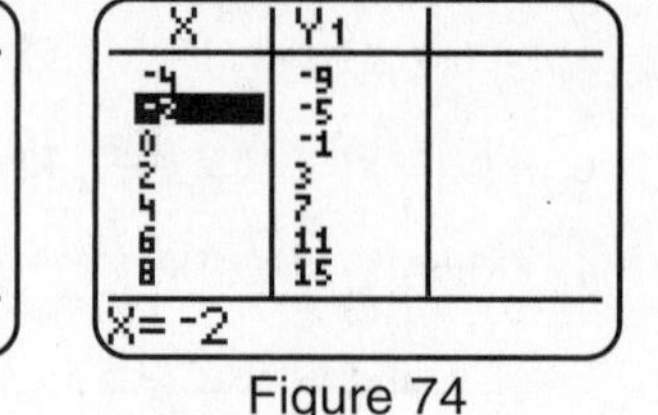

Figure 74

73. Let $Y_1 = 3X - 2$. From the table shown in Figure 73, $Y_1$ is between 10 and 4 (inclusive) for $x$-values between 1 and 4 (inclusive) $\Rightarrow [1, 4]$. In set-builder notation the interval is $\{x \mid 1 \leq x \leq 4\}$.

74. Let $Y_1 = 2X - 1$. From the table shown in Figure 74, $Y_1$ is between $-5$ and 15 for $x$-values between $-2$ and 8 $\Rightarrow (-2, 8)$. In set-builder notation the interval is $\{x \mid -2 < x < 8\}$.

75. Let $Y_1 = (2 - 5X)/3$. From the table shown in Figure 75, $Y_1$ is between $-0.75$ and 0.75 for $x$-values between $-0.05$ and 0.85 and $Y_1 = 0.75$ when $x = -0.05 \Rightarrow \left[-\frac{1}{20}, \frac{17}{20}\right)$. In set-builder notation the interval is $\left\{x \mid -\frac{1}{20} \leq x < \frac{17}{20}\right\}$.

76. Let $Y_1 = (3X - 1)/5$. From the table shown in Figure 76, $Y_1 \approx 15$ when $x = 25.3$. $Y_1 < 15$ when $x < 25.3$; $(-\infty, 25.3)$. In set-builder notation the interval is $\{x \mid x < 25.3\}$.

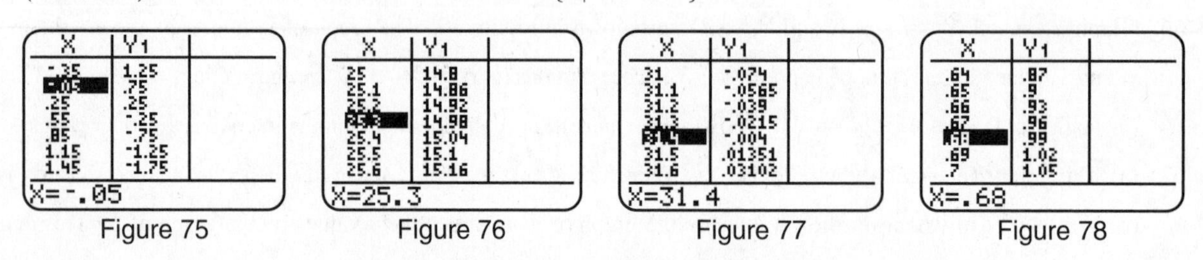

Figure 75

Figure 76

Figure 77

Figure 78

77. Let $Y_1 = (\sqrt{(11)} - \pi)X - 5.5$. From the table shown in Figure 77, $Y_1 \approx 0$ when $x = 31.4$. $Y_1 \leq 0$ when $x \leq 31.4$; $(-\infty, 31.4]$. In set-builder notation the interval is $\{x \mid x \leq 31.4\}$.

78. Let $Y_1 = 1.5(X - 0.7) + 1.5X$. From the table shown in Figure 78, $Y_1 \approx 1$ when $x = 0.68$. $Y_1 < 1$ when $x < 0.7$; $(-\infty, 0.7)$ In set-builder notation the interval is $\{x \mid x < 0.7\}$.

79. Symbolically: $2x - 8 > 5 \Rightarrow 2x > 13 \Rightarrow x > \frac{13}{2}$. The solution set is $\left(\frac{13}{2}, \infty\right)$. In set-builder notation the interval is $\left\{x \mid x > \frac{13}{2}\right\}$.

80. Symbolically: $5 < 4x - 2.5 \Rightarrow 7.5 < 4x \Rightarrow \frac{7.5}{4} < x \Rightarrow x > 1.875$. The solution set is $(1.875, \infty)$. In set-builder notation the interval is $\{x \mid x > 1.875\}$.

81. Graphically: Let $Y_1 = \pi X - 5.12$ and $Y_2 = \sqrt{(2)}X - 5.7(X - 1.1)$. Graph $Y_1$ and $Y_2$ as shown in Figure 81. The graphs intersect near (1.534, −0.302). The graph of $Y_1$ is below $Y_2$ for $x < 1.534$, so $Y_1 \le Y_2$ when $x \le 1.534$. The solution set is $(-\infty, 1.534]$.

82. Graphically: Let $Y_1 = 5.1X - \pi$ and $Y_2 = \sqrt{(3)} - 1.7X$. Graph $Y_1$ and $Y_2$ as shown in Figure 82. The graphs intersect near (0.717, 0.514). The graph of $Y_1$ is above $Y_2$ for $x > 0.717$, so $Y_1 \ge Y_2$ when $x \ge 0.717$. The solution set is $[0.717, \infty)$.

[−10, 10, 1] by [−10, 10, 1]

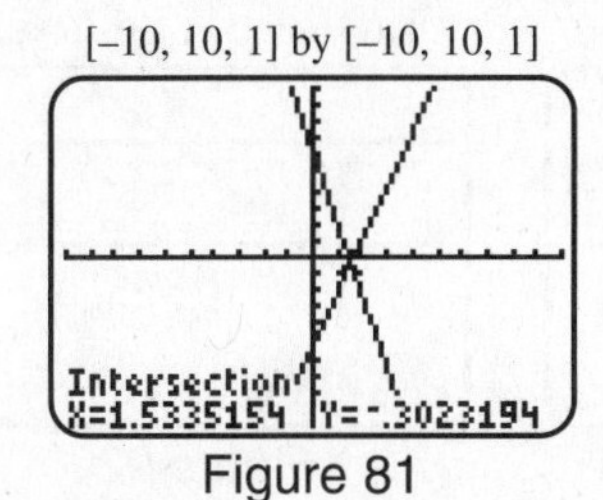

Figure 81

[−10, 10, 1] by [−10, 10, 1]

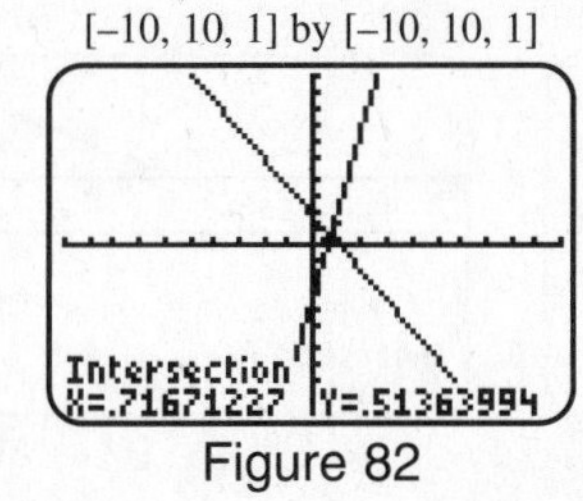

Figure 82

[0, 3, 1] by [0, 70, 10]

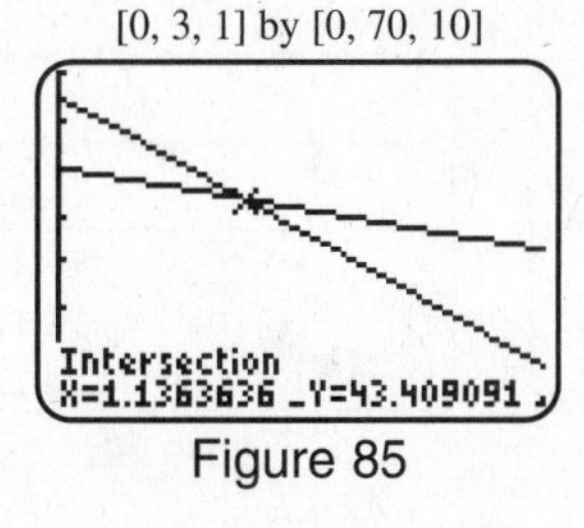

Figure 85

[0, 5, 1] by [0, 70, 10]

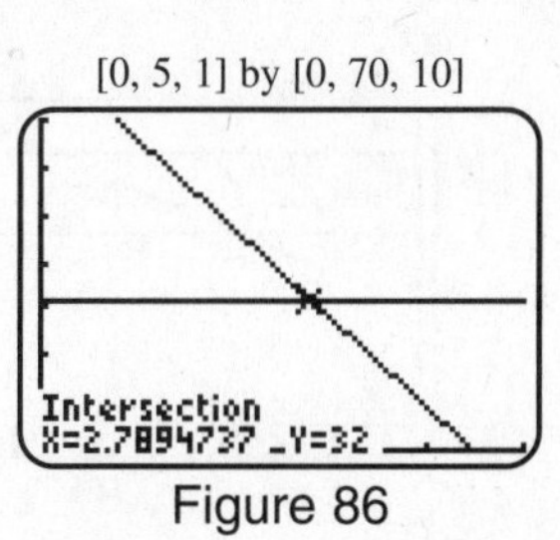

Figure 86

83. (a) Car A is traveling faster since it passes Car B. Its graph has the greater slope.

(b) The cars are the same distance from St. Louis when their graphs intersect. This point of intersection occurs at (2.5, 225). The cars are both 225 miles from St. Louis after 2.5 hours.

(c) Car B is ahead of Car A when $0 \le x < 2.5$.

84. (a) The car is moving away from Omaha since the graph has positive slope.

(b) The car is 100 miles from Omaha after 1 hour has elapsed and 200 miles away from Omaha after 3 hours.

(c) The car is 100 to 200 miles from Omaha between these times or when $1 \le x \le 3$.

(d) The distance is greater than 100 miles when $x > 1$.

85. (a) Graph $Y_1 = 65 - 19X$ and $Y_2 = 50 - 5.8X$. These graphs intersect near the point (1.14, 43.4) as shown in Figure 85. At an altitude of approximately 1.14 miles the temperature and the dew point are both equal to 43.4°F. The air temperature is greater than the dew point below 1.14 miles. The region where the clouds will not form is below 1.14 miles or when $0 \le x < 1.14$.

(b) $65 - 19x > 50 - 5.8x \Rightarrow 15 > 13.2x \Rightarrow \frac{15}{13.2} > x$ or $0 \le x < \frac{15}{13.2} \approx 1.14$

86. (a) Graph $Y_1 = 85 - 19X$ and $Y_2 = 32$. These graphs intersect near the point (2.8, 32) as shown in Figure 86. At an altitude of approximately 2.8 miles the temperature is 32°F. The temperature is below 32°F above this altitude. Since the domain is limited to an altitude of 6 miles, the region where the temperature is below freezing is above 2.8 miles and up to 6 miles. The solution is $2.8 < x \le 6$ (where 2.8 is approximate).

(b) The $x$-intercept represents the altitude where the temperature is 0°F.

(c) $T(x) = 32 \Rightarrow 85 - 19x = 32 \Rightarrow -19x = -53 \Rightarrow x = \frac{53}{19}$. Thus, $\frac{53}{19} < x \le 6$.

87. (a) The slope of the graph of $P$ is 8667. This means that the median price of a single-family home has increased by approximately \$8667 per year.

(b) Graph $Y_1 = 8667X + 90000$, $Y_2 = 142000$ and $Y_3 = 194000$. These graphs are shown in Figure 87. The points of intersection are located near (5.99, 142,000) and (11.99, 194,000). For approximately $5.99 \leq x \leq 11.99$ or, rounded to the nearest year, between 1996 and 2002, the median price was between \$142,000 and \$194,000. (Note that $x = 0$ corresponds to 1990.)

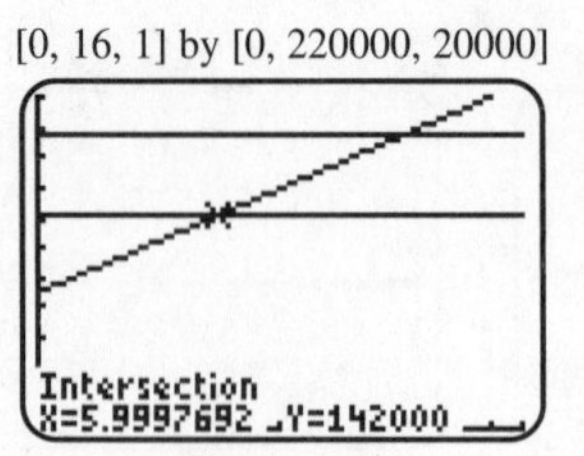

Figure 87

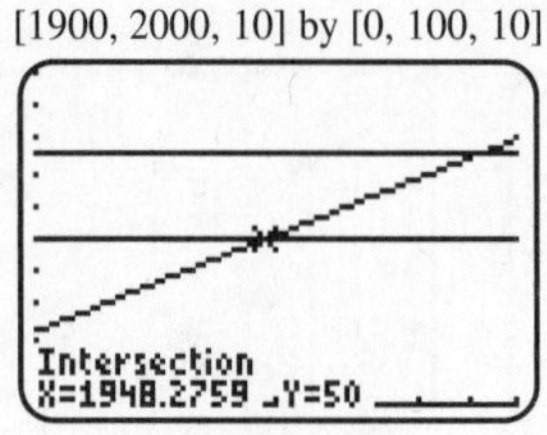

Figure 88

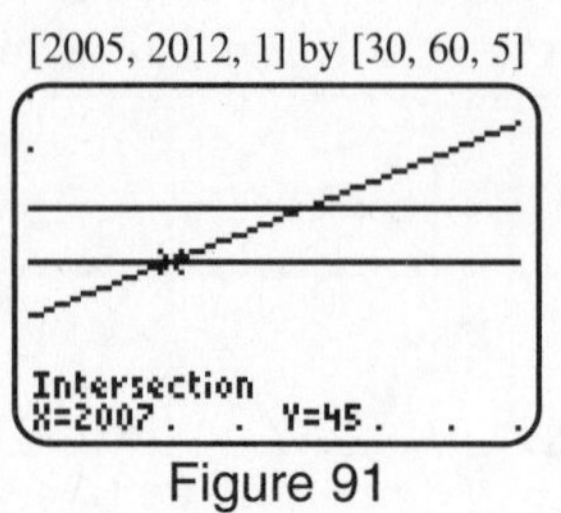

Figure 91

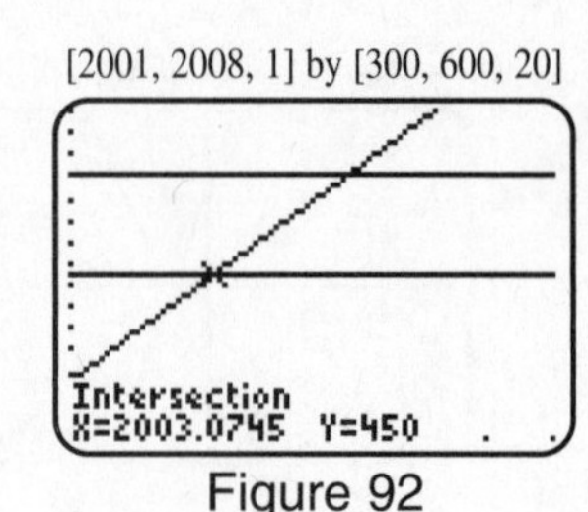

Figure 92

88. (a) The slope of the graph is 0.58. This means that the density increased on average by 0.58 people per square mile per year.

(b) Graph $Y_1 = 0.58X - 1080$, $Y_2 = 50$ and $Y_3 = 75$. The graphs are shown in Figure 88. The points of intersection are located near (1948.28, 50) and (1991.38, 75). Between approximately 1948 and 1991 the density varied between 50 and 75 in people per square mile.

89. (a) Using (2000, 6) and (2004, 30), find slope: $m = \dfrac{30 - 6}{2004 - 2000} = \dfrac{24}{4} = 6 \Rightarrow$

$B(x) = 6(x - 2000) + 6$ or $B(x) = 6(x - 2004) + 30$.

(b) $6(x - 2000) + 6 \geq 24 \Rightarrow 6x - 11{,}994 \geq 24 \Rightarrow 6x \geq 12{,}018 \Rightarrow x \geq 2003$, from 2003 to 2006.

90. (a) Using (2002, 4) and (2005, 10), find slope: $m = \dfrac{10 - 4}{2005 - 2002} = \dfrac{6}{3} = 2 \Rightarrow B(x) = 2(x - 2002) + 4$ or $B(x) = 2(x + 2005) + 10$.

(b) $2(x - 2002) + 4 \geq 6 \Rightarrow 2x - 4000 \geq 6 \Rightarrow 2x \geq 4006 \Rightarrow x \geq 2003$, consumer losses were more than \$6 billion from 2003 to 2007.

91. (a) The graph of linear function $P$ will contain the points (2005, 40) and (2011, 55).

$m = \dfrac{55 - 40}{2011 - 2005} = \dfrac{15}{6} = 2.5 \Rightarrow P(x) = 2.5(x - 2005) + 40 \Rightarrow P(x) = 2.5x - 4972.5$

(b) Let $Y_1 = 2.5X - 4972.5$, $Y_2 = 45$ and $Y_3 = 50$. The points of intersection are located at (2007, 45) and (2009, 50). The percentage was between 45% and 50% from 2007 to 2009. See Figure 91.

92. (a) The linear function $V$ will intersect the points (2002, 400) and (2007, 635).

$m = \dfrac{635 - 400}{2007 - 2002} = \dfrac{235}{5} = 47 \Rightarrow V(x) = 47(x - 2002) + 400 \Rightarrow V(x) = 47x - 93{,}694$

(b) Let $Y_1 = 47X - 93694$, $Y_2 = 450$ and $Y_3 = 540$. The points of intersection are located near (2003, 450) and (2005, 540). The annual VISA transactions were between \$450 and \$540 from 2003 to 2005. See Figure 92.

93. The graph of linear function will intersect the points (90, 6.5) and (129, 5.5).

$m = \frac{6.5 - 5.5}{90 - 129} = -\frac{1}{39} \Rightarrow f(x) = -\frac{1}{39}(x - 129) + 5.5 \Rightarrow 5.75 < -\frac{1}{39}(x - 129) + 5.5 < 6 \Rightarrow$

$0.25 < -\frac{1}{39}(x - 129) < 0.5 \Rightarrow -9.75 > x - 129 > 79.5 \Rightarrow 119.25 > x > 109.5$

94. The graph of linear function will intersect the points (77, 7) and (112, 6).

$m = \frac{7 - 6}{77 - 112} = -\frac{1}{35} \Rightarrow f(x) = -\frac{1}{35}(x - 77) + 7 \Rightarrow f(x) = -\frac{1}{35}x + 9.2 \Rightarrow$

$6\frac{1}{6} < -\frac{1}{35}x + 9.2 < 6\frac{2}{3} \Rightarrow \frac{37}{6} < -\frac{1}{35}x + \frac{46}{5} < \frac{20}{3} \Rightarrow -\frac{91}{30} < -\frac{1}{35}x < -\frac{38}{15} \Rightarrow$

$106\frac{1}{6} > x > 88\frac{2}{3}$; The sun rose between 6:10 a.m. and 6:40 a.m. from day 89 (Mar 29) to day 106 (Apr 15).

95. $r = \frac{C}{2\pi}$ and $1.99 \le r \le 2.01 \Rightarrow 1.99 \le \frac{C}{2\pi} \le 2.01 \Rightarrow 3.98\pi \le C \le 4.02\pi$

96. $s = \frac{P}{4}$ and $9.9 \le s \le 10.1 \Rightarrow 9.9 \le \frac{P}{4} \le 10.1 \Rightarrow 39.6 \le P \le 40.4$

97. (a) $m = \frac{4.5 - (-1.5)}{2 - 0} = \frac{6}{2} = 3$ and $y$-intercept $= -1.5$; $f(x) = 3x - 1.5$ models the data.

(b) $f(x) > 2.25 \Rightarrow 3x - 1.5 > 2.25 \Rightarrow 3x > 3.75 \Rightarrow x > 1.25$

98. (a) $m = \frac{3.5 - 0.4}{2 - 1} = 3.1$ and $y$-intercept $= 0.4 - 3.1 = -2.7$; $f(x) = 3.1x - 2.7$ models the data.

(b) $2 \le f(x) \le 8 \Rightarrow 2 \le 3.1x - 2.7 \le 8 \Rightarrow 4.7 \le 3.1x \le 10.7 \Rightarrow 1.52 \le x \le 3.45$ (approximate)

99. (a) Using the linear regression function on the calculator the function $f$ is found to be

$f(x) = 20.1x - 40{,}0096.7.$

(b) Let $Y_1 = 20.1X - 40096.7$, $Y_2 = 43$ and $Y_3 = 83$. The points of intersection are at (1997, 43) and near (1999, 83). Therefore, the number of cell phone subscribers was between 43 and 83 million between the years 1997 and 1999.

(c) The answer was a result of extrapolation.

100. (a) Using the linear regression function on the calculator the function $f$ is found to be

$f(x) \approx 0.21233x - 357.206.$

(b) Let $Y_1 = 0.21233X - 357.206$, $Y_2 = 58$ and $Y_3 = 60$. The points of intersection are near (1955, 58) and (1965, 60). The percentage of homes owned by the occupant was between 58% and 60% between the years 1955 and 1965.

(c) The answer was a result of interpolation.

## Extended and Discovery Exercises for Section 2.4

1. $a < b \Rightarrow 2a < a + b < 2b \Rightarrow a < \frac{a + b}{2} < b$

2. $0 < a < b \Rightarrow a^2 < ab < b^2 \Rightarrow a < \sqrt{ab} < b$

## Checking Basic Concepts for Sections 2.3 and 2.4

1. (a) Using the $x$-intercept method, graph $Y_1 = 4(x - 2) - 2(5 - x) + 3$. See Figure 1a.

   Since $Y_1 = 0$ when $x = 2.5$, the solution to the linear equation is 2.5.

   (b) Table $Y_1 = 4(x - 2) - 2(5 - x) + 3$ as shown in Figure 1b.

   Since $Y_1 = 0$ when $x = 2.5$, the solution to the linear equation is 2.5.

   (c) $4(x - 2) = 2(5 - x) - 3 \Rightarrow 4x - 8 = 10 - 2x - 3 \Rightarrow 6x = 15 \Rightarrow x = 2.5$

[−10, 10, 1] by [−10, 10, 1]

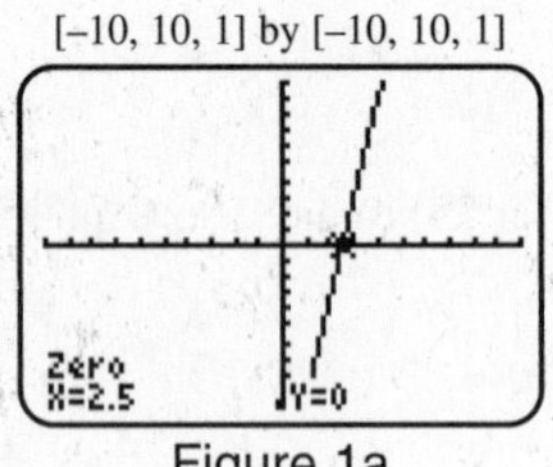
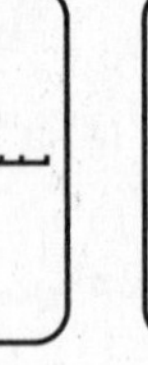


Figure 1a

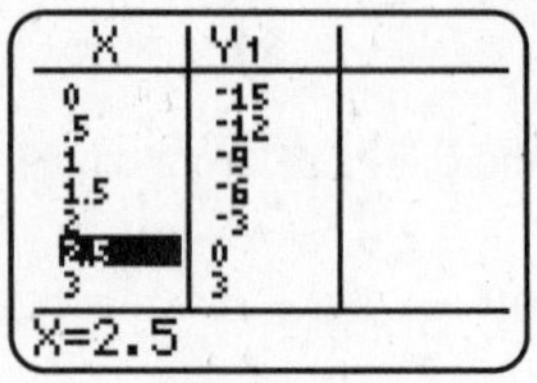

| X | $Y_1$ |
|---|---|
| 0 | −15 |
| .5 | −12 |
| 1 | −9 |
| 1.5 | −6 |
| 2 | −3 |
| 2.5 | 0 |
| 3 | 3 |

X=2.5

Figure 1b

2. $2(x - 4) > 1 - x \Rightarrow 2x - 8 > 1 - x \Rightarrow 3x > 9 \Rightarrow x > 3$; $\{x \mid x > 3\}$

3. $-2 \le 1 - 2x \le 3 \Rightarrow -3 \le -2x \le 2 \Rightarrow \frac{3}{2} \ge x \ge -1$, or $-1 \le x \le \frac{3}{2}$; $\left[-1, \frac{3}{2}\right]$ In set-builder notation the interval is $\left\{x \mid -1 \le x \le \frac{3}{2}\right\}$.

4. (a) $-3(2 - x) - \frac{1}{2}x - \frac{3}{2} = 0$ when $x = 3$; symbolically, $-3(2 - x) - \frac{1}{2}x - \frac{3}{2} = 0 \Rightarrow$

   $-6 + 3x - \frac{1}{2}x - \frac{3}{2} = 0 \Rightarrow \frac{5}{2}x - \frac{15}{2} = 0 \Rightarrow \frac{5}{2}x = \frac{15}{2} \Rightarrow x = 3$

   (b) $-3(2 - x) - \frac{1}{2}x - \frac{3}{2} > 0$ when $x > 3$; symbolically, $-3(2 - x) - \frac{1}{2}x - \frac{3}{2} > 0 \Rightarrow$

   $-6 + 3x - \frac{1}{2}x - \frac{3}{2} > 0 \Rightarrow \frac{5}{2}x - \frac{15}{2} > 0 \Rightarrow \frac{5}{2}x > \frac{15}{2} \Rightarrow x > 3 \Rightarrow (3, \infty)$. In set-builder notation the interval is $\{x \mid x > 3\}$.

   (c) $-3(2 - x) - \frac{1}{2}x - \frac{3}{2} \le 0$ when $x \le 3$; symbolically, $-3(2 - x) - \frac{1}{2}x - \frac{3}{2} \le 0 \Rightarrow$

   $-6 + 3x - \frac{1}{2}x - \frac{3}{2} \le 0 \Rightarrow \frac{5}{2}x - \frac{15}{2} \le 0 \Rightarrow \frac{5}{2}x \le \frac{15}{2} \Rightarrow x \le 3 \Rightarrow (-\infty, 3]$. In set-builder notation the interval is $\{x \mid x \le 3\}$.

## 2.5: Absolute Value Equations and Inequalities

1. $|x| = 3 \Rightarrow x = 3$ or $x = -3$

2. $|x| \le 3 \Rightarrow -3 \le x \le 3$; $[-3, 3]$

3. $|x| > 3 \Rightarrow x > 3$ or $x < -3$; $(-\infty, -3) \cup (3, \infty)$

4. $|ax + b| \le -2$ compared to form $|ax + b| \le k \Rightarrow k = -2$; $k < 0$. Thus, the absolute value equation has no solutions.

5. The graph of $y = |ax + b|$ is V-shaped with the vertex on the $x$-axis.

6. $|ax + b| = 0 \Rightarrow ax + b = 0 \Rightarrow ax = -b \Rightarrow x = -\frac{b}{a}$.

7. $\sqrt{36a^2} = |6a|$ since 36 and $a^2$ are always positive values.

8. $\sqrt{(ax + b)^2} = |ax + b|$ since $(ax + b)^2$ is always a positive value.

9. (a) $x + 1 = 0 \Rightarrow x = -1 \Rightarrow$ the vertex is $(-1, 0)$. Find any other point, $x = 0 \Rightarrow (0, 1)$; graph the absolute value graph with the vertex $(-1, 0)$, point $(0, 1)$ and its reflection through $x = -1$. See Figure 9.

   (b) $y = |x + 1|$ is increasing on $x \geq -1$ or $[-1, \infty)$ and decreasing on $x \leq -1$ or $(-\infty, -1]$.

10. (a) $1 - x = 0 \Rightarrow -x = -1 \Rightarrow$ the vertex is $(1, 0)$. Find another point such as $(0, 1)$, graph the absolute value function. See Figure 10.

    (b) $y = |1 - x|$ is increasing on $x \geq 1$ or $[1, \infty)$ and decreasing on $x \leq 1$ or $(-\infty, 1]$.

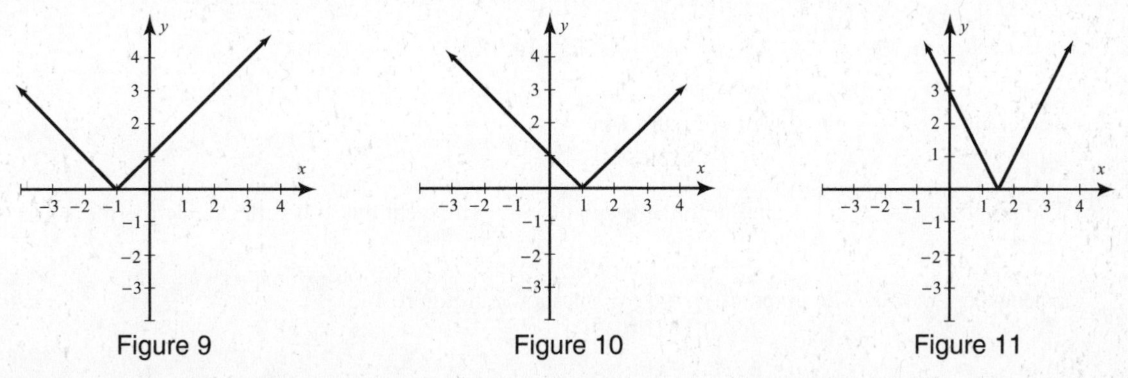


Figure 9 Figure 10 Figure 11

11. (a) $2x - 3 = 0 \Rightarrow 2x = 3 \Rightarrow x = \frac{3}{2} \Rightarrow$ the vertex is $\left(\frac{3}{2}, 0\right)$. Find another point such as $(0, 3)$; graph the absolute value function. See Figure 11.

    (b) $y = |2x - 3|$ is increasing on $x \geq \frac{3}{2}$ or $\left[\frac{3}{2}, \infty\right)$ and decreasing on $x \leq \frac{3}{2}$ or $\left(-\infty, \frac{3}{2}\right]$.

12. (a) $\frac{1}{2}x + 1 = 0 \Rightarrow \frac{1}{2}x = -1 \Rightarrow x = -2 \Rightarrow$ the vertex is $(-2, 0)$. Find another point such as $(0, 1)$; graph the absolute value function. See Figure 12.

    (b) $y = \left|\frac{1}{2}x + 1\right|$ is increasing on $x \geq -2$ or $[-2, \infty)$ and decreasing on $x \leq -2$ or $(-\infty, -2]$.

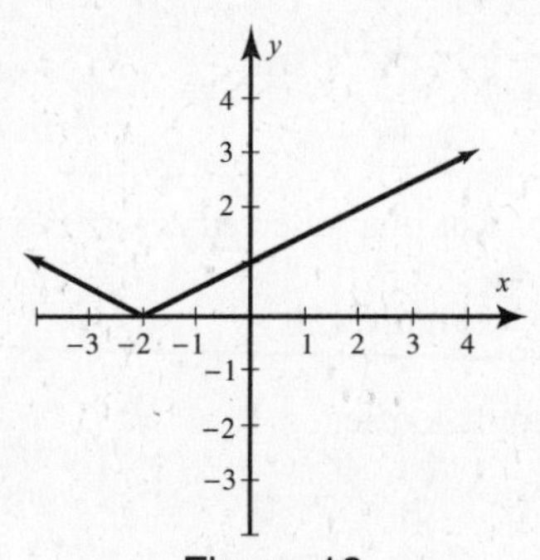


Figure 12

13. (a) The graph of $y_1 = 2x$ is shown in Figure 13a.

(b) The graph of $y = |2x|$ is similar to the graph of $y = 2x$ except that it is reflected across the $x$-axis whenever $2x < 0$. The graph of $y_1 = |2x|$ is shown in Figure 13b.

(c) The $x$-intercept occurs when $2x = 0$ or when $x = 0$. The $x$-intercept is 0.

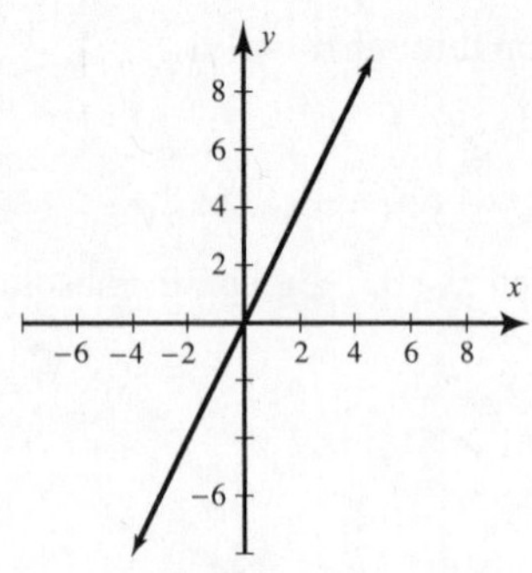

Figure 13a

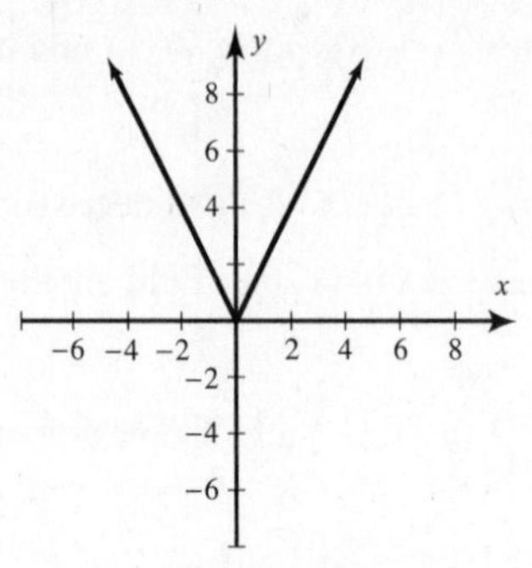

Figure 13b

14. (a) The graph of $y_1 = \frac{1}{2}x$ is shown in Figure 14a.

(b) The graph of $y = \left|\frac{1}{2}x\right|$ is similar to the graph of $y = \frac{1}{2}x$ except that it is reflected across the $x$-axis whenever $\frac{1}{2}x < 0$. The graph of $y_1 = \left|\frac{1}{2}x\right|$ is shown in Figure 14b.

(c) The $x$-intercept occurs when $\frac{1}{2}x = 0$ or when $x = 0$. The $x$-intercept is located at 0.

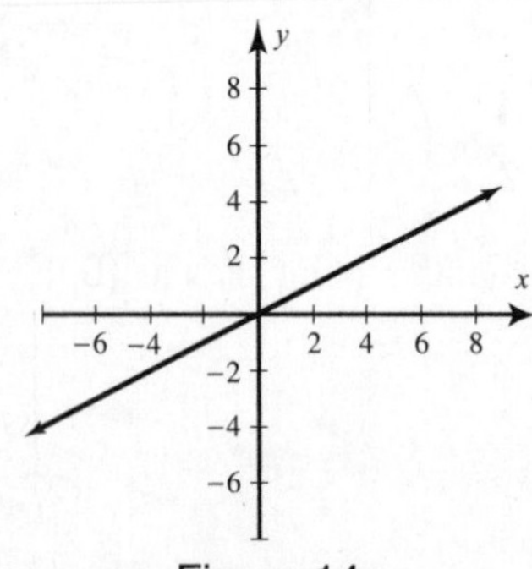

Figure 14a

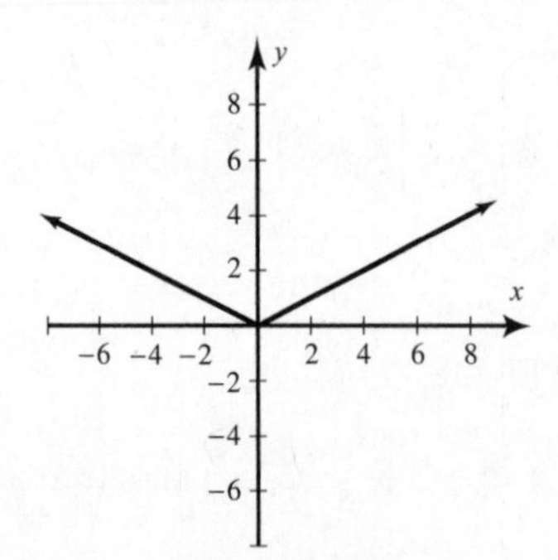

Figure 14b

15. (a) The graph of $y_1 = 3x - 3$ is shown in Figure 15a.

(b) The graph of $y = |3x - 3|$ is similar to the graph of $y = 3x - 3$ except that it is reflected across the $x$-axis whenever $3x - 3 < 0$ or $x < 1$. The graph of $y_1 = |3x - 3|$ is shown in Figure 15b.

(c) The $x$-intercept occurs when $3x - 3 = 0$ or when $x = 1$. The $x$-intercept is located at 1.

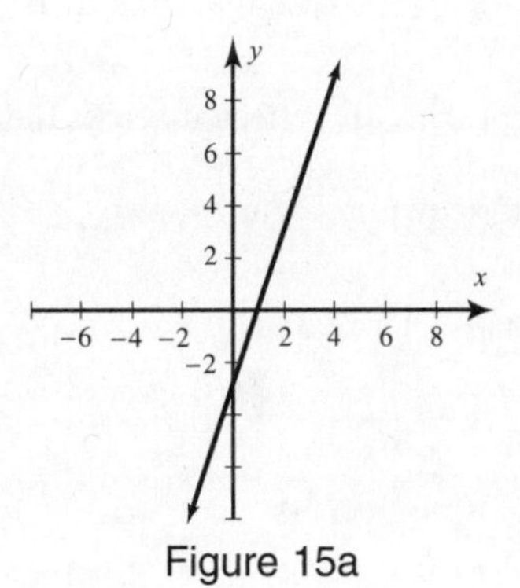


Figure 15a

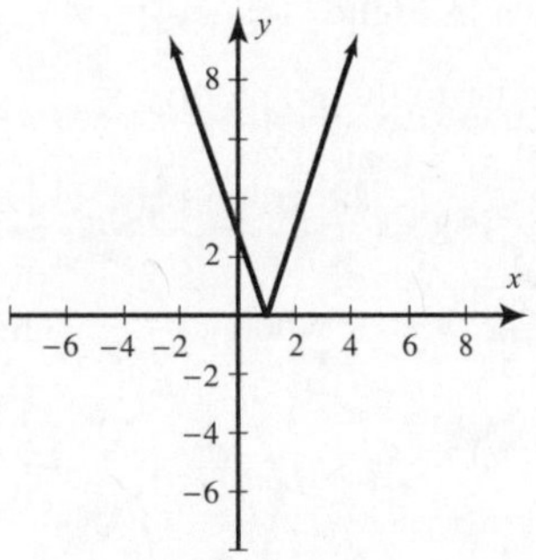

Figure 15b

16. (a) The graph of $y_1 = 2x - 4$ is shown in Figure 16a.

(b) The graph of $y = |2x - 4|$ is similar to the graph of $y = 2x - 4$ except that it is reflected across the $x$-axis whenever $2x - 4 < 0$ or $x < 2$. The graph of $y_1 = |2x - 4|$ is shown in Figure 16b.

(c) The $x$-intercept occurs when $2x - 4 = 0$ or when $x = 2$. The $x$-intercept is located at 2.

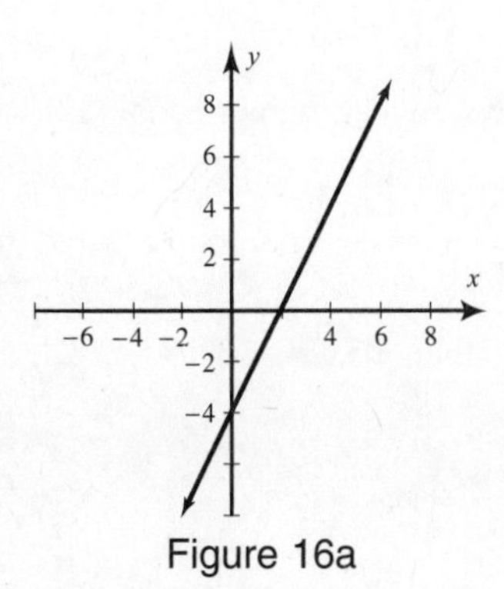


Figure 16a

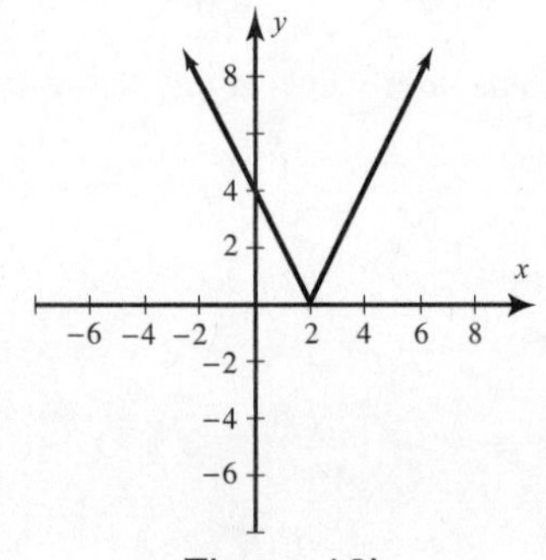


Figure 16b

17. (a) The graph of $y_1 = 6 - 2x$ is shown in Figure 17a.

(b) The graph of $y = |6 - 2x|$ is similar to the graph of $y = 6 - 2x$ except that it is reflected across the $x$-axis whenever $6 - 2x < 0$ or $x > 3$. The graph of $y_1 = |6 - 2x|$ is shown in Figure 17b.

(c) The $x$-intercept occurs when $6 - 2x = 0$ or when $x = 3$. The $x$-intercept is located at 3.

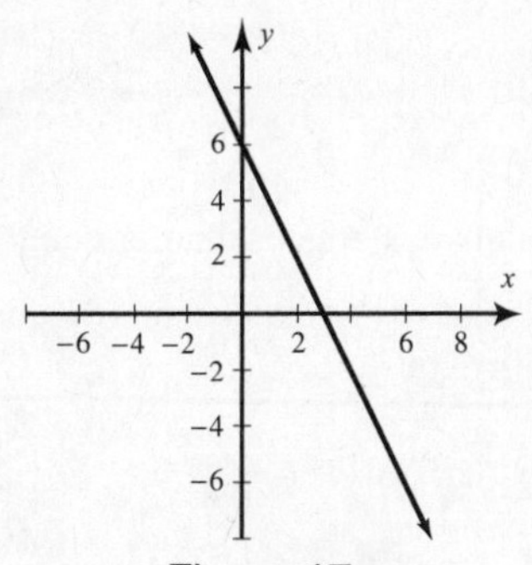


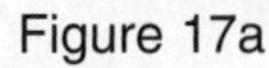

Figure 17a

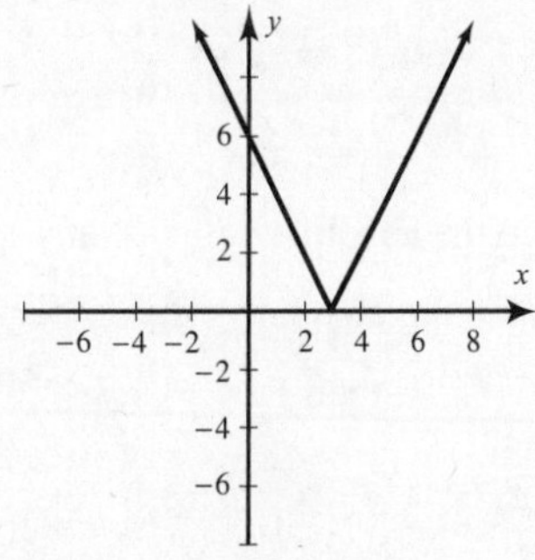


Figure 17b

18. (a) The graph of $y_1 = 2 - 4x$ is shown in Figure 18a.

(b) The graph of $y = |2 - 4x|$ is similar to the graph of $y = 2 - 4x$ except that it is reflected across the $x$-axis whenever $2 - 4x < 0$ or $x > \frac{1}{2}$. The graph of $y_1 = |2 - 4x|$ is shown in Figure 18b.

(c) The $x$-intercept occurs when $2 - 4x = 0$ or when $x = \frac{1}{2}$. The $x$-intercept is located at $\frac{1}{2}$.

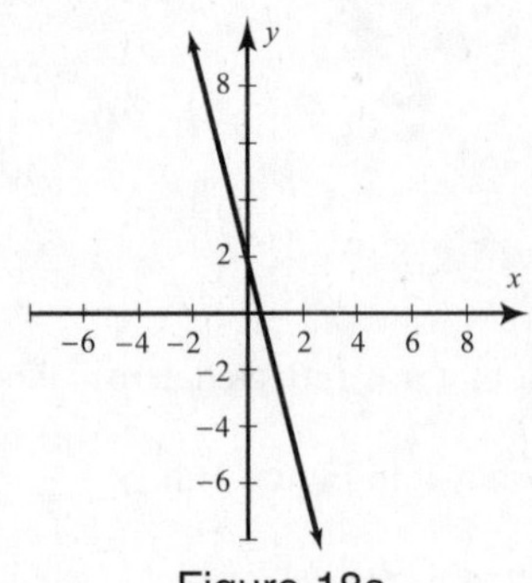

Figure 18a

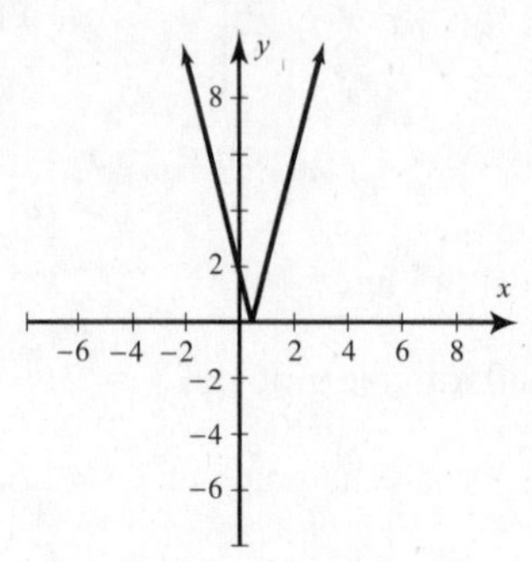

Figure 18b

19. $|-2x| = 4 \Rightarrow -2x = 4$ or $-2x = -4 \Rightarrow 2x = -4$ or $2x = 4 \Rightarrow x = -2$ or $2$

20. $|3x| = -6$ has no solutions since the absolute value of any quantity is always greater than or equal to 0.

21. $|5x - 7| = 2 \Rightarrow 5x - 7 = -2$ or $5x - 7 = 2$. If $5x - 7 = -2$, then $5x = 5 \Rightarrow x = 1$;

If $5x - 7 = 2$, then $5x = 9 \Rightarrow x = \frac{9}{5}$; $1, \frac{9}{5}$.

22. $|-3x - 2| = 5 \Rightarrow -3x - 2 = -5$ or $-3x - 2 = 5$. If $-3x - 2 = -5$, then $-3x = -3 \Rightarrow x = 1$;

If $-3x - 2 = 5$ then $-3x = 7 \Rightarrow x = -\frac{7}{3}$; $-\frac{7}{3}, 1$.

23. $|3 - 4x| = 5 \Rightarrow 3 - 4x = -5$ or $3 - 4x = 5$. If $3 - 4x = -5$, then $-4x = -8 \Rightarrow x = 2$;

If $3 - 4x = 5$ then $-4x = 2 \Rightarrow x = -\frac{1}{2}$; $-\frac{1}{2}, 2$.

24. $|2 - 3x| = 1 \Rightarrow 2 - 3x = -1$ or $2 - 3x = 1$. If $2 - 3x = -1$, then $-3x = -3 \Rightarrow x = 1$;

If $2 - 3x = 1$, then $-3x = -1 \Rightarrow x = \frac{1}{3}$; $\frac{1}{3}, 1$.

25. $|-6x - 2| = 0 \Rightarrow -6x - 2 = 0 \Rightarrow -6x = 2 \Rightarrow x = -\frac{1}{3}$.

26. $|6x - 9| = 0 \Rightarrow 6x - 9 = 0 \Rightarrow 6x = 9 \Rightarrow x = \frac{3}{2}$.

27. $|7 - 16x| = 0 \Rightarrow 7 - 16x = 0 \Rightarrow 7 = 16x \Rightarrow x = \frac{7}{16}$.

28. $|-x - 4| = 0 \Rightarrow -x - 4 = 0 \Rightarrow -4 = x \Rightarrow x = -4$.

29. $|17x - 6| = -3$ has no solutions since the absolute value of any quantity is always greater than or equal to 0.

30. $|-8x - 11| = -7$ has no solutions since the absolute value of any quantity is always greater than or equal to 0.

31. $|1.2x - 1.7| - 1 = 3 \Rightarrow |1.2x - 1.7| = 4$, then $1.2x - 1.7 = -4$ or $1.2x - 1.7 = 4$.

If $1.2x - 1.7 = -4$ then, $1.2x = -2.3 \Rightarrow x = -\frac{2.3}{1.2} \Rightarrow x = -\frac{23}{12}$; if $1.2x - 1.7 = 4$ then

$1.2x = 5.7 \Rightarrow x = \frac{5.7}{1.2} \Rightarrow x = \frac{19}{4}$; $\Rightarrow -\frac{23}{12}, \frac{19}{4}$.

32. $|3 - 3x| - 2 = 2 \Rightarrow |3 - 3x| = 4$, then $3 - 3x = -4$ or $3 - 3x = 4$. If $3 - 3x = -4$ then $-3x = -7 \Rightarrow x = \frac{7}{3}$; if $3 - 3x = 4$ then $-3x = 1 \Rightarrow x = -\frac{1}{3} \Rightarrow -\frac{1}{3}, \frac{7}{3}$.

33. $|4x - 5| + 3 = 2 \Rightarrow |4x - 5| = -1$ has no solution since the absolute value of any quantity is always greater than or equal to 0.

34. $|4.5 - 2x| + 1.1 = 9.7 \Rightarrow |4.5 - 2x| = 8.6 \Rightarrow 4.5 - 2x = -8.6$ or $4.5 - 2x = 8.6 \Rightarrow$ $x = -2.05, 6.55$

35. $|2x - 9| = |8 - 3x| \Rightarrow 2x - 9 = 8 - 3x$ or $2x - 9 = -(8 - 3x) \Rightarrow$ $2x + 3x = 8 + 9$ or $2x - 3x = -8 + 9 \Rightarrow 5x = 17$ or $-x = 1 \Rightarrow x = \frac{17}{5}, -1$

36. $|x - 3| = |8 - x| \Rightarrow x - 3 = 8 - x$ or $x - 3 = -(8 - x) \Rightarrow$ $x + x = 8 + 3$ or $x - x = -8 + 3 \Rightarrow 2x = 11$ or $0 = -5 \Rightarrow x = \frac{11}{2}$

37. $\left|\frac{3}{4}x - \frac{1}{4}\right| = \left|\frac{3}{4} - \frac{1}{4}x\right| \Rightarrow \frac{3}{4}x - \frac{1}{4} = \frac{3}{4} - \frac{1}{4}x$ or $\frac{3}{4}x - \frac{1}{4} = -\left(\frac{3}{4} - \frac{1}{4}x\right) \Rightarrow$ $\frac{3}{4}x + \frac{1}{4}x = \frac{3}{4} + \frac{1}{4}$ or $\frac{3}{4}x - \frac{1}{4}x = -\frac{3}{4} + \frac{1}{4} \Rightarrow x = 1$ or $\frac{1}{2}x = -\frac{1}{2} \Rightarrow x = -1, 1$

38. $\left|\frac{1}{2}x + \frac{3}{2}\right| = \left|\frac{3}{2}x - \frac{7}{2}\right| \Rightarrow \frac{1}{2}x + \frac{3}{2} = \frac{3}{2}x - \frac{7}{2}$ or $\frac{1}{2}x + \frac{3}{2} = -\left(\frac{3}{2}x - \frac{7}{2}\right) \Rightarrow$ $\frac{1}{2}x + \frac{3}{2} = \frac{3}{2}x - \frac{7}{2} \Rightarrow -x = -5 \Rightarrow x = 5$ or $\frac{1}{2}x + \frac{3}{2} = -\left(\frac{3}{2}x - \frac{7}{2}\right) \Rightarrow \frac{1}{2}x + \frac{3}{2} = -\frac{3}{2}x + \frac{7}{2} \Rightarrow$ $2x = 2 \Rightarrow x = 1 \Rightarrow x = 1, 5$

39. $\left|15x - 5\right| = \left|35 - 5x\right| \Rightarrow 15x - 5 = 35 - 5x$ or $15x - 5 = -(35 - 5x) \Rightarrow$ $15x - 5 = 35 - 5x \Rightarrow 20x = 40 \Rightarrow x = 2$ or $15x - 5 = -(35 - 5x) \Rightarrow 15x - 5 = -35 + 5x \Rightarrow$ $10x = -30 \Rightarrow x = -3 \Rightarrow x = -3$ or $2$

40. $|20x - 40| = |80 - 20x| \Rightarrow 20x - 40 = 80 - 20x$ or $20x - 40 = -(80 - 20x) \Rightarrow$ $20x + 20x = 80 + 40 \Rightarrow 40x = 120 \Rightarrow x = 3$; $20x - 20x = -80 + 40 \Rightarrow 0 = -40 \Rightarrow x = 3$

41. (a) $f(x) = g(x)$ when $x = -1$ or $7$.

(b) $f(x) < g(x)$ between these $x$-values or when $-1 < x < 7$; $(-1, 7)$

(c) $f(x) > g(x)$ outside of these $x$-values or when $x < -1$ or $x > 7$; $(-\infty, -1) \cup (7, \infty)$

42. (a) $f(x) = g(x)$ when $x = -4$ or $8$.

(b) $f(x) \le g(x)$ between and including these $x$-values or when $-4 \le x \le 8$; $[-4, 8]$

(c) $f(x) \ge g(x)$ outside of and including these $x$-values or when $x \le -4$ or $x \ge 8$; $(-\infty, -4] \cup [8, \infty)$

43. (a) $|2x - 3| = 1 \Rightarrow 2x - 3 = 1$ or $2x - 3 = -1$. If $2x - 3 = 1$, then $2x = 4 \Rightarrow x = 2$; If $2x - 3 = -1$ then $2x = 2 \Rightarrow x = 1$; $x = 1$ or $x = 2$

(b) $|2x - 3| < 1 \Rightarrow -1 < 2x - 3 < 1 \Rightarrow 2 < 2x < 4 \Rightarrow 1 < x < 2$; $(1, 2)$

(c) $|2x - 3| > 1 \Rightarrow 2x - 3 > 1$ or $2x - 3 < -1$. If $2x - 3 > 1$, then $2x > 4 \Rightarrow x > 2$. If $2x - 3 < -1$, then $2x < 2 \Rightarrow x < 1$. $x < 1$ or $x > 2$ or $(-\infty, 1) \cup (2, \infty)$

44. (a) $|5 - x| = 2 \Rightarrow 5 - x = 2$ or $5 - x = -2$. If $5 - x = 2$ then $-x = -3 \Rightarrow x = 3$. Or if

$5 - x = -2$ then $-x = -7 \Rightarrow x = 7$. $x = 3$ or $x = 7$.

(b) $|5 - x| \le 2 \Rightarrow -2 \le 5 - x \le 2 \Rightarrow -7 \le -x \le -3 \Rightarrow 7 \ge x \ge 3 \Rightarrow 3 \le x \le 7$; $[3, 7]$

(c) $|5 - x| \ge 2 \Rightarrow 5 - x \ge 2$ or $5 - x \le -2$. If $5 - x \ge 2$, then $-x \ge -3 \Rightarrow x \le 3$.

If $5 - x \le -2$, then $-x \le -7 \Rightarrow x \ge 7$; $x \le 3$ or $x \ge 7$; $(-\infty, 3] \cup [7, \infty)$

45. (a) Graph $Y_1 = \text{abs}(2X - 5)$ and $Y_2 = 10$. See Figures 45a and 45b. The solutions are $-2.5$ and $7.5$.

(b) Table $Y_1 = \text{abs}(2X - 5)$ starting at –5, incrementing by 2.5. See Figure 45c. The solutions are $-2.5$ and $7.5$.

(c) $|2x - 5| = 10 \Rightarrow 2x - 5 = -10$ or $2x - 5 = 10 \Rightarrow x = -\frac{5}{2}$ or $\frac{15}{2}$

From each method, the solution to $|2x - 5| < 10$ lies between –2.5 and 7.5, exclusively: $-2.5 < x < 7.5$

or $\left(-\frac{5}{2}, \frac{15}{2}\right)$.

[–10, 10, 1] by [–5, 15, 1]

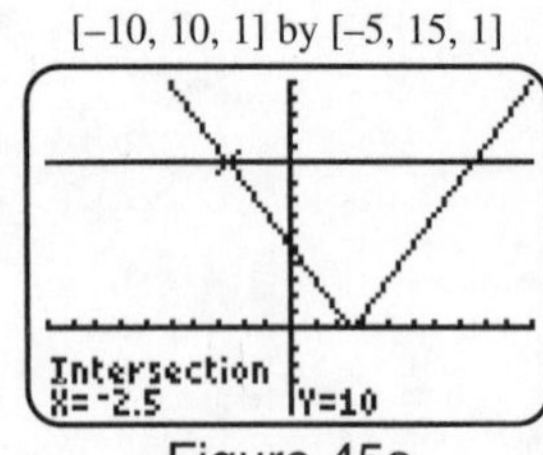

Figure 45a

[–10, 10, 1] by [–5, 15, 1]

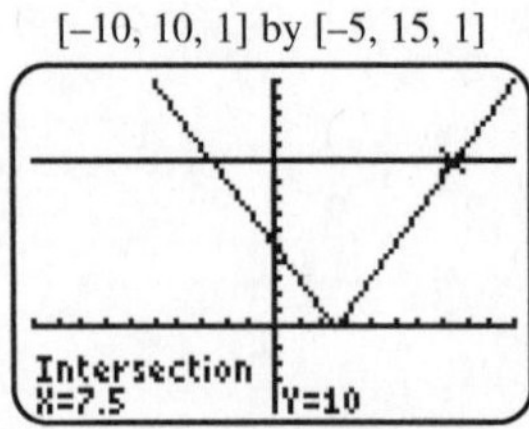

Figure 45b

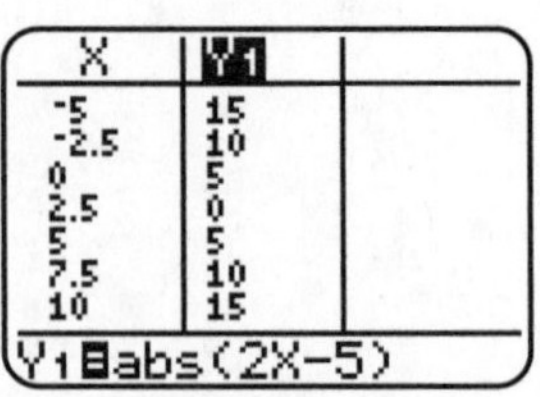

| X | Y1 |
|---|---|
| -5 | 15 |
| -2.5 | 10 |
| 0 | 5 |
| 2.5 | 0 |
| 5 | 5 |
| 7.5 | 10 |
| 10 | 15 |

Y1=abs(2X-5)

Figure 45c

46. (a) Graph $Y_1 = \text{abs}(3X - 4)$ and $Y_2 = 8$. See Figures 46a and 46b. The solutions are $-\frac{4}{3}$ and 4.

(b) Table $Y_1 = \text{abs}(3X - 4)$ starting at $-\frac{8}{3}$, incrementing by $\frac{4}{3}$. See Figure 46c. The solutions are $-\frac{4}{3}$ and 4.

(c) $|3x - 4| = 8 \Rightarrow 3x - 4 = -8$ or $3x - 4 = 8 \Rightarrow x = -\frac{4}{3}$ or 4

From each method, the solution to $|3x - 4| \le 8$ lies between $-\frac{4}{3}$ and 4, inclusively: $-\frac{4}{3} \le x \le 4$ or

$\left[-\frac{4}{3}, 4\right]$.

[–10, 10, 1] by [–5, 15, 1]

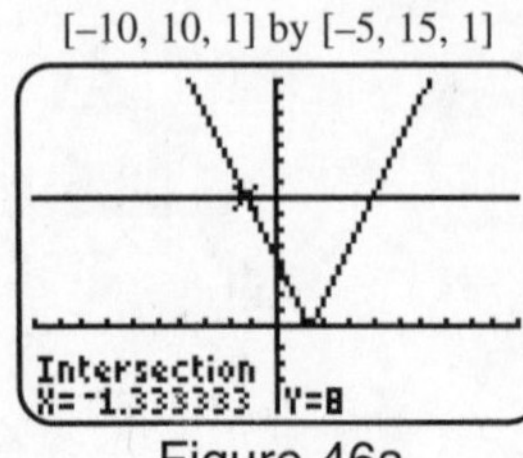

Figure 46a

[–10, 10, 1] by [–5, 15, 1]

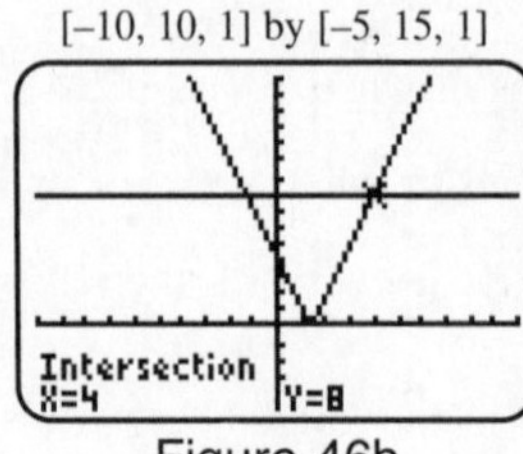

Figure 46b

| X | Y1 |
|---|---|
| -2.667 | 12 |
| -1.333 | 8 |
| 0 | 4 |
| 1.3333 | 0 |
| 2.6667 | 4 |
| 4 | 8 |
| 5.3333 | 12 |

Y1=abs(3X-4)

Figure 46c

47. (a) Graph $Y_1 = \text{abs}(5 - 3X)$ and $Y_2 = 2$. See Figures 47a and 47b. The solutions are 1 and $\frac{7}{3}$.

(b) Table $Y_1 = \text{abs}(5 - 3X)$ starting at $-\frac{1}{3}$, incrementing by $\frac{2}{3}$. See Figure 47c. The solutions are 1 and $\frac{7}{3}$.

(c) $|5 - 3x| = 2 \Rightarrow 5 - 3x = -2$ or $5 - 3x = 2 \Rightarrow x = \frac{7}{3}$ or 1

From each method, the solution to $|5 - 3x| > 2$ lies outside of 1 and $\frac{7}{3}$, exclusively: $x < 1$ or $x > \frac{7}{3}$ or $(-\infty, 1) \cup \left(\frac{7}{3}, \infty\right)$.

[-1, 4, 1] by [-1, 3, 1]

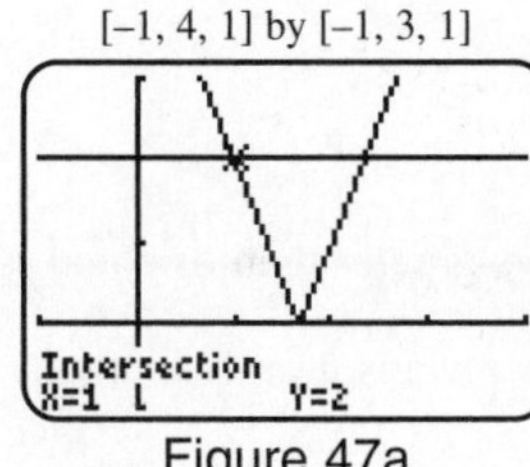


Figure 47a

[-1, 4, 1] by [-1, 3, 1]

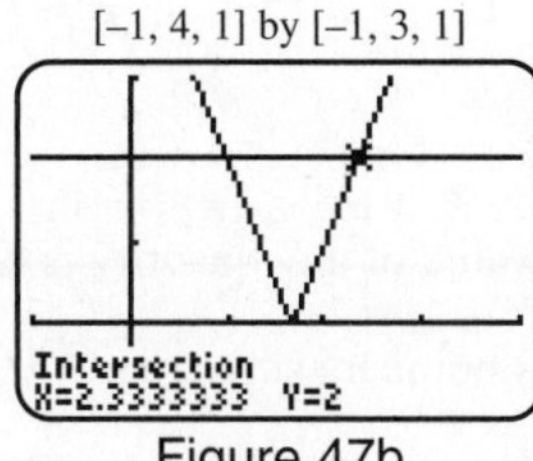


Figure 47b

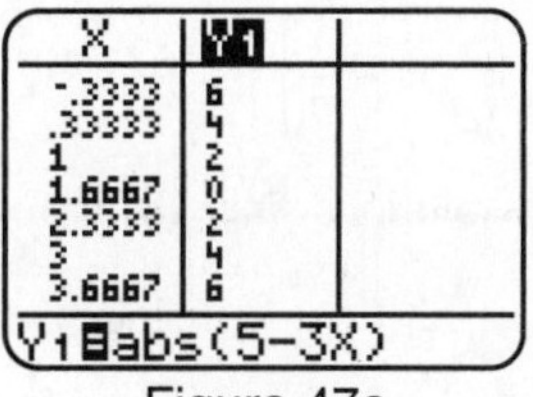

| X | Y1 |
|---|---|
| -.3333 | 6 |
| .33333 | 4 |
| 1 | 2 |
| 1.6667 | 0 |
| 2.3333 | 2 |
| 3 | 4 |
| 3.6667 | 6 |

Y1=abs(5-3X)

Figure 47c

48. (a) Graph $Y_1 = \text{abs}(4X - 7)$ and $Y_2 = 5$. See Figures 48a and 48b. The solutions are 0.5 and 3.

(b) Table $Y_1 = \text{abs}(4X - 7)$ starting at –2, incrementing by 1.25. See Figure 48c. The solutions are 0.5 and 3.

(c) $|4x - 7| = 5 \Rightarrow 4x - 7 = -5$ or $4x - 7 = 5 \Rightarrow x = \frac{1}{2}$ or 3

From each method, the solution to $|4x - 7| \geq 5$ lies outside of $\frac{1}{2}$ and 3, inclusively: $x \leq \frac{1}{2}$ or $x \geq 3$ or $\left(-\infty, \frac{1}{2}\right] \cup [3, \infty]$.

[-1, 4, 1] by [-3, 7, 1]

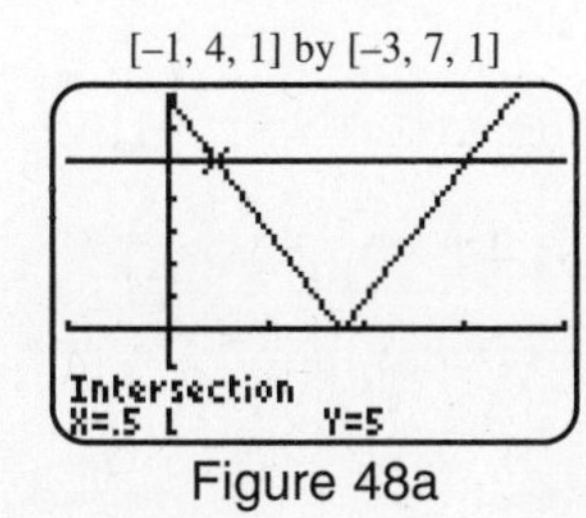


Figure 48a

[-1, 4, 1] by [-3, 7, 1]

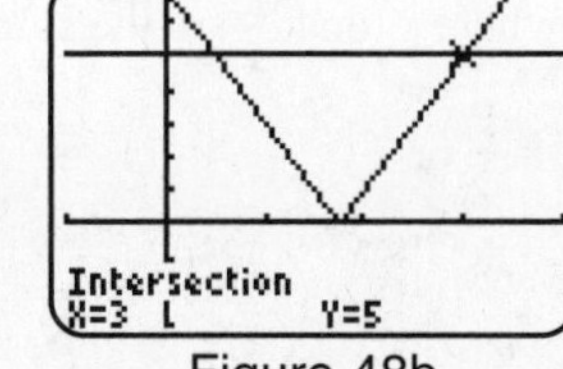


Figure 48b

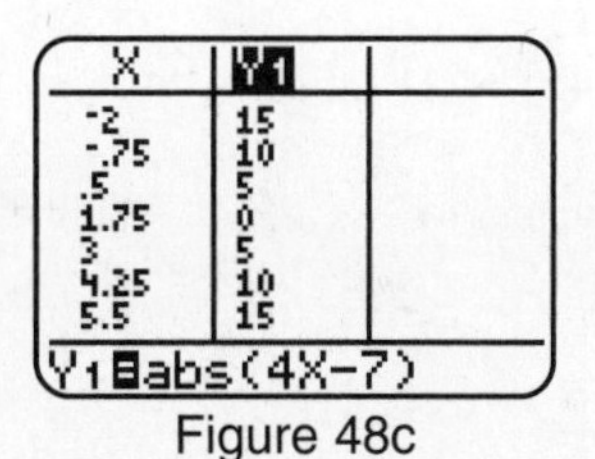

| X | Y1 |
|---|---|
| -2 | 15 |
| -.75 | 10 |
| .5 | 5 |
| 1.75 | 0 |
| 3 | 5 |
| 4.25 | 10 |
| 5.5 | 15 |

Y1=abs(4X-7)

Figure 48c

49. $|2.1x - 0.7| = 2.4 \Rightarrow 2.1x - 0.7 = -2.4$ or $2.1x - 0.7 = 2.4 \Rightarrow x = -\frac{17}{21}$ or $\frac{31}{21}$

The solution to $|2.1x - 0.7| \geq 2.4$ lies outside of $-\frac{17}{21}$ and $\frac{31}{21}$, inclusively: $x \leq -\frac{17}{21}$ or $x \geq \frac{31}{21}$ or $\left(-\infty, -\frac{17}{21}\right] \cup \left[\frac{31}{21}, \infty\right)$.

50. $\left|\frac{1}{2}x - \frac{3}{4}\right| = \frac{7}{4} \Rightarrow \frac{1}{2}x - \frac{3}{4} = -\frac{7}{4}$ or $\frac{1}{2}x - \frac{3}{4} = \frac{7}{4} \Rightarrow x = -2$ or 5

The solution to $\left|\frac{1}{2}x - \frac{3}{4}\right| \leq \frac{7}{4}$ lies between –2 and 5, inclusively: $-2 \leq x \leq 5$ or $[-2, 5]$.

51. $|3x| + 5 = 6 \Rightarrow |3x| = 1 \Rightarrow 3x = -1$ or $3x = 1 \Rightarrow x = -\frac{1}{3}$ or $\frac{1}{3}$.

The solution to $|3x| + 5 > 6$ lies outside of $-\frac{1}{3}$ and $\frac{1}{3}$, exclusively: $x < -\frac{1}{3}, x > \frac{1}{3}$,

$\left(-\infty, -\frac{1}{3}\right) \cup \left(\frac{1}{3}, \infty\right)$.

52. $|x| - 10 = 25 \Rightarrow |x| = 35 \Rightarrow x = -35$ or $35$.

The solution to $|x| - 10 < 25$ lies between –35 and 35, exclusively: $-35 < x < 35$ or $(-35, 35)$.

53. $\left|\frac{2}{3}x - \frac{1}{2}\right| = -\frac{1}{4}$ has no solutions since the absolute value of any quantity is always greater than or equal to 0.

There are no solutions to $\left|\frac{2}{3}x - \frac{1}{2}\right| \le -\frac{1}{4}$.

54. $|5x - 0.3| = -4$ has no solutions since the absolute value of any quantity is always greater than or equal to 0.

The solution set for $|5x - 0.3| > -4$ includes all real numbers since $|5x - 0.3|$ is always greater than any negative value.

55. The solutions to $|3x - 1| < 8$ satisfy $s_1 < x < s_2$ where $s_1$ and $s_2$, are the solutions to $|3x - 1| = 8$.

$|3x - 1| = 8$ is equivalent to $3x - 1 = -8 \Rightarrow x = -\frac{7}{3}$ or $3x - 1 = 8 \Rightarrow x = 3$.

The interval is $\left(-\frac{7}{3}, 3\right)$.

56. The solutions to $|15 - x| < 7$ satisfy $s_1 < x < s_2$, where $s_1$ and $s_2$ are the solutions to $|15 - x| = 7$.

$|15 - x| = 7$ is equivalent to $15 - x = -7 \Rightarrow x = 22$ or $15 - x = 7 \Rightarrow x = 8$.

The interval is $(8, 22)$.

57. The solutions to $|7 - 4x| \le 11$ satisfy $s_1 \le x \le s_2$, where $s_1$ and $s_2$ are the solutions to $|7 - 4x| = 11$.

$|7 - 4x| = 11$ is equivalent to $7 - 4x = -11 \Rightarrow x = \frac{9}{2}$ or $7 - 4x = 11 \Rightarrow x = -1$.

The interval is $\left[-1, \frac{9}{2}\right]$.

58. The solutions to $|-3x + 1| \le 5$ satisfy $s_1 \le x \le s_2$, where $s_1$ and $s_2$ are the solutions to $|-3x + 1| = 5$.

$|-3x + 1| = 5$ is equivalent to $-3x + 1 = -5 \Rightarrow x = 2$ or $-3x + 1 = 5 \Rightarrow x = -\frac{4}{3}$.

The interval is $\left[-\frac{4}{3}, 2\right]$.

59. The solutions to $|0.5x - 0.75| < 2$ satisfy $s_1 < x < s_2$, where $s_1$ and $s_2$ are the solutions to $|0.5x - 0.75| = 2$.

$|0.5x - 0.75| = 2$ is equivalent to $0.5x - 0.75 = -2 \Rightarrow x = -\frac{5}{2}$ or $0.5x - 0.75 = 2 \Rightarrow x = \frac{11}{2}$.

The interval is $\left(-\frac{5}{2}, \frac{11}{2}\right)$.

60. The solutions to $|2.1x - 5| \le 8$ satisfy $s_1 \le x \le s_2$, where $s_1$ and $s_2$ are the solutions to $|2.1x - 5| = 8$.

$|2.1x - 5| = 8$ is equivalent to $2.1x - 5 = -8 \Rightarrow x = -\frac{10}{7}$ or $2.1x - 5 = 8 \Rightarrow x = \frac{130}{21}$.

The interval is $\left[-\frac{10}{7}, \frac{130}{21}\right]$.

61. The solutions to $|2x - 3| > 1$ satisfy $x < s_1$ or $x > s_2$, where $s_1$ and $s_2$ are the solutions to $|2x - 3| = 1$.

$|2x - 3| = 1$ is equivalent to $2x - 3 = -1 \Rightarrow x = 1$ or $2x - 3 = 1 \Rightarrow x = 2$.

The solution set is $(-\infty, 1) \cup (2, \infty)$.

62. The solutions to $|5x - 7| > 2$ satisfy $x < s_1$ or $x > s_2$, where $s_1$ and $s_2$ are the solutions to $|5x - 7| = 2$.

$|5x - 7| = 2$ is equivalent to $5x - 7 = -2 \Rightarrow x = 1$ or $5x - 7 = 2 \Rightarrow x = \frac{9}{5}$.

The solution set is $(-\infty, 1) \cup \left(\frac{9}{5}, \infty\right)$.

63. The solutions to $|-3x + 8| \ge 3$ satisfy $x \le s_1$ or $x \ge s_2$, where $s_1$ and $s_2$ are the solutions to $|-3x + 8| = 3$.

$|-3x + 8| = 3$ is equivalent to $-3x + 8 = -3 \Rightarrow x = \frac{11}{3}$ or $-3x + 8 = 3 \Rightarrow x = \frac{5}{3}$.

The solution set is $\left(-\infty, \frac{5}{3}\right] \cup \left[\frac{11}{3}, \infty\right)$.

64. The solutions to $|-7x - 3| \ge 5$ satisfy $x \le s_1$ or $x \ge s_2$, where $s_1$ and $s_2$ are the solutions to $|-7x - 3| = 5$.

$|-7x - 3| = 5$ is equivalent to $-7x - 3 = -5 \Rightarrow x = \frac{2}{7}$ or $-7x - 3 = 5 \Rightarrow x = -\frac{8}{7}$.

The solution set is $\left(-\infty, -\frac{8}{7}\right] \cup \left[\frac{2}{7}, \infty\right)$.

65. The solutions to $|0.25x - 1| > 3$ satisfy $x < s_1$ or $x > s_2$, where $s_1$ and $s_2$ are the solutions to $|0.25x - 1| = 3$.

$|0.25x - 1| = 3$ is equivalent to $0.25x - 1 = -3 \Rightarrow x = -8$ or $0.25x - 1 = 3 \Rightarrow x = 16$.

The solution set is $(-\infty, -8) \cup (16, \infty)$.

66. The solutions to $|-0.5x + 5| \ge 4$ satisfy $x \le s_1$ or $x \ge s_2$, where $s_1$ and $s_2$ are the solutions to $|-0.5x + 5| = 4$.

$|-0.5x + 5| = 4$ is equivalent to $-0.5x + 5 = -4 \Rightarrow x = 18$ or $-0.5x + 5 = 4 \Rightarrow x = 2$.

The solution set is $(-\infty, 2] \cup [18, \infty)$.

67. $|-6| = 6$

68. $|17| = 17$

69. Since the inputs of absolute values can be positive or negative, the domain of $|f(x)|$ is also $[-2, 4]$.

70. Since the inputs of absolute values can be positive or negative, the domain of $|f(x)|$ is also $[-\infty, 0]$.

71. Since all solutions or the range of absolute values must be non-negative, all negative solutions will change to positive solutions; therefore, if the range of $f(x)$ is $(-\infty, 0]$, the range of $|f(x)|$ is $[0, \infty)$.

72. All negative solutions will change to positive solutions; therefore, if the range of $f(x)$ is $(-4, 5)$, the range of $|f(x)|$ is $[0, 5)$.

73. $|S - 57.5| = 17.5 \Rightarrow S - 57.5 = 17.5$ or $S - 57.5 = -17.5$. If $S - 57.5 = 17.5$, then $S = 75$. If $S - 57.5 = -17.5$, then $S = 40$. Therefore, the maximum speed limit is 75 mph and the minimum speed limit is 40 mph.

74. (a) Since the performer wants to land in a net with side length 70, the performer has 35 feet on each side of 180 feet to land safely. Therefore, the performer can travel a maximum of $180 + 35 = 215$ feet or a minimum of $180 - 35 = 145$ feet.

(b) The above scenario can be modeled using $|D - 180| \leq 35$.

75. (a) $0 \leq 80 - 19x \leq 32 \Rightarrow -80 \leq -19x \leq -48 \Rightarrow \frac{80}{19} \geq x \geq \frac{48}{19} \Rightarrow \frac{48}{19} \leq x \leq \frac{80}{19}$. The air temperature is between 0°F and 32°F when the altitudes are between $\frac{48}{19}$ and $\frac{80}{19}$ miles inclusively.

(b) The air temperature is between 0°F and 32°F inclusively when the altitude is within $\frac{16}{19}$ mile of $\frac{64}{19}$ miles. $\left|x - \frac{64}{19}\right| \leq \frac{16}{19}$.

76. (a) $50 \leq 80 - \frac{29}{5}x \leq 60 \Rightarrow -30 \leq -\frac{29}{5}x \leq -20 \Rightarrow \frac{150}{29} \geq x \geq \frac{100}{29} \Rightarrow \frac{100}{29} \leq x \leq \frac{150}{29}$. The dew point is between 50°F and 60°F when the altitudes are between $\frac{100}{29}$ and $\frac{150}{29}$ miles.

(b) The dew point is between 50°F and 60°F inclusively when the altitude is within $\frac{25}{29}$ mile of $\frac{125}{29}$ miles. $\left|x - \frac{125}{29}\right| \leq \frac{25}{29}$.

77. (a) $|T - 43| = 24 \Rightarrow T - 43 = -24$ or $T - 43 = 24 \Rightarrow T = 19$ or $67$. The average monthly temperature range is $19°\text{F} \leq T \leq 67°\text{F}$.

(b) The monthly average temperatures in Marquette vary between a low of 19°F and a high of 67°F. The monthly averages are always within 24° of 43°F.

78. (a) $|T - 62| = 19 \Rightarrow T - 62 = -19$ or $T - 62 = 19 \Rightarrow T = 43$ or $81$. The average monthly temperature range is $43°\text{F} \leq T \leq 81°\text{F}$.

(b) The monthly average temperatures in Memphis vary between a low of 43°F and a high of 81°F. The monthly averages are always within 19° of 62°F.

79. (a) $|T - 50| = 22 \Rightarrow T - 50 = -22$ or $T - 50 = 22 \Rightarrow T = 28$ or $72$. The average monthly temperature range is $28°\text{F} \leq T \leq 72°\text{F}$.

(b) The monthly average temperatures in Boston vary between a low of 28°F and a high of 72°F. The monthly averages are always within 22° of 50°F.

80. (a) $|T - 10| = 36 \Rightarrow T - 10 = -36$ or $T - 10 = 36 \Rightarrow T = -26$ or $46$. The average monthly temperature range is $-26°\text{F} \leq T \leq 46°\text{F}$.

(b) The monthly average temperatures in Chesterfield vary between a low of –26°F and a high of 46°F. The monthly averages are always within 36° of 10°F.

81. (a) $|T - 61.5| = 12.5 \Rightarrow T - 61.5 = -12.5$ or $T - 61.5 = 12.5 \Rightarrow T = 49$ or $74$. The average monthly temperature range is $49°\text{F} \leq T \leq 74°\text{F}$.

(b) The monthly average temperatures in Buenos Aires vary between a low of 49°F and a high of 74°F. The monthly averages are always within 12.5° of 61.5°F.

82. (a) $|T - 43.5| = 8.5 \Rightarrow T - 43.5 = -8.5$ or $T - 43.5 = 8.5 \Rightarrow T = 35$ or $52$. The average monthly temperature range is $35°\text{F} \leq T \leq 52°\text{F}$.

(b) The monthly average temperatures in Punta Arenas vary between a low of 35°F and a high of 52°F. The monthly averages are always within 8.5° of 43.5°F.

83. The solutions to $|d - 3| \leq 0.004$ satisfy $s_1 \leq d \leq s_2$ where $s_1$ and $s_2$ are the solutions to $|d - 3| = 0.004$. $|d - 3| = 0.004$ is equivalent to $d - 3 = -0.004 \Rightarrow d = 2.996$ and $d - 3 = 0.004 \Rightarrow d = 3.004$. The solution set is $\{d | 2.996 \leq d \leq 3.004\}$. The acceptable diameters are from 2.994 and 3.004 inches.

84. (a) $|L - 12| \leq 0.0002$

(b) $-0.0002 \leq L - 12 \leq 0.0002 \Rightarrow 11.9998 \leq L \leq 12.0002$; lengths between 11.9998 and 12.0002 inches are acceptable.

85. $\left|\frac{Q - A}{A}\right| \leq 0.02 \Rightarrow \left|\frac{Q - 35}{35}\right| \leq 0.02$, so $-0.02 \leq \frac{Q - 35}{35} \leq 0.02 \Rightarrow -0.7 \leq Q - 35 \leq 0.7 \Rightarrow$ $34.3 \leq Q \leq 35.7$

86. $\left|\frac{P - 50}{50}\right| \leq 0.04 \Rightarrow |P - 50| \leq 0.04(50)$, then $-2 \leq P - 50 \leq 2 \Rightarrow 48 \leq P \leq 52$; therefore, each side would be $P \div 4 \Rightarrow$ lengths between $\frac{48}{4} = 12$ and $\frac{52}{4} = 13$ feet are acceptable.

## Extended and Discovery Exercises for Section 2.5

1. The distance between points $x$ and $c$ on a number line can be shown by $|x - c|$. This distance is given to be less than some positive value $\delta$. Then $|x - c| < \delta$.

2. The distance between points $f(x)$ and $L$ on a number line can be shown by $|f(x) - L|$. This distance is given to be less than some positive value $\epsilon$. Then $|f(x) - L| < \epsilon$.

## Checking Basic Concepts for Section 2.5

1. $\sqrt{4x^2} = |2x|$

2. $y = |3x - 2|$, then the $x$-value of the vertex is given by $3x - 2 = 0 \Rightarrow 3x = 2 \Rightarrow x = \frac{2}{3}$. Another point is (0, 2). Use symmetry to graph the absolute value function. See Figure 2.

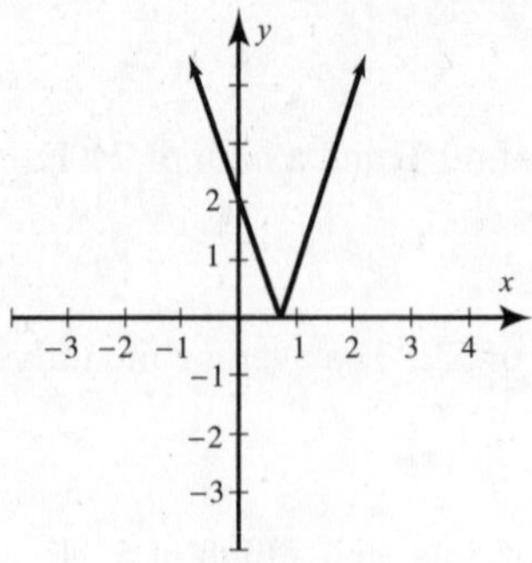

Figure 2

3. (a) Graphically: Graph $Y_1 = \text{abs}(2X - 1)$ and $Y_2 = 5$. Their graphs intersect at the points (–2, 5) and (3,5). The solutions are $-2, 3$. See Figures 3a & 3b.

   Numerically: Table $Y_1 = \text{abs}(2X - 1)$ starting $x$ at –2 and incrementing by 1. The solutions are $-2, 3$. See Figure 3c.

   Symbolically: $|2x - 1| = 5 \Rightarrow 2x - 1 = 5$ or $2x - 1 = -5 \Rightarrow 2x = 6$ or $2x = -4 \Rightarrow x = 3, -2$. The solutions are $-2, 3$.

   (b) The solutions to $|2x - 1| \le 5$ lie between $x = -2$ and $x = 3$, inclusively. Thus, $-2 \le x \le 3$ or $[-2, 3]$. The solutions to $|2x - 1| > 5$ lie left of $x = -2$ or right of $x = 3$. Thus, $x < -2$ or $x > 3$ or $(-\infty, -2) \cup (3, \infty)$.

[–10, 10, 1] by [–10, 10, 1]

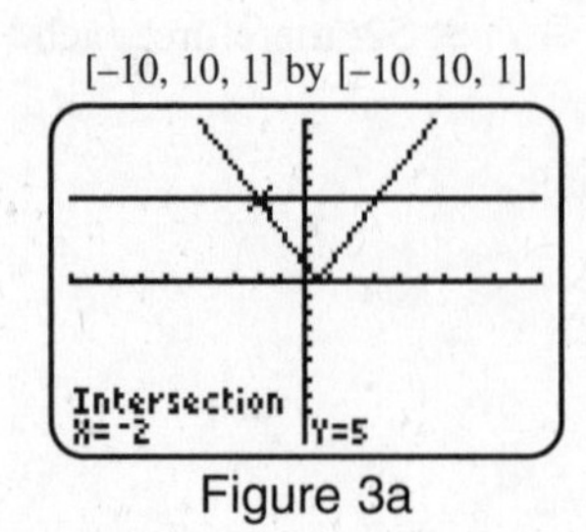

Figure 3a

[–10, 10, 1] by [–10, 10, 1]

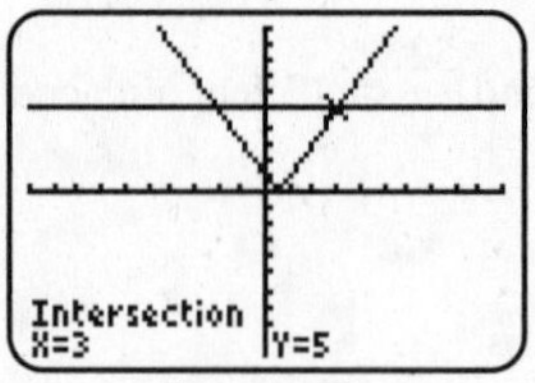

Intersection X=3 Y=5

Figure 3b

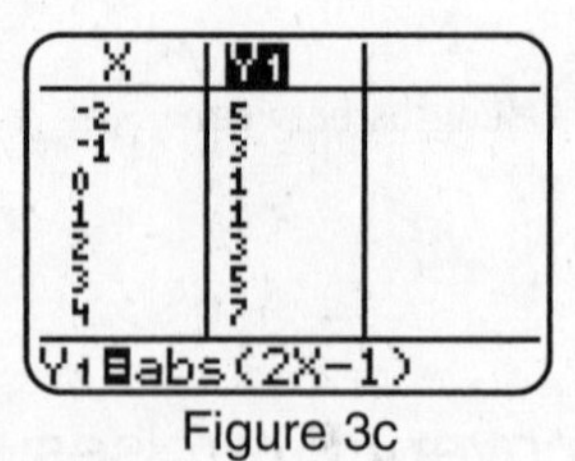

Figure 3c

4. (a) $|2 - 5x| - 4 = -1 \Rightarrow |2 - 5x| = 3 \Rightarrow 2 - 5x = -3$ or $2 - 5x = 3$. If $2 - 5x = -3$, then $-5x = -5 \Rightarrow x = 1$; if $2 - 5x = 3$, then $-5x = 1 \Rightarrow x = -\frac{1}{5} \Rightarrow -\frac{1}{5}, 1$

(b) The solutions to $|3x - 5| \leq 4$ satisfy $s_1 \leq x \leq s_2$ where $s_1$ and $s_2$, are the solutions to $|3x - 5| = 4$. $|3x - 5| = 4$ is equivalent to $3x - 5 = -4 \Rightarrow x = \frac{1}{3}$ or $3x - 5 = 4 \Rightarrow x = 3$.

The solution set is $\left[\frac{1}{3}, 3\right]$.

(c) The solutions to $\left|\frac{1}{2}x - 3\right| > 5$ satisfy $x < s_1$ or $x > s_2$ where $s_1$ and $s_2$, are the solutions to $\left|\frac{1}{2}x - 3\right| = 5$.

$\left|\frac{1}{2}x - 3\right| = 5$ is equivalent to $\frac{1}{2}x - 3 = -5 \Rightarrow x = -4$ or $\frac{1}{2}x - 3 = 5 \Rightarrow x = 16$.

The solution set is $(-\infty, -4) \cup (16, \infty)$.

5. $|x + 1| = |2x| \Rightarrow x + 1 = 2x$ or $x + 1 = -2x$. If $x + 1 = 2x$, then $x = 1$; $x + 1 = -2x \Rightarrow 1 = -3x \Rightarrow x = -\frac{1}{3}$; $-\frac{1}{3}, 1$

## Chapter 2 Review Exercises

1. (a) Using the points (0, 6) and (2, 2), $m = \frac{2 - 6}{2 - 0} = \frac{-4}{2} = -2$; $y$-intercept: 6; $x$-intercept: 3.

(b) $f(x) = -2x + 6$

(c) The zeros of $f$ are the same as the $x$-intercepts. That is $x = 3$.

2. (a) Using the points (0, −40) and (10, 10), $m = \frac{10 - (-40)}{10 - 0} = \frac{50}{10} = 5$; $y$-intercept: −40; $x$-intercept: 8.

(b) $f(x) = 5x - 40$

(c) The zeros of $f$ are the same as the $x$-intercepts. That is $x = 8$.

3. $m = \frac{0 - 2.5}{2 - 1} = \frac{-2.5}{1} = -2.5$; $(1, 2.5) \Rightarrow (1 - 1, 2.5 - (-2.5)) = (0, 5)$, so $b = 5$; $f(x) = -2.5x + 5$

4. $m = \frac{-1.2 - (-1.65)}{6 - (-3)} = \frac{0.45}{9} = 0.05$; since $\frac{0.05}{1} = \frac{0.15}{3}$, $(-3, -1.65) \Rightarrow (-3 + 3, -1.65 + 0.15) = (0, -1.5)$, so $b = -1.5$; $f(x) = 0.05x - 1.5$

5. See Figure 5.

6. See Figure 6.

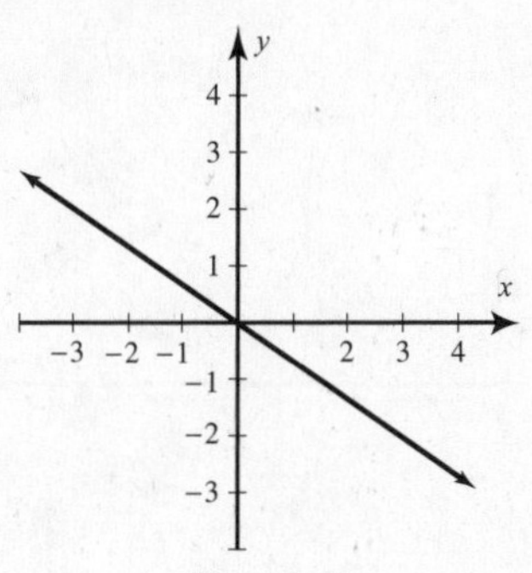

Figure 5

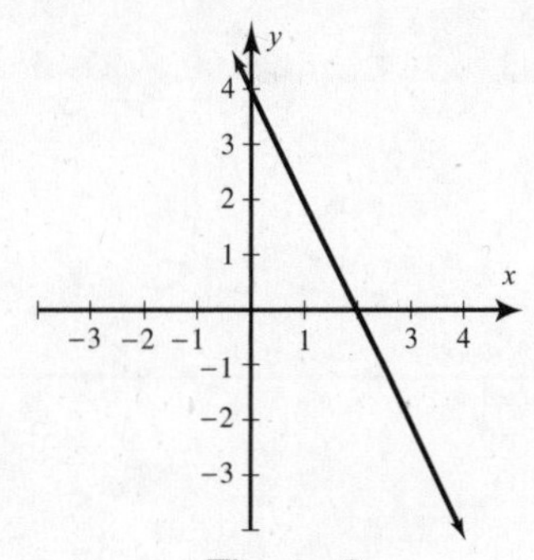

Figure 6

7. Using point-slope form $y = m(x - x_1) + y_1$, we get $y = -2(x + 2) + 3 \Rightarrow f(x) = -2x - 1$

8. $f(-2) = -3(-2) + 8 = 14$ or point $(-2, 14)$; $f(3) = -3(3) + 8 = -1$ or point $(3, -1)$. Find the slope of the line joining these points: $m = \frac{-1 - 14}{3 - (-2)} = \frac{-15}{5} = -3$; the average rate of change is $-3$.

9. $y = 7(x + 3) + 9 \Rightarrow y = 7x + 21 + 9 \Rightarrow y = 7x + 30$

10. $m = \frac{-3 - (-4)}{7 - 2} = \frac{1}{5}$; $y = \frac{1}{5}(x - 2) - 4 \Rightarrow y = \frac{1}{5}x - \frac{22}{5}$

11. Let $m = -3$. Then, $y = -3(x - 1) - 1 \Rightarrow y = -3x + 2$.

12. Let $m = -\frac{1}{2}$. Then, $y = -\frac{1}{2}(x + 2) + 1 \Rightarrow y = -\frac{1}{2}x$.

13. The line segment has slope $m = \frac{0 - 3.1}{5.7 - 0} = -\frac{31}{57}$; the parallel line has slope $m = -\frac{31}{57}$;

$y = -\frac{31}{57}(x - 1) - 7 \Rightarrow y = -\frac{31}{57}x - \frac{368}{57}$

14. The given line has slope $m = -\frac{5}{7}$; the perpendicular line has slope $m = \frac{7}{5}$;

$y = \frac{7}{5}\left(x - \frac{6}{7}\right) + 0 \Rightarrow y = \frac{7}{5}x - \frac{6}{5}$

15. The line is vertical passing through (6, –7), so the equation is $x = 6$.

16. The line is horizontal passing through (–3, 4), so the equation is $y = 4$.

17. The line is horizontal passing through (1, 3), so the equation is $y = 3$.

18. The line is vertical passing through (1.5, 1.9), so the equation is $x = 1.5$.

19. The equation of the vertical line with $x$-intercept 2.7 is $x = 2.7$.

20. The equation of the horizontal line with $y$-intercept –8 is $y = -8$.

21. For $x$-intercept: $y = 0 \Rightarrow 5x - 4(0) = 20 \Rightarrow 5x = 20 \Rightarrow x = 4$; for $y$-intercept: $x = 0 \Rightarrow$ $5(0) - 4y = 20 \Rightarrow -4y = 20 \Rightarrow y = -5$; use $(4, 0)$ and $(0, -5)$ to graph the equation. See Figure 21.

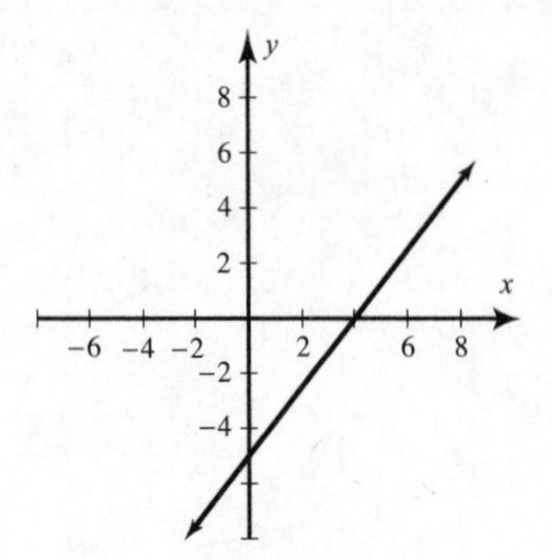

Figure 21

22. For $x$-intercept: $y = 0 \Rightarrow \frac{x}{3} - \frac{0}{2} = 1 \Rightarrow \frac{x}{3} = 1 \Rightarrow x = 3$; for $y$-intercept: $x = 0 \Rightarrow \frac{0}{3} - \frac{y}{2} = 1 \Rightarrow$ $-\frac{y}{2} = 1 \Rightarrow y = -2$; use (3, 0) and (0, −2) to graph the equation. See Figure 22.

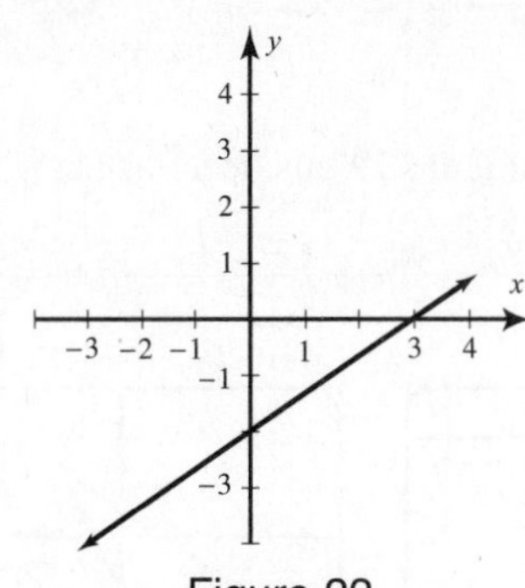

Figure 22

[−15, 15, 5] by [−15, 15, 5]
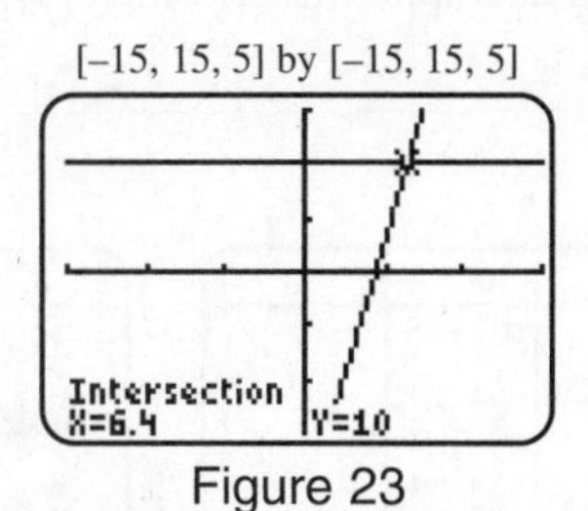

Figure 23

23. Graphical: Graph $Y_1 = 5X - 22$ and $Y_2 = 10$. Their graphs intersect at (6.4, 10) as shown in Figure 23. The solution is $x = 6.4$.

Symbolic: $5x - 22 = 10 \Rightarrow 5x = 32 \Rightarrow x = \frac{32}{5} = 6.4$

24. Graphical: Graph $Y_1 = 5(4 - 2X)$ and $Y_2 = 16$. Their graphs intersect at (0.4, 16) as shown in Figure 24. The solution is $x = 0.4$.

Symbolic: $5(4 - 2x) = 16 \Rightarrow 20 - 10x = 16 \Rightarrow 4 = 10x \Rightarrow x = \frac{2}{5} = 0.4$

25. Graphical: Graph $Y_1 = -2(3X - 7) + X$ and $Y_2 = 2X - 1$. Their graphs intersect near (2.143, 3.286) as shown in Figure 25. The solution is approximately 2.143.

Symbolic: $-2(3x - 7) + x = 2x - 1 \Rightarrow -6x + 14 + x = 2x - 1 \Rightarrow -7x = -15 \Rightarrow x = \frac{15}{7} \approx 2.143$

[−20, 20, 5] by [−10, 20, 5]
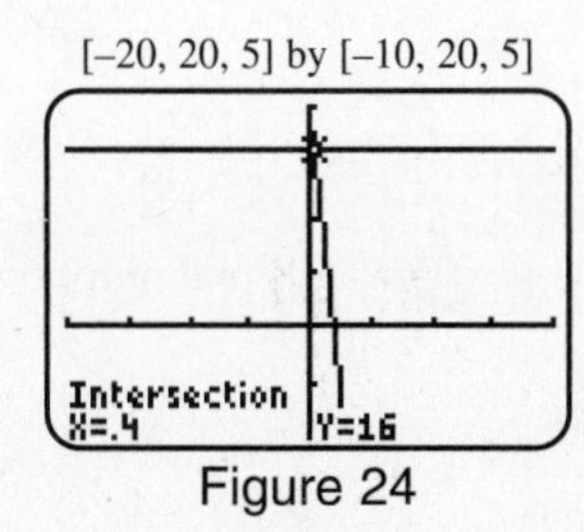

Figure 24

[−10, 10, 1] by [−10, 10, 1]
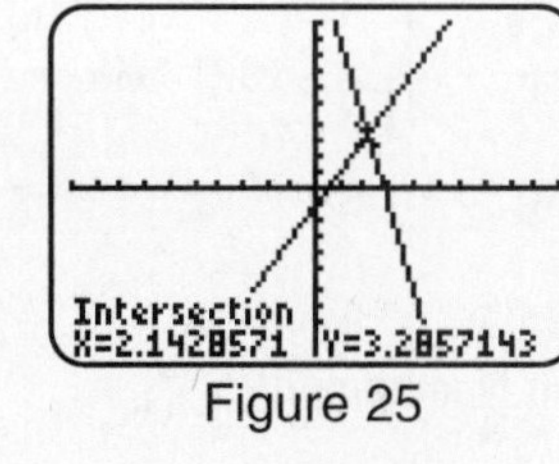

Figure 25

[−10, 10, 1] by [−10, 10, 1]
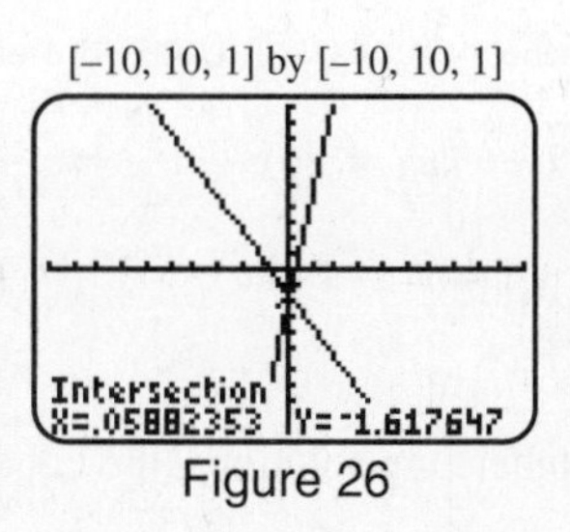

Figure 26

[−10, 10, 1] by [−10, 10, 1]
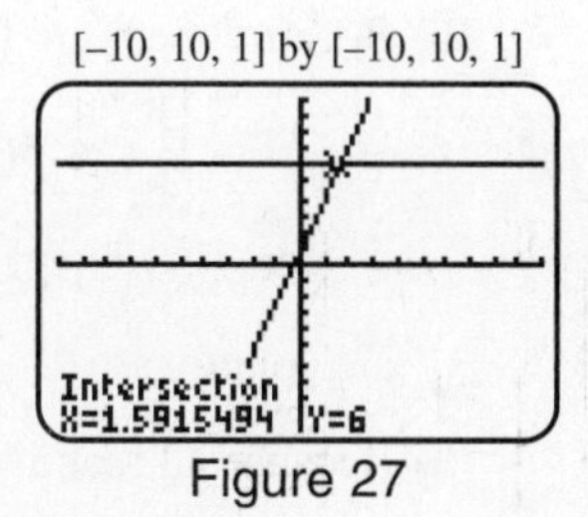

Figure 27

26. Graphical: Graph $Y_1 = 5X - 0.5(4 - 3X)$ and $Y_2 = 1.5 - (2X + 3)$. Their graphs intersect near (0.059, −1.618) as shown in Figure 26. The solution is approximately 0.059.

Symbolic: $5x - \frac{1}{2}(4 - 3x) = \frac{3}{2} - (2x + 3) \Rightarrow 10x - (4 - 3x) = 3 - 2(2x + 3) \Rightarrow$

$10x - 4 + 3x = 3 - 4x - 6 \Rightarrow 17x = 1 \Rightarrow x = \frac{1}{17} \approx 0.059$

27. Graphical: Graph $Y_1 = \pi X + 1$ and $Y_2 = 6$. Their graphs intersect near (1.592, 6) as shown in Figure 27. The solution is approximately 1.592.

Symbolic: $\pi x + 1 = 6 \Rightarrow \pi x = 5 \Rightarrow x = \frac{5}{\pi} \approx 1.592$

28. Graphical: Graph $Y_1 = (X - 4)/2$ and $Y_2 = X + (1 - 2X)/3$. Their graphs intersect at (14, 5) as shown in Figure 28. The solution is 14.

Symbolic: $\frac{x-4}{2} = x + \frac{1-2x}{3} \Rightarrow 3(x-4) = 6x + 2(1-2x) \Rightarrow 3x - 12 = 6x + 2 - 4x \Rightarrow$ $-14 = -x \Rightarrow x = 14$

29. Let $Y_1 = 3.1X - 0.2 - 2(X - 1.7)$ and approximate where $Y_1 = 0$. From Figure 29 this occurs when $x \approx -2.9$.

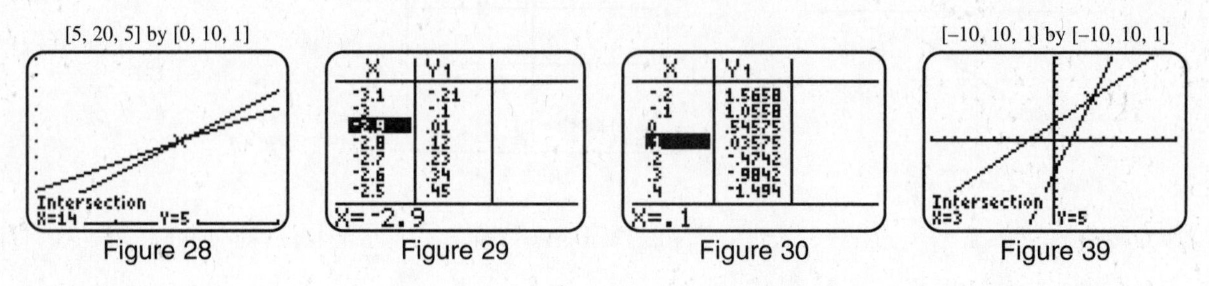


Figure 28 Figure 29 Figure 30 Figure 39

30. Let $Y_1 = \sqrt{(7)} - 3X - 2.1(1 + X)$ and approximate where $Y_1 = 0$. From Figure 30 this occurs when $x \approx 0.1$.

31. (a) $4(6 - x) = -4x + 24 \Rightarrow 24 - 4x = -4x + 24 \Rightarrow 0 = 0 \Rightarrow$ all real numbers are solutions.

(b) Because all real numbers are solutions, the equation is an identity.

32. (a) $\frac{1}{2}(4x - 3) + 2 = 3x - (1 + x) \Rightarrow 2x + \frac{1}{2} = 2x - 1 \Rightarrow \frac{1}{2} = -1 \Rightarrow$ no solutions.

(b) When an equation has no solutions, it is a contradiction.

33. (a) $5 - 2(4 - 3x) + x = 4(x - 3) \Rightarrow 5 - 8 + 6x + x = 4x - 12 \Rightarrow 7x - 3 = 4x - 12 \Rightarrow$ $3x = -9 \Rightarrow x = -3$

(b) Because there are finitely many solutions, the equation in condtional.

34. (a) $\frac{x-3}{4} + \frac{3}{4}x - 5(2 - 7x) = 36x - \frac{43}{4} \Rightarrow \frac{x-3}{4} + \frac{3}{4}x - 10 + 35x = 36x - \frac{43}{4} \Rightarrow$ $x - 3 + 3x - 40 + 140x = 144x - 43 \Rightarrow 144x - 43 = 144x - 43 \Rightarrow 0 = 0 \Rightarrow$ all real numbers are solutions.

(b) Because all real numbers are solutions, the equation is an identity.

35. $(-3, \infty)$

36. $(-\infty, 4]$

37. $\left[-2, \frac{3}{4}\right)$

38. $(-\infty, -2] \cup (3, \infty)$

39. Graphical: Graph $Y_1 = 3X - 4$ and $Y_2 = 2 + X$. Their graphs intersect at (3, 5). The graph of $Y_1$ is below the graph of $Y_2$ to the left of the point of intersection. Thus, $3x - 4 \leq 2 + x$ holds when $x \leq 3$ or $(-\infty, 3]$. See Figure 39. Symbolic: $3x - 4 \leq 2 + x \Rightarrow 2x \leq 6 \Rightarrow x \leq 3$ or $(-\infty, 3]$. In set-builder notation, the interval is $\{x \mid x \leq 3\}$.

40. Graphical: Graph $Y_1 = -2X + 6$ and $Y_2 = -3X$. Their graphs intersect at (–6, 18). The graph of $Y_1$ is below the graph of $Y_2$ to the left of the point of intersection. Thus, $-2x + 6 \leq -3x$ holds when $x \leq -6$ or $(-\infty, -6]$. See Figure 40. Symbolic: $-2x + 6 \leq -3x \Rightarrow x \leq -6$ or $(-\infty, -6]$. In set-builder notation the interval is $\{x \mid x \leq -6\}$.

41. Graphical: Graph $Y_1 = (2X - 5)/2$ and $Y_2 = (5X + 1)/5$. Their graphs are parallel and never intersect. The graph of $Y_1$ is always below the graph of $Y_2$, so $Y_1 < Y_2$ for all values of $x$; the inequality $\frac{2x - 5}{2} < \frac{5x + 1}{5}$ holds when $-\infty < x < \infty$, or $(-\infty, \infty)$. See Figure 41. In set-builder notation the interval is $\{x \mid -\infty < x < \infty\}$.

[–30, 30, 5] by [–30, 30, 5]

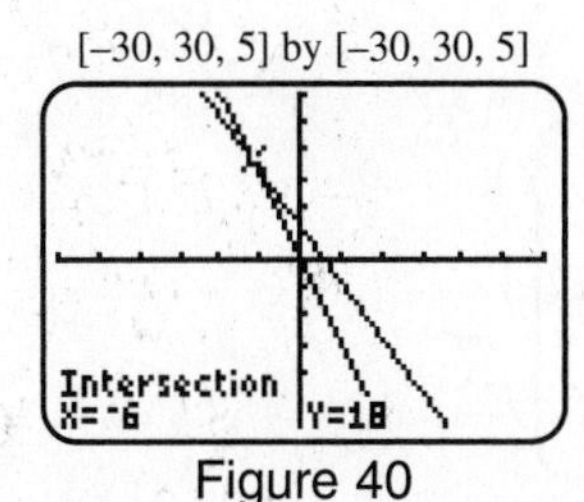

Figure 40

[–10, 10, 1] by [–10, 10, 1]

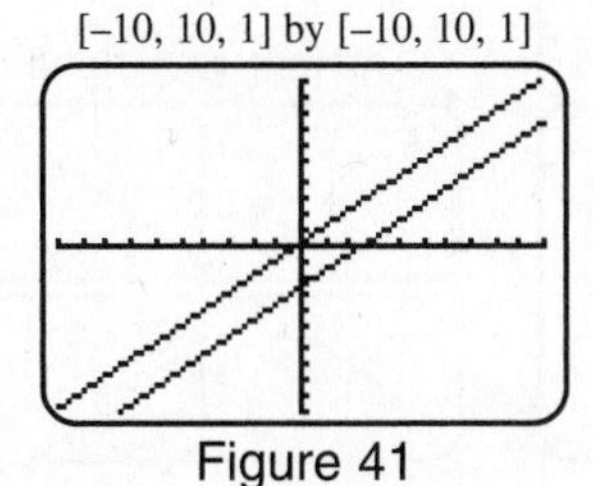
Figure 41

[–5, 5, 1] by [–30, 5, 5]

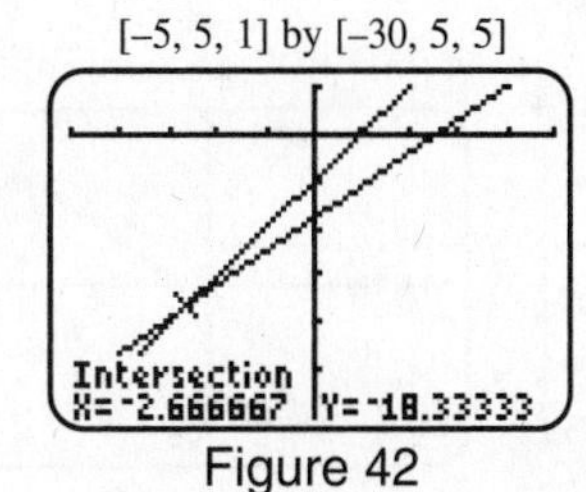

Figure 42

[–10, 10, 1] by [–10, 10, 1]

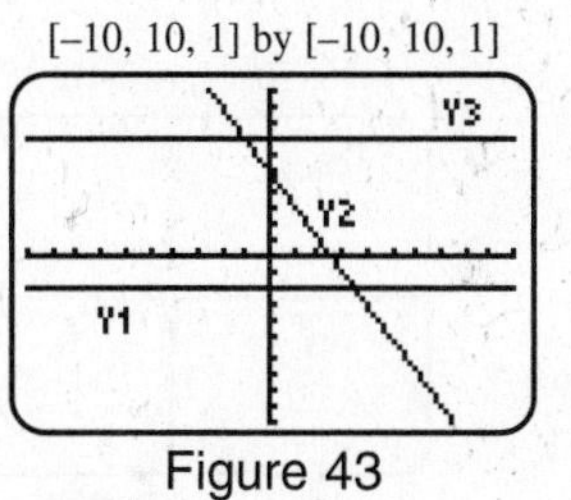

Figure 43

42. Graphical: Graph $Y_1 = -5(1 - X)$ and $Y_2 = 3(X - 3) + 0.5X$. Their graphs intersect near (–2.6667, –18.3333). The graph of $Y_1$ is above the graph of $Y_2$ to the right of the point of intersection. Thus, $-5(1 - x) > 3(x - 3) + \frac{1}{2}x$ holds when $x > -2.6667$ or $\left(-\frac{8}{3}, \infty\right)$. See Figure 42.

Symbolic: $-5(1 - x) > 3(x - 3) + \frac{1}{2}x \Rightarrow -5 + 5x > 3x - 9 + \frac{1}{2}x \Rightarrow \frac{3}{2}x > -4 \Rightarrow x > -\frac{8}{3}$, or $\left(-\frac{8}{3}, \infty\right)$. In set-builder notation, the interval is $\left\{x \mid x > -\frac{8}{3}\right\}$.

43. Graphical: Graph $Y_1 = -2$, $Y_2 = 5 - 2X$ and $Y_3 = 7$. See Figure 43. Their graphs intersect at the points (–1, 7) and (3.5, –2). The graph of $Y_2$ is between the graphs of $Y_1$ and $Y_3$ when $-1 < x \leq 3.5$. In interval notation the solution is (–1, 3.5].

Symbolic: $-2 \leq 5 - 2x < 7 \Rightarrow -7 \leq -2x < 2 \Rightarrow \frac{7}{2} \geq x > -1 \Rightarrow -1 < x \leq \frac{7}{2}$ or $\left(-1, \frac{7}{2}\right]$

In set-builder notation, the interval is $\left\{x \mid -1 < x \leq \frac{7}{2}\right\}$.

44. Graphical: Graph $Y_1 = -1$, $Y_2 = (3X - 5)/-3$, and $Y_3 = 3$. See Figure 44. Their graphs intersect at the points $\left(-\frac{4}{3}, 3\right)$ and $\left(\frac{8}{3}, -1\right)$. The graph of $Y_2$ is between the graphs of $Y_1$ and $Y_3$ when $-\frac{4}{3} < x < \frac{8}{3}$. In interval notation the solution is $\left(-\frac{4}{3}, \frac{8}{3}\right)$. Symbolic: $-1 < \frac{3x - 5}{-3} < 3 \Rightarrow 3 > 3x - 5 > -9 \Rightarrow$ $-9 < 3x - 5 < 3 \Rightarrow -4 < 3x < 8 \Rightarrow \left(-\frac{4}{3}, \frac{8}{3}\right)$. In set-builder notation the soultion set is $\left\{x \middle| -\frac{4}{3} < x < \frac{8}{3}\right\}$.

45. Graph $Y_1 = 2x$ and $Y_2 = x - 1$. See Figure 45. The lines intersect at $(-1, -2)$. $Y_1 > Y_2$ when the graph of $Y_1$ is above the graph of $Y_2$; this happens when $x > -1 \Rightarrow (-1, \infty)$. In set-builder notation the interval is $\{x | x > -1\}$.

[-10, 10, 1] by [-10, 10, 1] [-10, 10, 1] by [-10, 10, 1] [-10, 10, 1] by [-10, 10, 1]

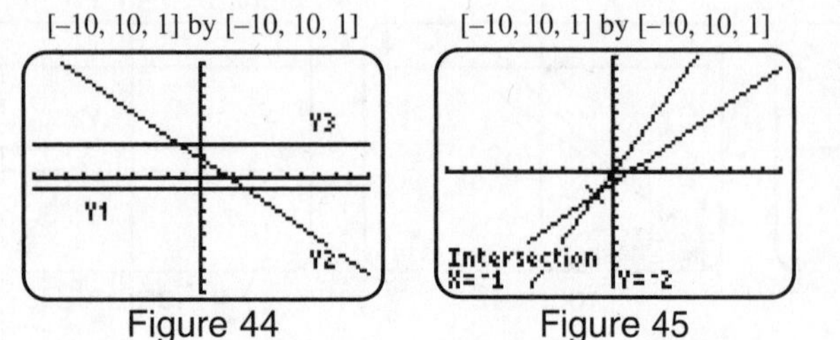


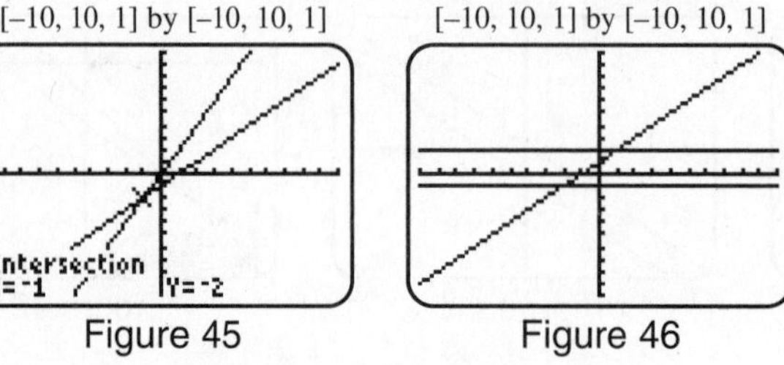

Figure 44 Figure 45 Figure 46

46. Graph $Y_1 = -1$, $Y_2 = 1 + x$ and $Y_3 = 2$. See Figure 46. The two points of intersection are $(-2, -1)$ and $(1, 2)$. $Y_1 \leq Y_2 \leq Y_3$ when the graph of $1 + x$ is between these two intersection points $\Rightarrow$ $-2 \leq x \leq 1 \Rightarrow [-2, 1]$.

47. (a) The graphs intersect at (2, 1). The solution to $f(x) = g(x)$ is 2.

(b) The graph of $f$ is below the graph of $g$ to the right of (2, 1).

Thus, $f(x) < g(x)$ when $x > 2$ or on $(2, \infty)$.

(c) The graph of $f$ is above the graph of $g$ to the left of (2, 1). Thus, $f(x) > g(x)$ when $x < 2$ or on $(-\infty, 2)$.

48. (a) The graphs of $f$ and $g$ intersect at (6, 2). The solution to $f(x) = g(x)$ is 6.

(b) The graphs of $g$ and $h$ intersect at (2, 4). The solution to $f(x) = g(x)$ is 2.

(c) The graph of $g$ is between the graphs of $f$ and $h$ when $2 < x < 6$. Thus, $f(x) < g(x) < h(x)$ when $x$ is in the interval (2, 6).

(d) The graph of $g$ is above the graph of $h$ to the left of the point (2, 4). Thus, $g(x) > h(x)$ when $x$ is in the interval [0, 2). (Remember: $D = \{x | 0 \leq x \leq 7\}$.)

49. (a) $f(-2) = 8 + 2(-2) = 4$; $f(-1) = 8 + 2(-1) = 6$; $f(2) = 5 - 2 = 3$; $f(3) = 3 + 1 = 4$.

(b) The graph of $f$ is shown in Figure 49. It is essentially a piecewise line graph with the points (–3, 2), (–1, 6), (2, 3), and (5, 6). Since there are no breaks in the graph, $f$ is continuous.

(c) From the graph we can see that there are two $x$-values where $f(x) = 3$. They occur when $8 + 2x = 3 \Rightarrow x = -2.5$ and when $5 - x = 3 \Rightarrow x = 2$. The solutions are $x = -2.5$ or 2.

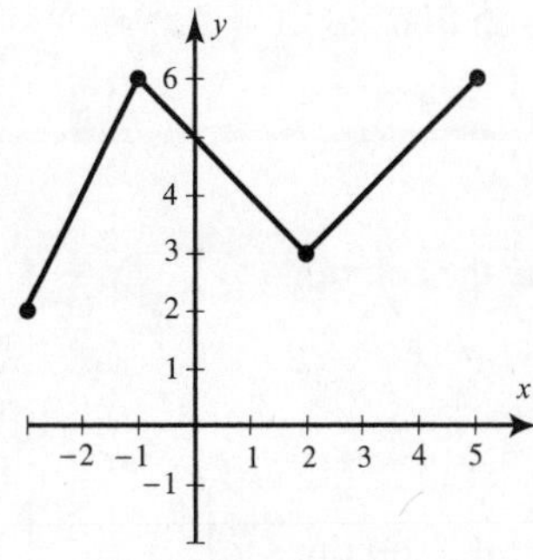

Figure 49

50. $f(-3.1) = [\![2(-3.1) - 1]\!] = [\![-7.2]\!] = -8$ and $f(2.5) = [\![2(2.5) - 1]\!] = [\![4]\!] = 4$

51. $|2x - 5| - 1 = 8 \Rightarrow |2x - 5| = 9 \Rightarrow 2x - 5 = -9$ or $2x - 5 = 9$; $2x - 5 = -9 \Rightarrow 2x = -4 \Rightarrow$ $x = -2$; $2x - 5 = 9 \Rightarrow 2x = 14 \Rightarrow x = 7 \Rightarrow -2, 7$

52. $|3 - 7x| = 10 \Rightarrow 3 - 7x = -10$ or $3 - 7x = 10$; $3 - 7x = -10 \Rightarrow -7x = -13 \Rightarrow x = \frac{13}{7}$; $3 - 7x = 10 \Rightarrow -7x = 7 \Rightarrow x = -1 \Rightarrow -1, \frac{13}{7}$

53. $|6 - 4x| = -2$ has no solutions since the absolute value of any quantity is always greater than or equal to 0.

54. $|9 + x| = |3 - 2x| \Rightarrow 9 + x = 3 - 2x$ or $9 + x = -(3 - 2x)$; $9 + x = 3 - 2x \Rightarrow 3x = -6 \Rightarrow$ $x = -2$; $9 + x = -(3 - 2x) \Rightarrow 9 + x = -3 + 2x \Rightarrow -x = -12 \Rightarrow x = 12 \Rightarrow -2, 12$

55. $|x| = 3 \Rightarrow x = \pm 3$. The solutions to $|x| > 3$ lie to the left of $-3$ and to the right of 3. That is, $x < -3$ or $x > 3$. This can be supported by graphing $Y_1 = |x|$ and $Y_2 = 3$ and determining where the graph of $Y_1$ is above the graph of $Y_2$. To support this result numerically, table $Y_1 = \text{abs}(X)$ starting at $-9$ and incrementing by 3.

56. $|-3x + 1| = 2 \Rightarrow -3x + 1 = -2$ or $-3x + 1 = 2 \Rightarrow x = 1$ or $-\frac{1}{3}$. The solutions to $|-3x + 1| < 2$ lie between 1 and $-\frac{1}{3}$; that is, $-\frac{1}{3} < x < 1$. This can be supported by graphing $Y_1 = |-3x + 1|$ and $Y_2 = 2$ and determining where the graph of $Y_1$ is below the graph of $Y_2$. To support this result numerically, table $Y_1 = \text{abs}(-3X + 1)$ starting at $-1$ and incrementing by $\frac{1}{3}$.

57. $|3x - 7| = 10 \Rightarrow 3x - 7 = 10$ or $3x - 7 = -10 \Rightarrow x = \frac{17}{3}$ or $x = -1$. The solutions to $|3x - 7| > 10$ lie to the left of $-1$ or to the right of $x = \frac{17}{3}$; that is, $x < -1$ or $x > \frac{17}{3}$. This can be supported by graphing $Y_1 = |3x - 7|$ and $Y_2 = 10$ and determining where the graph of $Y_1$ is above the graph of $Y_2$. To support this result numerically, table $Y_1 = \text{abs}(3X - 7)$ starting at $-3$ and incrementing by $\frac{1}{3}$.

58. $|4 - x| = 6 \Rightarrow 4 - x = 6$ or $4 - x = -6 \Rightarrow x = -2$ or $x = 10$. The solutions to $|4 - x| \le 2$ lie between $-2$ and 10, inclusively; that is, $-2 \le x \le 10$. This can be supported by graphing $Y_1 = |4 - x|$ and $Y_2 = 6$ and determining where the graph of $Y_1$ is below the graph of $Y_2$. To support this result numerically, table $Y_1 = \text{abs}(4 - X)$ starting at $-6$ and incrementing by 4.

59. The solutions to $|3 - 2x| < 9$ satisfy $s_1 < x < s_2$ where $s_1$ and $s_2$, are the solutions to $|3 - 2x| = 9$.

$|3 - 2x| = 9$ is equivalent to $3 - 2x = -9 \Rightarrow x = 6$ or $3 - 2x = 9 \Rightarrow x = -3$.

The solutions are $-3 < x < 6$ or $(-3, 6)$.

60. The solutions to $|-2x - 3| > 3$ satisfy $x < s_1$ or $x > s_2$, where $s_1$ and $s_2$ are the solutions to $|-2x - 3| = 3$.

$|-2x - 3| = 3$ is equivalent to $-2x - 3 = -3 \Rightarrow x = 0$ or $-2x - 3 = 3 \Rightarrow x = -3$.

The solutions are $x < -3$ or $x > 0$ or $(-\infty, -3) \cup (0, \infty)$.

61. The solutions to $\left|\frac{1}{3}x - \frac{1}{6}\right| \geq 1$ satisfy $x \leq s_1$ or $x \geq s_2$ where $s_1$ and $s_2$, are the solutions to $\left|\frac{1}{3}x + \frac{1}{6}\right| = 1$.

$\left|\frac{1}{3}x - \frac{1}{6}\right| = 1$ is equivalent to $\frac{1}{3}x - \frac{1}{6} = -1 \Rightarrow x = -\frac{5}{2}$ or $\frac{1}{3}x - \frac{1}{6} = 1 \Rightarrow x = \frac{7}{2}$.

The solutions are $x \leq -\frac{5}{2}$ or $x \geq \frac{7}{2}$ or $\left(-\infty, -\frac{5}{2}\right] \cup \left[\frac{7}{2}, \infty\right)$.

62. First rewrite the inequality: $\left|\frac{1}{2}x\right| - 3 \leq 5 \Rightarrow \left|\frac{1}{2}x\right| \leq 8$.

The solutions to $\left|\frac{1}{2}x\right| \leq 8$ satisfy $s_1 \leq x \leq s_2$, where $s_1$ and $s_2$ are the solutions to $\left|\frac{1}{2}x\right| = 8$.

$\left|\frac{1}{2}x\right| = 8$ is equivalent to $\frac{1}{2}x = -8 \Rightarrow x = -16$ or $\frac{1}{2}x = 8 \Rightarrow x = 16$. The solutions are $-16 \leq x \leq 16$ or $[-16, 16]$.

63. (a) Graph $Y_1 = 1450(x - 1980) + 20{,}000$ and $Y_2 = 34{,}500$. Their graphs intersect at the point (1990, 34,500). See Figure 63. This means that in 1990 the median income was $34,500.

(b) $1450(x - 1980) + 20{,}000 = 34{,}500 \Rightarrow 1450(x - 1980) = 14{,}500 \Rightarrow x = \frac{14{,}500}{1450} + 1980 = 1990$

[1980, 2005, 2] by [20000, 40000, 1000]

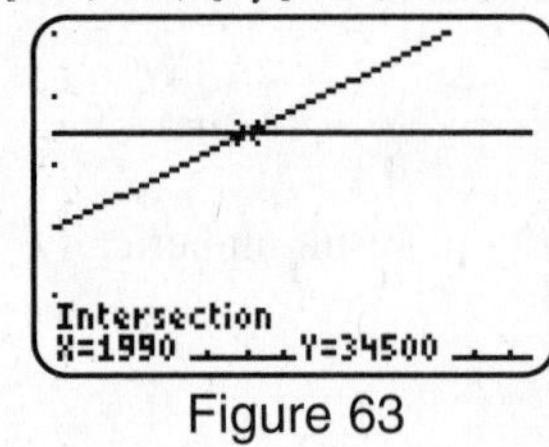


Figure 63

[1995, 2007, 1] by [200, 400, 50]

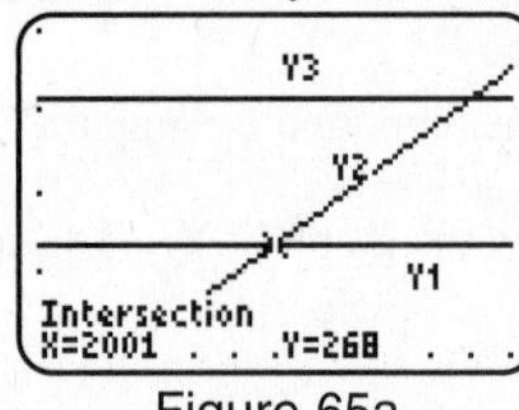


Figure 65a

[1995, 2007, 1] by [200, 400, 50]

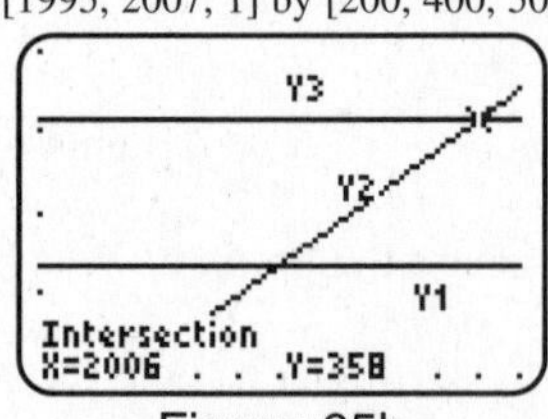


Figure 65b

64. Let $x$ be the minimum score received on the final exam. The total number of points possible in the course is $75 + 75 + 150 = 300$. Moreover, 80% of 300 is 240 points, which would result in a B grade. The minimum score $x$ on the final necessary to receive a B is given by the equation $55 + 72 + x = 240 \Rightarrow x = 113$. A score of 113 or higher will result in a B grade or better.

65. $268 \leq 18x - 35{,}750 \leq 358 \Rightarrow 36{,}018 \leq 18x \leq 36{,}108 \Rightarrow 2001 \leq x \leq 2006$. Medicare costs will be between 268 and 358 billion dollars from 2001 to 2006.

Graph $Y_1 = 268$, $Y_2 = 18X - 35{,}750$, and $Y_3 = 358$. Their graphs intersect at the points (2001, 268) and (2006, 358). See Figures 65a & 65b. Medicare costs will be between 268 and 358 billion dollars from 2001 to 2006.

66. (a) Plot the ordered pairs $(-40, -40)$, $(32, 0)$, $(59, 15)$, $(95, 35)$, and $(212, 100)$. The data appears to be linear. See Figure 66.

(b) We must determine the linear function whose graph passes through these points. To determine its equation we shall use the points $(32, 0)$ and $(212, 100)$, although any pair of points would work. The slope of the graph is $\frac{100 - 0}{212 - 32} = \frac{100}{180} = \frac{5}{9}$. The symbolic representation of this function is $C$ is $C(x) = \frac{5}{9}(x - 32) + 0$ or $C(x) = \frac{5}{9}(x - 32)$. A slope of $\frac{5}{9}$ means that the Celsius temperature changes 5° for every 9° change in the Fahrenheit temperature.

(c) $C(83) = \frac{5}{9}(83 - 32) = 28\frac{1}{3}°$ Celsius.

[-50, 250, 50] by [-50, 110, 50]

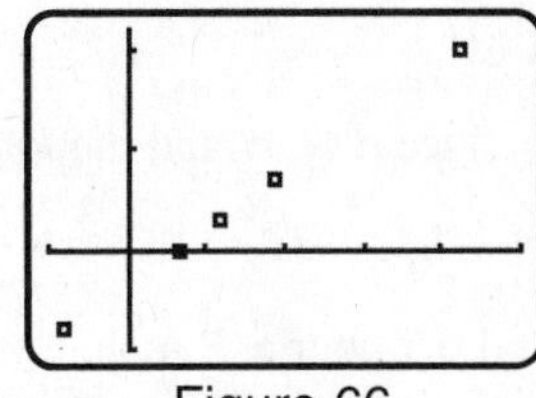

Figure 66

[1988, 1995, 1] by [20.5, 20.9, 0.1]

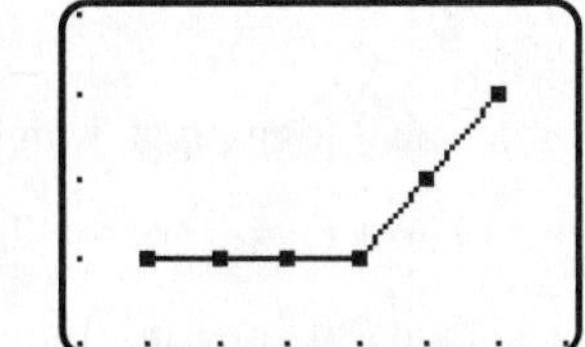

Figure 68

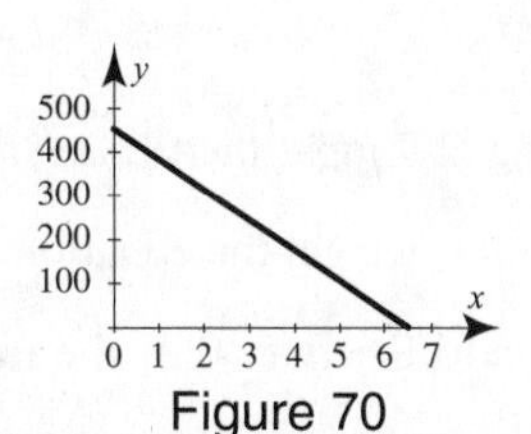


Figure 70

67. Since the graph is piecewise linear, the slope each line segment represents a constant speed. Initially, the car is home. After 1 hour it is 30 miles from home and has traveled at a constant speed of 30 mph. After 2 hours it is 50 miles away. During the second hour the car travels 20 mph. During the third hour the car travels toward home at 30 mph until it is 20 miles away. During the fourth hour the car travels away from home at 40 mph until it is 60 miles away from home. The last hour the car travels 60 miles at 60 mph until it arrives back at home.

68. (a) Make a line graph using the points $(1989, 20.6)$, $(1990, 20.6)$, $(1991, 20.6)$, $(1992, 20.6)$, $(1993, 20.7)$, and $(1994, 20.8)$. See Figure 68.

(b) From $x = 1989$ to $x = 1992$ the function $f$ is constant with $f(x) = 20.6$. From 1992 to 1994 the graph increases with a slope of 0.1. A piecewise-linear function can be defined by

$$f(x) = \begin{cases} 20.6, & \text{if } 1989 \le x \le 1992 \\ 0.1(x - 1992) + 20.6, & \text{if } 1992 < x \le 1994 \end{cases}$$

(c) [1989, 1994]

69. The midpoint is computed by $\left(\frac{2004 + 2008}{2}, \frac{143{,}247 + 167{,}933}{2}\right) = (2006, 155{,}590)$.

The population was about 155,590.

70. (a) $f(x) = 455 - 70x$, where $x$ is in hours.

(b) See Figure 70. $D = \{x \mid 0 \le x \le 6.5\}$ is an appropriate domain for $f$.

(c) $f(x) = 0 \Rightarrow 0 = 455 - 70x \Rightarrow x = \frac{455}{70} = 6.5$ ($x$-intercept); $f(0) = 455 - 7(0) = 455 \Rightarrow y = 455$ ($y$-intercept); the $x$-intercept indictaes that the driver arrives at home after 6.5 hours, and the $y$-intercept indicates that the driver starts out 455 miles from home.

71. Let $x$ = time it takes for both working together; the first worker can shovel $\frac{1}{50}$ of the sidewalk in 1 minute, and the second worker can shovel $\frac{1}{30}$ of the sidewalk in 1 minute; for the entire job, we get the equation $\frac{x}{50} + \frac{x}{30} = 1 \Rightarrow 3x + 5x = 150 \Rightarrow 8x = 150 \Rightarrow x = 18.75$; it takes the two workers 18.75 minutes to shovel the sidewalk together.

72. Let $x$ = number of gallons of the 80% antifreeze solution; then $20 + x$ = number of gallons of the final 50% antifreeze solution; the amount of antifreeze in the 30% and 80% solutions equals the amount of antifreeze in the 50% solution: $0.30(20) + 0.80x = 0.50(20 + x) \Rightarrow 3(20) + 8x = 5(20 + x) \Rightarrow$ $60 + 8x = 100 + 5x \Rightarrow 3x = 40 \Rightarrow x = \frac{40}{3} = 13\frac{1}{3}$; $13\frac{1}{3}$ gallons of the 80% antifreeze solution should be added.

73. Let $t$ = time spent jogging at 7 mph; then $1.8 - t$ = time spent jogging at 8 mph; since $d = rt$ and the total distance jogged is 13.5 miles, we get the equation $7t + 8(1.8 - t) = 13.5 \Rightarrow 7t + 14.4 - 8t = 13.5 \Rightarrow$ $-t = -0.9 \Rightarrow t = 0.9$ and $1.8 - t = 0.9$; the runner jogged 0.9 hour at 7 mph and 0.9 hour at 8 mph.

74. (a) The scatterplot in Figure 74 of the points (1960, 1394), (1970, 1763), (1980, 3176), (1990, 5136), and (2000, 6880) indicates that the correlation coefficient should be positive, and somewhat close to 1.

(b) $y = ax + b$, where $a = 143.45$ and $b \approx -280{,}361.2 \Rightarrow y = 143.45x - 280{,}361.2$; $r \approx 0.978$

(c) $y = 143.45(1995) - 280{,}361.2 \approx 5821.55$; the estimated cost of driving a mid-size car in 1995 was \$5821.55.

(d) $8000 = 143.45x - 280{,}361.2 \Rightarrow 288{,}361.2 = 143.45x \Rightarrow x \approx 2010.186$. Therefore, in the year 2010 the cost will be \$8000.

[1955, 2005, 10] by [1000, 7000, 1000]

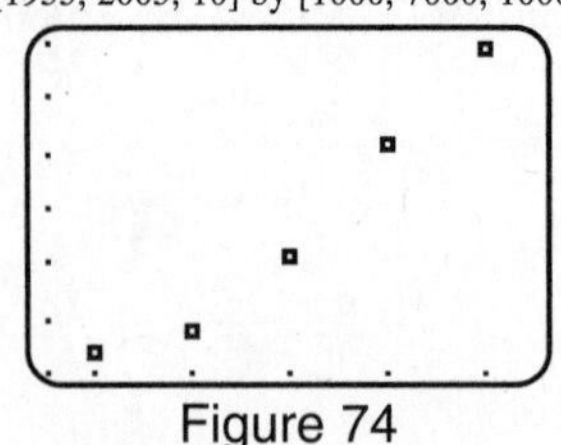

Figure 74

75. (a) Begin by selecting any two points to determine the equation of the line. For example, if we use $(-1, 4.2)$ and $(2, 0.6)$, then $m = \frac{4.2 - 0.6}{-1 - 2} = \frac{3.6}{-3} = -1.2$. $y - y_1 = m(x - x_1) \Rightarrow y - 0.6 = -1.2(x - 2) \Rightarrow$ $y - 0.6 = -1.2x + 2.4 \Rightarrow y = -1.2x + 3$.

(b) When $x = -1.5$, then $y = -1.2(-1.5) + 3 = 4.8$. This involves interpolation.

When $x = 3.5$, then $y = -1.2(3.5) + 3 = -1.2$. This involves extrapolation.

(c) $1.3 = -1.2x + 3 \Rightarrow -1.7 = -1.2x \Rightarrow x = \frac{17}{12}$.

76. Let $x$ = width of rectangle; then $2x$ = length of the rectangle; $P = 78$ inches and $P = 2w + 2l \Rightarrow$

$2x + 2(2x) = 78 \Rightarrow 2x + 4x = 78 \Rightarrow 6x = 78 \Rightarrow x = 13$ and $2x = 26$; the rectangle is 13 inches by 26 inches.

77. The tank is initially empty. When $0 \le x \le 3$, the slope is 5. The inlet pipe is open; the outlet pipe is closed. When $3 < x \le 5$, the slope is 2. Both pipes are open. When $5 < x \le 8$, the slope is 0. Both pipes are closed. When $8 < x \le 10$, the slope is –3. The inlet pipe is closed; the outlet pipe is open.

78. The tank initially contains 25 gallons.

On the interval [0, 4], the slope is 5. The 5 gal/min inlet pipe is open. The other pipes are closed.

On the interval (4, 8], the slope is –3 . Both inlet pipes are closed. The outlet pipe is open.

On the interval (8, 12], the slope is 7. Both inlet pipes are open. The outlet pipe is closed.

On the interval (12, 16], the slope is 4. All pipes are open.

On the interval (16, 24], the slope is –1. The 2 gal/min inlet pipe and the outlet pipe are open.

On the interval (24, 28], the slope is 0. All pipes are closed.

79. Let $x$ represent the distance above the ground and let $y$ represent the temperature. Since the ground temperature is 25°C, the point (0, 25) is on the graph of the function which models the situation. Since the rate of change is a constant –6°C per kilometer, the model is linear with a slope of $m = -6$. Therefore, the equation of the linear model is $y = -6x + 25$.

Graphically: Graph $Y_1 = 15$, $Y_2 = -6x + 25$, and $Y_3 = 5$ in $[0, 4, 1]$ by $[0, 30, 5]$. See Figure 79. The intersection points are $\left(1\frac{2}{3}, 15\right)$ and $\left(3\frac{1}{3}, 5\right)$. The distance above the ground is between $1\frac{2}{3}$ km and $3\frac{1}{3}$ km.

Symbolically: Solve $5 \le -6x + 25 \le 15 \Rightarrow -20 \le -6x \le -10 \Rightarrow \frac{20}{6} \ge x \ge \frac{10}{6} \Rightarrow 1\frac{2}{3} \le x \le 3\frac{1}{3}$.

The solution interval is the same for either method, $\left[1\frac{2}{3}, 3\frac{1}{3}\right]$. The distance above the ground is between $1\frac{2}{3}$ km and $3\frac{1}{3}$ km.

[0, 4, 1] by [0, 30, 5]

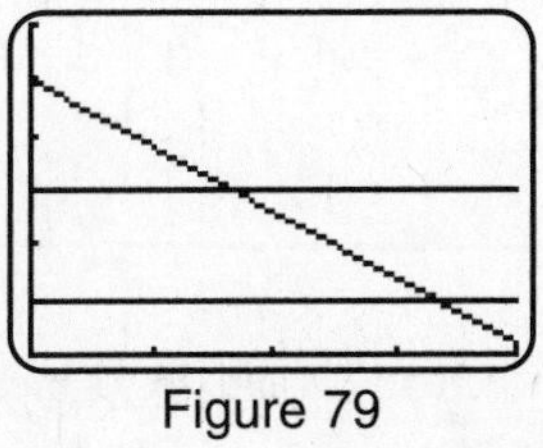

Figure 79

80. (a) $6.15x - 12{,}059 > 70 \Rightarrow 6.15x > 12{,}129 \Rightarrow x > 1972.20$; the number of species first exceeded 70 in 1972.

(b) $50 \le 6.15x - 12{,}059 \le 100 \Rightarrow 12{,}109 \le 6.15x \Rightarrow 12{,}159 \Rightarrow 1968.94 \le x \le 1977.07$. From 1969 to 1977, the number of species was between 50 and 100.

81. $\left|\dfrac{C - A}{A}\right| \le 0.003 \Rightarrow -0.003 \le \dfrac{C - 52.3}{52.3} \le 0.003 \Rightarrow -0.1569 \le C - 52.3 \le 0.1569 \Rightarrow$

$52.1431 \le C \le 52.4569 \Rightarrow$ between 52.1431 and 52.4569 ft.

82. (a) Because $1940 \le 1947 \le 1960$, $f(1947)$ is calculated using the formula

$f(1947) = \dfrac{11}{20}(1947 - 1940) + 7 = 10.85\%$. Similarly, $f(1972)$ is found using the second formula

$f(1972) = \dfrac{32}{15}(1972 - 1960) + 18 = 43.6\%$.

(b) See Figure 82.

(c) The graph has no breaks, so $f$ is continuous on its domain.

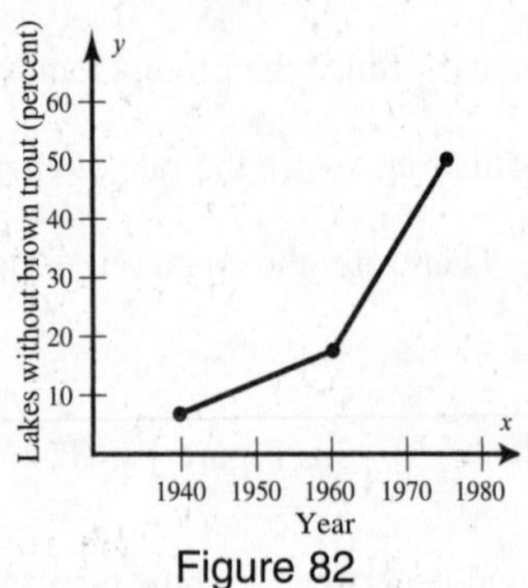

Figure 82

## Extended and Discovery Exercises for Chapter 2

1. (a) 62.8 inches

(b) The $(x, y)$ pairs for females are plotted in Figure 1a and for males in Figure 1b. Both sets of data appear to be linear.

(c) Female: 3.1 inches; male: 3.0 inches

(d) $f(x) = 3.1(x - 8) + 50.4$; $g(x) = 3.0(x - 8) + 53$

(e) $f(9.7) = 55.67$ and $f(10.1) = 56.91$. For a female, the height could vary between 55.67 and 56.91 inches. $g(9.7) = 58.1$ and $g(10.1) = 59.3$. For a male, the height could vary between 58.1 and 59.3 inches.

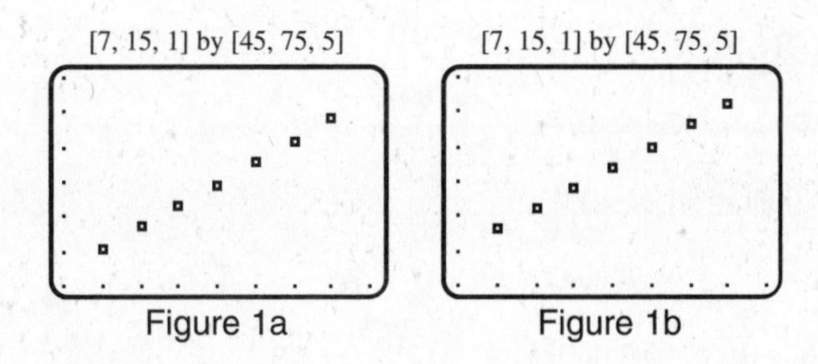


Figure 1a

Figure 1b

2. *Answers may vary.*

3. Let $x$ represent the distance walked by the 1st person. Let $z$ represent the distance walked by the 2nd person. Let $y$ represent the distance the car travels between dropping off the 2nd person and picking up the 1st person. Refer to Figure 3.

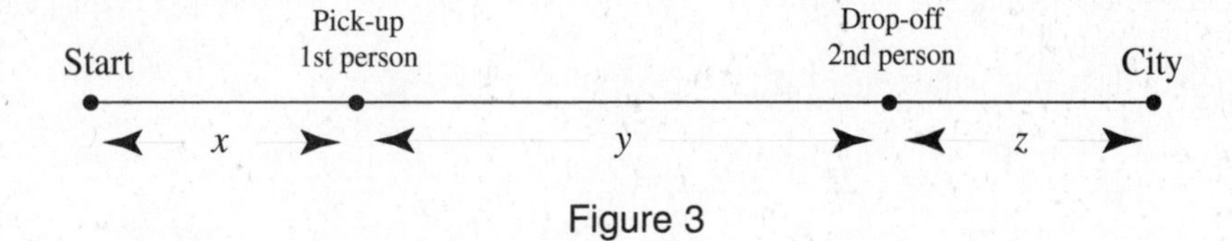


Figure 3

Using the formula time $= \dfrac{\text{distance}}{\text{rate}}$ we obtain the following results:

(1) (time for 1st person to walk distance $x$) $=$ (time for car to drive distance $x + 2y$) $\Rightarrow \dfrac{x}{4} = \dfrac{x + 2y}{28} \Rightarrow$

$28x = 4x + 8y \Rightarrow 24x = 8y \Rightarrow 3x = y.$

(2) (time for 2nd person to walk distance $z$) $=$ (time for car to drive distance $2y + z$) $\Rightarrow \dfrac{z}{4} = \dfrac{2y + z}{28} \Rightarrow$

$28z = 8y + 4z \Rightarrow 24z = 8y \Rightarrow 3z = y.$

(3) The total distance is 15 miles. Thus, $x + y + z = 15$.

Solving these three equations simultaneously results in $x = 3$, $y = 9$, $z = 3$. Each person walked 3 miles.

4. This problem can be solved using ratios; $\dfrac{200 \times 10^6}{4.45 \times 10^9} \approx 0.045$, so dinosaurs appeared 4.5% of the time before midnight December 31. 4.5% of 365 days is approximately 16.4 days; this corresponds to approximately December 15 at 2:24 P.M. Similarly, Homo sapiens first lived approximately $\dfrac{300 \times 10^3}{4.45 \times 10^9} \approx 0.000067$ or 0.0067% of the time before midnight December 31. $0.0067\% \times 365 \approx 0.025$ day. Since there are twenty-four hours in a day, this is equal to $0.025 \times 24 = 0.59$ hour or approximately 35 minutes before midnight. Thus, dinosaurs would have appeared on December 15 at 2:24 P.M., while Homo sapiens would have appeared on December 31 at 11:25 P.M.

5. If $|x - c| < \delta$, then $|f(x) - L| < \epsilon$.

## Chapters 1-2 Cumulative Review Exercises

1. Move the decimal point five places to the left; $123{,}000 = 1.23 \times 10^5$

   Move the decimal point three places to the right; $0.005 = 5.1 \times 10^{-3}$

2. Move the decimal point six places to the right; $6.7 \times 10^6 = 6{,}700{,}000$

   Move the decimal point four places to the left; $1.45 \times 10^{-4} = 0.000145$

3. $\dfrac{4 + \sqrt{2}}{4 - \sqrt{2}} \approx 2.09$

4. (a) Yes, each input has only one output.

   (b) $D = \{-1, 0, 1, 2, 3\}$; $R = \{0, 3, 4, 6\}$

5. The standard equation of a circle must fit the form $(x - h)^2 + (y - k)^2 = r^2$, where $(h, k)$ is the center and the radius $r$. The equation of the circle with center $(-2, 3)$ and radius 7 is $(x + 2)^2 + (y - 3)^2 = 49$.

6. $-5^2 - 2 - \dfrac{10 - 2}{5 - 1} = -25 - 2 - \dfrac{8}{4} = -25 - 2 - 2 = -29$

7. $d = \sqrt{[2 - (-3)]^2 + ((-3) - 5)^2} = \sqrt{25 + 64} = \sqrt{89}$

8. Midpoint $= \left(\dfrac{5 + (-3)}{2}, \dfrac{-2 + 1}{2}\right) = \left(\dfrac{2}{2}, \dfrac{-1}{2}\right) = \left(1, -\dfrac{1}{2}\right)$

9. (a) $D =$ all real numbers $\Rightarrow \{x \mid -\infty < x < \infty\}$; $R = \{y \mid y \geq -2\}$; $f(-1) = -1$

   (b) $D = \{x \mid -3 \leq x \leq 3\}$; $R = \{y \mid -3 \leq y \leq 2\}$; $f(-1) = -\dfrac{1}{2}$

10. (a) See Figure 10a.

    (b) See Figure 10b.

    (c) See Figure 10c.

    (d) See Figure 10d.

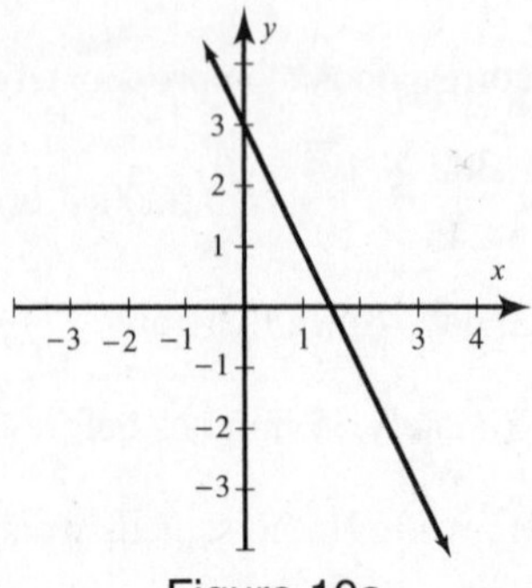

Figure 10a

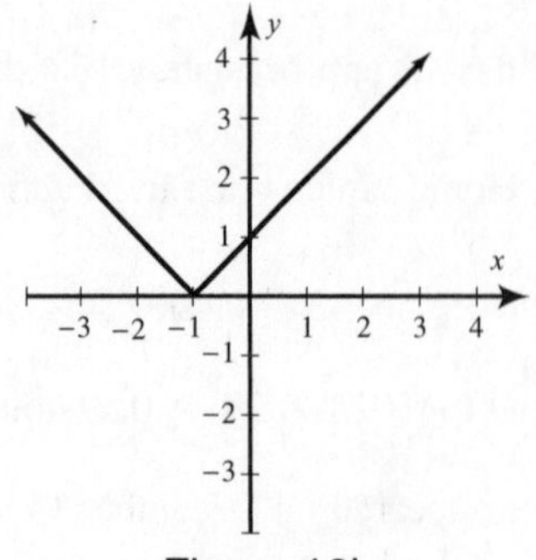

Figure 10b

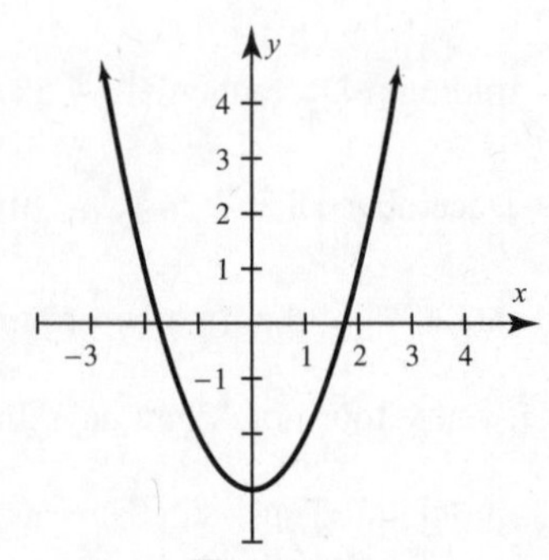

Figure 10c

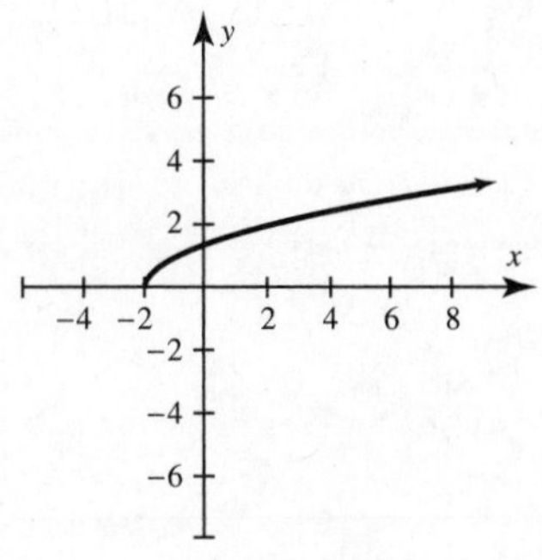

Figure 10d

11. (a) $f(2) = 5(2) - 3 = 7$; $f(a - 1) = 5(a - 1) - 3 = 5a - 5 - 3 = 5a - 8$

(b) The domain of $f$ includes all real numbers $\Rightarrow D = \{x \mid -\infty \leq x \leq \infty\}$

12. (a) $f(2) = \sqrt{2(2) - 1} = \sqrt{3}$; $f(a - 1) = \sqrt{2(a - 1) - 1} = \sqrt{2a - 2 - 1} = \sqrt{2a - 3}$

(b) The domain of $f$ includes all real numbers greater than or equal to $\frac{1}{2} \Rightarrow D = \left\{x \mid x \geq \frac{1}{2}\right\}$.

13. No, this is not a graph of a function because some vertical lines intersect the graph twice.

14. $f(x) = 80x + 89$

15. $f(1) = (1)^2 - 2(1) + 1 = 1 - 2 + 1 = 0 \Rightarrow (1, 0)$; $f(2) = (2)^2 - 2(2) + 1 = 4 - 4 + 1 = 1 \Rightarrow$

$(2, 1)$. The slope $m = \frac{1 - 0}{2 - 1} = \frac{1}{1} = 1$, so the average rate of change is 1.

16. $f(x) = 2x^2 - x$; $f(x + h) = 2(x + h)^2 - (x + h) = 2x^2 + 4xh + 2h^2 - x - h$. The difference quotient

$$= \frac{f(x + h) - f(x)}{h} = \frac{2x^2 + 4xh + 2h^2 - x - h - (2x^2 - x)}{h} = \frac{4xh + 2h^2 - h}{h} = 4x + 2h - 1$$

17. (a) $m = \frac{2}{3}$; $y$-intercept: $-2$, $x$-intercept: 3

(b) $f(x) = mx + b \Rightarrow f(x) = \frac{2}{3}x - 2$

(c) 3

18. (a) $m = -\frac{4}{3}$; $y$-intercept: 2; $x$-intercept: $\frac{3}{2}$

(b) $f(x) = mx + b \Rightarrow f(x) = -\frac{4}{3}x + 2$

(c) $\frac{3}{2}$

19. Using point-slope form

$$y = m(x - x_1) + y_1 \Rightarrow y = -3\left(x - \frac{2}{3}\right) - \frac{2}{3} \Rightarrow y = -3x + \frac{4}{3} \Rightarrow f(x) = -3x + \frac{4}{3}$$

20. The tank initially contains 200 gallons of water and the amount of water is decreasing at a rate of 10 gallons per minute.

21. $m = \frac{\frac{1}{2} - (-5)}{-3 - 1} = \frac{\frac{11}{2}}{-4} = -\frac{11}{8}$; using $(1, -5)$ and point-slope form: $y = -\frac{11}{8}(x - 1) - 5 \Rightarrow$

$y = -\frac{11}{8}x + \frac{11}{8} - 5 \Rightarrow y = -\frac{11}{8}x - \frac{29}{8}$

22. If the line is perpendicular to $y = \frac{2}{3}x - 7$ which has a slope of $\frac{2}{3}$, then its slope is $-\frac{3}{2}$.

Using point-slope form: $y = -\frac{3}{2}(x + 3) + 2 \Rightarrow y = -\frac{3}{2}x - \frac{5}{2}$

23. All lines parallel to the $y$-axis have undefined slope $\Rightarrow$ $y$ changes but $x$ remains constant $\Rightarrow x = -1$.

24. Using point-slope form $y = 30(x - 2002) + 50 \Rightarrow y = 30x - 60{,}010$

25. For the points $(2.4, 5.6)$ and $(3.9, 8.6)$ we get $m = \frac{8.6 - 5.6}{3.9 - 2.4} = \frac{3}{1.5} = 2$. A line parallel to this has the same slope. Using point-slope form: $y = 2(x + 3) + 5 \Rightarrow y = 2x + 11$.

26. Lines perpendicular to the $y$-axis have slope $0 \Rightarrow y = 0$.

27. For $-2x + 3y = 6$: $x$-intercept, then $y = 0 \Rightarrow -2x + 3(0) = 6 \Rightarrow -2x = 6 \Rightarrow x = -3$;

$y$-intercept, then $x = 0 \Rightarrow -2(0) + 3y = 6 \Rightarrow 3y = 6 \Rightarrow y = 2$. See Figure 27.

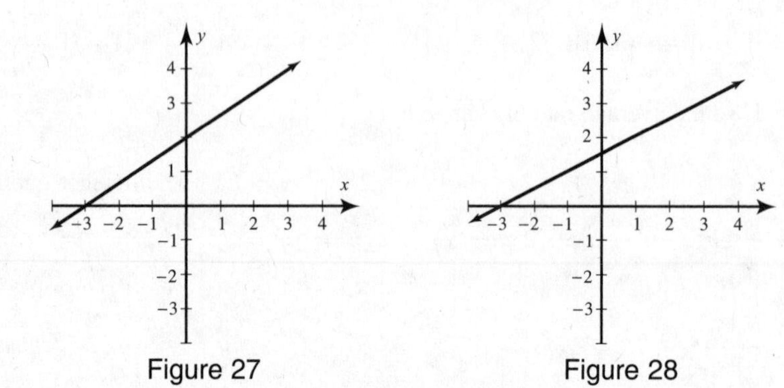


Figure 27 Figure 28

28. For $x = 2y - 3$: $x$-intercept, then $y = 0 \Rightarrow x = 2(0) - 3 \Rightarrow x = -3$;

$y$-intercept, then $x = 0 \Rightarrow 0 = 2y - 3 \Rightarrow 2y = 3 \Rightarrow y = \frac{3}{2}$. See Figure 28.

29. $4x - 5 = 1 - 2x \Rightarrow 6x = 6 \Rightarrow x = 1$; 1

30. $\frac{2x - 4}{2} = \frac{3x}{7} - 1 \Rightarrow 14\left(\frac{2x - 4}{2} = \frac{3x}{7} - 1\right) \Rightarrow 14x - 28 = 6x - 14 \Rightarrow 8x = 14 \Rightarrow x = \frac{14}{8} \Rightarrow$

$x = \frac{7}{4}$; $\frac{7}{4}$

31. $\frac{2}{3}(x - 2) - \frac{4}{5}x = \frac{4}{15} + x \Rightarrow \frac{2}{3}x - \frac{4}{3} - \frac{4}{5}x = \frac{4}{15} + x \Rightarrow 15\left(\frac{2}{3}x - \frac{4}{3} - \frac{4}{5}x = \frac{4}{15} + x\right) \Rightarrow$

$10x - 20 - 12x = 4 + 15x \Rightarrow -17x = 24 \Rightarrow x = -\frac{24}{17}$; $-\frac{24}{17}$

32. $-0.3(1 - x) - 0.1(2x - 3) = 0.4 \Rightarrow -0.3 + 0.3x - 0.2x + 0.3 = 0.4 \Rightarrow 0.1x = 0.4 \Rightarrow x = 4$; 4

33. Graph $Y_1 = X + 1$ and $Y_2 = 2X - 2$. See Figure 33a. The lines intersect at point $(3, 4) \Rightarrow x = 3$. Make a table of $Y_1 = X + 1$ and $Y_2 = 2X - 2$ for $x$ values from 0 to 5. See Figure 33b.

Both equations have $y$-value 4 at $x = 3$.

[−10, 10, 1] by [−10, 10, 1]

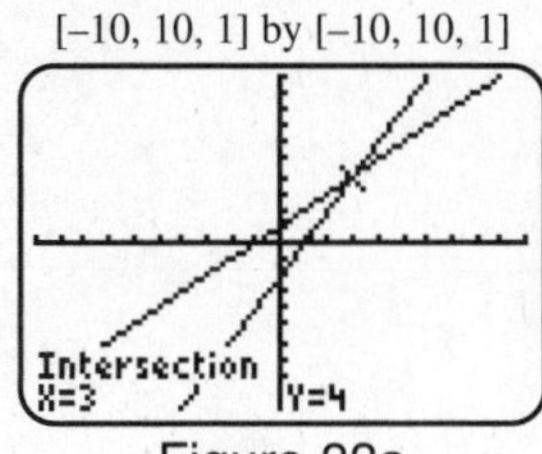

Figure 33a

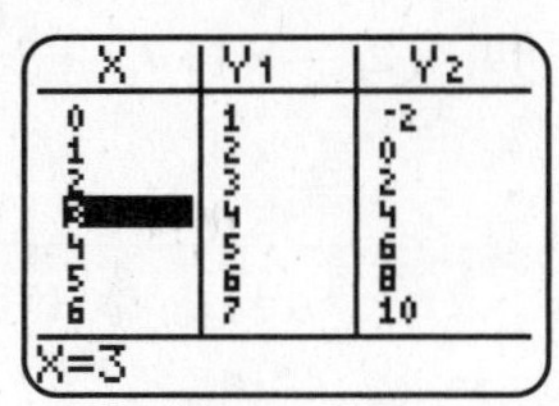

| X | Y1 | Y2 |
|---|---|---|
| 0 | 1 | -2 |
| 1 | 2 | 0 |
| 2 | 3 | 2 |
| 3 | 4 | 4 |
| 4 | 5 | 6 |
| 5 | 6 | 8 |
| 6 | 7 | 10 |

X=3

Figure 33b

34. $2x - (5 - x) = \dfrac{1 - 4x}{2} + 5(x - 2) \Rightarrow 3x - 5 = \dfrac{1 - 4x}{2} + 5x - 10 \Rightarrow$

$6x - 10 = 1 - 4x + 10x - 20 \Rightarrow 6x - 10 = 6x - 19 \Rightarrow -10 = -19$, no solutions $\Rightarrow$ The equation is a contradiction.

35. $(-\infty, 5)$

36. $[-2, 5]$

37. $(-\infty, -2) \cup (2, \infty)$

38. $[-3, \infty)$

39. $-3(1 - 2x) + x \le 4 - (x + 2) \Rightarrow -3 + 6x + x \le 4 - x - 2 \Rightarrow 7x - 3 \le -x + 2 \Rightarrow 8x \le 5 \Rightarrow$

$x \le \dfrac{5}{8} \Rightarrow \left(-\infty, \dfrac{5}{8}\right]$. In set builder notation the interval is $\left\{x \,|\, x \le \dfrac{5}{8}\right\}$.

40. $\dfrac{1}{3} \le \dfrac{2 - 3x}{2} < \dfrac{4}{3} \Rightarrow 6\left(\dfrac{1}{3} \le \dfrac{2 - 3x}{2} < \dfrac{4}{3}\right) \Rightarrow 2 \le 6 - 9x < 8 \Rightarrow -4 \le -9x < 2 \Rightarrow$

$\dfrac{4}{9} \ge x > -\dfrac{2}{9} \Rightarrow -\dfrac{2}{9} < x \le \dfrac{4}{9} \Rightarrow \left(-\dfrac{2}{9}, \dfrac{4}{9}\right]$. In set builder notation the interval is $\left\{x \,|\, -\dfrac{2}{9} < x \le \dfrac{4}{9}\right\}$.

41. (a) 2

(b) The graph of $f(x)$ is above the graph of $g(x)$ to the left of $x = 2 \Rightarrow x < 2$

(c) The graph of $f(x)$ intersects or is below the graph of $g(x)$ to the right of $x = 2 \Rightarrow f(x) \le g(x)$ when $x \ge 2$.

42. See Figure 42. $f$ has a break in it at $x = 2 \Rightarrow f$ is not continuous.

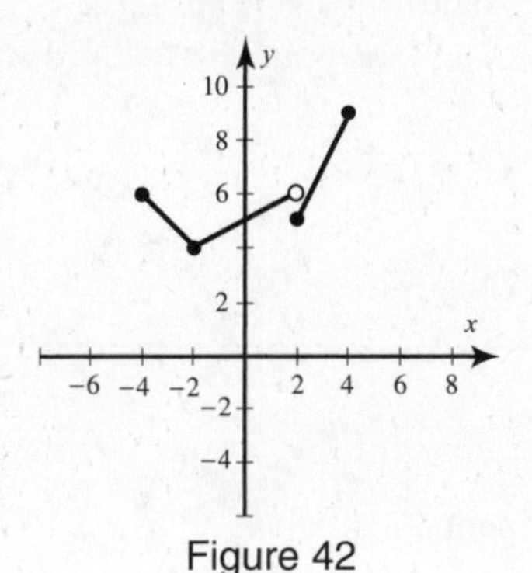

Figure 42

43. $|d + 1| = 5 \Rightarrow d + 1 = 5$ or $d + 1 = -5$. If $d + 1 = -5, d = -6$; if $d + 1 = 5, d = 4 \Rightarrow -6, 4$.

44. $|3 - 2x| = 7 \Rightarrow 3 - 2x = 7$ or $3 - 2x = -7$. If $3 - 2x = -7, -2x = -10 \Rightarrow x = 5$; if $3 - 2x = 7, -2x = 4 \Rightarrow x = -2 \Rightarrow -2, 5$.

45. $|2t| - 4 = 10 \Rightarrow |2t| = 14 \Rightarrow 2t = 14$ or $2t = -14$. If $2t = -14, t = -\frac{14}{2} \Rightarrow t = -7$; if $2t = 14, t = 7 \Rightarrow -7, 7$.

46. $|11 - 2x| = |3x + 1| \Rightarrow 11 - 2x = 3x + 1$ or $11 - 2x = -(3x + 1)$. If $11 - 2x = 3x + 1$, $-5x = -10 \Rightarrow x = 2$; if $11 - 2x = -(3x + 1), x = -12 \Rightarrow -12, 2$.

47. The solutions to $|2t - 5| \le 5$ satisfy $s_1 \le t \le s_2$ where $s_1$ and $s_2$, are the solutions to $|2t - 5| = 5$. $|2t - 5| = 5$ is equivalent to $2t - 5 = -5 \Rightarrow t = 0$ or $2t - 5 = 5 \Rightarrow t = 5$.
The interval is $[0, 5]$. In set-builder notation the interval is $\{t \mid 0 \le t \le 5\}$.

48. The solutions to $|5 - 5t| > 7$ satisfy $t < s_1$ or $t > s_2$, where $s_1$ and $s_2$ are the solutions to $|5 - 5t| = 7$. $|5 - 5t| = 7$ is equivalent to $5 - 5t = -7 \Rightarrow t = \frac{12}{5}$ or $5 - 5t = 7 \Rightarrow t = -\frac{2}{5}$.
The interval is $\left(-\infty, -\frac{2}{5}\right) \cup \left(\frac{12}{5}, \infty\right)$. In set-builder notation the interval is $\left\{t \mid t < -\frac{2}{5} \text{ or } t > \frac{12}{5}\right\}$.

49. $V = \pi r^2 h \Rightarrow 24 = \pi(1.5)^2 h \Rightarrow 24 = \pi(2.25)h \Rightarrow h \approx 3.40$ inches

50. Slope $= \frac{\text{rise}}{\text{run}} = \frac{20}{4} = 5, m_1 = 5$; gravel is being loaded into the truck at a rate of 5 tons per minute. $m_2 = \frac{0}{16} = 0$: no gravel is being loaded into or unloaded from the truck. $m_3 = -\frac{20}{2} = -10$: gravel is being unloaded from the truck at a rate of 10 tons per minute.

51. (a) $C(1500) = 500(1500) + 20{,}000 = 770{,}000$; it costs \$770,000 to manufacture 1500 computers.
(b) 500; each additional computer costs \$500 to manufacture.

52. If car $B$ is at the origin on a coordinate plane then car $A$ travels $60\left(\frac{5}{4}\right) = 75$ miles and ends up at the point $(0, 35)$, 35 miles north of where car $B$ started. Car $B$ travels $70\left(\frac{5}{4}\right) = 87.5$ miles west and ends up at $(-87.5, 0)$. Using the distance formula:

$$d = \sqrt{(-87.5 - 0)^2 + (0 - 35)^2} \Rightarrow d = \sqrt{7656.25 + 1225} \Rightarrow d = \sqrt{8881.25} \Rightarrow d \approx 94.2 \text{ mi.}$$

53. (a) $T(2) = 70 + \frac{3}{2}(2)^2 = 70 + 6 = 76$; $T(4) = 70 + \frac{3}{2}(4)^2 = 70 + 24 = 94$

Using (2, 76) and (4, 94): $m = \frac{94 - 76}{4 - 2} = \frac{18}{2} = 9$°F increase per hour.

(b) On average the temperature increased by 9°F per hour over this 2-hour period.

54. (a) $D(x) = 270 - 72x$

(b) Since $72x = 270 \Rightarrow x = 3.75$, the driver arrives home in 3.75 hours, so times after that are unnecessary. An appropriate domain is $\{x | 0 \leq x \leq 3.75\}$. See figure 54.

(c) $x$-intercept: when $y = 0 \Rightarrow 0 = 270 - 72(x) \Rightarrow 72x = 270 \Rightarrow x = 3.75$; the driver arrives home after 3.75 hours. $y$-intercept: when $x = 0 \Rightarrow y = 270 - 72(0) \Rightarrow y = 270$; the driver is initially 270 miles from home.

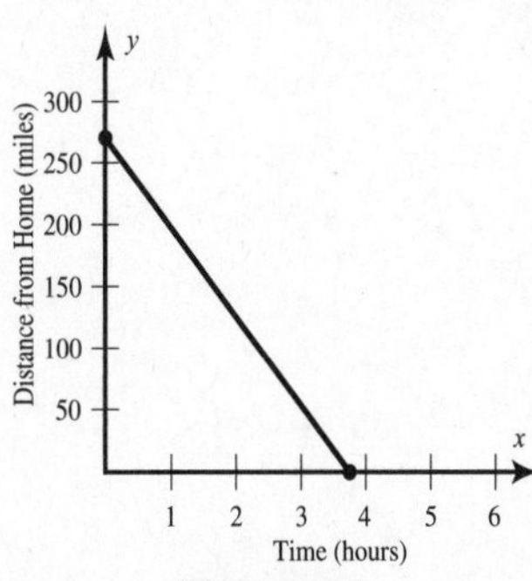

Figure 54

55. Let $t$ = time for the two to mow the lawn together. Then the first person mows $\frac{1}{5}t$ of the lawn and the second person mows $\frac{1}{12}t$ of the lawn $\Rightarrow \frac{1}{5}t + \frac{1}{12}t = 1 \Rightarrow \frac{12}{60}t + \frac{5}{60}t = 1 \Rightarrow \frac{17}{60}t = 1 \Rightarrow t = \frac{60}{17} = 3.53$ hours.

56. Let $x$ = time run at 8 mph and $\left(\frac{7}{4} - x\right)$ = time run at 10 mph. Then $8x + 10\left(\frac{7}{4} - x\right) = 15 \Rightarrow$

$8x + \frac{70}{4} - 10x = 15 \Rightarrow -2x = -\frac{10}{4} \Rightarrow x = \frac{5}{4} \Rightarrow$ 1.25 hours at 8mph and then 0.5 hour at 10 mph.

57. (a) Using (2001, 56) and (2012, 61), $m = \frac{61 - 56}{2012 - 2001} = \frac{5}{11}$; $f(x) = \frac{5}{11}(x - 2001) + 56$

(b) $f(2007) = \frac{5}{11}(2007 - 2001) + 56 = \frac{5}{11}(6) + 56 = \frac{30}{11} + 56 \approx 58.7$ lbs.

58. $\left|\frac{M - A}{A}\right| \leq 0.03 \Rightarrow \left|\frac{M - 65}{65}\right| \leq 0.03 \Rightarrow -0.03 \leq \frac{M - 65}{65} \leq 0.03 \Rightarrow -1.95 \leq M - 65 \leq 1.95 \Rightarrow$

$63.05 \leq M \leq 66.95 \Rightarrow$ 63.05 to 66.95

59. (a) Enter the data (1970, 4095), (1980, 10,182), (1990, 19,572) and (2000, 29,760);

$f(x) = 863.84x - 1{,}698{,}819.9$

(b) $f(1995) \approx 863.84(1995) - 1{,}698{,}819.9 \approx \$24{,}541$; this estimate is an interpolation.

60. (a) The slope of the line passing through (58, 91) and (64, 111) is $m = \frac{111 - 91}{64 - 58} = \frac{10}{3}$. Thus, let

$f(x) = \frac{10}{3}(x - 58) + 91.$

(b) $f(61) = \frac{10}{3}(61 - 58) + 91 = 101$. The recommended minimum weight is 101 pounds for a person 61 inches tall. Since 61 inches is the midpoint between 58 and 64 inches, we can use a midpoint approximation. The midpoint between (58, 91) and (64, 111) is $\left(\frac{58 + 64}{2}, \frac{91 + 111}{2}\right) = (61, 101)$. The recommended minimum weight is again 101. The midpoint formula gives the midpoint on the graph of $f$ between the two given points. The answers are the same.

# Chapter 3: Quadratic Functions and Equations

## 3.1: Quadratic Functions and Models

1. $f(x) = 1 - 2x + 3x^2$ is quadratic; $a = 3$; $f(-2) = 1 - 2(-2) + 3(-2)^2 = 17$.

2. $f(x) = -5x + 11$ is linear.

3. $f(x) = \dfrac{1}{x^2 - 1}$ is neither linear nor quadratic.

4. $f(x) = (x^2 + 1)^2 = x^4 + 2x^2 + 1$ is neither linear nor quadratic.

5. $f(x) = \dfrac{1}{2} - \dfrac{3}{10}x$ is linear.

6. $f(x) = \dfrac{1}{5}x^2$ is quadratic; a $= \dfrac{1}{5}$; $f(-2) = \dfrac{1}{5}(-2)^2 = \dfrac{4}{5}$

7. (a) $a > 0$

   (b) vertex: (1, 0)

   (c) axis of symmetry: $x = 1$

   (d) $f$ is increasing for $x \geq 1$ and decreasing for $x \leq 1$.

8. (a) $a < 0$

   (b) vertex: (–2, 2)

   (c) axis of symmetry: $x = -2$

   (d) $f$ is increasing for $x \leq -2$ and decreasing for $x \geq -2$.

9. (a) $a < 0$

   (b) vertex: (–3, –2)

   (c) axis of symmetry: $x = -3$

   (d) $f$ is increasing for $x \leq -3$ and decreasing for $x \geq -3$.

10. (a) $a > 0$

    (b) vertex: (0, 0)

    (c) axis of symmetry: $x = 0$

    (d) $f$ is increasing for $x \geq 0$ and decreasing for $x \leq 0$.

11. The graph of $g$ is narrower than the graph of $f$.

12. The graph of $g$ opens downward rather than upward.

13. The graph of $g$ is wider than the graph of $f$ and opens downward rather than upward.

14. The graph of $g$ is wider than the graph of $f$.

15. $f(x) = -3(x - 1)^2 + 2 \Rightarrow$ vertex: $(1, 2)$; leading coefficient: $-3$; $f(x) = -3x^2 + 6x - 1$

16. $f(x) = 5(x + 2)^2 - 5 \Rightarrow$ vertex: $(-2, -5)$; leading coefficient: 5; $f(x) = 5x^2 + 20x + 15$

17. $f(x) = 5 - 2(x - 4)^2 \Rightarrow$ vertex: $(4, 5)$; leading coefficient: $-2$; $f(x) = -2x^2 + 16x - 27$

18. $f(x) = \dfrac{1}{2}(x + 3)^2 - 5 \Rightarrow$ vertex: $(-3, -5)$; leading coefficient: $\dfrac{1}{2}$; $f(x) = \dfrac{1}{2}x^2 + 3x - \dfrac{1}{2}$

19. $f(x) = \frac{3}{4}(x+5)^2 - \frac{7}{4} \Rightarrow$ vertex: $\left(-5, -\frac{7}{4}\right)$; leading coefficient: $\frac{3}{4}$; $f(x) = \frac{3}{4}x^2 + \frac{15}{2}x + 17$

20. $f(x) = -5(x-4)^2 \Rightarrow$ vertex: $(4, 0)$; leading coefficient: $-5$; $f(x) = -5x^2 + 40x - 80$.

21. The vertex of the parabola is (2, –2), so $f(x) = a(x-h)^2 + k \Rightarrow f(x) = a(x-2)^2 - 2$; since (0, 2) is a point on the parabola, $f(0) = a(0-2)^2 - 2 \Rightarrow 2 = a(-2)^2 - 2 \Rightarrow 4 = 4a \Rightarrow a = 1$; $f(x) = (x-2)^2 - 2$.

22. The vertex of the parabola is (–1, –1), so $f(x) = a(x-h)^2 + k \Rightarrow f(x) = a(x+1)^2 - 1$; since (0, –3) is a point on the parabola, $f(0) = a(0+1)^2 - 1 \Rightarrow -3 = a - 1 \Rightarrow a = -2$; $f(x) = -2(x+1)^2 - 1$.

23. The vertex of the parabola is (2, –3), so $f(x) = a(x-h)^2 + k \Rightarrow f(x) = a(x-2)^2 - 3$; since (0, –1) is a point on the parabola, $f(0) = a(0-2)^2 - 3 \Rightarrow -1 = a(4) - 3 \Rightarrow -1 = 4a - 3 \Rightarrow 2 = 4a \Rightarrow$ $a = \frac{1}{2}$; $f(x) = \frac{1}{2}(x-2)^2 - 3$.

24. The vertex of the parabola is $(-2, -4)$, so $f(x) = a(x-h)^2 + k \Rightarrow f(x) = a(x+2)^2 - 4$; since (0, –2) is a point on the parabola, $f(0) = a(0+2)^2 - 4 \Rightarrow -2 = a(2)^2 - 4 \Rightarrow -2 = 4a - 4 \Rightarrow 2 = 4a \Rightarrow$ $a = \frac{1}{2}$; $f(x) = \frac{1}{2}(x+2)^2 - 4$.

25. The vertex of the parabola is (–1, 3), so $f(x) = a(x-h)^2 + k \Rightarrow f(x) = a(x+1)^2 + 3$; since (0, 1) is a point on the parabola, $f(0) = a(0+1)^2 + 3 \Rightarrow 1 = a(1) + 3 \Rightarrow 1 = a + 3 \Rightarrow a = -2$; $f(x) = -2(x+1)^2 + 3$.

26. The vertex of the parabola is $(1, -1)$, so $f(x) = a(x-h)^2 + k \Rightarrow f(x) = a(x-1)^2 - 1$; since (0, 1) is a point on the parabola, $f(0) = a(0-1)^2 - 1 \Rightarrow 1 = a - 1 \Rightarrow a = 2$; $f(x) = 2(x-1)^2 - 1$.

27. The vertex of the parabola is (2, 6), so $f(x) = a(x-h)^2 + k \Rightarrow f(x) = a(x-2)^2 + 6$; since $(0, -6)$ is a point on the parabola, $f(0) = a(0-2)^2 + 6 \Rightarrow -6 = 4a + 6 \Rightarrow -12 = 4a \Rightarrow a = -3$; $f(x) = -3(x-2)^2 + 6$.

28. The vertex of the parabola is (1, 1), so $f(x) = a(x-h)^2 + k \Rightarrow f(x) = a(x-1)^2 + 1$; since (0, –2) is a point on the parabola, $f(0) = a(0-1)^2 + 1 \Rightarrow -2 = a + 1 \Rightarrow a = -3$; $f(x) = -3(x-1)^2 + 1$.

29. $f(x) = x^2 + 4x - 5 \Rightarrow x = -\frac{b}{2a} = -\frac{4}{2(1)} = -2$ and $f(-2) = (-2)^2 + 4(-2) - 5 = -9 \Rightarrow$ vertex: $(-2, -9)$; since $a = 1$, $f(x) = 1(x - (-2))^2 - 9$, or $f(x) = (x+2)^2 - 9$

30. $f(x) = x^2 + 10x + 7 \Rightarrow x = -\frac{b}{2a} = -\frac{10}{2(1)} = -5$ and $f(-5) = (-5)^2 + 10(-5) + 7 = -18 \Rightarrow$ vertex: $(-5, -18)$; since $a = 1$, $f(x) = 1(x - (-5))^2 - 18$, or $f(x) = (x+5)^2 - 18$

31. $f(x) = x^2 - 3x \Rightarrow x = -\frac{b}{2a} = -\frac{(-3)}{2(1)} = \frac{3}{2}$ and $f\left(\frac{3}{2}\right) = \left(\frac{3}{2}\right)^2 - 3\left(\frac{3}{2}\right) = -\frac{9}{4} \Rightarrow$ vertex: $\left(\frac{3}{2}, -\frac{9}{4}\right)$; since $a = 1$, $f(x) = 1\left(x - \frac{3}{2}\right)^2 - \frac{9}{4}$, or $f(x) = \left(x - \frac{3}{2}\right)^2 - \frac{9}{4}$

32. $f(x) = x^2 - 7x + 5 \Rightarrow x = -\dfrac{b}{2a} = -\dfrac{(-7)}{2(1)} = \dfrac{7}{2}$ and

$f\left(\dfrac{7}{2}\right) = \left(\dfrac{7}{2}\right)^2 - 7\left(\dfrac{7}{2}\right) + 5 = -\dfrac{29}{4} \Rightarrow$ vertex: $\left(\dfrac{7}{2}, -\dfrac{29}{4}\right)$; since $a = 1$, $f(x) = 1\left(x - \dfrac{7}{2}\right)^2 - \dfrac{29}{4}$, or

$f(x) = \left(x - \dfrac{7}{2}\right)^2 - \dfrac{29}{4}$

33. $f(x) = 2x^2 - 5x + 3 \Rightarrow x = -\dfrac{b}{2a} = -\dfrac{(-5)}{2(2)} = \dfrac{5}{4}$ and

$f\left(\dfrac{5}{4}\right) = 2\left(\dfrac{5}{4}\right)^2 - 5\left(\dfrac{5}{4}\right) + 3 = -\dfrac{1}{8} \Rightarrow$ vertex: $\left(\dfrac{5}{4}, -\dfrac{1}{8}\right)$; since $a = 2$, $f(x) = 2\left(x - \dfrac{5}{4}\right)^2 - \dfrac{1}{8}$

34. $f(x) = 3x^2 + 6x + 2 \Rightarrow x = -\dfrac{b}{2a} = -\dfrac{6}{2(3)} = -1$ and

$f(-1) = 3(-1)^2 + 6(-1) + 2 = -1 \Rightarrow$ vertex: $(-1, -1)$; since $a = 3$, $f(x) = 3(x + 1)^2 - 1$

35. $f(x) = \dfrac{1}{3}x^2 + x + 1 \Rightarrow x = -\dfrac{b}{2a} = -\dfrac{1}{2(\frac{1}{3})} = -\dfrac{1}{\frac{2}{3}} = -\dfrac{3}{2}$ and

$f\left(-\dfrac{3}{2}\right) = \dfrac{1}{3}\left(-\dfrac{3}{2}\right)^2 - \dfrac{3}{2} + 1 = \dfrac{1}{4} \Rightarrow$ vertex: $\left(-\dfrac{3}{2}, \dfrac{1}{4}\right)$; since $a = \dfrac{1}{3}$, $f(x) = \dfrac{1}{3}\left(x + \dfrac{3}{2}\right)^2 + \dfrac{1}{4}$

36. $f(x) = -\dfrac{1}{2}x^2 - \dfrac{3}{2}x + 1 \Rightarrow x = -\dfrac{b}{2a} = -\dfrac{(-\frac{3}{2})}{2(-\frac{1}{2})} = -\dfrac{3}{2}$ and

$f\left(-\dfrac{3}{2}\right) = -\dfrac{1}{2}\left(-\dfrac{3}{2}\right)^2 - \dfrac{3}{2}\left(-\dfrac{3}{2}\right) + 1 = \dfrac{17}{8} \Rightarrow$

vertex: $\left(-\dfrac{3}{2}, \dfrac{17}{8}\right)$; since $a = -\dfrac{1}{2}$, $f(x) = -\dfrac{1}{2}\left(x + \dfrac{3}{2}\right)^2 + \dfrac{17}{8}$

37. $f(x) = 2x^2 - 8x - 1 \Rightarrow x = -\dfrac{b}{2a} = -\dfrac{(-8)}{2(2)} = 2$ and

$f(2) = 2(2)^2 - 8(2) - 1 = -9 \Rightarrow$ vertex: $(2, -9)$; since $a = 2$, $f(x) = 2(x - 2)^2 - 9$

38. $f(x) = -\dfrac{1}{2}x^2 - x \Rightarrow x = -\dfrac{b}{2a} = -\dfrac{(-1)}{2(-\frac{1}{2})} = -1$ and

$f(-1) = -\dfrac{1}{2}(-1)^2 - (-1) = \dfrac{1}{2} \Rightarrow$ vertex: $\left(-1, \dfrac{1}{2}\right)$; since $a = -\dfrac{1}{2}$, $f(x) = -\dfrac{1}{2}(x - (-1))^2 + \dfrac{1}{2}$, or

$f(x) = -\dfrac{1}{2}(x + 1)^2 + \dfrac{1}{2}$

39. $f(x) = 2 - 9x - 3x^2 \Rightarrow x = -\dfrac{b}{2a} = -\dfrac{(-9)}{2(-3)} = -1.5$ and

$f(-1.5) = 2 - 9(-1.5) - 3(-1.5)^2 = 8.75 \Rightarrow$ vertex: $(-1.5, 8.75)$; since $a = -3$,

$f(x) = -3(x - (-1.5))^2 + 8.75$, or $f(x) = -3(x + 1.5)^2 + 8.75$

40. $f(x) = 6 + 5x - 10x^2 \Rightarrow x = -\dfrac{b}{2a} = -\dfrac{5}{2(-10)} = \dfrac{1}{4} = 0.25$ and

$f(0.25) = 6 + 5(0.25) - 10(0.25)^2 = 6.625 \Rightarrow$ vertex: $(0.25, 6.625)$; since $a = -10$,

$f(x) = -10(x - 0.25)^2 + 6.625$

41. (a) It may be helpful to write $f$ in standard form as follows: $f(x) = -x^2 + 0x + 6$.

To find the vertex symbolically, use the vertex formula with $a = -1$ and $b = 0$.

$x = -\frac{b}{2a} = -\frac{0}{2(-1)} = \frac{0}{2} = 0$. The $x$-coordinate of the vertex is 0.

$y = f\left(-\frac{b}{2a}\right) = f(0) = 6 - (0)^2 = 6$. The $y$-coordinate of the vertex is 6. Thus, the vertex is $(0, 6)$.

The graph of $Y_1 = 6 - X\text{^}2$ shows graphical support for this vertex. See Figure 41.

(b) $f$ is increasing on $x \leq 0$ or $(-\infty, 0]$ and decreasing on $x \geq 0$ or $[0, \infty)$.

42. (a) The function is already in standard form: $f(x) = 2x^2 - 2x + 1$.

To find the vertex symbolically, use the vertex formula with $a = 2$ and $b = -2$.

$x = -\frac{b}{2a} = -\frac{(-2)}{2(2)} = \frac{2}{4} = \frac{1}{2}$. The $x$-coordinate of the vertex is $\frac{1}{2}$.

$y = f\left(-\frac{b}{2a}\right) = f\left(\frac{1}{2}\right) = 2\left(\frac{1}{2}\right)^2 - 2\left(\frac{1}{2}\right) + 1 = \frac{1}{2}$. The $y$-coordinate of the vertex is $\frac{1}{2}$. Thus, the vertex is $\left(\frac{1}{2}, \frac{1}{2}\right)$. The graph of $Y_1 = 2X\text{^}2 - 2X + 1$ shows graphical support for this vertex. See Figure 42.

(b) $f$ is increasing on $x \geq \frac{1}{2}$ or $\left[\frac{1}{2}, \infty\right)$ and decreasing on $x \leq \frac{1}{2}$ or $\left(-\infty, \frac{1}{2}\right]$.

[-10, 10, 1] by [-10, 10, 1]

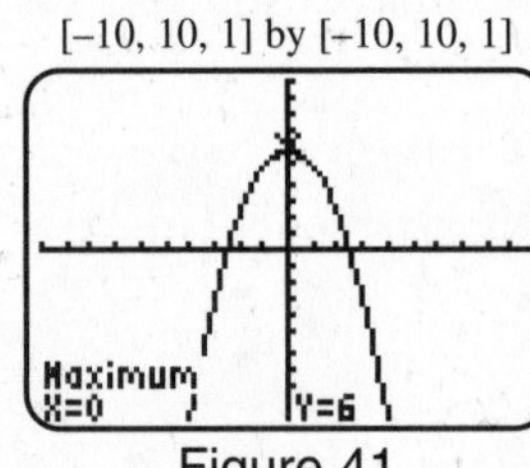

Figure 41

[-10, 10, 1] by [-10, 10, 1]

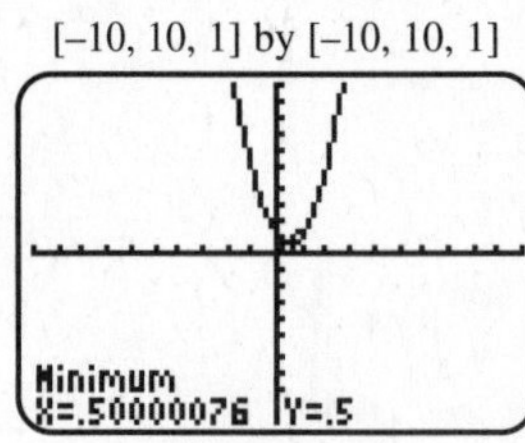

Figure 42

[-10, 10, 1] by [-15, 5, 1]

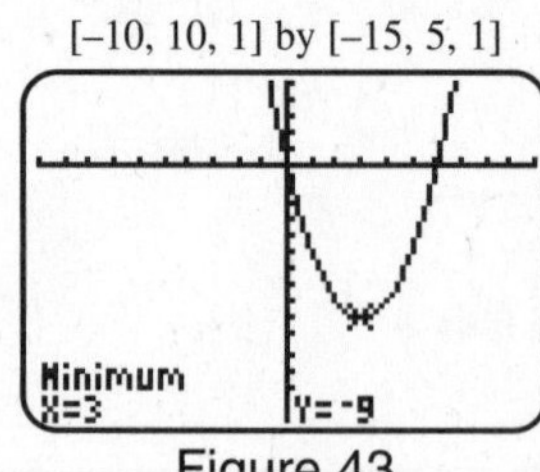

Figure 43

[-10, 10, 1] by [-10, 10, 1]

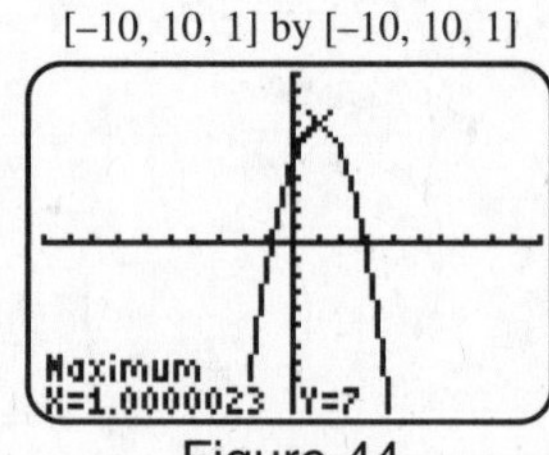

Figure 44

43. (a) It may be helpful to write $f$ in standard form as follows: $f(x) = x^2 - 6x + 0$.

To find the vertex symbolically, use the vertex formula with $a = 1$ and $b = -6$.

$x = -\frac{b}{2a} = -\frac{(-6)}{2(1)} = \frac{6}{2} = 3$. The $x$-coordinate of the vertex is 3.

$y = f\left(-\frac{b}{2a}\right) = f(3) = (3)^2 - 6(3) = -9$. The $y$-coordinate of the vertex is –9. Thus, the vertex is (3, –9). The graph of $Y_1 = X\text{^}2 - 6X$ shows graphical support for this vertex. See Figure 43.

(b) $f$ is increasing on $x \geq 3$ or $[3, \infty)$ and decreasing on $x \leq 3$ or $(-\infty, 3]$.

44. (a) The function is already in standard form: $f(x) = -2x^2 + 4x + 5$.

To find the vertex symbolically, use the vertex formula with $a = -2$ and $b = 4$.

$x = -\frac{b}{2a} = -\frac{4}{2(-2)} = \frac{4}{4} = 1$. The $x$-coordinate of the vertex is 1.

$y = f\left(-\frac{b}{2a}\right) = f(1) = -2(1)^2 + 4(1) + 5 = 7$. The $y$-coordinate of the vertex is 7. Thus, the vertex is (1, 7). The graph of $Y_1 = -2X\text{^}2 + 4X + 5$ shows graphical support for this vertex. See Figure 44.

(b) $f$ is increasing on $x \leq 1$ or $(-\infty, 1]$ and decreasing on $x \geq 1$ or $[1, \infty)$.

45. (a) The function is already in standard form: $f(x) = 2x^2 - 4x + 1$.

To find the vertex symbolically, use the vertex formula with $a = 2$ and $b = -4$.

$x = -\frac{b}{2a} = -\frac{(-4)}{2(2)} = \frac{4}{4} = 1$. The $x$-coordinate of the vertex is 1.

$y = f\left(-\frac{b}{2a}\right) = f(1) = 2(1)^2 - 4(1) + 1 = -1$. The $y$-coordinate of the vertex is $-1$. Thus, the vertex is $(1, -1)$. The graph of $Y_1 = 2X\text{^}2 - 4X + 1$ shows graphical support for this vertex. See Figure 45.

(b) $f$ is increasing on $x \geq 1$ or $[1, \infty)$ and decreasing on $x \leq 1$ or $(-\infty, 1]$.

46. (a) The function is already in standard form: $f(x) = -3x^2 + x - 2$.

To find the vertex symbolically, use the vertex formula with $a = -3$ and $b = 1$.

$x = -\frac{b}{2a} = -\frac{1}{2(-3)} = \frac{1}{6}$. The $x$-coordinate of the vertex is $\frac{1}{6}$.

$y = f\left(-\frac{b}{2a}\right) = f\left(\frac{1}{6}\right) = -3\left(\frac{1}{6}\right)^2 + \left(\frac{1}{6}\right) - 2 = -\frac{23}{12}$. The $y$-coordinate of the vertex is $-\frac{23}{12}$. Thus, the vertex is $\left(\frac{1}{6}, -\frac{23}{12}\right)$. The graph of $Y_1 = -3X\text{^}2 + X - 2$ shows graphical support for this vertex. See Figure 46.

(b) $f$ is increasing on $x \leq \frac{1}{6}$ or $\left(-\infty, \frac{1}{6}\right]$ and decreasing on $x \geq \frac{1}{6}$ or $\left[\frac{1}{6}, \infty\right)$.

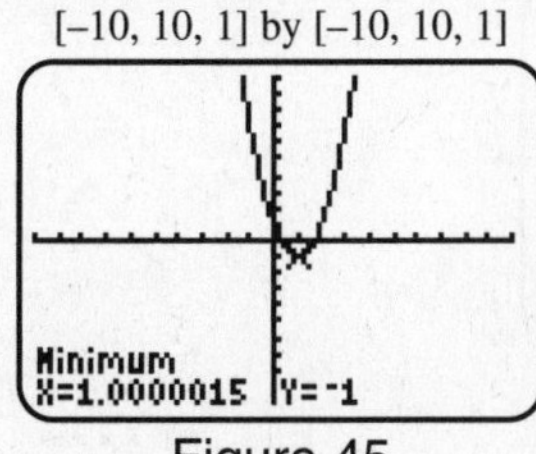

Figure 45

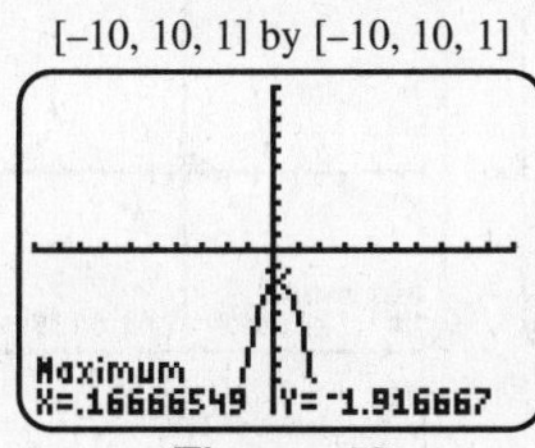

Figure 46

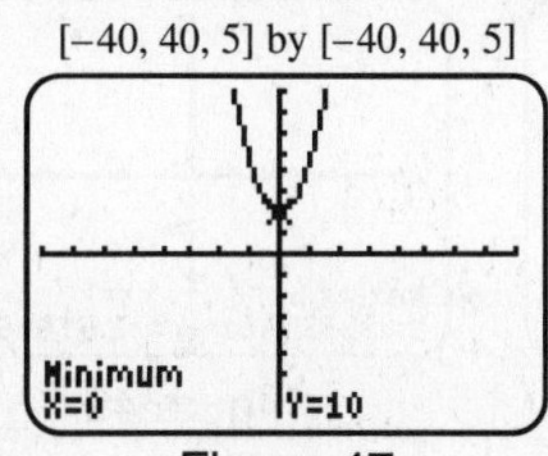

Figure 47

47. (a) It may be helpful to write $f$ in standard form as follows: $f(x) = \frac{1}{2}x^2 + 0x + 10$.

To find the vertex symbolically, use the vertex formula with $a = \frac{1}{2}$ and $b = 0$.

$x = -\frac{b}{2a} = -\frac{0}{2(\frac{1}{2})} = 0$. The $x$-coordinate of the vertex is 0.

$y = f\left(-\frac{b}{2a}\right) = f(0) = \frac{1}{2}(0)^2 + 0(0) + 10 = 10$. The $y$-coordinate of the vertex is 10. Thus, the vertex is (0, 10). The graph of $Y_1 = (1/2)X\text{^}2 + 10$ shows graphical support for this vertex. See Figure 47.

(b) $f$ is increasing on $x \geq 0$ or $[0, \infty)$ and decreasing on $x \leq 0$ or $(-\infty, 0]$.

48. (a) It may be helpful to write $f$ in standard form as follows: $f(x) = \frac{9}{10}x^2 + 0x - 12.$

To find the vertex symbolically, use the vertex formula with $a = \frac{9}{10}$ and $b = 0.$

$x = -\frac{b}{2a} = -\frac{0}{2(\frac{9}{10})} = 0.$ The $x$-coordinate of the vertex is 0.

$y = f\left(-\frac{b}{2a}\right) = f(0) = \frac{9}{10}(0)^2 + 0(0) - 12 = -12.$ The $y$-coordinate of the vertex is $-12$. Thus, the vertex is $(0, -12)$. The graph of $Y_1 = (9/10)X\text{^}2 - 12$ shows graphical support for this vertex. See Figure 48.

(b) $f$ is increasing on $x \geq 0$ or $[0, \infty)$ and decreasing on $x \leq 0$ or $(-\infty, 0]$.

49. (a) The function is already in standard form: $f(x) = -\frac{3}{4}x^2 + \frac{1}{2}x - 3.$

To find the vertex symbolically, use the vertex formula with $a = -\frac{3}{4}$ and $b = \frac{1}{2}.$

$x = -\frac{b}{2a} = -\frac{\frac{1}{2}}{2(-\frac{3}{4})} = \frac{1}{3}.$ The $x$-coordinate of the vertex is $\frac{1}{3}.$

$y = f\left(-\frac{b}{2a}\right) = f\left(\frac{1}{3}\right) = -\frac{3}{4}\left(\frac{1}{3}\right)^2 + \frac{1}{2}\left(\frac{1}{3}\right) - 3 = -\frac{35}{12}.$ The $y$-coordinate of the vertex is $-\frac{35}{12}.$

Thus, the vertex is $\left(\frac{1}{3}, -\frac{35}{12}\right)$. The graph of $Y_1 = (-3/4)X\text{^}2 + (1/2)X - 3$ shows graphical support for this vertex. See Figure 49.

(b) $f$ is increasing on $x \leq \frac{1}{3}$ or $\left(-\infty, \frac{1}{3}\right]$ and decreasing on $x \geq \frac{1}{3}$ or $\left[\frac{1}{3}, \infty\right)$.

[−40, 40, 5] by [−40, 40, 5]

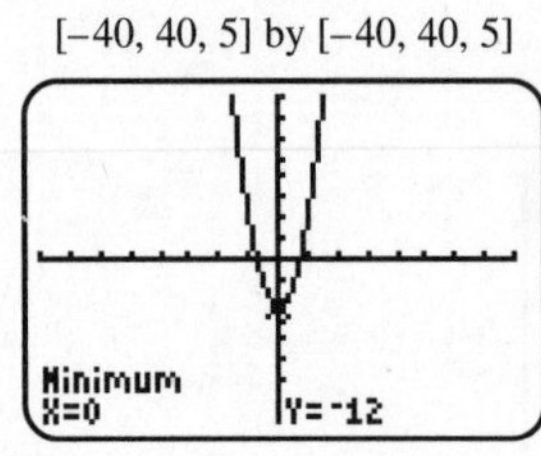

Figure 48

[−10, 10, 1] by [−10, 10, 1]

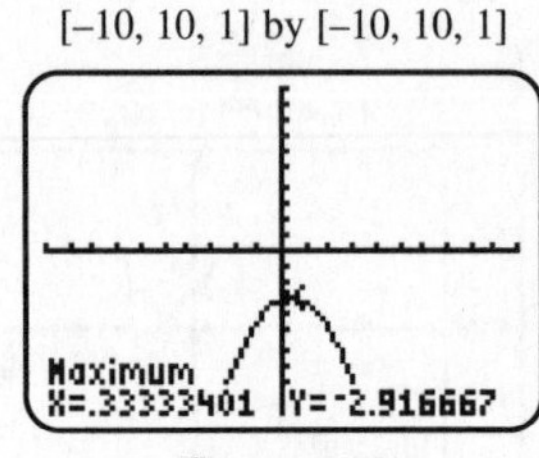

Figure 49

[−10, 10, 1] by [−10, 10, 1]

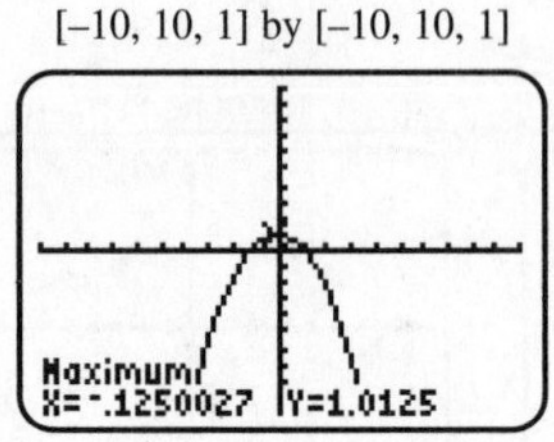

Figure 50

50. (a) The function is already in standard form: $f(x) = -\frac{4}{5}x^2 - \frac{1}{5}x + 1.$

To find the vertex symbolically, use the vertex formula with $a = -\frac{4}{5}$ and $b = -\frac{1}{5}.$

$x = -\frac{b}{2a} = -\frac{(-\frac{1}{5})}{2(-\frac{4}{5})} = -\frac{-\frac{1}{5}}{-\frac{8}{5}} = -\frac{1}{8}.$ The $x$-coordinate of the vertex is $-\frac{1}{8}.$

$y = f\left(-\frac{b}{2a}\right) = f\left(-\frac{1}{8}\right) = -\frac{4}{5}\left(-\frac{1}{8}\right)^2 - \frac{1}{5}\left(-\frac{1}{8}\right) + 1 = \frac{81}{80}.$ The $y$-coordinate of the vertex is $\frac{81}{80}.$

Thus, the vertex is $\left(-\frac{1}{8}, \frac{81}{80}\right)$. The graph of $Y_1 = (-4/5)X\text{^}2 - (1/5)X + 1$ shows graphical support for this vertex. See Figure 50.

(b) $f$ is increasing on $x \leq -\frac{1}{8}$ or $\left(-\infty, -\frac{1}{8}\right]$ and decreasing on $x \geq -\frac{1}{8}$ or $\left[-\frac{1}{8}, \infty\right)$.

51. (a) It may be helpful to write $f$ in standard form as follows: $f(x) = -6x^2 - 3x + 1.5$.

To find the vertex symbolically, use the vertex formula with $a = -6$ and $b = -3$.

$x = -\frac{b}{2a} = -\frac{(-3)}{2(-6)} = -\frac{3}{12} = -\frac{1}{4}$. The $x$-coordinate of the vertex is $-\frac{1}{4}$.

$y = f\left(-\frac{b}{2a}\right) = f\left(-\frac{1}{4}\right) = 1.5 - 3\left(-\frac{1}{4}\right) - 6\left(-\frac{1}{4}\right)^2 = 1\frac{7}{8}$. The $y$-coordinate of the vertex is $1\frac{7}{8}$. Thus, the vertex is $\left(-\frac{1}{4}, 1\frac{7}{8}\right)$. The graph of $Y_1 = 1.5 - 3X - 6X\text{^}2$ shows graphical support for this vertex. See Figure 51.

(b) $f$ is increasing on $x \le -\frac{1}{4}$ or $\left(-\infty, -\frac{1}{4}\right]$ and decreasing on $x \ge -\frac{1}{4}$ or $\left[-\frac{1}{4}, \infty\right)$.

[-3, 3, 1] by [-5, 5, 1]

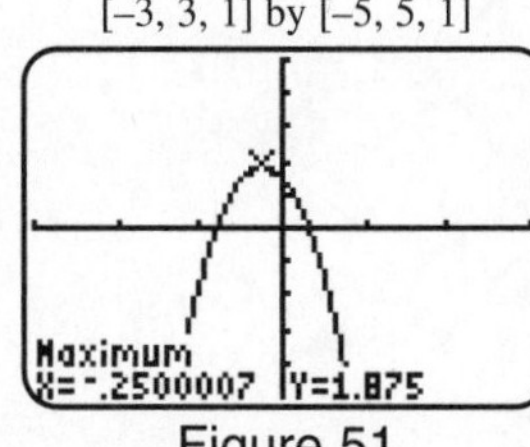

Figure 51

[-2, 8, 1] by [-2, 18, 2]

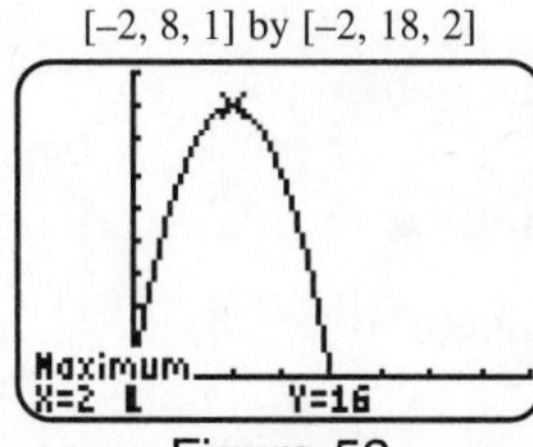

Figure 52

52. (a) It may be helpful to write $f$ in standard form as follows: $f(x) = -4x^2 + 16x + 0$.

To find the vertex symbolically, use the vertex formula with $a = -4$ and $b = 16$.

$x = -\frac{b}{2a} = -\frac{16}{2(-4)} = \frac{16}{8} = 2$. The $x$-coordinate of the vertex is 2.

$y = f\left(-\frac{b}{2a}\right) = f(2) = -4(2)^2 + 16(2) = 16$. The $y$-coordinate of the vertex is 16. Thus, the vertex is (2, 16). The graph of $Y_1 = -4X\text{^}2 + 16X$ shows graphical support for this vertex. See Figure 52.

(b) $f$ is increasing on $x \le 2$ or $(-\infty, 2]$ and decreasing on $x \ge 2$ or $[2, \infty)$.

53. The graph of $f(x) = x^2$ is shown in Figure 53.

54. The graph of $f(x) = -2x^2$ is shown in Figure 54.

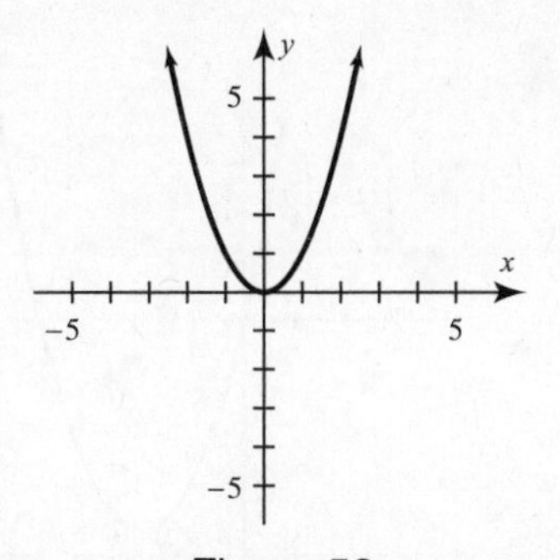

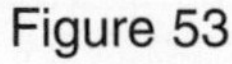
Figure 53

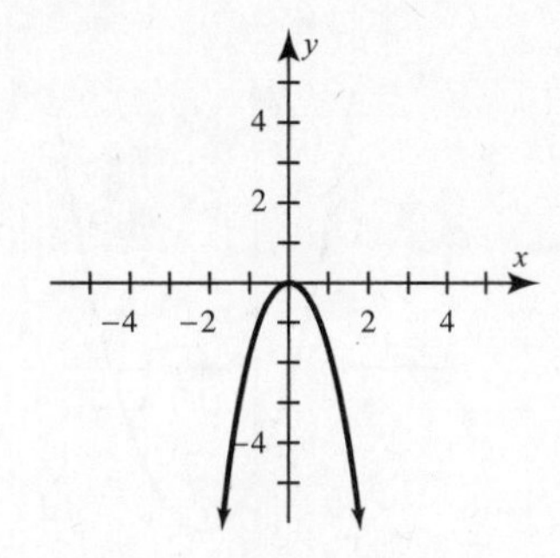

Figure 54

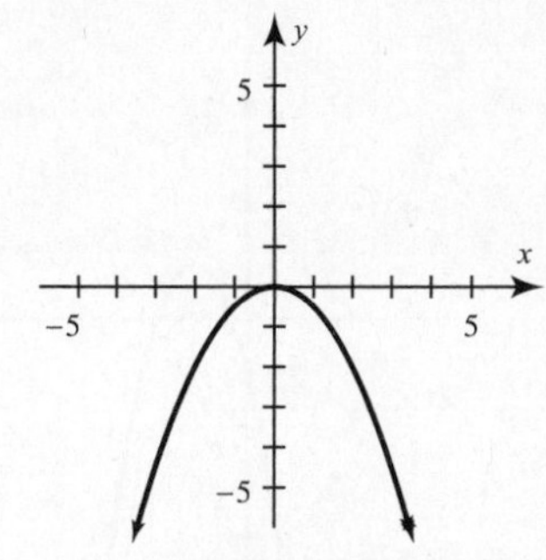

Figure 55

55. The graph of $f(x) = -\frac{1}{2}x^2$ is shown in Figure 55.

56. The graph of $f(x) = 4 - x^2$ is shown in Figure 56.

57. The graph of $f(x) = x^2 - 3$ is shown in Figure 57.

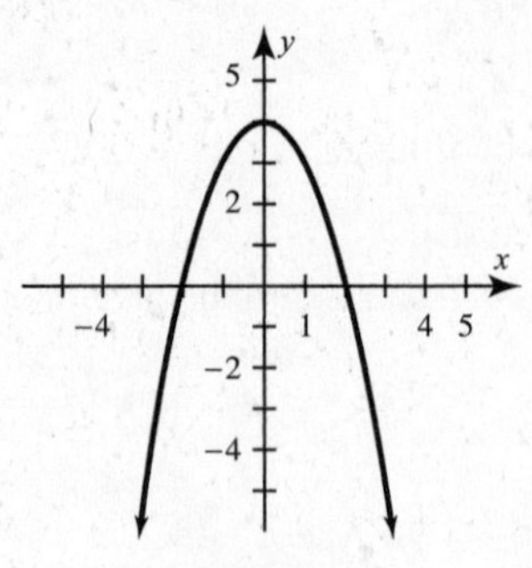

Figure 56

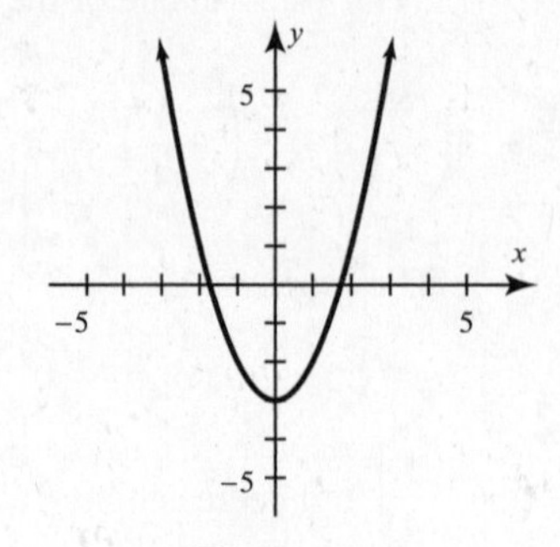

Figure 57

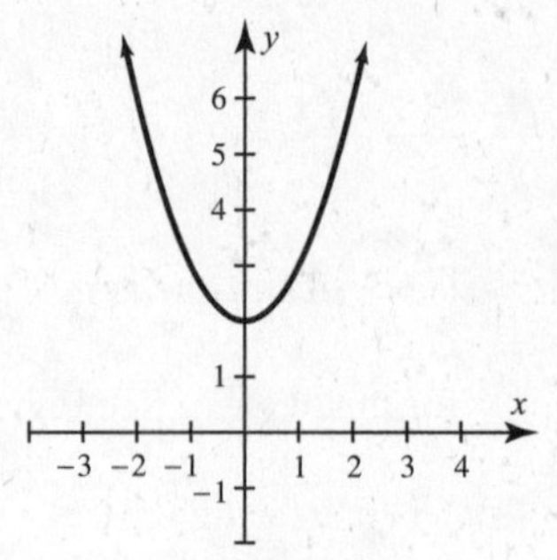

Figure 58

58. The graph of $f(x) = x^2 + 2$ is shown in Figure 58.

59. The graph of $f(x) = (x - 2)^2 + 1$ is shown in Figure 59.

60. The graph of $f(x) = (x + 1)^2 - 2$ is shown in Figure 60.

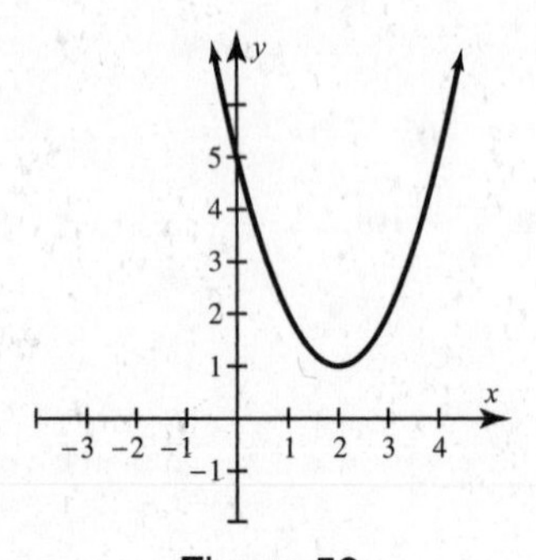

Figure 59

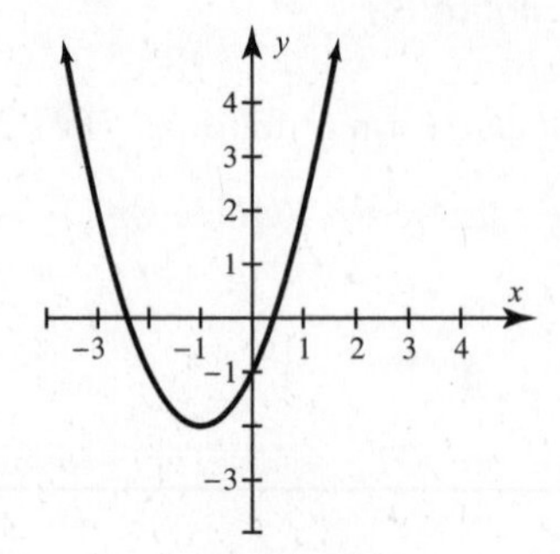

Figure 60

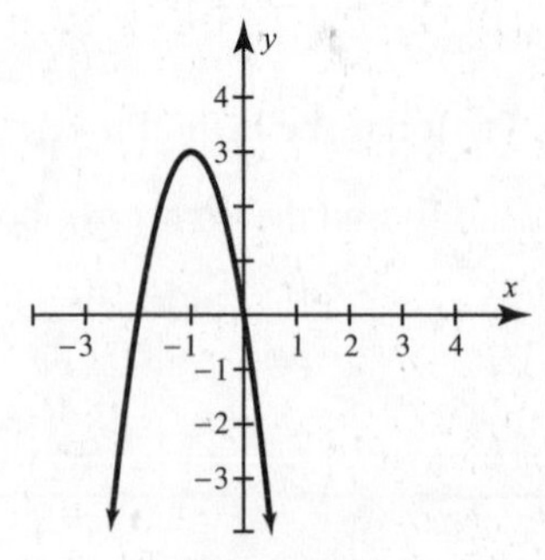

Figure 61

61. The graph of $f(x) = -3(x + 1)^2 + 3$ is shown in Figure 61.

62. The graph of $f(x) = -2(x - 1)^2 + 1$ is shown in Figure 62.

63. The graph of $f(x) = x^2 - 2x - 2$ is shown in Figure 63.

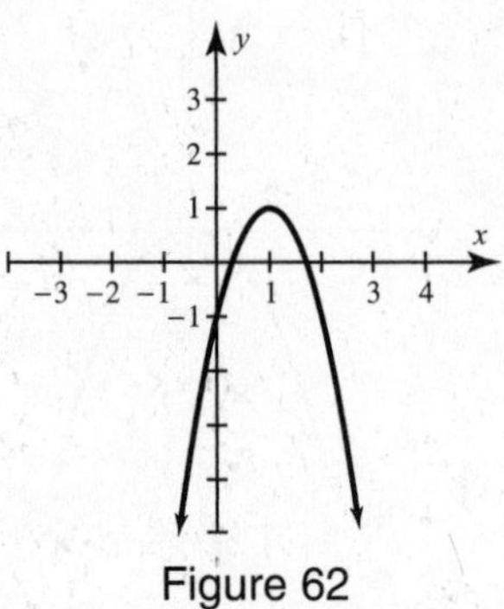

Figure 62

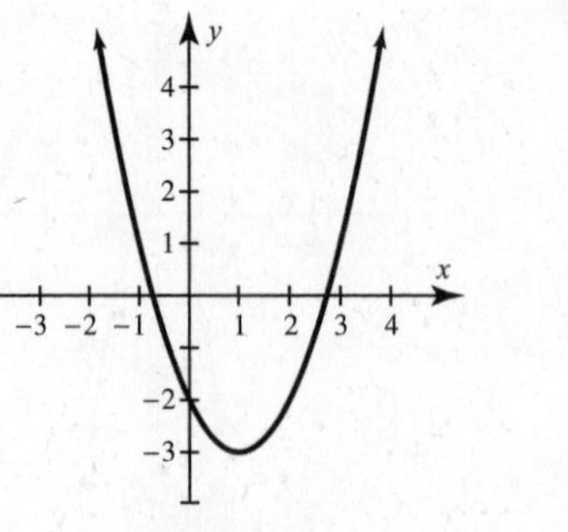

Figure 63

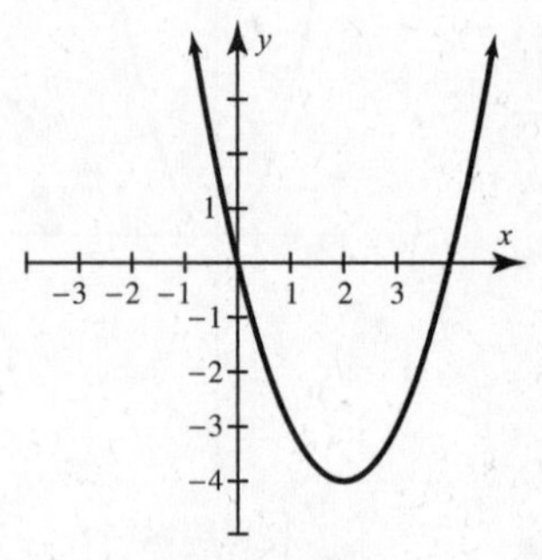

Figure 64

64. The graph of $f(x) = x^2 - 4x$ is shown in Figure 64.

65. The graph of $f(x) = -x^2 + 4x - 2$ is shown in Figure 65.

66. The graph of $f(x) = -x^2 + 2x + 1$ is shown in Figure 66.

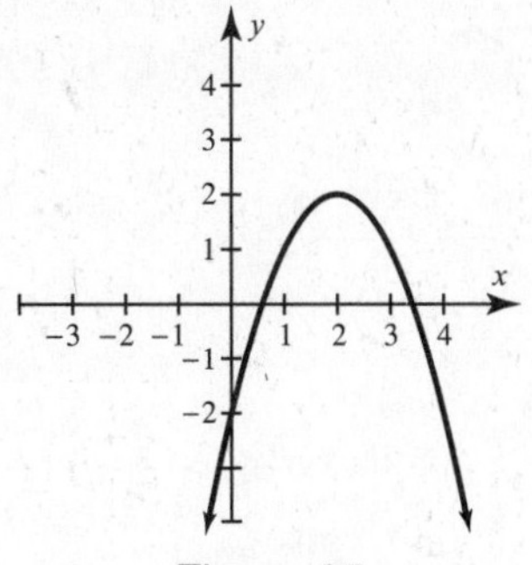

Figure 65

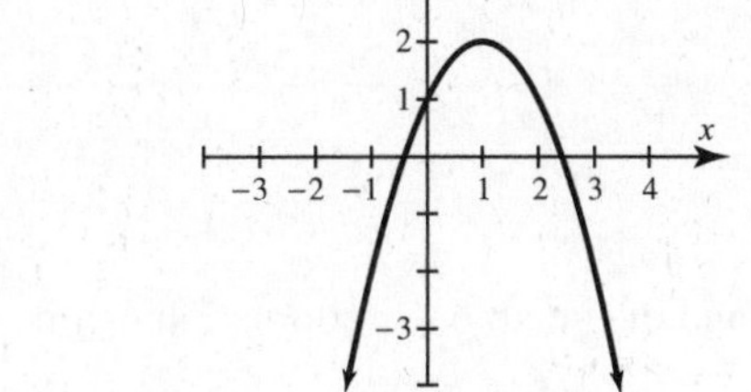

Figure 66

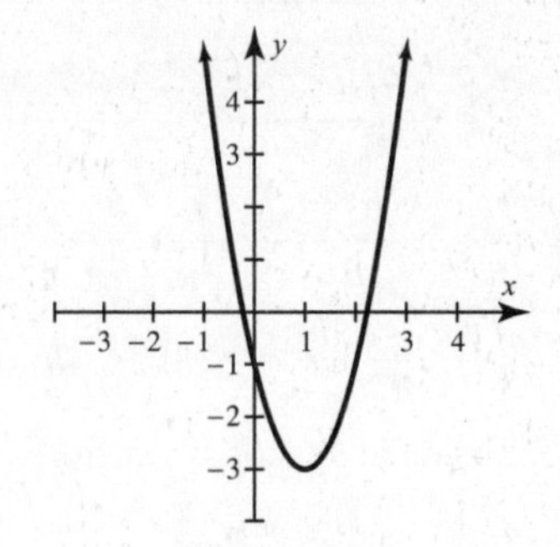

Figure 67

67. The graph of $f(x) = 2x^2 - 4x - 1$ is shown in Figure 67.

68. The graph of $f(x) = 3x^2 + 6x$ is shown in Figure 68.

69. The graph of $f(x) = -3x^2 - 6x + 1$ is shown in Figure 69.

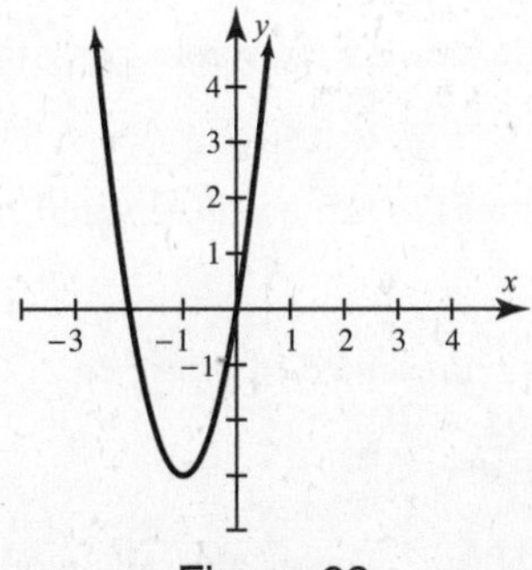

Figure 68

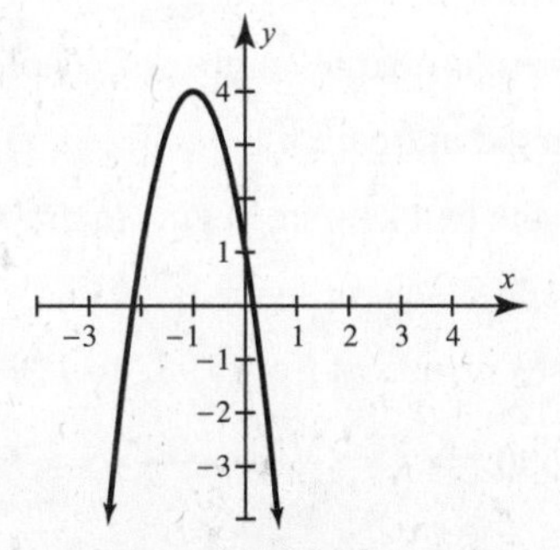

Figure 69

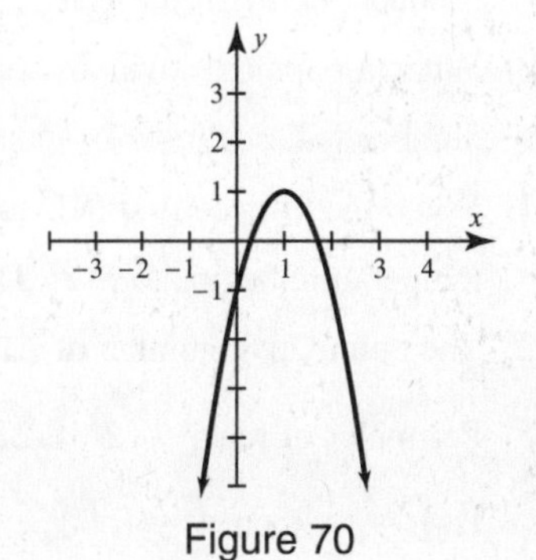

Figure 70

70. The graph of $f(x) = -2x^2 + 4x - 1$ is shown in Figure 70.

71. The graph of $f(x) = -\frac{1}{2}x^2 + x + 1$ is shown in Figure 71.

72. The graph of $f(x) = \frac{1}{2}x^2 - 2x + 2$ is shown in Figure 72.

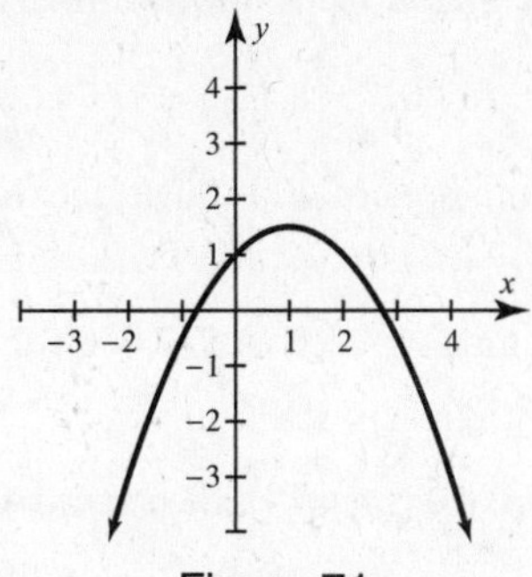

Figure 71

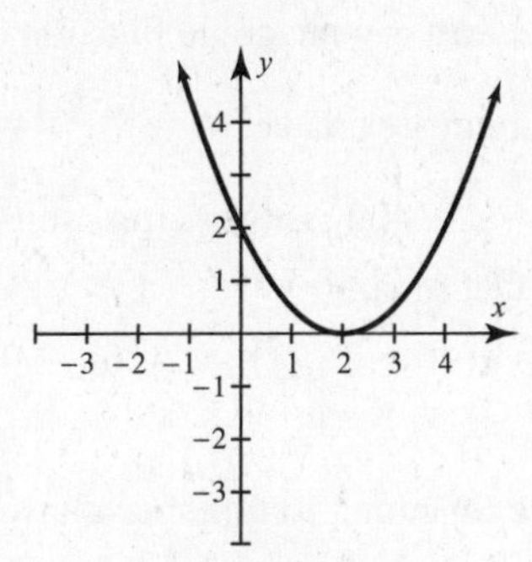

Figure 72

73. The average rate of change from 1 to 3 for $f(x) = -3x^2 + 5x$ is $\dfrac{f(3) - f(1)}{3 - 1} = \dfrac{-14}{2} = -7.$

74. The average rate of change from 1 to 3 for $f(x) = 4x^2 - 3x + 1$ is $\dfrac{f(3) - f(1)}{3 - 1} = \dfrac{26}{2} = 13.$

75. $\dfrac{f(x + h) - f(x)}{h} = \dfrac{3(x + h)^2 - 2(x + h) - [3x^2 - 2x]}{h} =$
$\dfrac{3x^2 + 6xh + 3h^2 - 2x - 2h - 3x^2 + 2x}{h} = \dfrac{6xh + 3h^2 - 2h}{h} = 6x + 3h - 2$

76. $\dfrac{f(x + h) - f(x)}{h} = \dfrac{5 - 4(x + h)^2 - [5 - 4x^2]}{h} = \dfrac{5 - 4x^2 - 8xh - 4h^2 - 5 + 4x^2}{h} =$
$\dfrac{-8xh - 4h^2}{h} = -8x - 4h$

77. Since the axis of symmetry is $x = 3$ and the graph passes through the point (3, 1), the vertex is (3, 1).
$f(x) = a(x - h)^2 + k \Rightarrow f(x) = a(x - 3)^2 + 1$. Using the point (1, 9) to find $a$ gives
$9 = a(1 - 3)^2 + 1 \Rightarrow a = 2;\ f(x) = 2(x - 3)^2 + 1.$

78. $f(x) = a(x - h)^2 + k \Rightarrow f(x) = a(x + 3)^2 + 4$. Using the point $(-2, 1)$ to find $a$ gives
$1 = a(-2 + 3)^2 + 4 \Rightarrow a = -3;\ f(x) = -3(x + 3)^2 + 4.$

79. A stone thrown from ground level would first rise to some maximum height and then fall back to the ground. This is represented in figure d.

80. When a popular movie first opens, there is a large number of people in attendance. As the weeks pass, this number will decline. This is represented in figure b.

81. When the furnace first fails to work, the temperature begins to drop. Then, after the furnace is repaired, the temperature begins to rise. This is represented in figure a.

82. The cumulative number of AIDS cases increased from 1982 to 1994. This is represented in figure c.

83. Perimeter of fence $= 2l + 2w = 1000 \Rightarrow l = \dfrac{1000 - 2w}{2} \Rightarrow l = 500 - w.$
If $A = lw$ then $A = (500 - w)w \Rightarrow A = 500w - w^2 \Rightarrow A = -w^2 + 500w$. This is a parabola opening downward and by the vertex formula, the maximum area occurs when $w = -\dfrac{b}{2a} = -\dfrac{500}{2(-1)} = 250.$
The dimensions that maximize area are 250 ft. by 250 ft.

84. The perimeter of a rectangle is $P = 2w + 2l$, so $2w + 2l = 80$; to maximize the area of this rectangle, we need to write a formula for the area in terms of one variable: $A = lw$ and $w = \dfrac{80 - 2l}{2} = 10 - l \Rightarrow$
$A = l(40 - l) = 40l - l^2$; thus, the area is a quadratic function of $l$ whose graph opens downward. The vertex of this function gives the maximum area value; $l = -\dfrac{b}{2a} = -\dfrac{40}{2(-1)} = 20.$
$A(20) = 40(20) - (20)^2 = 400 \Rightarrow (20, 400)$ is the vertex, so the maximum area of 400 square feet occurs when the rectangle is a 20 feet by 20 feet square.

85. (a) $R(x) = x(40 - 2x) \Rightarrow R(2) = 2(40 - 2(2)) = 2(36) = 72$; the company receives \$72,000 for producing 2000 CD players.

(b) $R(x) = 40x - 2x^2$ is a quadratic function; to find the value at which the maximum value occurs, we need to find the vertex: $x = -\dfrac{b}{2a} = -\dfrac{40}{2(-2)} = 10$ and $R(10) = 40(10) - 2(10)^2 = 200 \Rightarrow (10, 200)$ is the vertex, thus, the company needs to produce 10,000 CD players to maximize its revenue.

(c) Since $R(10) = 200$, the maximum revenue for the company is \$200,000.

86. (a) $R(x) = x(120 - 2x)$

(b) The graph of $R(x) = x(120 - 2x)$ or $R(x) = -2x^2 + 120x$ is shown in Figure 86; since the cost to rent 60 rooms is \$0, a reasonable domain is $D = \{0 \le x \le 60\}$.

(c) The graph is a parabola opening downward, by the vertex formula, maximum area occurs when $x = -\frac{b}{2a} \Rightarrow x = -\frac{120}{2(-2)} = 30$; maximum revenue occurs when 30 rooms are rented $\Rightarrow R(30) = -2(30)^2 + 120(30) = -1800 + 3600 = \$1800$ is the maximum revenue.

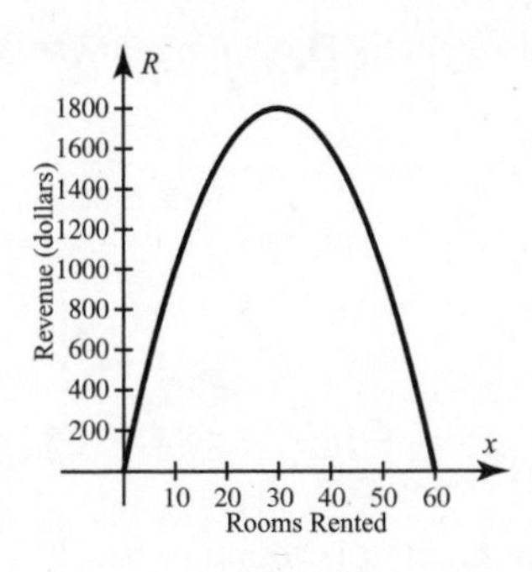

Figure 86

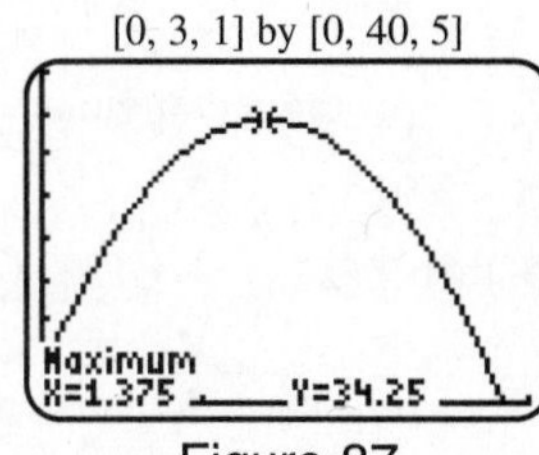

Figure 87

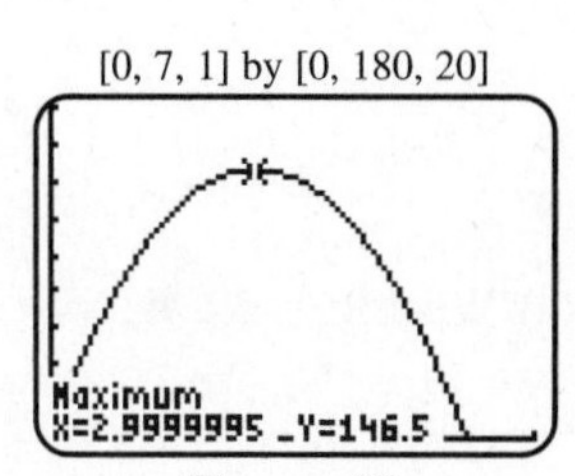

Figure 88

87. (a) $s(1) = -16(1)^2 + 44(1) + 4 = 32$; the baseball is 32 feet high after 1 second.

(b) For $s(t) = -16t^2 + 44t + 4$, the vertex formula gives $t = -\frac{b}{2a} = -\frac{44}{2(-16)} = 1.375$ and $f(1.375) = -16(1.375)^2 + 44(1.375) + 4 = 34.25$; the maximum height 34.25 feet. See Figure 87.

88. (a) Because $v_0 = 96$ and the initial height is $h_0 = 2.5$, $s(t) = -16t^2 + v_0 t + h_0 \Rightarrow s(t) = -16t^2 + 96t + 2.5$.

(b) $s(4) = -16(4)^2 + 96(4) + 2.5 = 130.5$ ft.

(c) Because $a = -16$, the graph of $s$ is a parabola opening downward. The vertex is the highest point on the graph, with a $t$-coordinate of $t = -\frac{b}{2a} = -\frac{96}{2(-16)} = 3$;
$s(3) = -16(3)^2 + 96(3) + 2.5 = 146.5$ ft. Thus, the vertex is (3, 146.5) and the maximum height of the baseball is 146.5 ft. after 3 seconds. See Figure 88.

89. (a) The initial velocity $v_0 = -66$ and the initial height is $h_0 = 120$, so $s(t) = -16t^2 + v_0 t + h_0 \Rightarrow s(t) = -16t^2 - 66t + 120$.

(b) When the stone hits the water, $s(t) = 0$; $0 = -16t^2 - 66t + 120 \Rightarrow 0 = -2(8t^2 + 33t - 60) \Rightarrow 0 = 8t^2 + 33t - 60$; using the quadratic formula or graphing the parabola, we find that $s(t) = 0$ when $t \approx 1.37$ seconds, so the stone hits the water within the first 2 seconds.

90. (a) Since $s(t) = -16t^2 + v_0 t + h_0$ where $v_0$ is the initial velocity and $h_0$ is the initial height, then given $s(t) = -16t^2 + 60t \Rightarrow h_0 = 0$. Therefore, the golf ball begins at ground level.

(b) $s(1.5) = -16(1.5)^2 + 60(1.5) = 54$ feet. The ball is 54 feet high after 1.5 seconds.

(c) Because $a = -16$, the graph of $s$ is a parabola opening downward. The vertex is the highest point on the graph, with a $t$-coordinate of $t = -\frac{b}{2a} = -\frac{60}{2(-16)} = 1.875$;
$s(1.875) = -16(1.875)^2 + 60(1.875) = 56.25$ feet. Thus, the vertex is (1.875, 56.25) and the maximum height of the golf ball is 56.25 feet after 1.875 seconds.

91. Using the wall of the barn for one side gives us $W + L + W = 160$ for the three sides $\Rightarrow L = 160 - 2W$.

If $A = LW$ then $A = (160 - 2W)W \Rightarrow A = 160W - 2W^2$. Since this is a parabola opening downward,

maximum area occurs when $W = -\dfrac{b}{2a} \Rightarrow W = \dfrac{-160}{2(-2)} \Rightarrow W = 40$. Then $L = 160 - 2(40) = 80$. Thus,

the dimensions that yield maximum area are 40 feet by 80 feet.

92. Using the river for one side gives us $W + L + W = P \Rightarrow L = P - 2W$. If $A = LW$ then

$A = (P - 2W)W \Rightarrow A = PW - 2W^2$ or $A = -2W^2 + PW$; since this is a parabola opening downward,

maximum area occurs when $W = -\dfrac{b}{2a} \Rightarrow W = -\dfrac{P}{2(-2)} \Rightarrow W = \dfrac{P}{4}$ and

$L = P - 2\left(\dfrac{P}{4}\right) \Rightarrow L = P - \dfrac{P}{2} \Rightarrow L = \dfrac{P}{2}$; the rectangle is $\dfrac{P}{4}$ ft by $\dfrac{P}{2}$ ft.

93. (a) When $g = 32$, $v_0 = 88$, and $h_0 = 25$, then $f(x) = -\dfrac{1}{2}(32)x^2 + 88x + 25 = -16x^2 + 88x + 25$.

Graph $Y_1 = -16X\text{^}2 + 88X + 25$. By using the calculator, the maximum height is found to be

approximately 146 feet. The maximum height of 146 ft occurs when $x = 2.75$ seconds. See Figure 93.

(b) To find the maximum height symbolically, use the vertex formula with $a = -16$ and $b = 88$.

$x = -\dfrac{b}{2a} = -\dfrac{88}{2(-16)} = \dfrac{88}{32} = 2.75$. The maximum height occurs at $x = 2.75$ seconds.

$y = f\left(-\dfrac{b}{2a}\right) = f(2.75) = -16(2.75)^2 + 88(2.75) + 25 = 146$. The maximum height is 146 feet.

94. (a) When $g = 5.1$, $v_0 = 88$, and $h_0 = 25$, then $f(x) = -\dfrac{1}{2}(5.1)x^2 + 88x + 25 = -2.55x^2 + 88x + 25$.

Graph $Y_1 = -2.55X\text{^}2 + 88X + 25$. By using the calculator, the maximum height is found to be

approximately 784 feet. The maximum height of about 784 ft occurs when $x \approx 17.3$ seconds. See Figure 94.

(b) To find the maximum height symbolically, use the vertex formula with $a = -2.55$ and $b = 88$.

$x = -\dfrac{b}{2a} = -\dfrac{88}{2(-2.55)} = \dfrac{88}{5.1} \approx 17.3$. The maximum height occurs at $x \approx 17.3$ seconds.

$y = f\left(-\dfrac{b}{2a}\right) = f(17.3) = -2.55(17.3)^2 + 88(17.3) + 25 \approx 784.2$. The maximum height approximately

784 feet.

[0, 6, 1] by [0, 160, 10]

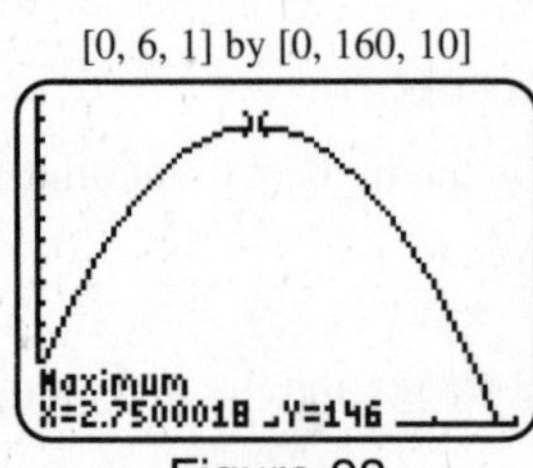


Figure 93

[0, 40, 10] by [0, 800, 100]

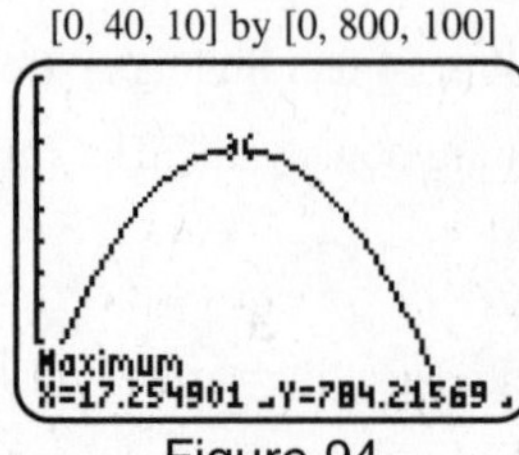


Figure 94

[0, 15, 5] by [0, 400, 100]

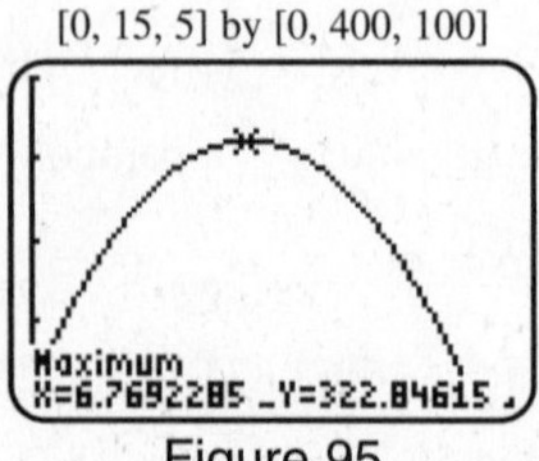


Figure 95

[0, 3, 1] by [0, 100, 10]

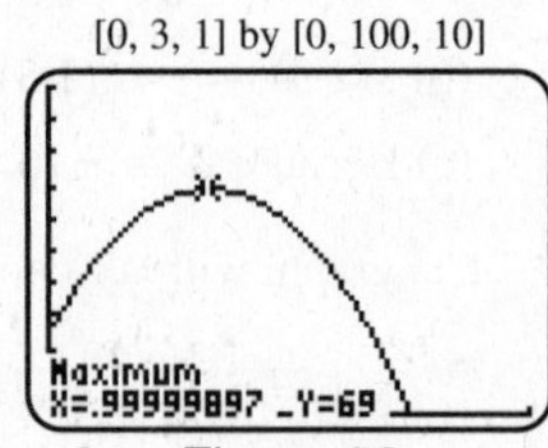


Figure 96

95. (a) When $g = 13$, $v_0 = 88$, and $h_0 = 25$, then $f(x) = -\frac{1}{2}(13)x^2 + 88x + 25 = -6.5x^2 + 88x + 25.$

Graph $Y_1 = -6.5X\text{^}2 + 88X + 25$. By using the calculator, the maximum height is found to be approximately 323 feet. The maximum height of about 323 ft occurs when $x \approx 6.77$ seconds. See Figure 95.

(b) To find the maximum height symbolically, use the vertex formula with $a = -6.5$ and $b = 88$.

$x = -\frac{b}{2a} = -\frac{88}{2(-6.5)} = \frac{88}{13} \approx 6.77$. The maximum height occurs at $x \approx 6.77$ seconds.

$y = f\left(-\frac{b}{2a}\right) = f(6.77) = -6.5(6.77)^2 + 88(6.77) + 25 \approx 323$. The maximum height is about 323 feet.

96. (a) When $g = 88$, $v_0 = 88$, and $h_0 = 25$, then $f(x) = -\frac{1}{2}(88)x^2 + 88x + 25 = -44x^2 + 88x + 25.$

Graph $Y_1 = -44X\text{^}2 + 88X + 25$. By using the calculator, the maximum height is found to be approximately 69 feet. The maximum height of about 69 ft occurs when $x \approx 1$ second. See Figure 96.

(b) To find the maximum height symbolically, use the vertex formula with $a = -44$ and $b = 88$.

$x = -\frac{b}{2a} = -\frac{88}{2(-44)} = \frac{88}{88} = 1$. The maximum height occurs at $x = 1$ second.

$y = f\left(-\frac{b}{2a}\right) = f(1) = -44(1)^2 + 88(1) + 25 = 69$. The maximum height is 69 feet.

97. The smallest $y$-value is –3 when $x = 1$; the symmetry in the $y$-values about $x = 1$ indicates that the axis of symmetry is $x = 1$ and the vertex is (1, –3), so $f(x) = a(x - 1)^2 - 3$. Since (0, –1) is a data point, $f(0) = -1$; $f(0) = a(0 - 1)^2 - 3 \Rightarrow -1 = a - 3 \Rightarrow a = 2$; the function $f(x) = 2(x - 1)^2 - 3$ models the data exactly.

98. The largest $y$-value is 4 when $x = -1$; the symmetry in the $y$-values about $x = -1$ indicates the axis of symmetry is $x = -1$ and the vertex is (–1, 4), so $f(x) = a(x + 1)^2 + 4$; since (0, 2) is a data point, $f(0) = 2$; $f(0) = a(0 + 1)^2 + 4 \Rightarrow 2 = a + 4 \Rightarrow a = -2$; the function $f(x) = -2(x + 1)^2 + 4$ models the data exactly.

99. The cables drawn as a parabola can be placed in the coordinate plane. Use (0, 20) as the vertex.

$f(x) = a(x - h)^2 + k \Rightarrow f(x) = a(x - 0)^2 + 20 = f(x) = ax^2 + 20$; since the parabola passes through (150, 120), $f(150) = 120$; $f(150) = a(150)^2 + 20 \Rightarrow 120 = 22{,}500a + 20 \Rightarrow 100 = 22{,}500a \Rightarrow$

$a = \frac{1}{225}$; $f(x) = \frac{1}{225}x^2 + 20$, or $f(x) \approx 0.0044x^2 + 20$.

100. The cables drawn as a parabola can be placed in the coordinate plane. See Figure 100. Use (0, 15) as the vertex.

$f(x) = a(x - h)^2 + k \Rightarrow f(x) = a(x - 0)^2 + 15 \Rightarrow f(x) = ax^2 + 15$; since the parabola passes through the point (100, 100), $f(100) = a(100)^2 + 15 \Rightarrow 100 = a(10{,}000) + 15 \Rightarrow 85 = 10{,}000a \Rightarrow$ $a = 0.0085$; $f(x) = 0.0085x^2 + 15$.

[–100, 100, 10] by [0, 100, 10]

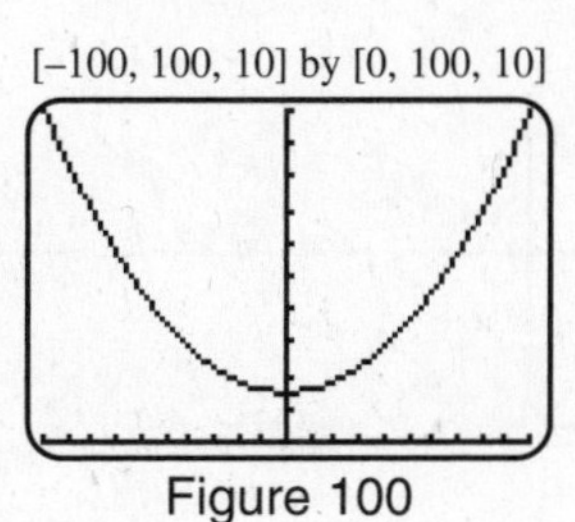

Figure 100

101. (a) Since the minimum occurs at $t = 4$, let $(4, 90)$ be the vertex and write $H(t) = a(t - 4)^2 + 90$. Use the data point $(0, 122)$ to find $a$: $H(0) = a(0 - 4)^2 + 90 \Rightarrow 122 = a(0 - 4)^2 + 90 \Rightarrow$ $122 = 16a + 90 \Rightarrow 16a = 32 \Rightarrow a = 2$; $H(t) = 2(t - 4)^2 + 90$; Domain of $H = \{0 \le t \le 4\}$

(b) $H(1.5) = 2(1.5 - 4)^2 + 90 \Rightarrow H(1.5) = 2(-2.5)^2 + 90 \Rightarrow H(1.5) = 12.5 + 90 \Rightarrow$ $H(1.5) = 102.5$ beats per minute.

102. (a) The data increases and then decreases.

(b) Using the quadratic regression function on your calculator, the function $f(x) \approx -8.7857x^2 + 35.2429x + 84.2286$.

(c) Domain: $\{x | 0 \le x \le 4\}$ or $[0, 4]$

103. (a) Using the coordinates (1982, 1.6), $f(x) = a(x - 1982)^2 + 1.6$. To find $a$, use (1994, 442) $\Rightarrow$ $442 = a(1994 - 1982)^2 + 1.6 \Rightarrow 440.4 = a(144) \Rightarrow a \approx 3.06$; $f(x) = 3.06(x - 1982)^2 + 1.6$.

*Answers may vary.*

(b) See Figure 103.

(c) $f(1991) = 3.06(1991 - 1982)^2 + 1.6 = 3.06(81) + 1.6 = 249.46$. By 1991, a total of about 250,000 AIDS cases had been reported.

[1980, 1996, 2] by [–50, 500, 100]

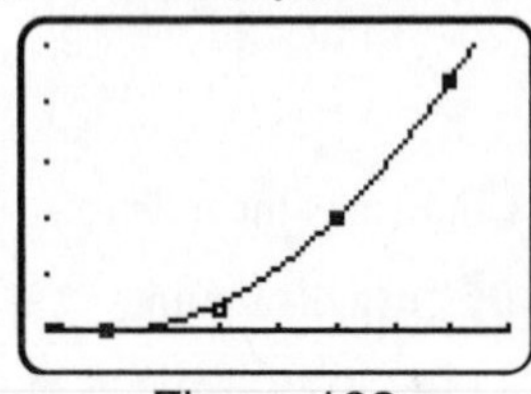

Figure 103

[1980, 1996, 2] by [–50, 500, 100]

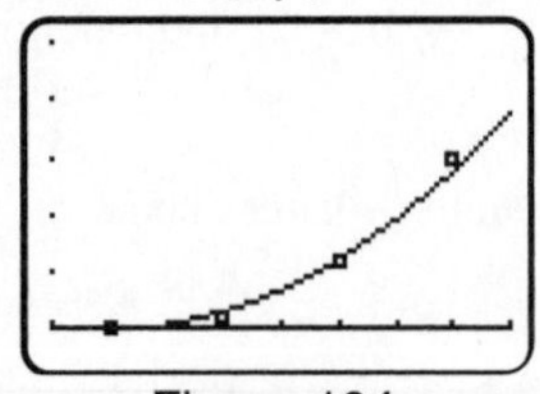

Figure 104

104. (a) Using the coordinates (1982, 0.6), $f(x) = a(x - 1982)^2 + 0.6$, to find $a$, use (1990, 122) $\Rightarrow$ $122 = a(1990 - 1982)^2 + 0.6 \Rightarrow 121.4 = a(64) \Rightarrow a \approx 1.9$; $f(x) = 1.9(x - 1982)^2 + 0.6$.

*Answers may vary.*

(b) See Figure 104.

(c) $f(1991) = 1.9(1991 - 1982)^2 + 0.6 = 154.5$. By 1991 a total of about 155,000 AIDS deaths had occured.

105. Enter the data into your calculator. See Figure 105a. Select quadratic regression from the STAT menu. See Figure 105b. In Figure 105c, the modeling function is given (approximately) by $f(x) = 3.125x^2 + 2.05x - 0.9$. $f(3.5) = 3.125(3.5)^2 + 2.05(3.5) - 0.9 \approx 44.56$.

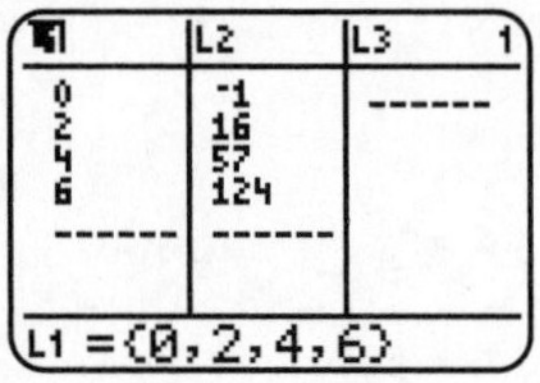

Figure 105a

Figure 105b

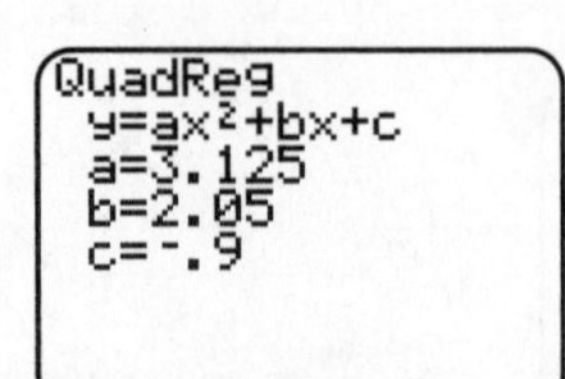


Figure 105c

106. Enter the data into your calculator. See Figure 106a. Select quadratic regression from the STAT menu. See Figure 106b. In figure 106c, the modeling function is given (approximately) by

$f(x) = 0.1995x^2 - 3.983x + 24.1$; $f(3.5) = 0.1995(3.5)^2 - 3.983(3.5) + 24.1 \approx 12.60$.

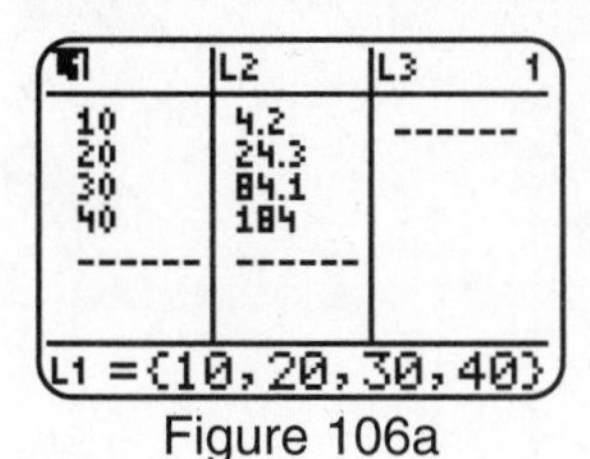

Figure 106a

Figure 106b

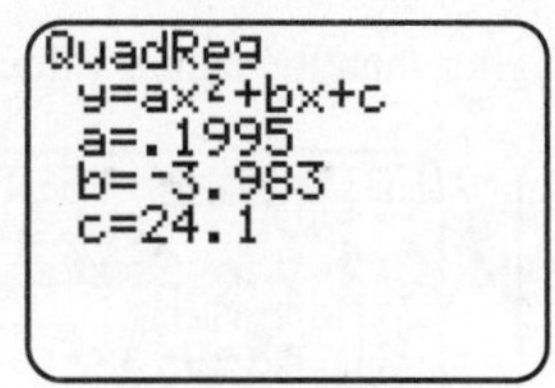

Figure 106c

107. (a) $f(x) = 0.00019838x^2 - 0.79153x + 791.46$. See Figure 107.

(b) $f(1975) = 0.00019838(1975)^2 - 0.79153(1975) + 791.46 \approx 1.99$, which compares favorably with the actual value of 2.01.

[1935, 2005, 5] by [1.9, 2.6, 0.1]

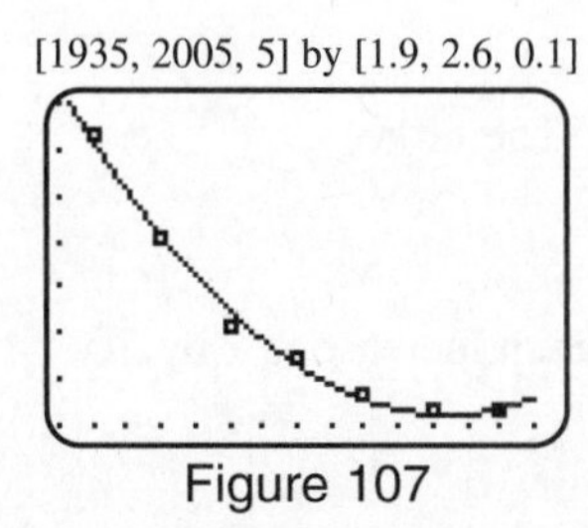
Figure 107

[1945, 2005, 5] by [20, 180, 20]

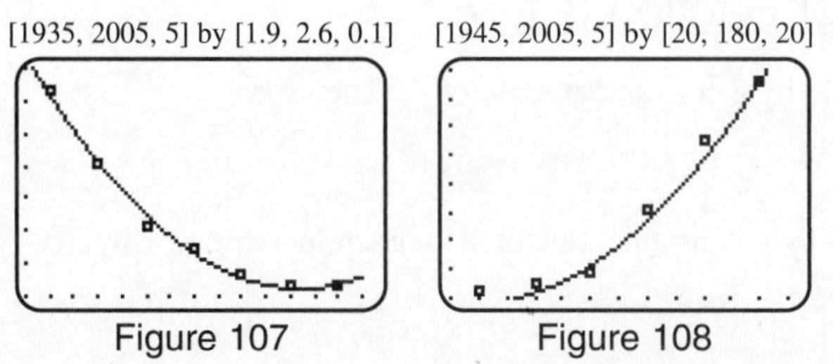
Figure 108

108. (a) Entering the data and using quadratic regression gives the function

$f(x) = 0.06007x^2 - 234.17529x + 228{,}242.2$. See Figure 108.

(b) $f(1995) = 0.06007(1995)^2 - 234.17529(1995) + 228{,}242.2 \approx 142.6$. Note: If the regression equation is not rounded, the result is approximately 148.3, which compares favorably with the actual value of 152.4.

109. (a) Enter data into your calculator. See Figure 109a. Select quadratic regression from the STAT menu. See Figure 109b. In Figure 109c, the modeling function is given by approximately

$f(x) = 0.59462x^2 - 2350.82x + 2{,}323{,}895$.

(b) $f(1985) = 0.59462(1985)^2 - 2350.82(1985) + 2{,}323{,}895 = 453.8895$. In 1985, the approximate enrollment was 454 thousand.

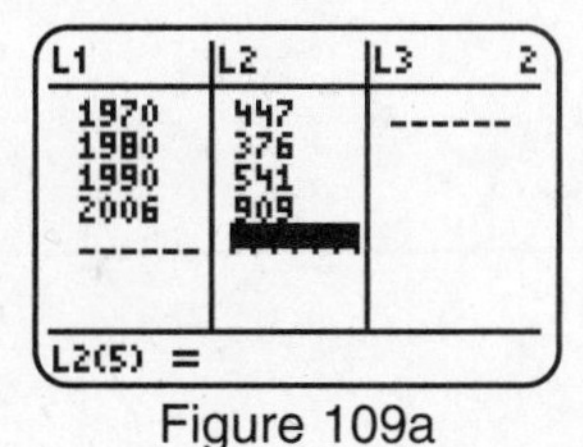

Figure 109a

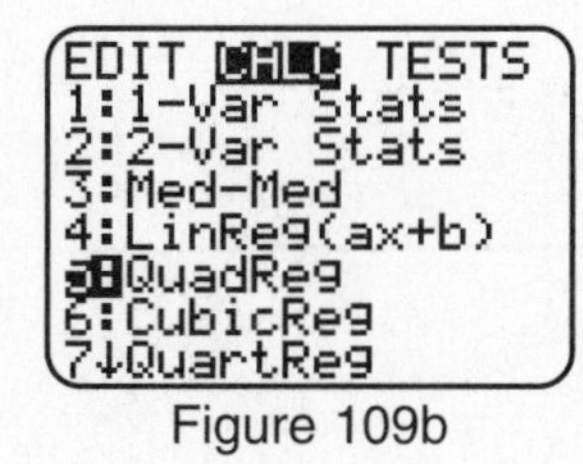

Figure 109b

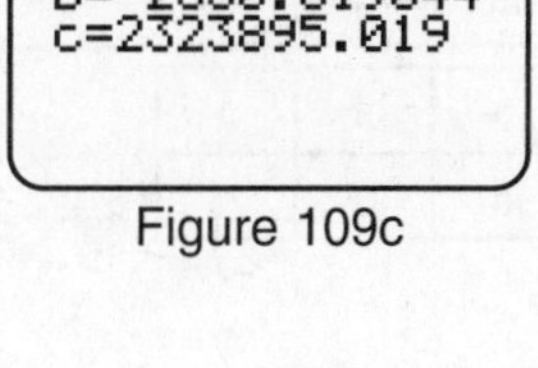

Figure 109c

110. (a) Enter data into your calculator. See Figure 110a. Select quadratic regression from the STAT menu. See Figure 110b. In Figure 110c, the modeling function is given by approximately

$f(x) = 0.0069196x^2 - 24.929x + 22{,}459.$

(b) $f(1980) = 0.0069196(1980)^2 - 24.929(1980) + 22{,}459 = 227.18$. The estimated value of 227 million is about 1 million higher than the actual value of 226 million.

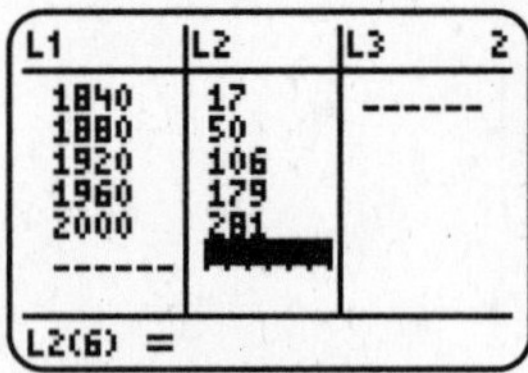

Figure 110a

Figure 110b

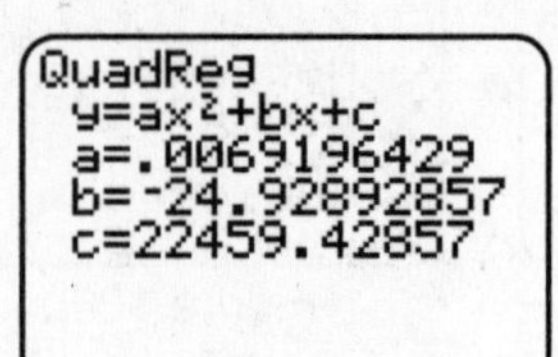

Figure 110c

## Extended and Discovery Exercises for Section 3.1

1. The data are quadratic since the slopes are decreasing by a constant amount of 4. Therefore, $y = -61$ when $x = 6$.

2. The data are linear since the $y$-values are decreasing by a constant value of 1 for each increase in $x$ by 5. Therefore, $y = 4$ when $x = 30$.

3. This data are neither linear nor quadratic. There is neither a constant slope nor a constant amount of difference between slopes of consecutive data points.

4. The data are quadratic since the slopes are decreasing by a constant amount of 4. Therefore, $y = 41$ when $x = 6$.

5. (a) See Figure 5.

(b) For $(1, -2)$ and $(2, 1)$, $m = \dfrac{1 - (-2)}{2 - 1} = 3$; for $(2, 1)$ and $(3, 6)$, $m = \dfrac{6 - 1}{3 - 2} = 5$;

for $(3, 6)$ and $(4, 13)$, $m = \dfrac{13 - 6}{4 - 3} = 7$; for $(4, 13)$ and $(5, 22)$, $m = \dfrac{22 - 13}{5 - 4} = 9 \Rightarrow 3, 5, 7, 9.$

(c) $f(x + h) = (x + h)^2 - 3 = x^2 + 2xh + h^2 - 3$;

the difference quotient $= \dfrac{f(x + h) - f(x)}{h} = \dfrac{x^2 + 2xh + h^2 - 3 - (x^2 - 3)}{h} = \dfrac{2xh + h^2}{h} = 2x + h$;

when $h = 1$, the difference quotient is $2x + 1$.

(d) $x = 1, 2(1) + 1 = 3$; $x = 2, 2(2) + 1 = 5$; $x = 3, 2(3) + 1 = 7$; $x = 4, 2(4) + 1 = 9$;

the results are the same.

| $x$ | 1 | 2 | 3 | 4 | 5 |
|---|---|---|---|---|---|
| $f(x)$ | −2 | 1 | 6 | 13 | 22 |

Figure 5

6. (a) See Figure 6.

(b) For $(1, 1)$ and $(2, 0)$, $m = \dfrac{0 - 1}{2 - 1} = -1$; for $(2, 0)$ and $(3, -3)$, $m = \dfrac{-3 - 0}{3 - 2} = -3$; for $(3, -3)$ and $(4, -8)$, $m = \dfrac{-8 - (-3)}{4 - 3} = -5$; for $(4, -8)$ and $(5, -15)$, $m = \dfrac{-15 - (-8)}{5 - 4} = -7 \Rightarrow$ $-1, -3, -5, -7$.

(c) $f(x) = 2x - x^2$, $f(x + h) = 2(x + h) - (x + h)^2 = 2x + 2h - (x^2 + 2xh + h^2) =$ $2x + 2h - x^2 - 2xh - h^2$; the difference quotient $= \dfrac{f(x + h) - f(x)}{h} =$ $\dfrac{2x + 2h - x^2 - 2xh - h^2 - (2x - x^2)}{h} = \dfrac{2h - 2xh - h^2}{h} = 2 - 2x - h = -2x + 2 - h$; when $h = 1$, the difference quotient is $-2x + 1$.

(d) $x = 1, -2(1) + 1 = -1$; $x = 2, -2(2) + 1 = -3$; $x = 3, -2(3) + 1 = -5$; $x = 4, -2(4) + 1 = -7$; the results are the same.

| $x$ | 1 | 2 | 3 | 4 | 5 |
|---|---|---|---|---|---|
| $f(x)$ | 1 | 0 | −3 | −8 | −15 |

Figure 6

7. (a) See Figure 7.

(b) For $(1, 0)$ and $(2, -3)$, $m = \dfrac{-3 - 0}{2 - 1} = -3$; for $(2, -3)$ and $(3, -10)$, $m = \dfrac{-10 - (-3)}{3 - 2} = -7$; for $(3, -10)$ and $(4, -21)$, $m = \dfrac{-21 - (-10)}{4 - 3} = -11$; for $(4, -21)$ and $(5, -36)$, $m = \dfrac{-36 - (-21)}{5 - 4} = -15 \Rightarrow -3, -7, -11, -15$.

(c) $f(x) = -2x^2 + 3x - 1$, $f(x + h) = -2(x + h)^2 + 3(x + h) - 1 =$ $-2x^2 - 4xh - 2h^2 + 3x + 3h - 1$; the difference quotient $= \dfrac{f(x + h) - f(x)}{h} =$ $\dfrac{-2x^2 - 4xh - 2h^2 + 3x + 3h - 1 - (-2x^2 + 3x - 1)}{h} =$ $\dfrac{-4xh - 2h^2 + 3h}{h} = -4x - 2h + 3$; when $h = 1$, the difference quotient is $-4x + 1$.

(d) $x = 1, -4(1) + 1 = -3$; $x = 2, -4(2) + 1 = -7$; $x = 3, -4(3) + 1 = -11$; $x = 4, -4(4) + 1 = -15$; the results are the same.

| $x$ | 1 | 2 | 3 | 4 | 5 |
|---|---|---|---|---|---|
| $f(x)$ | 0 | −3 | −10 | −21 | −36 |

Figure 7

8. (a) See Figure 8.

(b) For $(1, 6)$ and $(2, 16)$, $m = \dfrac{16 - 6}{2 - 1} = 10$; for $(2, 16)$ and $(3, 32)$, $m = \dfrac{32 - 16}{3 - 2} = 16$;

for $(3, 32)$ and $(4, 54)$, $m = \dfrac{54 - 32}{4 - 3} = 22$; for $(4, 54)$ and $(5, 82)$, $m = \dfrac{82 - 54}{5 - 4} = 28 \Rightarrow$

10, 16, 22, 28.

(c) $f(x) = 3x^2 + x + 2$, $f(x + h) = 3(x + h)^2 + (x + h) + 2 = 3x^2 + 6xh + 3h^2 + x + h + 2$;

the difference quotient $= \dfrac{f(x + h) - f(x)}{h} = \dfrac{3x^2 + 6xh + 3h^2 + x + h + 2 - (3x^2 + x + 2)}{h} =$

$\dfrac{6xh + 3h^2 + h}{h} = 6x + 3h + 1$; when $h = 1$, the difference quotient is $6x + 4$.

(d) $x = 1, 6(1) + 4 = 10$; $x = 2, 6(2) + 4 = 16$; $x = 3, 6(3) + 4 = 22$; $x = 4, 6(4) + 4 = 28$;

the results are the same.

| $x$ | 1 | 2 | 3 | 4 | 5 |
|---|---|---|---|---|---|
| $f(x)$ | 6 | 16 | 32 | 54 | 82 |

Figure 8

## 3.2: Quadratic Equations and Problem Solving

1. $x^2 + x - 11 = 1 \Rightarrow x^2 + x - 12 = 0$. Factoring this we get: $(x + 4)(x - 3) = 0$. Then $x + 4 = 0 \Rightarrow$ $x = -4$ or $x - 3 = 0 \Rightarrow x = 3$. Therefore $x = -4, 3$.

   Check: $(-4)^2 + (-4) - 11 = 1 \Rightarrow 16 - 4 - 11 = 1 \Rightarrow 12 - 11 = 1 \Rightarrow 1 = 1$;

   $(3)^2 + (3) - 11 = 1 \Rightarrow 9 + 3 - 11 = 1 \Rightarrow 12 - 11 = 1 \Rightarrow 1 = 1$

2. $x^2 - 9x + 10 = -8 \Rightarrow x^2 - 9x + 18 = 0$. Factoring this we get: $(x - 6)(x - 3) = 0$.

   Then $x - 6 = 0 \Rightarrow x = 6$ or $x - 3 = 0 \Rightarrow x = 3$. Therefore $x = 3, 6$.

   Check: $(3)^2 - 9(3) + 10 = -8 \Rightarrow 9 - 27 + 10 = -8 \Rightarrow -18 + 10 = -8 \Rightarrow -8 = -8$;

   $(6)^2 - 9(6) + 10 = -8 \Rightarrow 36 - 54 + 10 = -8 \Rightarrow -18 + 10 = -8 \Rightarrow -8 = -8$

3. $t^2 = 2t \Rightarrow t^2 - 2t = 0$. Factoring this we get: $t(t - 2) = 0$. Then $t = 0$ or $t - 2 = 0 \Rightarrow t = 2$.

   Therefore $t = 0, 2$. Check: $0^2 = 2(0) \Rightarrow 0 = 0$; $2^2 = 2(2) \Rightarrow 4 = 4$

4. $t^2 - 7t = 0$. Factoring this we get: $t(t - 7) = 0$. Then $t = 0$ or $t - 7 = 0 \Rightarrow t = 7$. Therefore $t = 0, 7$.

   Check: $0^2 - 7(0) = 0 \Rightarrow 0 = 0$; $7^2 - 7(7) = 0 \Rightarrow 49 - 49 = 0 \Rightarrow 0 = 0$

5. $3x^2 - 7x = 0$. Factoring we get $x(3x - 7) = 0$. Then $x = 0$ or $3x - 7 = 0 \Rightarrow x = \dfrac{7}{3}$. Therefore $x = 0, \dfrac{7}{3}$.

   Check: $3(0)^2 - 7(0) = 0 \Rightarrow 0 = 0$; $3\left(\dfrac{7}{3}\right)^2 - 7\left(\dfrac{7}{3}\right) = 0 \Rightarrow \dfrac{49}{3} - \dfrac{49}{3} = 0 \Rightarrow 0 = 0$

6. $5x = 9x^2 \Rightarrow 5x - 9x^2 = 0$. Factoring we get $x(5 - 9x) = 0$. Then $x = 0$ or $5 - 9x = 0 \Rightarrow x = \dfrac{5}{9}$.

   Therefore $x = 0, \dfrac{5}{9}$. Check: $5(0) = 9(0)^2 \Rightarrow 0 = 0$; $5(\frac{5}{9}) = 9(\frac{5}{9})^2 \Rightarrow \dfrac{25}{9} = \dfrac{25}{9} \Rightarrow 0 = 2$

7. $2z^2 = 13z + 15 \Rightarrow 2z^2 - 13z - 15 = 0$. Factoring we get $(2z - 15)(z + 1) = 0$. Then $2z - 15 = 0 \Rightarrow$
$z = \frac{15}{2}$ or $z + 1 = 0 \Rightarrow z = -1$. Check: $2\left(\frac{15}{2}\right)^2 = 13\left(\frac{15}{2}\right) + 15 \Rightarrow \frac{225}{2} = \frac{195}{2} + \frac{30}{2} \Rightarrow \frac{225}{2} = \frac{225}{2}$;
$2(-1)^2 = 13(-1) + 15 \Rightarrow 2 = -13 + 15 \Rightarrow 2 = 2$.

8. $4z^2 = 7 - 27z \Rightarrow 4z^2 + 27z - 7 = 0$. Factoring we get $(4z - 1)(z + 7) = 0$. Then $4z - 1 = 0 \Rightarrow z = \frac{1}{4}$
or $z + 7 = 0 \Rightarrow z = -7$. Check: $4\left(\frac{1}{4}\right)^2 = 7 - 27\left(\frac{1}{4}\right) \Rightarrow \frac{1}{4} = \frac{28}{4} - \frac{27}{4} \Rightarrow \frac{1}{4} = \frac{1}{4}$;
$4(-7)^2 = 7 - 27(-7) \Rightarrow 196 = 7 + 189 \Rightarrow 196 = 196$.

9. $x(3x + 14) = 5 \Rightarrow 3x^2 + 14x - 5 = 0$. Factoring this we get: $(3x - 1)(x + 5) = 0$.
Then $3x - 1 = 0 \Rightarrow 3x = 1 \Rightarrow x = \frac{1}{3}$ or $x + 5 = 0 \Rightarrow x = -5$. Therefore $x = -5, \frac{1}{3}$.
Check: $-5(3(-5) + 14) = 5 \Rightarrow -5(-1) = 5 \Rightarrow 5 = 5$; $\frac{1}{3}\left(3\left(\frac{1}{3}\right) + 14\right) = 5 \Rightarrow \frac{1}{3}\left(15\right) = 5 \Rightarrow 5 = 5$

10. $x(5x + 19) = 4 \Rightarrow 5x^2 + 19x - 4 = 0$. Factoring this we get: $(5x - 1)(x + 4) = 0$.
Then $5x - 1 = 0 \Rightarrow 5x = 1 \Rightarrow x = \frac{1}{5}$ or $x + 4 = 0 \Rightarrow x = -4$. Therefore $x = -4, \frac{1}{5}$.
Check: $-4(5(-4) + 19) = 4 \Rightarrow -4(-1) = 4 \Rightarrow 4 = 4$;
$\frac{1}{5}\left(5\left(\frac{1}{5}\right) + 19\right) = 4 \Rightarrow \frac{1}{5}\left(20\right) = 4 \Rightarrow 4 = 4$

11. $6x^2 + \frac{5}{2} = 8x \Rightarrow 6x^2 - 8x + \frac{5}{2} = 0 \Rightarrow 12x^2 - 16x + 5 = 0$. Factoring this we get:
$(2x - 1)(6x - 5) = 0$.
Then $2x - 1 = 0 \Rightarrow 2x = 1 \Rightarrow x = \frac{1}{2}$ or $6x - 5 = 0 \Rightarrow 6x = 5 \Rightarrow x = \frac{5}{6}$. Therefore $x = \frac{1}{2}, \frac{5}{6}$.
Check: $6\left(\frac{1}{2}\right)^2 + \frac{5}{2} = 8\left(\frac{1}{2}\right) \Rightarrow \frac{3}{2} + \frac{5}{2} = 4 \Rightarrow 4 = 4$;
$6\left(\frac{5}{6}\right)^2 + \frac{5}{2} = 8\left(\frac{5}{6}\right) \Rightarrow \frac{25}{6} + \frac{15}{6} = \frac{40}{6} \Rightarrow \frac{40}{6} = \frac{40}{6}$

12. $8x^2 + 63 = -46x \Rightarrow 8x^2 + 46x + 63 = 0$. Factoring this we get: $(2x + 7)(4x + 9) = 0$.
Then $2x + 7 = 0 \Rightarrow 2x = -7 \Rightarrow x = -\frac{7}{2}$ or $4x + 9 = 0 \Rightarrow 4x = -9 \Rightarrow x = -\frac{9}{4}$.
Therefore $x = -\frac{7}{2}, -\frac{9}{4}$.
Check: $8\left(-\frac{7}{2}\right)^2 + 63 = -46\left(-\frac{7}{2}\right) \Rightarrow 98 + 63 = 161 \Rightarrow 161 = 161$;
$8\left(-\frac{9}{4}\right)^2 + 63 = -46\left(-\frac{9}{4}\right) \Rightarrow \frac{81}{2} + \frac{126}{2} = \frac{207}{2} \Rightarrow \frac{207}{2} = \frac{207}{2}$

13. $(t + 3)^2 = 5 \Rightarrow t^2 + 6t + 4 = 0$. Using the quadratic formula: $t = \frac{-b \pm \sqrt{b^2 - 4ac}}{2a} \Rightarrow$
$t = \frac{-6 \pm \sqrt{6^2 - 4(1)(4)}}{2(1)} \Rightarrow t = \frac{-6 \pm \sqrt{20}}{2} \Rightarrow t = \frac{-6 \pm 2\sqrt{5}}{2} \Rightarrow t = -3 \pm \sqrt{5}$

14. $(t-2)^2 = 11 \Rightarrow t^2 - 4t - 7 = 0$. Using the quadratic formula: $t = \dfrac{-b \pm \sqrt{b^2 - 4ac}}{2a} \Rightarrow$

$t = \dfrac{4 \pm \sqrt{(-4)^2 - 4(1)(-7)}}{2(1)} \Rightarrow t = \dfrac{4 \pm \sqrt{16 + 28}}{2} \Rightarrow t = \dfrac{4 \pm \sqrt{44}}{2} \Rightarrow \dfrac{4 \pm 2\sqrt{11}}{2} \Rightarrow$

$t = 2 \pm \sqrt{11}$

15. $4x^2 - 13 = 0 \Rightarrow 4x^2 + 0x - 13 = 0$. Using the quadratic formula: $x = \dfrac{-b \pm \sqrt{b^2 - 4ac}}{2a} \Rightarrow$

$x = \dfrac{0 \pm \sqrt{0^2 - 4(4)(-13)}}{2(4)} \Rightarrow x = \dfrac{\pm\sqrt{208}}{8} \Rightarrow x = \dfrac{\pm 4\sqrt{13}}{8} \Rightarrow x = \dfrac{\pm\sqrt{13}}{2}$

16. $9x^2 - 11 = 0 \Rightarrow 9x^2 + 0x - 11 = 0$. Using the quadratic formula: $x = \dfrac{-b \pm \sqrt{b^2 - 4ac}}{2a} \Rightarrow$

$x = \dfrac{-0 \pm \sqrt{0^2 - 4(9)(-11)}}{2(9)} \Rightarrow x = \dfrac{\pm\sqrt{396}}{18} \Rightarrow x = \dfrac{\pm 6\sqrt{11}}{18} \Rightarrow x = \dfrac{\pm\sqrt{11}}{3}$

17. $2(x-1)^2 + 4 = 0 \Rightarrow 2(x^2 - 2x + 1) + 4 = 0 \Rightarrow 2x^2 - 4x + 6 = 0$. Using the quadratic formula:

$x = \dfrac{-b \pm \sqrt{b^2 - 4ac}}{2a} \Rightarrow x = \dfrac{-(-4) \pm \sqrt{(-4)^2 - 4(2)(6)}}{2(2)} \Rightarrow x = \dfrac{4 \pm \sqrt{-32}}{4} = \dfrac{4 \pm 4\sqrt{-2}}{4} =$

$1 \pm \sqrt{-2}$. Since $\sqrt{-2}$ is not real, there is no real solution to the equation.

18. $-3(x+5)^2 - 6 = 0 \Rightarrow -3(x^2 + 10x + 25) - 6 = 0 \Rightarrow -3x^2 - 30x - 81 = 0$. Using the quadratic formula: $x = \dfrac{-b \pm \sqrt{b^2 - 4ac}}{2a} \Rightarrow x = \dfrac{-(-30) \pm \sqrt{(-30)^2 - 4(-3)(-81)}}{2(-3)} \Rightarrow x = \dfrac{30 \pm \sqrt{-72}}{-6}$.

Since $\sqrt{-72}$ is not real, there is no real solution to the equation.

19. $\dfrac{1}{2}x^2 - 3x + \dfrac{1}{2} = 0 \Rightarrow x^2 - 6x + 1 = 0$. Using the quadratic formula: $x = \dfrac{-b \pm \sqrt{b^2 - 4ac}}{2a} \Rightarrow$

$x = \dfrac{-(-6) \pm \sqrt{(-6)^2 - 4(1)(1)}}{2(1)} \Rightarrow x = \dfrac{6 \pm \sqrt{32}}{2} \Rightarrow x = \dfrac{6 \pm 4\sqrt{2}}{2} \Rightarrow x = 3 \pm 2\sqrt{2}$

20. $\dfrac{3}{4}x^2 + \dfrac{1}{2}x - \dfrac{1}{2} = 0 \Rightarrow 3x^2 + 2x - 2 = 0$. Using the quadratic formula: $x = \dfrac{-b \pm \sqrt{b^2 - 4ac}}{2a} \Rightarrow$

$x = \dfrac{-2 \pm \sqrt{2^2 - 4(3)(-2)}}{2(3)} \Rightarrow x = \dfrac{-2 \pm \sqrt{28}}{6} \Rightarrow x = \dfrac{-2 \pm 2\sqrt{7}}{6} \Rightarrow x = \dfrac{-1 \pm \sqrt{7}}{3}$

21. $-3z^2 - 2z + 4 = 0$. Using the quadratic formula: $x = \dfrac{-b \pm \sqrt{b^2 - 4ac}}{2a} \Rightarrow$

$x = \dfrac{-(-2) \pm \sqrt{(-2)^2 - 4(-3)(4)}}{2(-3)} \Rightarrow x = \dfrac{2 \pm \sqrt{52}}{-6} \Rightarrow x = \dfrac{-2 \pm 2\sqrt{13}}{6} \Rightarrow x = \dfrac{-1 \pm \sqrt{13}}{3}$

22. $-4z^2 + z + 1 = 0$. Using the quadratic formula: $x = \dfrac{-b \pm \sqrt{b^2 - 4ac}}{2a} \Rightarrow$

$x = \dfrac{-1 \pm \sqrt{1^2 - 4(-4)(1)}}{2(-4)} \Rightarrow x = \dfrac{-1 \pm \sqrt{17}}{-8} \Rightarrow x = \dfrac{1 \pm \sqrt{17}}{8}$

23. $25k^2 + 1 = 10k \Rightarrow 25k^2 - 10k + 1 = 0$. Using the quadratic formula: $x = \dfrac{-b \pm \sqrt{b^2 - 4ac}}{2a} \Rightarrow$

$x = \dfrac{-(-10) \pm \sqrt{(-10)^2 - 4(25)(1)}}{2(25)} \Rightarrow x = \dfrac{10 \pm \sqrt{0}}{50} \Rightarrow x = \dfrac{1}{5}$

24. $49k^2 + 4 = -28k \Rightarrow 49k^2 + 28k + 4 = 0$. Using the quadratic formula: $x = \dfrac{-b \pm \sqrt{b^2 - 4ac}}{2a} \Rightarrow$

$x = \dfrac{-28 \pm \sqrt{28^2 - 4(49)(4)}}{2(49)} \Rightarrow x = \dfrac{-28 \pm \sqrt{0}}{98} \Rightarrow x = \dfrac{-28}{98} \Rightarrow x = \dfrac{-2}{7}$

25. $-0.3x^2 + 0.1x = -0.02 \Rightarrow -30x^2 + 10x + 2 = 0$.

Using the quadratic formula: $x = \dfrac{-b \pm \sqrt{b^2 - 4ac}}{2a} \Rightarrow$

$x = \dfrac{-10 \pm \sqrt{10^2 - 4(-30)(2)}}{2(-30)} \Rightarrow x = \dfrac{-10 \pm \sqrt{340}}{-60} \Rightarrow x = \dfrac{10 \pm 2\sqrt{85}}{60} \Rightarrow x = \dfrac{5 \pm \sqrt{85}}{30}$

26. $-0.1x^2 + 1 = 0.5x \Rightarrow -x^2 - 5x + 10 = 0$. Using the quadratic formula: $x = \dfrac{-b \pm \sqrt{b^2 - 4ac}}{2a} \Rightarrow$

$x = \dfrac{-(-5) \pm \sqrt{(-5)^2 - 4(-1)(10)}}{2(-1)} \Rightarrow x = \dfrac{5 \pm \sqrt{25 + 40}}{-2} \Rightarrow x = \dfrac{5 \pm \sqrt{65}}{-2} \Rightarrow x = \dfrac{-5 \pm \sqrt{65}}{2}$

27. $2x(x + 2) = (x - 1)(x + 2) \Rightarrow 2x^2 + 4x = x^2 + x - 2 \Rightarrow x^2 + 3x + 2 = 0$. Factoring we get $(x + 2)(x + 1) = 0$. Then $x + 2 = 0 \Rightarrow x = -2$ or $x + 1 = 0 \Rightarrow x = -1$.

28. $(2x - 1)(x + 2) = (x + 3)(x + 1) \Rightarrow 2x^2 + 3x - 2 = x^2 + 4x + 3 \Rightarrow x^2 - x - 5 = 0$. Using the quadratic formula: $x = \dfrac{-b \pm \sqrt{b^2 - 4ac}}{2a} \Rightarrow x = \dfrac{1 \pm \sqrt{1 - 4(1)(-5)}}{2(1)} \Rightarrow x = \dfrac{1 \pm \sqrt{21}}{2}$.

29. For the $x$-intercepts, $y = 0 \Rightarrow 6x^2 + 13x - 5 = 0$. Factoring this we get $(2x + 5)(3x - 1) = 0$. Then $2x + 5 = 0 \Rightarrow 2x = -5 \Rightarrow x = -\dfrac{5}{2}$ or $3x - 1 = 0 \Rightarrow 3x = 1 \Rightarrow x = \dfrac{1}{3}$. Therefore $x = -\dfrac{5}{2}, \dfrac{1}{3}$.

30. For the $x$-intercepts, $y = 0 \Rightarrow 6x^2 + 4x - 2 = 0 \Rightarrow 3x^2 + 2x - 1 = 0$. Using the quadratic formula:

$x = \dfrac{-2 \pm \sqrt{2^2 - 4(3)(-1)}}{2(3)} \Rightarrow x = \dfrac{-2 \pm \sqrt{16}}{6} \Rightarrow x = \dfrac{-2 \pm 4}{6} \Rightarrow x = -1, \dfrac{1}{3}$.

31. For the $x$-intercept, $y = 0 \Rightarrow -4x^2 + 12x - 9 = 0$. Using the quadratic formula:

$x = \dfrac{-12 \pm \sqrt{12^2 - 4(-4)(-9)}}{2(-4)} \Rightarrow x = \dfrac{-12 \pm \sqrt{144 - 144}}{-8} \Rightarrow x = \dfrac{-12 \pm \sqrt{0}}{-8} \Rightarrow x = \dfrac{3}{2}$

32. For the $x$-intercept, $y = 0 \Rightarrow 9x^2 + 30x + 25 = 0$. Using the quadratic formula:

$x = \dfrac{-30 \pm \sqrt{30^2 - 4(9)(25)}}{2(9)} \Rightarrow x = \dfrac{-30 \pm \sqrt{900 - 900}}{18} \Rightarrow x = \dfrac{-30 \pm \sqrt{0}}{18} \Rightarrow x = \dfrac{-30}{18} \Rightarrow$

$x = -\dfrac{5}{3}$

33. For the $x$-intercepts, $y = 0 \Rightarrow -3x^2 + 11x - 6 = 0$. Using the quadratic formula:

$x = \dfrac{-11 \pm \sqrt{11^2 - 4(-3)(-6)}}{2(-3)} \Rightarrow x = \dfrac{-11 \pm \sqrt{121 - 72}}{-6} \Rightarrow x = \dfrac{-11 \pm \sqrt{49}}{-6} \Rightarrow x = \dfrac{11 \pm 7}{6} \Rightarrow$

$x = \dfrac{2}{3}, 3$

34. For the $x$-intercepts, $y = 0 \Rightarrow -7x^2 - 15x - 2 = 0$. Factoring this we get $(-7x - 1)(x + 2) = 0$. Then $-7x - 1 = 0 \Rightarrow -7x = 1 \Rightarrow x = -\dfrac{1}{7}$ or $x + 2 = 0 \Rightarrow x = -2$. Therefore $x = -2, -\dfrac{1}{7}$.

35. (a) Graphical: Graph $Y_1 = X^\wedge 2 + 2X$ and locate the $x$-intercepts. See Figure 35a and Figure 35b; the solutions to the equation are $-2$ and 0.

(b) Numerical: Table $Y_1 = X^\wedge 2 + 2X$ starting at $x = -4$, incrementing by 1. $Y_1 = 0$ when $x = -2$ or 0. See Figure 35c.

(c) Symbolic: $x^2 + 2x = 0 \Rightarrow x(x + 2) = 0$. Then $x = 0$ or $x + 2 = 0 \Rightarrow x = -2$. Therefore $x = -2, 0$.

[−10, 10, 1] by [−10, 10, 1]

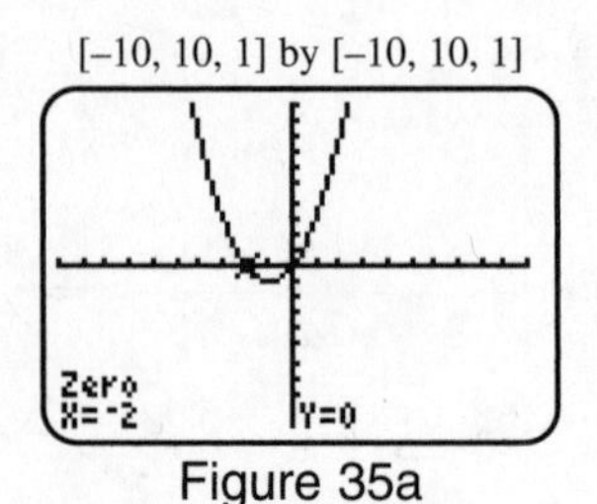


Figure 35a

[−10, 10, 1] by [−10, 10, 1]

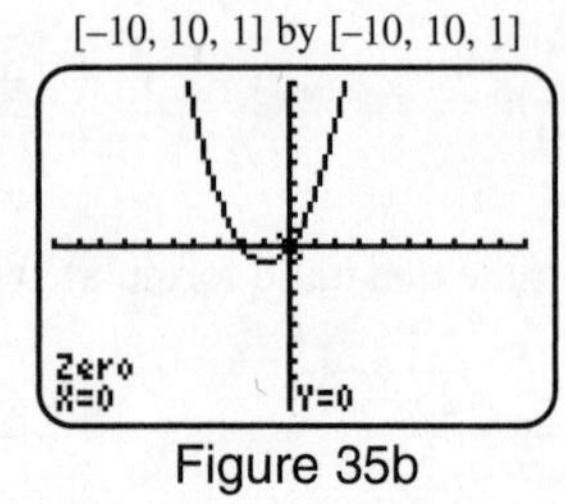


Figure 35b

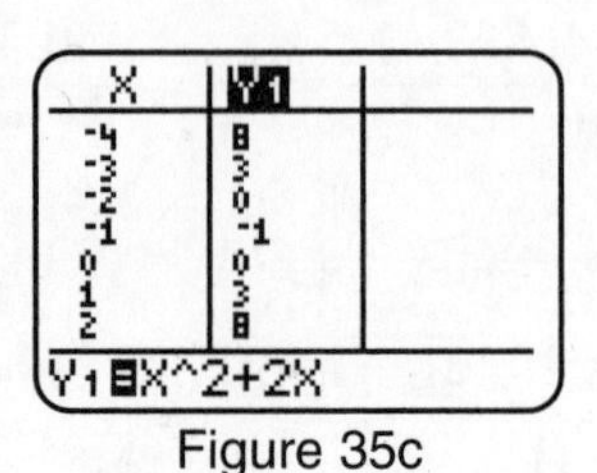


Figure 35c

36. (a) Graphical: Graph $Y_1 = X^\wedge 2 - 4$ and locate the $x$-intercepts. See Figure 36a and Figure 36b; the solutions to the equation are $-2$ and 2.

(b) Numerical: Table $Y_1 = X^\wedge 2 - 4$ starting at $x = -3$, incrementing by 1. $Y_1 = 0$ when $x = -2, 2$. See Figure 36c.

(c) Symbolic: $x^2 - 4 = 0 \Rightarrow (x + 2)(x - 2) = 0$. Therefore $x = -2, 2$.

[−10, 10, 1] by [−10, 10, 1]

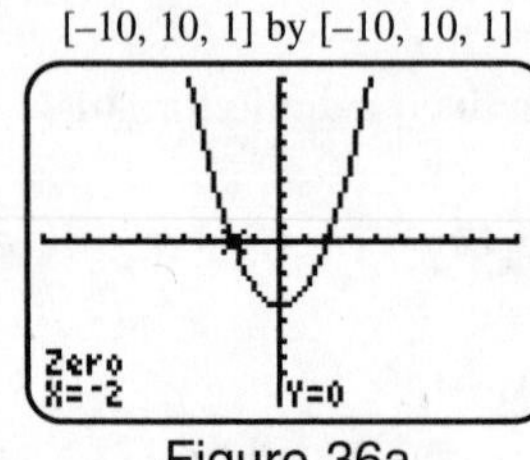


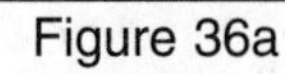

Figure 36a

[−10, 10, 1] by [−10, 10, 1]

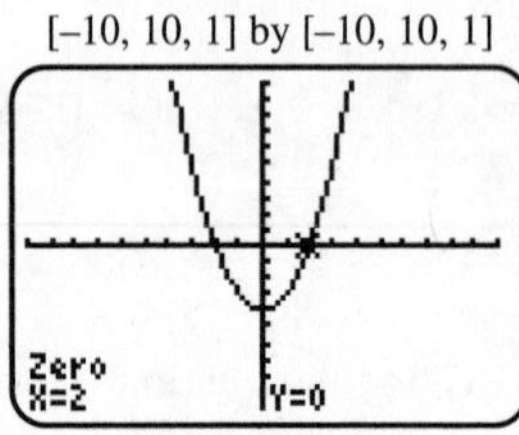


Figure 36b

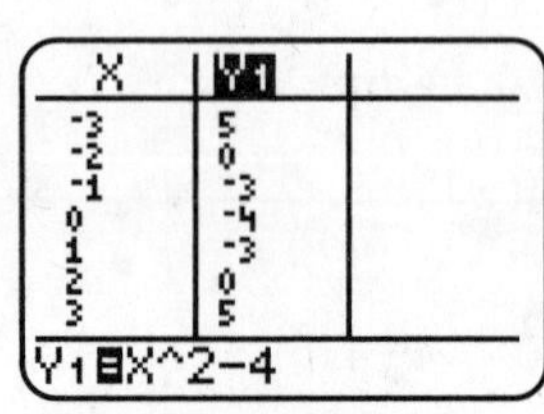


Figure 36c

37. (a) Graphical: Graph $Y_1 = X^\wedge 2 - X - 6$ and locate the $x$-intercepts. See Figures 37a and 37b; the solutions to the equation are $-2$ and 3.

(b) Numerical: Table $Y_1 = X^\wedge 2 - X - 6$ starting at $x = -3$, incrementing by 1. $Y_1 = 0$ when $x = -2$ or 3. See Figure 37c.

(c) Symbolic: $x^2 - x - 6 = 0 \Rightarrow (x - 3)(x + 2) = 0 \Rightarrow x = 3$ or $-2$.

[−10, 10, 1] by [−10, 10, 1]

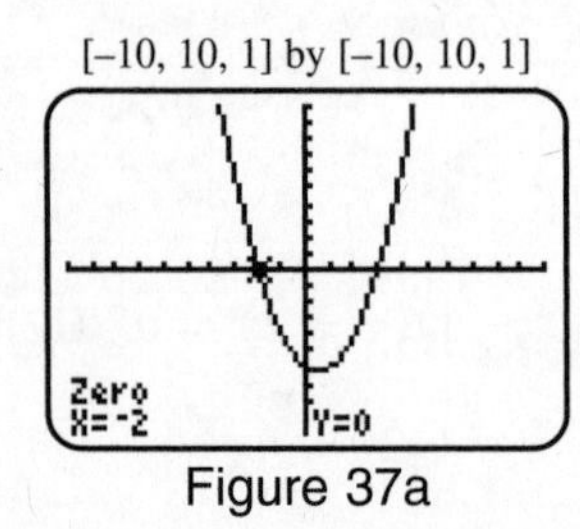


Figure 37a

[−10, 10, 1] by [−10, 10, 1]

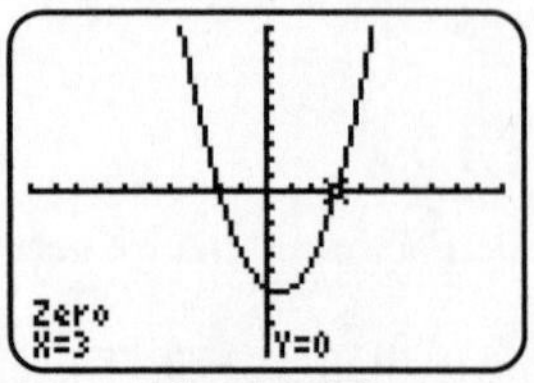

Figure 37b

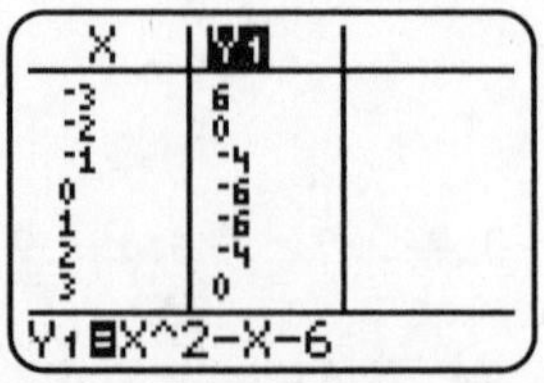

Figure 37c

38. (a) Graphical: Graph $Y_1 = 2X\wedge2 + 5X - 3$ and locate the $x$-intercepts. See Figures 38a and 38b; the solutions to the equation are $-3$ and 0.5.

(b) Numerical: Table $Y_1 = 2X\wedge2 + 5X - 3$ starting at $x = -3$, incrementing by 0.7. $Y_1 = 0$ when $x = -3$ or 0.5. See Figure 38c.

(c) Symbolic: $2x^2 + 5x - 3 = 0 \Rightarrow (2x - 1)(x + 3) = 0 \Rightarrow x = \frac{1}{2}$ or $-3$.

[−10, 10, 1] by [−10, 10, 1]

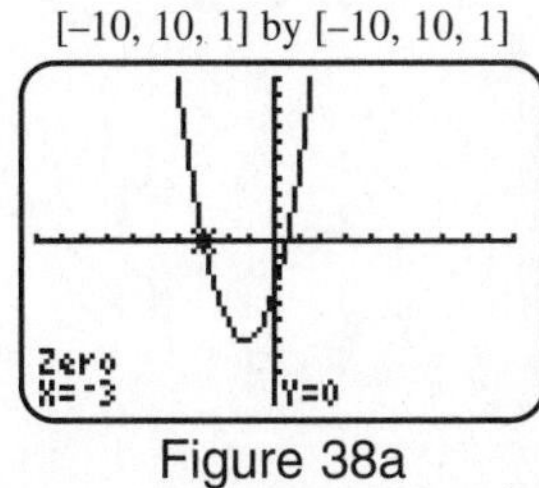
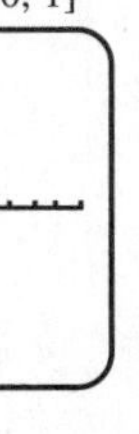

Figure 38a

[−10, 10, 1] by [−10, 10, 1]

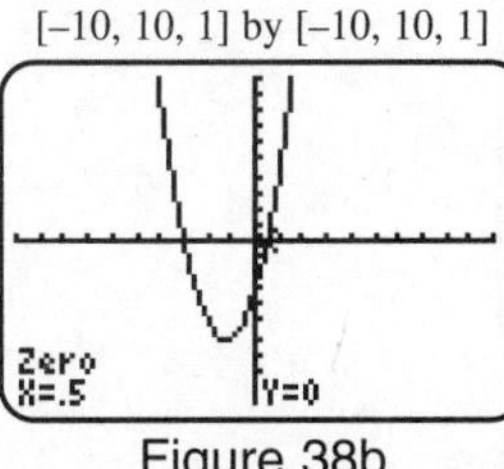

Figure 38b

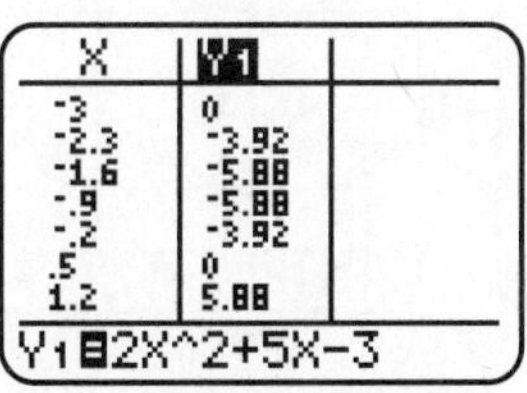

| X | Y1 |
|---|---|
| -3 | 0 |
| -2.3 | -3.92 |
| -1.6 | -5.88 |
| -.9 | -5.88 |
| -.2 | -3.92 |
| .5 | 0 |
| 1.2 | 5.88 |

Y1=2X^2+5X-3

Figure 38c

39. (a) Graphical: Graph $Y_1 = 2X\wedge2 - 6$ and locate the $x$-intercepts. See Figures 39a and 39b; the solutions to the equation are $x \approx \pm1.7$.

(b) Numerical: Table $Y_1 = 2X\wedge2 - 6$ starting at $x = -2\sqrt{3}$, incrementing by $\sqrt{3}$. $Y_1 \approx 0$ when $x \approx \pm1.7$. See Figure 39c.

(c) Symbolic: $2x^2 = 6 \Rightarrow x^2 = 3 \Rightarrow x = \pm\sqrt{3} \approx \pm1.7$.

[−10, 10, 1] by [−10, 10, 1]

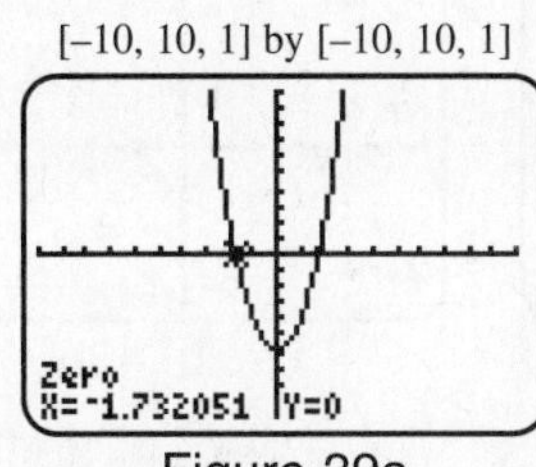
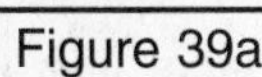

Figure 39a

[−10, 10, 1] by [−10, 10, 1]

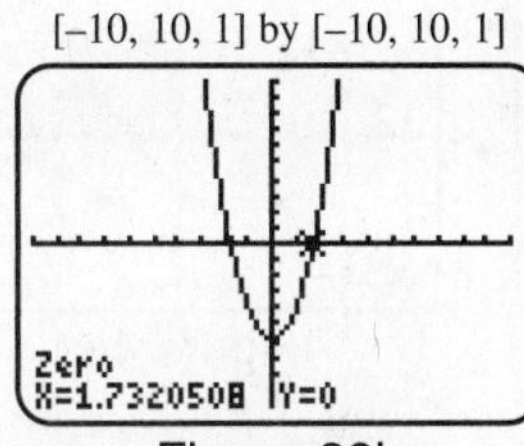

Figure 39b

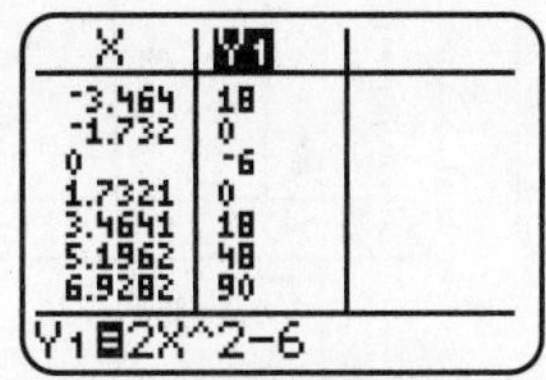

| X | Y1 |
|---|---|
| -3.464 | 18 |
| -1.732 | 0 |
| 0 | -6 |
| 1.7321 | 0 |
| 3.4641 | 18 |
| 5.1962 | 48 |
| 6.9282 | 90 |

Y1=2X^2-6

Figure 39c

40. (a) Graphical: Graph $Y_1 = X\wedge2 - 225$ and locate the $x$-intercepts. See Figures 40a and 40b; the solutions to the equation are $x = \pm15$.

(b) Numerical: Table $Y_1 = X\wedge2 - 225$ starting at $x = -25$, incrementing by 10. $Y_1 = 0$ when $x = \pm15$. See Figure 40c.

(c) Symbolic: $x^2 - 225 = 0 \Rightarrow x^2 = 225 \Rightarrow x = \pm15$.

[−50, 50, 5] by [−300, 300, 50]

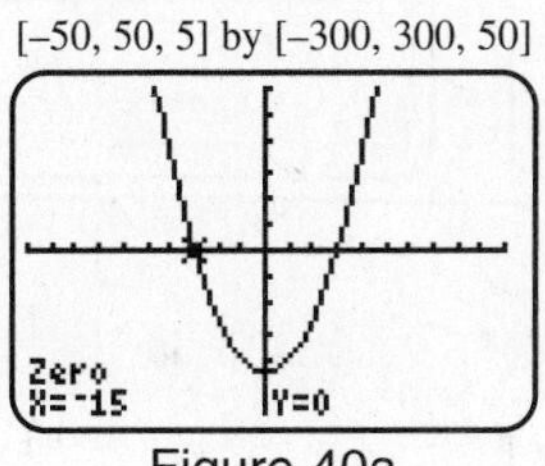

Figure 40a

[−50, 50, 5] by [−300, 300, 50]

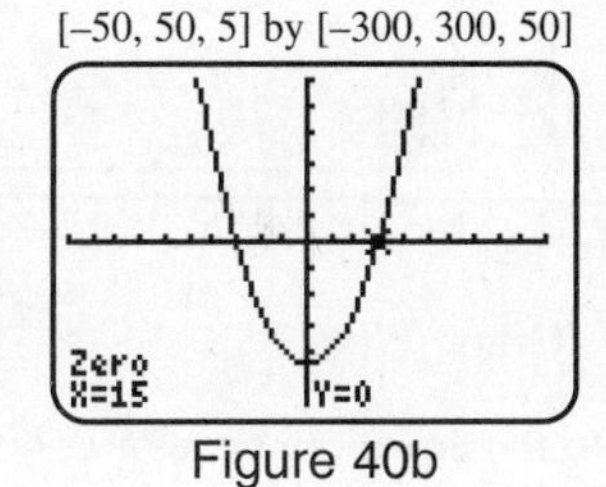

Figure 40b

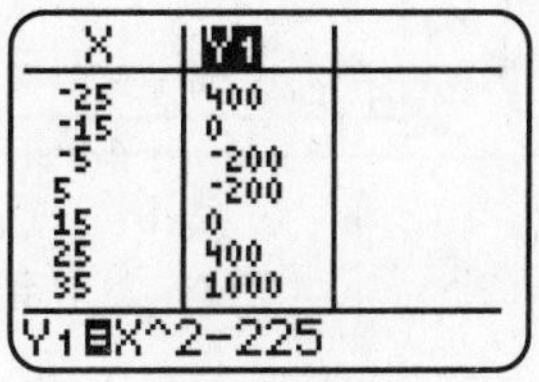

| X | Y1 |
|---|---|
| -25 | 400 |
| -15 | 0 |
| -5 | -200 |
| 5 | -200 |
| 15 | 0 |
| 25 | 400 |
| 35 | 1000 |

Y1=X^2-225

Figure 40c

41. (a) Graphical: Graph $Y_1 = 4X^2 - 12X + 9$ and locate the $x$-intercept. See Figure 41a; the solution to the equation is $x = 1.5$.

(b) Numerical: Table $Y_1 = 4X^2 - 12X + 9$ starting at $x = 0$, incrementing by 0.5. $Y_1 = 0$ when $x = 1.5$. See Figure 41b.

(c) Symbolic: $4x^2 - 12x + 9 = 0 \Rightarrow (2x - 3)(2x - 3) = 0 \Rightarrow x = \frac{3}{2}$.

[−5, 5, 1] by [−5, 5, 1]

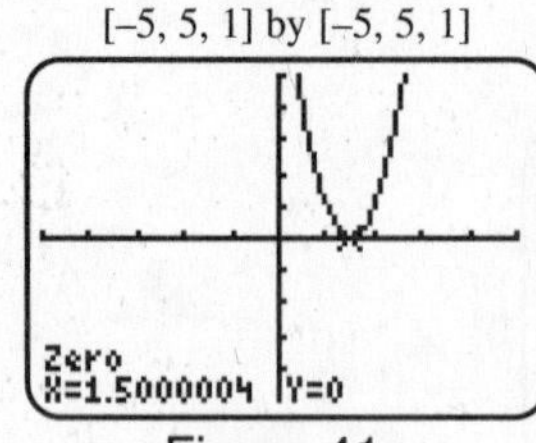

Figure 41a

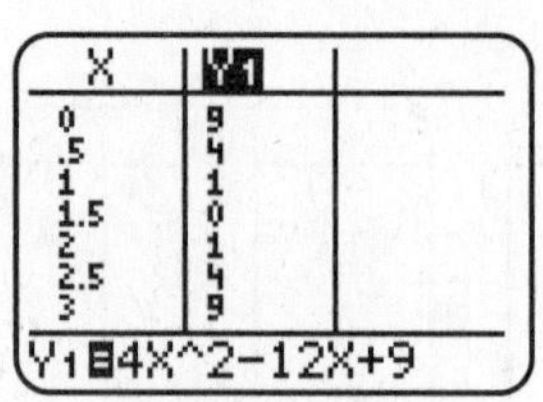

Figure 41b

42. (a) Graphical: Graph $Y_1 = -4X^2 + 4X - 1$ and locate the $x$-intercept. See Figure 42a; the solution to the equation is $x = 0.5$.

(b) Numerical: Table $Y_1 = -4X^2 + 4X - 1$ starting at $x = 0$, incrementing by 0.5. $Y_1 = 0$ when $x = 0.5$. See Figure 42b.

(c) Symbolic: $-4x^2 + 4x - 1 = 0 \Rightarrow 4x^2 - 4x + 1 = 0 \Rightarrow (2x - 1)(2x - 1) = 0 \Rightarrow x = \frac{1}{2}$.

[−5, 5, 1] by [−5, 5, 1]

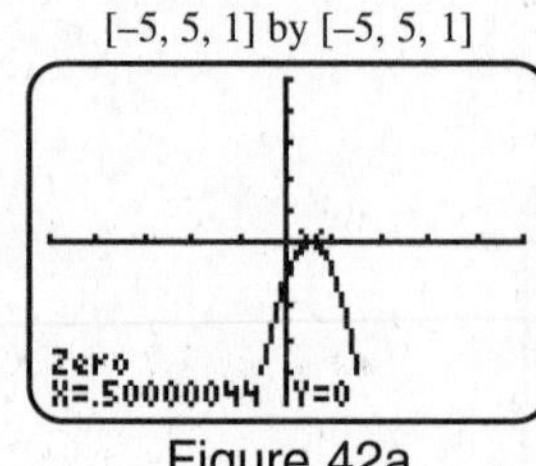

Figure 42a

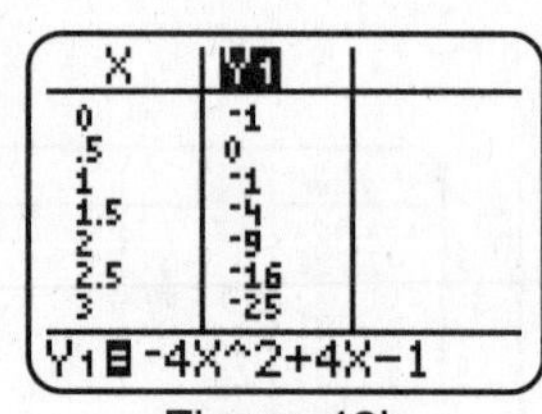

Figure 42b

[−1, 1, 0.1] by [−10, 10, 1]

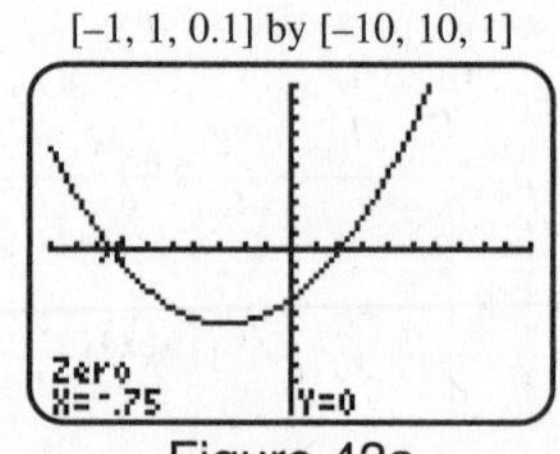

Figure 43a

[−1, 1, 0.1] by [−10, 10, 1]

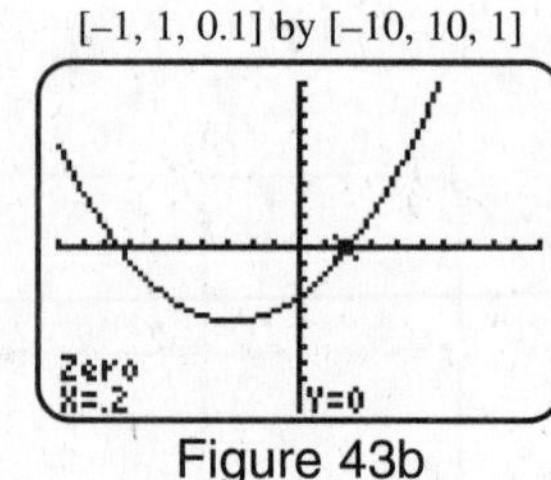

Figure 43b

43. $20x^2 + 11x = 3 \Rightarrow 20x^2 + 11x - 3 = 0$. Graph $Y_1 = 20X^2 + 11X - 3$ and locate the $x$-intercepts. See Figures 43a and 43b; the solutions to the equation are $x = -0.75$ or $0.2$.

44. $-2x^2 + 4x = 1.595 \Rightarrow -2x^2 + 4x - 1.595 = 0$. Graph $Y_1 = -2X^2 + 4X - 1.595$ and locate the $x$-intercepts. See Figures 44a and 44b; the solutions to the equation are $x = 0.55$ or $1.45$.

[0, 2, 0.1] by [−1, 1, 0.1]

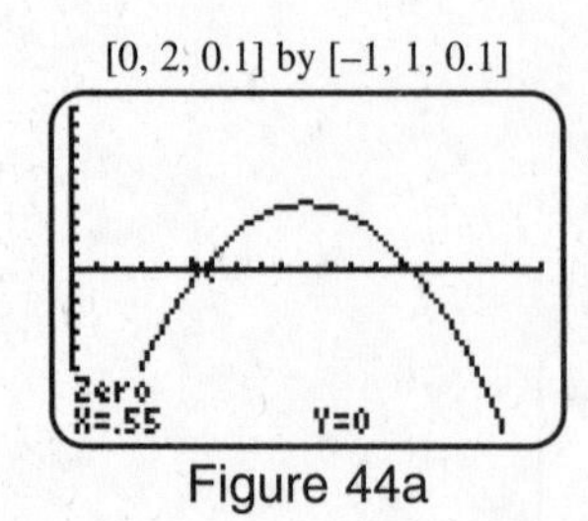

Figure 44a

[0, 2, 0.1] by [−1, 1, 0.1]

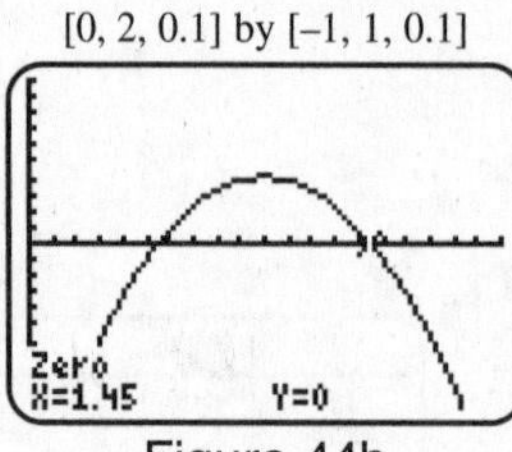

Figure 44b

[0, 2, 0.1] by [−1, 1, 0.1]

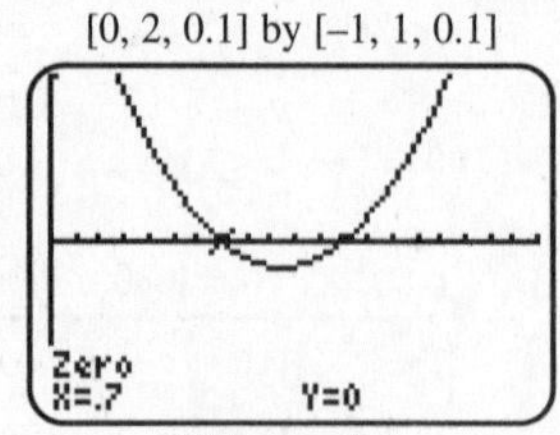

Figure 45a

[0, 2, 0.1] by [−1, 1, 0.1]

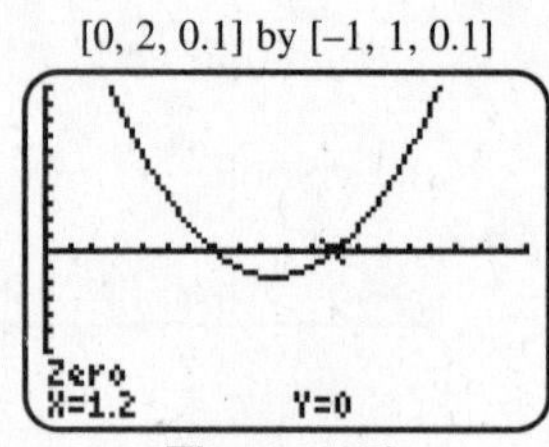

Figure 45b

45. $2.5x^2 = 4.75x - 2.1 \Rightarrow 2.5x^2 - 4.75x + 2.1 = 0$. Graph $Y_1 = 2.5X^2 - 4.75X + 2.1$ and locate the $x$-intercepts. See Figures 45a and 45b; the solutions to the equation are $x = 0.7$ or $1.2$.

46. $x(x + 24) = 6912 \Rightarrow x^2 + 24x - 6912 = 0$. Graph $Y_1 = X\text{^}2 + 24X - 6912$ and locate the $x$-intercepts. See Figures 46a & 46b; the solutions to the equation are $x = -96$ or $72$.

[−200, 200, 50] by [−10000, 10000, 5000]

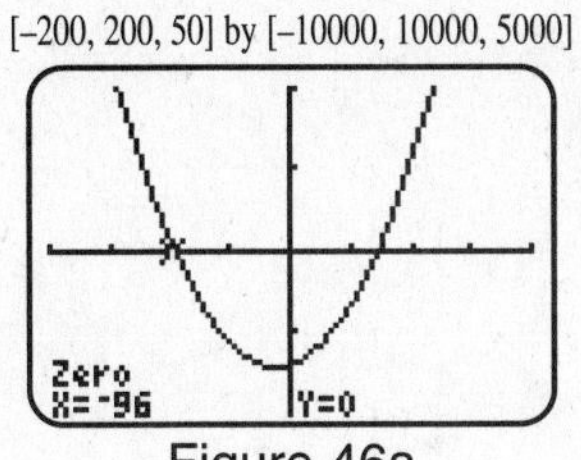

Figure 46a

[−200, 200, 50] by [−10000, 10000, 5000]

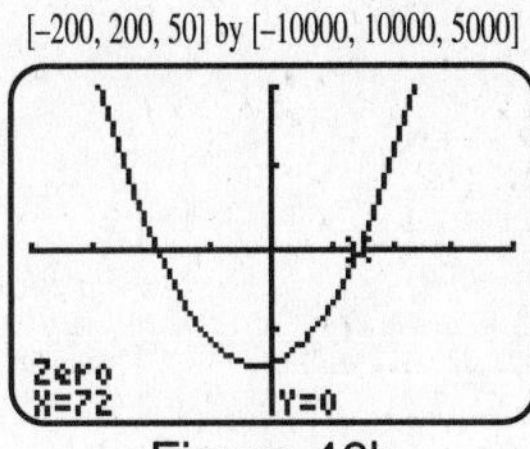

Figure 46b

47. $x^2 + 4x - 6 = 0 \Rightarrow x^2 + 4x = 6 \Rightarrow x^2 + 4x + 4 = 6 + 4 \Rightarrow (x + 2)^2 = 10 \Rightarrow$
$x + 2 = \pm\sqrt{10} \Rightarrow x = -2 \pm \sqrt{10}$

48. $x^2 - 10x = 1 \Rightarrow x^2 - 10x + 25 = 1 + 25 \Rightarrow (x - 5)^2 = 26 \Rightarrow x - 5 = \pm\sqrt{26} \Rightarrow x = 5 \pm \sqrt{26}$

49. $x^2 + 5x = 4 \Rightarrow x^2 + 5x + \frac{25}{4} = 4 + \frac{25}{4} \Rightarrow \left(x + \frac{5}{2}\right)^2 = \frac{41}{4} \Rightarrow$
$x + \frac{5}{2} = \pm\sqrt{\frac{41}{4}} \Rightarrow x = -\frac{5}{2} \pm \frac{\sqrt{41}}{2} \Rightarrow x = -\frac{5}{2} \pm \frac{1}{2}\sqrt{41}$

50. $x^2 + 6x - 5 = 0 \Rightarrow x^2 + 6x = 5 \Rightarrow x^2 + 6x + 9 = 5 + 9 \Rightarrow (x + 3)^2 = 14 \Rightarrow$
$x + 3 = \pm\sqrt{14} \Rightarrow x = -3 \pm \sqrt{14}$

51. $3x^2 - 6x = 2 \Rightarrow x^2 - 2x = \frac{2}{3} \Rightarrow x^2 - 2x + 1 = \frac{2}{3} + 1 \Rightarrow (x - 1)^2 = \frac{5}{3} \Rightarrow$
$x - 1 = \pm\sqrt{\frac{5}{3}} \Rightarrow x = 1 \pm \sqrt{\frac{5}{3}} \Rightarrow 1 \pm \frac{\sqrt{15}}{3}$

52. $2x^2 - 3x + 1 = 0 \Rightarrow 2x^2 - 3x = -1 \Rightarrow x^2 - \frac{3}{2}x = -\frac{1}{2} \Rightarrow x^2 - \frac{3}{2}x + \frac{9}{16} = -\frac{1}{2} + \frac{9}{16} \Rightarrow$
$\left(x - \frac{3}{4}\right)^2 = \frac{1}{16} \Rightarrow x - \frac{3}{4} = \pm\frac{1}{4} \Rightarrow x = \frac{3}{4} \pm \frac{1}{4} \Rightarrow x = \frac{1}{2}$ or $1$

53. $x^2 - 8x = 10 \Rightarrow x^2 - 8x + 16 = 10 + 16 \Rightarrow (x - 4)^2 = 26 \Rightarrow x - 4 = \pm\sqrt{26} \Rightarrow x = 4 \pm \sqrt{26}$

54. $x^2 - 2x = 2 \Rightarrow x^2 - 2x + 1 = 2 + 1 \Rightarrow (x - 1)^2 = 3 \Rightarrow x - 1 = \pm\sqrt{3} \Rightarrow x = 1 \pm \sqrt{3}$

55. $\frac{1}{2}t^2 - \frac{3}{2}t = 1 \Rightarrow t^2 - 3t = 2 \Rightarrow t^2 - 3t + \frac{9}{4} = 2 + \frac{9}{4} \Rightarrow \left(t - \frac{3}{2}\right)^2 = \frac{17}{4} \Rightarrow t - \frac{3}{2} = \pm\sqrt{\frac{17}{4}} \Rightarrow$
$t = \frac{3}{2} \pm \frac{\sqrt{17}}{2} \Rightarrow t = \frac{3 \pm \sqrt{17}}{2}$

56. $\frac{1}{3}t^2 + \frac{1}{2}t = 2 \Rightarrow t^2 + \frac{3}{2}t = 6 \Rightarrow t^2 + \frac{3}{2}t + \frac{9}{16} = 6 + \frac{9}{16} \Rightarrow \left(t + \frac{3}{4}\right)^2 = \frac{105}{16} \Rightarrow$
$t + \frac{3}{4} = \pm\sqrt{\frac{105}{16}} \Rightarrow t = -\frac{3}{4} \pm \frac{\sqrt{105}}{4} \Rightarrow t = \frac{-3 \pm \sqrt{105}}{4}$

57. $-2z^2 + 3z + 1 = 0 \Rightarrow z^2 - \frac{3}{2}z = \frac{1}{2} \Rightarrow z^2 - \frac{3}{2}z + \frac{9}{16} = \frac{1}{2} + \frac{9}{16} \Rightarrow \left(z - \frac{3}{4}\right)^2 = \frac{17}{16} \Rightarrow$
$z - \frac{3}{4} = \pm\sqrt{\frac{17}{16}} \Rightarrow z = \frac{3}{4} \pm \frac{\sqrt{7}}{4} \Rightarrow z = \frac{3 \pm \sqrt{17}}{4}$

58. $-3z^2 - 5z + 3 = 0 \Rightarrow z^2 + \frac{5}{3}z = 1 \Rightarrow z^2 + \frac{5}{3}z + \frac{25}{36} = 1 + \frac{25}{36} \Rightarrow \left(z + \frac{5}{6}\right)^2 = \frac{61}{36} \Rightarrow$

$z + \frac{5}{6} = \pm\sqrt{\frac{61}{36}} \Rightarrow z = -\frac{5}{6} \pm \frac{\sqrt{61}}{6} \Rightarrow z = \frac{-5 \pm \sqrt{61}}{6}$

59. $-\frac{3}{2}z^2 - \frac{1}{4}z + 1 = 0 \Rightarrow z^2 + \frac{1}{6}z = \frac{2}{3} \Rightarrow z^2 + \frac{1}{6}z + \frac{1}{144} = \frac{2}{3} + \frac{1}{144} \Rightarrow \left(z + \frac{1}{12}\right)^2 = \frac{97}{144} \Rightarrow$

$z + \frac{1}{12} = \pm\sqrt{\frac{97}{144}} \Rightarrow z = -\frac{1}{12} \pm \frac{\sqrt{97}}{12} \Rightarrow z = \frac{-1 \pm \sqrt{97}}{12}$

60. $-\frac{1}{5}z^2 - \frac{1}{2}z + 2 = 0 \Rightarrow z^2 + \frac{5}{2}z = 10 \Rightarrow z^2 + \frac{5}{2}z + \frac{25}{16} = 10 + \frac{25}{16} \Rightarrow \left(z + \frac{5}{4}\right)^2 = \frac{185}{16} \Rightarrow$

$z + \frac{5}{4} = \pm\sqrt{\frac{185}{16}} \Rightarrow z = -\frac{5}{4} \pm \frac{\sqrt{185}}{4} \Rightarrow z = \frac{-5 \pm \sqrt{185}}{4}$

61. $D =$ all real numbers except when the denominator $x^2 - 5 = 0 \Rightarrow x^2 = 5 \Rightarrow x = \pm\sqrt{5} \Rightarrow$

$D = \{x \mid x \neq \sqrt{5}, x \neq -\sqrt{5}\}$

62. $D =$ all real numbers except when the denominator

$7 - x^2 = 0 \Rightarrow -x^2 = -7 \Rightarrow x^2 = 7 \Rightarrow x = \pm\sqrt{7} \Rightarrow D = \{x \mid x \neq \sqrt{7}, x \neq -\sqrt{7}\}$

63. $D =$ all real numbers except when the denominator

$t^2 - t - 2 = 0 \Rightarrow (t - 2)(t + 1) = 0 \Rightarrow t = -1, 2 \Rightarrow D = \{t \mid t \neq -1, t \neq 2\}$

64. $D =$ all real numbers except when the denominator $2t - 11t - 21 = 0 \Rightarrow (2t + 3)(t - 7) = 0 \Rightarrow$

$2t + 3 = 0$ or $t - 7 = 0 \Rightarrow t = -\frac{3}{2}, 7 \Rightarrow D = \{t \mid t \neq -\frac{3}{2}, t \neq 7\}$

65. $4x^2 + 3y = \frac{y + 1}{3} \Rightarrow 3y - \frac{y + 1}{3} = -4x^2 \Rightarrow 9y - y - 1 = -12x^2 \Rightarrow 8y - 1 = -12x^2 \Rightarrow$

$8y = -12x^2 + 1 \Rightarrow y = \frac{-12x^2 + 1}{8}$; yes, $y$ is a function of $x$ since each $x$-input produces only one $y$-output.

66. $\frac{x^2 + y}{2} = y - 2 \Rightarrow x^2 + y = 2y - 4 \Rightarrow -2y + y = -x^2 - 4 \Rightarrow -y = -x^2 - 4 \Rightarrow y = x^2 + 4$;

yes, $y$ is a function of $x$ since each $x$-input produces only one $y$-output.

67. $3y = \frac{2x - y}{3} \Rightarrow 9y = 2x - y \Rightarrow 10y = 2x \Rightarrow y = \frac{x}{5}$; yes, $y$ is a function of $x$ since each $x$-input produces only one $y$-output.

68. $\frac{5 - y}{3} = \frac{x + 3y}{4} \Rightarrow 20 - 4y = 3x + 9y \Rightarrow -13y = 3x - 20 \Rightarrow y = \frac{-3x + 20}{13}$. Yes, $y$ is a function of $x$ since each $x$-input produces only one $y$-output.

69. $x^2 + (y - 3)^2 = 9 \Rightarrow (y - 3)^2 = 9 - x^2 \Rightarrow y - 3 = \pm\sqrt{9 - x^2} \Rightarrow y = 3 \pm \sqrt{9 - x^2}$; no, $y$ is not a function of $x$ since some $x$-inputs produce two $y$-outputs.

70. $(x + 2)^2 + (y + 1)^2 = 1 \Rightarrow (y + 1)^2 = 1 - (x + 2)^2 \Rightarrow y + 1 = \pm\sqrt{1 - (x + 2)^2} \Rightarrow$

$y = -1 \pm \sqrt{1 - (x + 2)^2}$; No, $y$ is not a function of $x$ since some $x$-inputs produce two $y$-outputs.

71. $3x^2 + 4y^2 = 12 \Rightarrow 4y^2 = 12 - 3x^2 \Rightarrow 2y = \pm\sqrt{12 - 3x^2} \Rightarrow y = \pm\frac{\sqrt{12 - 3x^2}}{2}$;

no, $y$ is not a function of $x$ because some $x$-inputs produce two $y$-outputs.

72. $x - 25y^2 = 50 \Rightarrow -25y^2 = -x + 50 \Rightarrow 25y^2 = x - 50 \Rightarrow 5y = \pm\sqrt{x - 50} \Rightarrow y = \pm\dfrac{\sqrt{x-50}}{5}$;

no, $y$ is not a function of $x$ because some $x$-inputs produce two $y$-outputs.

73. $V = \frac{1}{3}\pi r^2 h$ for $r \Rightarrow \frac{3V}{\pi h} = r^2 \Rightarrow r = \pm\sqrt{\frac{3V}{\pi h}}$

74. $V = \frac{1}{2}gt^2 + h$ for t $\Rightarrow V - h = \frac{1}{2}gt^2 \Rightarrow \frac{2(V-h)}{g} = t^2 \Rightarrow t = \pm\sqrt{\frac{2(V-h)}{g}}$

75. $K = \frac{1}{2}mv^2$ for $v \Rightarrow \frac{2K}{m} = v^2 \Rightarrow v = \pm\sqrt{\frac{2K}{m}}$

76. $W = I^2R$ for $I \Rightarrow \frac{W}{R} = I^2 \Rightarrow I = \pm\sqrt{\frac{W}{R}}$

77. $a^2 + b^2 = c^2$ for $b \Rightarrow b^2 = c^2 - a^2 \Rightarrow b = \pm\sqrt{c^2 - a^2}$

78. $S = 4\pi r^2 + x^2$ for $r \Rightarrow S - x^2 = 4\pi r^2 \Rightarrow \frac{S - x^2}{4\pi} \Rightarrow r^2 \Rightarrow r = \pm\frac{1}{2}\sqrt{\frac{S - x^2}{\pi}}$

79. $s = -16t^2 + 100t$ for $t \Rightarrow -s = 16t^2 - 100t \Rightarrow \frac{-s}{16} = t^2 - \frac{25}{4}t \Rightarrow \frac{-s}{16} + \frac{625}{64} = t^2 - \frac{25}{4}t + \frac{625}{64} \Rightarrow$

$\left(t - \frac{25}{8}\right)^2 = \frac{625 - 4s}{64} \Rightarrow t - \frac{25}{8} = \pm\sqrt{\frac{625 - 4s}{64}} \Rightarrow t = \frac{25}{8} \pm \sqrt{\frac{625 - 4s}{64}} \Rightarrow$

$t = \dfrac{25 \pm \sqrt{625 - 4s}}{8}$

80. $T^2 - kT - k^2 = 0$ for $T$, $T^2 - kT = k^2 \Rightarrow T^2 - kT + \frac{k^2}{4} = k^2 + \frac{k^2}{4} \Rightarrow \left(T - \frac{k}{2}\right)^2 = \frac{5k^2}{4} \Rightarrow$

$T - \frac{k}{2} = \pm\sqrt{\frac{5k^2}{4}} \Rightarrow T = \frac{k}{2} \pm \sqrt{\frac{5K^2}{4}} \Rightarrow T = \frac{k \pm \sqrt{5k^2}}{2}$

81. (a) $3x^2 = 12 \Rightarrow 3x^2 - 12 = 0$

(b) $b^2 - 4ac = 0^2 - 4(3)(-12) = 144 > 0$. There are two real solutions.

(c) $3x^2 = 12 \Rightarrow x^2 = 4 \Rightarrow x = \pm 2$

82. (a) $8x^2 - 2 = 14 \Rightarrow 8x^2 - 16 = 0$

(b) $b^2 - 4ac = 0^2 - 4(8)(-16) = 512 > 0$. There are two real solutions.

(c) $8x^2 = 16 \Rightarrow x^2 = 2 \Rightarrow x = \pm\sqrt{2}$

83. (a) $x^2 - 2x = -1 \Rightarrow x^2 - 2x + 1 = 0$

(b) $b^2 - 4ac = (-2)^2 - 4(1)(1) = 0$. There is one real solution.

(c) $x^2 - 2x + 1 = 0 \Rightarrow (x - 1)^2 = 0 \Rightarrow x = 1$

84. (a) $6x^2 = 4x \Rightarrow 6x^2 - 4x = 0$

(b) $b^2 - 4ac = (-4)^2 - 4(6)(0) = 16 > 0$. There are two real solutions.

(c) $6x^2 - 4x = 0 \Rightarrow 3x^2 - 2x = 0 \Rightarrow x(3x - 2) = 0 \Rightarrow x = 0$ or $3x - 2 = 0 \Rightarrow 3x = 2 \Rightarrow x = \frac{2}{3}$.

Therefore $x = 0, \frac{2}{3}$.

85. (a) $4x = x^2 \Rightarrow x^2 - 4x = 0$

(b) $b^2 - 4ac = (-4)^2 - 4(1)(0) = 16 > 0$. There are two real solutions.

(c) $x^2 - 4x = 0 \Rightarrow x(x - 4) = 0 \Rightarrow x = 0$ or $x - 4 = 0 \Rightarrow x = 4$. Therefore, $x = 0, 4$.

86. (a) $16x^2 + 9 = 24x \Rightarrow 16x^2 - 24x + 9 = 0$

(b) $b^2 - 4ac = (-24)^2 - 4(16)(9) = 0$. There is one real solution.

(c) $16x^2 - 24x + 9 = 0 \Rightarrow (4x - 3)^2 = 0 \Rightarrow 4x = 3 \Rightarrow x = \frac{3}{4}$

87. (a) $x^2 + 1 = x \Rightarrow x^2 - x + 1 = 0$

(b) $b^2 - 4ac = (-1)^2 - 4(1)(1) = -3 < 0$. There are no real solutions.

(c) There are no real solutions.

88. (a) $2x^2 + x = 2 \Rightarrow 2x^2 + x - 2 = 0$

(b) $b^2 - 4ac = 1^2 - 4(2)(-2) = 17 > 0$. There are two real solutions.

(c) $x = \frac{-1 \pm \sqrt{1^2 - 4(2)(-2)}}{2(2)} \Rightarrow x = \frac{-1 \pm \sqrt{17}}{4}$

89. (a) $2x^2 + 3x = 12 - 2x \Rightarrow 2x^2 + 5x - 12 = 0$.

(b) $b^2 - 4ac = (5)^2 - 4(2)(-12) = 121 > 0$. There are two real solutions.

(c) $2x^2 + 5x - 12 = 0 \Rightarrow (2x - 3)(x + 4) = 0 \Rightarrow 2x = 3 \Rightarrow x = 1.5$ or $x = -4$. So, $x = 1.5, -4$.

90. (a) $3x^2 + 3 = 5x \Rightarrow 3x^2 - 5x + 3 = 0$

(b) $b^2 - 4ac = (-5)^2 - 4(3)(3) = -11 < 0$. There are no real solutions.

(c) There are no real solutions.

91. (a) $9x(x - 4) = -36 \Rightarrow 9x^2 - 36x + 36 = 0$

(b) $b^2 - 4ac = (-36)^2 - 4(9)(36) = 0$. There is one real solution.

(c) $9x^2 - 36x + 36 = 0 \Rightarrow x^2 - 4x + 4 = 0 \Rightarrow (x - 2)^2 = 0 \Rightarrow x = 2$

92. (a) $\frac{1}{4}x^2 + 3x = x - 4 \Rightarrow \frac{1}{4}x^2 + 2x + 4 = 0$

(b) $b^2 - 4ac = (2)^2 - 4\left(\frac{1}{4}\right)(4) = 0$. There is one real solution.

(c) $\frac{1}{4}x^2 + 2x + 4 = 0 \Rightarrow x^2 + 8x + 16 = 0 \Rightarrow (x + 4)^2 = 0 \Rightarrow x = -4$

93. (a) $x\left(\frac{1}{2}x + 1\right) = -\frac{13}{2} \Rightarrow \frac{1}{2}x^2 + x + \frac{13}{2} = 0$

(b) $b^2 - 4ac = (1)^2 - 4\left(\frac{1}{2}\right)\left(\frac{13}{2}\right) = -12 < 0$. There are no real solutions.

(c) There are no real solutions.

94. (a) $4x = 6 + x^2 \Rightarrow x^2 - 4x + 6 = 0$

(b) $b^2 - 4ac = (-4)^2 - 4(1)(6) = -8 < 0$. There are no real solutions.

(c) There are no real solutions.

95. (a) $3x^2 = 1 - x \Rightarrow 3x^2 + x - 1 = 0$

(b) $b^2 - 4ac = 1^2 - 4(3)(-1) = 13 > 0$. There are two real solutions.

(c) $x = \dfrac{-1 \pm \sqrt{1^2 - 4(3)(-1)}}{2(3)} = \dfrac{-1 \pm \sqrt{13}}{2(3)} = \dfrac{-1 \pm \sqrt{13}}{6}$

96. (a) $x(5x - 3) = 1 \Rightarrow 5x^2 - 3x - 1 = 0$

(b) $b^2 - 4ac = (-3)^2 - 4(5)(-1) = 29 > 0$. There are two real solutions.

(c) $x = \dfrac{-(-3) \pm \sqrt{(-3)^2 - 4(5)(-1)}}{2(5)} = \dfrac{3 \pm \sqrt{29}}{2(5)} = \dfrac{-3 \pm \sqrt{29}}{10}$

97. (a) Since the parabola opens upward, $a > 0$.

(b) Since the zeros of $f$ are $-6$ and 2, the solutions to $ax^2 + bx + c = 0$ are also $-6$ and 2.

(c) Since there are two real solutions, the discriminant is positive.

98. (a) Since the parabola opens downward, $a < 0$.

(b) Since the zeros of $f$ are 0 and 4, the solutions are also 0 and 4.

(c) Since there are two real solutions, the discriminant is positive.

99. (a) Since the parabola opens upward, $a > 0$.

(b) Since the only zero of $f$ is $-4$, the solution is also $-4$.

(c) Since there is one real solutions, the discriminant is equal to zero.

100. (a) Since the parabola opens upward, $a > 0$.

(b) Since $f$ has no real zeros, there are no solutions to the quadratic equation.

(c) Since there are no real solutions, the discriminant is negative.

101. The height when it hits the ground will be $0 \Rightarrow 75 - 16t^2 = 0 \Rightarrow -16t^2 = -75 \Rightarrow t^2 = \dfrac{75}{16} \Rightarrow$

$t = \sqrt{\dfrac{75}{16}} \Rightarrow t = \dfrac{\sqrt{75}}{4} \Rightarrow t \approx 2.2$ seconds.

102. The height when it hits the ground will be $0 \Rightarrow 80 - 16t^2 - 30t = 0$ or $-16t^2 - 30t + 80 = 0$. Using the quadratic formula we get $t = \dfrac{30 \pm \sqrt{900 - 4(-16)(80)}}{2(-16)} \Rightarrow t \approx \dfrac{30 \pm 77.6}{-32} \Rightarrow t \approx -3.4$ or 1.5.

Since $-3.4$ seconds makes no sense, the time is about 1.5 seconds.

103. $90{,}000 = 2375x^2 + 5134x + 5020 \Rightarrow 2375x^2 + 5134x - 84{,}980 = 0$. Using the quadratic formula we get:

$x = \dfrac{-5134 \pm \sqrt{(5134)^2 - 4(2375)(-84{,}980)}}{2(2375)} \Rightarrow x \approx -7.2$ or 5. Since $-7.2$ does not apply, the number of years is 5. Therefore $1984 + 5 = 1989$.

104. $200{,}000 = 3034x^2 + 14{,}018x + 6400 \Rightarrow 3034x^2 + 14{,}018x - 193{,}600 = 0$. Using the quadratic formula we get: $x = \dfrac{-14{,}018 \pm \sqrt{(14{,}018)^2 - 4(3034)(-193{,}600)}}{2(3034)} \Rightarrow x \approx -10.6$ or 6. Since $-10.6$ does not apply, the number of years is 6. Therefore $1984 + 6 = 1990$.

105. Graphical: First, we must determine a formula for the area. Let $x$ represent the height of the computer screen. Then, $x + 2.5$ is the width. The area of the screen is height times width, computed $A(x) = x(x + 2.5)$. We must solve the quadratic equation $x(x + 2.5) = 93.5$ or $x^2 + 2.5x - 93.5 = 0$. Graph $Y_1 = X\text{^}2 + 2.5X - 93.5$ and determine any zeros. Figure 105a shows that the equation has two zeros, one negative and one positive. The positive zero is located at $x = 8.5$. The height is 8.5 inches and the width is $8.5 + 2.5 = 11$ inches.

Symbolic: The quadratic equation $x^2 + 2.5x - 93.5 = 0$ can be solved by the quadratic formula. $x = \dfrac{-b \pm \sqrt{b^2 - 4ac}}{2a} = \dfrac{-2.5 \pm \sqrt{2.5^2 - 4(1)(-93.5)}}{2(1)} = \dfrac{-2.5 \pm 19.5}{2} = 8.5, -11$. The positive answer gives a height of 8.5 inches. It follows that the width is 11 inches.

The numerical solution is shown in Figure 105b. Yes, the symbolic, graphical and numerical answers agree.

106. (a) Graphical: First we must determine a formula for the area. Let $x$ represent the width of the pen. Since the pen is rectangular and there is 100 feet of fence, the width plus the length must equal 50 feet. Thus, the length is equal to $50 - x$. The area of the pen is computed by $A(x) = x(50 - x) = 50x - x^2$. We must determine $x$ when $A(x)$ is equal to 576. To do this, graph $Y_1 = 50X - X\text{^}2$ and $Y_2 = 576$. Figure 106 shows the graph of a parabola opening down along with the horizontal line $y = 576$. The intersection points are (18, 576) and (32, 576). The point (18, 576) corresponds to a width of 18 feet. In this case, the length would be $50 - 18 = 32$ feet. The point (32, 576) corresponds to the width of 32 feet. In this case, the length would be $50 - 32 = 18$ feet. In both cases, the dimensions are 18 feet by 32 feet.

Symbolic: Solve $50x - x^2 = 576 \Rightarrow x^2 - 50x + 576 = 0 \Rightarrow (x - 18)(x - 32) = 0 \Rightarrow$ $x = 18$ or $x = 32$. In either case, the dimensions are 18 feet by 32 feet.

(b) The graph of $y = 50x - x^2 = -x^2 + 50x$ is a parabola opening down. The maximum $y$-value will occur at the vertex. The $x$-coordinate of the vertex is $x = -\dfrac{b}{2a} = -\dfrac{50}{2(-1)} = 25$. If the width is 25, then the length is $50 - x = 25$ feet. The dimensions are 25 feet by 25 feet.

[−15, 15, 1] by [−100, 100, 10]

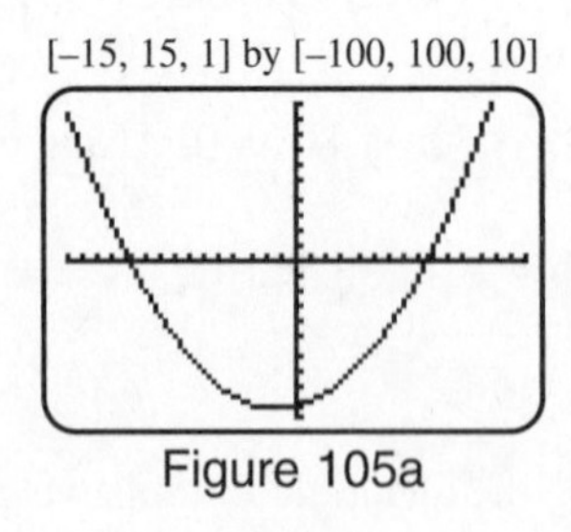

Figure 105a

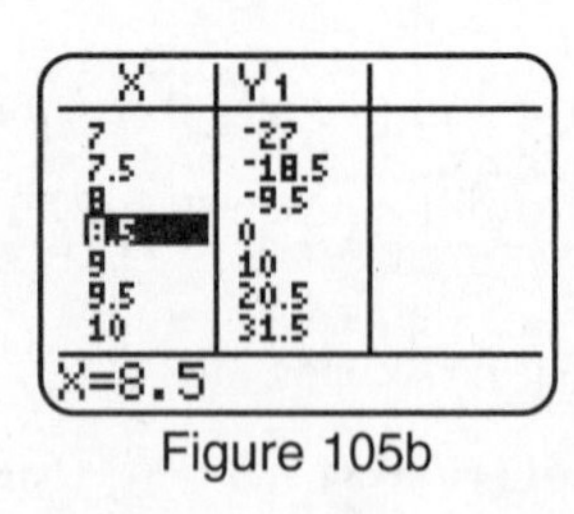

| X | Y1 |
|---|---|
| 7 | -27 |
| 7.5 | -18.5 |
| 8 | -9.5 |
| 8.5 | 0 |
| 9 | 10 |
| 9.5 | 20.5 |
| 10 | 31.5 |

X=8.5

Figure 105b

[0, 60, 10] by [0, 800, 100]

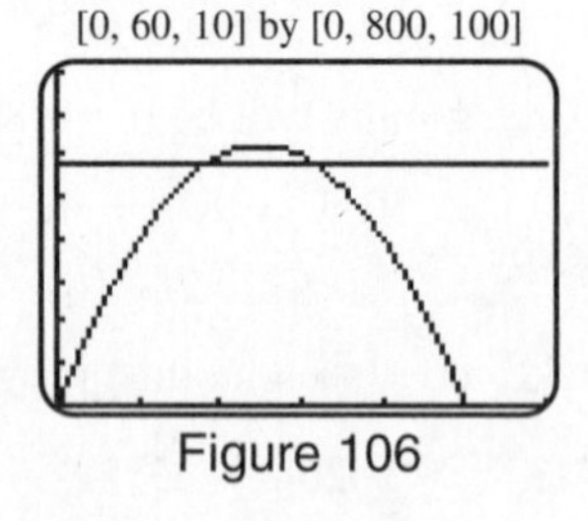

Figure 106

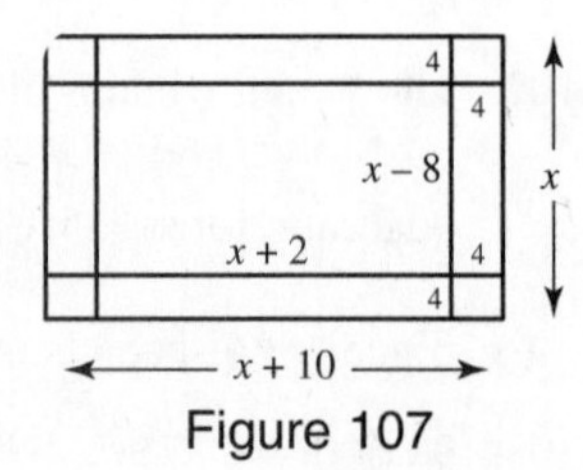


Figure 107

107. Let $x$ = width of the metal sheet in inches and $x + 10$ = length of the metal sheet in inches. Make a sketch to find expressions for the dimensions of the box. See Figure 107. The width of the box is $x - 8$ inches, the length of the box is $x + 2$ inches, and the height of the box is 4 inches; the volume of the box, which is given as 476 cubic inches, is determined by the length times the width times the height: $4(x - 8)(x + 2) = 476 \Rightarrow$ $(x - 8)(x + 2) = 119 \Rightarrow x^2 - 6x - 16 = 119 \Rightarrow x^2 - 6x - 135 = 0 \Rightarrow (x + 9)(x - 15) = 0 \Rightarrow$ $x = -9$ or $x = 15$. Since width cannot be negative, $x = 15$ inches; thus, the dimensions of the metal sheet is 15 inches by 25 inches.

108. Let $x$ = width of the square metal sheet. Then the width and length of the metal sheet after 2 inch squares have been cut out of the corners will be $x - 4$. Therefore, the volume will be represented by $V = l \cdot w \cdot h \Rightarrow (x - 4)(x - 4)(2) = 1058 \Rightarrow 2(x^2 - 8x + 16) = 1058 \Rightarrow x^2 - 8x + 16 = 529 \Rightarrow$ $x^2 - 8x - 513 = 0 \Rightarrow (x - 27)(x + 19) = 0 \Rightarrow x = 27$ or $x = -19$. Since $x$ cannot equal $-19$ inches, the dimensions of the original metal sheet are 27 by 27 inches.

109. $V = \pi r^2 h$, $V = 28$ cubic inches, and $h = 4$ inches $\Rightarrow 28 = \pi r^2(4) \Rightarrow r^2 = \dfrac{28}{4\pi} \Rightarrow r = \sqrt{\dfrac{28}{4\pi}} \approx 1.49$; the radius of the cylinder is approximately 1.49 inches.

110. (a) $k = 0.3 \Rightarrow D(x) = \dfrac{x^2}{30(0.3)} = \dfrac{x^2}{9}$; $D(60) = \dfrac{60^2}{9} = 400$; a car traveling at 60 mph requires about 400 feet to stop.

(b) $k = 0.25 \Rightarrow D(x) = \dfrac{x^2}{30(0.25)} = \dfrac{x^2}{7.5}$; $300 = \dfrac{x^2}{7.5} \Rightarrow x^2 = 2250 \Rightarrow x \approx \pm 47.4$; a braking distance of 300 feet corresponds to a velocity of approximately 47.4 mph. (We reject $x \approx -47.4$ since a negative velocity does not fit the physical situation of the problem.)

111. Since the diameter of the semicircle is $x$, the radius is $\dfrac{x}{2}$; the area of the semicircle $= \dfrac{1}{2}\pi\left(\dfrac{x}{2}\right)^2 = \dfrac{1}{2}\pi\left(\dfrac{x^2}{4}\right) = \dfrac{1}{8}\pi x^2$. The area of the square $= x^2$; thus, the total area of the window, which is 463 square inches, is $x^2 + \dfrac{1}{8}\pi x^2$; $463 = x^2 + \dfrac{1}{8}\pi x^2 \Rightarrow 463 = \left(1 + \dfrac{\pi}{8}\right)x^2 \Rightarrow x^2 = \dfrac{463}{(1 + \frac{\pi}{8})} \Rightarrow$ $x = \sqrt{\dfrac{463}{1 + \frac{\pi}{8}}} \approx 18.23$ inches.

112. The dimensions of the picture are $x$ inches by $x + 4$ inches; since the area of the picture is 320 square inches, $A = lw \Rightarrow 320 = x(x + 4) \Rightarrow x^2 + 4x = 320 \Rightarrow x^2 + 4x - 320 = 0 \Rightarrow (x - 16)(x + 20) = 0 \Rightarrow$ $x = 16$ or $x = -20$; since $x = -20$ has no physical meaning, $x = 16$ inches; thus, the picture is 16 inches by 20 inches, and so the frame is $16 + 4 = 20$ inches by $20 + 4 = 24$ inches.

113. Let $x$ be the number of shirts ordered. Revenue equals the number of shirts sold times the price of each shirt. If $x$ shirts are sold, then the price in dollars of each shirt is $20 - 0.10(x - 1)$. The revenue $R(x)$ is given by $R(x) = x(20 - 0.10(x - 1))$. We must solve the equation $989 = x(20 - 0.10(x - 1)) \Rightarrow$ $-0.10x^2 + 20.1x - 989 = 0$. Let $y_1 = -0.10x^2 + 20.1x - 989$ and use the graphing calculator to find the $x$-intercept. Because the discount applies to orders up to 100 shirts, we find that $x = 86$ shirts. See Figure 113.

[0, 150, 10] by [-20, 50, 10]

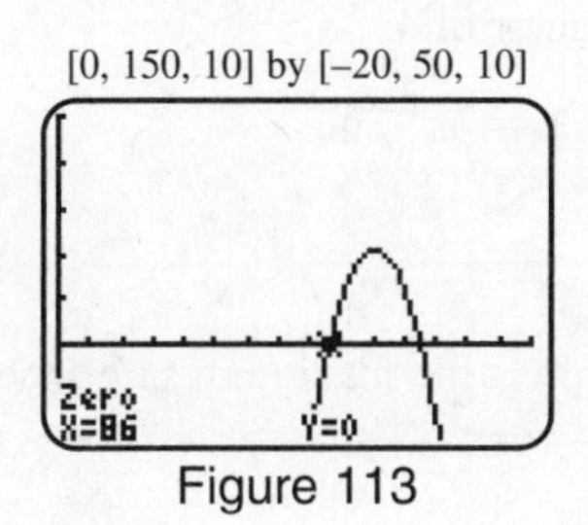

Figure 113

114. (a) $f(x) = x(252 - 2x) = 252x - 2x^2$, where $x$ is the number of tickets.

(b) $f(5) = 252(5) - 2(5)^2 = 1210$; the cost of 5 tickets is \$1210.

(c) $5200 = 252x - 2x^2 \Rightarrow 2x^2 - 252x + 5200 = 0 \Rightarrow x^2 - 126x + 2600 = 0 \Rightarrow$

$(x - 26)(x - 100) = 0 \Rightarrow x = 26$ or $x = 100$; either 26 tickets or 100 tickets were sold for \$5200.

(d) We need to find the $x$-value of the vertex for the function $f(x) = 252x - 2x^2$;

$x = -\dfrac{b}{2a} = -\dfrac{252}{2(-2)} = 63$; since the maximum value occurs at the value $x = 63$, the greatest cost is when 63 tickets are sold.

115. (a) Since $s(0) = 32$, $s(t) = -16t^2 + v_0t + h_0 \Rightarrow 32 = -16(0)^2 + v_0(0) + h_0 \Rightarrow h_0 = 32$ and so $s(t) = -16t^2 + v_0t + 32$; since $s(1) = 176$, $176 = -16(1)^2 + v_0(1) + 32 \Rightarrow v_0 = 160$; thus, $s(t) = -16t^2 + 160t + 32$ models the data.

(b) When the projectile strikes the ground, $s(t) = 0$; $0 = -16t^2 + 160t + 32 \Rightarrow 0 = t^2 - 10t - 2 \Rightarrow$

$t = \dfrac{10 \pm \sqrt{10^2 - 4(1)(-2)}}{2} \approx 10.2$ or $-0.2$; since $t$ cannot be negative, $t \approx 10.2$; the projectile strikes the ground after about 10.2 seconds.

116. (a) Plot the ordered pairs (0, 0), (1, 32), (2, 64), (3, 96), (4, 128), and (5, 160) together with the ordered pairs (0, 0), (1, 16), (2, 64), (3, 144), (4, 256), and (5, 400). These scatterplots are shown in Figure 116.

(b) Since the speed increases by 32 feet per second every second, a linear function models the velocity. The function $v$ is given by $v(x) = 32x$.

(d) $200 = 16x^2 \Rightarrow \dfrac{200}{16} = x^2 \Rightarrow \dfrac{25}{2} = x^2 \Rightarrow x = \sqrt{\dfrac{25}{2}} \Rightarrow x = \dfrac{5}{\sqrt{2}} \Rightarrow x = \dfrac{5\sqrt{2}}{2} \approx 3.536$ seconds.

Its velocity at this time is computed as follows:

$v(x) = 32x \Rightarrow v\left(\dfrac{5\sqrt{2}}{2}\right) = 32\left(\dfrac{5\sqrt{2}}{2}\right) = 80\sqrt{2} \approx 113.1$ feet per second.

[-1, 6, 1] by [-10, 450, 50]

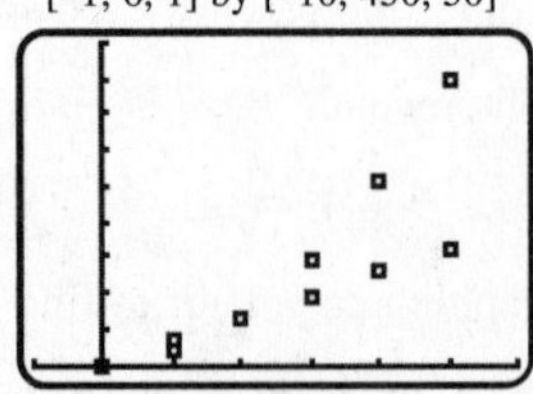

Figure 116

117. (a) If the speed doubles, the radius of the curve quadruples, or increases by a factor of 4.

(b) Any ordered pair in the table may be used to determine the constant $a$. $R(x) = ax^2$ and

$R(10) = 50 \Rightarrow a(10)^2 = 50 \Rightarrow a = \dfrac{50}{10^2} = 0.5$.

(c) If $R = 500$, $500 = 0.5x^2 \Rightarrow 1000 = x^2 \Rightarrow x = \sqrt{1000} \approx 31.6$. 31.6 mph is the maximum safe speed on a curve with a 500 foot radius.

118. (a) Use the quadratic regression function on your graphing calculator to find

$f(x) \approx -0.00138x^2 - 0.0757x + 50.1$.

(b) See Figure 118b.

(c) Use the graphing calculator to graph the regession equation found in part (a). See Figure 118c. Use the CALC function on your calculator to find the $x$-intercepts of $x \approx -220$ or $x \approx 165$. The negative solution does not have real meaning for the context of the problem. The value $x \approx 165$ represents the number of days for all the worms to die.

[−10, 170, 10] by [0, 60, 10]

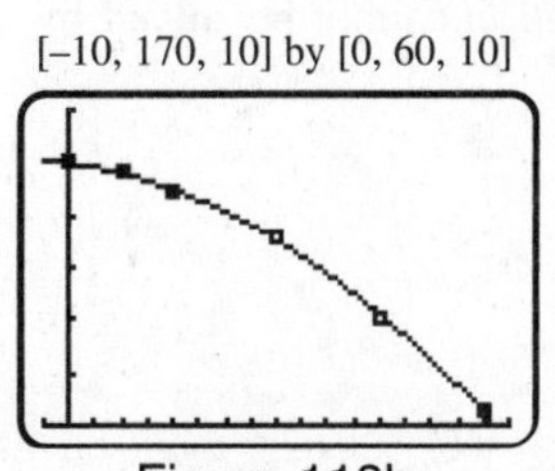

Figure 118b

[−250, 250, 50] by [−50, 100, 10]

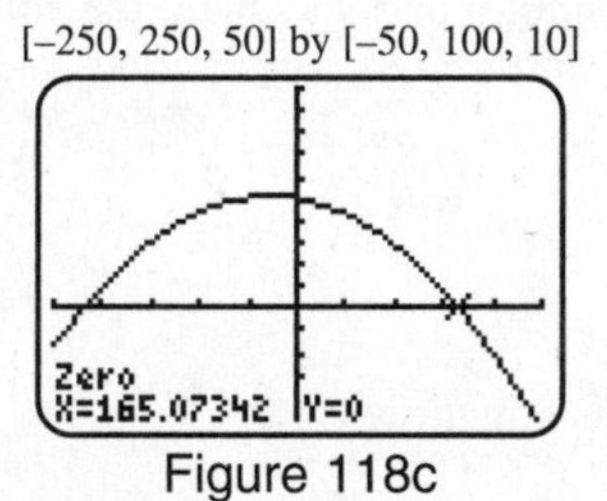


Figure 118c

119. (a) $E(15) = 1.4$, $1987 + 15 = 2002$; in 2002 there were 1.4 million Wal-Mart employees.

(b) Use the quadratic regression function on your graphing calculator to find

$f(x) = 0.00474x^2 + 0.00554x + 0.205$. *Answers may vary.*

(c) See Figure 119c.

(d) Let $Y_1 = (0.00474)X$^$2 + 0.00554X + 0.205$ and $Y_2 = 3$. Use the CALC function on your calculator to find the intersection points of the $Y_1$ and $Y_2$. See Figure 119d. When $x \approx 24$, $f(x) = 3$. Therefore, in the year 2011 the number of employees may reach 3 million. *Answers may vary.*

[0, 25, 5] by [0, 2.6, 0.2]

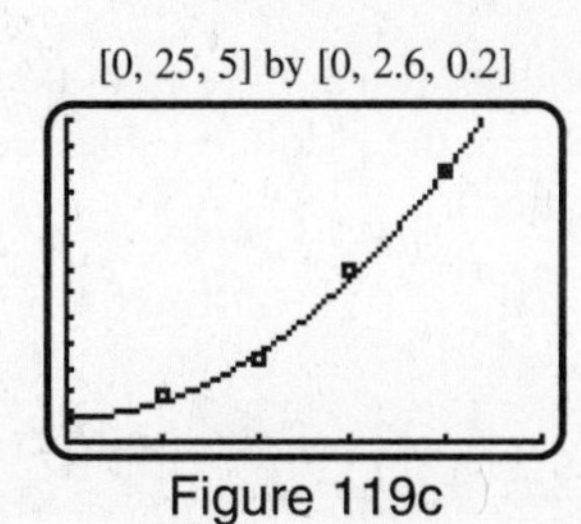

Figure 119c

[0, 25, 5] by [0, 3.6, 0.2]

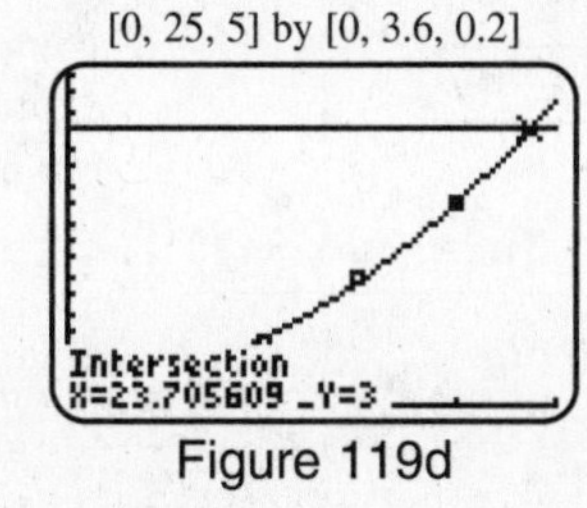


Figure 119d

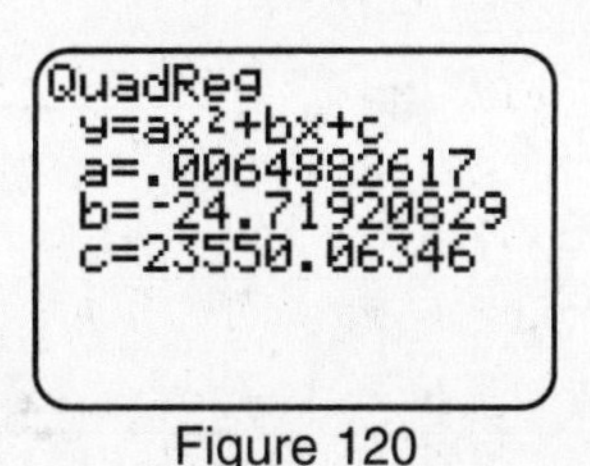


Figure 120

120. (a) Use the quadratic regression function on your graphing calculator to find

$f(x) = 0.00648826x^2 - 24.7192x + 23{,}550$. See Figure 120.

(b) Calculate $f(2020) \approx 91.966$. About 92 million women will be in the labor force in 2020.

*Answers may vary.*

## Extended and Discovery Exercises for Section 3.2

1. $b^2 - 4ac = 14^2 - 4(8)(-15) = 676 = 26^2$. Since 676 is a perfect square the equation can be solved by factoring. $8x^2 + 14x - 15 = 0 \Rightarrow (4x - 3)(2x + 5) = 0$. Then $4x - 3 = 0 \Rightarrow x = \frac{3}{4}$ or $2x + 5 = 0 \Rightarrow x = -\frac{5}{2}$.

2. $b^2 - 4ac = (-17)^2 - 4(15)(-4) = 529 = 23^2$. Since 529 is a perfect square the equation can be solved by factoring. $15x^2 - 17x - 4 = 0 \Rightarrow (5x + 1)(3x - 4) = 0$. Then $5x + 1 = 0 \Rightarrow x = -\dfrac{1}{5}$ or $3x - 4 = 0 \Rightarrow x = \dfrac{4}{3}$.

3. $b^2 - 4ac = (-3)^2 - 4(5)(-3) = 69$. Since 69 is not a perfect square the equation cannot be solved by factoring. $x = \dfrac{-b \pm \sqrt{b^2 - 4ac}}{2a} \Rightarrow x = \dfrac{3 \pm \sqrt{(-3)^2 - 4(5)(-3)}}{2(5)} \Rightarrow x = \dfrac{3 \pm \sqrt{69}}{10}$.

4. $b^2 - 4ac = (-2)^2 - 4(3)(-4) = 52$. Since 52 is not a perfect square the equation cannot be solved by factoring. $x = \dfrac{-b \pm \sqrt{b^2 - 4ac}}{2a} \Rightarrow x = \dfrac{2 \pm \sqrt{(-2)^2 - 4(3)(-4)}}{2(3)} \Rightarrow x = \dfrac{2 \pm \sqrt{52}}{6} \Rightarrow$ $x = \dfrac{2 \pm 2\sqrt{13}}{6} \Rightarrow x = \dfrac{1 \pm \sqrt{13}}{3}$.

5. (a) Follow the steps for completing the square in this equation:

$$ax^2 + bx + c = 0 \Rightarrow x^2 + \frac{b}{a}x + \frac{c}{a} = 0 \Rightarrow x^2 + \frac{b}{a}x = -\frac{c}{a}$$

(b) Add $\left(\dfrac{b}{2a}\right)^2 = \dfrac{b^2}{4a^2}$ to both sides to obtain $x^2 + \dfrac{b}{a}x + \dfrac{b^2}{4a^2} = -\dfrac{c}{a} + \dfrac{b^2}{4a^2}$ or $\left(x + \dfrac{b}{2a}\right)^2 = \dfrac{b^2 - 4ac}{4a^2}$.

(c) In order to derive the quadratic formula we must solve this second equation for $x$.

$$\left(x + \frac{b}{2a}\right)^2 = \frac{b^2 - 4ac}{4a^2} \Rightarrow \left(x + \frac{b}{2a}\right) = \pm\sqrt{\frac{b^2 - 4ac}{4a^2}} \Rightarrow$$ {Square root property}

$$x = -\frac{b}{2a} \pm \sqrt{\frac{b^2 - 4ac}{4a^2}} \Rightarrow x = -\frac{b}{2a} \pm \frac{\sqrt{b^2 - 4ac}}{|2a|} \Rightarrow$$ $\{\sqrt{4a^2} = |2a|\}$

$$x = -\frac{b}{2a} \pm \frac{\sqrt{b^2 - 4ac}}{2a} \Rightarrow x = \frac{-b \pm \sqrt{b^2 - 4ac}}{2a}$$ {Since there is a $\pm$ in front of the expression, the absolute value does not matter.}

6. $$\frac{f(x + h) - f(x)}{h} = \frac{a(x + h)^2 - b(x + h) + 1 - (ax^2 - bx + 1)}{h} =$$

$$\frac{ax^2 + 2axh + ah^2 - bx - bh + 1 - ax^2 + bx - 1}{h} = \frac{2axh + ah^2 - bh}{h} = 2ax + ah - b.$$

Since $2ax + ah - b = 2x + h - 4$, $a = 1$ and $b = 4$.

7. $x^2 = k \Rightarrow \sqrt{x^2} = \sqrt{k} \Rightarrow |x| = \sqrt{k} \Rightarrow x = \pm\sqrt{k}$

## Checking Basic Concepts for Sections 3.1 and 3.2

1. Vertex: $(1, -4)$; axis of symmetry: $x = 1$; $x$-intercepts: $-1, 3$. See Figure 1.

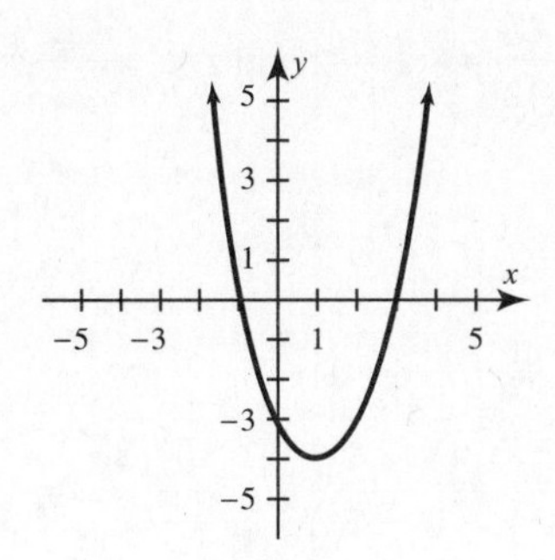


Figure 1

2. (a) Negative; the parabola opens downward, so $a < 0$.

   (b) Vertex: $(1, 2)$; axis of symmetry: $x = 1$

   (c) The solutions to $ax^2 + bx + c = 0$ are the $x$-intercepts of the parabola, so $x = -1, 3$ are the two solutions.

   (d) Since there are two solutions, the discriminant $b^2 - 4ac$ is positive.

3. Since 3 is the smallest $y$-value and there is symmetry of the $y$-values around $x = -1$, the vertex is $(-1, 3)$; $f(x) = a(x - h)^2 + k \Rightarrow f(x) = a(x + 1)^2 + 3$; since $(0, 5)$ is a data point, $f(0) = 5$; $5 = a(0 + 1)^2 + 3 \Rightarrow a = 2$; $f(x) = 2(x + 1)^2 + 3$ models the data exactly.

4. For $y = 3x^2 - 9x - 2$, $x = -\dfrac{b}{2a} \Rightarrow x = -\dfrac{-9}{2(3)} = \dfrac{3}{2}$; at $x = \dfrac{3}{2}$, $y = 3\left(\dfrac{3}{2}\right)^2 - 9\left(\dfrac{3}{2}\right) - 2 = -\dfrac{35}{4}$; the vertex of the graph of $y = 3x^2 - 9x - 2$ is $\left(\dfrac{3}{2}, -\dfrac{35}{4}\right)$.

5. Find the vertex:

   $x = -\dfrac{b}{2a} \Rightarrow x = -\dfrac{4}{2(1)} \Rightarrow x = -2$. Since $f(-2) = (-2)2 + 4(-2) - 3 \Rightarrow f(-2) = -7$, $(-2, -7)$ is the vertex. The leading coefficient is $a = 1$. Converting to $f(x) = a(x - h)^2 + k$, we get $f(x) = 1(x - (-2))^2 + (-7) \Rightarrow f(x) = (x + 2)^2 - 7$. The minimum value is at the vertex or $-7$.

6. (a) $16x^2 = 81 \Rightarrow x^2 = \dfrac{81}{16} \Rightarrow x = \pm\sqrt{\dfrac{81}{16}} = \pm 2.25$

   (b) $2x^2 + 3x = 2 \Rightarrow 2x^2 + 3x - 2 = 0 \Rightarrow (2x - 1)(x + 2) = 0 \Rightarrow x = \dfrac{1}{2}$ or $x = -2$

   (c) $x^2 = x - 3 \Rightarrow x^2 - x + 3 = 0$; $b^2 - 4ac = (-1)^2 - 4(1)(3) = -11 < 0$; since the discriminant is negative, there are no real solutions.

   (d) $2x^2 = 3x + 4 \Rightarrow 2x^2 - 3x - 4 = 0$. Using the quadratic formula we get:

   $$x = \frac{3 \pm \sqrt{(-3)^2 - 4(2)(-4)}}{2(2)} \Rightarrow x = \frac{3 \pm \sqrt{41}}{4}$$

7. Let $x =$ width of rectangle, then $x + 4 =$ length of rectangle; since area $= 165$ square inches, $x(x + 4) = 165 \Rightarrow x^2 + 4x - 165 = 0 \Rightarrow (x - 11)(x + 15) = 0 \Rightarrow x = 11, -15$; since $x = -15$ has no physical meaning for the width, the width of the rectangle is 11 inches and the length is $11 + 4 = 15$ inches.

8. (a) $h(1) = -16(1)^2 + 96(1) + 2 \Rightarrow h(1) = -16 + 96 + 2 \Rightarrow h(1) = 82$ feet

(b) $142 = -16t^2 + 96t + 2 \Rightarrow -16t^2 + 96t - 140 = 0$. Using the quadratic formula we get:

$$t = \frac{-96 \pm \sqrt{(96)^2 - 4(-16)(-140)}}{2(-16)} \Rightarrow t = \frac{-96 \pm 16}{-32} \Rightarrow t = \frac{-80}{-32} \Rightarrow t = 2.5 \text{ or } t = \frac{-112}{-32} \Rightarrow$$

$x = 3.5$, so the height is 142 feet at 2.5 seconds and 3.5 seconds.

(c) The maximum height occurs at the vertex. $\frac{-b}{2a} \Rightarrow t = \frac{-96}{2(-16)} \Rightarrow t = 3;$

$f(3) = -16(3)^2 + 96(3) + 2 \Rightarrow f(3) = -144 + 288 + 2 \Rightarrow f(3) = 146$ feet.

(d) $0 = -16t^2 + 96t + 2$, using the quadratic formula we get: $t = \frac{-96 \pm \sqrt{(96)^2 - 4(-16)(2)}}{2(-16)} \Rightarrow$

$t \approx -0.021$ and $6.021$. Since time must be positive the maximum height occurs after about 6 seconds.

## 3.3: Complex Numbers

1. $\sqrt{-4} = i\sqrt{4} = 2i$
2. $\sqrt{-16} = i\sqrt{16} = 4i$
3. $\sqrt{-100} = i\sqrt{100} = 10i$
4. $\sqrt{-49} = i\sqrt{49} = 7i$
5. $\sqrt{-23} = i\sqrt{23}$
6. $\sqrt{-11} = i\sqrt{11}$
7. $\sqrt{-12} = i\sqrt{12} = i\sqrt{4}\sqrt{3} = 2i\sqrt{3}$
8. $\sqrt{-32} = i\sqrt{32} = i\sqrt{16}\sqrt{2} = 4i\sqrt{2}$
9. $\sqrt{-54} = \sqrt{(9)(6)(-1)} = \sqrt{9(-1)}\sqrt{6} = 3i\sqrt{6}$
10. $\sqrt{-28} = \sqrt{(4)(7)(-1)} = \sqrt{4(-1)}\sqrt{7} = 2i\sqrt{7}$
11. $\frac{4 \pm \sqrt{-16}}{2} = \frac{4 \pm \sqrt{(16)(-1)}}{2} = \frac{4 \pm 4i}{2} = 2 \pm 2i$
12. $\frac{-2 \pm \sqrt{-36}}{6} = \frac{-2 \pm \sqrt{(36)(-1)}}{6} = \frac{-2 \pm 6i}{6} = -\frac{1}{3} \pm i$
13. $\frac{-6 \pm \sqrt{-72}}{3} = \frac{-6 \pm \sqrt{(36)(-1)}\sqrt{2}}{3} = \frac{-6 \pm 6i\sqrt{2}}{3} = -2 \pm 2i\sqrt{2}$
14. $\frac{2 \pm \sqrt{-8}}{4} = \frac{2 \pm \sqrt{(4)(-1)}\sqrt{2}}{4} = \frac{2 \pm 2i\sqrt{2}}{4} = \frac{1}{2} \pm \frac{\sqrt{2}}{2}i$
15. $\sqrt{-5} \cdot \sqrt{-5} = \sqrt{5}\sqrt{-1} \cdot \sqrt{5}\sqrt{-1} = \sqrt{5}i \cdot \sqrt{5}i = \sqrt{25}i^2 = 5(-1) = -5$
16. $\sqrt{-8} \cdot \sqrt{-8} = (\sqrt{4}\sqrt{2}\sqrt{-1})(\sqrt{4}\sqrt{2}\sqrt{-1}) = (2\sqrt{2}i)(2\sqrt{2}i) = 4i^2\sqrt{4} = 4(-1)(2) = -8$
17. $\sqrt{-18} \cdot \sqrt{-2} = (\sqrt{9}\sqrt{2}\sqrt{-1})(\sqrt{2}\sqrt{-1}) = (3\sqrt{2}\,i)(\sqrt{2}\,i) = 3\sqrt{4}i^2 = (3)(2)(-1) = -6$
18. $\sqrt{-20} \cdot \sqrt{-5} = (\sqrt{4}\sqrt{5}\sqrt{-1})(\sqrt{5}\sqrt{-1}) = (2\sqrt{5}\,i)(\sqrt{5}\,i) = 2\sqrt{25}i^2 = 2(5)(-1) = -10$
19. $\sqrt{-3} \cdot \sqrt{-6} = (\sqrt{3}\sqrt{-1})(\sqrt{6}\sqrt{-1}) = (\sqrt{3}i)(\sqrt{6}i) = \sqrt{18}i^2 = \sqrt{9}\sqrt{2}(-1) = -3\sqrt{2}$
20. $\sqrt{-15} \cdot \sqrt{-5} = (\sqrt{15}\sqrt{-1})(\sqrt{5}\sqrt{-1}) = (\sqrt{15}i)(\sqrt{5}i) = \sqrt{75}i^2 = \sqrt{25}\sqrt{3}(-1) = -5\sqrt{3}$

21. $3i + 5i = (3 + 5)i = 8i$

22. $-7i + 5i = (-7 + 5)i = -2i$

23. $(3 + i) + (-5 - 2i) = (3 + (-5)) + (1 - 2)i = -2 - i$

24. $(-4 + 2i) + (7 + 35i) = (-4 + 7) + (2 + 35)i = 3 + 37i$

25. $2i - (-5 + 23i) = (-5) + (2 - 23)i = 5 - 21i$

26. $(12 - 7i) - (-1 + 9i) = (12 - (-1)) + (-7 - 9)i = 13 - 16i$

27. $3 - (4 - 6i) = (3 - 4) + i = -1 + 6i$

28. $(7 + i) - (-8 + 5i) = (7 - (-8)) + (1 - 5)i = 15 - 4i$

29. $(2)(2 + 4i) = 4 + 8i$

30. $(-5)(-7 + 3i) = 35 - 15i$

31. $(1 + i)(2 - 3i) = (1)(2) + (1)(-3i) + (i)(2) + (i)(-3i) = 2 - i - 3i^2 = 2 - i - 3(-1) = 5 - i$

32. $(-2 + i)(1 - 2i) = (-2)(1) + (-2)(-2i) + (i)(1) + (i)(-2i) = -2 + 5i - 2i^2 =$
$-2 + 5i - 2(-1) = 0 + 5i = 5i$

33. $(-3 + 2i)(-2 + i) = (-3)(-2) + (-3)(i) + (2i)(-2) + (2i)(i) = 6 - 7i + 2i^2 =$
$6 - 7i + 2(-1) = 4 - 7i$

34. $(2 - 3i)(1 + 4i) = (2)(1) + (2)(4i) + (-3i)(1) + (-3i)(4i) = 2 + 5i - 12i^2 =$
$2 + 5i - 12(-1) = 14 + 5i$

35. $(-2 + 3i)^2 = (-2 + 3i)(-2 + 3i) = (-2)(-2) + (-2)(3i) + (-2)(3i) + (3i)(3i) =$
$4 + (-12i) + (9i^2) = 4 - 12i + (-9) = -5 - 12i$

36. $(2 - 3i)^2 = (2 - 3i)(2 - 3i) = (2)(2) + (2)(-3i) + (2)(-3i) + (-3i)(-3i) =$
$4 + (-12i) + (9i^2) = 4 - 12i + (-9) = -5 - 12i$

37. $2i(1 - i)^2 = 2i(1 - i)(1 - i) = 2i[(1)(1) + (1)(-i) + (1)(-i) + (-i)(-i)] =$
$2i[1 - 2i + (-1)] = 2i(-2i) = -4i^2 = 4$

38. $-i(5 - 2i)^2 = -i(5 - 2i)(5 - 2i) = -i[(5)(5) + (5)(-2i) + (5)(-2i) + (-2i)(-2i)] =$
$-i(25 - 20i + 4i^2) = -i[25 - 20i + 4(-1)] = -i(21 - 20i) = -21i + 20i^2 = -21i + 20(-1) =$
$-20 - 21i$

39. $\dfrac{1}{1+i} = \dfrac{1}{1+i} \cdot \dfrac{1-i}{1-i} = \dfrac{1-i}{(1+i)(1-i)} = \dfrac{1-i}{1-i^2} = \dfrac{1-i}{2} = \dfrac{1}{2} - \dfrac{1}{2}i$

40. $\dfrac{1-i}{2+3i} = \dfrac{1-i}{2+3i} \cdot \dfrac{2-3i}{2-3i} = \dfrac{(1-i)(2-3i)}{(2+3i)(2-3i)} = \dfrac{2-5i+3i^2}{4-9i^2} = \dfrac{-1-5i}{13} = -\dfrac{1}{13} - \dfrac{5}{13}i$

41. $\dfrac{4+i}{5-i} = \dfrac{4+i}{5-i} \cdot \dfrac{5+i}{5+i} = \dfrac{(4+i)(5+i)}{(5-i)(5+i)} = \dfrac{20+9i+i^2}{25-i^2} = \dfrac{19+9i}{26} = \dfrac{19}{26} + \dfrac{9}{26}i$

42. $\dfrac{10}{1-4i} = \dfrac{10}{1-4i} \cdot \dfrac{1+4i}{1+4i} = \dfrac{10+40i}{(1-4i)(1+4i)} = \dfrac{10+40i}{1-16i^2} = \dfrac{10+40i}{17} = \dfrac{10}{17} + \dfrac{40}{17}i$

43. $\dfrac{2i}{10-5i} = \dfrac{2i}{10-5i} \cdot \dfrac{10+5i}{10+5i} = \dfrac{20i+10i^2}{(10-5i)(10+5i)} = \dfrac{-10+20i}{100-25i^2} = \dfrac{-10+20i}{125} = -\dfrac{2}{25} + \dfrac{4}{25}i$

44. $\dfrac{3-2i}{1+2i}=\dfrac{3-2i}{1+2i}\cdot\dfrac{1-2i}{1-2i}=\dfrac{(3-2i)(1-2i)}{(1+2i)(1-2i)}=\dfrac{3-6i-2i+4i^2}{1-4i^2}=\dfrac{-1-8i}{5}=-\dfrac{1}{5}-\dfrac{8}{5}i$

45. $\dfrac{3}{-i}\cdot\dfrac{i}{i}=\dfrac{3i}{-i^2}=\dfrac{3i}{-i^2}=\dfrac{3i}{-(-1)}=3i$

46. $\dfrac{4-2i}{i}\cdot\dfrac{i}{i}=\dfrac{4i-2i^2}{i^2}=\dfrac{4i-2(-1)}{-1}=\dfrac{4i+2}{-1}=-2-4i$

47. $\dfrac{-2+i}{(1+i)^2}=\dfrac{-2+i}{(1+i)(1+i)}=\dfrac{-2+i}{(1)(1)+(1)(i)+(1)(i)+(i)(i)}=\dfrac{-2+i}{1+2i+i^2}=\dfrac{-2+i}{1+2i-1}=$

$\dfrac{-2+i}{2i}\cdot\dfrac{i}{i}=\dfrac{-2i+i^2}{2i^2}=\dfrac{-2i-1}{2(-1)}=\dfrac{-2i-1}{-2}=\dfrac{1}{2}+i$

48. $\dfrac{3}{(2-i)^2}=\dfrac{3}{(2-i)(2-i)}=\dfrac{3}{(2)(2)+(2)(-i)+(2)(-i)+(-i)(-i)}=\dfrac{3}{4+(-4i)+i^2}=$

$\dfrac{3}{4-4i-1}=\dfrac{3}{3-4i}\cdot\dfrac{3+4i}{3+4i}=\dfrac{9+12i}{9-16i^2}=\dfrac{9+12i}{25}=\dfrac{9}{25}+\dfrac{12}{25}i$

49. $(23-5.6i)+(-41.5+93i)=-18.5+87.4i$

50. $(-8.05-4.67i)+(3.5+5.37i)=-4.55+0.7i$

51. $(17.1-6i)-(8.4+0.7i)=8.7-6.7i$

52. $\left(\dfrac{3}{4}-\dfrac{1}{10}i\right)-\left(-\dfrac{1}{8}+\dfrac{4}{25}i\right)=0.875-0.26i$

53. $(-12.6-5.7i)(5.1-9.3i)=-117.27+88.11i$

54. $(7.8+23i)(-1.04+2.09i)=-56.182-7.618i$

55. $\dfrac{17-135i}{18+142i}\approx-0.921-0.236i$

56. $\dfrac{141+52i}{102-31i}\approx 1.124+0.851i$

57. $x^2+5=0\Rightarrow x^2=-5\Rightarrow x=\pm\sqrt{-5}=\pm i\sqrt{5}$

58. $4x^2+3=0\Rightarrow x^2=-\dfrac{3}{4}\Rightarrow x=\pm\dfrac{\sqrt{-3}}{2}\Rightarrow x=\pm\dfrac{i\sqrt{3}}{2}$

59. $5x^2+1=3x^2\Rightarrow 2x^2=-1\Rightarrow x^2=-\dfrac{1}{2}\Rightarrow x=\pm i\sqrt{\dfrac{1}{2}}$

60. $x(3x+1)=-1\Rightarrow 3x^2+x+1=0$; use the quadratic formula with $a=3$, $b=1$, and $c=1$.

$$x=\frac{-1\pm\sqrt{1^2-4(3)(1)}}{2(3)}=\frac{-1\pm\sqrt{1-12}}{6}=\frac{-1\pm\sqrt{-11}}{6}=\frac{-1\pm i\sqrt{11}}{6}=-\frac{1}{6}\pm\frac{i\sqrt{11}}{6}$$

61. $3x=5x^2+1\Rightarrow 5x^2-3x+1=0$; use the quadratic formula with $a=5$, $b=-3$, and $c=1$.

$$x=\frac{-(-3)\pm\sqrt{(-3)^2-4(5)(1)}}{2(5)}=\frac{3\pm\sqrt{9-20}}{10}=\frac{3\pm\sqrt{-11}}{10}=\frac{3\pm i\sqrt{11}}{10}=\frac{3}{10}\pm\frac{i\sqrt{11}}{10}$$

62. $4x^2=x-1\Rightarrow 4x^2-x+1=0$; use the quadratic formula with $a=4$, $b=-1$, and $c=1$.

$$x=\frac{-(-1)\pm\sqrt{(-1)^2-4(4)(1)}}{2(4)}=\frac{1\pm\sqrt{1-16}}{8}=\frac{1\pm\sqrt{-15}}{8}=\frac{1\pm i\sqrt{15}}{8}=\frac{1}{8}\pm\frac{i\sqrt{15}}{8}$$

63. $x(x-4)=-5 \Rightarrow x^2-4x=-5 \Rightarrow x^2-4x+5=0$; use the quadratic formula to solve $x^2-4x+5=0$ with $a=1, b=-4$, and $c=5$.

$$x=\frac{-(-4)\pm\sqrt{(-4)^2-4(1)(5)}}{2(1)}=\frac{4\pm\sqrt{16-20}}{2}=\frac{4\pm\sqrt{-4}}{2}=\frac{4\pm 2i}{2}=2\pm i$$

64. Use the quadratic formula to solve $2x^2+x+1=0$ with $a=2, b=1$, and $c=1$.

$$x=\frac{-1\pm\sqrt{1^2-4(2)(1)}}{2(2)}=\frac{-1\pm\sqrt{1-8}}{4}=\frac{-1\pm\sqrt{-7}}{4}=\frac{-1\pm i\sqrt{7}}{4}=-\frac{1}{4}\pm\frac{i\sqrt{7}}{4}$$

65. Use the quadratic formula to solve $x^2-3x+5=0$ with $a=1, b=-3$, and $c=5$.

$$x=\frac{-(-3)\pm\sqrt{(-3)^2-4(1)(5)}}{2(1)}=\frac{3\pm\sqrt{9-20}}{2}=\frac{3\pm\sqrt{-11}}{2}=\frac{3\pm i\sqrt{11}}{2}=\frac{3}{2}\pm\frac{i\sqrt{11}}{2}$$

66. Use the quadratic formula to solve $x^2-3x+5=0$ with $a=1, b=-3$, and $c=5$.

$$x=\frac{-(-3)\pm\sqrt{(-3)^2-4(1)(5)}}{2(1)}=\frac{3\pm\sqrt{9-20}}{2}=\frac{3\pm\sqrt{-11}}{2}=\frac{3\pm i\sqrt{11}}{2}=\frac{3}{2}\pm\frac{i\sqrt{11}}{2}$$

67. Use the quadratic formula to solve $x^2+2x+4=0$ with $a=1, b=2$, and $c=4$.

$$x=\frac{-2\pm\sqrt{2^2-4(1)(4)}}{2(1)}=\frac{-2\pm\sqrt{4-16}}{2}=\frac{-2\pm\sqrt{-12}}{2}=\frac{-2\pm 2i\sqrt{3}}{2}=-1\pm i\sqrt{3}$$

68. Use the quadratic formula to solve $x^2-4x+8=0$ with $a=1, b=-4$, and $c=8$.

$$x=\frac{-(-4)\pm\sqrt{(-4)^2-4(1)(8)}}{2(1)}=\frac{4\pm\sqrt{16-32}}{2}=\frac{4\pm\sqrt{-16}}{2}=\frac{4\pm 4i}{2}=2\pm 2i$$

69. $3x^2-4x=x^2-3 \Rightarrow 2x^2-4x+3=0$. Using the quadratic formula we get:

$$\frac{4\pm\sqrt{16-4(2)(3)}}{2(2)}=\frac{4\pm\sqrt{-8}}{4}=\frac{4\pm 2\sqrt{-2}}{4}=1+\frac{\sqrt{-2}}{2}=1\pm\frac{i\sqrt{2}}{2}$$

70. $2x^2+3=1-x \Rightarrow 2x^2+x+2=0$

Using the quadratic formula we get: $\dfrac{-1\pm\sqrt{(1)^2-4(2)(2)}}{2(2)}=\dfrac{-1\pm\sqrt{-15}}{4}=\dfrac{-1}{4}\pm\dfrac{i\sqrt{15}}{4}$

71. $2x(x-2)=x-4 \Rightarrow 2x^2-4x=x-4 \Rightarrow 2x^2-5x+4=0$.

Using the quadratic formula we get: $\dfrac{5\pm\sqrt{(5)^2-4(2)(4)}}{2(2)}=\dfrac{5\pm\sqrt{-7}}{4}=\dfrac{5}{4}\pm\dfrac{i\sqrt{7}}{4}$

72. $3x^2+x=x(5-x)-2 \Rightarrow 3x^2+x=5x-x^2-2 \Rightarrow 4x^2-4x+2=0$.

Using the quadratic formula we get: $\dfrac{4\pm\sqrt{(-4)^2-4(4)(2)}}{2(4)}=\dfrac{4\pm\sqrt{-16}}{8}=\dfrac{4}{8}\pm\dfrac{4i}{8}=\dfrac{1}{2}\pm\dfrac{1}{2}i$

73. $3x(3-x)-8=x(x-2) \Rightarrow 9x-3x^2-8=x^2-2x \Rightarrow -4x^2+11x-8=0$.

Using the quadratic formula we get: $\dfrac{-11\pm\sqrt{(11)^2-4(-4)(-8)}}{2(-4)}=\dfrac{-11\pm\sqrt{-7}}{-8}=\dfrac{11}{8}\pm\dfrac{i\sqrt{7}}{8}$

74. $-x(7-2x)=-6-(3-x) \Rightarrow -7x+2x^2=-6-3+x \Rightarrow 2x^2-8x+9=0$.

Using the quadratic formula we get: $\dfrac{8\pm\sqrt{(-8)^2-4(2)(9)}}{2(2)}=\dfrac{8\pm\sqrt{-8}}{4}=\dfrac{8\pm 2\sqrt{-2}}{4}=2\pm\dfrac{i\sqrt{2}}{2}$

75. (a) The graph of $y = 2x^2 - x - 3$ intersects the $x$-axis twice, so there are two real zeros.

(b) $x = \dfrac{-b \pm \sqrt{b^2 - 4ac}}{2a} = \dfrac{1 \pm \sqrt{(-1)^2 - 4(2)(-3)}}{2(2)} = \dfrac{1 \pm 5}{4} = \dfrac{3}{2}, -1$

76. (a) The graph of $y = -x^2 + 4.6x - 5.29$ appears to intersects the $x$-axis once, so there is one real zero.

(b) $x = \dfrac{-b \pm \sqrt{b^2 - 4ac}}{2a} = \dfrac{-4.6 \pm \sqrt{4.6^2 - 4(-1)(-5.29)}}{2(-1)} = \dfrac{-4.6 \pm 0}{-2} = 2.3$

77. (a) The graph of $f(x) = x^2 + x + 2$ does not intersect the $x$-axis. Both of its zeros are imaginary.

(b) $x = \dfrac{-b \pm \sqrt{b^2 - 4ac}}{2a} = \dfrac{-1 \pm \sqrt{1^2 - 4(1)(2)}}{2(1)} = \dfrac{-1 \pm \sqrt{-7}}{2} = -\dfrac{1}{2} \pm \dfrac{i\sqrt{7}}{2}$

78. (a) The graph of $y = -2x^2 + 2x - 3$ does not intersect the $x$-axis. Both of its zeros are imaginary.

(b) $x = \dfrac{-b \pm \sqrt{b^2 - 4ac}}{2a} = \dfrac{-2 \pm \sqrt{2^2 - 4(-2)(-3)}}{2(-2)} = \dfrac{-2 \pm \sqrt{-20}}{-4} = \dfrac{1}{2} \pm \dfrac{1}{4}\sqrt{20}i = \dfrac{1}{2} \pm \dfrac{i\sqrt{5}}{2}$

79. (a) The graph of $y = -x^2 - 2$ does not intersect the $x$-axis. Both of its zeros are imaginary.

(b) $x = \dfrac{-b \pm \sqrt{b^2 - 4ac}}{2a} = \dfrac{0 \pm \sqrt{0^2 - 4(-1)(-2)}}{2(-1)} = \dfrac{\pm\sqrt{-8}}{-2} = \dfrac{\pm 2i\sqrt{2}}{-2} = \pm i\sqrt{2}$

80. (a) The graph of $y = x^2 - x + 1$ does not intersect the $x$-axis. Both of its zeros are imaginary.

(b) $x = \dfrac{-b \pm \sqrt{b^2 - 4ac}}{2a} = \dfrac{-1 \pm \sqrt{1^2 - 4(1)(1)}}{2(1)} = \dfrac{-1 \pm \sqrt{-3}}{2} = -\dfrac{1}{2} \pm \dfrac{i\sqrt{3}}{2}$

## Extended and Discovery Exercise for Section 3.3

1. (a) $i^1 = i, i^2 = -1, i^3 = -i, i^4 = 1, i^5 = i, i^6 = -1, i^7 = -i, i^8 = 1$, and so on.

(b) Divide $n$ by 4. If the remainder is $r$, then $i^n = i^r$, where $i^0 = 1, i^1 = i, i^2 = -1$ and $i^3 = -i$.

## 3.4: Quadratic Inequalities

1. (a) The inequality $f(x) < 0$ is satisfied when the graph of $f$ is below the $x$-axis. This occurs when $-3 < x < 2$.

(b) The inequality $f(x) \geq 0$ is satisfied when the graph of $f$ is above the $x$-axis or intersects it. This occurs when $x \leq -3$ or $x \geq 2$.

2. (a) The inequality $f(x) > 0$ is satisfied when the graph of $f$ is above the $x$-axis. This occurs when $-1 < x < 4$.

(b) The inequality $f(x) < 0$ is satisfied when the graph of $f$ is below the $x$-axis. This occurs when $x < -1$ or $x > 4$.

3. (a) The inequality $f(x) \leq 0$ is satisfied when the graph of $f$ is below the $x$-axis or intersects it. This occurs only when $x = -2$.

   (b) The inequality $f(x) > 0$ is satisfied when the graph of $f$ is above the $x$-axis. This occurs when $x \neq -2$.

4. (a) The inequality $f(x) \geq 0$ is satisfied when the graph of $f$ is above the $x$-axis or intersects it. This occurs for all real values of $x$.

   (b) The inequality $f(x) \leq 0$ is satisfied when the graph of $f$ is below the $x$-axis or intersects it. Since the graph of $f$ is always above the $x$-axis, this inequality has no solutions.

5. (a) The inequality $f(x) > 0$ is satisfied when the graph of $f$ is above the $x$-axis. Since the graph of $f$ is always below the $x$-axis, this inequality has no solutions.

   (b) The inequality $f(x) < 0$ is satisfied when the graph of $f$ is below the $x$-axis. This occurs for all real values of $x$.

6. (a) The inequality $f(x) \geq 0$ is satisfied when the graph of $f$ is above the $x$-axis or intersects it. This occurs only when $x = -1$.

   (b) The inequality $f(x) < 0$ is satisfied when the graph of $f$ is below the $x$-axis. This occurs when $x \neq -1$.

7. (a) The $x$-intercepts are the solutions to $f(x) = 0$: $0 = 2x^2 + 6x + \frac{5}{2} \Rightarrow 4x^2 + 12x + 5 = 0$.

$$x = \frac{-12 \pm \sqrt{(12)^2 - 4(4)(5)}}{2(4)} \Rightarrow x = \frac{-12 \pm \sqrt{64}}{8} \Rightarrow x = \frac{-12 \pm 8}{8} \Rightarrow x = \frac{-4}{8} \Rightarrow$$

$$x = -\frac{1}{2} \text{ or } x = -\frac{20}{8} \Rightarrow x = -2\frac{1}{2}, x = -2\frac{1}{2}, -\frac{1}{2}$$

   (b) The inequality $f(x) < 0$ is satisfied when the graph of $f$ is above the $x$-axis. This occurs in the interval $\left(-\frac{5}{2}, -\frac{1}{2}\right)$ or $\left\{x \mid -\frac{5}{2} < x < -\frac{1}{2}\right\}$.

   (c) The inequality $f(x) > 0$ is satisfied when the graph of $f$ is above the $x$-axis. This occurs in the interval $\left(-\infty, -\frac{5}{2}\right) \cup \left(-\frac{1}{2}, \infty\right)$ or $\left\{x \mid x < -\frac{5}{2} \text{ or } x > -\frac{1}{2}\right\}$.

8. (a) The $x$-intercepts are the solutions to $f(x) = 0$: $0 = 3x^2 + 4x - 4$.

$$x = \frac{-4 \pm \sqrt{(4)^2 - 4(3)(-4)}}{2(3)} \Rightarrow x = \frac{-4 \pm \sqrt{64}}{6} \Rightarrow x = \frac{-4 \pm 8}{6} \Rightarrow x = -2, \frac{2}{3}$$

   (b) The inequality $f(x) < 0$ is satisfied when the graph of $f$ is above the $x$-axis. This occurs in the interval $\left(-2, \frac{2}{3}\right)$ or $\left\{x \mid -2 < x < \frac{2}{3}\right\}$.

   (c) The inequality $f(x) > 0$ is satisfied when the graph of $f$ is above the $x$-axis. This occurs in the interval $(-\infty, -2) \cup \left(\frac{2}{3}, \infty\right)$ or $\left\{x \mid x < -2 \text{ or } x > \frac{2}{3}\right\}$.

9. (a) The $x$-intercepts are the solutions to $f(x) = 0$: $0 = -5x^2 + 2x + 7$.

$$x = \frac{-2 \pm \sqrt{(2)^2 - 4(-5)(7)}}{2(-5)} \Rightarrow x = \frac{-2 \pm \sqrt{144}}{-10} \Rightarrow x = \frac{-2 \pm 12}{-10} \Rightarrow x = -1, \frac{7}{5}$$

(b) The inequality $f(x) < 0$ is satisfied when the graph of $f$ is above the $x$-axis. This occurs in the interval $(-\infty, -1) \cup \left(\frac{7}{5}, \infty\right)$ or $\left\{x \mid x < -1 \text{ or } x > \frac{7}{5}\right\}$

(c) The inequality $f(x) > 0$ is satisfied when the graph of $f$ is above the $x$-axis. This occurs in the interval $\left(-1, \frac{7}{5}\right)$ or $\left\{x \mid -1 < x < \frac{7}{5}\right\}$

10. (a) The $x$-intercepts are the solutions to $f(x) = 0$: $0 = -3x^2 + \frac{5}{2}x + 3 \Rightarrow 0 = -6x^2 + 5x + 6$.

$$x = \frac{-5 \pm \sqrt{(5)^2 - 4(-6)(6)}}{2(-6)} \Rightarrow x = \frac{-5 \pm \sqrt{169}}{-12} \Rightarrow x = \frac{-5 \pm 13}{-12} \Rightarrow x = -\frac{2}{3}, \frac{3}{2}$$

(b) The inequality $f(x) < 0$ is satisfied when the graph of $f$ is above the $x$-axis. This occurs in the interval $\left(-\infty, -\frac{2}{3}\right) \cup \left(\frac{3}{2}, \infty\right)$ or $\left\{x \mid x < -\frac{2}{3} \text{ or } x > \frac{3}{2}\right\}$

(c) The inequality $f(x) > 0$ is satisfied when the graph of $f$ is above the $x$-axis. This occurs in the interval $\left(-\frac{2}{3}, \frac{3}{2}\right)$ or $\left\{x \mid -\frac{2}{3} < x < \frac{3}{2}\right\}$

11. (a) $x^2 - x - 12 = 0 \Rightarrow (x - 4)(x + 3) = 0 \Rightarrow x = -3, 4$.

(b) Using test intervals, $x^2 - x - 12 < 0$ on $(-3, 4)$ or $\{x \mid -3 < x < 4\}$.

(c) Using test intervals, $x^2 - x - 12 > 0$ on $(-\infty, -3) \cup (4, \infty)$ or $\{x \mid x < -3 \text{ or } x > 4\}$.

12. (a) $x^2 - 8x + 12 = 0 \Rightarrow (x - 6)(x - 2) = 0 \Rightarrow x = 2, 6$.

(b) Using test intervals, $x^2 - 8x + 12 < 0$ on $(2, 6)$ or $\{x \mid 2 < x < 6\}$.

(c) Using test intervals, $x^2 - 8x + 12 > 0$ on $(-\infty, 2) \cup (6, \infty)$ or $\{x \mid x < 2 \text{ or } x > 6\}$.

13. (a) $k^2 - 5 = 0 \Rightarrow k^2 = 5 \Rightarrow k = \pm\sqrt{5}$.

(b) Using test intervals, $k^2 - 5 \le 0$ on $[-\sqrt{5}, \sqrt{5}]$ or $\{k \mid -\sqrt{5} \le k \le \sqrt{5}\}$.

(c) Using test intervals, $k^2 - 5 \ge 0$ on $(-\infty, -\sqrt{5}] \cup [\sqrt{5}, \infty)$ or $\{k \mid k \le -\sqrt{5} \text{ or } k \ge \sqrt{5}\}$.

14. (a) $n^2 - 17 = 0 \Rightarrow n^2 = 17 \Rightarrow n = \pm\sqrt{17}$.

(b) Using test intervals, $n^2 - 17 \le 0$ on $[-\sqrt{17}, \sqrt{17}]$ or $\{n \mid -\sqrt{17} \le n \le \sqrt{17}\}$.

(c) Using test intervals, $n^2 - 17 \ge 0$ on $(-\infty, -\sqrt{17}] \cup [\sqrt{17}, \infty)$ or $\{n \mid n \le -\sqrt{17} \text{ or } x \ge \sqrt{17}\}$.

15. (a) $3x^2 + 8x = 0 \Rightarrow x(3x + 8) = 0 \Rightarrow x = -\frac{8}{3}, 0$. Using $x = -1$, which is inbetween $-\frac{8}{3}$ and 0 produces $3(-1)^2 + 8(-1) = -5 \Rightarrow$ less than 0.

(b) Using test intervals, $3x^2 + 8x \le 0$ on $\left[-\frac{8}{3}, 0\right]$ or $\left\{x \mid -\frac{8}{3} \le x \le 0\right\}$.

(c) Using test intervals, $3x^2 + 8x \ge 0$ on $\left(-\infty, -\frac{8}{3}\right] \cup [0, \infty)$ or $\left\{x \mid x \le -\frac{8}{3} \text{ or } x \ge 0\right\}$.

16. (a) $7x^2 - 4x = 0 \Rightarrow x(7x - 4) = 0 \Rightarrow x = 0, \frac{4}{7}.$

(b) Using test intervals, $7x^2 - 4x \le 0$ on $\left[0, \frac{4}{7}\right]$ or $\left\{x \mid 0 \le x \le \frac{4}{7}\right\}$

(c) Using test intervals, $7x^2 - 4x \ge 0$ on $(-\infty, 0] \cup \left[\frac{4}{7}, \infty\right)$ or $\left\{x \mid x \le 0 \text{ or } x \ge \frac{4}{7}\right\}$

17. (a) $-4x^2 + 12x - 9 = 0 \Rightarrow (2x - 3)(-2x + 3) = 0 \Rightarrow x = \frac{3}{2}.$

(b) Using test intervals, $-4x^2 + 12x - 9 < 0$ on $x \ne \frac{3}{2}$ on $\left(-\infty, \frac{3}{2}\right) \cup \left(\frac{3}{2}, \infty\right)$ or $\left\{x \mid x < \frac{3}{2} \text{ or } x > \frac{3}{2}\right\}$

(c) Using test intervals, $-4x^2 + 12x - 9 > 0$ has no solution

18. (a) $x^2 + 2x + 1 = 0 \Rightarrow (x + 1)^2 = 0 \Rightarrow x = -1.$

(b) Using test intervals, $x^2 + 2x + 1 < 0$ has no solutions

(c) Using test intervals, $x^2 + 2x + 1 > 0$ on $x \ne -1$ or $(-\infty, -1) \cup (-1, \infty)$ or $\{x \mid x < -1 \text{ or } x > -1\}$

19. (a) $12z^2 - 23z + 10 = 0 \Rightarrow (3z - 2)(4z - 5) = 0 \Rightarrow z = \frac{2}{3}, \frac{5}{4}.$

(b) Using test intervals, $12z^2 - 23z + 10 \le 0$ on $\left[\frac{2}{3}, \frac{5}{4}\right]$ or $\left\{z \mid \frac{2}{3} \le z \le \frac{5}{4}\right\}$

(c) Using test intervals, $12z^2 - 23z + 10 \ge 0$ on $\left(-\infty, \frac{2}{3}\right] \cup \left[\frac{5}{4}, \infty\right)$ or $\left\{z \mid z \le \frac{2}{3} \text{ or } z \ge \frac{5}{4}\right\}$

20. (a) $18z^2 + 9z - 20 = 0 \Rightarrow (6z - 5)(3z + 4) = 0 \Rightarrow z = -\frac{4}{3}, \frac{5}{6}.$

(b) Using test intervals, $18z^2 + 9z - 20 \le 0$ on $\left[-\frac{4}{3}, \frac{5}{6}\right]$ or $\left\{z \mid -\frac{4}{3} \le z \le \frac{5}{6}\right\}$

(c) Using test intervals, $18z^2 + 9z - 20 \ge 0$ on $\left(-\infty, -\frac{4}{3}\right] \cup \left[\frac{5}{6}, \infty\right)$ or $\left\{z \mid z \le -\frac{4}{3} \text{ or } z \ge \frac{5}{6}\right\}$

21. (a) $x^2 + 2x - 1 = 0$, using the quadratic formula we get: $x = \frac{-2 \pm \sqrt{(2)^2 - 4(1)(-1)}}{2(1)} \Rightarrow$

$x = \frac{-2 \pm \sqrt{8}}{2} \Rightarrow x = \frac{-2 \pm 2\sqrt{2}}{2} \Rightarrow x = -1 \pm \sqrt{2}.$

(b) Using test intervals, $x^2 + 2x - 1 < 0$ on $(-1 - \sqrt{2}, -1 + \sqrt{2})$ or $\{x \mid -1 - \sqrt{2} < x < -1 + \sqrt{2}\}$

(c) Using test intervals, $x^2 + 2x - 1 > 0$ on $(-\infty, -1 - \sqrt{2}) \cup (-1 + \sqrt{2}, \infty)$ or

$\{x \mid x < -1 - \sqrt{2} \text{ or } x > -1 + \sqrt{2}\}$

22. (a) $x^2 + 4x - 3 = 0$, using the quadratic formula we get: $x = \dfrac{-4 \pm \sqrt{(4)^2 - 4(1)(-3)}}{2(1)} \Rightarrow$

$x = \dfrac{-4 \pm \sqrt{28}}{2} \Rightarrow x = -2 \pm \sqrt{7}$.

(b) Using test intervals, $x^2 + 4x - 3 < 0$ on $(-2 - \sqrt{7}, -2 + \sqrt{7})$ or $\{x \mid -2 - \sqrt{7} < x < -2 + \sqrt{7}\}$

(c) Using test intervals, $x^2 + 4x - 3 > 0$ on $(-\infty, -2 - \sqrt{7}) \cup (-2 + \sqrt{7}, \infty)$ or

$\{x \mid x < -2 - \sqrt{7}$ or $x > -2 + \sqrt{7}\}$

23. (a) $f(x) > 0$ when $x < -1$ or $x > 1$

(b) $f(x) \leq 0$ when $-1 \leq x \leq 1$

24. (a) $f(x) > 0$ when $-4 < x < 5$

(b) $f(x) \leq 0$ when $x \leq -4$ or $x \geq 5$

25. (a) $f(x) > 0$ when $-6 < x < -2$

(b) $f(x) \leq 0$ when $x \leq -6$ or $x \geq -2$

26. (a) $f(x) > 0$ when $x < -2$ or $x > 4$

(b) $f(x) \leq 0$ when $-2 \leq x \leq 4$

27. Start by solving $2x^2 + 5x + 2 = 0 \Rightarrow (2x + 1)(x + 2) = 0 \Rightarrow x = -2$ or $-0.5$; thus,

$2x^2 + 5x + 2 \leq 0$ when $-2 \leq x \leq -0.5$.

28. Start by solving $x^2 - 3x - 4 = 0 \Rightarrow (x - 4)(x + 1) = 0 \Rightarrow x = -1$ or $4$; thus,

$x^2 - 3x - 4 < 0$ when $-1 < x < 4$.

29. Start by solving $x^2 + x - 6 = 0 \Rightarrow (x + 3)(x - 2) = 0 \Rightarrow x = -3$ or $2$; thus,

$x^2 + x - 6 > 0$ when $x < -3$ or $x > 2$.

30. Start by solving $12x^2 - 3x - 9 = 0 \Rightarrow 3(4x^2 - x - 3) = 0 \Rightarrow 3(4x + 3)(x - 1) = 0 \Rightarrow$

$x = -0.75$ or $1$; thus, $12x^2 - 3x - 9 \geq 0$ when $x \leq -0.75$ or $x \geq 1$.

31. Start by solving the equation $x^2 = 4 \Rightarrow x = \pm 2$. Next write the quadratic inequality with $a > 0$.

$x^2 \leq 4 \Rightarrow x^2 - 4 \leq 0$. The graph of $y = x^2 - 4$ is a parabola opening up. It will be less than or equal to 0 between (and including) the solutions to the equation. The solutions are $-2 \leq x \leq 2$.

32. Start by solving the equation $2x^2 = 16 \Rightarrow x^2 = 8 \Rightarrow x = \pm\sqrt{8}$. Next write the quadratic inequality with $a > 0$. $2x^2 > 16 \Rightarrow 2x^2 - 16 > 0$. The graph of $y = 2x^2 - 16$ is a parabola opening up. The solutions are $x < -\sqrt{8}$ or $x > \sqrt{8}$.

33. Since $x(x - 4) \geq 4 \Rightarrow x^2 - 4x + 4 \geq 0 \Rightarrow (x - 2)^2 \geq 0$, the solutions are all real numbers.

34. $x^2 - 3x - 10 = 0 \Rightarrow (x + 2)(x - 5) = 0 \Rightarrow x = -2$ or $5$. The solutions to $x^2 - 3x - 10 < 0$ will be between (and not include) these two solutions. The solutions are $-2 < x < 5$.

35. Start by solving the equation $-x^2 + x + 6 = 0 \Rightarrow x^2 - x - 6 = 0 \Rightarrow (x + 2)(x - 3) = 0 \Rightarrow$

$x = -2, 3$. The graph of $y = -x^2 + x + 6$ is a parabola opening downward. It will be below the $x$-axis or intersect it outside of the solutions of the equation. The solutions are $x \leq -2$ or $x \geq 3$.

36. Start by solving the equation $-x^2 - 2x + 8 = 0 \Rightarrow x^2 + 2x - 8 = 0 \Rightarrow (x + 4)(x - 2) = 0 \Rightarrow$ $x = -4, 2$. The graph of $y = -x^2 - 2x + 8$ is a parabola opening downward. It is above the $x$-axis between the solutions of the equation. The solutions are $-4 < x < 2$.

37. Start by solving the equation $6x^2 - x = 1 \Rightarrow 6x^2 - x - 1 = 0 \Rightarrow (3x + 1)(2x - 1) = 0 \Rightarrow$ $x = -\frac{1}{3}, \frac{1}{2}$. The graph of $y = 6x^2 - x - 1$ is a parabola opening up. It will be below the $x$-axis between the solutions of the equation. The solutions to $6x^2 - x < 1$ are $-\frac{1}{3} < x < \frac{1}{2}$.

38. Start by solving the equation $5x^2 + 5x - 10 = 0 \Rightarrow x^2 + x - 2 = 0 \Rightarrow (x + 2)(x - 1) = 0 \Rightarrow$ $x = -2, 1$. The graph of $y = 5x^2 + 5x - 10$ is a parabola opening up. It will intersect or be below the $x$-axis between (and including) the solutions of the equation. The solutions to $5x^2 \le 10 - 5x$ are $-2 \le x \le 1$.

39. Start by solving the equation $(x + 4)(x - 10) = 0 \Rightarrow x = -4, 10$. The graph of $y = (x + 4)(x - 10) = x^2 - 6x - 40$ is a parabola opening up. It will intersect or be below the $x$-axis between (and including) the solutions of the equation. The solutions to $(x + 4)(x - 10) \le 0$ are $-4 \le x \le 10$.

40. Start by solving the equation $(x - 3.1)(x + 2.7) = 0 \Rightarrow x = -2.7, 3.1$. The graph of $y = (x - 3.1)(x + 2.7) = x^2 - 0.4x - 8.37$ is a parabola opening up. It will be above the $x$-axis outside the solutions of the equation. The solutions to $(x - 3.1)(x + 2.7) > 0$ are $x < -2.7$ or $x > 3.1$.

41. Since $2x^2 + 4x + 3 > 0$ for all values of $x$, there are no solutions to $2x^2 + 4x + 3 < 0$.

42. Since $2x^2 + x + 4 > 0$ for all values of $x$, there are no solutions to $2x^2 + x + 4 < 0$.

43. Start by solving the equation $9x^2 - 12x + 4 = 0 \Rightarrow (3x - 2)(3x - 2) = 0 \Rightarrow x = \frac{2}{3}$. The graph of $y = 9x^2 - 12x + 4 = (3x - 2)^2$ is a parabola opening up and intersecting the $x$-axis at $x = \frac{2}{3}$. It will always be above the $x$-axis except at $x = \frac{2}{3}$. The solutions to $9x^2 + 4 > 12x$ are all real numbers except $\frac{2}{3}$.

44. Start by solving the equation $x^2 + 2x - 35 = 0 \Rightarrow (x + 7)(x - 5) = 0 \Rightarrow x = -7, 5$. The graph of $y = x^2 + 2x - 35$ is a parabola opening up. It will be above or intersect the $x$-axis outside (and including) the solutions of the equation. The solutions to $x^2 + 2x \ge 35$ are $x \le -7$ or $x \ge 5$.

45. Start by solving the equation $x^2 = x \Rightarrow x^2 - x = 0 \Rightarrow x(x - 1) = 0 \Rightarrow x = 0, 1$. The graph of $y = x^2 - x$ is a parabola opening up. It will be above or intersect the $x$-axis outside (and including) the solutions of the equation. The solutions to $x^2 \ge x$ are $x \le 0$ or $x \ge 1$.

46. Since $x^2 \ge 0$ for all real numbers, $x^2 \ge -3$ is always true. The solutions are all real numbers.

47. Start by solving the equation $x(x - 1) - 6 = 0 \Rightarrow x^2 - x - 6 = 0 \Rightarrow (x + 2)(x - 3) = 0 \Rightarrow$ $x = -2, 3$. The graph of $y = x^2 - x - 6$ is a parabola opening up. It will be above or intersect the $x$-axis outside (and including) the solutions of the equation. The solutions to $x(x - 1) \ge 6$ are $x \le -2$ or $x \ge 3$.

48. Start by solving the equation $x^2 - 9 = 0 \Rightarrow (x + 3)(x - 3) = 0 \Rightarrow x = -3, 3$. The graph of $y = x^2 - 9$ is a parabola opening up. It will be below the $x$-axis between the solutions of the equation. The solutions to $x^2 - 9 < 0$ are $-3 < x < 3$.

49. Start by solving the equation $x^2 - 5 = 0 \Rightarrow x^2 = 5 \Rightarrow x = \pm\sqrt{5}$. The graph of $y = x^2 - 5$ is a parabola opening up. It will intersect or be below the $x$-axis between (and including) the solutions of the equation. The solutions are $-\sqrt{5} \leq x \leq \sqrt{5}$.

50. Start by graphing $Y_1 = 0.5X^2 - 3.2X + 0.9$ in $[-10, 10, 1]$ by $[-10, 10, 1]$. The inequality given by $0.5x^2 - 3.2x + 0.9 > 0$ is satisfied when the graph $Y_1$ is above the $x$-axis. This occurs when $x < k_1$ or $x > k_2$, where $k_1 \approx 0.3$ and $k_2 \approx 6.1$.

51. Start by graphing $Y_1 = 7X^2 - 179.8X + 515.2$ in $[-4, 30, 2]$ by $[-750, 250, 50]$. The inequality given by $7x^2 - 179.8x + 515.2 \geq 0$ is satisfied when the graph $Y_1$ is above or intersects the $x$-axis. This occurs when $x \leq k$ or $x \geq 22.4$, where $k = \frac{23}{7}$.

52. $-10 < 3x - x^2 \Rightarrow x^2 - 3x - 10 < 0$. Start by solving the equation $x^2 - 3x - 10 = 0 \Rightarrow (x + 2)(x - 5) = 0 \Rightarrow x = -2, 5$. The graph of $y = x^2 - 3x - 10$ is a parabola opening up. It will be below the $x$-axis between the solutions of the equation. The solutions are $-2 < x < 5$.

53. For $x^2 - 9x + 14 \leq 0$, first solve $x^2 - 9x + 14 = 0 \Rightarrow (x - 7)(x - 2) = 0 \Rightarrow x = 2, 7$. These boundary numbers give us the disjoint intervals: $(-\infty, 2), (2, 7), (7, \infty)$. See Figure 53. $x^2 - 9x + 14 \leq 0$ when $2 \leq x \leq 7$.

| Interval | Test Value $x$ | $x^2 - 9x + 14$ | Positive or Negative? |
|---|---|---|---|
| $(-\infty, 2)$ | 0 | 14 | Positive |
| $(2, 7)$ | 4 | $-6$ | Negative |
| $(7, \infty)$ | 10 | 24 | Positive |

Figure 53

| Interval | Test Value $x$ | $x^2 + 10x + 21$ | Positive or Negative? |
|---|---|---|---|
| $(-\infty, -7)$ | $-10$ | 21 | Positive |
| $(-7, -3)$ | $-5$ | $-4$ | Negative |
| $(-3, \infty)$ | 0 | 21 | Positive |

Figure 54

54. For $x^2 + 10x + 21 > 0$, first solve $x^2 + 10x + 21 = 0 \Rightarrow (x + 7)(x + 3) = 0 \Rightarrow x = -7, -3$. These boundary numbers give us the disjoint intervals: $(-\infty, -7), (-7, -3), (-3, \infty)$. See Figure 54. $x^2 + 10x + 21 > 0$ when $x < -7$ or $x > -3$.

55. For $x^2 \geq 3x + 10 \Rightarrow x^2 - 3x - 10 \geq 0$, first solve $x^2 - 3x - 10 = 0 \Rightarrow (x - 5)(x + 2) = 0 \Rightarrow x = -2, 5$. These boundary numbers give us the disjoint intervals: $(-\infty, -2), (-2, 5), (5, \infty)$. See Figure 55. $x^2 - 3x - 10 \geq 0$ when $x \leq -2$ or $x \geq 5$.

| Interval | Test Value $x$ | $x^2 - 3x - 10$ | Positive or Negative? |
|---|---|---|---|
| $(-\infty, -2)$ | $-3$ | 8 | Positive |
| $(-2, 5)$ | 0 | $-10$ | Negative |
| $(5, \infty)$ | 6 | 8 | Positive |

Figure 55

| Interval | Test Value $x$ | $x^2 - 3x - 4$ | Positive or Negative? |
|---|---|---|---|
| $(-\infty, -1)$ | $-2$ | 6 | Positive |
| $(-1, 4)$ | 0 | $-4$ | Negative |
| $(4, \infty)$ | 5 | 6 | Positive |

Figure 56

56. For $x^2 < 3x + 4 \Rightarrow x^2 - 3x - 4 < 0$, first solve $x^2 - 3x - 4 = 0 \Rightarrow (x - 4)(x + 1) = 0 \Rightarrow x = -1, 4$. These boundary numbers give us the disjoint intervals: $(-\infty, -1), (-1, 4), (4, \infty)$. See Figure 56. $x^2 - 3x - 4 < 0$ when $-1 < x < 4$.

57. For $\frac{1}{8}x^2 + x + 2 \geq 0 \Rightarrow x^2 + 8x + 16 \geq 0$, first solve $x^2 + 8x + 16 = 0 \Rightarrow (x + 4)(x + 4) = 0 \Rightarrow$ $x = -4$. This boundary gives us the disjoint intervals: $(-\infty, -4), (-4, \infty)$. See Figure 57.
$\frac{1}{8}x^2 + x + 2 \geq 0$ for all real numbers.

| Interval | Test Value $x$ | $1/8x^2 + x + 2$ | Positive or Negative? |
|---|---|---|---|
| $(-\infty, -4)$ | $-8$ | 2 | Positive |
| $(-4, \infty)$ | 0 | 2 | Positive |

Figure 57

| Interval | Test Value $x$ | $x^2 - 1/2x - 5$ | Positive or Negative? |
|---|---|---|---|
| $(-\infty, -2)$ | $-4$ | 13 | Positive |
| $(-2, 5/2)$ | 0 | $-5$ | Negative |
| $(5/2, \infty)$ | 4 | 9 | Positive |

Figure 58

58. For $x^2 - \frac{1}{2}x - 5 < 0$, first solve $x^2 - \frac{1}{2}x - 5 = 0 \Rightarrow 2x^2 - x - 10 = 0 \Rightarrow (2x - 5)(x + 2) = 0 \Rightarrow$ $x = -2, \frac{5}{2}$. These boundary numbers give us the disjoint intervals: $(-\infty, -2), \left(-2, \frac{5}{2}\right), \left(\frac{5}{2}, \infty\right)$. See Figure 58.
$x^2 - \frac{1}{2}x - 5 < 0$ when $-2 < x < \frac{5}{2}$.

59. For $x^2 > 3 - 4x \Rightarrow x^2 + 4x - 3 > 0$, first solve $x^2 + 4x - 3 = 0$. Using the quadratic formula we get:
$x = \frac{-4 \pm \sqrt{(4)^2 - 4(1)(-3)}}{2(1)} \Rightarrow x = \frac{-4 \pm \sqrt{28}}{2} \Rightarrow x = -2 + \sqrt{7}$ or $x = -2 - \sqrt{7}$. These boundary numbers give us the disjoint intervals:
$(-\infty, -2 - \sqrt{7}), (-2 - \sqrt{7}, -2 + \sqrt{7}), (-2 + \sqrt{7}, \infty)$. See Figure 59. $x^2 + 4x - 3 > 0$ when $x < -2 - \sqrt{7}$ or $x > -2 + \sqrt{7}$.

| Interval | Test Value $x$ | $x^2 + 4x - 3$ | Positive or Negative? |
|---|---|---|---|
| $(-\infty, -4.6)$ | $-5$ | 2 | Positive |
| $(-4.6, 0.6)$ | 0 | $-3$ | Negative |
| $(0.6, \infty)$ | 1 | 2 | Positive |

Figure 59

| Interval | Test Value $x$ | $2x^2 + 4x - 1$ | Positive or Negative? |
|---|---|---|---|
| $(-\infty, -2.2)$ | $-3$ | 5 | Positive |
| $(-2.2, 0.2)$ | 0 | $-1$ | Negative |
| $(0.2, \infty)$ | 1 | 5 | Positive |

Figure 60

60. For $2x^2 \leq 1 - 4x \Rightarrow 2x^2 + 4x - 1 \leq 0$, first solve $2x^2 + 4x - 1 = 0$. Using the quadratic formula we get:
$x = \frac{-4 \pm \sqrt{(4)^2 - 4(2)(-1)}}{2(2)} \Rightarrow x = \frac{-4 \pm \sqrt{24}}{4} \Rightarrow x = \frac{-2 \pm \sqrt{6}}{2} \Rightarrow$
$x = \frac{-2 - \sqrt{6}}{2}$ or $x = \frac{-2 + \sqrt{6}}{2}$. These boundary numbers give us the disjoint intervals:
$\left(-\infty, \frac{-2 - \sqrt{6}}{2}\right), \left(\frac{-2 - \sqrt{6}}{2}, \frac{-2 + \sqrt{6}}{2}\right), \left(\frac{-2 + \sqrt{6}}{2}, \infty\right)$. See Figure 60. $2x^2 + 4x - 1 \leq 0$ when $\frac{-2 - \sqrt{6}}{2} \leq x \leq \frac{-2 + \sqrt{6}}{2}$.

61. Graph $Y_1 = (1/9)X^2 + (11/3)X$, $Y_2 = 300$ in $[30, 40, 1]$ by $[0, 400, 100]$ (Not Shown). The intersection is (38.018, 300). Thus, the safe stopping speed is to be no more than 38 mph. The speed limit might be 35 mph.

62. Graph $Y_1 = (1/12)X^2 + (11/9)X$, $Y_2 = 300$ and $Y_3 = 500$ in [40, 100, 10] by [100, 600, 50] (Not shown). The intersections are approximately (53.113154, 300) and (70.472693, 500). From the graphs, we see that $300 \le Y_1 \le 500$ when $53 \le X \le 70$. Thus, the stopping distances are between 300 and 500 feet, inclusively, when the driving speed is between 53 mph and 70 mph inclusive.

63. To find the possible values of the radius of the can, solve the following inequality: $24\pi \le \pi(r^2)6 \le 54\pi \Rightarrow 24 \le 6r^2 \le 54 \Rightarrow 4 \le r^2 \le 9 \Rightarrow 2 \le r \le 3$. The possible values of $r$ range between 2 and 3 inches.

64. The area of the rectangle is given as follows: $A = l \cdot w \Rightarrow (x + 4)x \le 672 \Rightarrow x^2 + 4x - 672 \le 0 \Rightarrow (x + 28)(x - 24) \le 0$. The graph of $y = x^2 + 4x - 672$ opens upward and the $x$-intercepts are $x = -28$ and $x = 24$. Therefore, $x^2 + 4x - 672 \le 0$ when $x$ is $-28 \le x \le 24$. Since width cannot be negative, the possible values of the width are between 0 and 24 feet.

65. (a) $f(0) = \frac{4}{5}(0 - 10)^2 + 80 = 160$ and $f(2) = \frac{4}{5}(2 - 10)^2 + 80 = 131.2$. Initially when the person stops exercising the heart rate is 160 beats per minute, and after 2 minutes the heart rate has dropped to about 131 beats per minute.

(b) Graph $Y_1 = 100$, $Y_2 = 0.8(X - 10)^2 + 80$ and $Y_3 = 120$ (Not shown). To find the points of intersection, use the calc function on the calculator. The person's heart rate is between 100 and 120 when the graph of $Y_2$ is between the graphs of $Y_1$ and $Y_3$. This occurs between approximately 2.9 minutes and 5 minutes after the person stops exercising.

66. Graph $Y_1 = 0.0079X^2 - 1.53X + 76$, $Y_2 = 4$ and $Y_3 = 5$ (Not shown). To find the points of intersection use the CALC function on the calculator. The time is between 4 and 5 hours when x is between approximately 77.1 and 80.6 ppm.

67. Graph $Y_1 = 2375X^2 + 5134X - 5020$, $Y_2 = 90{,}000$ and $Y_3 = 200{,}000$ in [–1, 11, 1] by [5000, 210000, 10000] (Not shown). The intersection points are approximately (4.9977492, 90000) and (8.044127, 200,000). From the graphs, we see that $90{,}000 \le Y_1 \le 200{,}000$ when $4.998 \le X \le 8.044$. Since 1984 corresponds to $x = 0$, the number of AIDS deaths was from 90,000 to 200,000 for the years from 1989 to 1992.

68. (a) The altitude of Denver is approximately one mile or 5280 feet. This is approximately equivalent to $5280(0.305) \approx 1610$ meters. At sea level, the density of air is

$D(0) = (3.32 \times 10^{-9})0^2 - (1.14 \times 10^{-4})0 + 1.22 = 1.22 \text{ kg/m}^3$. If the elevation of Denver is 1610 meters, then the density of the air is approximately

$D(1610) = (3.32 \times 10^{-9})1610^2 - (1.14 \times 10^{-4})1610 + 1.22 \approx 1.05 \text{ kg/m}^3$.

(b) Graph $Y_1 = (3.32E{-}9)X^2 - (1.14E{-}4)X + 1.22$ and $Y_2 = 1$ (Not shown). The point of intersection is near (2053, 1). Thus, The density is greater than 1 kilogram per cubic meter for altitudes below about 2053 meters.

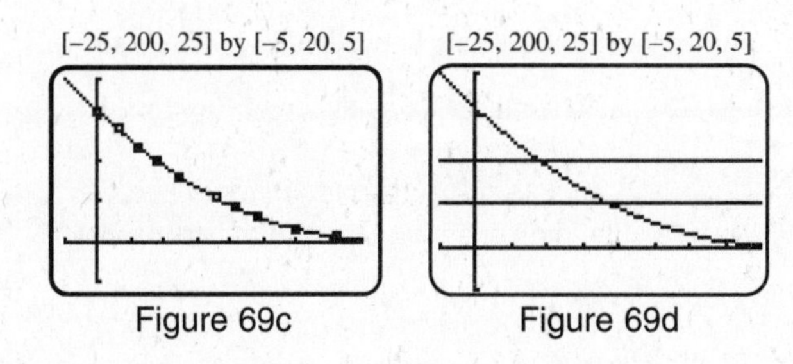


Figure 69c Figure 69d

69. (a) The data cannot be modeled by a linear function because the rate at which the height of the water decreases is not constant. When the tank first starts to drain, the large quantity of water in the tank will cause the water to drain rapidly. As the tank empties, there will be less water in the tank and the draining rate will decrease. This is evident in the data.

(b) From the table, it appears that the height of the water was between 5 and 10 centimeters from approximately 43 to 95 seconds after draining began.

(c) The graph of $Y_1 = 0.00036706X\text{^}2 - 0.1517X + 15.94$ with the data shown in Figure 69c.

(d) To find the times when the water height was between 5 and 10 centimeters, graph the function $Y_1 = 5$, $Y_2 = 0.00036706X\text{^}2 - 0.1517X + 15.94$, and $Y_3 = 10$ in the same window. The intersection points are approximately (93.1, 5) and (43.8, 10). See Figure 69d. The water level was between 5 and 10 centimeters from approximately 43.8 to 93.1 seconds after draining started.

70. (a) Letting (4, 90) be the vertex gives $f(x) = a(x - h)^2 + k \Rightarrow f(x) = a(x - 4)^2 + 90$; since (0, 154) is a data point, $f(0) = 154 \Rightarrow 154 = a(0 - 4)^2 + 90 \Rightarrow a = 4$; $f(x) = 4(x - 4)^2 + 90$ models the data.

(b) $f(1) = 4(1 - 4)^2 + 90 = 126$; a person's heart rate is 126 beats per minute after exercising 1 minute.

(c) To find the times when the heart rate was from 115 to 125 beats per minute, graph the function $Y_1 = 4(X - 4)\text{^}2 + 90$, $Y_2 = 115$, and $Y_3 = 125$ in the window [0, 3, 1] by [110, 130, 5]. The intersection points are approximately (1.04, 125) and (1.5, 115). Thus, between the times of 1.04 and 1.5 minutes, the heart rate was between 125 and 115 beats per minute.

## Checking Basic Concepts for Sections 3.3 and 3.4

1. (a) $\sqrt{-25} = \sqrt{25}\sqrt{-1} = 5i$

(b) $\sqrt{-3} \cdot \sqrt{-18} = (\sqrt{3}\sqrt{-1})(\sqrt{9}\sqrt{2}\sqrt{-1}) = (i\sqrt{3})(3i\sqrt{2}) = 3i^2\sqrt{6} = -3\sqrt{6}$

(c) $\dfrac{7 + \sqrt{-98}}{14} = \dfrac{7 \pm \sqrt{49}\sqrt{2}\sqrt{-1}}{14} = \dfrac{7 \pm 7i\sqrt{2}}{14} = \dfrac{1}{2} \pm \dfrac{i\sqrt{2}}{2}$

2. (a) $-3i - (5 - 2i) = -3i - 5 + 2i = -5 - i$

(b) $(6 - 7i) + (-1 + i) = (6 + (-1)) + (-7i + i) = 5 - 6i$

(c) $i(1 - i)(1 + i) = i(1 - i^2) = i(1 + 1) = 2i$

(d) $\dfrac{1 + 2i}{4 - i} = \dfrac{1 + 2i}{4 - i} \cdot \dfrac{4 + i}{4 + i} = \dfrac{4 + 9i + 2i^2}{16 - i^2} = \dfrac{2 + 9i}{17}$

3. (a) The $x$-intercepts are $-3$ and 0. The graph of $y = f(x)$ is below the $x$-axis between these values, so $f(x) \leq 0$ on the interval $[-3, 0]$. The graph of $y = f(x)$ is above the $x$-axis outside of these values, so $f(x) > 0$ on the intervals $(-\infty, -3) \cup (0, \infty)$ or $\{x \mid x < -3 \text{ or } x > 0\}$.

(b) The $x$-intercept is $-2$. The graph of $y = f(x)$ is always below the $x$-axis for all real numbers except at $x = -2$. That is, $f(x) \leq 0$ on $(-\infty, \infty)$. The graph of $y = f(x)$ is never above the $x$-axis, so there are no solutions to $f(x) > 0$.

4. (a) $2x^2 + 7x - 4 = 0 \Rightarrow (2x - 1)(x + 4) = 0 \Rightarrow 2x - 1 = 0 \Rightarrow x = \frac{1}{2}$ or $x + 4 = 0 \Rightarrow x = -4$. So $x = -4, \frac{1}{2}$.

(b) $2x^2 + 7x - 4 < 0$ on $\left(-4, \frac{1}{2}\right)$ or $\left\{x \mid -4 < x < \frac{1}{2}\right\}$.

(c) $2x^2 + 7x - 4 > 0$ on $(-\infty, -4) \cup \left(\frac{1}{2}, \infty\right)$ or $\left\{x \mid x < -4 \text{ or } x > \frac{1}{2}\right\}$.

5. (a) Start by solving the equation $x^2 - 5 = 0 \Rightarrow x^2 = 5 \Rightarrow x = \pm\sqrt{5}$. The graph of $x^2 - 5$ is a parabola opening up. It will be above the $x$-axis outside the solutions of the equation. The solutions to $x^2 - 5 \geq 0$ are $(-\infty, -\sqrt{5}\,] \cup [\sqrt{5}, \infty)$ or $\{x \mid x \leq -\sqrt{5} \text{ or } x \geq \sqrt{5}\}$.

(b) Start by solving the equation $4x^2 + 9 = 9x \Rightarrow 4x^2 - 9x + 9 = 0$. Using the quadratic formula we get: $x = \frac{9 \pm \sqrt{81 - 4(4)(9)}}{2(4)} \Rightarrow x = \frac{9 \pm \sqrt{-63}}{8} \Rightarrow$ no real solutions $\Rightarrow$ no intersection with the $x$-axis. This is a parabola opening up completely above the $x$-axis $\Rightarrow$ the solutions to $4x^2 + 9 > 9x$ are all real numbers.

(c) Start by solving the equation $2x(x - 1) = 2 \Rightarrow 2x^2 - 2x = 2 \Rightarrow 2x^2 - 2x - 2 = 0$.
Using the quadratic formula we get: $x = \frac{2 \pm \sqrt{4 - 4(2)(-2)}}{2(2)} \Rightarrow x = \frac{2 \pm \sqrt{20}}{4} \Rightarrow \frac{1 \pm \sqrt{5}}{2}$.
The graph of $y = 2x^2 - 2x - 2$ is a parabola opening up. It will be below the $x$-axis between the solutions of the equation. The solutions to $2x(x - 1) \leq 2$ is $\left[\frac{1 - \sqrt{5}}{2}, \frac{1 + \sqrt{5}}{2}\right]$ or $\left\{x \mid \frac{1 - \sqrt{5}}{2} \leq x \leq \frac{1 + \sqrt{5}}{2}\right]$.

6. Find $x$ so that $80 \leq d(x) \leq 180$. To do this solve: $\frac{1}{9}x^2 + \frac{11}{3}x = 80$ and $\frac{1}{9}x^2 + \frac{11}{3}x = 180$.

First, $\frac{1}{9}x^2 + \frac{11}{3}x = 80 \Rightarrow x^2 + 33x - 720 = 0 \Rightarrow (x - 15)(x + 48) = 0 \Rightarrow x = -48, 15$.

Second, $\frac{1}{9}x^2 + \frac{11}{3}x = 180 \Rightarrow x^2 + 33x - 1620 = 0 \Rightarrow (x - 27)(x + 60) = 0 \Rightarrow x = -60, 27$. Now from the first equation $\frac{1}{9}x^2 + \frac{11}{3}x \geq 80$ the value of $x \geq 15$ because all negative stopping distances make no sense. From the second equation $\frac{1}{9}x^2 + \frac{11}{3} \leq 180$ the value $x \leq 27$ because all negative stopping distances make no sense. Therefore $15 \leq x \leq 27$ or speeds from 15 to 27 miles per hour.

## 3.5: Transformations of Graphs

1. The vertex is (–2, 0 ). The parabola $y = x^2$ has been shifted 2 units to the left. The equation is $y = (x + 2)^2$.
2. The vertex is (2, –3). The parabola $y = x^2$ has been shifted 2 units to the right and 3 units down. The equation is $y = (x - 2)^2 - 3$.
3. The endpoint is (–3, 0). The curve $y = \sqrt{x}$ has been shifted 3 units to the left. The equation is $y = \sqrt{x + 3}$.
4. The endpoint is (0, –1). The curve $y = \sqrt{x}$ has been shifted 1 unit down. The equation is $y = \sqrt{x} - 1$.
5. The vertex is (–2, –1). The graph of $y = |x|$ has been shifted 2 units to the left and 1 unit down. The equation is $y = |x + 2| - 1$.
6. The vertex is (1, 2). The graph of $y = |x|$ has been shifted 1 unit to the right and 2 units up. The equation is $y = |x - 1| + 2$.
7. The endpoint is (–2, –3). The curve $y = \sqrt{x}$ has been shifted 2 units to the left and 3 units down. The equation is $y = \sqrt{x + 2} - 3$.
8. The vertex is (–1, –4). The parabola $y = x^2$ has been shifted 1 unit to the left and 4 units down. The equation is $y = (x + 1)^2 - 4$.
9. To shift the graph of $f(x) = x^2$ to the right 2 units, replace $x$ with $(x - 2)$ in the formula for $f(x)$. This results in $y = f(x - 2) = (x - 2)^2$. To shift the graph of this new equation down 3 units, subtract 3 from the formula to obtain $y = f(x - 2) - 3 = (x - 2)^2 - 3$. See Figure 9.
10. To shift the graph of $f(x) = 3x - 4$ to the left 3 units, replace $x$ with $(x + 3)$ in the formula for $f(x)$. This results in $y = f(x + 3) = 3(x + 3) - 4$. To shift the graph of this new equation up 1 unit, add 1 to the formula to obtain $y = f(x + 3) + 1 = 3(x + 3) - 4 + 1 = 3(x + 3) - 3$. See Figure 10.

[–10, 10, 1] by [–10, 10, 1]

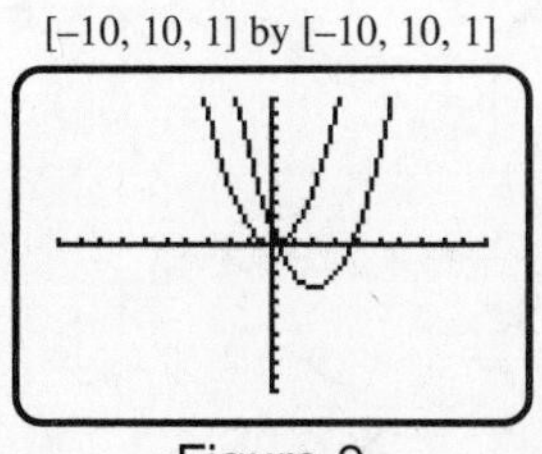

Figure 9

[–10, 10, 1] by [–10, 10, 1]

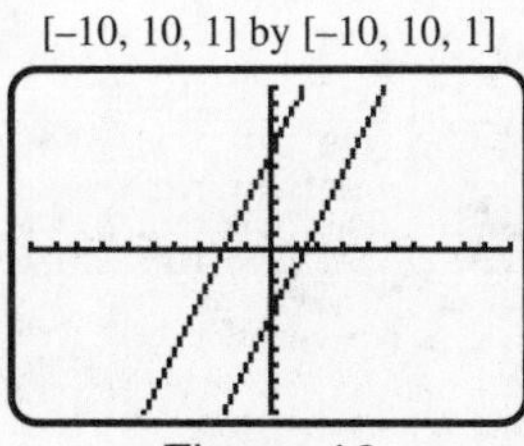

Figure 10

[–10, 10, 1] by [–10, 10, 1]

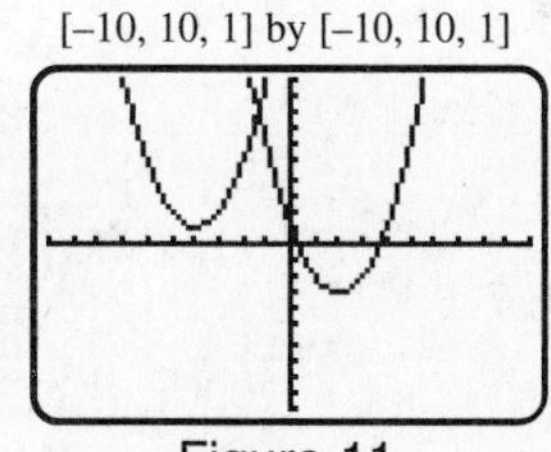

Figure 11

[–10, 10, 1] by [–10, 10, 1]

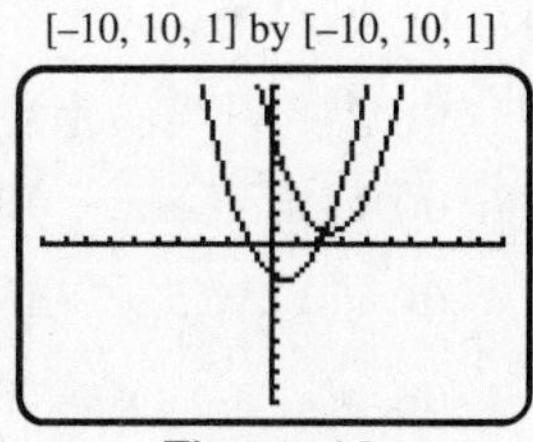

Figure 12

11. To shift the graph of $f(x) = x^2 - 4x + 1$ to the left 6 units, replace $x$ with $(x + 6)$ in the formula for $f(x)$. This results in $y = f(x + 6) = (x + 6)^2 - 4(x + 6) + 1$. To shift the graph of this new equation up 4 units, add 4 to the formula to obtain
$y = f(x + 6) + 4 = (x + 6)^2 - 4(x + 6) + 1 + 4 = (x + 6)^2 - 4(x + 6) + 5$. See Figure 11.
12. The shift to the graph of $f(x) = x^2 - x - 2$ to the right 2 units, replace $x$ with $(x - 2)$ in the formula for $f(x)$. The result is $y = f(x - 2) = (x - 2)^2 - (x - 2) - 2$. To shift the graph of this new equation up 3 units, add 3 to obtain $y = f(x - 2) + 3 = (x - 2)^2 - (x - 2) - 2 + 3 = (x - 2)^2 - (x - 2) + 1$. See Figure 12.

13. To shift the graph of $f(x) = \frac{1}{2}x^2 + 2x - 1$ to the left 3 units, replace $x$ with $(x + 3)$ in the formula for $f(x)$.

The result is $y = f(x + 3) = \frac{1}{2}(x + 3)^2 + 2(x + 3) - 1$. To shift the graph of this new equation down 2 units, subtract 2 to obtain $y = f(x + 3) - 2 = \frac{1}{2}(x + 3)^2 + 2(x + 3) - 1 - 2 \Rightarrow$

$y = \frac{1}{2}(x + 3)^2 + 2(x + 3) - 3$. See Figure 13.

[−10, 10, 1] by [−10, 10, 1]

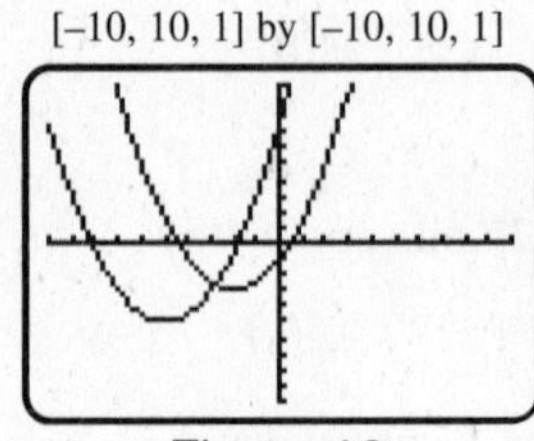

Figure 13

[−10, 10, 1] by [−10, 10, 1]

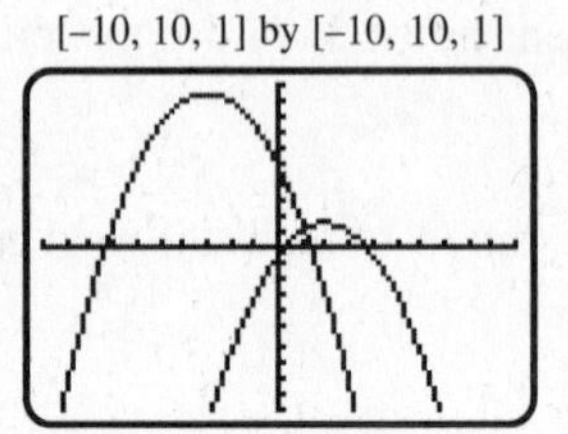

Figure 14

14. To shift the graph of $f(x) = 5 - 3x - \frac{1}{2}x^2$ to the right 5 units, replace $x$ with $(x - 5)$ in the formula for $f(x)$.

This results in $y = f(x - 5) = 5 - 3(x - 5) - \frac{1}{2}(x - 5)^2$.

To shift the graph of this new equation down 8 units, subtract 8 from the formula to obtain

$y = f(x - 5) - 8 = 5 - 3(x - 5) - \frac{1}{2}(x - 5)^2 - 8 = -3 - 3(x - 5) - \frac{1}{2}(x - 5)^2$. See Figure 14.

15. (a) $g(x) = 3(x + 3)^2 + 2(x + 3) - 5$

(b) $g(x) = 3x^2 + 2x - 9$

16. (a) $g(x) = 2(x - 8)^2 - 3(x - 8) + 2$

(b) $g(x) = 2x^2 - 3x + 4$

17. (a) $g(x) = 2(x - 2)^2 - 4(x - 2) + 5$

(b) $g(x) = 2(x + 8)^2 - 4(x + 8) - 4$

18. (a) $g(x) = 5(x + 10)^2 - 9$

(b) $g(x) = 5(x - 1)^2 + 7$

19. (a) $g(x) = 3(x - 2000)^2 - 3(x - 2000) + 72$

(b) $g(x) = 3(x + 300)^2 - 3(x + 300) - 28$

20. (a) $g(x) = |x - 4| - 6$

(b) $g(x) = |x + 5| - 1$

21. (a) $g(x) = -\sqrt{x - 4}$

(b) $g(x) = \sqrt{-x + 2}$

22. (a) $g(x) = -\sqrt{(x + 2)}$

(b) $g(x) = \sqrt{-(x - 3)}$ or $g(x) = \sqrt{3 - x}$

23. $(x - 3)^2 + (y + 4)^2 = 4$; Center: $(3, -4)$; Radius $= 2$

24. $(x - 2)^2 + (y + 6)^2 = 9$; Center: $(2, -6)$; Radius $= 3$

25. $(x + 5)^2 + (y - 3)^2 = 5$; Center: $(-5, 3)$; Radius $= \sqrt{5}$

26. $(x + 3)^2 + (y + 7)^2 = 7$; Center: $(-3, -7)$; Radius $= \sqrt{7}$

27. (a) See Figure 27a.

(b) See Figure 27b.

(c) See Figure 27c.

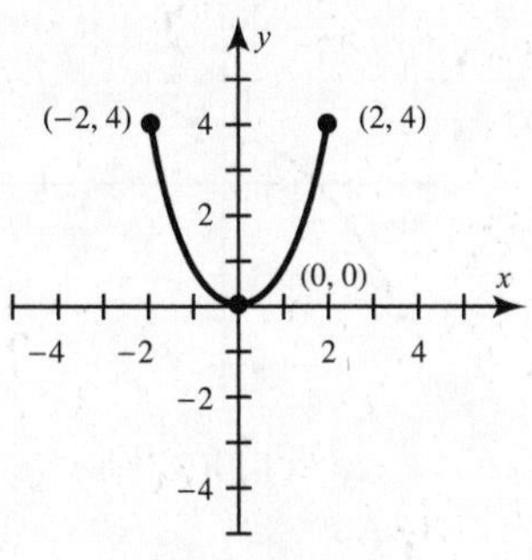

Figure 27a

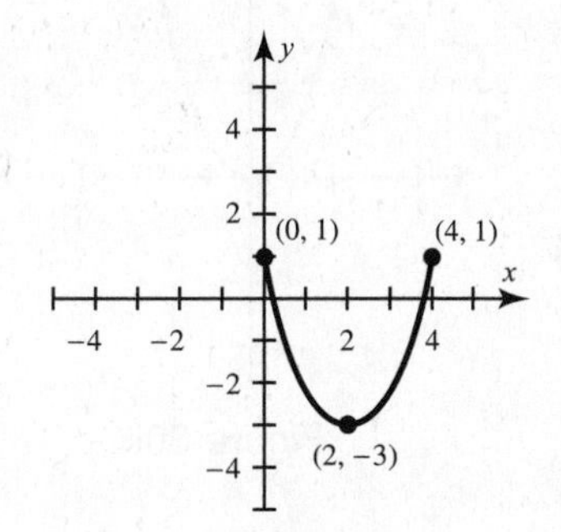

Figure 27b

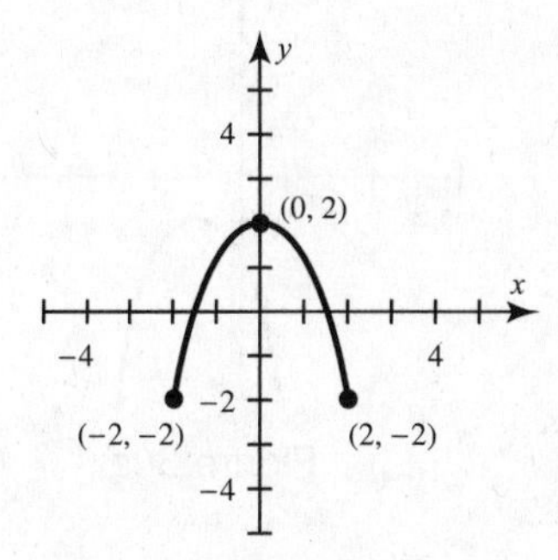

Figure 27c

28. (a) See Figure 28a.

(b) See Figure 28b.

(c) See Figure 28c.

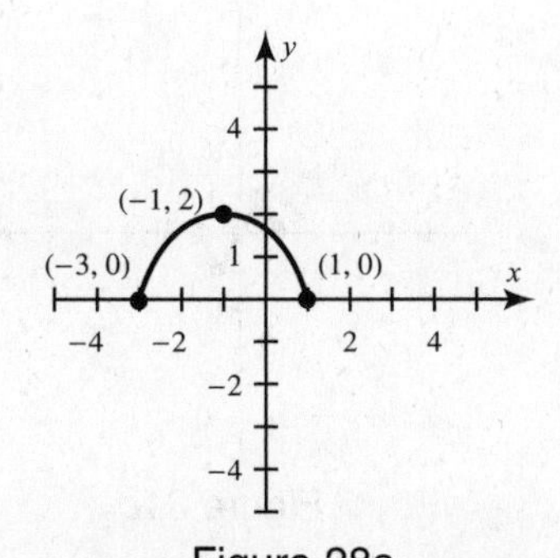

Figure 28a

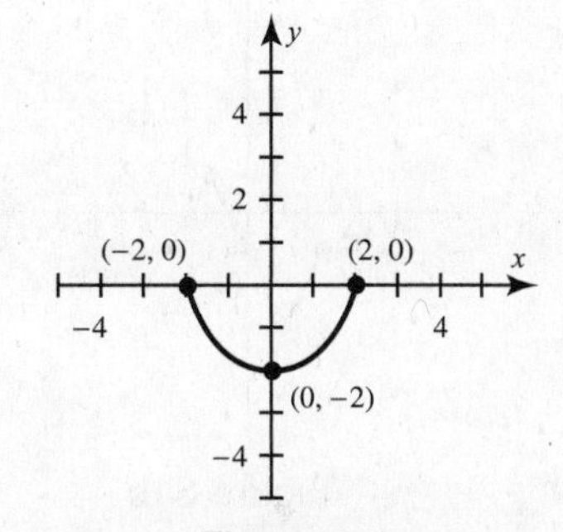

Figure 28b

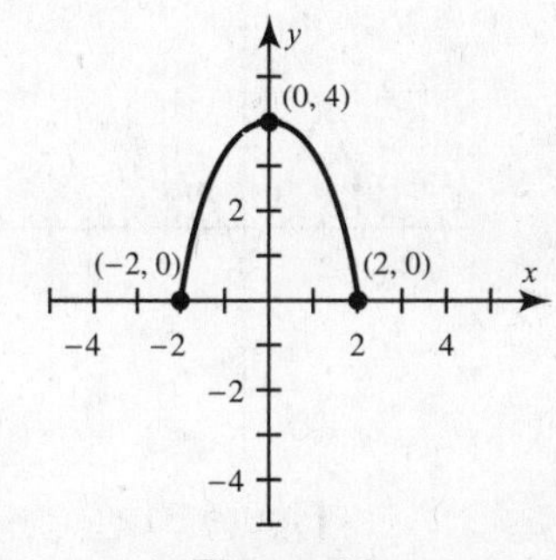

Figure 28c

29. (a) See Figure 29a.

(b) See Figure 29b.

(c) See Figure 29c.

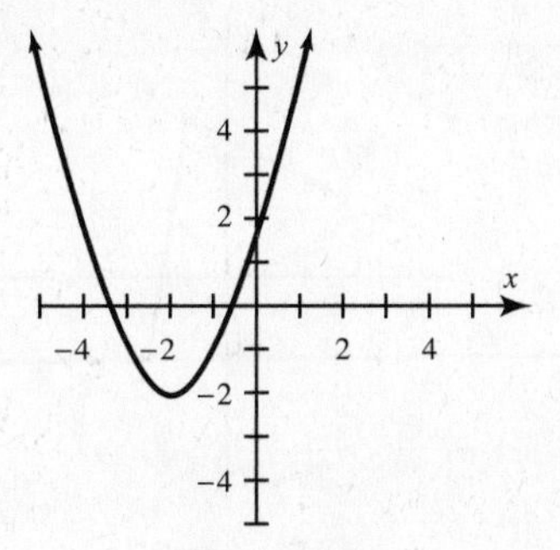

Figure 29a

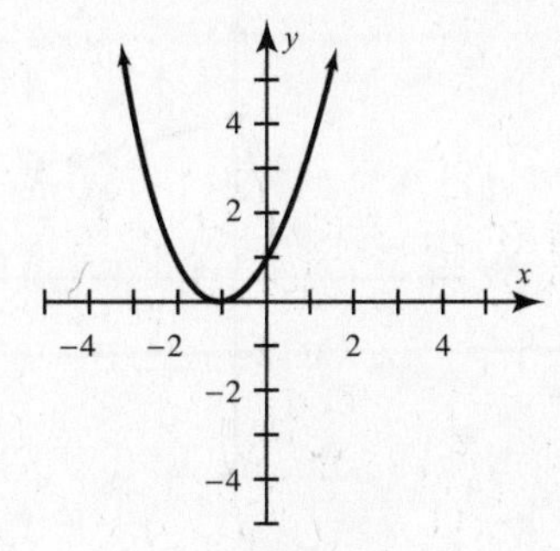

Figure 29b

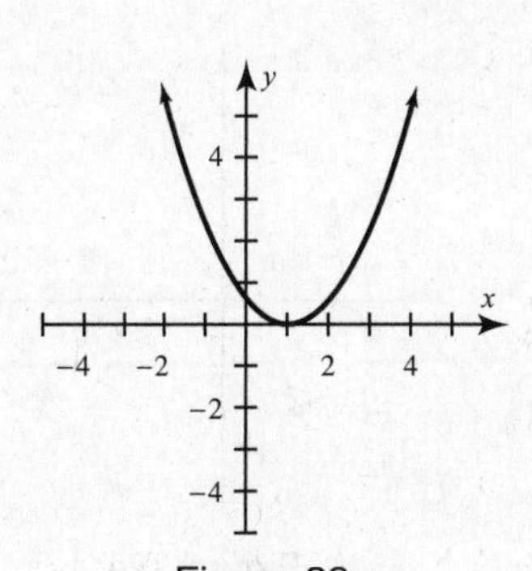

Figure 29c

30. (a) See Figure 30a.

(b) See Figure 30b.

(c) See Figure 30c.

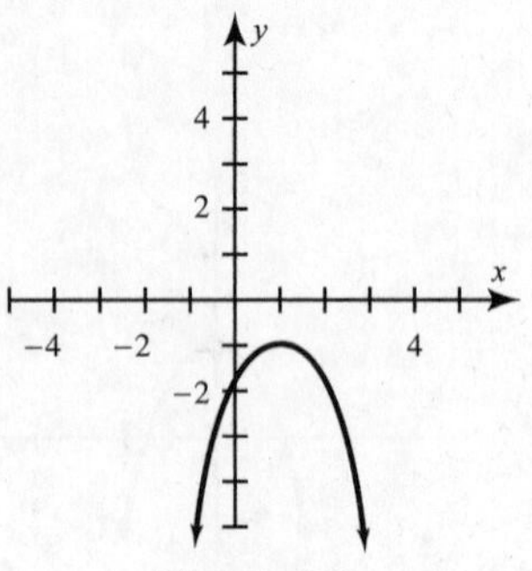

Figure 30a

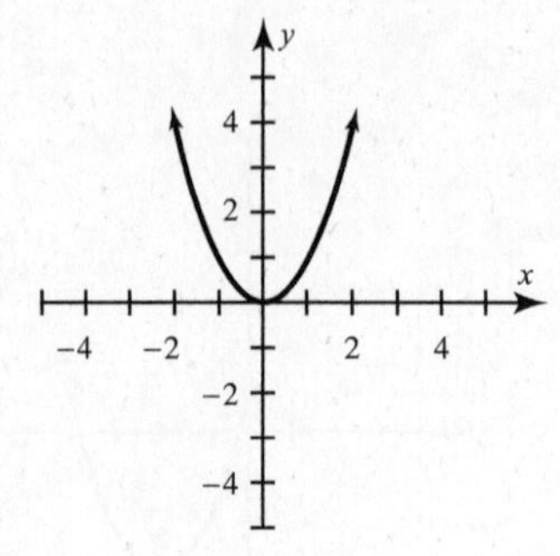

Figure 30b

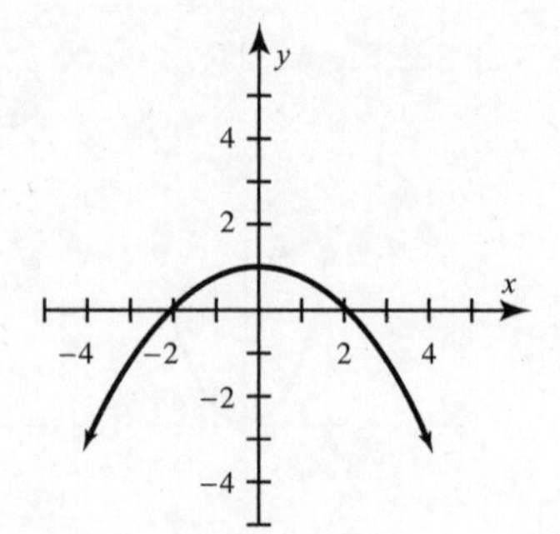

Figure 30c

31. (a) See Figure 31a.

(b) See Figure 31b.

(c) See Figure 31c.

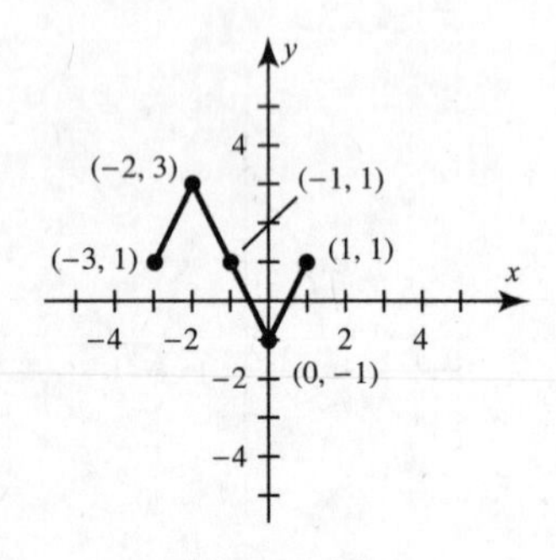


Figure 31a

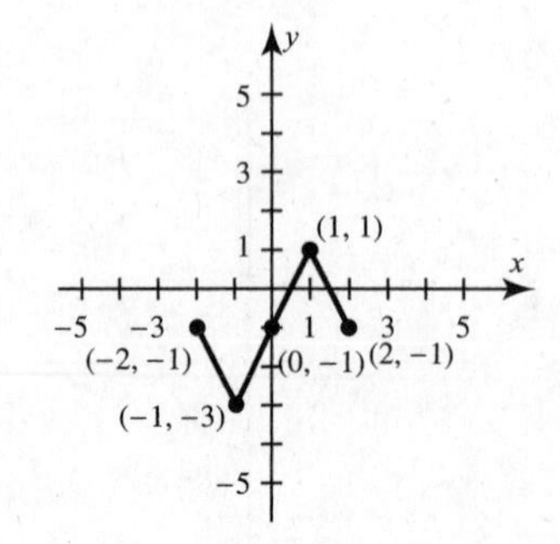


Figure 31b

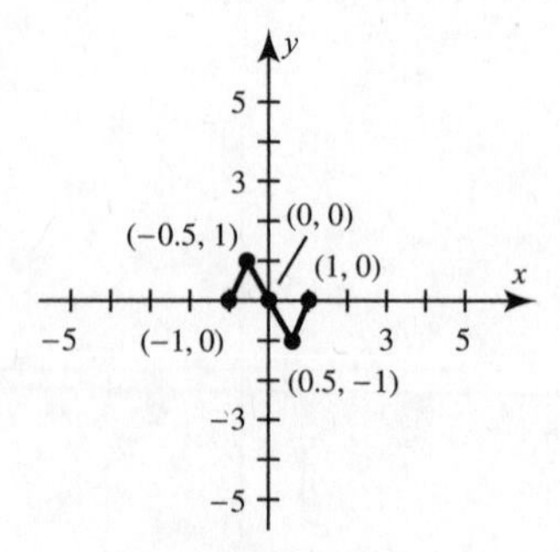


Figure 31c

32. (a) See Figure 32a.

(b) See Figure 32b.

(c) See Figure 32c.

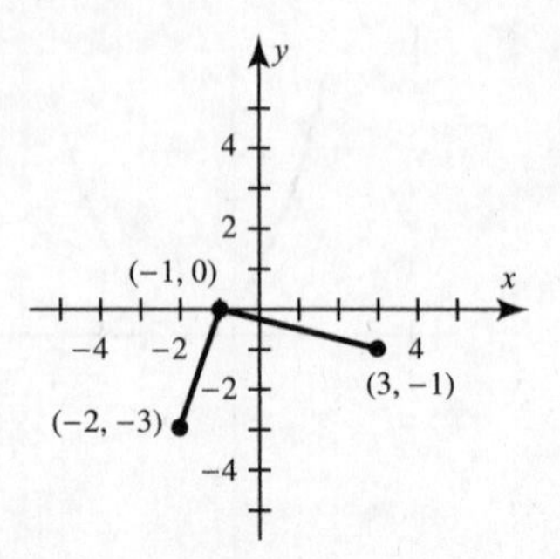


Figure 32a

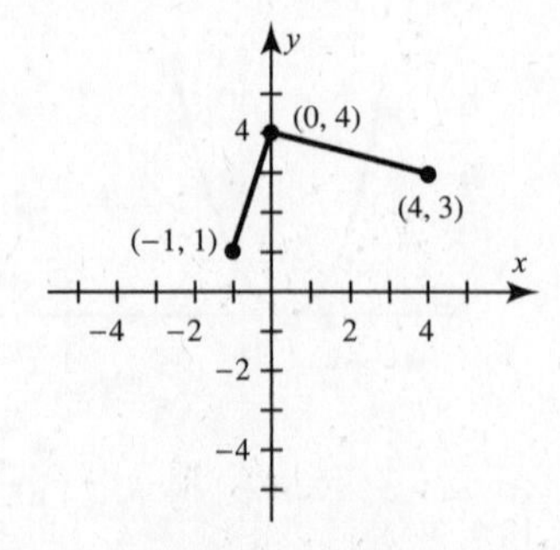


Figure 32b

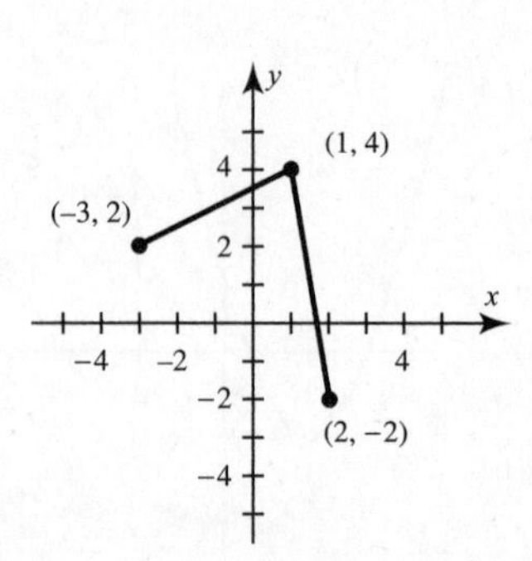


Figure 32c

33. (a) See Figure 33a.

(b) See Figure 33b.

(c) See Figure 33c.

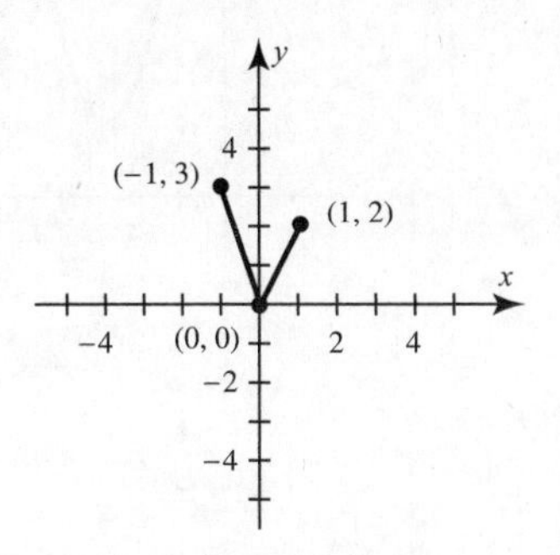


Figure 33a

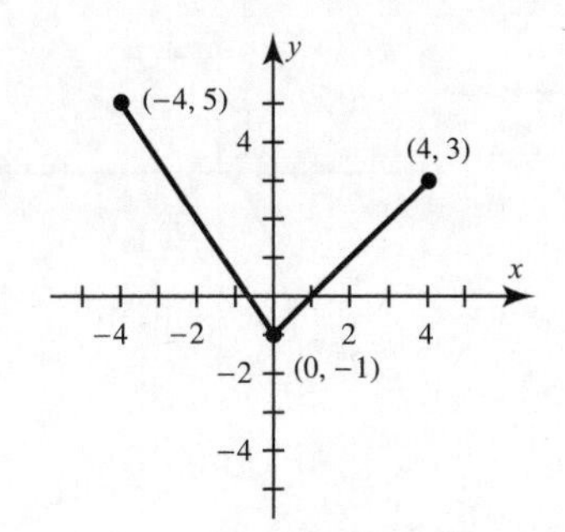


Figure 33b

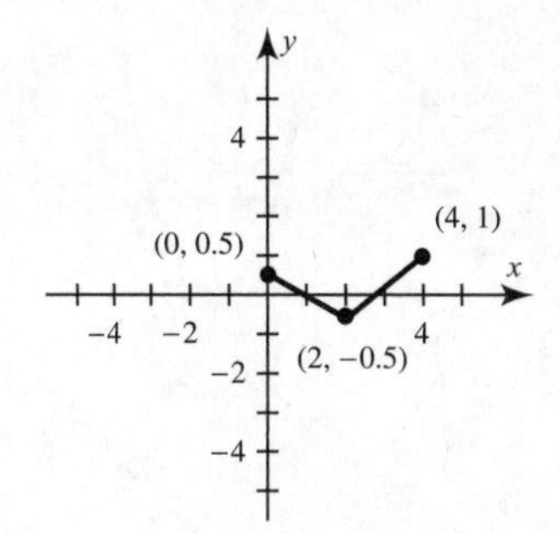


Figure 33c

34. (a) See Figure 34a.

(b) See Figure 34b.

(c) See Figure 34c.

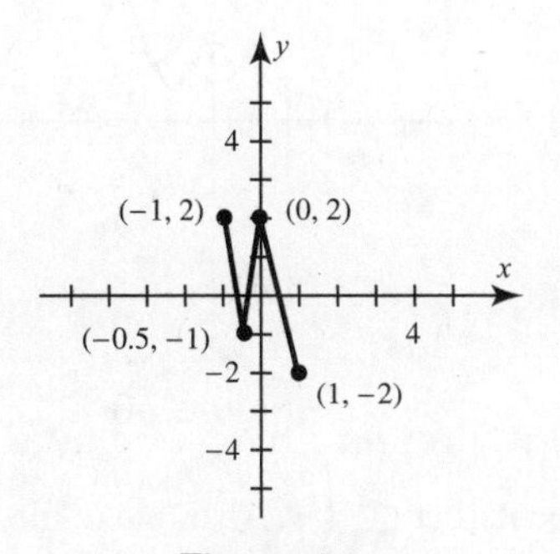


Figure 34a

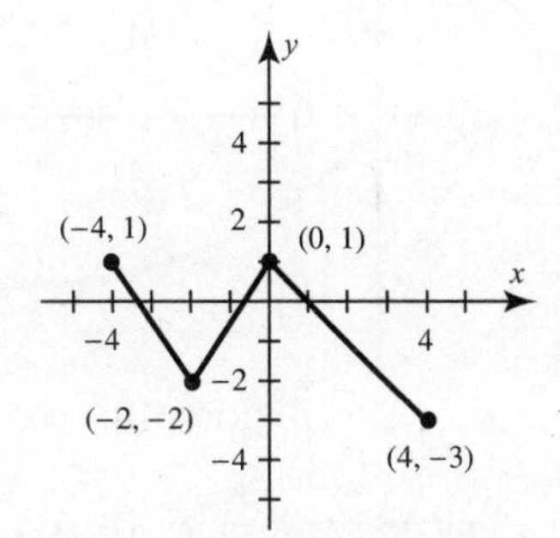


Figure 34b

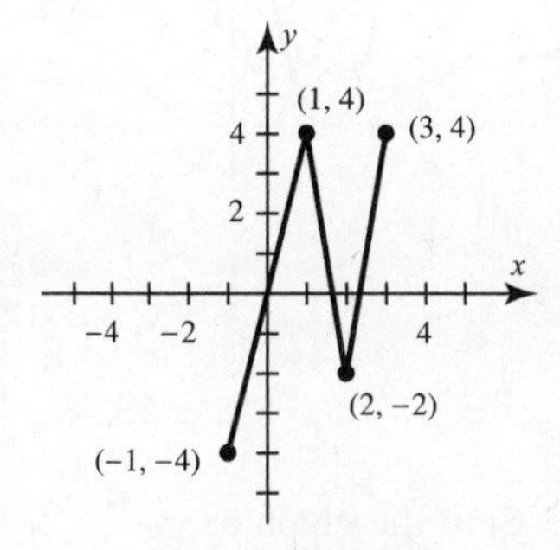


Figure 34c

35. Shift the graph of $y = x^2$ right 3 units and upward 1 unit.

36. Shift the graph of $y = x^2$ left 2 units and downward 3 units.

37. Shift the graph of $y = x^2$ left 1 unit and vertically shrink it with factor $\frac{1}{4}$.

38. Shift the graph of $y = x^2$ right 4 units and vertically stretch it with factor 2.

39. Reflect the graph of $y = \sqrt{x}$ across the $x$-axis and shift it left 5 units.

40. Reflect the graph of $y = \sqrt{x}$ across the $x$-axis and shift it downward 3 units.

41. Reflect the graph of $y = \sqrt{x}$ across the $y$-axis and vertically stretch it with factor 2.

42. Reflect the graph of $y = \sqrt{x}$ across the $y$-axis and horizontally shrink it with factor $\frac{1}{2}$.

43. Reflect the graph of $y = |x|$ across the $y$-axis and shift it left 1 unit.

44. Reflect the graph of $y = |x|$ across the $y$-axis and shift it right 4 units.

45. Shift the graph of $y = x^2$ down 3 units. The vertex is located at $(0, -3)$. See Figure 45.

46. Reflect the graph of $y = x^2$ across the $x$-axis. See Figure 46.

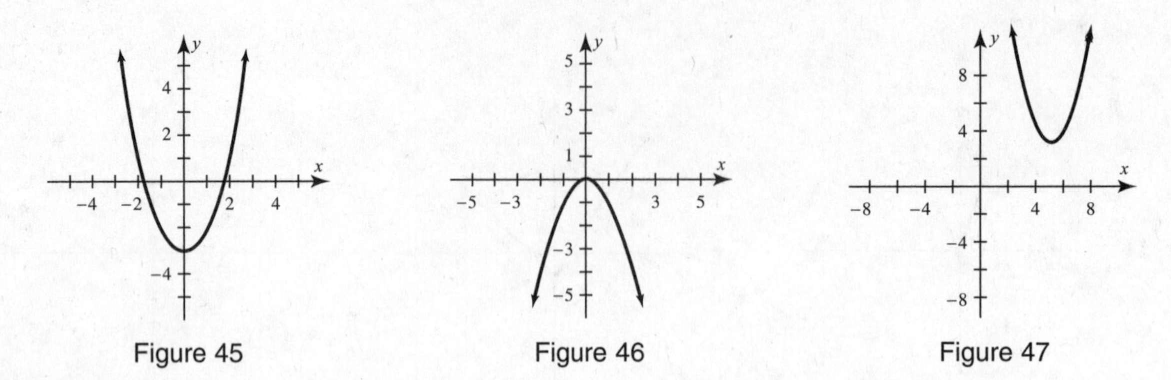


Figure 45 Figure 46 Figure 47

47. Shift the graph of $y = x^2$ to the right 5 units and up 3 units. The vertex is located at $(5, 3)$. See Figure 47.

48. Shift the graph of $y = x^2$ to the left 4 units. The vertex is located at $(-4, 0)$. See Figure 48.

49. Reflect the graph of $y = \sqrt{x}$ across the $x$-axis. See Figure 49.

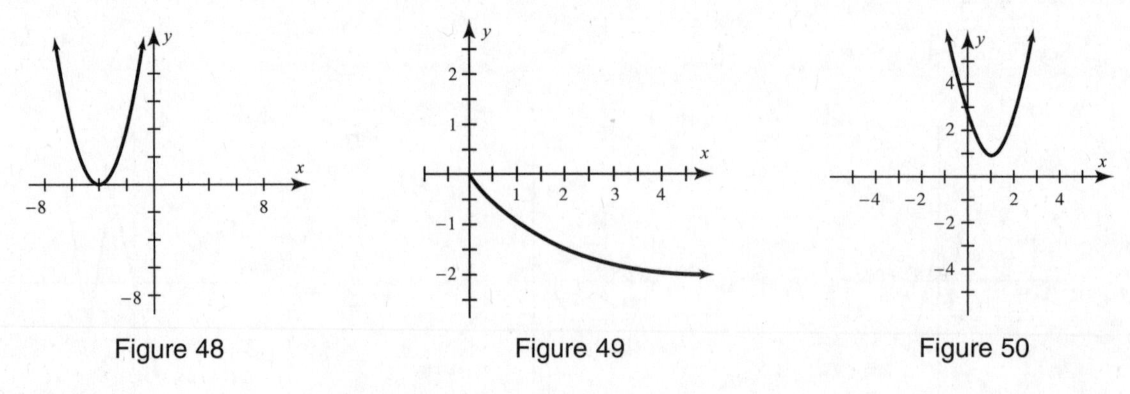


Figure 48 Figure 49 Figure 50

50. Shift the graph of $y = x^2$ to the right 1 unit and up 1 unit. The vertex is located at $(1, 1)$. Also, make the graph narrower since there is a vertical stretch. See Figure 50.

51. Reflect the graph of $y = x^2$ across the $x$-axis and shift the graph 4 units up. See Figure 51.

52. Reflect the graph of $y = \sqrt{x}$ across the $y$-axis. See Figure 52.

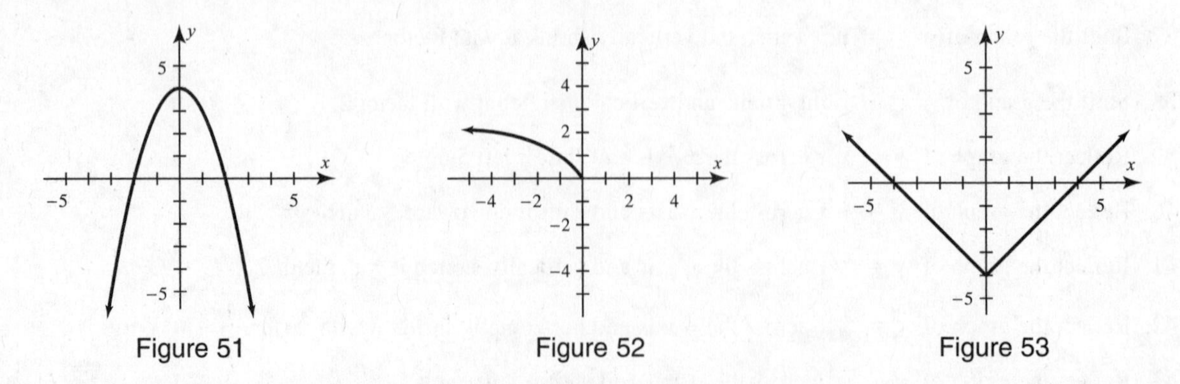


Figure 51 Figure 52 Figure 53

53. Shift the graph of $y = |x|$ down 4 units. See Figure 53.

54. Shift the graph of $y = \sqrt{x}$ up 1 unit. See Figure 54.

55. Shift the graph of $y = \sqrt{x}$ to the right 3 units and up 2 units. See Figure 55.

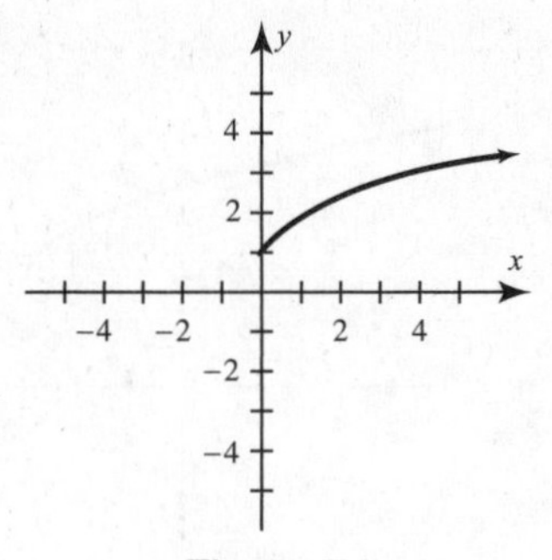

Figure 54

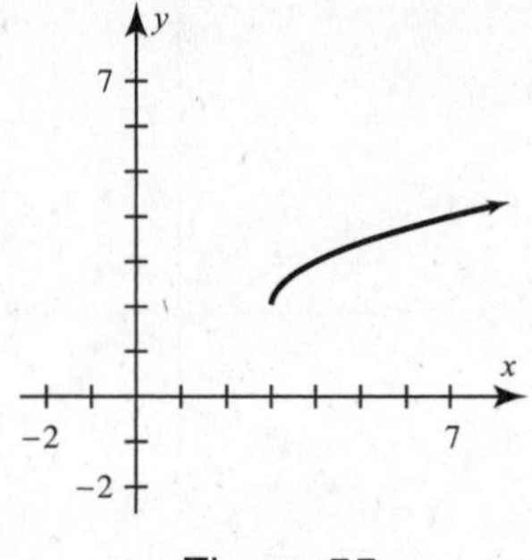

Figure 55

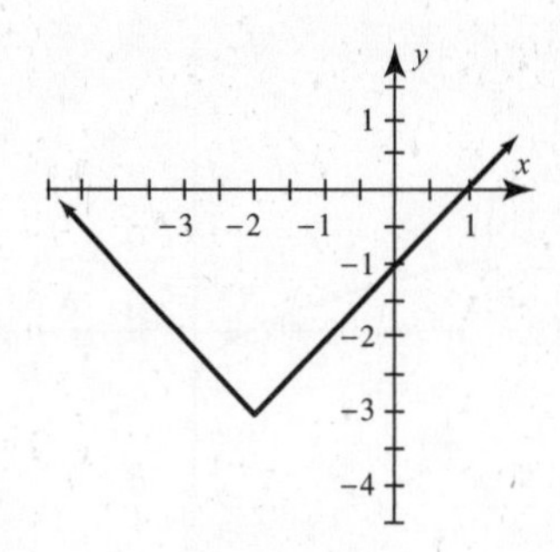

Figure 56

56. Shift the graph of $y = |x|$ to the left 2 units and down 3 units. See Figure 56.

57. The graph is like $f(x) = |x|$ but narrower by a factor of 2, vertex $(0, 0)$. See Figure 57.

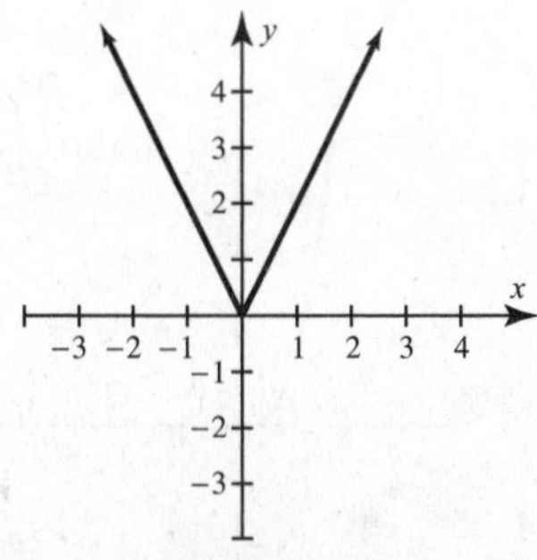

Figure 57

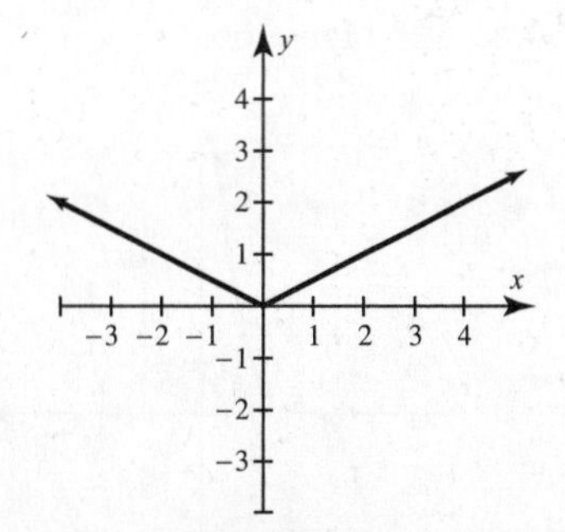

Figure 58

58. The graph is like $f(x) = |x|$ but wider by a factor of 2, reciprocal of $\frac{1}{2}$, vertex $(0, 0)$. See Figure 58.

59. Reflect the graph of $f(x) = \sqrt{x}$ across the $x$-axis and then shift up 1 unit, the vertex is $(0, 1)$. See Figure 59.

60. Shift the graph of $f(x) = \sqrt{x}$ right 2 units and down 1 unit, the vertex is $(2, -1)$. Also, stretch the graph vertically by a factor of 2, since the coefficient of $\sqrt{(x - 2)}$ is 2. See Figure 60.

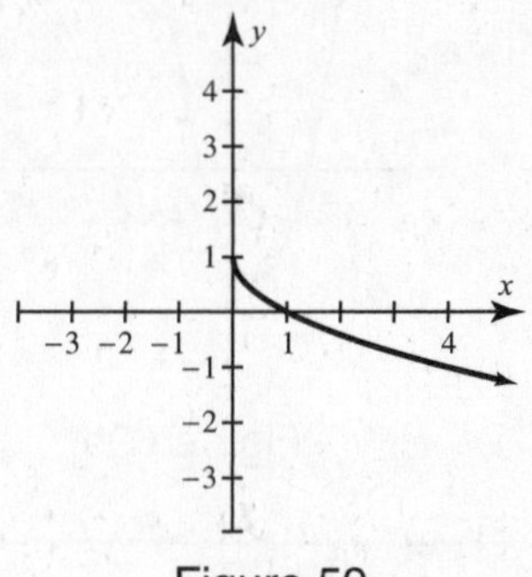

Figure 59

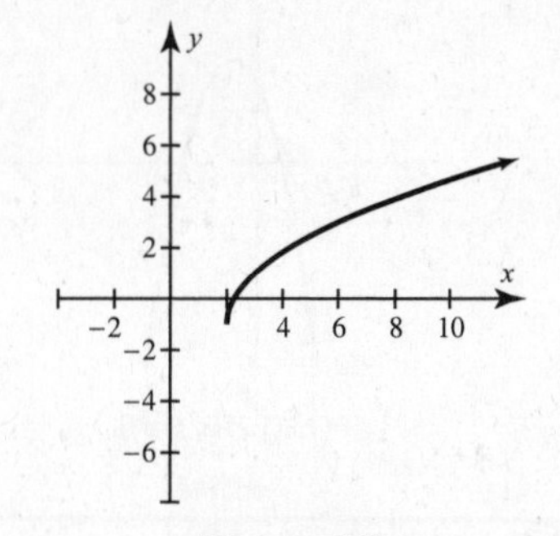

Figure 60

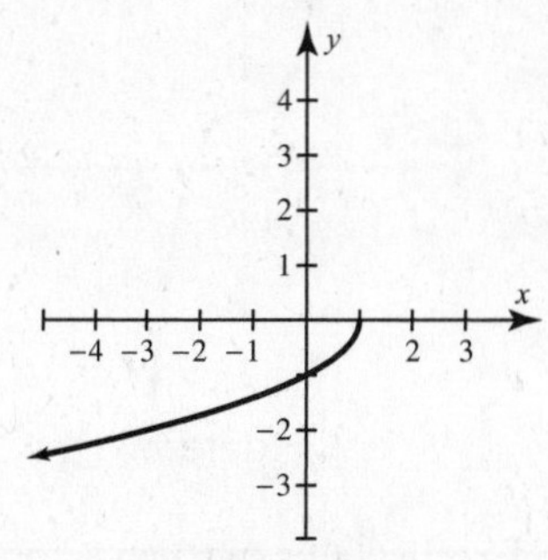

Figure 61

61. Shift the graph of $f(x) = \sqrt{x}$ left 1 unit, then reflect this graph across the $y$-axis and then reflect this graph across the $x$-axis. See Figure 61.

62. Reflect the graph of $f(x) = \sqrt{x}$ across the $y$-axis, then shift down 1 unit. See Figure 62.

63. Reflect the graph of $f(x) = \sqrt{x}$ across the $y$-axis, then shift left 1 unit. See Figure 63.

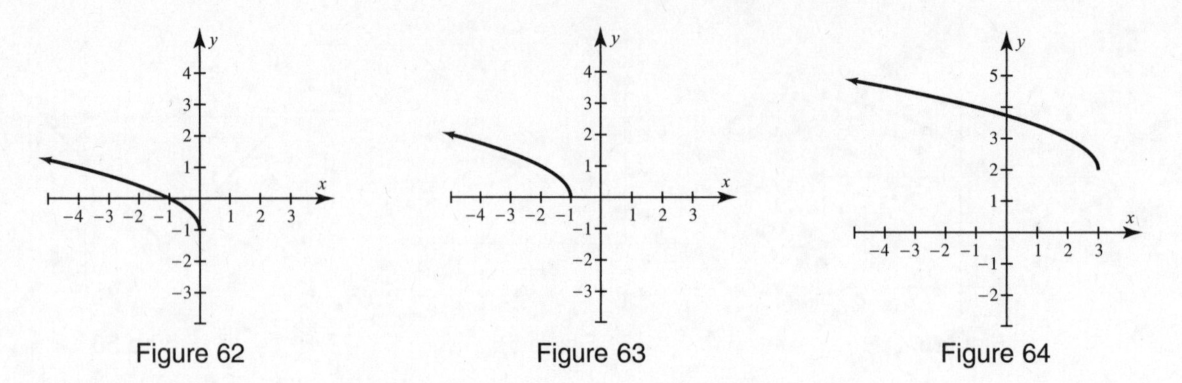

Figure 62 Figure 63 Figure 64

64. Reflect the graph of $f(x) = \sqrt{x}$ across the $y$-axis, shift right 3 units, then up 2 units. See Figure 64.

65. Shift the graph of $f(x) = x^3$ right 1 unit. See Figure 65.

66. Shift the graph of $f(x) = x^3$ left 2 units. See Figure 66.

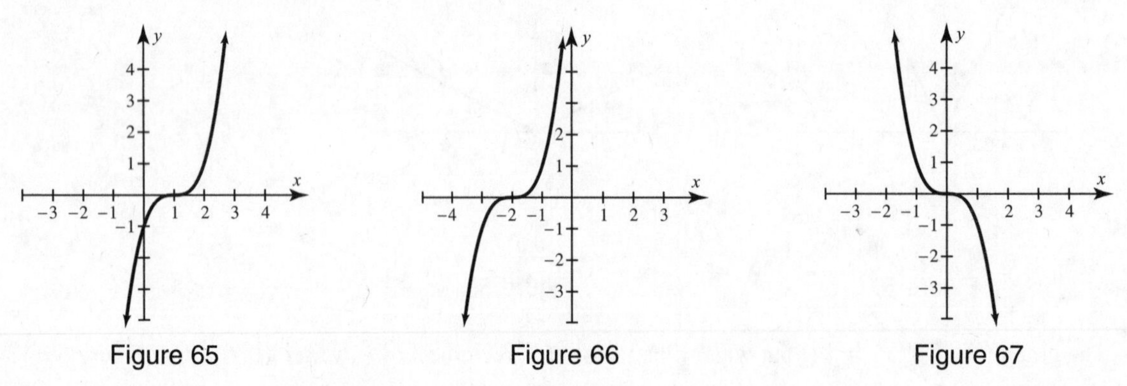

Figure 65 Figure 66 Figure 67

67. Reflect the graph of $f(x) = x^3$ across the $x$-axis. See Figure 67.

68. Reflect the graph of $f(x) = x^3$ across the $y$-axis, then shift up 1 unit. See Figure 68.

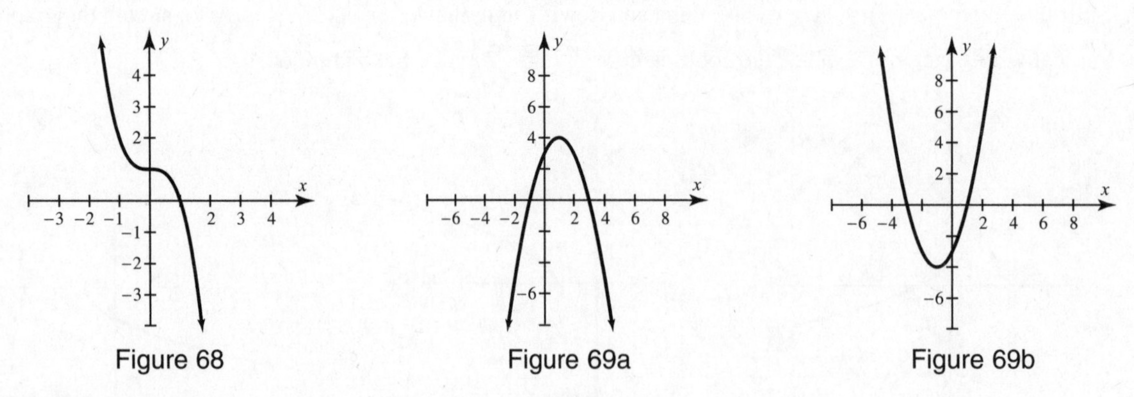

Figure 68 Figure 69a Figure 69b

69. To reflect this function across the $x$-axis, graph $y = -f(x) = -(x^2 - 2x - 3) = -x^2 + 2x + 3$.
See Figure 69a.

To reflect this function across the $y$-axis, graph $y = f(-x) = (-x)^2 - 2(-x) - 3 = x^2 + 2x - 3$.
See Figure 69b.

70. To reflect this function across the $x$-axis, graph $y = -f(x) = -(4 - 7x - 2x^2) = 2x^2 + 7x - 4$.

See Figure 70a.

To reflect this function across the $y$-axis, graph $y = f(-x) = 4 - 7(-x) - 2(-x)^2 = 4 + 7x - 2x^2$.

See Figure 70b.

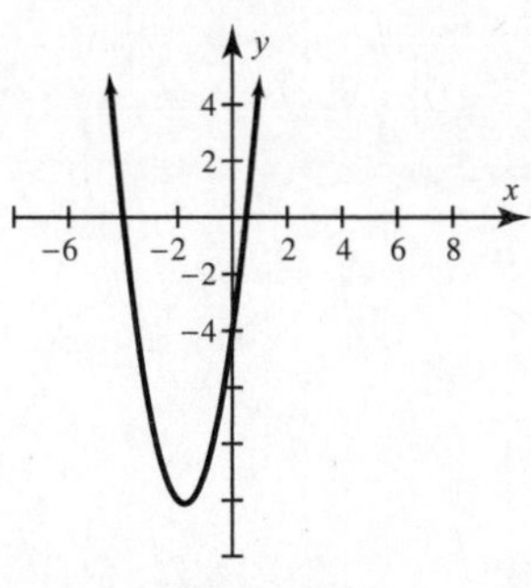


Figure 70a

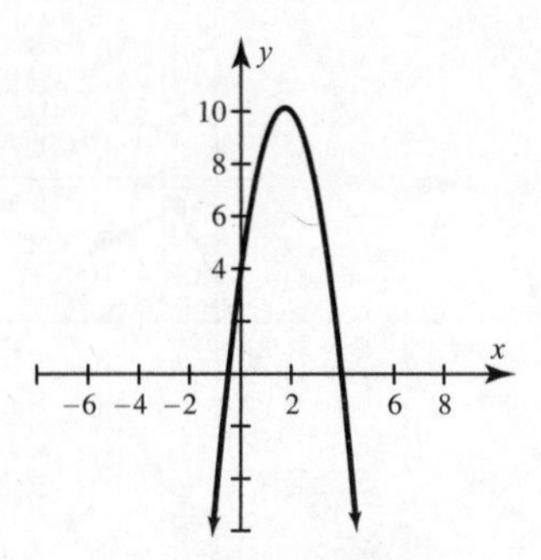


Figure 70b

71. To reflect this function across the $x$-axis, graph $y = -f(x) = -(|x + 1| - 1) = -|x + 1| + 1$.

See Figure 71a.

To reflect this function across the $y$-axis, graph $y = f(-x) = |-x + 1| - 1 = |-x + 1| - 1$.

See Figure 71b.

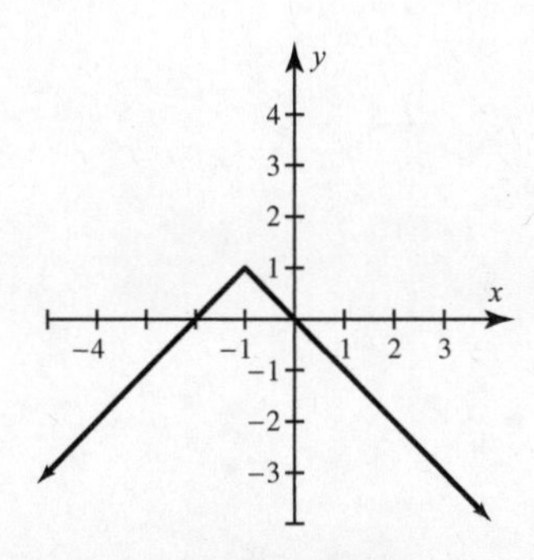


Figure 71a

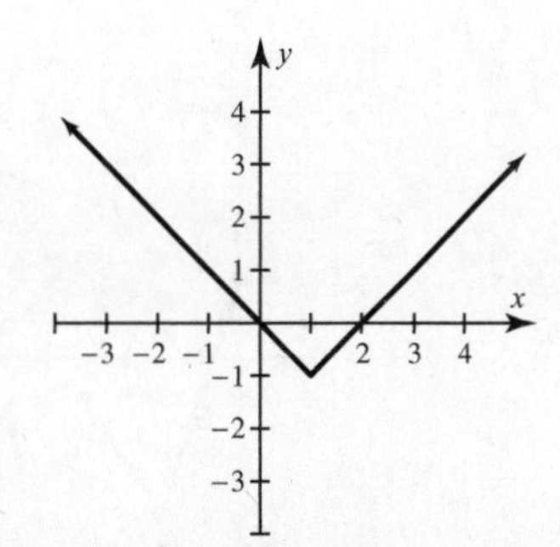


Figure 71b

72. To reflect this function across the $x$-axis, graph $y = -f(x) = -\left(\frac{1}{2}|x - 2| + 2\right) = -\frac{1}{2}|x - 2| - 2$.

See Figure 72a.

To reflect this function across the $y$-axis, graph $y = f(-x) = \frac{1}{2}|-x - 2| + 2$. See Figure 72b.

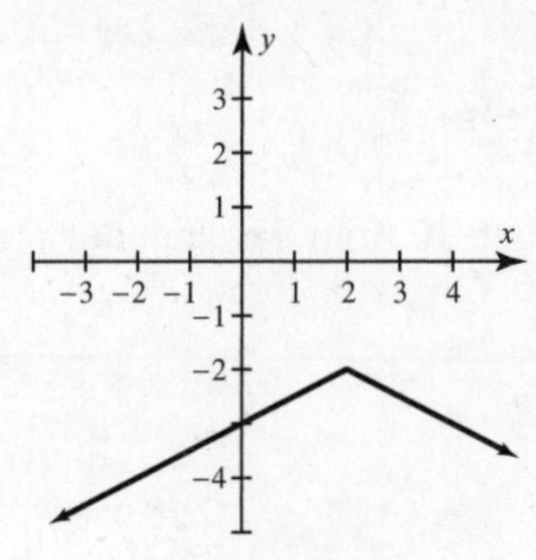


Figure 72a

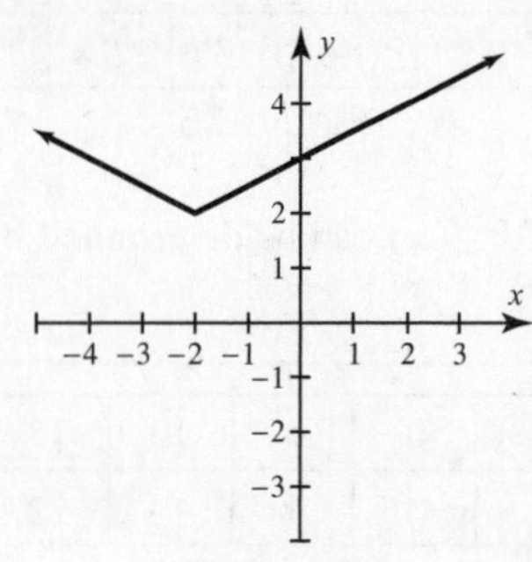


Figure 72b

73. (a) To reflect this line graph across the $x$-axis, make a table of values for $y = -f(x)$; that is, change each $(x, y)$ to $(x, -y)$. Plot the points $(-3, -2)$, $(-1, -3)$, $(1, 1)$, and $(2, 2)$. See Figure 73a.

(b) To reflect this line graph across the $y$-axis, make a table of values for $y = f(-x)$; that is, change each $(x, y)$ to $(-x, y)$. Plot the points $(3, 2)$, $(1, 3)$, $(-1, -1)$, and $(-2, -2)$. See Figure 73b.

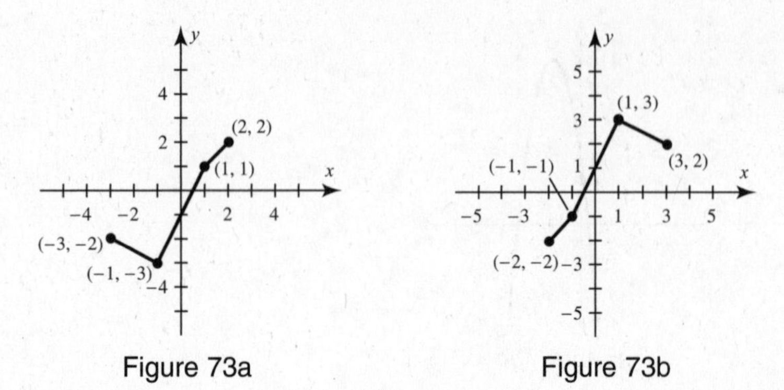


Figure 73a

Figure 73b

74. (a) To reflect this line graph across the $x$-axis, make a table of values for $y = -f(x)$; that is, change each $(x, y)$ to $(x, -y)$. Plot the points $(-4, 1)$, $(-2, 4)$, $(0, -2)$, and $(1, -2)$. See Figure 74a.

(b) To reflect this line graph across the $y$-axis, make a table of values for $y = f(-x)$; that is, change each $(x, y)$ to $(-x, y)$. Plot the points $(4, -1)$, $(2, -4)$, $(0, 2)$, and $(-1, 2)$. See Figure 74b.

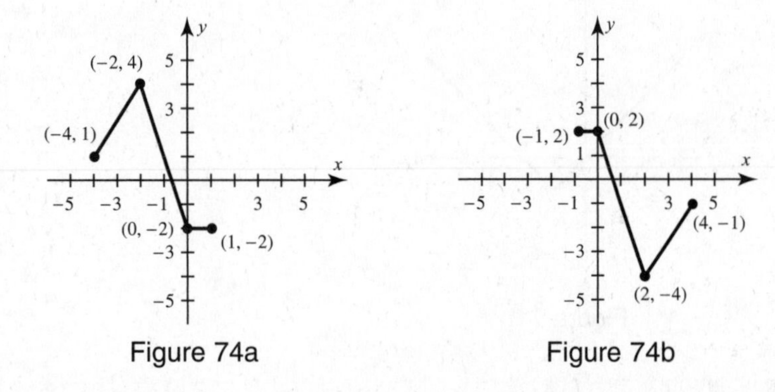


Figure 74a

Figure 74b

75. Since $g(x) = f(x) + 7$, the output for $g(x)$ can be determined by adding 7 to the output of $f(x)$. See Figure 75.

| $x$ | 1 | 2 | 3 | 4 | 5 | 6 |
|---|---|---|---|---|---|---|
| $g(x)$ | 12 | 8 | 13 | 9 | 14 | 16 |

Figure 75

76. Since $g(x) = f(x) - 10$, the output for $g(x)$ can be determined by subtracting 10 from the output of $f(x)$. See Figure 76.

| $x$ | 0 | 5 | 10 | 15 | 20 |
|---|---|---|---|---|---|
| $g(x)$ | $-15$ | 1 | 11 | 22 | 37 |

Figure 76

77. Since $g(x) = f(x - 2)$, each input value of $g$ is found by shifting each input value of $f$ two units right.

For example, $g(4) = f(4 - 2) = f(2) = -5$ and $g(2) = f(2 - 2) = f(0) = -3$.

However, the value of $g(-4) = f(-4 - 2) = f(-6)$ is undefined because $-6$ is not in the domain of $f$.

See Figure 77.

| $x$ | $-2$ | 0 | 2 | 4 | 6 |
|---|---|---|---|---|---|
| $g(x)$ | 5 | 2 | $-3$ | $-5$ | $-9$ |

Figure 77

78. Since $g(x) = f(x + 50)$, each input value of $g$ is found by shifting the input value of $f$ fifty units left.

For example, $g(-100) = f(-100 + 50) = f(-50) = 80$ and $g(-50) = f(-50 + 50) = f(0) = 120$.

However, the value of $g(100) = f(100 + 50) = f(150)$ is undefined because 150 is not in the domain of $f$.

See Figure 78.

| $x$ | $-150$ | $-100$ | $-50$ | 0 | 50 |
|---|---|---|---|---|---|
| $g(x)$ | 25 | 80 | 120 | 150 | 100 |

Figure 78

79. Since $g(x) = f(x + 1) - 2$, each input value of $g$ is found by shifting each input value of $f$ one unit left. Then each output of $g$ is found by shifting the cooresponding output of $f$ two units down.

For example, $g(1) = f(1 + 1) - 2 = f(2) - 2 = 4 - 2 = 2$ and

$g(1) = f(1 + 1) - 2 = f(2) - 2 = 4 - 2 = 2$ and $g(2) = f(2 + 1) - 2 = f(3) - 2 = 3 - 2 = 1$.

$g(5) = f(6) - 2 = 10 - 2 = 8$; $g(6) = f(7) - 2$ is undefined because 7 is not in the domain of $f$.

See Figure 79.

| $x$ | 0 | 1 | 2 | 3 | 4 | 5 |
|---|---|---|---|---|---|---|
| $g(x)$ | 0 | 2 | 1 | 5 | 6 | 8 |

Figure 79

80. Since $g(x) = f(x - 3) + 5$, each input value of $g$ is found by shifting each input value of $f$ three units right. Then each output of $g$ is found by shifting the cooresponding output of $f$ five units up. For example,

$g(9) = f(9 - 3) + 5 = f(6) + 5 = 27 + 5 = 32$ and $g(6) = f(6 - 3) + 5 = f(3) + 5 = 15 + 5 = 20$.

However, the value of $g(-3) = f(-3 - 3) + 5 = f(-6) + 5$ is undefined because $-6$ is not in the domain of $f$. See Figure 80.

| $x$ | 0 | 3 | 6 | 9 | 12 |
|---|---|---|---|---|---|
| $g(x)$ | 8 | 13 | 20 | 32 | 36 |

Figure 80

81. Since $g(x) = f(-x) + 1$, each input value of $g$ is the opposite of each input value of $f$.

Then each output of $g$ is found by shifting the cooresponding output of $f$ one unit up.

For example, $g(-2) = f(-(-2)) + 1 = f(2) + 1 = -1 + 1 = 0$ and

$g(-1) = f(-(-1)) + 1 = f(1) + 1 = 2 + 1 = 3$. See Figure 81.

| $x$ | $-2$ | $-1$ | $0$ | $1$ | $2$ |
|---|---|---|---|---|---|
| $g(x)$ | $0$ | $3$ | $6$ | $9$ | $12$ |

Figure 81

82. Since $g(x) = -f(x + 2)$, each input value of $g$ is found by shifting each input value of $f$ two units left. Then each output of $g$ is the opposite of the cooresponding output of $f$. For example,

$g(-4) = -f(-4 + 2) = -f(-2) = -8$ and $g(-2) = -f(-2 + 2) = -f(0) = -10$. However, the value of $g(4) = -f(4 + 2) = -f(6)$ is undefined because 6 is not defined in the domain of $f$. See Figure 82.

| $x$ | $-6$ | $-4$ | $-2$ | $0$ | $2$ |
|---|---|---|---|---|---|
| $g(x)$ | $-5$ | $-8$ | $-10$ | $-8$ | $-5$ |

Figure 82

83. The graph of $f(x)$ is shifted up 2 units $\Rightarrow (-12, 8), (0, 10)$, and $(8, -2)$.

84. The graph of $f(x)$ is shifted down 3 units $\Rightarrow (-12, 3), (0, 5)$, and $(8, -7)$.

85. The graph of $f(x)$ is shifted right 2 units and up 1 unit $\Rightarrow (-10, 7), (2, 9)$, and $(10, -3)$.

86. The graph of $f(x)$ is shifted left 1 unit and down 1 unit $\Rightarrow (-13, 5), (-1, 7)$, and $(7, -5)$.

87. The graph is reflected across the $x$-axis $\Rightarrow$ the $y$-coordinate is $-\frac{1}{2}$ times the given $y$-coordinate $\Rightarrow$

$(-12, -3), (0, -4)$, and $(8, 2)$.

88. The graph is reflected across the $x$-axis $\Rightarrow$ the $y$-coordinate is $-2$ times the given $y$-coordinate $\Rightarrow$

$(-12, -12), (0, -16)$, and $(8, 8)$.

89. The graph is reflected across the $y$-axis $\Rightarrow$ the $x$-coordinate is the reciprocal of $-2$ or $-\frac{1}{2}$ times the given $x$-coordinate $\Rightarrow (6, 6), (0, 8)$, and $(-4, -4)$.

90. The graph is reflected across the $y$-axis $\Rightarrow$ the $x$-coordinate is the reciprocal of $-\frac{1}{2}$ or $-2$ times the given $x$-coordinate $\Rightarrow (24, 6), (0, 8)$, and $(-16, -4)$.

91. Let $(1997, 3.8)$ be the vertex $(h, k)$. Translate the graph of $y = x^2$ right 1997 units and upward 3.8 units. To determine a value for $a$, graph the data and $y = a(x - 1997)^2 + 3.8$ for different values of $a$. By trial and error a value of $a = \frac{1}{4}$ appears to fit the data. Thus $f(x) = \frac{1}{4}(x - 1997)^2 + 3.8$.

92. Let $(1998, 2049)$ be the vertex $(h, k)$. Translate the graph of $y = x^2$ right 1998 units and upward 2049 units. To determine a value for $a$, graph the data and $y = a(x - 1998)^2 + 2049$ for different values of $a$. By trial and error a value of $a = 1400$ appears to fit the data. Thus $f(x) = 1400(x - 1998)^2 + 2049$.

93. Let $(1970, 30)$ be the vertex $(h, k)$. Translate the graph of $y = x^2$ right 1970 units and upward 30 units. To determine a value for $a$, graph the data and $y = a(x - 1970)^2 + 30$ for different values of $a$. By trial and error a value of $a = 0.22$ appears to fit the data. Thus $f(x) = 0.22(x - 1970)^2 + 30$.

94. Let $(1998, 3247)$ be the vertex $(h, k)$. Translate the graph of $y = x^2$ right 1998 units and upward 3247 units. To determine a value for $a$, graph the data and $y = a(x - 1998)^2 + 3247$ for different values of $a$. By trial and error a value of $a = 42$ appears to fit the data. Thus $f(x) = 42(x - 1998)^2 + 3247$.

95. We must determine a function $g$ such that $g(1991) = P(1)$, $g(1992) = P(2)$.... Thus, the relationship $g(x) = P(x - 1990)$ holds for $x = 1990, 1991, 1992$.... It follows that the representation for $g(x)$ is $g(x) = 0.00075(x - 1990)^2 + 0.17(x - 1990) + 44$.

96. For $g(x)$ change $x$ to $(x - 1984) \Rightarrow g(x) = 2375(x - 1984)^2 + 5134(x - 1984) + 5020$

97. (a) When $x = 2$, the $y$-value is about 9. There are about 9 hours of daylight on February 21 at 60°N latitude.

(b) Since February 21 is 2 months after the shortest day and October 21 is 2 months before the shortest day, the days should have about the same number of daylight hours. A reasonable conjecture would be 9 hours.

(c) The amount of daylight would increase to the left or right of $x = 0$. There are approximately the same number of daylight hours either $x$ months before or after December 21. the graph should be symmetric about the $y$-axis, as shown in Figure 97.

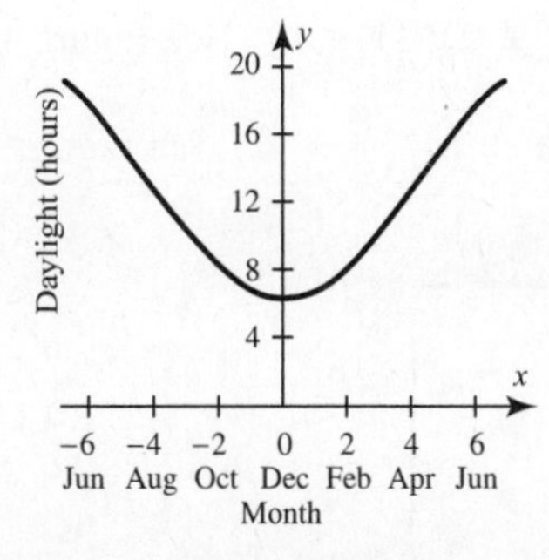

Figure 97

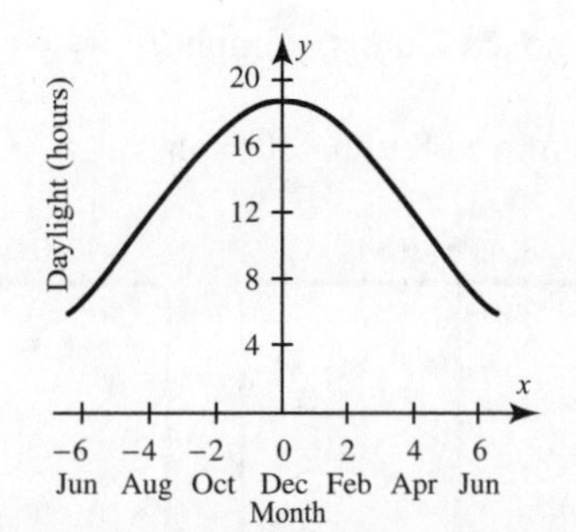

Figure 98

98. Since June and December are reversed, shift the graph showing 60°N latitude 6 units to the left. See Figure 98.

99. In 15 seconds, the plane has moved $15(0.2) = 3$ kilometers to the left. To show this movement, translate the graph of the mountain 3 kilometers (units) to the right; $y = -0.4(x - 3)^2 + 4$. See Figure 99.

100. In 20 seconds, the plane has moved $20(0.1) = 2$ kilometers to the right and $20(0.05) = 1$ kilometer up. To show this movement, translate the graph of the mountain 2 kilometers (units) to the left and 1 kilometer (unit) down; $y = -0.4(x + 2)^2 + 4 - 1 \Rightarrow y = -0.4(x + 2)^2 + 3$. See Figure 100.

[−4, 4, 1] by [0, 6, 1]

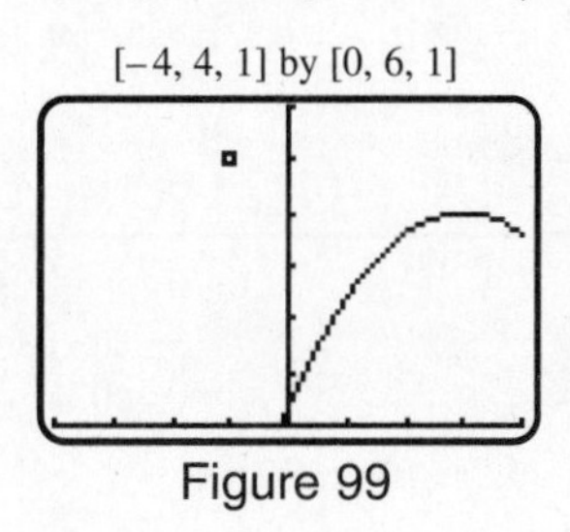
Figure 99

[−4, 4, 1] by [0, 6, 1]

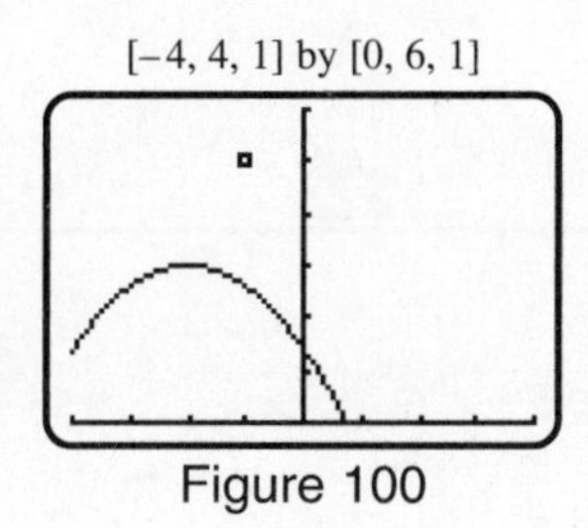
Figure 100

101. (a) In 4 hours, the cold front has moved $4(40) = 160$ miles, which is $\frac{160}{100} = 1.6$ units on the graph. To show this movement, shift the graph 1.6 units down; $y = \frac{1}{20}x^2 - 1.6$. See Figure 101a.

(b) The graph of the cold front has shifted $\frac{250}{100} = 2.5$ units down and $\frac{210}{100} = 2.1$ units to the right. To show this movement, the new equation should be $y = \frac{1}{20}(x - 2.1)^2 - 2.5$. The location of Columbus, Ohio is at $(5.5, -0.8)$ relative to the location of Des Moines at $(0, 0)$. Since the parabola representing the cold front at midnight has past the point $(5.5, -0.8)$, the front reaches Columbus by midnight. See Figure 101b.

[−15, 15, 1] by [−10, 10, 1]

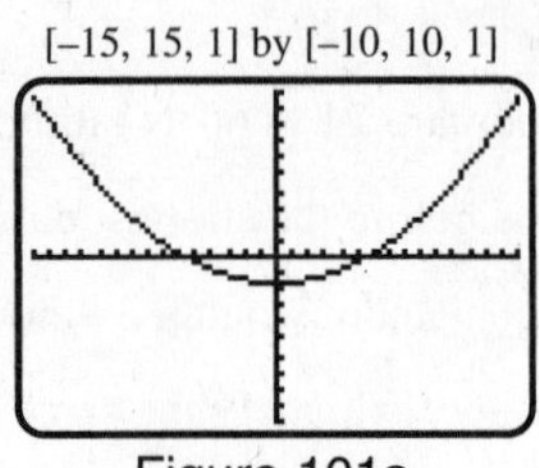

Figure 101a

[−15, 15, 1] by [−10, 10, 1]

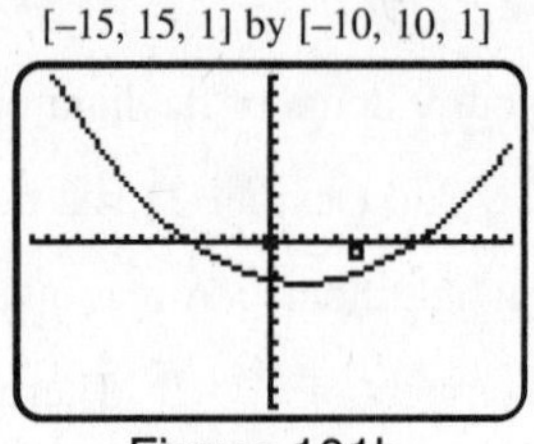

Figure 101b

102. (a) Graph $Y_1 = \sqrt{}(9 - X^2) + 12$. See Figure 102a.

(b) After 1 second the person has moved 2 units. Graph $Y_1 = \sqrt{}(9 - (X + 2)^2) + 12$. See Figure 102b.

After 4 seconds the person has moved 8 units. Graph $Y_1 = \sqrt{}(9 - (X + 8)^2) + 12$. See Figure 102c.

[−12, 12, 1] by [0, 16, 1]

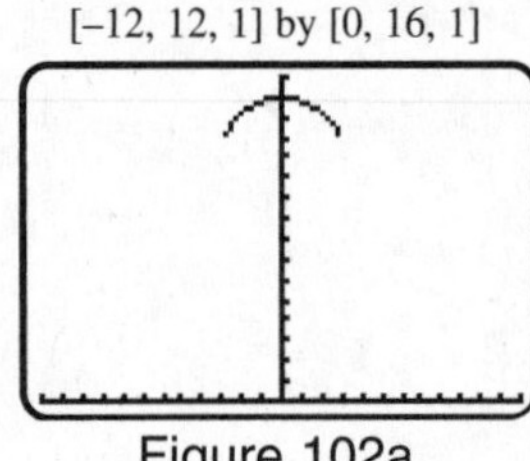

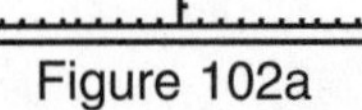

Figure 102a

[−12, 12, 1] by [0, 16, 1]

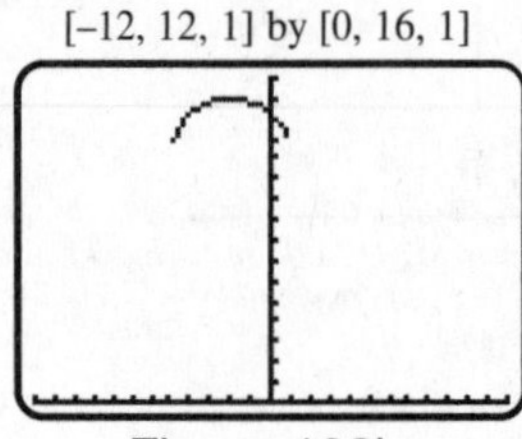

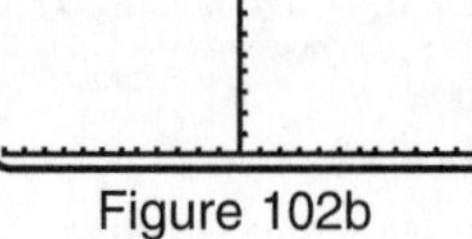

Figure 102b

[−12, 12, 1] by [0, 16, 1]

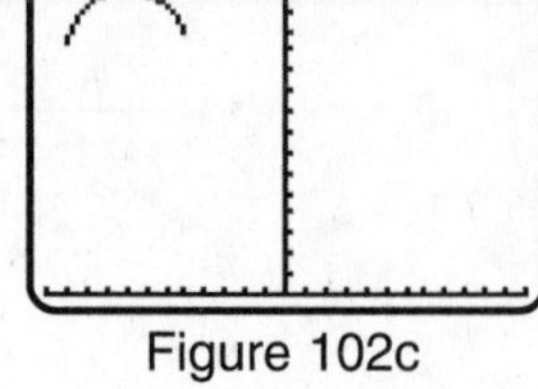

Figure 102c

## Extended and Discovery Exercises for Section 3.5

1. No, the two transformations are not equivalent.
2. Yes, the two transformations are equivalent.
3. Yes, the two transformations are equivalent.
4. No, the two transformations are not equivalent.

## Checking Basic Concepts for Section 3.5

1. (a) The graph of $y = (x + 4)^2$ is the graph of $f(x) = x^2$ shifted 4 units to the left.

   (b) The graph of $y = x^2 - 3$ is the graph of $f(x) = x^2$ shifted 3 units down.

   (c) The graph of $y = (x - 5)^2 + 3$ is the graph of $f(x) = x^2$ shifted 5 units to the right and 3 units up.

2. (a) See Figure 2a.

   (b) See Figure 2b.

   (c) See Figure 2c.

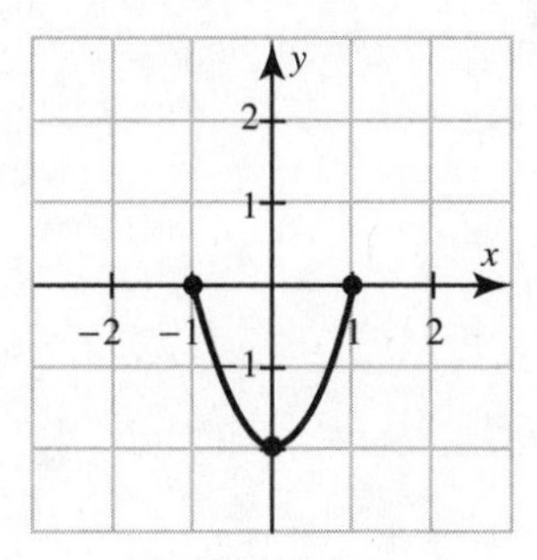

Figure 2a

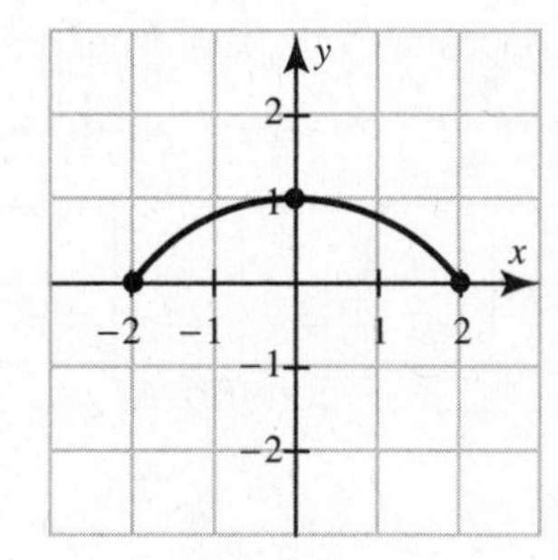

Figure 2b

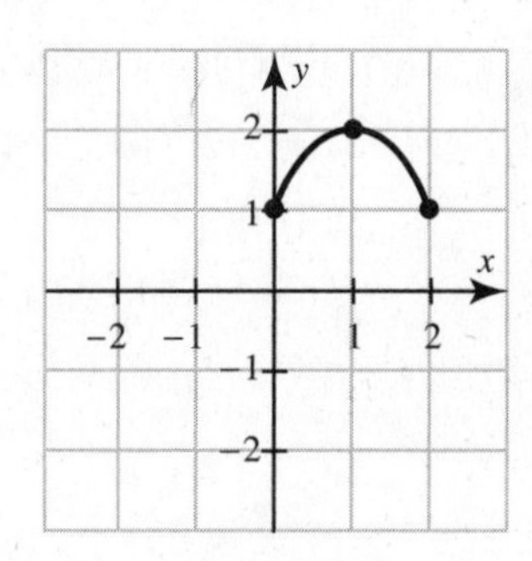

Figure 2c

3. (a) To shift the graph of $f(x) = x^2 - 4x + 1$ to the right 3 units, replace $x$ with $(x - 3)$ in the formula for $f(x)$. This results in $y = f(x - 3) = (x - 3)^2 - 4(x - 3) + 1$. To shift the graph of this new equation down 4 units, subtract 4 to obtain $y = f(x - 3) - 4 = (x - 3)^2 - 4(x - 3) + 1 - 4 =$ $(x - 3)^2 - 4(x - 3) - 3$.

   (b) To reflect the graph of $f(x) = x^2 - 4x + 1$ about the $x$-axis, replace $f(x)$ with $-f(x)$ in the formula for $f(x)$. This results in $y = -f(x) = -(x^2 - 4x + 1) = -x^2 + 4x - 1$.

   (c) To shift the graph of $f(x) = x^2 - 4x + 1$ to the left 6 units, replace $x$ with $(x + 6)$ in the formula for $f(x)$. This results in $y = f(x + 6) = (x + 6)^2 - 4(x + 6) + 1$. To reflect the graph of this new equation about the $y$-axis, replace $x$ with $-x$. This results in $y = f(-x + 6) = (-x + 6)^2 - 4(-x + 6) + 1$.

   (d) To reflect the graph of $f(x) = x^2 - 4x + 1$ about the $y$-axis, replace $x$ with $-x$. This results in $y = f(-x) = (-x)^2 - 4(-x) + 1$. To shift the new equation to the left 6 units, replace $x$ with $(x + 6)$. This results in $f(-(x + 6)) = (-(x + 6))^2 - 4(-(x + 6)) + 1$.

4. See Figure 4.

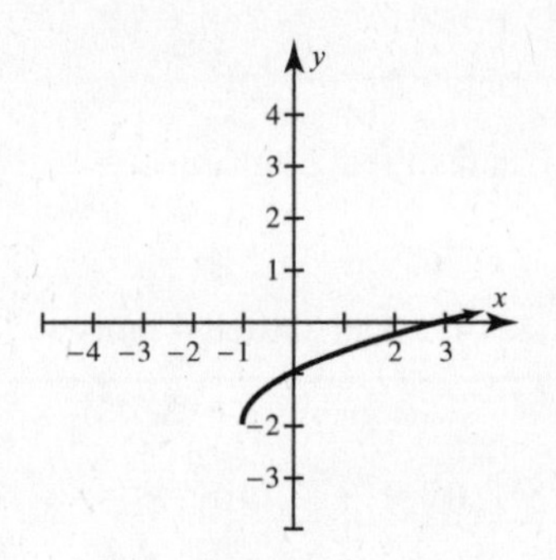

Figure 4

5. (a) Since $g(x) = f(x - 2) + 3$, each input value of $g$ is found by shifting each input value of $f$ two units right. Then each output of $g$ is found by shifting the cooresponding output of $f$ three units up. For example, $g(-2) = f(-2 - 2) + 3 = f(-4) + 3 = 1 + 3 = 4$. See Figure 5a.

| $x$ | $-2$ | $0$ | $2$ | $4$ | $6$ |
|---|---|---|---|---|---|
| $g(x)$ | $4$ | $6$ | $9$ | $11$ | $12$ |

Figure 5a

(b) Since $h(x) = -2(f(x + 1))$, each input value of $g$ is found by shifting each input value of $f$ one unit left. Then each output of $g$ is twice the opposite of the cooresponding output of $f$. For example, $h(-3) = -2(f(-3 + 1)) = -2(f(-2)) = -2(3) = -6$. See Figure 5b.

| $x$ | $-5$ | $-3$ | $-1$ | $1$ | $3$ |
|---|---|---|---|---|---|
| $h(x)$ | $-2$ | $-6$ | $-12$ | $-16$ | $-18$ |

Figure 5b

## Chapter 3 Review Exercises

1. (a) The parabola opens downward, so $a < 0$.

(b) Vertex: $(2, 4)$

(c) Axis of symmetry: $x = 2$.

(d) $f$ is increasing for $x \leq 2$ and decreasing for $x \geq 2$.

2. (a) The parabola opens upward, so $a > 0$.

(b) Vertex: $(-3, 2)$

(c) Axis of symmetry: $x = -3$.

(d) $f$ is increasing for $x \geq -3$ and decreasing for $x \leq -3$.

3. $f(x) = -2(x - 5)^2 + 1 \Rightarrow f(x) = -2(x^2 - 10x + 25) + 1 \Rightarrow f(x) = -2x^2 + 20x - 49$

The leading coefficient is –2.

4. $f(x) = \frac{1}{3}(x + 1)^2 - 2 \Rightarrow f(x) = \frac{1}{3}(x^2 + 2x + 1) - 2 \Rightarrow f(x) = \frac{1}{3}x^2 + \frac{2}{3}x - \frac{5}{3}$

The leading coefficient is $\frac{1}{3}$.

5. The graph of $y = x^2$ has been shifted 1 unit left, reflected across the $x$-axis, and shifed 2 units up $\Rightarrow$ $f(x) = -(x + 1)^2 + 2$.

6. The graph of $y = x^2$ has been shifted 2 units left, is narrower by the scale factor 2, and shifted 4 units down $\Rightarrow$ $f(x) = 2(x + 2)^2 - 4$.

7. $f(x) = x^2 + 6x - 1 \Rightarrow f(x) = x^2 + 6x + 9 - 9 - 1 \Rightarrow f(x) = (x^2 + 6x + 9) - 10 \Rightarrow$ $f(x) = (x + 3)^2 - 10$; the vertex is (–3, –10).

8. $f(x) = 2x^2 + 4x - 5 \Rightarrow f(x) = 2(x^2 + 2x) - 5 \Rightarrow f(x) = 2(x^2 + 2x + 1) - 2 - 5 \Rightarrow$
$f(x) = 2(x^2 + 2x + 1) - 7 \Rightarrow f(x) = 2(x + 1)^2 - 7$; the vertex is $(-1, -7)$.

9. $-\dfrac{b}{2a} = -\dfrac{2}{2(-3)} = \dfrac{1}{3}$ and $f\left(\dfrac{1}{3}\right) = -3\left(\dfrac{1}{3}\right)^2 + 2\left(\dfrac{1}{3}\right) - 4 = -\dfrac{11}{3}$; the vertex is $\left(\dfrac{1}{3}, -\dfrac{11}{3}\right)$.

10. $-\dfrac{b}{2a} = -\dfrac{8}{2(1)} = -4$ and $f(-4) = (-4)^2 + 8(-4) - 5 = -21$; the vertex is $(-4, -21)$.

11. Shift the graph of $f(x) = x^2$ up 3 units, reflect it across the $x$-axis, and make it narrower by the scale factor 3. The vertex is located at $(0, 3)$. See Figure 11.

12. Shift the graph of $g(x) = x^2$ right 1 unit, down 3 units, and make it narrower by the scale factor 2. The vertex is located at $(1, -3)$. See Figure 12.

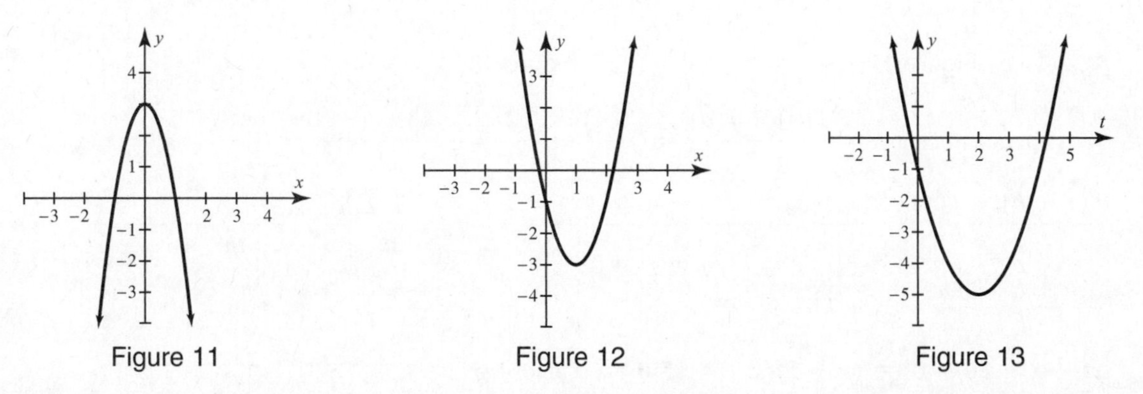


Figure 11 Figure 12 Figure 13

13. $h(t) = t^2 - 4t - 1 \Rightarrow h(t) = t^2 - 4t + 4 - 5 \Rightarrow h(t) = (t - 2)^2 - 5$. Shift the graph of $h(t) = t^2$ right 2 units, and down 5 units. The vertex is $(2, -5)$. See Figure 13.

14. Shift the graph of $f(x) = |x|$ right 1 unit, and down 2 units. The vertex is located at $(1, -2)$. See Figure 14.

15. Shift the graph of $f(x) = |x|$ left 3 units, and reflect it across the $x$-axis. The vertex is located at $(-3, 0)$. See Figure 15.

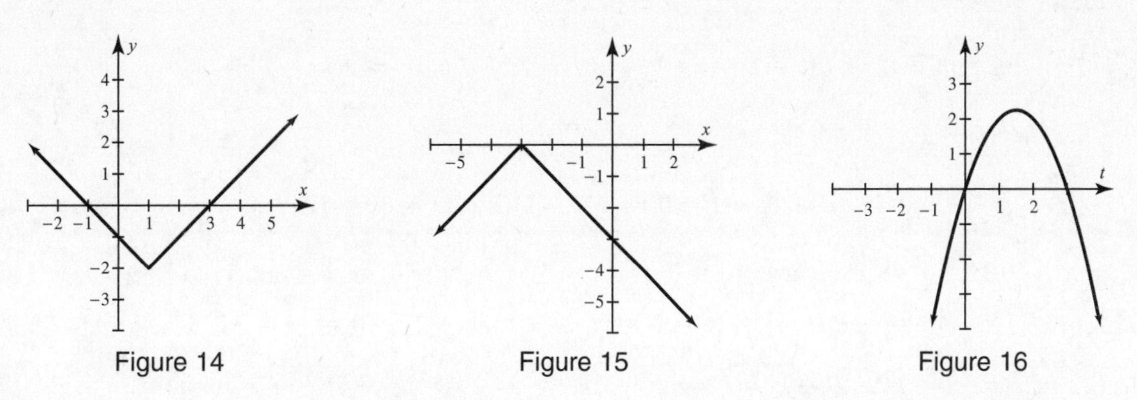


Figure 14 Figure 15 Figure 16

16. $g(t) = 3t - t^2 \Rightarrow g(t) = -\left(t^2 - 3t + \dfrac{9}{4}\right) + \dfrac{9}{4} \Rightarrow g(t) = -\left(t - \dfrac{3}{2}\right)^2 + \dfrac{9}{4}$. Shift the graph of $g(t) = t^2$ right $\dfrac{3}{2}$ units, up $\dfrac{9}{4}$ units, and reflect across the $x$-axis. The vertex is $\left(\dfrac{3}{2}, \dfrac{9}{4}\right)$. See Figure 16.

17. Shift the graph of $f(x) = \sqrt{x}$ left 1 unit and reflect across the $x$-axis. The vertex is $(-1, 0)$. See Figure 17.

18. $f(x) = \sqrt{2 - x} \Rightarrow f(x) = \sqrt{-x + 2}$. Shift the graph of $f(x) = \sqrt{x}$ left 2 units then reflect across the $y$-axis. The vertex is $(2, 0)$. See Figure 18.

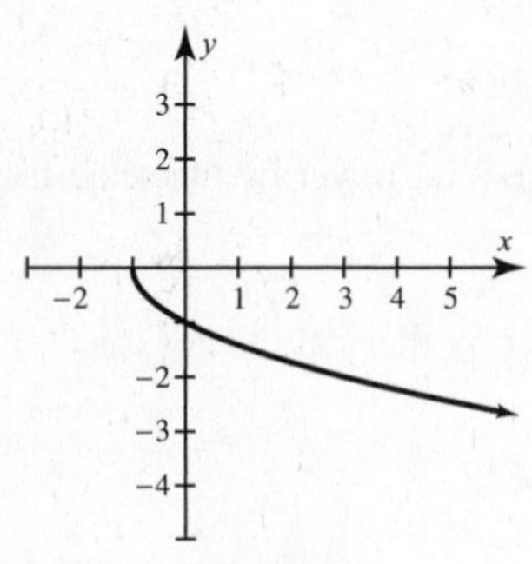

Figure 17

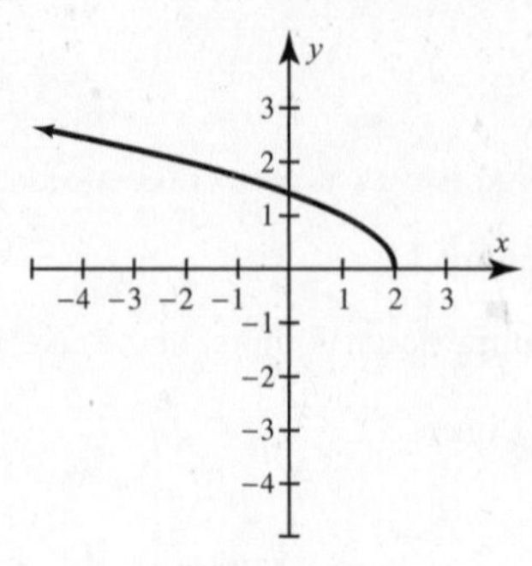

Figure 18

19. Average rate of change $= \dfrac{f(b) - f(a)}{b - a} \Rightarrow \dfrac{f(4) - f(2)}{4 - 2} = \dfrac{-63 - (-5)}{2} = \dfrac{-58}{2} = -29$

20. $\dfrac{f(x + h) - f(x)}{h} = \dfrac{(x + h)^2 - 2(x + h) - (x^2 - 2x)}{h} = \dfrac{x^2 + 2xh + h^2 - 2x - 2h - x^2 + 2x}{h} =$

$\dfrac{2xh + h^2 - 2h}{h} = 2x + h - 2$

21. $x^2 - x - 20 = 0 \Rightarrow (x - 5)(x + 4) = 0 \Rightarrow x = -4, 5$

22. $3x^2 + 4x = -1 \Rightarrow 3x^2 + 4x + 1 = 0 \Rightarrow (3x + 1)(x + 1) = 0 \Rightarrow x = -1, -\dfrac{1}{3}$

23. $x^2 = 4x \Rightarrow x^2 - 4x = 0 \Rightarrow x(x - 4) = 0 \Rightarrow x = 0, 4$

24. $-5x^2 - 3x = 0 \Rightarrow x(-5x - 3) = 0 \Rightarrow x = 0$ or $-5x - 3 = 0 \Rightarrow -5x = 3 \Rightarrow x = -\dfrac{3}{5} \Rightarrow x = -\dfrac{3}{5}, 0$

25. $4z^2 - 7 = 0 \Rightarrow 4z^2 = 7 \Rightarrow z^2 = \dfrac{7}{4} \Rightarrow z = \pm\sqrt{\dfrac{7}{4}} \Rightarrow z = \pm\dfrac{\sqrt{7}}{2}$

26. $25z^2 = 9 \Rightarrow z^2 = \dfrac{9}{25} \Rightarrow z = \pm\sqrt{\dfrac{9}{25}} \Rightarrow z = \pm\dfrac{3}{5}$

27. $-2t^2 - 3t + 14 = 0 \Rightarrow (2t + 7)(-t + 2) = 0 \Rightarrow 2t + 7 = 0 \Rightarrow 2t = -7 \Rightarrow$

$t = -\dfrac{7}{2}$ or $-t + 2 = 0 \Rightarrow -t = -2 \Rightarrow t = 2 \Rightarrow t = -\dfrac{7}{2}, 2$

28. $\dfrac{1}{2}t^2 + \dfrac{3}{4}t + \dfrac{1}{4} = 0 \Rightarrow 2t^2 + 3t + 1 = 0 \Rightarrow (2t + 1)(t + 1) = 0 \Rightarrow t = -1, -\dfrac{1}{2}$

29. $0.1x^2 - 0.3x = 1 \Rightarrow x^2 - 3x - 10 = 0 \Rightarrow (x - 5)(x + 2) = 0 \Rightarrow x = -2, 5$

30. $x(6 - x) = -16 \Rightarrow -x^2 + 6x + 16 = 0 \Rightarrow (-x + 8)(x + 2) = 0 \Rightarrow x = -2, 8$

31. $(k - 1)^2 = \dfrac{9}{4} \Rightarrow k^2 - 2k + 1 = \dfrac{9}{4} \Rightarrow k^2 - 2k - \dfrac{5}{4} = 0 \Rightarrow 4k^2 - 8k - 5 = 0 \Rightarrow$

$(2k - 5)(2k + 1) = 0 \Rightarrow 2k - 5 = 0 \Rightarrow 2k = 5 \Rightarrow k = \dfrac{5}{2}$ or $2k + 1 = 0 \Rightarrow 2k = -1 \Rightarrow$

$k = -\dfrac{1}{2} \Rightarrow k = -\dfrac{1}{2}, \dfrac{5}{2}$

32. $(k+2)^2 = 7 \Rightarrow k^2 + 4k + 4 = 7 \Rightarrow k^2 + 4k - 3 = 0$. Using the quadratic formula we get:

$$\frac{-4 \pm \sqrt{(4)^2 - 4(1)(-3)}}{2(1)} = \frac{-4 \pm \sqrt{28}}{2} = -2 \pm \sqrt{7}$$

33. (a) Since the parabola is opening upward, $a > 0$.

(b) The real solutions to $ax^2 + bx + c = 0$ appear to be $-3, 2$, the $x$-intercepts.

(c) The discriminant must be positive since $ax^2 + bx + c = 0$ has two real solutions.

34. (a) Since the parabola is opening downward, $a < 0$.

(b) There are no real solutions to $ax^2 + bx + c = 0$ since there are no $x$-intercepts.

(c) The discriminant must be negative since $ax^2 + bx + c = 0$ has no real solutions.

35. $x^2 + 2x = 5 \Rightarrow x^2 + 2x + 1 = 5 + 1 \Rightarrow (x+1)^2 = 6 \Rightarrow x + 1 = \pm\sqrt{6} \Rightarrow x = -1 \pm \sqrt{6}$

36. $x^2 - 3x = 3 \Rightarrow x^2 - 3x + \frac{9}{4} = 3 + \frac{9}{4} \Rightarrow \left(x - \frac{3}{2}\right)^2 = \frac{21}{4} \Rightarrow x - \frac{3}{2} = \pm\sqrt{\frac{21}{4}} \Rightarrow x = \frac{3}{2} \pm \frac{\sqrt{21}}{2} \Rightarrow$

$x = \frac{3 \pm \sqrt{21}}{2}$

37. $2z^2 - 6z - 1 = 0 \Rightarrow z^2 - 3z = \frac{1}{2} \Rightarrow z^2 - 3z + \frac{9}{4} = \frac{1}{2} + \frac{9}{4} \Rightarrow \left(z - \frac{3}{2}\right)^2 = \frac{11}{4} \Rightarrow$

$z - \frac{3}{2} = \pm\sqrt{\frac{11}{4}} \Rightarrow z = \frac{3}{2} \pm \frac{\sqrt{11}}{2} \Rightarrow z = \frac{3 \pm \sqrt{11}}{2}$

38. $-3z^2 - 2z + 2 = 0 \Rightarrow z^2 + \frac{2}{3}z - \frac{2}{3} = 0 \Rightarrow z^2 + \frac{2}{3}z + \frac{1}{9} = \frac{2}{3} + \frac{1}{9} \Rightarrow \left(z + \frac{1}{3}\right)^2 = \frac{7}{9} \Rightarrow$

$z + \frac{1}{3} = \pm\sqrt{\frac{7}{9}} \Rightarrow z = -\frac{1}{3} \pm \frac{\sqrt{7}}{3} \Rightarrow z = \frac{-1 \pm \sqrt{7}}{3}$

39. $\frac{1}{2}x^2 - 4x + 1 = 0 \Rightarrow x^2 - 8x + 2 = 0 \Rightarrow x^2 - 8x + 16 = -2 + 16 \Rightarrow (x-4)^2 = 14 \Rightarrow$

$x - 4 = \pm\sqrt{14} \Rightarrow x = 4 \pm \sqrt{14}$

40. $-\frac{1}{4}x^2 - \frac{1}{2}x + 1 = 0 \Rightarrow x^2 + 2x - 4 = 0 \Rightarrow x^2 + 2x + 1 = 4 + 1 \Rightarrow (x+1)^2 = 5 \Rightarrow$

$x + 1 = \pm\sqrt{5} \Rightarrow x = -1 \pm \sqrt{5}$

41. $2x^2 - 3y^2 = 6 \Rightarrow -3y^2 = -2x^2 + 6 \Rightarrow y^2 = \frac{2x^2 - 6}{3} \Rightarrow y = \pm\sqrt{\frac{2x^2 - 6}{3}}$

Since there are two output values for each input, $y$ is not a function of $x$.

42. $h = -\frac{1}{2}gt^2 + 100 \Rightarrow -\frac{1}{2}gt^2 = h - 100 \Rightarrow gt^2 = -2h + 200 \Rightarrow t^2 = \frac{-2h + 200}{g} \Rightarrow$

$t = \pm\sqrt{\frac{-2h + 200}{g}}$ or $t = \pm\sqrt{\frac{-2(h - 100)}{g}}$

43. (a) $\sqrt{-16} = \sqrt{16}\sqrt{-1} = 4i$

(b) $\sqrt{-48} = \sqrt{16}\sqrt{-1}\sqrt{3} = 4i\sqrt{3}$

(c) $\sqrt{-5} \cdot \sqrt{-15} = i\sqrt{5} \cdot i\sqrt{5}\sqrt{3} = i^2(5)\sqrt{3} = 5(-1)\sqrt{3} = -5\sqrt{3}$

44. (a) $(2 - 3i) + (-3 + 3i) = (2 + (-3)) + (-3 + 3)i = -1$

(b) $(-5 + 3i) - (-3 - 5i) = (-5 - (-3)) + (3 - (-5))i = -2 + 8i$

(c) $(3 + 2i)(-4 - i) = -12 - 3i - 8i - 2i^2 = -12 - 11i - 2(-1) = -10 - 11i$

(d) $\dfrac{3 + 2i}{2 - i} = \dfrac{3 + 2i}{2 - i} \cdot \dfrac{2 + i}{2 + i} = \dfrac{6 + 7i + 2i^2}{4 - (-1)} = \dfrac{4 + 7i}{5} = \dfrac{4}{5} + \dfrac{7}{5}i$

45. (a) The $x$-intercepts of $f$ are $-\dfrac{5}{2}$ and $\dfrac{1}{2}$.

(b) The complex zeros of $f$ are $-\dfrac{5}{2}$ and $\dfrac{1}{2}$.

46. (a) The $x$-intercept of $f$ is $\dfrac{3}{2}$.

(b) The complex zero of $f$ is $\dfrac{3}{2}$.

47. (a) There are no $x$-intercepts of $f$.

(b) Use the quadratic formula to find the complex zeros. $x = \dfrac{-b \pm \sqrt{b^2 - 4ac}}{2} \Rightarrow$

$$x = \frac{-1 \pm \sqrt{1^2 - 4(1)(2)}}{2(1)} \Rightarrow x = \frac{-1 \pm \sqrt{-7}}{2} \Rightarrow x = -\frac{1}{2} \pm \frac{i\sqrt{7}}{2}$$

48. (a) There are no $x$-intercepts of $f$.

(b) Use the quadratic formula to find the complex zeros. $x = \dfrac{-b \pm \sqrt{b^2 - 4ac}}{2} \Rightarrow$

$$x = \frac{-2 \pm \sqrt{(-2)^2 - 4(-2)(-1)}}{2(-2)} \Rightarrow x = \frac{-2 \pm \sqrt{-4}}{-4} \Rightarrow x = \frac{-2 \pm 2i}{-4} \Rightarrow x = \frac{1}{2} \pm \frac{1}{2}i$$

49. $4x^2 + 9 = 0 \Rightarrow 4x^2 = -9 \Rightarrow x^2 = -\dfrac{9}{4} \Rightarrow x = \pm\sqrt{-\dfrac{9}{4}} = \pm\dfrac{3}{2}i$

50. Use the quadratic formula noting that $2x^2 + 3 = 2x \Rightarrow 2x^2 - 2x + 3 = 0$.

$$\frac{-(-2) \pm \sqrt{(-2)^2 - 4(2)(3)}}{2(2)} = \frac{2 \pm \sqrt{4 - 24}}{4} = \frac{2 \pm \sqrt{-20}}{4} = \frac{2 \pm 2i\sqrt{5}}{4} = \frac{1}{2} \pm \frac{i\sqrt{5}}{2}$$

51. (a) The graph of $y = f(x)$ has $x$-intercepts at $x = -3, 2$. It is above the $x$-axis between these values, which are solutions to $f(x) = 0$, so $f(x) > 0$ when $-3 < x < 2$ or on $(-3, 2)$.

(b) The graph of $y = f(x)$ is below or intersects the $x$-axis outside of and including the values where $f(x) = 0$, so $f(x) \leq 0$ when $x \leq -3$ or $x \geq 2$ or on $(-\infty, -3] \cup [2, \infty)$.

52. (a) According to the table, $f(x) < 0$ when $-5 < x < 3$.

(b) According to the table, $f(x) \geq 0$ when $x \leq -5$ or $x \geq 3$.

53. (a) $x^2 - 3x + 2 = 0 \Rightarrow (x - 2)(x - 1) = 0 \Rightarrow x = 1, 2$.

(b) Using test intervals, $x^2 - 3x + 2 < 0$ on $(1, 2)$, (when $1 < x < 2$).

(c) Using test intervals, $x^2 - 3x + 2 > 0$ on $(-\infty, 1) \cup (2, \infty)$, (when $x < 1$ or $x > 2$).

54. Using the $x$-intercept method, let $Y_1 = 2X\wedge 2 + 1.3X - 0.4$ and determine where the graph of $Y_1$ is below or intersecting the $x$-axis. From Figures 54a & 54b we see that the $x$-intercepts are $x \approx -0.88$ or $x \approx 0.23$. The solution includes these $x$-values and all $x$-values between: $-0.88 \le x \le 0.23$ (approximate).

[-3, 3, 1] by [-2, 2, 1]

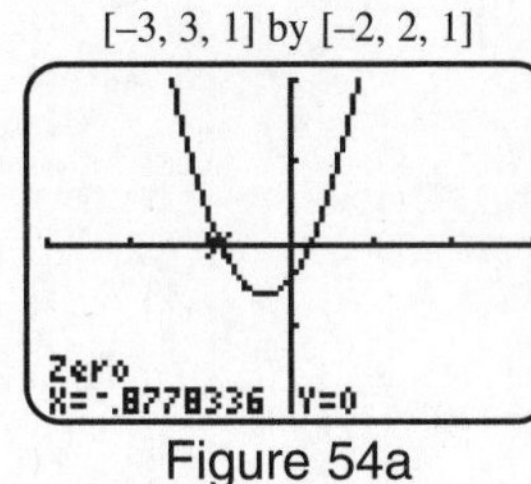

Figure 54a

[-3, 3, 1] by [-2, 2, 1]

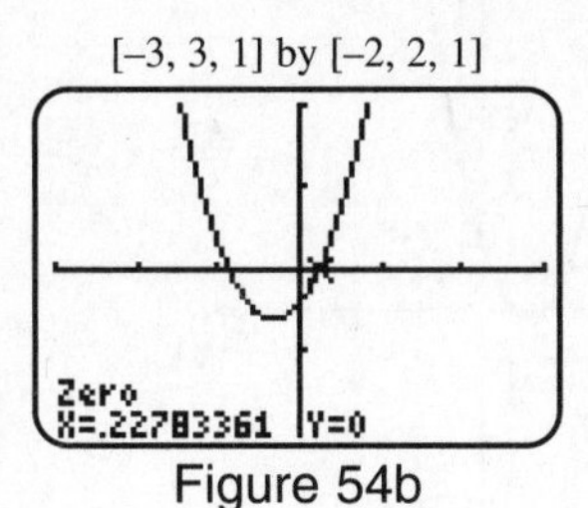

Figure 54b

55. Start by solving $x^2 - 3x + 2 = 0 \Rightarrow (x - 1)(x - 2) = 0 \Rightarrow x = 1$ or $2$; thus, $x^2 - 3x + 2 \le 0$ on $[1, 2]$ or $\{x \mid 1 \le x \le 2\}$. Note that a graph of $y = x^2 - 3x + 2$ intersects or is below the $x$-axis for values of $x$ between the $x$-intercepts.

56. Start by solving $x^2 - 2x = 0 \Rightarrow x(x - 2) = 0 \Rightarrow x = 0$ or $2$; thus, $x^2 - 2x \ge 0$ on $(-\infty, 0] \cup [2, \infty)$ or $\{x \mid x \le 0 \text{ or } x \ge 2\}$. Note that a graph of $y = x^2 - 2x$ intersects or is above the $x$-axis for values of $x$ outside of the $x$-intercepts.

57. Start by solving $2x^2 + 3x + 1 = 0 \Rightarrow x = -1$ or $-\frac{1}{2}$; thus, $2x^2 + 3x + 1 < 0$ on $\left(-1, -\frac{1}{2}\right)$ or $\left\{x \mid -1 < x < -\frac{1}{2}\right\}$. Note that a graph of $y = 2x^2 + 3x + 1$ is below the $x$-axis for values of $x$ between the $x$-intercepts.

58. Start by solving $9x^2 - 4 = 0 \Rightarrow (3x + 2)(3x - 2) = 0 \Rightarrow x = -\frac{2}{3}$ or $\frac{2}{3}$; thus, $9x^2 - 4 > 0$ on $\left(-\infty, -\frac{2}{3}\right) \cup \left(\frac{2}{3}, \infty\right)$ or $\left\{x \mid x < -\frac{2}{3} \text{ or } x > \frac{2}{3}\right\}$. Note that a graph of $y = 9x^2 - 4$ is above the $x$-axis for values of $x$ outside of the $x$-intercepts.

59. Start by solving $n(n - 2) = 15 \Rightarrow n^2 - 2n - 15 = 0 \Rightarrow (n - 5)(n + 3) = 0 \Rightarrow n = -3$ or $5$; thus, $n(n - 2) \ge 15$ on $(-\infty, -3] \cup [5, \infty)$ or $\{x \mid x \le -3 \text{ or } x \ge 5\}$. Note that a graph of $y = n^2 - 2n - 15$ intersects or is above the $n$-axis for values of $n$ outside of the $n$-intercepts.

60. Start by solving $n^2 + 4 = 6n \Rightarrow n^2 - 6n + 4 = 0$. Using the quadratic formula we get: $\frac{6 \pm \sqrt{36 - 4(1)(4)}}{2(1)} = \frac{6 \pm \sqrt{20}}{2} = 3 \pm \sqrt{5}$; thus, $n^2 + 4 \le 6n$ on $[3 - \sqrt{5}, 3 + \sqrt{5}]$ or $\{x \mid 3 - \sqrt{5} \le x \le 3 + \sqrt{5}\}$. Note that a graph of $y = n^2 - 6n + 4$ intersects or is below the $n$-axis for values of $n$ between the $n$-intercepts.

61. $y = -f(x) = -(2x^2 - 3x + 1) = -2x^2 + 3x - 1$. See Figure 61a.

$y = f(-x) = 2(-x)^2 - 3(-x) + 1 = 2x^2 + 3x + 1$. See Figure 61b.

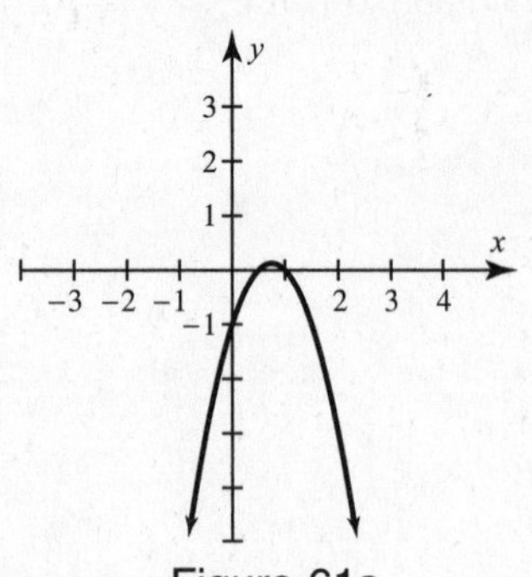

Figure 61a

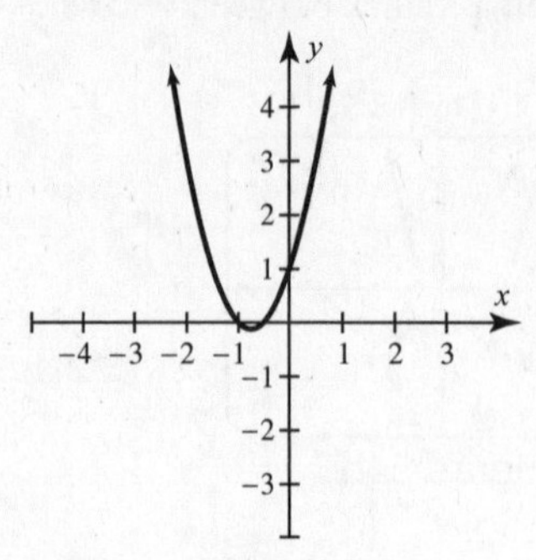

Figure 61b

62. (a) See Figure 62a.

(b) See Figure 62b.

(c) See Figure 62c.

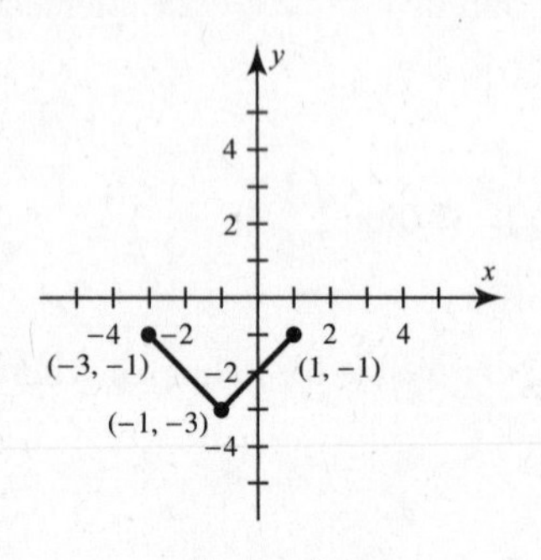

Figure 62a

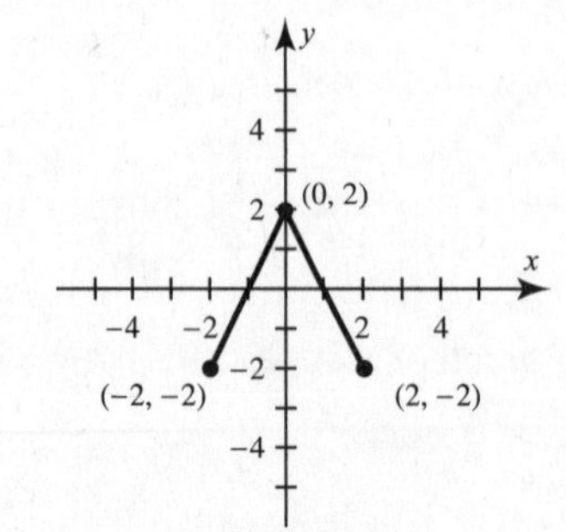

Figure 62b

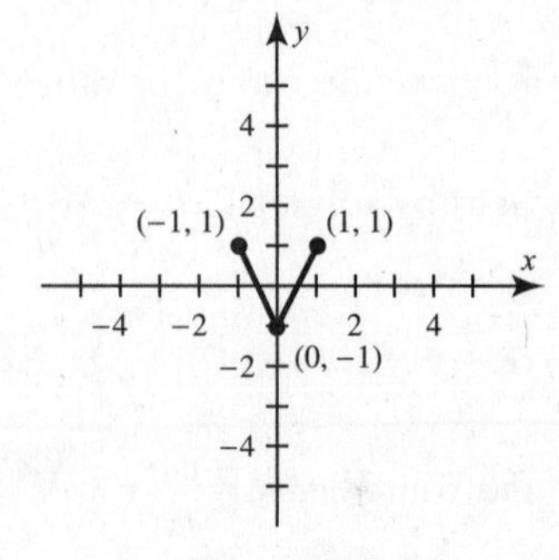

Figure 62c

63. Shift the graph of $y = x^2$ four units down. See Figure 63.

64. Shift the graph of $y = |x|$ two units right and one unit up and stretch it vertically. See Figure 64.

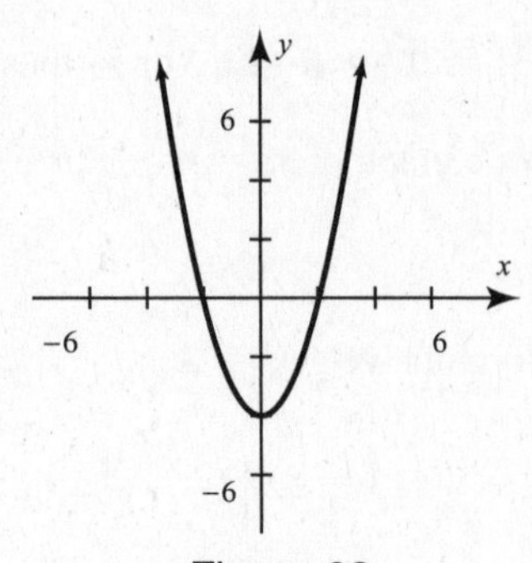

Figure 63

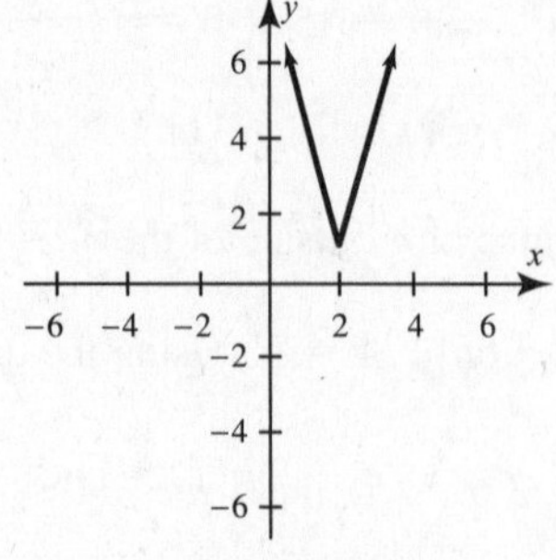

Figure 64

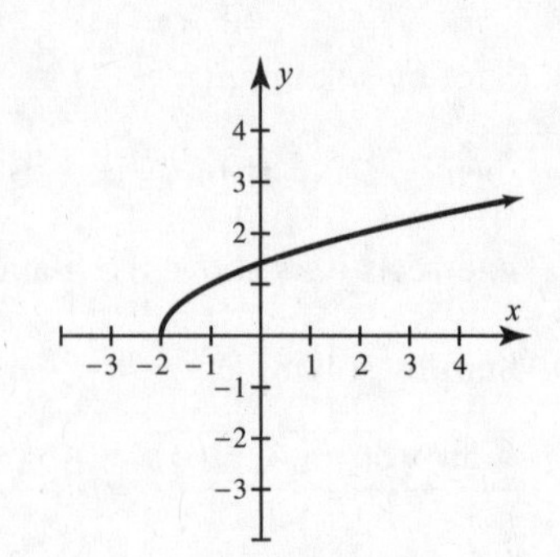

Figure 65

65. Shift the graph of $y = \sqrt{x}$ two units left. See Figure 65.

66. Reflect the graph of $y = \sqrt{x}$ across the $x$-axis and the $y$-axis, then stretch it vertically. See Figure 66.

67. Reflect the graph of $y = x^2$ across the $x$-axis, shift it two units right and three unnits up, then stretch it vertically. See Figure 67.

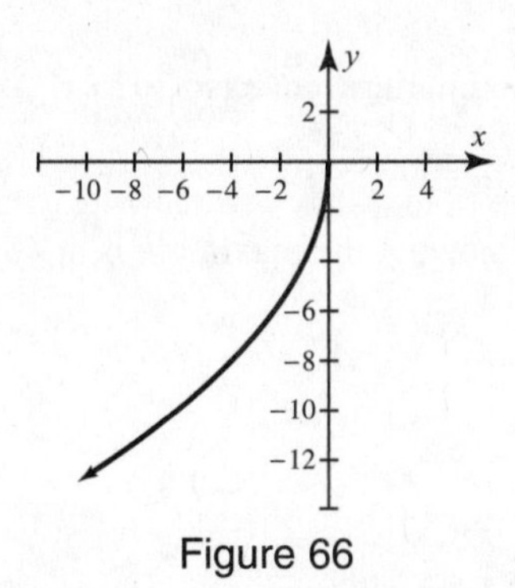
Figure 66

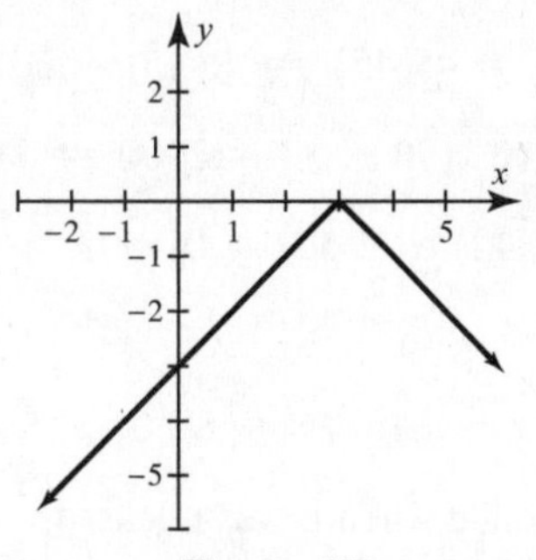
Figure 67

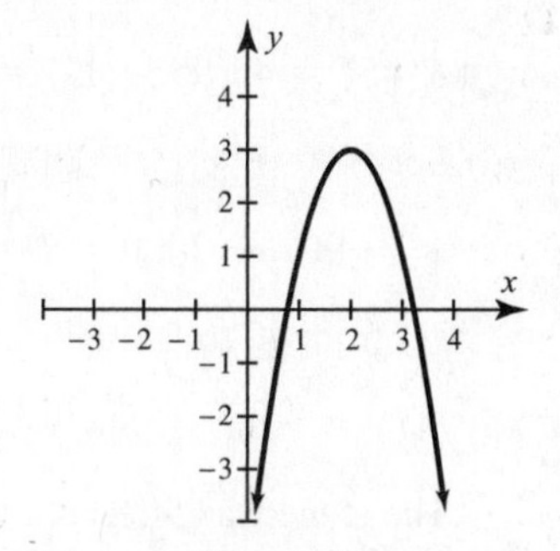
Figure 68

68. Reflect the graph of $y = |x|$ across the $x$-axis and shift it three units right. See Figure 68.

69. For example $g(2) = (-3)f(2 + 1) + 2 \Rightarrow -3f(3) + 2 = -3(4) + 2 = -10$. See Figure 69.

| $x$ | 0 | 1 | 2 | 3 |
|---|---|---|---|---|
| $g(x)$ | 11 | −7 | −10 | −19 |

Figure 69

70. Since the axis of symmetry is $x = 2$, the point (2, 3) is the vertex of the parabola. Because (4, –1) is a point on the parabola and $-1 < 3$, the parabola opens downward. $f(x) = a(x - h)^2 + k \Rightarrow f(x) = a(x - 2)^2 + 3$; $f(4) = -1 \Rightarrow -1 = a(4 - 2)^2 + 3 \Rightarrow a = -1$; thus $f(x) = -(x - 2)^2 + 3$. See Figure 70.

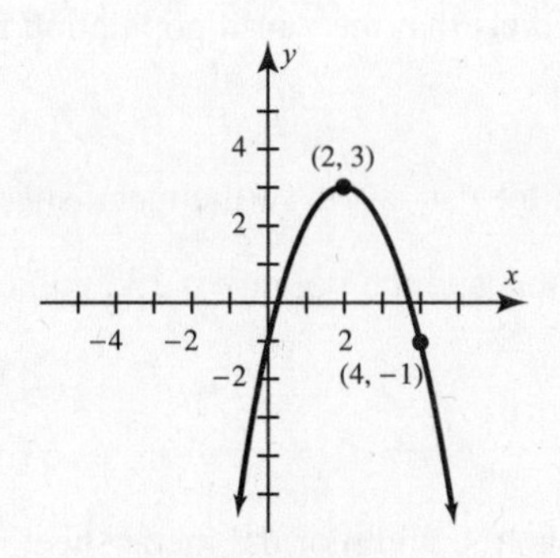

Figure 70

71. Let $W + L + W = 44 \Rightarrow L = 44 - 2W$. If $A = L \cdot W$ then $A = (44 - 2W)(W) \Rightarrow A = 44W - 2W^2$ or $A = -2W^2 + 44W$. Now use the vertex formula: $W = -\dfrac{44}{2(-2)} \Rightarrow W = 11$ and $L = 44 - 2(11) \Rightarrow L = 22$. So the dimensions are 11 feet by 22 feet.

72. (a) $R(20) = 20(90 - 20) \Rightarrow R(20) = 20(70) \Rightarrow R(20) = 1400$; the revenue from selling 20 radios is \$1400.

(b) $R(x) = x(90 - x) \Rightarrow R(x) = -x^2 + 90x$. Using the vertex formula: $-\dfrac{90}{2(-1)} = 45$ radios should be sold to maximize revenue.

(c) $R(45) = 45(95 - 45) \Rightarrow R(45) = 45(45) \Rightarrow R(45) = 2025$; the maximum revenue is \$2025.

(d) Let $x(90 - x) \geq 2000$. First solve $x(90 - x) = 2000 \Rightarrow 90x - x^2 = 2000 \Rightarrow$ $x^2 - 90x + 2000 = 0 \Rightarrow (x - 40)(x - 50) = 0 \Rightarrow x = 40, 50$. Knowing the maximum is at 45, we get from 40 to 50 radios.

73. (a) $h(t) = -16t^2 + 88t + 5 \Rightarrow h(0) = -16(0)^2 + 88(0) + 5 \Rightarrow h(0) = 5$

The stone was 5 feet above the ground when it was released.

(b) $h(2) = -16(2)^2 + 88(2) + 5 = 117$; the stone was 117 feet high after 2 seconds.

(c) $t = -\dfrac{b}{2a} = -\dfrac{88}{2(-16)} = 2.75$ and $h(2.75) = -16(2.75)^2 + 88(2.75) + 5 = 126$; the maximum height of the stone was 126 feet.

(d) $h(t) = 117 \Rightarrow 117 = -16t^2 + 88t + 5 \Rightarrow 16t^2 - 88t + 112 = 0 \Rightarrow$

$$t = \frac{88 \pm \sqrt{(-88)^2 - 4(16)(112)}}{2(16)} \Rightarrow t = 3.5 \text{ or } t = 2$$

The stone was 117 feet high after 2 seconds and after 3.5 seconds.

74. (a) $f(1985) = 0.000478(1985)^2 - 1.813(1985) + 1720.1 \approx 4.7$; in 1985 there were about 4.7 billion people.

(b) $f(2000) = 0.000478(2000)^2 - 1.813(2000) + 1720.1 \approx 6.1$; in 2000 there were about 6.1 billion people.

(c) Graph $Y_1 = 0.000478X\text{^}2 - 1.813X + 1720.1$ and $Y_2 = 7$ in [1980, 2030, 20] by [5, 9, 1] (not shown). The intersection point is approximately (2008.7235, 7). The model predicts that the world population may reach 7 billion in 2009 or late 2008.

75. Use the sketch shown in Figure 75 to determine the dimensions of the box; let $x$ = width of the metal sheet. The dimensions of the box are 3 inches by $(x - 6)$ inches by $(x - 2)$ inches, and the volume is 135 cubic inches.

$135 = 3(x - 6)(x - 2) \Rightarrow 135 = 3x^2 - 24x + 36 \Rightarrow 0 = 3x^2 - 24x - 99 \Rightarrow 0 = x^2 - 8x - 33 \Rightarrow$ $0 = (x - 11)(x + 3) \Rightarrow x = 11$ or $x = -3$. Since $x = -3$ is impossible, the width of the metal sheet is 11 inches and the length is $11 + 4 = 15$ inches.

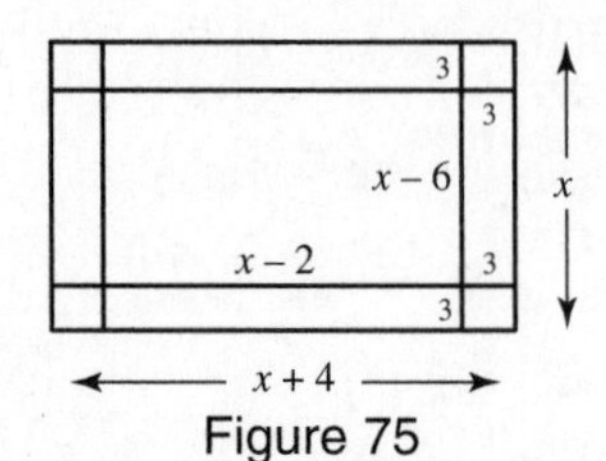

Figure 75

76. (a) $C(x) = x(103 - 3x)$

(b) $C(6) = 6(103 - 3(6)) = 510$; the cost of renting 6 rooms is \$510.

(c) $730 = x(103 - 3x) \Rightarrow 730 = 103x - 3x^2 \Rightarrow 3x^2 - 103x + 730 = 0 \Rightarrow (3x - 73)(x - 10) = 0 \Rightarrow$ $x = \frac{73}{3}$ or $x = 10$. Since $\frac{73}{3}$ has no physical meaning for the number of rooms, 10 rooms.

(d) $C(x) = 103x - 3x^2 \Rightarrow x = -\frac{b}{2a} = -\frac{103}{2(-3)} \approx 17$; the maximum cost occurs when $x = 17$ rooms.

The greatest cost is $C(17) = 103(17) - 3(17)^2 = \$884$.

77. (a) Using least squares regression, we get the function $f(x) \approx 0.00051x^2 - 0.00604x + 1.6$. See Figure 77a.

(b) Graph $Y_1 = 0.00051X^\wedge 2 - 0.00604X + 1.6$ and $Y_2 = 3.7$ in [0, 120, 20] by [1, 6.2, 1]. See Figure 77b.

The intersection point is approximately (70.363108, 3.7), so $x \approx 70.4$. The yield will be 3.7 tons per hectare when 70.4% of the area is irrigated.

Figure 77a

[0, 120, 10] by [1, 6.2, 1]

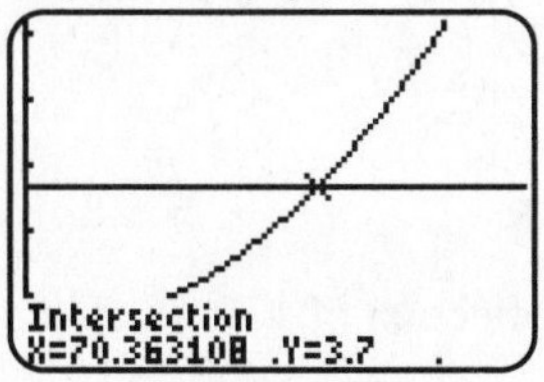

Intersection
X=70.363108 .Y=3.7

Figure 77b

78. (a) No, the change in debt is not constant for each 4-year period.

(b) Using (1980, 82) as the vertex, let $h = 1980$ and $k = 82$ in $f(x) = a(x - h)^2 + k$. Then the function can be written $f(x) = a(x - 1980)^2 + 82$. To find the value of $a$, note that $f(1996) = 444$. By substitution, $444 = a(1996 - 1980)^2 + 82 \Rightarrow 362 = 256a \Rightarrow a = \frac{362}{256} \approx 1.4$. When the data is plotted along with the graph of $f(x) = 1.4(x - 1980)^2 + 82$, it may be reasonable to adjust the value of $a$. A good fit appears to be obtained when $f(x) = 1.3(x - 1980)^2 + 82$. To solve $f(x) = 212$, substitute 212 for $f(x)$. $212 = 1.3(x - 1980)^2 + 82 \Rightarrow 130 = 1.3(x - 1980)^2 \Rightarrow 100 = (x - 1980)^2 \Rightarrow$ $\sqrt{100} = x - 1980 \Rightarrow x = 1980 + \sqrt{100} = 1990$. Note that only the positive square root of 100 is necessary for dates after 1980. Visa and Mastercard debt reached \$212 billion in 1990.

## Extended and Discovery Exercises for Chapter 3

1. (a) For $y = 10$ and $x = 15$, $y = \frac{-16x^2}{0.434v^2} + 1.15x + 8 \Rightarrow 10 = \frac{-16(15)^2}{0.434v^2} + 1.15(15) + 8 \Rightarrow$ $10 = \frac{-3600}{0.434v^2} + 17.25 + 8 \Rightarrow -15.25 = \frac{-3600}{0.434v^2} \Rightarrow v^2 \approx 543.93 \Rightarrow v \approx 23.32$ feet per second.

(b) Graph $Y_1 = (-16X^\wedge 2/(0.434 \times 543.93)) + 1.15X + 8$ along with the points (0, 8) and (15, 10) in the window $[-1, 16, 1]$ by $[-1, 16, 1]$. See Figure 1. The graph passes through both points.

(c) Using the maximum finder feature on the graphing calculator, we see that the maximum point is approximately (8.48, 12.88). The maximum height of the basketball is about 12.88 feet.

2. (a) For $y = 10$ and $x = 15$, $y = \dfrac{-16x^2}{0.117v^2} + 2.75x + 3 \Rightarrow 10 = \dfrac{-16(15)^2}{0.117v^2} + 2.75(15) + 3 \Rightarrow$

$10 = \dfrac{-3600}{0.117v^2} + 41.25 + 3 \Rightarrow -34.25 = \dfrac{-3600}{0.117v^2} \Rightarrow v^2 \approx 898.37 \Rightarrow v \approx 29.97$ feet per second.

(b) Graph $Y_1 = (-16X\text{^}2/(0.117 \times 898.37)) + 2.75X + 3$ along with the points (0, 3) and (15, 10) in the window $[-1, 16, 1]$ by $[-1, 16, 1]$. See Figure 2. The graph passes through both points.

(c) Using the maximum finder feature on the graphing calculator, we see that the maximum point is approximately (9.03, 15.42). The maximum height of the basketball is about 15.42 feet.

The underhand shot produces a higher arc.

[-1, 16, 1] by [-1, 16, 1]

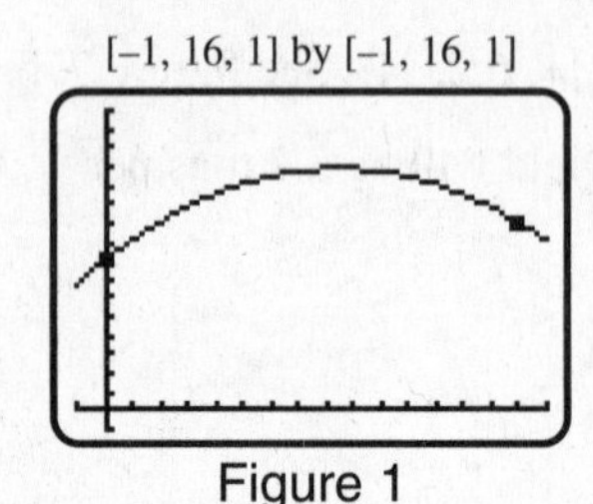

Figure 1

[-1, 16, 1] by [-1, 16, 1]

Figure 2

3. (a) See Figure 3.

(b) The graph of $y = f(2k - x) = f(4 - x)$ is a reflection of $y = f(x)$ across the line $x = 2$.

4. (a) See Figure 4.

(b) The graph of $y = f(2k - x) = f(-6 - x)$ is a reflection of $y = f(x)$ across the line $x = -3$.

[-1, 8, 1] by [-4, 4, 1]

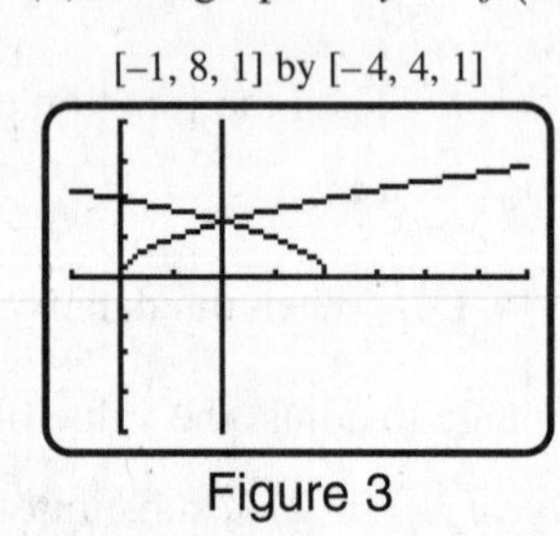

Figure 3

[-12, 6, 1] by [-6, 6, 1]

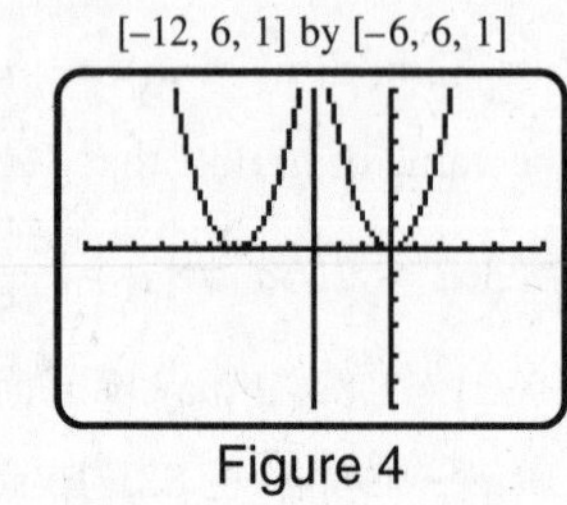

Figure 4

[-15, 3, 1] by [-3, 9, 1]

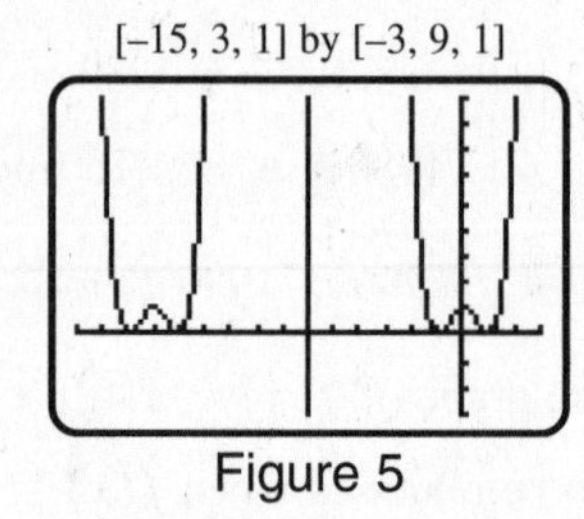

Figure 5

[-6, 18, 1] by [-8, 8, 1]

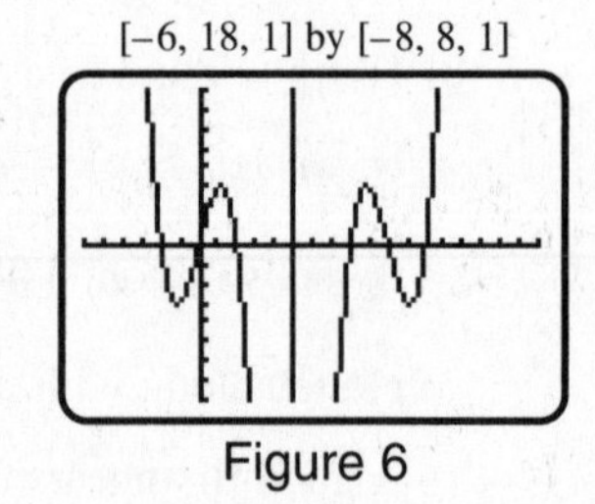

Figure 6

5. (a) See Figure 5.

(b) The graph of $y = f(2k - x) = f(-12 - x)$ is a reflection of $y = f(x)$ across the line $x = -6$.

6. (a) See Figure 6.

(b) The graph of $y = f(2k - x) = f(10 - x)$ is a reflection of $y = f(x)$ across the line $x = 5$.

7. (a) The front reached St. Louis, but not Nashville. See Figure 7a.

(b) $g(x) = -\sqrt{750^2 - (x - 160)^2} - 110$

(c) The front reached both cities in less than 12 hours. See Figure 7c.

[0, 1200, 100] by [-800, 0, 100]

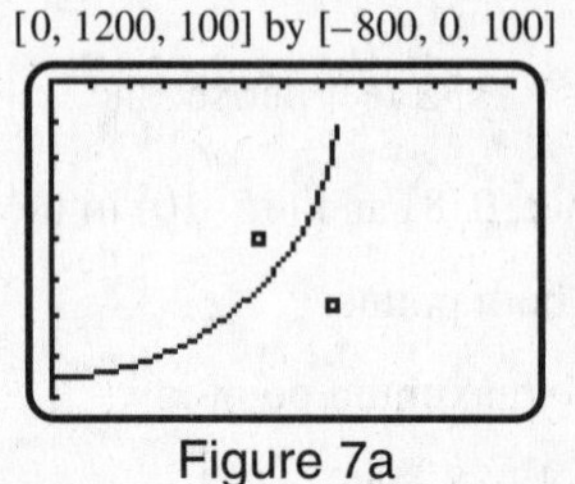

Figure 7a

[0, 1200, 100] by [-800, 0, 100]

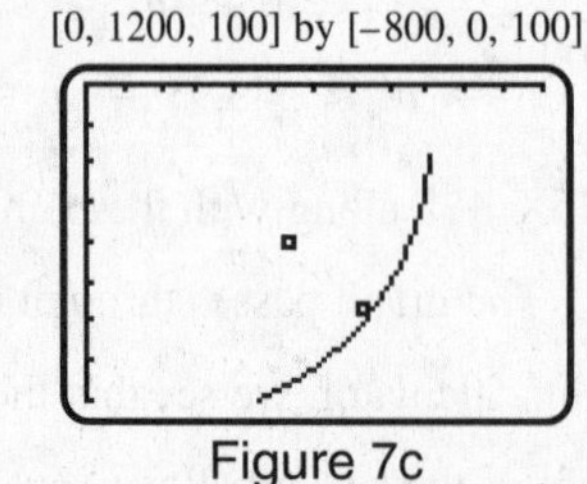

Figure 7c

# Chapter 4: Nonlinear Functions and Equations

## 4.1: Nonlinear Functions and Their Graphs

1. $f(x) = 2x^3 - x + 5$ is a polynomial; degree: 3; leading coefficient: 2.
2. $f(x) = -x^4 + 1$ is a polynomial; degree: 4; leading coefficient: –1.
3. $f(x) = \sqrt{x}$ is not a polynomial.
4. $f(x) = 2x^3 - \sqrt[3]{x}$ is not a polynomial.
5. $f(x) = 1 - 4x - 5x^4$ is a polynomial; degree: 4; leading coefficient: –5.
6. $f(x) = 5 - 4x$ is a polynomial; degree: 1; leading coefficient: $-4$.
7. $g(t) = \dfrac{1}{t^2 + 3t - 1}$ is not a polynomial.
8. $g(t) = \dfrac{1}{1 - t}$ is not a polynomial.
9. $g(t) = 22$ is a polynomial; degree: 0; leading coefficient: 22.
10. $g(t) = |2t|$ is not a polynomial.
11. (a) A local maximum of approximately 5.5 occurs when $x \approx -2$. A local minimum of approximately –5.5 occurs when $x \approx 2$. *Answers may vary slightly.*

    (b) There are no absolute extrema.
12. (a) A local maximum of 0 occurs when $x = 0$. A local minimum of approximately –5 occurs when $x \approx \pm 3$. *Answers may vary slightly.*

    (b) There is no absolute maximum. The absolute minimum is –5 and occurs when $x \approx \pm 3$.
13. (a) Local maxima of approximately 17 and 27 occur when $x \approx -3$ and 2, respectively. Local minima of approximately –10 and 24 occur when $x \approx -1$ and 3, respectively. *Answers may vary slightly.*

    (b) There are no absolute extrema.
14. (a) A local maximum of 2 occurs when $x = 0$. There are no local minima.

    (b) The absolute maximum is 2 and occurs when $x = 0$. There is no absolute minimum.
15. (a) Local maxima of approximately 0.5 and 2.8 occur when $x \approx 1$ and $-2$, respectively. A local minimum of approximately 0 occur when $x = 0$. *Answers may vary slightly.*

    (b) The absolute maximum is 2.8 when $x \approx -2$. There is no absolute minimum.
16. (a) A Local maximum of approximately 2.5 occurs when $x \approx -2$. A local minimum of approximately $-2.1$ occurs when $x \approx 1$. *Answers may vary slightly.*

    (b) There are no absolute extrema.
17. (a) A Local maximum of 0 occurs when $x = 0$. A local minimum of $-1{,}000$ occurs when $x = \pm 8$.

    (b) There is no absolute maximum. The absolute minimum of $-1{,}000$ occurs when $x = \pm 8$.
18. (a) A Local maximum of 0 occurs when $x = 0$. There is no local minimum.

    (b) The absolute maximum of 0 occurs when $x = 0$. There is no absolute minimum.

19. (a) Each local minimum is –1. Each local maximum is 1.

    (b) The absolute minimum is –1 and the absolute maximum is 1.

20. (a) The local minima are approximately 2 and –12. The local maximum is approximately 2.5.

    (b) The absolute minimum is approximately –12. There is no absolute maximum.

21. (a) A local minimum of approximately –3.2 occurs when $x \approx 0.5$. There are no local maxima.

    *Answers may vary slightly.*

    (b) The absolute minimum is approximately –3.2. The absolute maximum is 3 and occurs when $x = -2$.

22. (a) A local maximum of approximately 3.1 occurs when $x \approx 1.2$. A local minimum of approximately –3.1 occurs when $x \approx -1.2$. *Answers may vary slightly.*

    (b) The absolute maximum is approximately 3.1 and the absolute minimum is approximately –3.1.

23. (a) Local minima are approximately –0.5 and –2. Local maxima are approximately 0.5 and 2.

    (b) The absolute minimum is –2 and the absolute maximum is 2.

24. (a) The local minimum is –2. Local maxima are 1 and 2.

    (b) The absolute minimum is –2 and the absolute maximum is 2.

25. (a) There is no local maximum. A local minimum of $-2$ occurs when $x \approx 1$.

    (b) There is no absolute maximum. An absolute minimum of $-2$ occurs when $x \approx 1$.

26. (a) A local maximum of 1 occurs when $x \approx -1$. There is no local minimum.

    (b) An absolute maximum of 1 occurs when $x \approx -1$. There is no absolute minimum.

27. (a) The graph of $g$ is linear $\Rightarrow$ no local extrema.

    (b) The graph of $g$ is linear $\Rightarrow$ no absolute extrema.

28. (a) The graph of $g$ is linear $\Rightarrow$ no local extrema.

    (b) The graph of $g$ is linear $\Rightarrow$ no absolute extrema.

29. (a) The graph of $g$ is a parabola opening up with a vertex $(0, 1)$ $\Rightarrow$ it has a local minimum: 1; and no local maximum.

    (b) The graph of $g$ is a parabola opening up with a vertex $(0, 1)$ $\Rightarrow$ it has an absolute minimum: 1; and no absolute maximum.

30. (a) The graph of $g$ is a parabola opening down with a vertex $(0, 1)$ $\Rightarrow$ it has a local maximum: 1; and no local minimum.

    (b) The graph of $g$ is a parabola opening down with a vertex $(0, 1)$ $\Rightarrow$ it has an absolute maximum: 1; and no absolute minimum.

31. (a) The graph of $g$ is a parabola opening down with a vertex $(-3, 4)$ $\Rightarrow$ it has a local maximum: 4; and no local minimum.

    (b) The graph of $g$ is a parabola opening down with a vertex $(-3, 4)$ $\Rightarrow$ it has an absolute maximum: 4; and no absolute minimum.

32. (a) The graph of $g$ is a parabola opening up with a vertex $(1, -2) \Rightarrow$ it has a local minimum: $-2$; and no local maximum.

 (b) The graph of $g$ is a parabola opening up with a vertex $(1, -2) \Rightarrow$ it has an absolute minimum: $-2$; and no absolute maximum.

33. (a) The graph of $g$ is a parabola opening up with a vertex $\left(\frac{3}{4}, -\frac{1}{8}\right) \Rightarrow$ it has a local minimum: $-\frac{1}{8}$; and no local maximum.

 (b) The graph of $g$ is a parabola opening up with a vertex $\left(\frac{3}{4}, -\frac{1}{8}\right) \Rightarrow$ it has an absolute minimum: $-\frac{1}{8}$; and no absolute maximum.

34. (a) The graph of $g$ is a parabola opening down with a vertex $\left(\frac{2}{3}, \frac{1}{3}\right) \Rightarrow$ it has a local maximum: $\frac{1}{3}$; and no local minimum.

 (b) The graph of $g$ is a parabola opening down with a vertex $\left(\frac{2}{3}, \frac{1}{3}\right) \Rightarrow$ it has an absolute maximum: $\frac{1}{3}$; and no absolute minimum.

35. (a) The absolute value graph opening up has a vertex $(-3, 0) \Rightarrow$ it has a local minimum: $0$; and no local maximum.

 (b) The absolute value graph opening up has a vertex $(-3, 0) \Rightarrow$ it has an absolute minimum: $0$; and no absolute maximum.

36. (a) The absolute value graph opening down has a vertex $(0, 2) \Rightarrow$ it has a local maximum: $2$; and no local minimum.

 (b) The absolute value graph opening down has a vertex $(0, 2) \Rightarrow$ it has an absolute maximum: $2$; and no absolute minimum.

37. (a) The graph of $g$ is the basic $\sqrt[3]{x}$ graph and has no local extrema.

 (b) The graph of $g$ is the basic $\sqrt[3]{x}$ graph and has no absolute extrema.

38. (a) The graph of $g$ is the basic $x^3$ graph reflected across the $x$-axis, has no local extrema.

 (b) The graph of $g$ is the basic $x^3$ graph reflected across the $x$-axis, has no absolute extrema.

39. (a) The cubic function graph of $g$ has turning points $(-1, -2)$ and $(1, 2) \Rightarrow$ it has a local minimum: $-2$; and a local maximum: 2.

 (b) The cubic function graph of $g$ has turning points $(-1, -2)$ and $(1, 2)$ but then continues on to $-\infty$ and $\infty \Rightarrow$ it has no absolute extrema.

40. (a) The graph of $g$ as an inverted V type absolute graph with each leg getting closer to the asymptote $y = 0$ and a vertex at $(0, 1) \Rightarrow$ it has a local maximum: 1; and no local minimum.

 (b) The graph of $g$ as an inverted V type absolute graph with each leg getting closer to the asymptote $y = 0$ and a vertex at $(0, 1) \Rightarrow$ it has an absolute maximum: 1; and no absolute minimum.

41. (a) A graph of $f(x) = -3x^4 + 8x^3 + 6x^2 - 24x$ is shown in Figure 41. Local maxima of 19 and $-8$ occur at $x \approx -1$ and $x \approx 2$ respectively. A local minima of $-13$ occurs when $x \approx 1$.

(b) The absolute maximum of 19 occurs at $x \approx -1$, and there is no absolute minimum.

42. (a) A graph of $f(x) = -x^4 + 4x^3 - 4x^2$ is shown in Figure 42. A local maximum of 0 occurs at $x \approx 0$ and $x \approx 2$. A local minimum of $-1$ occurs when $x \approx 1$.

(b) The absolute maximum of 0 occurs at $x \approx 0$ and $x \approx 2$. There is no absolute minimum.

[–5, 5, 1] by [–30, 30, 5]

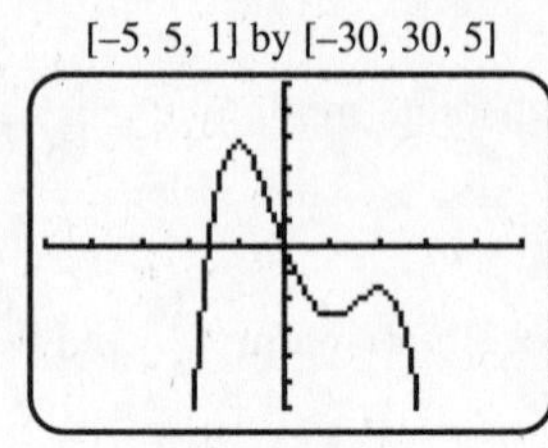

Figure 41

[–5, 5, 1] by [–5, 5, 1]

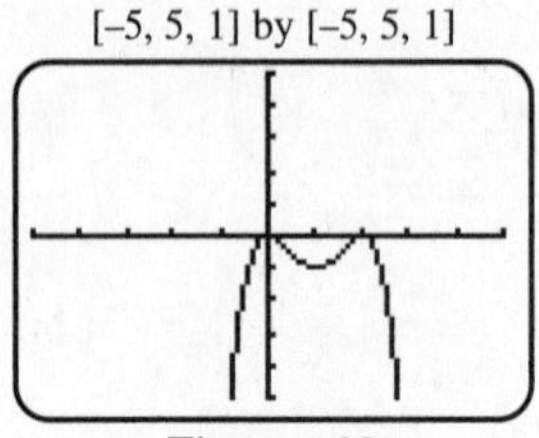

Figure 42

43. (a) A graph of $f(x) = 0.5x^4 - 5x^2 + 4.5$ is shown in Figure 43. A local maximum of 4.5 occurs at $x = 0$. A local minimum of –8 occurs when $x \approx \pm 2.236$.

(b) There is no absolute maximum. An absolute minimum of –8 occurs at $x \approx \pm 2.236$.

44. (a) A graph of $f(x) = 0.01x^5 + 0.02x^4 - 0.35x^3 - 0.36x^2 + 1.8x$ is shown in Figure 44. Local maxima of approximately 7.009 and 1.125 occur at $x \approx -4.955$ and 1.066, respectively. Local minima of approximately –2.356 and –5.6 occur when $x \approx -1.705$ and 3.995, respectively.

(b) There are no absolute extrema.

[–10, 10, 1] by [–10, 10, 1]

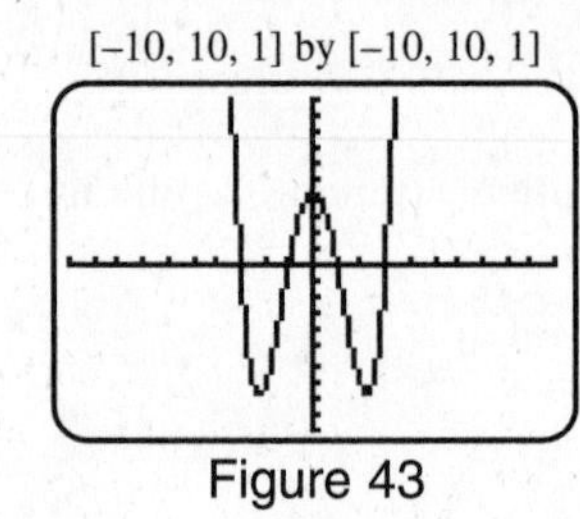

Figure 43

[–10, 10, 1] by [–10, 10, 1]

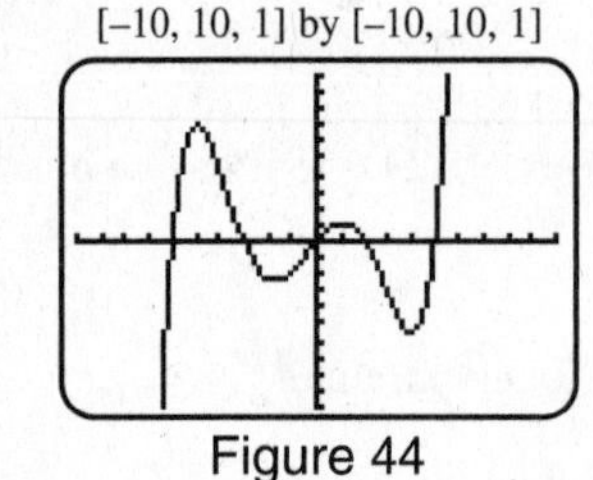

Figure 44

[–10, 10, 1] by [–10, 10, 1]

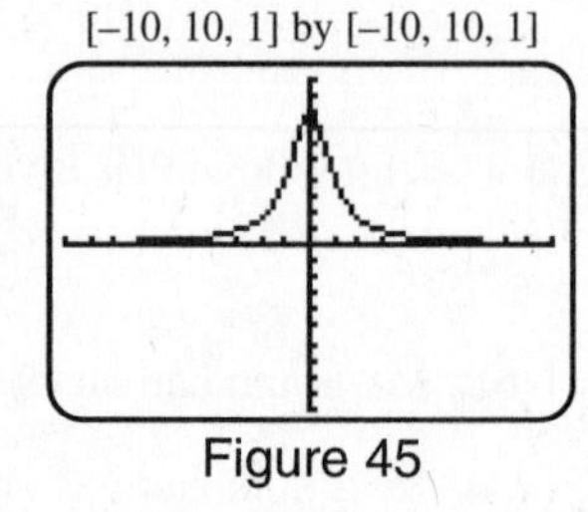

Figure 45

[–10, 10, 1] by [–10, 10, 1]

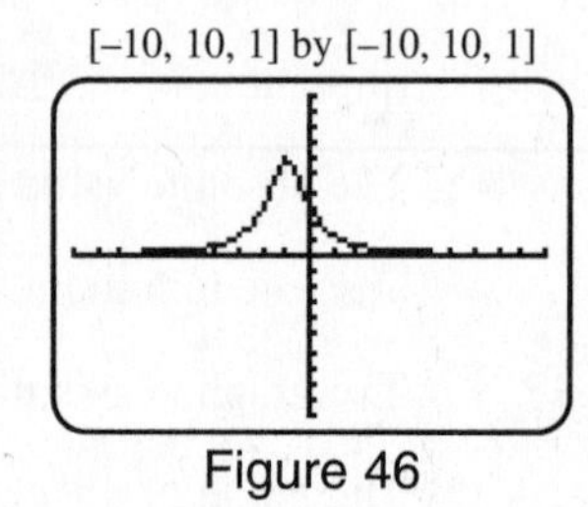

Figure 46

45. (a) A graph of $f(x) = \dfrac{8}{1 + x^2}$ is shown in Figure 45. A local maximum of 8 occurs at $x = 0$. There are no local minima.

(b) An absolute maximum of 8 occurs at $x = 0$. There is no absolute minimum.

46. (a) A graph of $f(x) = \dfrac{6}{x^2 + 2x + 2}$ is shown in Figure 46. Local maximum of 6 and occurs when $x \approx -1$. There are no local minima.

(b) The absolute maximum of 6 occurs at $x \approx -1$. There are no absolute minima.

47. From the graph we can see that the function $f$ is neither even or odd.

48. From the graph we can see that the function is odd. Since the point $\left(\dfrac{1}{2}, \dfrac{1}{2}\right)$ is located on the graph of $f$, the point $\left(-\dfrac{1}{2}, -\dfrac{1}{2}\right)$ must also be located on the graph.

49. From the graph we can see that the function is even. Since the point $(1, -1)$ is on the graph of $f$, the point $(-1, -1)$ must also be located on the graph.

50. From the graph we can see that the function is odd. Since the point $(1, -1)$ is on the graph of $f$, the point $(-1, 1)$ must also be located on the graph.

51. The function $f$ is a monomial with only an odd power $\Rightarrow$ it is odd.

52. The function $f$ is a monomial with only an odd power $\Rightarrow$ it is odd.

53. The function $f$ is a polynomial with an odd power and a constant term, which is an even power $\Rightarrow$ it is neither.

54. The function $f$ is a polynomial with an odd power and a constant term, which is an even power $\Rightarrow$ it is neither.

55. The function $f$ is a polynomial with an even power and a constant term, which is also even $\Rightarrow$ it is even.

56. The function $f$ is a polynomial with an even power and a constant term, which is also even $\Rightarrow$ it is even.

57. The function $f$ is a polynomial with all even powers and a constant term, which is also even $\Rightarrow$ it is even.

58. The function $f$ is a polynomial with all even powers $\Rightarrow$ it is even.

59. The function $f$ is a polynomial with all odd powers $\Rightarrow$ it is odd.

60. The function $f$ is a monomial with only an odd power $\Rightarrow$ it is odd.

61. The function $f$ is a polynomial with both an odd powered term and an even powered term $\Rightarrow$ it is neither.

62. The function $f$ is a polynomial with an odd power and a constant term, which is an even power $\Rightarrow$ it is neither.

63. If $f(x) = \sqrt[3]{x^2}$, then $f(-x) = \sqrt[3]{(-x)^2} = \sqrt[3]{x^2}$, which is equal to $f(x) \Rightarrow$ it is even.

64. If $f(x) = \sqrt{-x}$, then $f(-x) = \sqrt{-(-x)} = \sqrt{x}$, and $-f(x) = -\sqrt{-x}$. Since, $f(-x) \neq -f(x)$ and $f(-x) \neq f(x)$. It is neither.

65. If $f(x) = \sqrt{1 - x^2}$, then $f(-x) = \sqrt{1 - (-x)^2} = \sqrt{1 - x^2}$, which is equal to $f(x) \Rightarrow$ it is even.

66. If $f(x) = \sqrt{x^2}$, then $f(-x) = \sqrt{(-x)^2} = \sqrt{x^2}$, which is equal to $f(x) \Rightarrow$ it is even.

67. If $f(x) = \dfrac{1}{1 + x^2}$, then $f(-x) = \dfrac{1}{1 + (-x)^2} = \dfrac{1}{1 + x^2}$, which is equal to $f(x) \Rightarrow$ it is even.

68. If $f(x) = \dfrac{1}{x}$, then $f(-x) = \dfrac{1}{-x} = -\dfrac{1}{x}$, and $-f(x) = -\dfrac{1}{x}$. Since $f(-x) = -f(x)$ it is odd.

69. If $f(x) = |\, x + 2 \,|$, then $f(-x) = |\, -x + 2 \,|$, and $-f(x) = -|\, x + 2 \,|$. Since $f(x) \neq f(-x)$ and $f(-x) \neq -f(x)$. It is neither.

70. If $f(x) = \dfrac{1}{x + 1}$, then $f(-x) = \dfrac{1}{-x + 1}$, and $-f(x) = -\dfrac{1}{x + 1}$. Since, $f(x) \neq f(-x)$ and $f(-x) \neq -f(x)$. It is neither.

71. Notice that $f(-100) = 56$ and $f(100) = -56$. In general, since $f(-x) = -f(x)$ holds for each $x$ in the table, $f$ is odd.

72. Since $f(3) = -4$ and $f(-3) = -2$, $f$ is neither odd nor even.

73. Since $f$ is even, the condition $f(-x) = f(x)$ must hold. For example, since $f(-3) = 21$, $f(3)$ must also equal 21. The value assigned to $f(0)$ makes no difference. See Figure 73.

| $x$ | $-3$ | $-2$ | $-1$ | 0 | 1 | 2 | 3 |
|---|---|---|---|---|---|---|---|
| $f(x)$ | 21 | $-12$ | $-25$ | 1 | $-25$ | $-12$ | 21 |

Figure 73

74. Since $f$ is odd, the condition $f(-x) = -f(x)$ must hold. For example, since $f(-5) = 13$, $f(5)$ must equal $-13$. See Figure 74. Note that for any odd function $f(0) = 0$.

| $x$ | $-5$ | $-3$ | $-2$ | 0 | 2 | 3 | 5 |
|---|---|---|---|---|---|---|---|
| $f(x)$ | 13 | 1 | $-5$ | 0 | 5 | $-1$ | $-13$ |

Figure 74

75. Since $f$ is an odd function and $(-5, -6)$ and $(-3, 4)$ are on the graph of $f$, then $(5, 6)$ and $(3, -4)$ are on the graph. Thus, $f(5) = 6$ and $f(3) = -4$.

76. Since $f$ is an even function and $(1 - a, b + 1)$ is on the graph of $f$, then $(-(1 - a), b + 1)$ is on the graph. Thus, $f(a - 1) = b + 1$.

77. Sketch any linear function that passes through the origin will work. For example, the graph of $y = x$ is shown in Figure 77.

78. Since a constant function is also a linear function, any constant function will work. For example, the graph of $y = 2$ is shown in Figure 78.

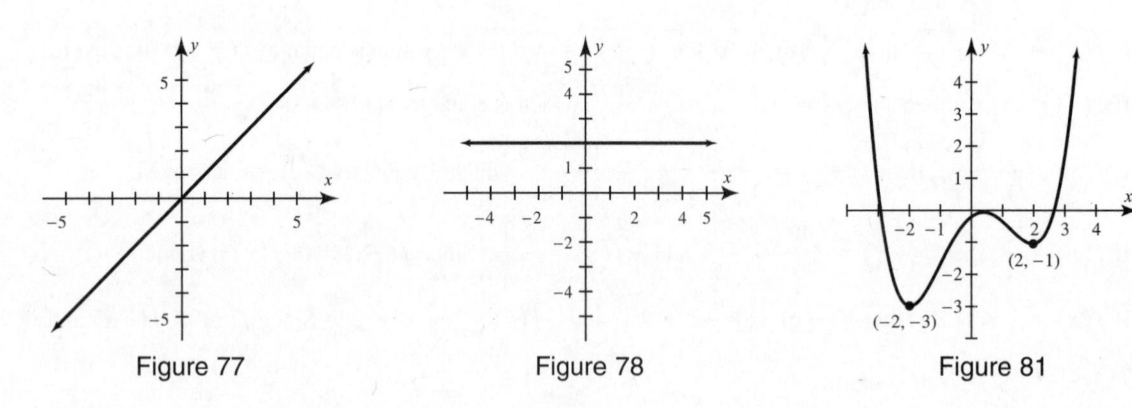


Figure 77 Figure 78 Figure 81

79. No. If (2, 5) is on the graph of an odd function $f$, then so is (–2, –5). Since $f$ would pass through (–3, –4) and then (–2, –5), it could not always be increasing.

80. No. If $(x, y)$ is on the graph of $f$, then so is $(-x, y)$. A decreasing function cannot have two points on it's graph with the same $y$-coordinate.

81. Plot points $(-2, -3)$ and $(2, -1)$ and make them minima. See Figure 81.

82. Plot point $(-1, -2)$ and make it a minima and point $(1, 2)$ and make it a maxima. See Figure 82.

83. Plot point $(2, 3)$ and make it a maxima. See Figure 83. Yes, it could be quadratic, but it does not have to be quadratic.

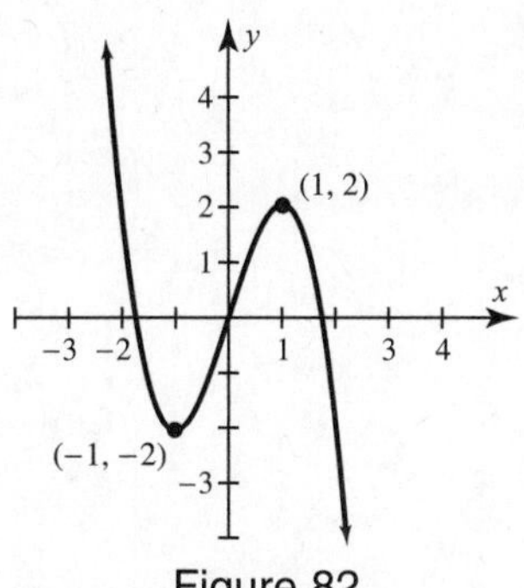


Figure 82

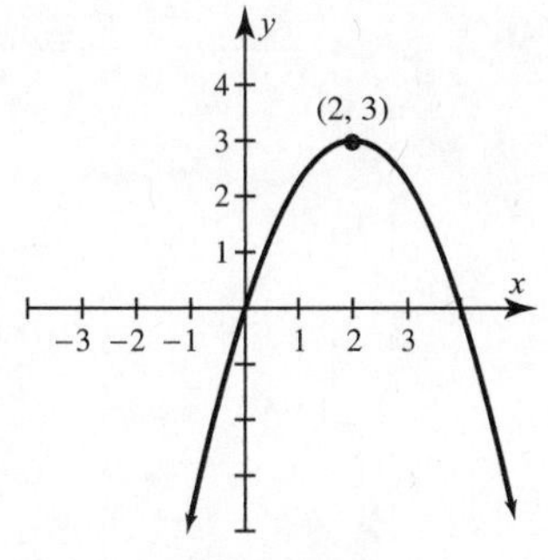


Figure 83

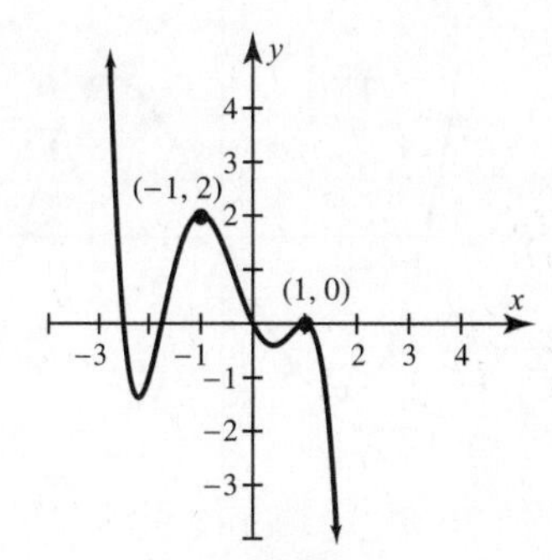


Figure 84

84. Plot points $(-1, 2)$ and $(1, 0)$ and make them both maxima. See Figure 84.

85. Shift the graph of $y = f(x) = 4x - \frac{x^3}{3}$ to the left 1 unit to get the graph of

$y = f(x + 1) = 4(x + 1) - \frac{(x + 1)^3}{3}$. See Figure 85.

86. Shift the graph of $y = f(x) = 4x - \frac{x^3}{3}$ down 2 units to get the graph of $y = f(x) - 2 = 4x - \frac{x^3}{3} - 2$. See Figure 86.

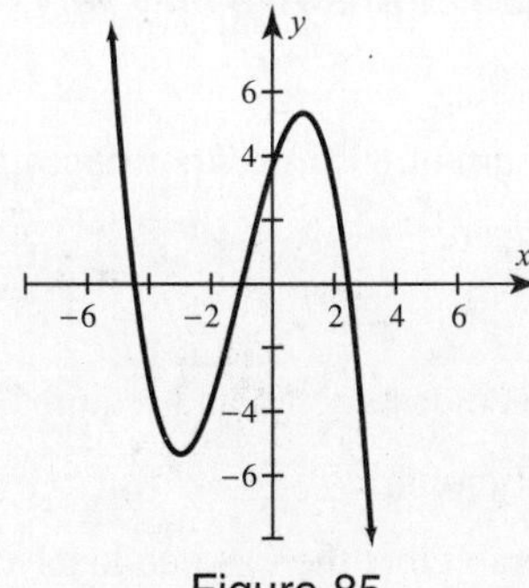


Figure 85

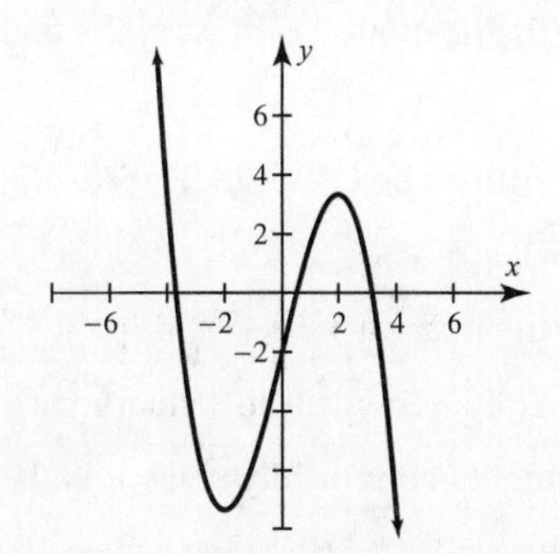


Figure 86

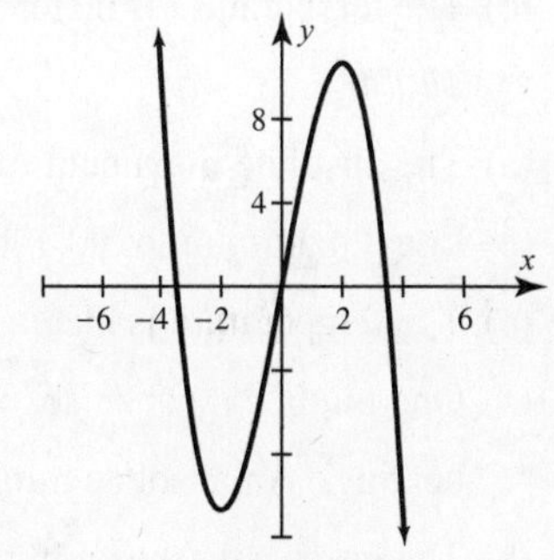


Figure 87

87. Sketch the graph of $y = f(x) = 4x - \frac{x^3}{3}$ vertically by multiplying each $y$-value by 2, that is, each $(x, y)$ point becomes $(x, 2y)$, to get the graph of $y = 2f(x) = 2\left(4x - \frac{x^3}{3}\right) = 8x - \frac{2}{3}x^3$. See Figure 87.

88. Sketch the graph of $y = f(x) = 4x - \frac{x^3}{3}$ horizontally by multiplying each $x$-value by 2, that is, each $(x, y)$ point becomes $(2x, y)$, to get the graph of $y = f\left(\frac{1}{2}x\right) = 4\left(\frac{1}{2}x\right) - \frac{(\frac{1}{2}x)^3}{3} = 2x - \frac{x^3}{24}$. See Figure 88.

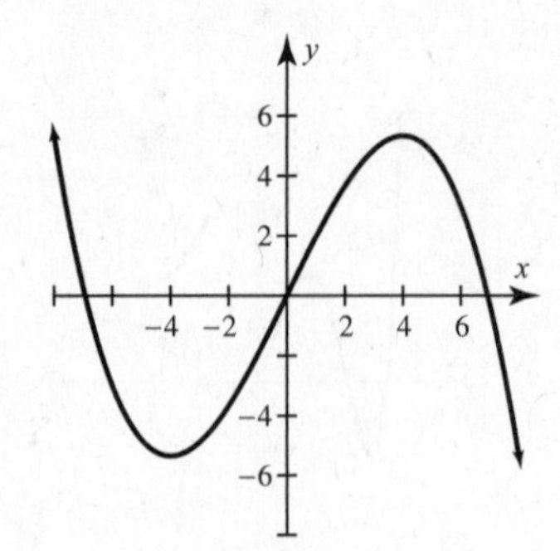

Figure 88

89. The first equation graph is transformed 1 unit left $\Rightarrow y = f(x+1) - 2$ increases on $[0, 3]$. The second equation graph is transformed across the $x$-axis and transformed 2 units right $\Rightarrow y = -f(x-2)$ decreases on $[3, 6]$.

90. The first equation graph is reflected across the $y$-axis $\Rightarrow y = f(-x) + 1$ increases on$(-\infty, 0]$. The second equation graph is reflected across the $x$-axis $\Rightarrow y = -f(x) - 1$ increases on $[0, \infty)$.

91. (a) An absolute maximum of approximately 84°F occurs when $x \approx 5$. An absolute minumum of approximately 63°F occurs when $x \approx 1.6$. These are the high and low temperatures between 1 p.m. and 6 p.m. *Answers may vary slightly.*

(b) Local maxima of approximately 78°F and 84°F occur when $x \approx 2.9$ and 5, respectively. Local mimima of approximately 63°F and 72°F occur when $x \approx 1.6$ and 3.8. *Answers may vary slightly.*

(c) The temperature is increasing on the intervals $1.6 \le x \le 2.9$ and $3.8 \le x \le 5$. *Answers may vary slightly.*

92. (a) The absolute maximum of 90°F occurs when $x \approx 7$. The absolute minumum of 69°F occurs when $x \approx 1$.

(b) Local maximum of 90°F occurs when $x \approx 7$.

(c) The temperature is increasing on the interval $1 \le x \le 7$.

93. (a) One might expect an absolute maximum to occur in January since it is the coldest month and requires the heating. An absolute minimum might occur in July since it is the warmest month.

(b) The graph $f$ is shown in both Figures 93a & 93b. One can see from the graph that there is one local maximum and one local minimum where $1 \le x \le 12$. The peak is near the point (1.46, 140.06) and the valley is located near (7.12, 14.78). This means that the peak heating expense of \$140 occurs in January $(x \approx 1)$. The minimum heating cost is during July $(x \approx 7)$ when it is roughly \$15.

[1, 12, 1] by [0, 150, 10]

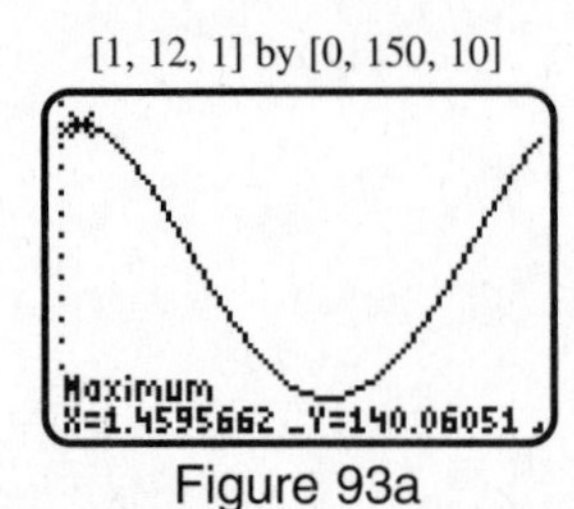

Figure 93a

[1, 12, 1] by [0, 150, 10]

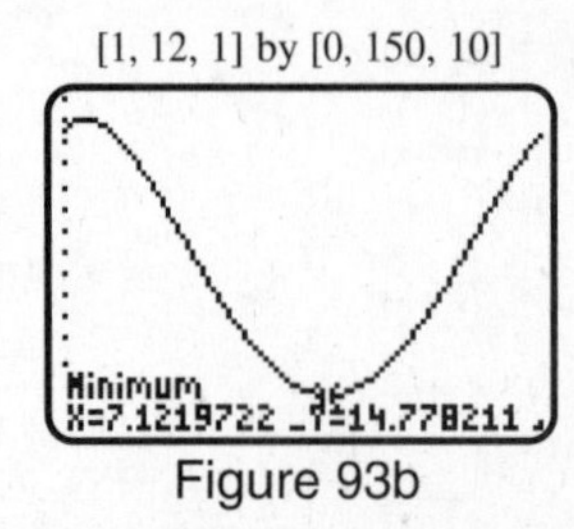

Figure 93b

94. (a) $f(65) = -0.0000285(65)^3 + 0.0057(65)^2 - 0.48(65) + 34.4 \approx 19.45568 \Rightarrow 19.5$. In 1965 there were approximately 19.5 births per 1000 people.

(b) From the graphs of $f$ we see that the absolute maximum of 34.4 occurs when $x = 0$ and the absolute minimum of 13.9 occurs when $x = 105$. Therefore, the maximum birth rate of 34.4 was in 1900 and the minimum birth rate was 13.9 in 2005. See Figures 94a & 94b.

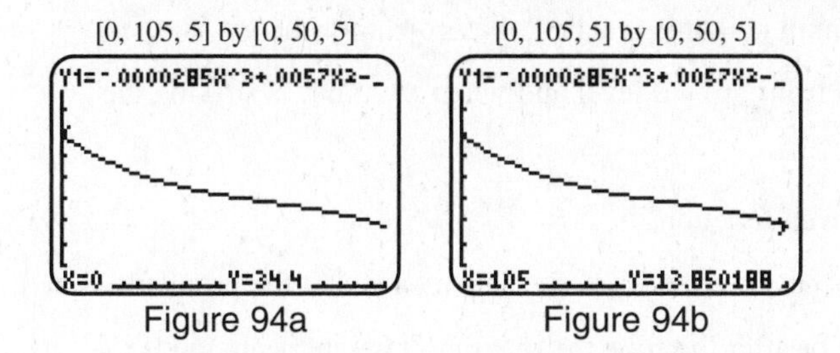

Figure 94a Figure 94b

95. (a) $f(5) = -0.00113(5)^3 + 0.0408(5)^2 - 0.432(5) + 7.66 \approx 8.32$; in 1955 U.S. consumption of energy was about 8.32 quadrillion Btu.

(b) The graph of $f$ is shown in Figure 95b; the energy consumption increased, reached a maximum value, and the started to decrease.

(c) The local maximum is approximately 14.5 when $x \approx 23.5$. In 1973 energy use peaked at 14.5 quadrillion Btu. See Figure 95c.

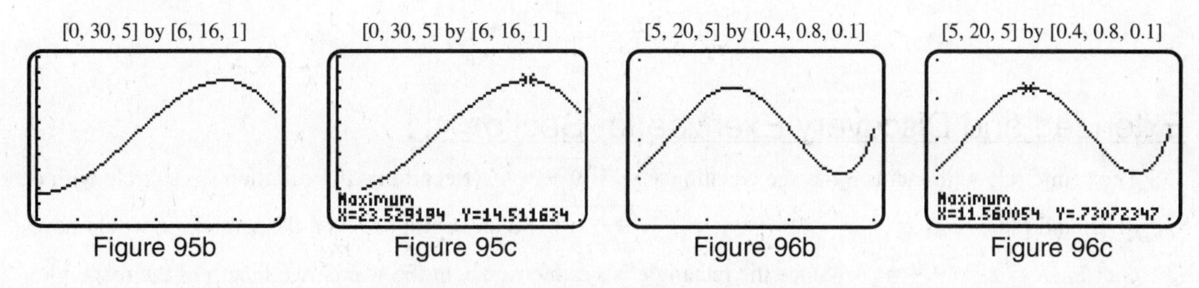

Figure 95b Figure 95c Figure 96b Figure 96c

96. (a) $f(10) = 0.0001234(10)^4 - 0.005689(10)^3 + 0.08792(10)^2 - 0.5145(10) + 1.514 \approx 0.706$; in 1970 U.S. consumption of natural gas was about 0.706 trillion cubic feet.

(b) The graph of $f$ is shown in Figure 96b; the natural gas consumption increased, reached a maximum value, decreased, reached a minimum value, and then started to increase again.

(c) There is a local maximum of approximately 0.73 when $x \approx 11.6$. In 1971 natural gas use peaked at 0.73 trillion cubic feet. There is a local minimum of approximately 0.51 when $x \approx 18$. In 1978 the natural gas consumption reached a minimum of 0.51 trillion cubic feet. See Figure 96c.

97. (a) Since the graph of $f$ is symmetric with respect to the $y$-axis, it is a graphical representation of an even function.

(b) If $f$ represents the average temperature in the month $x$, $f(1) = f(-1)$. Thus, the average monthly temperature in August is also 83°F.

(c) The average monthly temperatures in March and November are equal, since $f(-4) = f(4)$.

(d) In Austin the average monthly temperature is symmetric about July. In July the highest average monthly temperature occurs. In January the lowest temperature occurs. The pairs June-August, May-September, April-October, March-November, and February-December have approximately the same average temperatures.

98. (a) Since $h(x) = -16x^2 + h_{\text{max}}$ and $h_{\text{max}} = 400$. Let $h(x) = -16x^2 + 400$. Then, it follows that $h(-2) = h(2) = -16(\pm 2)^2 + 400 = 336$. Two seconds before $(x = -2)$ and two seconds after $(x = 2)$ the time when the maximum height is reached, the projectile's height is 336 feet. When $x = -2$, the projectile is moving upward, whereas when $x = 2$, the projectile is moving downward.

(b) $h(x) = -16x^2 + 400 \Rightarrow h(-5) = h(5) = -16(\pm 5)^2 + 400 = 0$. Five seconds before $(x = -5)$ and five seconds after $(x = 5)$ when the maximum height is reached, the projectile's height is 0 feet. When $x = -5$, the object is being shot upward from ground level and when $x = 5$, it is striking the ground.

(c) The graph of $h$ is shown in Figure 98. $h$ is an even function.

(d) Since $h$ is an even function, $h(-x) = h(x)$ whenever $-5 \le x \le 5$. This means that the projectile is at exactly the same height either $x$ seconds before or after the time the maximum height is attained.

[-5, 5, 1] by [0, 500, 100]

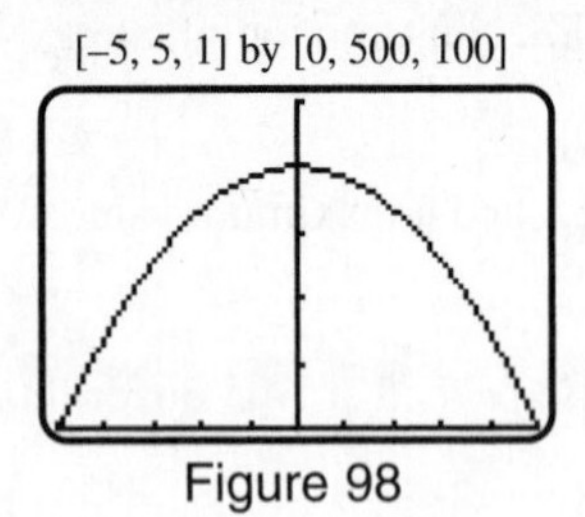

Figure 98

## Extended and Discovery Exercise for Section 4.1

1. The semicircle with radius 3 has the equation $y = \sqrt{9 - x^2}$. (Recall that the equation for a circle with center (0, 0) and radius 3 is $x^2 + y^2 = 9 \Rightarrow y = \pm\sqrt{9 - x^2}$. So any point $(x, y)$ on the semicircle would have coordinates $(x, \sqrt{9 - x^2})$. Since the rectangle is symmetric about the $y$-axis, the length of the rectangle $= 2x$, as shown in Figure 1a. The width of the rectangle $= y$.

The area of the rectangle is: $A = lw = 2x(y) = 2x(\sqrt{9 - x^2})$. To find the maximum area, graph the function $A(x) = 2x\sqrt{9 - x^2}$ on a graphing calculator, and then find the maximum value. See Figure 1b. The maximum area of 9 occurs when $x \approx 2.12$. Thus, the length of the rectangle is $2x \approx 2(2.12) \approx 4.24$, and the height is $y = \sqrt{9 - x^2} \approx \sqrt{9 - (2.12)^2} \approx 2.12$.

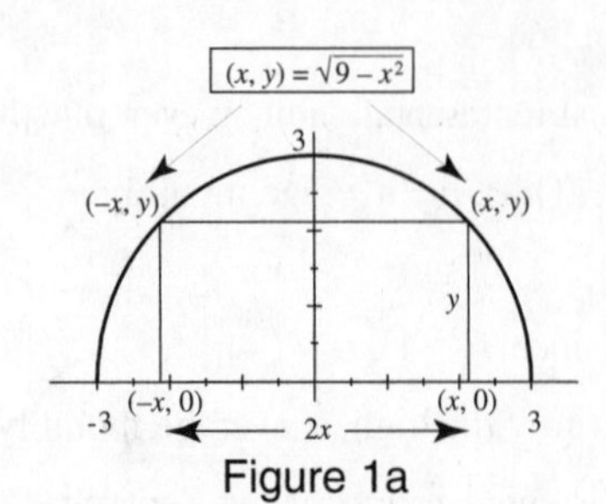


Figure 1a

[0, 5, 1] by [0, 10, 1]

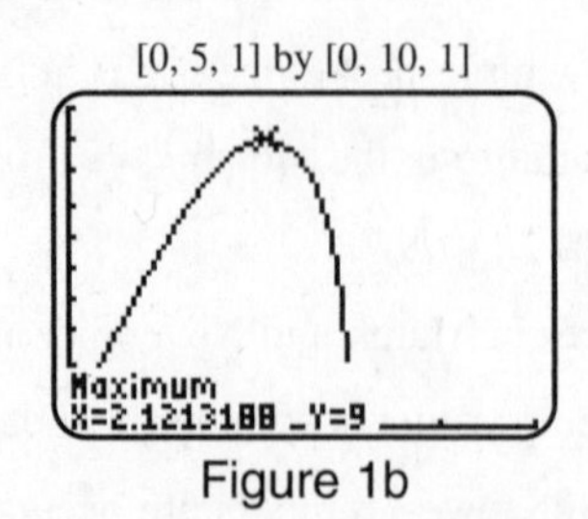


Figure 1b

2. (a) Let $x =$ the length of the side of the square, then the area of the square is $x^2$, then the length of the wire remaining is $20 - 4x$. This length is then divided evenly into 3 sides or $y = \frac{20-4x}{3}$. The height of this triangle by the 30-60-90 rule is $\frac{1}{2} \cdot \frac{20-4x}{3} \cdot \sqrt{3} = \frac{\sqrt{3}}{2}\left(\frac{20-4x}{3}\right)$. To find area of the triangle we take $\frac{1}{2} \cdot b \cdot h \Rightarrow \frac{1}{2} \cdot \frac{20-4x}{3} \cdot \frac{20-4x}{3} \cdot \frac{\sqrt{3}}{2} = \frac{\sqrt{3}}{4}\left(\frac{20-4x}{3}\right)^2$. Therefore the area of both the square and triangle is $x^2 + \frac{\sqrt{3}}{4}\left(\frac{20-4x}{3}\right)^2$.

(b) To find the minimum combined area, graph the function $A(x) = x^2 + \frac{\sqrt{3}}{4}\left(\frac{20-4x}{3}\right)^2$ on a graphing calculator for $x$-values between 0 and 20, then find the minimum value. See Figure 2. The minimum value occurs when $x \approx 2.175$. The length of wire used for the square should be about $4(2.175) = 8.7$ inches.

[0, 10, 1] by [0, 20, 2]

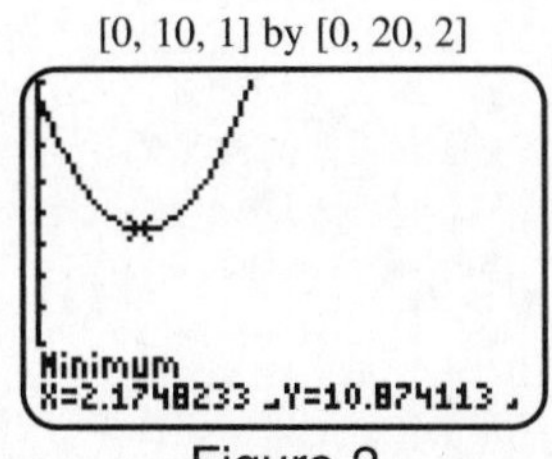


Figure 2

[0, 20, 2] by [0, 5, 1]

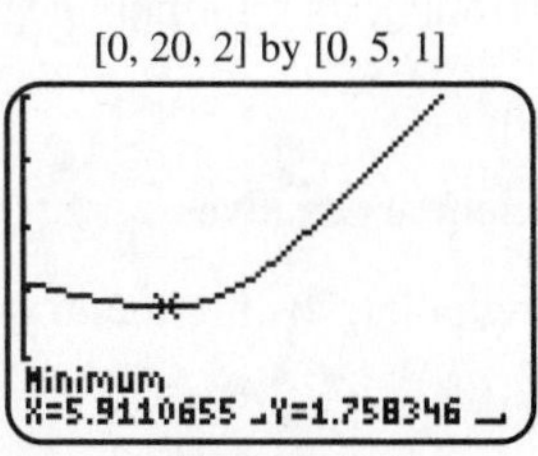


Figure 3

3. (a) Since $r \cdot t = D$ the time to shore is $4 \cdot t = 3 \Rightarrow t = \frac{3}{4}$ hour or 45 minutes; and the time to the cabin is $7 \cdot t = 8 \Rightarrow t = \frac{8}{7}$ hours or about 69 minutes. Therefore the combined time is $45 + 69 = 114$ minutes or 1 hour and 54 minutes.

(b) Using pythagorean theorem; the distance to the cabin is $3^2 + 8^2 = d^2 \Rightarrow 9 + 64 = d^2 \Rightarrow d^2 = 73 \Rightarrow d \approx 8.5$. Now the time is $4 \cdot t = 8.5 \Rightarrow t = \frac{8.5}{4} \Rightarrow t \approx 128$ minutes or 2 hours and 8 minutes.

(c) Let $x =$ the distance jogged, then the distance rowed by using pythagorean theorem is;

$3^2 + (8 - x)^2 = d^2$ or $d = \sqrt{x^2 - 16x + 73} \Rightarrow$ the time needed to reach the cabin if $t = \frac{d}{r}$ is

$t = \frac{d(\text{jogged})}{7} + \frac{d(\text{rowed})}{4}$ or $t = \frac{x}{7} + \frac{\sqrt{x^2 - 16x + 73}}{4}$. Graph this equation to find the minimum time. See Figure 3. The minimum time is $t \approx 1.76$ hours or about 1 hour 46 minutes.

## 4.2: Polynomial Functions and Models

1. (a) Turning points occur near (1.6, 3.6), (3, 1.2), and (4.4, 3.6).

   (b) The turning points represent the times and distances where the runner turned around and jogged the other direction. In this example, after 1.6 minutes the runner is 360 feet from the starting line. The runner turns and jogs toward the starting line. After 3 minutes the runner is 120 feet from the starting line, turns, and jogs away from the starting line. After 4.4 minutes the runner is again 360 feet from the starting line. The runner turns and jogs back to the starting line.

2. (a) The turning point corresponds to the vertex. Its coordinates are approximately (2, 64).

   (b) This point represents the time and height when the stone started to fall. That is, after traveling for 2 seconds and reaching maximum height of 64 feet, the stone began to fall.

3. (a) It has no turning points and one $x$-intercept of 0.5.

   (b) The leading coefficient is positive, since the slope of the line is positive.

   (c) Since the graph appears to be a line that is not horizontal, its minimum degree is 1.

4. (a) It has one turning point and 2 $x$-intercepts of $-3$ and 2.

   (b) Since the parabola opens down, the leading coefficient is negative.

   (c) The graph appears to be a parabola with one turning point. Its minimum degree is 2.

5. (a) It has three turning points and three $x$-intercepts of $-6, -1, 6$.

   (b) Since the graph goes down for large values of $x$, the leading coefficient is negative.

   (c) Since the graph has three turning points, its minimum degree is 4.

6. (a) It has two turning points and three $x$-intercepts of $-2, 0, 2$.

   (b) Since the graph goes up on the left and down on the right, the leading coefficient is negative.

   (c) The graph has two turning points. The minimum degree of $f$ is 3.

7. (a) It has four turning points and five $x$-intercepts of $-3, -1, 0, 1$, and 2.

   (b) Since the graph goes up for large values of $x$, the leading coefficient is positive.

   (c) Since the graph has four turning points, its minimum degree is 5.

8. (a) It has three turning points and four $x$-intercepts of $-4, -2, 2$, and 3.

   (b) Since the graph goes up on the left and up on the right, the leading coefficient is positive.

   (c) The graph has three turning points. The minimum degree of $f$ is 4.

9. (a) It has two turning points and one $x$-intercept of $-3$.

   (b) Since the graph goes down to the left and up to the right, the leading coefficient is positive.

   (c) The graph has two turning points. The minimum degree of $f$ is 3.

10. (a) It has four turning points and five $x$-intercepts of $-2, -1, 0, 1$, and 2.

    (b) Since the graph goes up to the left and down to the right, the leading coefficient is negative.

    (c) The graph has four turning points. The minimum degree of $f$ is 5.

11. (a) It has one turning point and two $x$-intercepts of $-1$, and 2.

    (b) Since the graph is a parabola opening up, the leading coefficient is positive.

    (c) The graph has one turning point. The minimum degree of $f$ is 2.

12. (a) It has zero turning points and one $x$-intercept of 0.5.

    (b) The leading coefficient is negative, since the slope of the line is negative.

    (c) The graph appears to be a line that is not horizontal. The minimum degree of $f$ is 1.

13. (a) Graph d.

    (b) There is one turning point at (1, 0).

    (c) It has one $x$-intercept: $x = 1$.

    (d) The only local minimum is 0.

    (e) The absolute minimum is 0. There is no absolute maximum.

14. (a) Graph c.

    (b) The turning points are at (–1, –2) and (1, 2).

    (c) The three $x$-intercepts are $x \approx -1.7$, $x = 0$, and $x \approx 1.7$.

    (d) The local minimum is –2, and the local maximum is 2.

    (e) There are no absolute extrema.

15. (a) Graph b.

    (b) The turning points are at (–3, 27) and (1, –5).

    (c) The three $x$-intercepts are $x \approx -4.9$, $x = 0$, and $x \approx 1.9$.

    (d) The local minimum is –5, and the local maximum is 27.

    (e) There are no absolute extrema.

16. (a) Graph f.

    (b) The turning points are at (–2, –16), (0, 0), and (2, –16).

    (c) The three $x$-intercepts are $x \approx -2.8$, $x = 0$, and $x \approx 2.8$.

    (d) The local minimum is –16, and the local maximum is 0.

    (e) The absolute minimum is $-16$, and there is no absolute maximum.

17. (a) Graph a.

    (b) The turning points are at (–2, 16), (0, 0), and (2, 16).

    (c) The three $x$-intercepts are $x \approx -2.8$, $x = 0$, and $x \approx 2.8$.

    (d) The local minimum is 0, and the local maximum is 16.

    (e) The absolute maximum is 16. There is no absolute minimum.

18. (a) Graph e.

    (b) The turning points are near (–2, 1.3), (–1, –1.8), (0, 0), and (1, –3.2).

    (c) The four $x$-intercepts are $x \approx -2.3$, $x \approx -1.6$, $x = 0$, and $x \approx 1.4$.

    (d) The two local minimums are approximately –1.8 and –3.2. The two local maximums are approximately 1.4 and 0.

    (e) There are no absolute extrema.

19. (a) The graph of $f(x) = \frac{1}{9}x^3 - 3x$ is shown in Figure 19.

    (b) There are two turning points located at (–3, 6) and (3, –6).

    (c) At $x = -3$ there is a local maximum of 6 and at $x = 3$ there is a local minimum of –6.

20. (a) The graph of $f(x) = x^2 - 4x - 3$ is shown in Figure 20.

    (b) There is one turning point located at (2, –7).

    (c) At $x = 2$ there is a local minimum of –7.

[–10, 10, 1] by [–10, 10, 1]

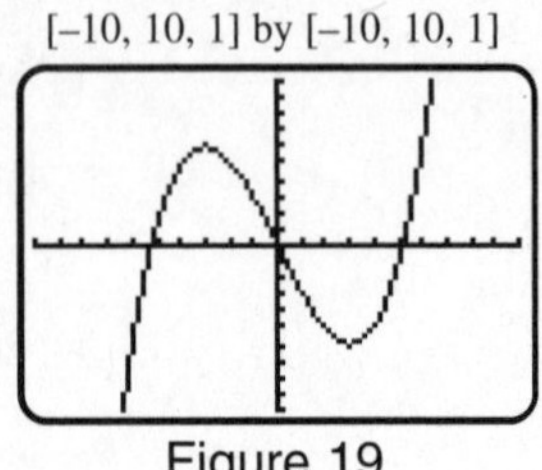

Figure 19

[–10, 10, 1] by [–10, 10, 1]

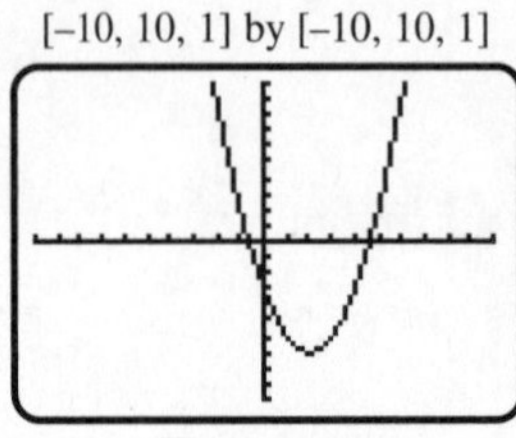

Figure 20

[–10, 10, 1] by [–10, 10, 1]

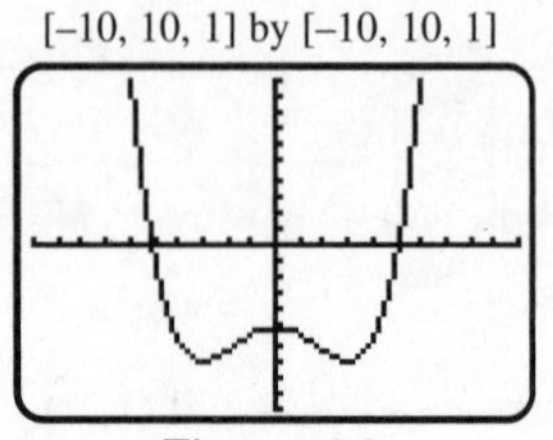

Figure 21

[–10, 10, 1] by [–10, 10, 1]

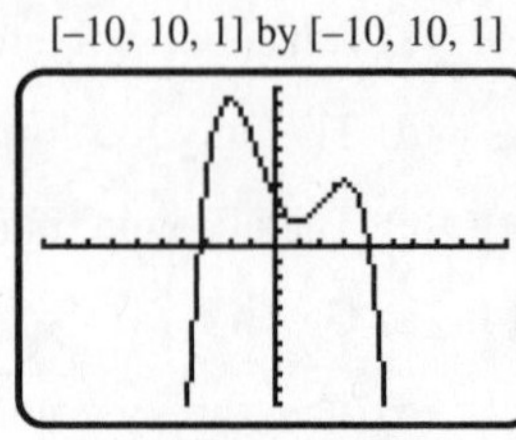

Figure 22

21. (a) The graph of $f(x) = 0.025x^4 - 0.45x^2 - 3$ is shown in Figure 21.

    (b) There are three turning points located at (–3, –7.025), (0, –5), and (3, –7.025).

    (c) At $x = \pm 3$ there is a local minimum of –7.025. At $x = 0$ there is a local maximum of –5.

22. (a) The graph of $f(x) = -\frac{1}{8}x^4 + \frac{1}{3}x^3 + \frac{5}{4}x^2 - 3x + 3$ is shown in Figure 22.

    (b) There are three turning points located at $(-2, 9.\overline{3})$, $(1, 1.458\overline{3})$, and (3, 4.125).

    (c) At $x = -2$ and 3 there are local maximums of $9.\overline{3}$ and 4.125, respectively. At $x = 1$ there is a local minimum of $1.458\overline{3}$

23. (a) The graph of $f(x) = 1 - 2x + 3x^2$ is shown in Figure 23.

    (b) There is one turning point located at $\left(\frac{1}{3}, \frac{2}{3}\right) \approx (0.333, 0.667)$.

    (c) At $x = \frac{1}{3}$ there is a local minimum of $\frac{2}{3} \approx 0.667$.

[–10, 10, 1] by [–10, 10, 1]

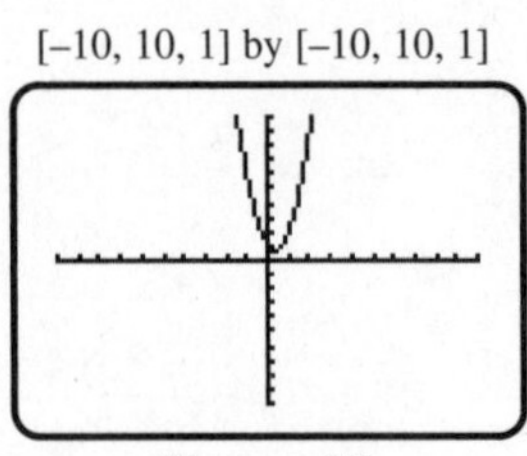

Figure 23

[–10, 10, 1] by [–10, 10, 1]

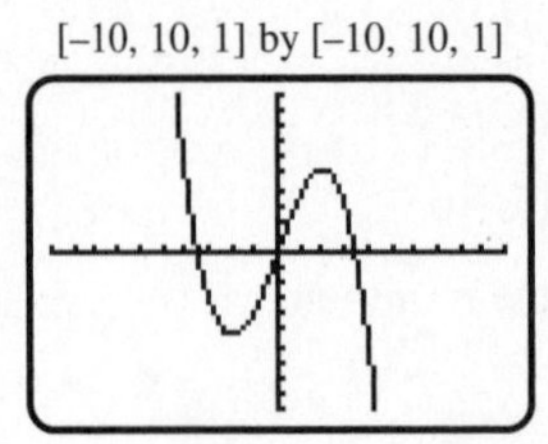

Figure 24

24. (a) The graph of $f(x) = 4x - \frac{1}{3}x^3$ is shown in Figure 24.

    (b) There are two turning points located at $(-2, -5.\overline{3})$ and $(2, 5.\overline{3})$.

    (c) There is a local minimum of $-5.\overline{3}$, and there is a local maximum of $5.\overline{3}$.

25. (a) The graph of $f(x) = \frac{1}{3}x^3 + \frac{1}{2}x^2 - 2x$ is shown in Figure 25.

    (b) The turning points are at $\left(-2, \frac{10}{3}\right) \approx (-2, 3.333)$ and $\left(1, -\frac{7}{6}\right) \approx (1, -1.167)$.

    (c) There is a local minimum of $-\frac{7}{6} \approx -1.167$, and there is a local maximum of $\frac{10}{3} \approx 3.333$.

[−10, 10, 1] by [−10, 10, 1]

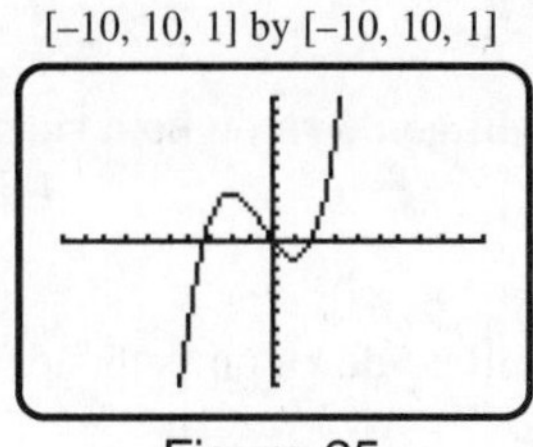

Figure 25

[−10, 10, 1] by [−10, 10, 1]

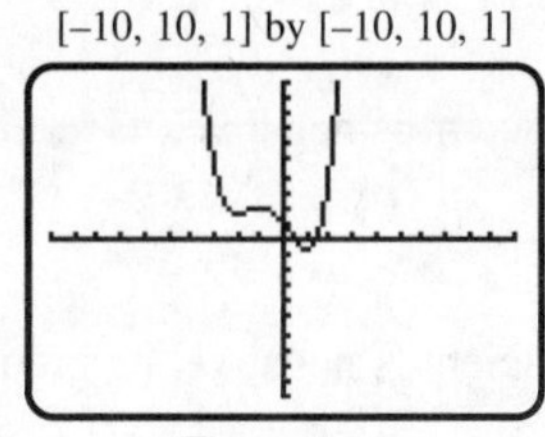

Figure 26

26. (a) The graph of $f(x) = \frac{1}{4}x^4 + \frac{2}{3}x^3 - \frac{1}{2}x^2 - 2x + 1$ is shown in Figure 26.

    (b) The turning points are at $(-2, 1.\overline{6})$, $(-1, 2.08\overline{3})$, and $(1, -0.58\overline{3})$.

    (c) There is a local maximum of $2.08\overline{3}$, and there are local minimum values of $1.\overline{6}$ and $-0.58\overline{3}$.

27. (a) The degree is 1 and the leading coefficient is $-2$.

    (b) Since the degree of $f$ is 1 and the lead coefficient is negative the graph is a line with a negative slope $\Rightarrow$ it goes up on the left end and down on the right.

28. (a) The degree is 1 and the leading coefficient is $\frac{2}{3}$.

    (b) Since the degree of $f$ is 1 and the lead coefficient is positive the graph is a line with a positive slope $\Rightarrow$ it goes down on the left end and up on the right.

29. (a) The degree is 2 and the leading coefficient is 1.

    (b) Since the degree of $f$ is 2 and the lead coefficient is positive the graph is a parabola that opens up on each side.

30. (a) The degree is 2 and the leading coefficient is $-\frac{1}{2}$.

    (b) Since the degree of $f$ is 2 and the lead coefficient is negative the graph is a parabola that opens down on each side.

31. (a) The degree is 3 and the leading coefficient is $-2$.

    (b) Since the degree of $f$ is odd and the lead coefficient is negative its graph will go up on the left and down on the right.

32. (a) The degree is 3 and the leading coefficient is $-\frac{1}{3}$.

    (b) Since the degree of $f$ is odd and the lead coefficient is negative its graph will go up on the left and down on the right.

33. (a) The degree is 3 and the leading coefficient is $-1$.

    (b) Since the degree of $f$ is odd and the leading coefficient is negative, its graph will go up on the left and down on the right.

34. (a) The degree is 4 and the leading coefficient is 1.

    (b) Since the degree of $f$ is even and the leading coefficient is positive, its graph will go up on both sides.

35. (a) The degree is 5 and the leading coefficient is 0.1.

    (b) Since the degree of $f$ is odd and the leading coefficient is positive, its graph will go down on the left and up on the right.

36. (a) The degree is 4 and the leading coefficient is –1.

    (b) Since the degree of $f$ is even and the leading coefficient is negative, its graph will go down on both sides.

37. (a) The degree is 2 and the leading coefficient is $-\frac{1}{2}$.

    (b) Since the degree of $f$ is even and the leading coefficient is negative, its graph will go down on both sides.

38. (a) The degree is 5 and the leading coefficient is $-0.2$.

    (b) Since the degree of $f$ is odd and the leading coefficient is negative, its graph will go up on the left and down on the right.

39. (a) A line graph of the data is shown in Figure 39.

    (b) The data appears to decrease, increase, and decrease. The line graph crosses the $x$-axis three times. Neither a linear or quadratic function could do this. Thus, $f$ must be degree 3.

    (c) Since $f$ rises to the left and falls to the right $a < 0$.

    (d) Using the cubic regession function on the calculator we find $f(x) = -x^3 + 8x$.

40. (a) A line graph of the data is shown in Figure 40.

    (b) The data appears linear so $f$ could be degree 1 with one $x$-intercept.

    (c) Since $f$ is always decreasing $a < 0$.

    (d) Using the linear regession function on the calculator we find $f(x) = -2x + 5$.

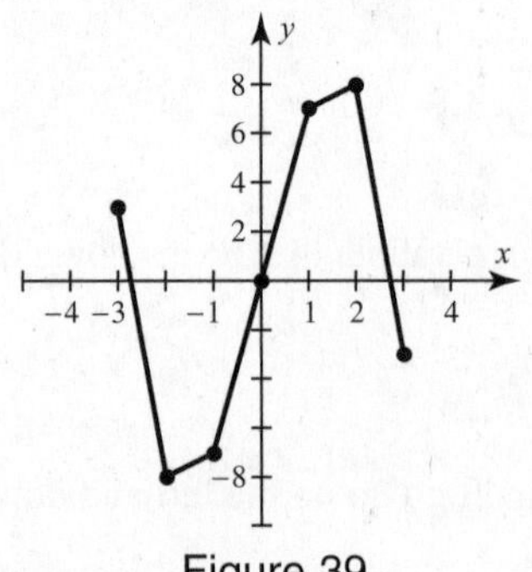


Figure 39

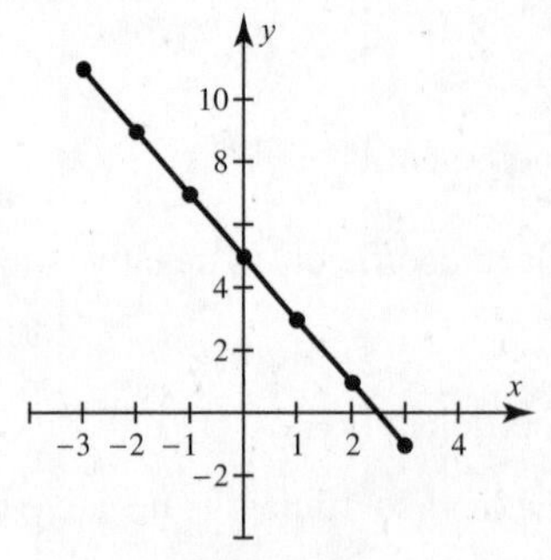


Figure 40

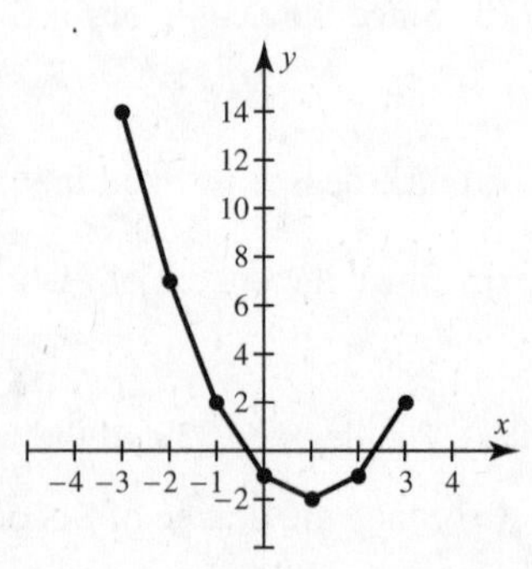


Figure 41

41. (a) A line graph of the data is shown in Figure 41.

    (b) The data decreases and then increases. This could not be a linear function. The data appears to be parabolic and the line graph crosses the $x$-axis twice. Since all zeros are real and between –3 and 3, $f$ must be degree 2 with two real zeros.

    (c) Since $f$ is opening upward $a > 0$.

    (d) Using the quadratic regession function on the calctator we find $f(x) = x^2 - 2x - 1$.

42. (a) A line graph of the data is shown in Figure 42.

    (b) The data increases and then decreases. The line graph crosses the $x$-axis two times. Since the data outlines a parabolic shape and the line graph crosses the $x$-axis twice, $f$ is degree 2.

    (c) Since $f$ is opening downward $a < 0$.

    (d) Using the quadratic regession function on the calclator we find $f(x) = -x^2 + 2x + 2$.

43. (a) See Figure 43.

    (b) The data increases then decreases then increases and the decreases. The graph crosses the $x$-axis 4 times. Therefore, $f$ is degree 4.

    (c) Since both ends of $f$ go down $a < 0$.

    (d) Using the quartic regession function on the calculator we find $f(x) = -x^4 + 3x^2 - 1$.

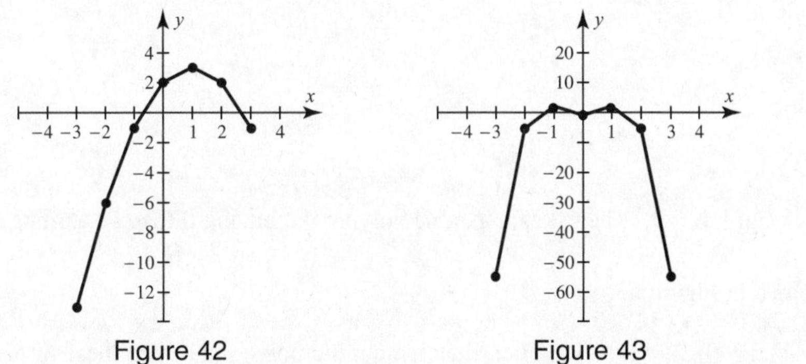

Figure 42 Figure 43

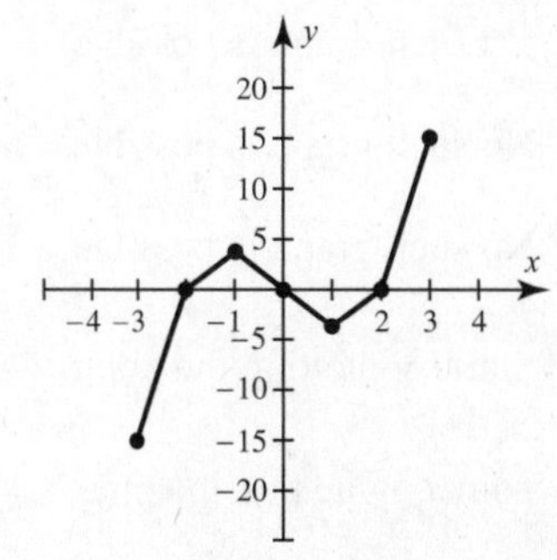

Figure 44

44. (a) See Figure 44.

    (b) The data increases then decreases and then increases. The graph crosses the $x$-axis 3 times. Therefore, $f$ is degree 3.

    (c) Since $f$ falls to the left and rises to the right $a > 0$.

    (d) Using the cubic regession function on the calculator we find $f(x) = x^3 - 4x$.

45. One possible graph is shown in Figure 45.

46. One possible graph is shown in Figure 46.

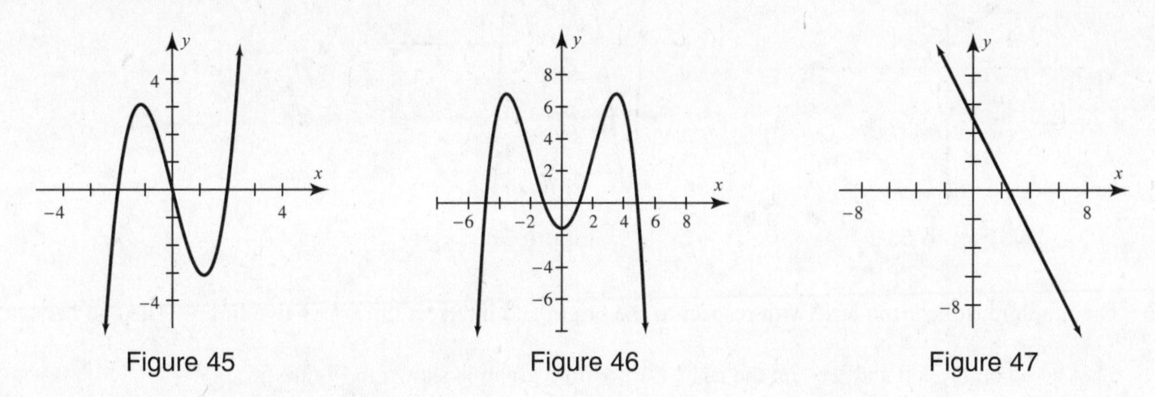

Figure 45 Figure 46 Figure 47

47. One possible graph is shown in Figure 47.

48. One possible graph is shown in Figure 48.

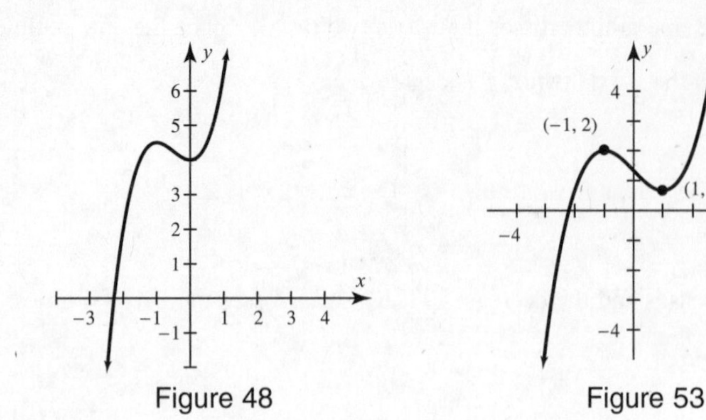

Figure 48 Figure 53

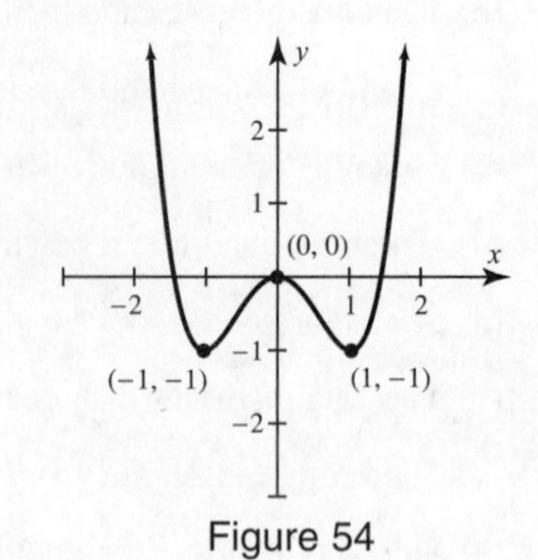

Figure 54

49. No such graph is possible.

50. No such graph is possible.

51. No such graph is possible.

52. No such graph is possible.

53. Start by plotting the points $(-1, 2)$ and $\left(1, \frac{2}{3}\right)$. Then sketch a cubic polynomial having these two turning points. One possible graph is shown in Figure 53.

54. Start by plotting the points $(-1, -1)$, $(0, 0)$, and $(1, -1)$. Then sketch a quartic polynomial with these turning points. One possible graph is shown in Figure 54.

55. Since a quadratic polynomial has only one turning point, $(-1, 2)$ must be the vertex. Plot the points $(-1, 2)$, $(-3, 4)$, and $(1, 4)$. Sketch a parabola passing through these points with a vertex of $(-1, 2)$. The parabola must open up. See Figure 55.

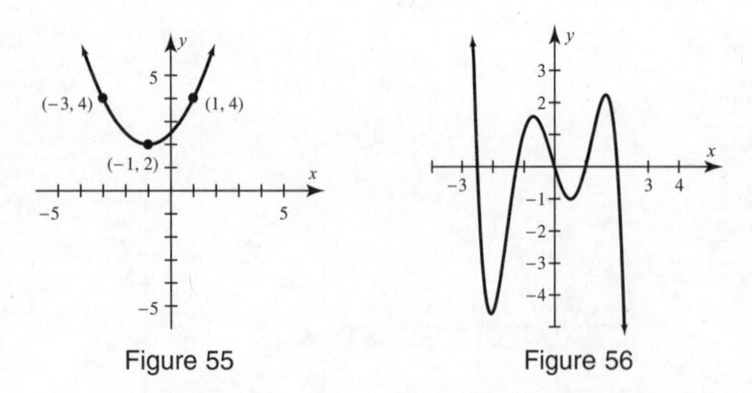

Figure 55 Figure 56

56. The graph must be symmetric with respect to the origin and intersect the $x$-axis five times. The end behavior must be $\infty$ on the left and $-\infty$ on the right. A possible graph is shown in Figure 56.

57. The graphs of $f(x) = 2x^4$, $g(x) = 2x^4 - 5x^2 + 1$, and $h(x) = 2x^4 + 3x^2 - x - 2$ are shown in Figures 57a-c. As the viewing rectangle increases in size, the graphs begin to look alike. Each formula contains the term $2x^4$. This term determines the end behavior of the graph for large values of $|x|$. The other terms are relatively small in absolute value by comparison when $|x| \geq 100$. End behavior is determined by the leading term.

[−4, 4, 1] by [−4, 4, 1]

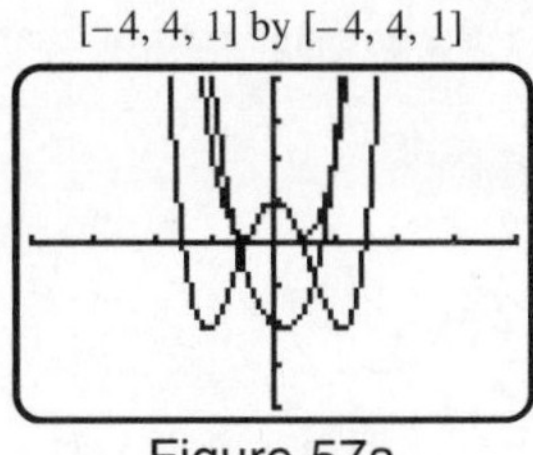

Figure 57a

[−10, 10, 1] by [−100, 100, 10]

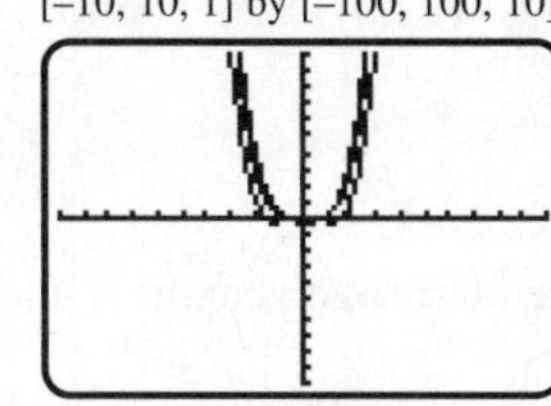

Figure 57b

[−100, 100, 10] by [$-10^6$, $10^6$, $10^5$]

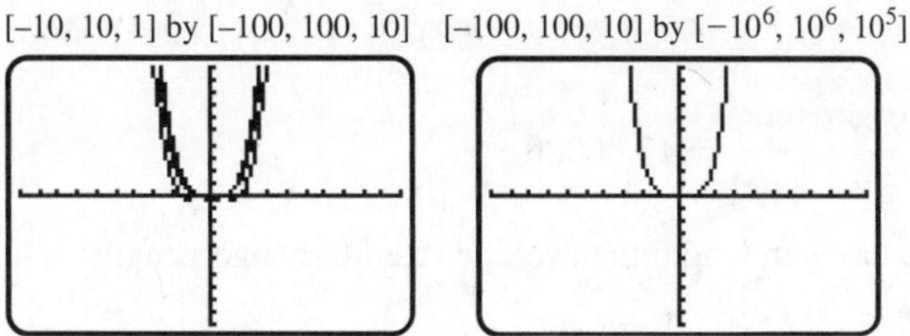

Figure 57c

58. The graphs of $f(x) = -x^3$, $g(x) = -x^3 + x^2 + 2$, and $h(x) = -x^3 - 2x^2 + x - 1$ are shown in Figures 58a-c. As the viewing rectangle increases in size, the graphs begin to look alike. Each formula contains the term $-x^3$. This term determines the end behavior of the graph for large values of $|x|$. The other terms are relatively small in absolute value by comparison when $|x| \geq 100$. End behavior is determined by the leading term.

[−4, 4, 1] by [−4, 4, 1]

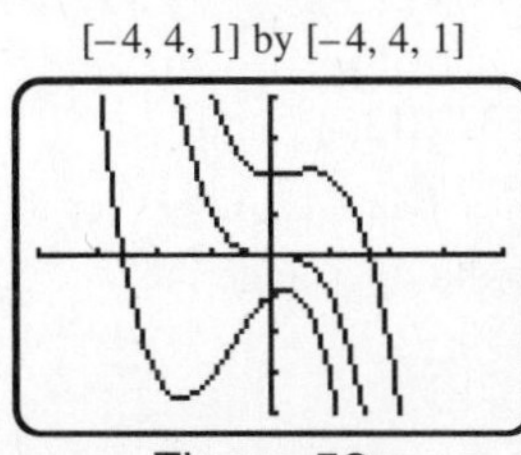

Figure 58a

[−10, 10, 1] by [−100, 100, 10]

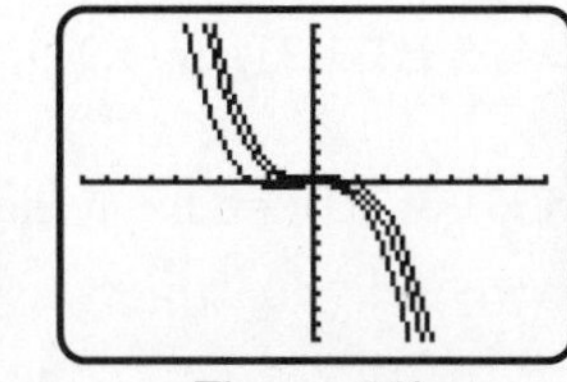

Figure 58b

[−100, 100, 10] by [$-10^5$, $10^5$, $10^4$]

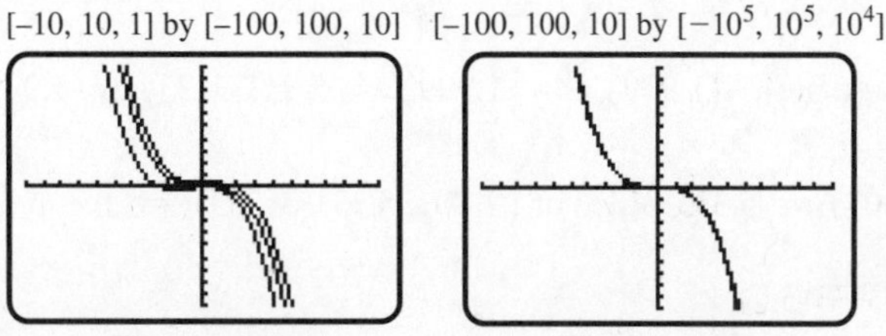

Figure 58c

59. For $f(x) = x$ we get $(0, 0)$ and $\left(\frac{1}{2}, \frac{1}{2}\right)$ $\Rightarrow$ the average rate of change is $\dfrac{\frac{1}{2} - 0}{\frac{1}{2} - 0} = \dfrac{\frac{1}{2}}{\frac{1}{2}} = 1$

For $g(x) = x^2$ we get $(0, 0)$ and $\left(\frac{1}{2}, \frac{1}{4}\right)$ $\Rightarrow$ the average rate of change is $\dfrac{\frac{1}{4} - 0}{\frac{1}{2} - 0} = \dfrac{\frac{1}{4}}{\frac{1}{2}} = 0.5$

For $h(x) = x^3$ we get $(0, 0)$ and $\left(\frac{1}{2}, \frac{1}{8}\right)$ $\Rightarrow$ the average rate of change is $\dfrac{\frac{1}{8} - 0}{\frac{1}{2} - 0} = \dfrac{\frac{1}{8}}{\frac{1}{2}} = 0.25$

It decreases with higher degree.

60. For $f(x) = x$ we get $(1, 1)$ and $\left(\frac{3}{2}, \frac{3}{2}\right)$ $\Rightarrow$ the average rate of change is $\dfrac{\frac{3}{2} - 1}{\frac{3}{2} - 1} = \dfrac{\frac{1}{2}}{\frac{1}{2}} = 1$

For $g(x) = x^2$ we get $(1, 1)$ and $\left(\frac{3}{2}, \frac{9}{4}\right)$ $\Rightarrow$ the average rate of change is $\dfrac{\frac{9}{4} - 1}{\frac{3}{2} - 1} = \dfrac{\frac{5}{4}}{\frac{1}{2}} = 2.5$

For $h(x) = x^3$ we get $(1, 1)$ and $\left(\frac{3}{2}, \frac{27}{8}\right)$ $\Rightarrow$ the average rate of change is $\dfrac{\frac{27}{8} - 1}{\frac{3}{2} - 1} = \dfrac{\frac{19}{8}}{\frac{1}{2}} = 4.75$

It increases with higher degree.

61. (a) For $[1.9, 2.1]$ we get: $(1.9, 6.859)$ and $(2.1, 9.261) \Rightarrow$ the average rate of change is $\dfrac{9.261 - 6.859}{2.1 - 1.9} = 12.01$

(b) For $[1.99, 2.01]$ we get: $(1.99, 7.880599)$ and $(2.01, 8.120601) \Rightarrow$ the average rate of change is

$\dfrac{8.120601 - 7.880599}{2.01 - 1.99} = 12.0001$

(c) For $[1.999, 2.001]$ we get: $(1.999, 7.988005999)$ and $(2.001, 8.012006001) \Rightarrow$ the average rate of change is

$\dfrac{8.012006001 - 7.988005999}{2.001 - 1.999} = 12.000001$

As the interval decreases in length the average rate of change is approaching 12.

62. (a) For $[1.9, 2.1]$ we get: $4(1.9) - \dfrac{1}{3}(1.9)^3 = 5.3137$ or $(1.9, 5.313\overline{6})$ and $4(2.1) - \dfrac{1}{3}(2.1)^3 = 5.313$ or

$(2.1, 5.313) \Rightarrow$ the average rate of change is: $\dfrac{5.313 - 5.313\overline{6}}{2.1 - 1.9} = -0.00\overline{3}$

(b) For $[1.99, 2.01]$ we get: $4(1.99) - \dfrac{1}{3}(1.99)^3 = 5.333133\overline{6}$ or $(1.99, 5.333133\overline{6})$ and $4(2.01) - \dfrac{1}{3}(2.01)^3 =$

$5.333133$ or $(2.01, 5.333133) \Rightarrow$ the average rate of change is: $\dfrac{5.333133 - 5.333133\overline{6}}{2.01 - 1.99} = \dfrac{-0.000000\overline{6}}{0.02} =$

$-0.0000\overline{3}$

(c) For $[1.999, 2.001]$ we get: $4(1.999) - \dfrac{1}{3}(1.999)^3 = 5.333331334$ or $(1.999, 5.333331334)$ and

$4(2.001) - \dfrac{1}{3}(2.001)^3 = 5.333331333$ or $(2.001, 5.333331333) \Rightarrow$ the average rate of change is:

$\dfrac{5.333331333 - 5.3333313334}{2.001 - 1.999} = -0.000000\overline{3}$

As the interval decreases in length the average rate of change is approaching 0.

63. (a) For $[1.9, 2.1]$ we get: $\dfrac{1}{4}(1.9)^4 - \dfrac{1}{3}(1.9)^3 = 0.97169\overline{16}$ or $(1.9, 0.97169\overline{16})$ and $\dfrac{1}{4}(2.1)^4 - \dfrac{1}{3}(2.1)^3 =$

$1.775025$ or $(2.1, 1.775025) \Rightarrow$ the average rate of change is: $\dfrac{1.775025 - 0.97169\overline{16}}{2.1 - 1.9} = 4.01\overline{6}$

(b) For $[1.99, 2.01]$ we get: $\dfrac{1}{4}(1.99)^4 - \dfrac{1}{3}(1.99)^3 = 1.29373\overline{16}$ or $(1.99, 1.29373\overline{16})$ and

$\dfrac{1}{4}(2.01)^4 - \dfrac{1}{3}(2.01)^3 = 1.373735003$ or $(2.01, 1.373735003) \Rightarrow$ the average rate of change is:

$\dfrac{1.373735003 - 1.29373\overline{16}}{2.01 - 1.99} = 4.0001\overline{6}$

(c) For $[1.999, 2.001]$ we get: $\dfrac{1}{4}(1.999)^4 - \dfrac{1}{3}(1.999)^3 = 1.329337332$ or $(1.999, 1.329337332)$ and

$\dfrac{1}{4}(2.001)^4 - \dfrac{1}{3}(2.001)^3 = 1.337337335$ or $(2.001, 1.337337335) \Rightarrow$ the average rate of change is:

$\dfrac{1.337337335 - 1.329337332}{2.001 - 1.999} = 4.000001\overline{6}$

As the interval decreases in length the average rate of change is approaching 4.

64. (a) For $[1.9, 2.1]$ we get: $4(1.9)^2 - \frac{1}{2}(1.9)^4 = 7.92395$ or $(1.9, 7.92395)$ and $4(2.1)^2 - \frac{1}{2}(2.1)^4 = 7.91595$ or $(2.1, 7.91595) \Rightarrow$ the average rate of change is: $\dfrac{7.91595 - 7.92395}{21 - 1.9} = -0.04$

(b) For $[1.99, 2.01]$ we get: $4(1.99)^2 - \frac{1}{2}(1.99)^4 = 7.999203995$ or $(1.99, 7.999203995)$ and $4(2.01)^2 - \frac{1}{2}(2.01)^4 = 7.999195995$ or $(2.01, 7.999195995) \Rightarrow$ the average rate of change is: $\dfrac{7.999195995 - 7.999203995}{2.01 - 1.99} = -0.0004$

(c) For $[1.999, 2.001]$ we get: $4(1.999)^2 - \frac{1}{2}(1.999)^4 = 7.999992004$ or $(1.999, 7.999992004)$ and $4(2.001)^2 - \frac{1}{2}(2.001)^4 = 7.999991996$ or $(2.001, 7.999991996) \Rightarrow$ the average rate of change is: $\dfrac{7.999991996 - 7.999992004}{2.001 - 1.999} = -0.000004$. As the interval decreases in length the average rate of change is approaching 0.

65. Use $\dfrac{f(x+h) - f(x)}{h}$, then $\dfrac{3(x+h)^3 - 3x^3}{h} = \dfrac{3x^3 + 9x^2h + 9xh^2 + 3h^3 - 3x^3}{h} = 9x^2 + 9xh + 3h^2$

66. Use $\dfrac{f(x+h) - f(x)}{h}$, then $\dfrac{-2(x+h)^3 - (-2x^3)}{h} = \dfrac{-2x^3 - 6x^2h - 6xh^2 - 2h^3 + 2x^3}{h} =$ $-6x^2 - 6xh - 2h^2$

67. Use $\dfrac{f(x+h) - f(x)}{h}$, then $\dfrac{1 + (x+h) - (x+h)^3 - (1 + x - x^3)}{h} =$ $\dfrac{1 + x + h - x^3 - 3x^2h - 3xh^2 - h^3 - 1 - x + x^3}{h} = -3x^2 - 3xh - h^2 + 1$

68. Use $\dfrac{f(x+h) - f(x)}{h}$, then $\dfrac{\frac{1}{2}(x+h)^3 - 2(x+h) - (\frac{1}{2}x^3 - 2x)}{h} =$ $\dfrac{\frac{1}{2}x^3 + \frac{3}{2}x^2h + \frac{3}{2}xh^2 + \frac{1}{2}h^3 - 2x - 2h - \frac{1}{2}x^3 + 2x}{h} = \dfrac{3}{2}x^2 + \dfrac{3}{2}xh + \dfrac{1}{2}h^2 - 2$

69. $f(-2) \approx 5$ and $f(1) \approx 0$

70. $f(-1) \approx 0,\ f(0) \approx -0.7$, and $f(3) \approx 2$

71. $f(-1) \approx -1,\ f(1) \approx 1$, and $f(2) \approx -2$

72. $f(-2) \approx 0,\ f(0) \approx -3$, and $f(2) \approx 2$

73. $f(-3) = (-3)^3 - 4(-3)^2 = -27 - 36 = -63,\ f(1) = 3(1)^2 = 3$, and $f(4) = (4)^3 - 54 = 64 - 54 = 10$

74. $f(-4) = -4(-4) = 16,\ f(0) = (0)^3 + 2 = 2$, and $f(4) = 4 - (4)^2 = 4 - 16 = -12$

75. $f(-2) = (-2)^2 + 2(-2) + 6 = 6,\ f(1) = 1 + 6 = 7$, and $f(2) = 2^3 + 1 = 9$

76. $f(1975) = 0.2(1975 - 1970)^3 + 60 = 85,\ f(1980) = 190 - (1980 - 1980)^2 = 190$, and $f(1998) = 2(1998 - 1990) + 100 = 116$

77. (a) The graph of $f$ is shown in Figure 77.

(b) The function $f$ is discontinuous at $x = 0$.

(c) First solve: $4 - x^2 = 0 \Rightarrow -x^2 = -4 \Rightarrow x^2 = 4 \Rightarrow x = -2, 2$; only $x = -2$ is in the domain for the equation. Now solve: $x^2 - 4 = 0 \Rightarrow x^2 = 4 \Rightarrow x = -2, 2$; only $x = 2$ is in the domain for the equation $\Rightarrow x = -2, 2$.

78. (a) The graph of $f$ is shown in Figure 78.

(b) The function $f$ is discontinuous at $x = 0$.

(c) First solve: $x^2 = 0 \Rightarrow x = 0$; this is not in the domain for the equation.

Now solve: $x + 1 = 0 \Rightarrow x = -1$; this also is not in the domain for the equation $\Rightarrow$ no solution.

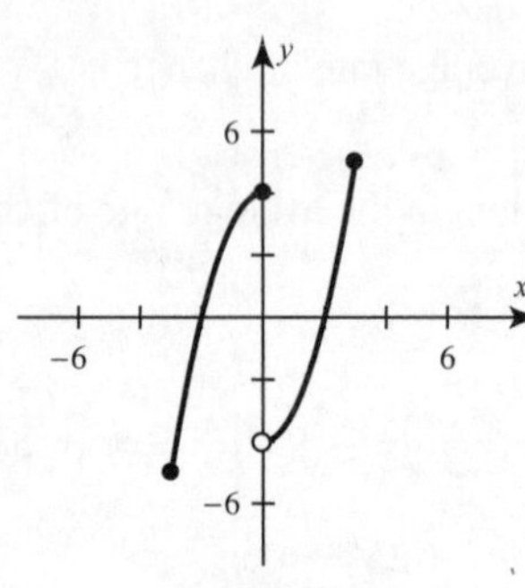

Figure 77

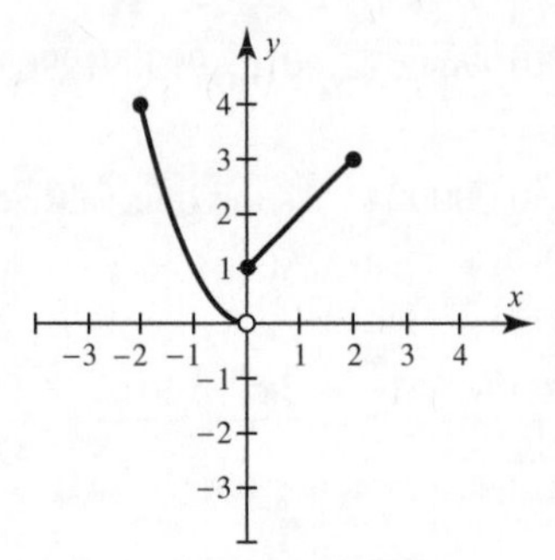

Figure 78

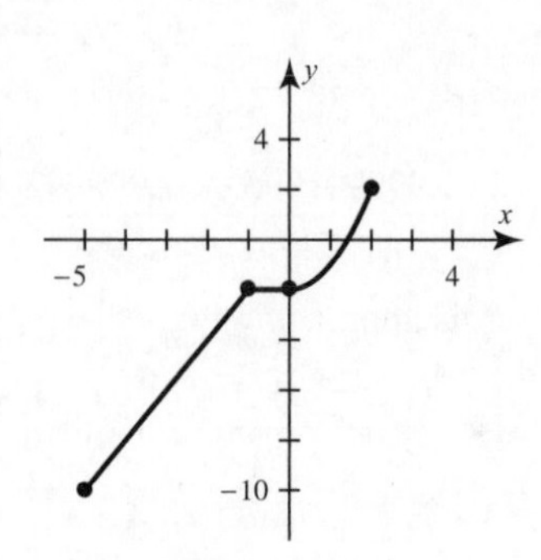

Figure 79

79. (a) The graph of $f$ is shown in Figure 79.

(b) $f$ is continuous.

(c) First solve: $2x = 0 \Rightarrow x = 0$; this is not in the domain for the equation.

$-2 \neq 0 \Rightarrow$ no solutions $-1 \leq x \leq 0$. Finally solve: $x^2 - 2 = 0 \Rightarrow x^2 = 2 \Rightarrow x = \pm\sqrt{2}$; only $\sqrt{2}$ is in the domain for the equation $\Rightarrow x = \sqrt{2}$.

80. (a) The graph of $f$ is shown in Figure 80.

(b) $f$ is discontinuous at $x = -2$ and $x = 2$.

(c) First solve: $0.5x^2 = 0 \Rightarrow x^2 = 0 \Rightarrow x = 0$; this is not in the domain for the equation.

Now solve: $x = 0$; this is in the domain for the second equation.

Finally solve: $x^2 - 4 = 0 \Rightarrow x^2 = 4 \Rightarrow x = \pm 2$; only 2 is in the domain for the equation $\Rightarrow x = 0, 2$.

81. (a) The graph of $f$ is shown in Figure 81.

(b) $f$ is continuous on its domain.

(c) First solve: $x^3 + 3 = 0 \Rightarrow x^3 = -3 \Rightarrow x = \sqrt[3]{-3}$ or $-\sqrt[3]{3}$; this is in the domain for the equation.

Now solve: $x + 3 = 0 \Rightarrow x = -3$; this is not in the domain for the equation.

Finally solve: $4 + x - x^2 = 0 \Rightarrow$ using quadratic formula for $-x^2 + x + 4 = 0$ we get:

$\dfrac{-1 \pm \sqrt{1 - 4(-1)(4)}}{2(-1)} = \dfrac{-1 \pm \sqrt{17}}{-2}$; only $\dfrac{1 + \sqrt{17}}{2}$ is in the domain of the equation $\Rightarrow$

$x = -\sqrt[3]{3}, \dfrac{\sqrt{17} + 1}{2}$.

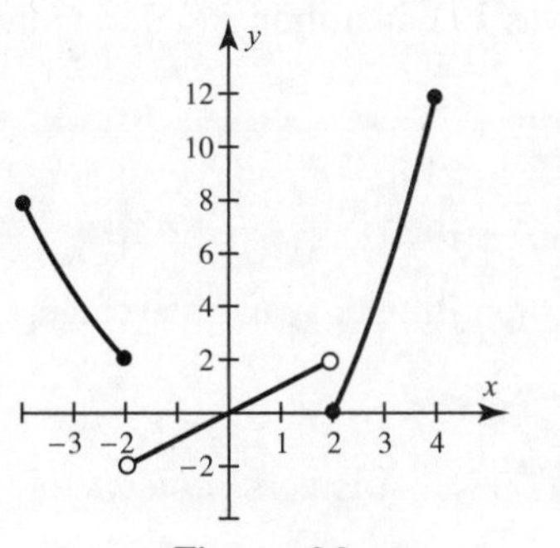


Figure 80

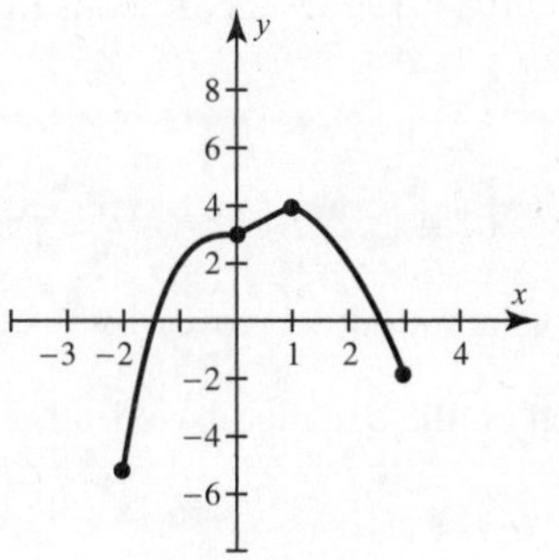

Figure 81

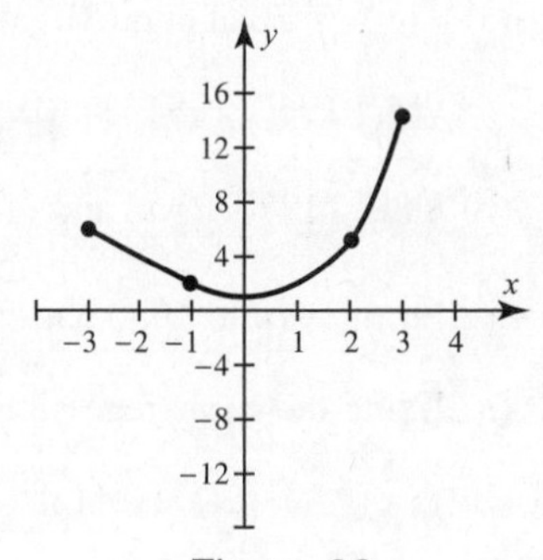


Figure 82

82. (a) The graph of $f$ is shown in Figure 82.

    (b) $f$ is continuous on its domain.

    (c) First solve: $-2x = 0 \Rightarrow x = 0$; this is not in the domain for the equation.

    Now solve: $x^2 + 1 = 0 \Rightarrow x^2 = -1$; there is no real solution for this equation.

    Finally solve: $\frac{1}{2}x^3 + 1 = 0 \Rightarrow \frac{1}{2}x^3 = -1 \Rightarrow x^3 = -2 \Rightarrow x = \sqrt[3]{-2}$; this is not in the domain for the equation $\Rightarrow$ no solution.

83. (a) $H(-2) = 0$, because $t < 0$; $H(0) = 1$, because $t \geq 0$; $H(3.5) = 1$, because $t \geq 0$

    (b) See Figure 83.

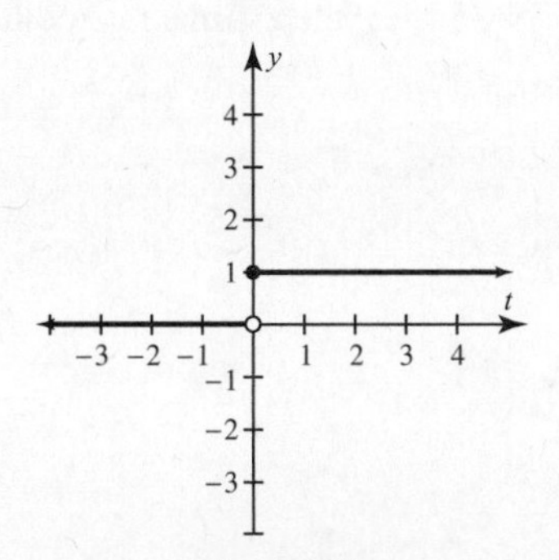


Figure 83

84. (a) $f\left(-\frac{3}{4}\right) = 0$, because $-\frac{3}{4}$ is a rational number; $f(-\sqrt{2}\,) = 1$, because $-\sqrt{2}$ is an irrational number; $f(\pi) = 1$, because $\pi$ is an irrational number

    (b) $f$ is a function because each input has exactly one output.

    (c) Between any two input values $x_1$ and $x_2$, there are infinitely many rational and irrational numbers.

85. (a) There are two turning points that occur near (1, 13) and (7, 72).

    (b) The point (1, 13) means that in January the average temperature is 13ºF. This is the minimum average monthly temperature in Minneapolis. After this the average temperature begins to increase. The point (7, 72) means that in July the average temperature is 72ºF. This is the maximum average monthly temperature in Minneapolis. After this the average temperature begins to decrease.

86. (a) $f(x) = 20$ at approximately 1967, 1984, 1994; energy consumption was 20 quadrillion Btu during the years 1967, 1984, and 1994.

(b) Since $(1970, 21.8)$ and $(1980, 20.4)$ the average rate of change is; $\dfrac{20.4 - 21.8}{1980 - 1970} = -0.14.$

From 1970 to 1980 natural gas consumption decreased by 0.14 quadrillion Btu per year, on average.

87. (a) Using the cubic regession function on the calculator we find

$f(x) \approx -0.15311111x^3 + 914.695238x^2 - 1{,}821{,}416.18x + 1{,}208{,}942{,}069.3$ *Answers may vary.*

(b) $f(1998) = -0.15311111(1998)^3 + 914.695238(1998)^2 - 1{,}821{,}416.18(1998) + 1{,}208{,}942{,}069.3 \approx 1704.$

The result that was found using interpolation.

(c) Using the graph of $f(x)$ we can see that in approximately 1996 the number of endangered and threatened species will be 1600.

88. (a) A line graph of the data is shown in Figure 88. Marijuana use among seniors peaked in 1978 $(x = 3)$ at 37%. There was a decline until 1990. Marijuana use then increased significantly from 1990 to 1995. The line graph suggests that a cubic polynomial might be used to model the data. Selecting cubic regression on the calculator, we get $f(x) \approx 0.02352x^3 - 0.7088x^2 + 4.444x + 27.46.$

(b) In the table, 1997 corresponds to $x = 22;$

$f(22) = 0.02352(22)^3 - 0.7088(22)^2 + 4.444(22) + 27.64 \approx 32.6$, or 32.6%; the estimate is too high compared to the actual value of 23%.

(c) The estimate in part b uses extrapolation.

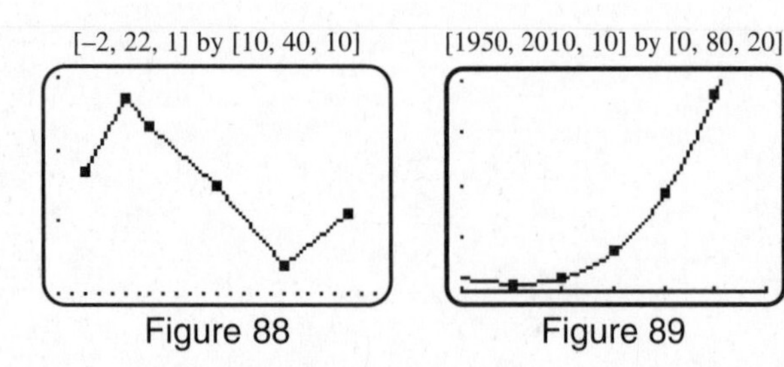


Figure 88 Figure 89

89. (a) Using the cubic regression function on the calculator we find

$f(x) = 0.000667x^3 - 3.9x^2 + 7604.7333x - 4{,}942725.$

(b) See Figure 89.

(c) $f(1994) = 0.000667(1994)^3 - 3.9(1994)^2 + 7604.7333(1994) - 4{,}942{,}725 \approx 50.05.$ This result is very close to the actual value of 50 thousand.

$f(2010) = 0.000667(1994)^3 - 3.9(2010)^2 + 7604.7333(2010) - 4{,}942{,}725 \approx 133.$ This result is 4 thousand higher than the actual result of 129 thousand.

(d) The estimate found for 1994 involved interpolation, and the estimate found for 2010 involved extrapolation.

90. (a) A line graph of the data is shown in Figure 90. The height begins to decrease after 4 seconds. The object appears to have dropped after 4 seconds.

(b) From 0 to 4 seconds, when the object is being lifted, the height could be modeled with a linear function. From 4 to 7 seconds, when the object begins to fall, the height can be modeled with a nonlinear function.

(c) The altitude increases by 36 feet each second, during the first four seconds. Therefore, let $m = 36$. When $x = 4$, the height is 144 feet. Let $b = 144$. When $x = 7$, the height was 0,

$a(7-4)^2 + 144 = 0 \Rightarrow a = -16$. Thus, $f(x) = \begin{cases} 36x, & \text{if } 0 \le x \le 4 \\ -16(x-4)^2 + 144, & \text{if } 4 < x \le 7 \end{cases}$

(d) Using $f(x) = 36x$, $f(x) = 100 \Rightarrow 100 = 36x \Rightarrow x \approx 2.8$;

using $f(x) = -16(x-4)^2 + 144$, $f(x) = 100 \Rightarrow 100 = -16(x-4)^2 + 144 \Rightarrow$

$-44 = -16(x-4)^2 \Rightarrow x \approx 5.7$; the object is 100 feet high at about 2.8 seconds and at about 5.7 second

[−1, 8, 1] by [−10, 170, 10]

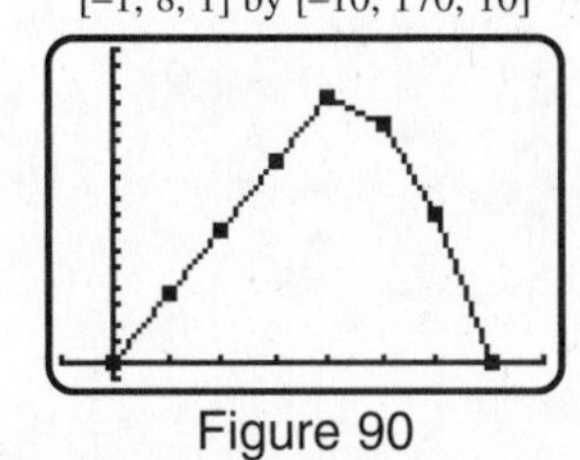

Figure 90

91. (a) See Figure 91a.

(b) Water entering the container can be modeled with a linear formula and occurs in the first 2 minutes. The height increases 16 centimeters in 2 minutes. Thus, $m = 8$, $f(x) = 8x$ for $0 \le x \le 2$. The water leaks out over the time interval of 2 to 5 minutes and can be modeled with a nonlinear formula. Use quadratic regression to find $f(x) = 1.32x^2 - 14.4x + 39.39$ for $2 < x \le 5$.

Thus, $f(x) = \begin{cases} 8x, & \text{if } 0 \le x \le 2 \\ 1.32x^2 - 14.4 + 39.39, & \text{if } 2 < x \le 5 \end{cases}$

(c) When $x = 1.25$, water was flowing into the tank and $f(x) = 8x$. $f(1.25) = 8(1.25) = 10$ cm. When $x = 3.2$, water is flowing out of the tank and $f(x) = 1.32x^2 - 14.4x + 39.39$.

$f(3.2) = 1.32(3.2)^2 - 14.4(3.2) + 39.39 \approx 7$ cm.

(d) The water level in figure 91 equals 5 centimeters twice. This occurs when the water is entering the container and when it is leaking out. Solve $8x = 5$ and $1.32x^2 - 14.4x + 39.39 = 5$. Thus, after $\frac{5}{8}$ minute the water level was 5 centimeters. The equation $1.32x^2 - 14.4x + 39.39 = 5$ is solved graphically. See Figure 91d. Intersection: $y = 5$ and $x = 3.5312577$. The solution satisfying $2 < x \le 5$ is $x \approx 3.53$ min. *Answers may vary.*

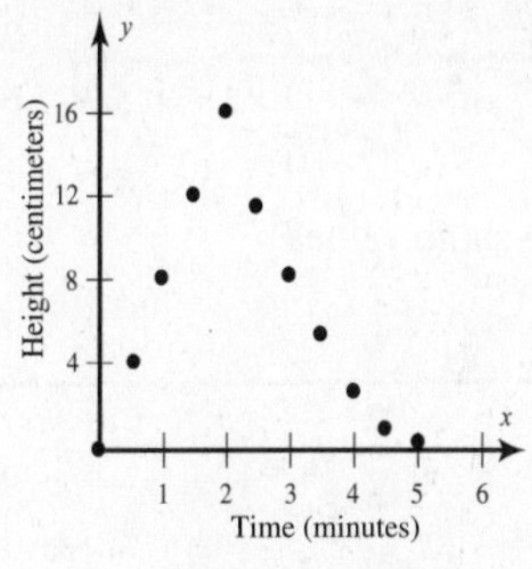


Figure 91a

[0, 5, 1] by [0, 18, 2]

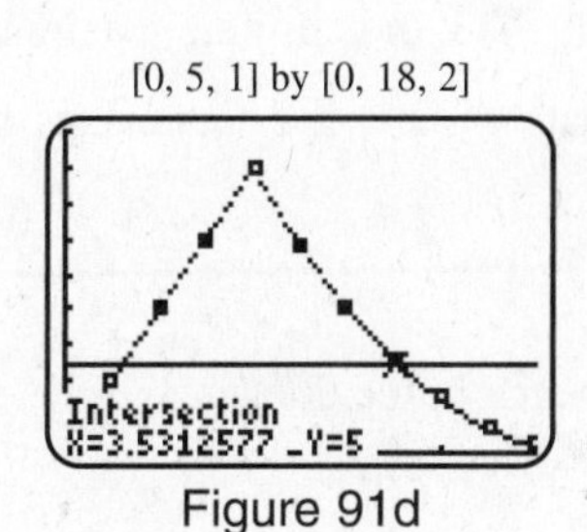


Figure 91d

92. Using $f(t) = 9t$, $f(t) = 12 \Rightarrow 12 = 9t \Rightarrow t \approx 1.3$;

using $f(t) = 4t^2 - 56t + 196$, $f(t) = 12 \Rightarrow 12 = 4t^2 - 56t + 196 \Rightarrow 4t^2 - 56t + 184 = 0 \Rightarrow$

$t^2 - 14t + 46 = 0 \Rightarrow t = \dfrac{14 \pm \sqrt{(-14)^2 - 4(1)(46)}}{2} \Rightarrow t \approx 8.7$ or $t \approx 5.3$. Since $8.7 > 7$, the value 8.7 does not satisfy the conditions of the problem, and so $t \approx 5.3$; the tank has 12 gallons of water after about 1.3 minutes and after about 5.3 minutes.

## Extended and Discovery Exercise for Section 4.2

1. (a) $D = [0, 10]$

(b) $A(1) = 500\left(1 - \frac{1}{10}\right)^2 \Rightarrow A(1) = 500\left(\frac{9}{10}\right)^2 \Rightarrow A(1) = 500\left(\frac{81}{100}\right) \Rightarrow A(1) = 405$

After one minute of draining the tank it contains 405 gallons of water.

(c) $500\left(1 - \frac{t}{10}\right)^2 = 500\left(1 - \frac{2t}{10} + \frac{t^2}{100}\right) = 5t^2 - 100t + 500 \Rightarrow$ the degree is: 2.

The leading coefficient is: 5.

(d) $A(5) = 500\left(1 - \frac{5}{10}\right)^2 \Rightarrow A(5) = 500\left(\frac{1}{2}\right)^2 \Rightarrow A(5) = 500\left(\frac{1}{4}\right) \Rightarrow A(5) = \frac{500}{4} \Rightarrow$

$A(5) = 125$ gallons remaining. No more than half is drained. This is reasonable because the water will drain faster at first.

2. $f$ is concave up on $(-\infty, \infty)$ and is not concave down.
3. $f$ is concave down on $(-\infty, \infty)$ and is not concave up.
4. $f$ is concave up on $(-\infty, 0)$ and is concave down on $(0, \infty)$.
5. $f$ is concave up on $(1, \infty)$ and is concave down on $(-\infty, 1)$.
6. $f$ is concave up on $(-\infty, -1) \cup (1, \infty)$ and is concave down on $(-1, 1)$.
7. $f$ is concave up on $(-2, 2)$ and is concave down on $(-\infty, -2) \cup (2, \infty)$.

## Checking Basic Concepts for Section 4.1 and 4.2

1. (a) In the set builder notation, these intervals are $\{x \mid -2 \le x \le 1 \text{ or } x \ge 3\}$ and $\{x \mid x \le -2 \text{ or } 1 \le x \le 3\}$ respectively.

(b) Local maximum: approximately 3; local minimum; approximately $-13, -2$.

(c) Absolute minimum: approximately $-13$; no absolute maximum.

(d) From the graph they are approximately $-3.1$, 0, 2.2, and 3.6; they are the same values.

2. (a) $f(-4) \approx 0$, $f(0) \approx 4$, and $f(4) \approx 0$

(b) $y$-axis symmetry.

(c) Even, because $f(-x) = f(x)$ for all $x$ in the domain.

(d) Domain: $[-4, 4]$, range: $[0, 4]$

3. (a) Cubic graphs have a range from $-\infty$ to $\infty$ $\Rightarrow$ must have an $x$-intercept $\Rightarrow$ not possible.

   (b) See Figure 3b.

   (c) See Figure 3c.

   (d) Cubic graphs have at most two turning points $\Rightarrow$ have at most 3 $x$-intercept $\Rightarrow$ not possible.

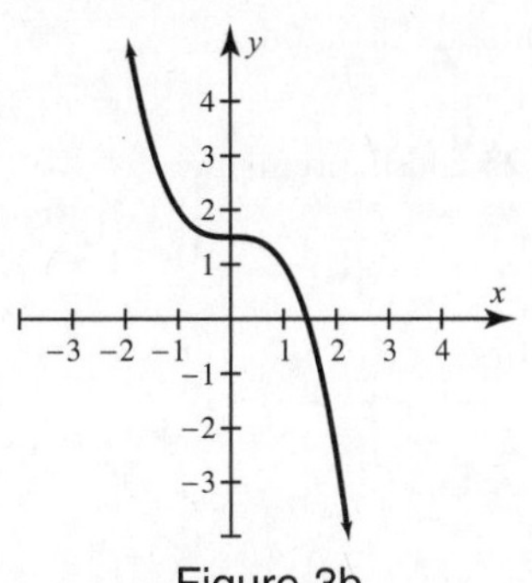


Figure 3b

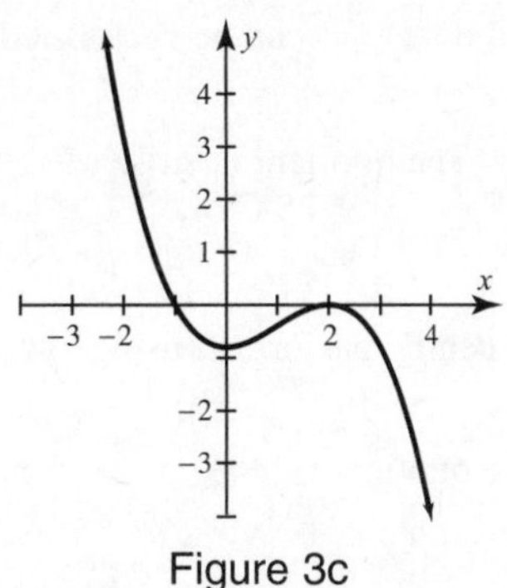


Figure 3c

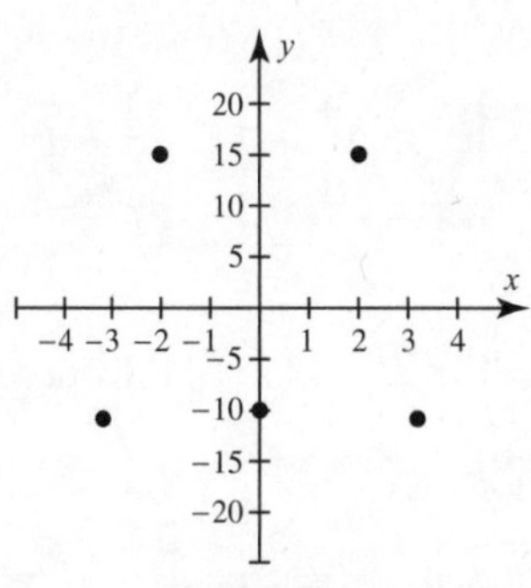


Figure 4

4. (a) A polynomial of minimum degree 4 would be needed to model the data because the graph of $f$ has at least four $x$-intercepts. See Figure 4.

   (b) $f$ is even because the data points are symmetric with respect to the $y$-axis.

   (c) The leading coefficient is negative because the graph falls both to the left and the right.

5. $f(x) \approx -1.01725x^4 + 10.319x^2 - 10$

## 4.3: Division of Polynomials

1. $\dfrac{5x^4 - 15}{10x} = \dfrac{5x^4}{10x} - \dfrac{15}{10x} = \dfrac{x^3}{2} - \dfrac{3}{2x}$

2. $\dfrac{x^2 - 5x}{5x} = \dfrac{x^2}{5x} - \dfrac{5x}{5x} = \dfrac{x}{5} - 1$

3. $\dfrac{3x^4 - 2x^2 - 1}{3x^3} = \dfrac{3x^4}{3x^3} - \dfrac{2x^2}{3x^3} - \dfrac{1}{3x^3} = x - \dfrac{2}{3x} - \dfrac{1}{3x^3}$

4. $\dfrac{5x^3 - 10x^2 + 5x}{15x^2} = \dfrac{5x^3}{15x^2} - \dfrac{10x^2}{15x^2} + \dfrac{5x}{15x^2} = \dfrac{x}{3} - \dfrac{2}{3} + \dfrac{1}{3x}$

5. $\dfrac{x^3 - 4}{4x^3} = \dfrac{x^3}{4x^3} - \dfrac{4}{4x^3} = \dfrac{1}{4} - \dfrac{1}{x^3}$

6. $\dfrac{2x^4 - 3x^2 + 4x - 7}{-4x} = \dfrac{2x^4}{-4x} - \dfrac{3x^2}{-4x} + \dfrac{4x}{-4x} - \dfrac{7}{-4x} = -\dfrac{x^3}{2} + \dfrac{3x}{4} - 1 + \dfrac{7}{4x}$

7. $\dfrac{5x(3x^2 - 6x + 1}{3x^2} = \dfrac{15x^3 - 30x^2 + 5x}{3x^2} = \dfrac{15x^3}{3x^2} - \dfrac{30x^2}{3x^2} + \dfrac{5x}{3x^2} = 5x - 10 + \dfrac{5}{3x}$

8. $\dfrac{(1 - 5x^2)(x + 1) + x^2}{2x} = \dfrac{x + 1 - 5x^3 - 5x^2 + x^2}{2x} = \dfrac{-5x^3 - 4x^2 + x + 1}{2x} = \dfrac{-5x^2}{2} - 2x + \dfrac{1}{2} + \dfrac{1}{2x}$

9. $x^3 - 2x^2 - 5x + 6$ divided by $x - 3$ can be performed using synthetic division.

$$\begin{array}{r|rrrr} 3 & 1 & -2 & -5 & 6 \\ & & 3 & 3 & -6 \\ \hline & 1 & 1 & -2 & 0 \end{array}$$

The quotient is $x^2 + x - 2$ and the remainder is 0.

10. $3x^3 - 10x^2 - 27x + 10$ divided by $x + 2$ can be performed using synthetic division.

$$\begin{array}{r|rrrr} -2 & 3 & -10 & -27 & 10 \\ & & -6 & 32 & -10 \\ \hline & 3 & -16 & 5 & 0 \end{array}$$

The quotient is $3x^2 - 16x + 5$ and the remainder is 0.

11. $2x^4 - 7x^3 - 5x^2 - 19x + 17$ divided by $x + 1$ can be performed using synthetic division.

$$\begin{array}{r|rrrrr} -1 & 2 & -7 & -5 & -19 & 17 \\ & & -2 & 9 & -4 & 23 \\ \hline & 2 & -9 & 4 & -23 & 40 \end{array}$$

The quotient is $2x^3 - 9x^2 + 4x - 23$ and the remainder is 40.

12. $x^4 - x^3 - 4x + 1$ divided by $x - 2$ can be performed using synthetic division.

$$\begin{array}{r|rrrrr} 2 & 1 & -1 & 0 & -4 & 1 \\ & & 2 & 2 & 4 & 0 \\ \hline & 1 & 1 & 2 & 0 & 1 \end{array}$$

The quotient is $x^3 + x^2 + 2x$ and the remainder is 1.

13. $3x^3 - 7x + 10$ divided by $x - 1$ can be performed using synthetic division.

$$\begin{array}{r|rrrr} 1 & 3 & 0 & -7 & 10 \\ & & 3 & 3 & -4 \\ \hline & 3 & 3 & -4 & 6 \end{array}$$

The quotient is $3x^2 + 3x - 4$ and the remainder is 6.

This can also be found using long division as shown.

$$\begin{array}{r} 3x^2 + 3x - 4 \phantom{)} \\ x - 1 \overline{)\, 3x^3 - 0x^2 - 7x + 10} \\ \underline{3x^3 - 3x^2} \phantom{- 7x + 10} \\ 3x^2 - 7x \phantom{+ 10} \\ \underline{3x^2 - 3x} \phantom{+ 10} \\ -4x + 10 \\ \underline{-4x + \phantom{1}4} \\ 6 \end{array}$$

14. $x^4 - 16x^2 + 1$ divided by $x + 4$ can be performed using synthetic division.

$$\begin{array}{r|rrrrr} -4 & 1 & 0 & -16 & 0 & 1 \\ & & -4 & 16 & 0 & 0 \\ \hline & 1 & -4 & 0 & 0 & 1 \end{array}$$

The quotient is $x^3 - 4x^2$ and the remainder is 1.

15. We can use synthetic division to divide $x^4 - 3x^3 - x + 3$ by $x - 3$.

$$\begin{array}{r|rrrrr} 3 & 1 & -3 & 0 & -1 & 3 \\ & & 3 & 0 & 0 & -3 \\ \hline & 1 & 0 & 0 & -1 & 0 \end{array}$$

The quotient is $x^3 - 1$ and the remainder is 0.

16. We can use synthetic division to divide $x^3 - 2x^2 - x + 3$ by $x + 1$.

$$\begin{array}{r|rrrr} -1 & 1 & -2 & -1 & 3 \\ & & -1 & 3 & -2 \\ \hline & 1 & -3 & 2 & 1 \end{array}$$

The quotient is $x^2 - 3x + 2 + \dfrac{1}{x + 1}$.

17. We can use long division to divide $4x^3 - x^2 - 5x + 6$ by $x - 1$.

$$\begin{array}{rl} & 4x^2 + 3x - 2 \\ x - 1 & \overline{)4x^3 - x^2 - 5x + 6} \\ & \underline{4x^3 - 4x^2} \\ & \qquad 3x^2 - 5x \\ & \qquad \underline{3x^2 - 3x} \\ & \qquad\qquad -2x + 6 \\ & \qquad\qquad \underline{-2x + 2} \\ & \qquad\qquad\qquad 4 \end{array}$$

The quotient is $4x^2 + 3x - 2 + \dfrac{4}{x - 1}$.

18. We can use long division to divide $x^4 + 3x^3 - 4x + 1$ by $x + 2$.

$$\begin{array}{rl} & x^3 + x^2 - 2x \\ x + 2 & \overline{)x^4 + 3x^3 + 0x^2 - 4x + 1} \\ & \underline{x^4 + 2x^3} \\ & \qquad x^3 + 0x^2 \\ & \qquad \underline{x^3 + 2x^2} \\ & \qquad\qquad -2x^2 - 4x \\ & \qquad\qquad \underline{-2x^2 - 4x} \\ & \qquad\qquad\qquad 0x + 1 = 1 \end{array}$$

The quotient is $x^3 + x^2 - 2x + \dfrac{1}{x + 2}$.

19. We can use synthetic division to divide $x^3 + 1$ by $x + 1$.

$$\begin{array}{r|rrrr} -1 & 1 & 0 & 0 & 1 \\ & & -1 & 1 & -1 \\ \hline & 1 & -1 & 1 & 0 \end{array}$$

The quotient is $x^2 - x + 1$and the remainder is 0.

20. We can use synthetic division to divide $x^5 + 3x^4 - x - 3$ by $x + 3$.

$$\begin{array}{r|rrrrrr} -3 & 1 & 3 & 0 & 0 & -1 & -3 \\ & & -3 & 0 & 0 & 0 & 3 \\ \hline & 1 & 0 & 0 & 0 & -1 & 0 \end{array}$$

The quotient is $x^4 - 1$ and the remainder is 0.

21. We can use long division to divide $6x^3 + 5x^2 - 8x + 4$ by $2x - 1$.

$$\begin{array}{rl} & 3x^2 + 4x - 2 \\ 2x - 1 & \overline{)6x^3 + 5x^2 - 8x + 4} \\ & \underline{6x^3 - 3x^2} \\ & \qquad 8x^2 - 8x + 4 \\ & \qquad \underline{8x^2 - 4x} \\ & \qquad\qquad -4x + 4 \\ & \qquad\qquad \underline{-4x + 2} \\ & \qquad\qquad\qquad 2 \end{array}$$

The quotient is $3x^2 + 4x - 2 + \dfrac{2}{2x - 1}$.

22. We can use long division to divide $12x^3 - 14x^2 + 7x - 7$ by $3x - 2$.

$$\begin{array}{rl} & 4x^2 - 2x + 1 \\ 3x - 2 & \overline{)12x^3 - 14x^2 + 7x - 7} \\ & \underline{12x^3 - 8x^2} \\ & \qquad -6x^2 + 7x - 7 \\ & \qquad \underline{-6x^2 + 4x} \\ & \qquad\qquad 3x - 7 \\ & \qquad\qquad \underline{3x - 2} \\ & \qquad\qquad\qquad -5 \end{array}$$

The quotient is $4x^2 - 2x + 1 + \dfrac{-5}{3x - 2}$.

23. We can use long division to divide $3x^4 - 7x^3 + 6x - 16$ by $3x - 7$.

$$\begin{array}{rl} & x^3 + 2 \\ 3x - 7 & \overline{)\,3x^4 - 7x^3 + 0x^2 + 6x - 16} \\ & \underline{3x^4 - 7x^3} \\ & \qquad\qquad\qquad 6x - 16 \\ & \qquad\qquad\qquad \underline{6x - 14} \\ & \qquad\qquad\qquad\qquad -2 \end{array}$$

The quotient is $x^3 + 2 + \frac{-2}{3x - 7}$.

24. We can use long division to divide $20x^4 + 6x^3 - 2x^2 + 15x - 2$ by $5x - 1$.

$$\begin{array}{rl} & 4x^3 + 2x^2 + 3 \\ 5x - 1 & \overline{)\,20x^4 + 6x^3 - 2x^2 + 15x - 2} \\ & \underline{20x^4 - 4x^3} \\ & \qquad 10x^3 - 2x^2 + 15x - 2 \\ & \qquad \underline{10x^3 - 2x^2} \\ & \qquad\qquad\qquad 15x - 2 \\ & \qquad\qquad\qquad \underline{15x - 3} \\ & \qquad\qquad\qquad\qquad 1 \end{array}$$

The quotient is $4x^3 + 2x^2 + 3 + \frac{1}{5x - 1}$.

25. We can use long division to divide $5x^4 - 2x^2 + 6$ by $x^2 + 2$.

$$\begin{array}{rl} & 5x^2 - 12 \\ x^2 + 2 & \overline{)\,5x^4 - 2x^2 + 6} \\ & \underline{5x^4 + 10x^2} \\ & \qquad -12x^2 + 6 \\ & \qquad \underline{-12x^2 - 24} \\ & \qquad\qquad\quad 30 \end{array}$$

The quotient is $5x^2 - 12 + \frac{30}{x^2 + 2}$.

26. We can use long division to divide $x^3 - x^2 + 2x - 3$ by $x^2 + 3$.

$$\begin{array}{rl} & x - 1 \\ x^2 + 3 & \overline{)\,x^3 - x^2 + 2x - 3} \\ & \underline{x^3 \qquad\quad + 3x} \\ & \qquad -x^2 - x - 3 \\ & \qquad \underline{-x^2 \qquad - 3} \\ & \qquad\qquad -x \end{array}$$

The quotient is $x - 1 + \frac{-x}{x^2 + 3}$.

27. We can use long division to divide $8x^3 + 10x^2 - 12x - 15$ by $2x^2 - 3$.

$$\begin{array}{rl} & 4x + 5 \\ 2x^2 - 3 & \overline{)\,8x^3 + 10x^2 - 12x - 15} \\ & \underline{8x^3 \qquad\quad - 12x} \\ & \qquad 10x^2 \qquad - 15 \\ & \qquad \underline{10x^2 \qquad - 15} \\ & \qquad\qquad\qquad\quad 0 \end{array}$$

The quotient is $4x + 5$.

28. We can use long division to divide $3x^4 - 2x^2 - 5$ by $3x^2 - 5$.

$$\begin{array}{rl} & x^2 + 1 \\ 3x^2 - 5 & \overline{)\,3x^4 \qquad - 2x^2 \qquad - 5} \\ & \underline{3x^4 \qquad - 5x^2} \\ & \qquad\qquad 3x^2 \qquad - 5 \\ & \qquad\qquad \underline{3x^2 \qquad - 5} \\ & \qquad\qquad\qquad\qquad 0 \end{array}$$

The quotient is $x^2 + 1$.

29. We can use long division to divide $2x^4 - x^3 + 4x^2 + 8x + 7$ by $2x^2 + 3x + 2$.

$$
\begin{array}{r}
x^2 - 2x + 4 \\
2x^2 + 3x + 2 \overline{\smash{)}\, 2x^4 - x^3 + 4x^2 + 8x + 7} \\
\underline{2x^4 + 3x^3 + 2x^2 \phantom{+ 8x + 7}} \\
-4x^3 + 2x^2 + 8x \phantom{+ 7} \\
\underline{-4x^3 - 6x^2 - 4x \phantom{+ 7}} \\
8x^2 + 12x + 7 \\
\underline{8x^2 + 12x + 8} \\
-1
\end{array}
$$

The quotient is $x^2 - 2x + 4 + \dfrac{-1}{2x^3 + 3x + 2}$.

30. We can use long division to divide $3x^4 + 2x^3 - x^2 + 4x - 3$ by $x^2 + x - 1$.

$$
\begin{array}{r}
3x^2 - x + 3 \\
x^2 + x - 1 \overline{\smash{)}\, 3x^4 + 2x^3 - x^2 + 4x - 3} \\
\underline{3x^4 + 3x^3 - 3x^2 \phantom{+ 4x - 3}} \\
-x^3 + 2x^2 + 4x \phantom{- 3} \\
\underline{-x^3 - x^2 + x \phantom{- 3}} \\
3x^2 + 3x - 3 \\
\underline{3x^2 + 3x - 3} \\
0
\end{array}
$$

The quotient is $3x^2 - x + 3$.

31. The divisor times the quotient will be equal to the dividend, $(x - 2)(x^2 - 6x + 3) = x^3 - 8x^2 + 15x - 6$.

32. The dividend equals the divisor times the quotient add to the remainder,

$x^4 - 15 = (x + 2)(x^3 - 2x^2 + 4x - 8) + 1$.

33.
$$
\begin{array}{r}
x - 1 \\
x - 2 \overline{\smash{)}\, x^2 - 3x + 1} \\
\underline{x^2 - 2x \phantom{+ 1}} \\
-x + 1 \\
\underline{-x + 2} \\
-1
\end{array}
\qquad (x - 2)(x - 1) - 1
$$

34.
$$
\begin{array}{r}
2x - 9 \\
x + 4 \overline{\smash{)}\, 2x^2 - x + 2} \\
\underline{2x^2 + 8x \phantom{+ 2}} \\
-9x + 2 \\
\underline{-9x - 36} \\
38
\end{array}
\qquad (x + 4)(2x - 9) + 38
$$

35.
$$
\begin{array}{r}
x^2 - 1 \\
2x + 1 \overline{\smash{)}\, 2x^3 - x^2 - 2x} \\
\underline{2x^3 + x^2 \phantom{- 2x}} \\
-2x + 0 \\
\underline{-2x - 1} \\
1
\end{array}
\qquad (2x + 1)(x^2 - 1) + 1
$$

36.
$$
\begin{array}{r}
x^2 \phantom{+ 0x + 1} \\
x - 1 \overline{\smash{)}\, x^3 - x^2 + 0x + 1} \\
\underline{x^3 - x^2 \phantom{+ 0x + 1}} \\
0x + 1
\end{array}
\qquad (x - 1)(x^2) + 1
$$

37.

$$\begin{array}{r} x - 1 \\ x^2 + 0x + 1\overline{)x^3 - \phantom{0}x^2 + x + 1} \\ \underline{x^3 + 0x^2 + x\phantom{+1}} \\ -x^2 \phantom{+x} + 1 \\ \underline{-x^2 \phantom{+x} - 1} \\ 2 \end{array} \quad (x^2 + 1)(x - 1) + 2$$

38.

$$\begin{array}{r} 2x - 1 \\ x^2 + x + 0\overline{)2x^3 + \phantom{2}x^2 - \phantom{0}x + 4} \\ \underline{2x^3 + 2x^2 + 0x\phantom{+4}} \\ -x^2 - x + 4 \\ \underline{x^2 - x - 0} \\ 4 \end{array} \quad (x^2 + x)(2x - 1) + 4$$

39. $\begin{array}{r|rrrr} -5 & 1 & 2 & -17 & -10 \\ & & -5 & 15 & 10 \\ \hline & 1 & -3 & -2 & 0 \end{array}$ The quotient is $x^2 - 3x - 2$.

40. $\begin{array}{r|rrrr} -4 & 1 & 0 & -2 & 1 \\ & & -4 & 16 & -56 \\ \hline & 1 & -4 & 14 & -55 \end{array}$ The quotient is $x^2 - 4x + 14 - \dfrac{55}{x + 4}$.

41. $\begin{array}{r|rrrr} 5 & 3 & -11 & -20 & 3 \\ & & 15 & 20 & 0 \\ \hline & 3 & 4 & 0 & 3 \end{array}$ The quotient is $3x^2 + 4x + \dfrac{3}{x - 5}$.

42. $\begin{array}{r|rrrrr} 3 & 1 & -3 & -5 & 2 & -16 \\ & & 3 & 0 & -15 & -39 \\ \hline & 1 & 0 & -5 & -13 & -55 \end{array}$ The quotient is $x^3 - 5x - 13 - \dfrac{55}{x - 3}$.

43. $\begin{array}{r|rrrrr} 2 & 1 & -3 & -4 & 12 & 0 \\ & & 2 & -2 & -12 & 0 \\ \hline & 1 & -1 & -6 & 0 & \end{array}$ The quotient is $x^3 + x^2 - 6x$ .

44. $\begin{array}{r|rrrrrr} -\frac{1}{4} & 1 & \frac{1}{4} & -1 & -\frac{1}{4} & 3 & -\frac{5}{4} \\ & & -\frac{1}{4} & 0 & \frac{1}{4} & 0 & -\frac{3}{4} \\ \hline & 1 & 0 & -1 & 0 & 3 & -2 \end{array}$ The quotient is $x^4 - x^2 + 3 - \dfrac{2}{x + 0.25}$.

45. $\begin{array}{r|rrrrrr} -\frac{1}{2} & 2 & -1 & -1 & 0 & 4 & 3 \\ & & -1 & 1 & 0 & 0 & -2 \\ \hline & 2 & -2 & 0 & 0 & 4 & 1 \end{array}$ The quotient is $2x^4 - 2x^3 + 4 + \dfrac{1}{x + 0.5}$.

46. $\begin{array}{r|rrrrr} \frac{1}{2} & 1 & -\frac{1}{2} & 3 & -\frac{5}{2} & \frac{9}{2} \\ & & \frac{1}{2} & 0 & \frac{3}{2} & -\frac{1}{2} \\ \hline & 1 & 0 & 3 & -1 & 4 \end{array}$ The quotient is $x^3 + 3x - 1 + \dfrac{4}{x - 0.5}$.

47. Using the remainder theorem we find: $f(1), \Rightarrow 5(1)^2 - 3(1) + 1 = 5 - 3 + 1 = 3$

48. Using the remainder theorem we find: $f(-4), \Rightarrow -4(-4)^2 + 6(-4) - 7 = -64 - 24 - 7 = -95$

49. Using the remainder theorem we find:

    $f(-2), \Rightarrow 4(-2)^3 - (-2)^2 + 4(-2) + 2 = -32 - 4 - 8 + 2 = -42$

50. Using the remainder theorem we find: $f(3), \Rightarrow -(3)^4 + 4(3)^3 - (3) + 3 = -81 + 108 - 3 + 3 = 27$

51. If we divide the Area by the Width we will find the Length:

$$\begin{array}{r} 4x + 3 \\ 3x + 1 \overline{)12x^2 + 13x + 3} \\ \underline{12x^2 + 4x} \\ 9x + 3 \\ \underline{9x + 3} \\ 0 \end{array}$$

The length is $4x + 3$. When $x = 10$, the Length is $4(10) + 3 = 43$ feet.

52. If we divide the Area by the Length we will find the Width:

$$\begin{array}{r} 3x - 5 \\ x^2 + 1 \overline{)3x^3 - 5x^2 + 3x - 5} \\ \underline{3x^3 \qquad + 3x} \\ -5x^2 \qquad - 5 \\ \underline{-5x^2 \qquad - 5} \\ 0 \end{array}$$

The Width is $3x - 5$. When $x = 5$, the Width is $3(5) - 5 = 10$ inches.

## 4.4: Real Zeros of Polynomial Functions

1. The $x$-intercepts of $f$ are $-1$, 1, and 2. Since $f(-1) = 0$, the factor theorem states that $(x + 2)$ is a factor of $f(x)$. Similarly, $f(-1) = 0$ implies that $(x + 1)$ is a factor, and $f(1) = 0$ implies that $(x - 1)$ is a factor.

2. The $x$-intercepts of $f$ are $-1$, 1, and 2. Since $f(-1) = 0$, the factor theorem states that $(x + 1)$ is a factor of $f(x)$. Similarly, $f(1) = 0$ implies that $(x - 1)$ is a factor, and $f(2) = 0$ implies that $(x - 2)$ is a factor.

3. The $x$-intercepts of $f$ are $-2, -1, 1$ and 2. Since $f(-2) = 0$, the factor theorem states that $(x + 2)$ is a factor of $f(x)$. Similarly, $f(-1) = 0$ implies that $(x + 1)$ is a factor, $f(1) = 0$ implies that $(x - 1)$ is a factor and $f(2) = 0$ implies that $(x - 2)$ is a factor.

4. The $x$-intercepts of $f$ are $-1, 0, 1$ and 3. Since $f(-1) = 0$, the factor theorem states that $(x + 1)$ is a factor of $f(x)$. Similarly, $f(0) = 0$ implies that $x$ is a factor, $f(1) = 0$ implies that $(x - 1)$ is a factor and $f(3) = 0$ implies that $(x - 3)$ is a factor.

5. $f(x) = 2x^2 - 25x + 77$ and zeros: $\frac{11}{2}$ and $7 \Rightarrow f(x) = 2\left(x - \frac{11}{2}\right)(x - 7)$

6. $f(x) = 6x^2 + 21x + 90$ and zeros: $-6$ and $\frac{5}{2} \Rightarrow f(x) = 6(x + 6)\left(x - \frac{5}{2}\right)$

7. $f(x) = x^3 - 2x^2 - 5x + 6$ and zeros: $-2, 1$, and $3 \Rightarrow f(x) = (x + 2)(x - 1)(x - 3)$

8. $f(x) = x^3 + 6x^2 + 11x + 6$ and zeros: $-3, -2$, and $-1 \Rightarrow f(x) = (x + 3)(x + 2)(x + 1)$

9. $f(x) = -2x^3 + 3x^2 + 59x - 30$ and zeros: $-5, \frac{1}{2}$, and $6 \Rightarrow f(x) = -2(x + 5)\left(x - \frac{1}{2}\right)(x - 6)$

10. $f(x) = 3x^4 - 8x^3 - 67x^2 + 112x + 240$ and zeros: $-4, -\frac{4}{3}$, 3, and 5 $\Rightarrow$

    $f(x) = 3(x + 4)\left(x + \frac{4}{3}\right)(x - 3)(x - 5)$

11. If $f(-3) = 0$ then the quadratic equation has a factor of $x - (-3)$ or $x + 3$, likewise if $f(2) = 0$ then the quadratic equation has a factor $x - 2$. If this quadratic equation has a leading coefficient 7, the complete factored form of $f(x)$ is $f(x) = 7(x + 3)(x - 2)$.

12. If $g(-2) = 0$ then the cubic equation has a factor of $x - (-2)$ or $x + 2$, likewise if $g(1) = 0$ then the cubic equation has a factor $x - 1$, and if $g(4) = 0$ then the cubic equation also has a factor $x - 4$. If this cubic equation has a leading coefficient $-4$, the complete factored form of $g(x)$ is $g(x) = -4(x + 2)(x - 1)(x - 4)$.

13. To factor $f(x)$ we need to determine the leading coefficient and zeros of $f$. The leading coefficient is $-2$ and the zeros are $-1$, 0, and 1. The complete factorization is $f(x) = -2x(x + 1)(x - 1)$.

14. To factor $f(x)$ we need to determine the leading coefficient and zeros of $f$. The leading coefficient is $\frac{1}{4}$ and the zeros are $-2$, 1, 3 and 4. The complete factorization is $f(x) = \frac{1}{4}(x + 2)(x - 1)(x - 3)(x - 4)$.

15. From the graph the zeros are $-4$, 2, and 8. $f(x)$ is a cubic with a positive leading coefficient. Therefore, $f(x) = (x + 4)(x - 2)(x - 8)$.

16. From the graph the zeros are $-4$, $-1$, and 3. $f(x)$ is a cubic with a negative leading coefficient. Therefore, $f(x) = -1(x + 4)(x + 1)(x - 3)$.

17. From the graph the zeros are $-8$, $-4$, $-2$, and 4. $f(x)$ is a quartic polynomial with a negative leading coefficient. Therefore, $f(x) = -1(x + 8)(x + 4)(x + 2)(x - 4)$.

18. From the graph the zeros are $-5$, $-2$, 1, and 3. $f(x)$ is a quartic polynomial with a positive leading coefficient. Therefore, $f(x) = (x + 5)(x + 2)(x - 1)(x - 3)$.

19. Since the polynomial has zeros of $-1$, 2, and 3, it has factors $(x + 1)(x - 2)(x - 3)$.
    If $f$ passes through $(0, 3)$ then $a(0 + 1)(0 - 2)(0 - 3) = 3 \Rightarrow a(1)(-2)(-3) = 3 \Rightarrow 6a = 3 \Rightarrow a = \frac{1}{2}$.
    The complete factored form is: $f(x) = \frac{1}{2}(x + 1)(x - 2)(x - 3)$.

20. Since the polynomial has zeros of $-2, -1, 1$, and 2, it has factors $(x + 2)(x + 1)(x - 1)(x - 2)$. If $g$ passes through $(0, 8)$ then $a(0 + 2)(0 + 1)(0 - 1)(0 - 2) = 8 \Rightarrow a(2)(1)(-1)(-2) = 8 \Rightarrow 4a = 8 \Rightarrow a = 2$. The complete factored form is: $g(x) = 2(x + 2)(x + 1)(x - 1)(x - 2)$.

21. Since $f$ has zeros $-1$, 1, and 2, it has factors $(x + 1)(x - 1)(x - 2)$. If $f(0) = 1$ then $a(1)(-1)(-2) = 1$ or $2a = 1 \Rightarrow a = \frac{1}{2}$. The complete factored form is: $f(x) = \frac{1}{2}(x + 1)(x - 1)(x - 2)$.

22. Since $f$ has zeros $-3, -2, -1$, and 1, it has factors $(x + 3)(x + 2)(x + 1)(x - 1)$. If $f(0) = 2$ then $a(3)(2)(1)(-1) = 2 \Rightarrow -6a = 2 \Rightarrow a = -\frac{1}{3}$.

    The complete factored form is: $f(x) = -\frac{1}{3}(x + 3)(x + 2)(x + 1)(x - 1)$.

23. Since $f$ has zeros $-2, -1, 1$, and 2, it has factors $(x + 2)(x + 1)(x - 1)(x - 2)$. If $f(0) = -8$ then $a(2)(1)(-1)(-2) = -8 \Rightarrow 4a = -8 \Rightarrow a = -2$.
The complete factored form is: $f(x) = -2(x + 2)(x + 1)(x - 1)(x - 2)$.

24. Since $f$ has zeros $-4, 0, 2$, and 4, it has factors $(x + 4)(x)(x - 2)(x - 4)$. If $f(0) = 0$ then we have to use a different point so we will use $f(-2) = -6$, then $a(-2 + 4)(-2)(-2 - 2)(-2 - 4) = -6 \Rightarrow$ $a(2)(-2)(-4)(-6) = -6 \Rightarrow -96a = -6 \Rightarrow a = \frac{1}{16}$.
The complete factored form is: $f(x) = \frac{1}{16}(x + 4)(x)(x - 2)(x - 4)$.

25. A graph of $Y_1 = 10X\text{^}2 + 17X - 6$ is shown in Figure 25. Its zeros are –2 and 0.3. Since the leading coefficient is 10, the complete factorization is $f(x) = 10(x + 2)\left(x - \frac{3}{10}\right)$.

26. A graph of $Y_1 = 2X\text{^}3 + 7X\text{^}2 + 2X - 3$ is shown in Figure 26. Its zeros are –3, –1, and 0.5. Since the leading coefficient is 2, the complete factorization is $f(x) = 2(x + 3)(x + 1)\left(x - \frac{1}{2}\right)$.

[–5, 5, 1] by [–20, 20, 5]

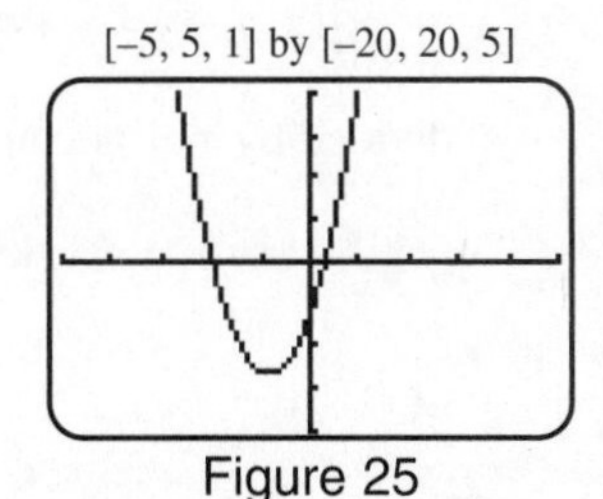

Figure 25

[–5, 5, 1] by [–6, 6, 1]

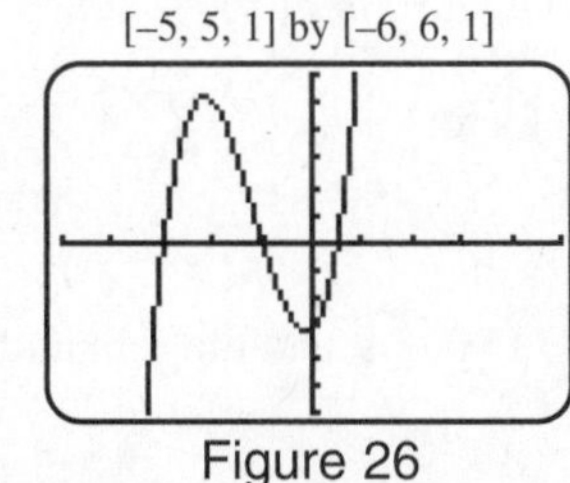

Figure 26

[–5, 5, 1] by [–40, 40, 5]

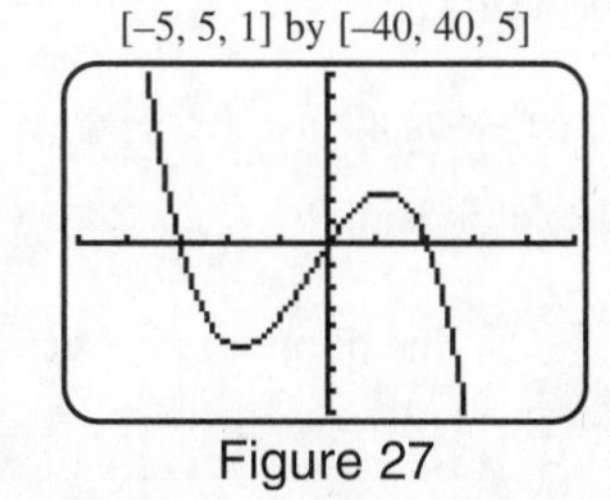

Figure 27

[–5, 5, 1] by [–5, 5, 1]

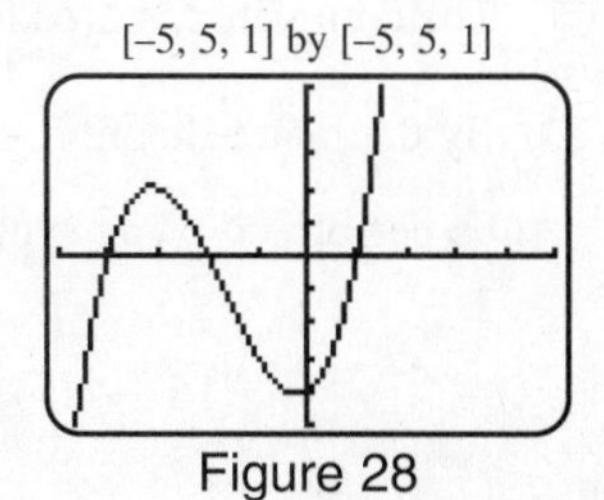

Figure 28

27. A graph of $Y_1 = -3X\text{^}3 - 3X\text{^}2 + 18X$ is shown in Figure 27. Its zeros are –3, 0, and 2. Since the leading coefficient is –3, the complete factorization is $f(x) = -3(x - 0)(x - 2)(x + 3) = -3x(x - 2)(x + 3)$.

28. A graph of $Y_1 = (1/2)X\text{^}3 + (5/2)X\text{^}2 + X - 4$ is shown in Figure 28. Its zeros are –4, –2, and 1. Since the leading coefficient is $\frac{1}{2}$, the complete factorization is $f(x) = \frac{1}{2}(x + 4)(x + 2)(x - 1)$.

29. A graph of $Y_1 = X\text{^}4 + (5/2)X\text{^}3 - 3X\text{^}2 - (9/2)X$ is shown in Figure 29. Its zeros are –3, –1, 0, and $\frac{3}{2}$.
Since the leading coefficient is 1, the complete factorization is
$f(x) = (x + 3)(x + 1)(x - 0)\left(x - \frac{3}{2}\right) = x(x + 3)(x + 1)\left(x - \frac{3}{2}\right)$.

[–5, 5, 1] by [–10, 10, 1]

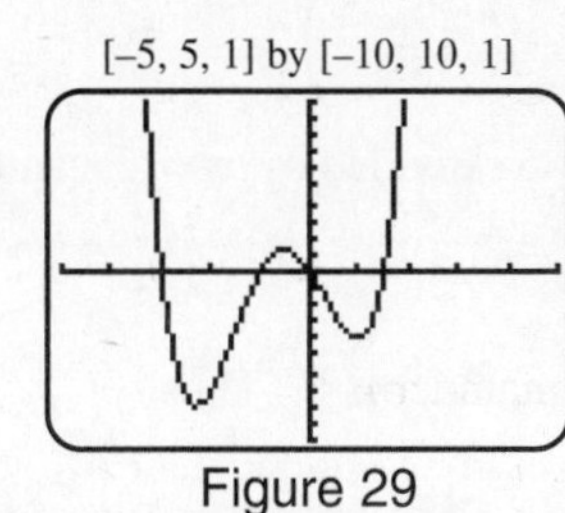

Figure 29

[–3, 3, 1] by [–40, 40, 5]

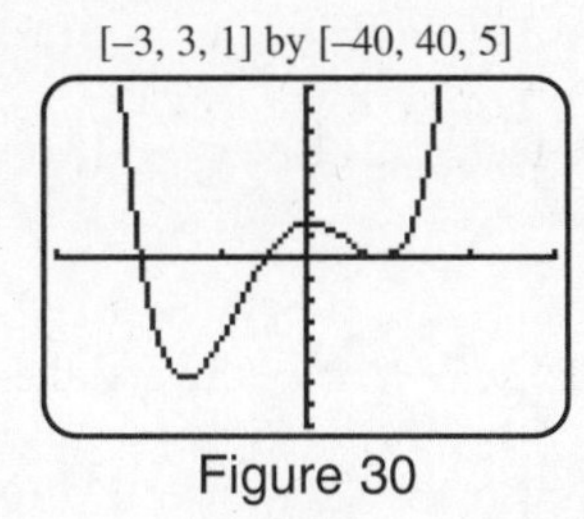

Figure 30

30. A graph of $Y_1 = 10X\text{^}4 + 7X\text{^}3 - 27X\text{^}2 + 2X + 8$ is shown in Figure 30. Its zeros are –2, $-\frac{1}{2}$, 0.8, and 1.
Since the leading coefficient is 10, the complete factorization is
$f(x) = 10(x + 2)\left(x + \frac{1}{2}\right)(x - 0.8)(x - 1)$.

31. By the factor theorem, since 1 is a zero, $(x - 1)$ is a factor. $x^3 - 9x^2 + 23x - 15$ divided by $x - 1$ can be performed using synthetic division.

| 1⌋ | 1 | −9 | 23 | −15 |
|---|---|---|---|---|
| | | 1 | −8 | 15 |
| | 1 | −8 | 15 | 0 |

The quotient is $x^2 - 8x + 15$ and the remainder is 0.

Thus, $x^3 - 9x^2 + 23x - 15 = (x - 1)(x^2 - 8x + 15) = (x - 1)(x - 3)(x - 5)$.

The complete factored form of $f(x) = x^3 - 9x^2 + 23x - 15$ is $f(x) = (x - 1)(x - 3)(x - 5)$.

32. By the factor theorem, since –2 is a zero, $(x + 2)$ is a factor. $2x^3 + x^2 - 11x - 10$ divided by $x + 2$ can be performed using synthetic division.

| −2⌋ | 2 | 1 | −11 | −10 |
|---|---|---|---|---|
| | | −4 | 6 | 10 |
| | 2 | −3 | −5 | 0 |

The quotient is $2x^2 - 3x - 5$ and the remainder is 0.

Thus, $2x^3 + x^2 - 11x - 10 = (x + 2)(2x^2 - 3x - 5) = (x + 2)(2x - 5)(x + 1)$.

The complete factored form of $f(x) = 2x^3 + x^2 - 11x - 10$ is $f(x) = 2(x + 2)\left(x - \frac{5}{2}\right)(x + 1)$.

33. By the factor theorem, since –4 is a zero, $(x + 4)$ is a factor. $-4x^3 - x^2 + 51x - 36$ divided by $x + 4$ can be performed using synthetic division.

| −4⌋ | −4 | −1 | 51 | −36 |
|---|---|---|---|---|
| | | 16 | −60 | 36 |
| | −4 | 15 | −9 | 0 |

The quotient is $-4x^2 + 15x - 9$ and the remainder is 0.

Thus, $-4x^3 - x^2 + 51x - 36 = (x + 4)(-4x^2 + 15x - 9) = (x + 4)(-4x + 3)(x - 3)$.

The complete factored form of $f(x) = -4x^3 - x^2 + 51x - 36$ is $f(x) = -4(x + 4)\left(x - \frac{3}{4}\right)(x - 3)$.

34. By the factor theorem, since 5 is a zero, $(x - 5)$ is a factor. $3x^3 - 11x^2 - 35x + 75$ divided by $x - 5$ can be performed using synthetic division.

| 5⌋ | 3 | −11 | −35 | 75 |
|---|---|---|---|---|
| | | 15 | 20 | −75 |
| | 3 | 4 | −15 | 0 |

The quotient is $3x^2 + 4x - 15$ and the remainder is 0.

Thus, $3x^3 - 11x^2 - 35x + 75 = (x - 5)(3x^2 + 4x - 15) = (x - 5)(3x - 5)(x + 3)$.

The complete factored form of $f(x) = 3x^3 - 11x^2 - 35x + 75$ is $f(x) = 3(x + 3)\left(x - \frac{5}{3}\right)(x - 5)$.

35. By the factor theorem, since –2 is a zero, $(x + 2)$ is a factor. $2x^4 - x^3 - 13x^2 - 6x$ divided by $x + 2$ can be performed using synthetic division.

| −2⌋ | 2 | −1 | −13 | −6 | 0 |
|---|---|---|---|---|---|
| | | −4 | 10 | 6 | 0 |
| | 2 | −5 | −3 | 0 | 0 |

The quotient is $2x^3 - 5x^2 - 3x$ and the remainder is 0. Thus,

$2x^4 - x^3 - 13x^2 - 6x = (x + 2)(2x^3 - 5x^2 - 3x) = (x + 2)x(2x^2 - 5x - 3) =$
$x(x + 2)(2x + 1)(x - 3)$.

The complete factored form of $f(x) = 2x^4 - x^3 - 13x^2 - 6x$ is $f(x) = 2x(x + 2)\left(x + \frac{1}{2}\right)(x - 3)$.

36. By the factor theorem, since $\frac{3}{7}$ is a zero, $\left(x - \frac{3}{7}\right)$ is a factor. $35x^4 + 48x^3 - 41x^2 + 6x$ divided by $x + \frac{3}{7}$ can be performed using synthetic division.

$$\begin{array}{c|ccccc} \frac{3}{7} & 35 & 48 & -41 & 6 & 0 \\ & & 15 & 27 & -6 & 0 \\ \hline & 35 & 63 & -14 & 0 & 0 \end{array}$$

The quotient is $35x^3 + 63x^2 - 14x$ and the remainder is 0.

Thus, $35x^4 + 48x^3 - 41x^2 + 6x = \left(x - \frac{3}{7}\right)(35x^3 + 63x^2 - 14x) = 7x\left(x - \frac{3}{7}\right)(5x^2 + 9x - 2) = 7x\left(x - \frac{3}{7}\right)(5x - 1)(x + 2)$.

The complete factored form of $f(x) = 35x^4 + 48x^3 - 41x^2 + 6x$ is $f(x) = 35x\left(x - \frac{3}{7}\right)\left(x - \frac{1}{5}\right)(x + 2)$.

37. $f(2) = (2)^3 - 6(2)^2 + 11(2) - 6 = 0$; since $f(2) = 0$, by the factor theorem, $x - 2$ is a factor of $f(x) = x^3 - 6x^2 + 11x - 6$.

38. $f(-3) = (-3)^3 + (-3)^2 - 14(-3) - 24 = 0$; since $f(-3) = 0$, by the factor theorem, $x - (-3) = x + 3$ is a factor of $f(x) = x^3 + x^2 - 14x - 24$.

39. $f(3) = (3)^4 - 2(3)^3 - 13(3)^2 - 10(3) = -120$; since $f(-3) \neq 0$, by the factor theorem, $x - 3$ is not a factor of $x^4 - 2x^3 - 13x^2 - 10x$.

40. $f\left(\frac{1}{2}\right) = 2\left(\frac{1}{2}\right)^4 - 11\left(\frac{1}{2}\right)^3 + 9\left(\frac{1}{2}\right)^2 + 14\left(\frac{1}{2}\right) = 8$; since $f\left(\frac{1}{2}\right) \neq 0$, by the factor theorem, $x - \frac{1}{2}$ is not a factor of $2x^4 - 11x^3 + 9x^2 + 14x$.

41. The zeros of $f(x)$ are 4 and –2. Since the graph does not cross the $x$-axis at $x = 4$, the zero of 4 has even multiplicity. The graph crosses the $x$-axis at $x = -2$. The zero of –2 has odd multiplicity. Since the graph levels off, crossing the $x$-axis at $x = -2$, this zero has at least multiplicity 3, and the zero of 4 has at least multiplicity 2. Thus, the minimum degree of $f(x)$ is $3 + 2$, or 5.

42. The zeros of $f(x)$ are –8, –4, and 2. Since the graph does not cross the $x$-axis at $x = -8$, the zero of –8 has even multiplicity. The graph crosses the $x$-axis at $x = -4$ and 2. These zeros have odd multiplicity. Since the graph levels off, crossing the $x$-axis at $x = -4$ and $x = 2$, these zeros both have at least multiplicity 3, and the zero of –8 has at least multiplicity 2. Thus, the minimum degree of $f(x)$ is $3 + 3 + 2$, or 8.

43. Degree: 3; zeros: –1 with multiplicity 2 and 6 with multiplicity 1. $f(x) = (x + 1)^2(x - 6)$

44. Degree: 4; zeros: 5 and 7, both with multiplicity 2. $f(x) = (x - 5)^2(x - 7)^2$

45. Degree: 4; zeros: 2 with multiplicity 3 and 6 with multiplicity 1. $f(x) = (x - 2)^3(x - 6)$

46. Degree: 5; zeros: –2 with multiplicity 2 and 4 with multiplicity 3. $f(x) = (x + 2)^2(x - 4)^3$

47. The graph shows a cubic polynomial with a positive leading coefficient and zeros of 4 and –2. The zero of 4 has odd multiplicity, whereas the zero of –2 has even multiplicity. Since the graph has a degree three, its complete factored form is $f(x) = (x - 4)(x + 2)^2$.

48. The graph shows a cubic polynomial with a negative leading coefficient and zeros of –2 and 6. The zero of –2 has odd multiplicity, whereas the zero of 6 has even multiplicity. Since the graph shows a cubic, its complete factored form is $f(x) = -1(x + 2)(x - 6)^2$.

49. The graph shows a quartic polynomial with a negative leading coefficient and zeros of –3 and 3. Both zeros have even multiplicity. Since the graph has a degree four polynomial, its complete factored form is $f(x) = -1(x + 3)^2(x - 3)^2$.

50. The graph shows a quartic polynomial with a positive leading coefficient and zeros of $-4$ and 2. Both zeros have odd multiplicity. However, the zero at 2 has a higher multiplicity since the graph levels off more at $x = 2$ than at $x = -4$. Since the graph shows a quartic, the zero of $-4$ has multiplicity 1 and the zero of 2 has multiplicity 3. Its factored form is $f(x) = (x + 4)(x - 2)^3$.

51. The graph shows a fifth degree polynomial with a positive leading coefficient and zeros of – 1 and 1. The $-1$ has an even multiplicity, whereas the zero of 1 has an odd multiplicity. Since the graph shows a fifth degree polynomial the factors are $(x + 1)^2(x - 1)^3$. To find the leading coefficient we use $f(0) = -2 \Rightarrow a(1)^2(-1)^3 = -2 \Rightarrow -a = -2 \Rightarrow a = 2$. Its factored form is $f(x) = 2(x + 1)^2(x - 1)^3$.

52. The graph shows a quartic polynomial with a negative leading coefficient and zeros of $-3$, $-1$, and 2. The $-3$ and $-1$ zeros have odd multiplicity, and the zero 2 has an even multiplicity. Since the graph shows a quartic, the factors are $(x + 3)(x + 1)(x - 2)^2$. To find the leading coefficient we use $f(0) = -6 \Rightarrow$ $a(3)(1)(-2)^2 = -6 \Rightarrow 12a = -6 \Rightarrow a = -\frac{1}{2}$. Its factored form is $f(x) = -\frac{1}{2}(x + 3)(x + 1)(x - 2)^2$.

53. (a) From the factors the $x$-intercepts are: $-2, -1$. To find the $y$-intercept set $x = 0 \Rightarrow$

$2(0 + 2)(0 + 1)^2 = 2(2)(1)^2 = 4$

(b) The zero $-2$ has multiplicity 1. The zero $-1$ has multiplicity 2.

(c) See Figure 53.

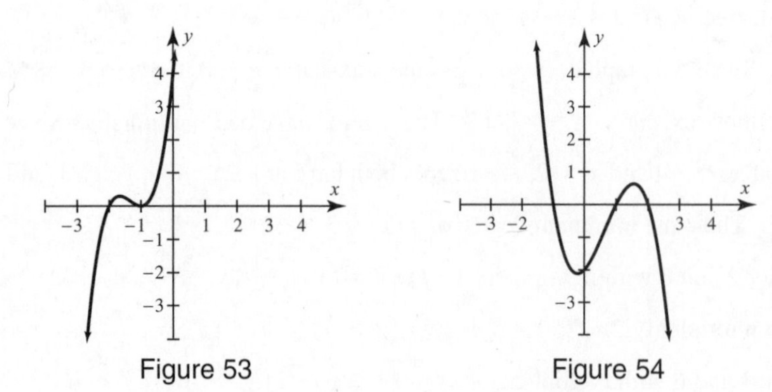

Figure 53 Figure 54

54. (a) From the factors the $x$-intercepts are: $-1$, 1, and 2. To find the $y$-intercept set $x = 0 \Rightarrow$

$-(0 + 1)(0 - 1)(0 - 2) = -(1)(-1)(-2) = -2$

(b) The zero $-1$ has multiplicity 1. The zero 1 has multiplicity 1. The zero 2 has multiplicity 1.

(c) See Figure 54.

55. (a) From the factors the $x$-intercepts are: $-2, 0$, and 2. To find the $y$-intercept set $x = 0 \Rightarrow$

$0(0 + 2)(0 - 2) = 0(2)(-2) = 0$

(b) The zero $-2$ has multiplicity 1. The zero 0 has multiplicity 2. The zero 2 has multiplicity 1.

(c) See Figure 55.

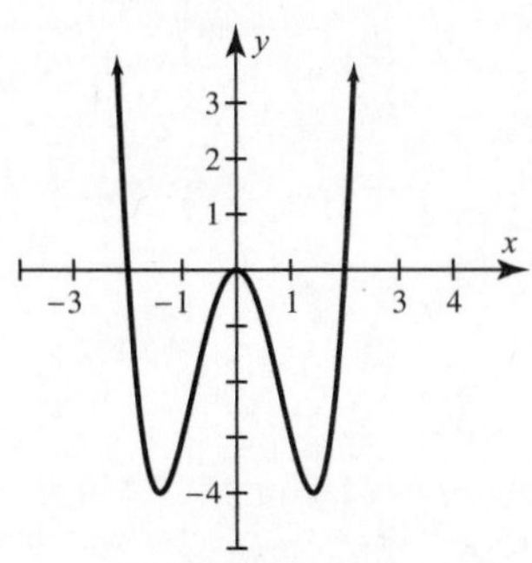

Figure 55

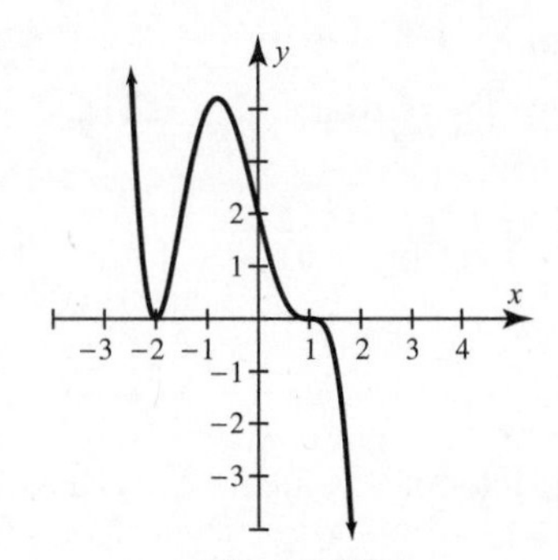

Figure 56

56. (a) From the factors the $x$-intercepts are: $-2, 1$. To find the $y$-intercept set $x = 0 \Rightarrow$

$-\frac{1}{2}(0 + 2)^2(0 - 1)^3 = -\frac{1}{2}(2)^2(-1)^3 = 2$

(b) The zero $-2$ has multiplicity 2. The zero 1 has multiplicity 3.

(c) See Figure 56.

57. $f(x) = 2x^3 + 3x^2 - 8x + 3$

(a) If $\frac{p}{q}$ is a rational zero, then $p$ is a factor of 3, which are $\pm 1$ and $\pm 3$ and $q$ is a factor of 2, which are $\pm 1$ or $\pm 2$. Thus, any rational zero must be in the list $\pm\frac{1}{2}, \pm 1, \pm\frac{3}{2}$, or $\pm 3$. From Figure 57 we see that there are three rational zeros of $\frac{1}{2}$, 1, and –3.

(b) The complete factored form is $f(x) = 2\left(x - \frac{1}{2}\right)(x - 1)(x + 3)$.

| $x$ | $\frac{1}{2}$ | $-\frac{1}{2}$ | 1 | $-1$ | $\frac{3}{2}$ | $-\frac{3}{2}$ | 3 | $-3$ |
|---|---|---|---|---|---|---|---|---|
| $f(x)$ | 0 | $\frac{15}{2}$ | 0 | 12 | $\frac{9}{2}$ | 15 | 60 | 0 |

Figure 57

58. $f(x) = x^3 - 7x + 6$

(a) If $\frac{p}{q}$ is a rational zero, then $p$ is a factor of 6, which are $\pm 1, \pm 2, \pm 3$, and $\pm 6$ and $q$ is a factor of 1, which are $\pm 1$. Thus, any rational zero must be in the list $\pm 1, \pm 2, \pm 3$, or $\pm 6$. From Figure 58 we see that there are three rational zeros of –3, 1, and 2.

(b) The complete factored form is $f(x) = (x + 3)(x - 1)(x - 2)$.

| $x$ | 1 | $-1$ | 2 | $-2$ | 3 | $-3$ | 6 | $-6$ |
|---|---|---|---|---|---|---|---|---|
| $f(x)$ | 0 | 12 | 0 | 12 | 12 | 0 | 180 | $-168$ |

Figure 58

59. $f(x) = 2x^4 + x^3 - 8x^2 - x + 6$

(a) If $\frac{p}{q}$ is a rational zero, then $p$ is a factor of 6, which are $\pm1$, $\pm2$, $\pm3$, and $\pm6$ and $q$ is a factor of 2, which are $\pm1$ and $\pm2$. Thus, any rational zero must be in the list $\pm\frac{1}{2}$, $\pm1$, $\pm\frac{3}{2}$, $\pm2$, $\pm3$, or $\pm6$. By evaluating $f(x)$ at each of these values, we find that the zeros are $-2$, $-1$, 1, and $\frac{3}{2}$.

(b) The complete factored form is $f(x) = 2(x + 2)(x + 1)(x - 1)\left(x - \frac{3}{2}\right)$.

60. $f(x) = 2x^4 + x^3 - 19x^2 - 9x + 9$

(a) If $\frac{p}{q}$ is a rational zero, then $p$ is a factor of 9, which are $\pm1$, $\pm3$, and $\pm9$ and $q$ is a factor of 2, which are $\pm1$ and $\pm2$. Thus, any rational zero must be in the list $\pm\frac{1}{2}$, $\pm1$, $\pm\frac{3}{2}$, $\pm3$, $\pm\frac{9}{2}$, or $\pm9$. By evaluating $f(x)$ at each of these values, we find that the zeros are $-3$, $-1$, $\frac{1}{2}$, and 3.

(b) The complete factored form is $f(x) = 2(x + 3)(x + 1)\left(x - \frac{1}{2}\right)(x - 3)$.

61. $f(x) = 3x^3 - 16x^2 + 17x - 4$

(a) If $\frac{p}{q}$ is a rational zero, then $p$ is a factor of 4, which are $\pm1$, $\pm2$, and $\pm4$ and $q$ is a factor of 3, which are $\pm1$ and $\pm3$. Thus, any rational zero must be in the list $\pm\frac{1}{3}$, $\pm1$, $\pm\frac{2}{3}$, $\pm2$, $\pm\frac{4}{3}$, or $\pm4$. By evaluating $f(x)$ at each of these values, we find that the zeros are $\frac{1}{3}$, 1, and 4.

(b) The complete factored form is $f(x) = 3\left(x - \frac{1}{3}\right)(x - 1)(x - 4)$.

62. $f(x) = x^3 + 2x^2 - 3x - 6$

(a) If $\frac{p}{q}$ is a rational zero, then $p$ is a factor of 6, which are $\pm1$, $\pm2$, $\pm3$, and $\pm6$ and $q$ is a factor of 1, which are $\pm1$. Thus, any rational zero must be in the list $\pm1$, $\pm2$, $\pm3$, or $\pm6$. By evaluating $f(x)$ at each of these values, we find that the only rational zero is $-2$.

(b) In order to find the complete factored form of $f(x)$ we need to divide the factor $(x + 2)$ into $x^3 + 2x^2 - 3x - 6$ using synthetic division.

$$\begin{array}{r|rrrr} -2 & 1 & 2 & -3 & -6 \\ & & -2 & 0 & 6 \\ \hline & 1 & 0 & -3 & 0 \end{array}$$

Thus $x^3 + 2x^2 - 3x - 6 = (x + 2)(x^2 - 3)$.

The complete factored form is $f(x) = (x + 2)(x - \sqrt{3})(x + \sqrt{3})$.

63. $f(x) = x^3 - x^2 - 7x + 7$

(a) If $\frac{p}{q}$ is a rational zero, then $p$ is a factor of 7, which are $\pm 1$, and $\pm 7$ and $q$ is a factor of 1, which are $\pm 1$.

Thus, any rational zero must be in the list $\pm 1$ or $\pm 7$. By evaluating $f(x)$ at each of these values, we find that the only rational zero is 1.

(b) In order to find the complete factored form of $f(x)$ we need to divide the factor $(x - 1)$ into $x^3 - x^2 - 7x + 7$ using synthetic division.

$$\begin{array}{r|rrrr} 1 & 1 & -1 & -7 & 7 \\ & & 1 & 0 & 7 \\ \hline & 1 & 0 & -7 & 0 \end{array}$$

Thus $x^3 - x^2 - 7x + 7 = (x - 1)(x^2 - 7)$.

The complete factored form is $f(x) = (x - 1)(x - \sqrt{7})(x + \sqrt{7})$.

64. $f(x) = 2x^3 - 5x^2 - 7x + 10$

(a) If $\frac{p}{q}$ is a rational zero, then $p$ is a factor of 10, which are $\pm 1$, $\pm 2$, $\pm 5$, and $\pm 10$ and $q$ is a factor of 2, which are $\pm 1$ and $\pm 2$. Thus, any rational zero must be in the list $\pm \frac{1}{2}$, $\pm 1$, $\pm 2$, $\pm \frac{5}{2}$, $\pm 5$, or $\pm 10$. By evaluating $f(x)$ at each of these values, we find that the only rational zero is $\frac{5}{2}$.

(b) In order to find the complete factored form of $f(x)$ we need to divide the factor $\left(x - \frac{5}{2}\right)$ into $2x^3 - 5x^2 - 4x + 10$ using synthetic division.

$$\begin{array}{r|rrrr} \frac{5}{2} & 2 & -5 & -4 & 10 \\ & & 5 & 0 & -10 \\ \hline & 2 & 0 & -4 & 0 \end{array}$$

Thus $2x^3 - 5x^2 - 4x + 10 = \left(x - \frac{5}{2}\right)(2x^2 - 4)$.

The complete factored form is $f(x) = 2\left(x - \frac{5}{2}\right)(x - \sqrt{2})(x + \sqrt{2})$.

65. $P(x) = 2x^3 - 4x^2 + 2x + 7$, $P(x)$ has two sign changes, therefore are 2 or $2 - 2 = 0$ possible positive zeros. $P(-x) = 2(-x)^3 - 4(-x)^2 + 2(-x) + 7 = -2(x)^3 - 4x^2 - 2x + 7$, $P(-x)$ has one sign change, therefore there is one possible negative zero. From the graph of $P(x)$ in Figure 65, we see that the actual number of positive and negative zeros are 0 and 1 repectively.

[-4, 4, 1] by [-25, 25, 5]

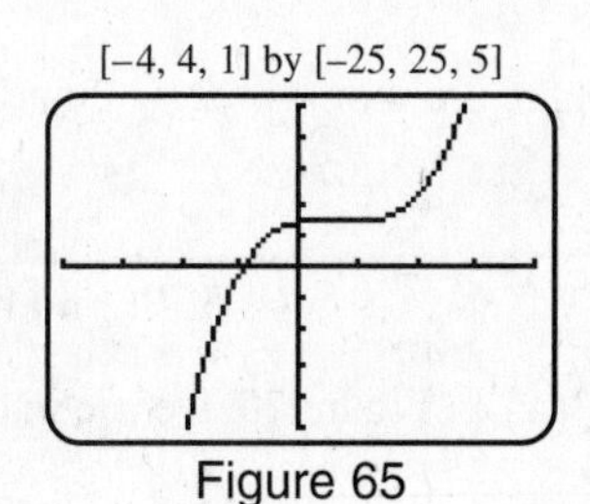

Figure 65

66. $P(x) = x^3 + 2x^2 + x - 10$, $P(x)$ has one sign change, thereforethere is one possible positive zero. $P(-x) = (-x)^3 + 2(-x)^2 + (-x) - 10 = -x^3 + 2x - x - 10$, $P(-x)$ has two sign changes, therefore there are 2 or $2 - 2 = 0$ possible negative zeros. From the graph of $P(x)$ in Figure 66, we see that the actual number of positive and negative zeros are 1 and 0 respectively.

67. $P(x) = 5x^4 + 3x^2 + 2x - 9$, $P(x)$ has one sign change, therefore there is one possible positive zero. $P(-x) = 5(-x)^4 + 3(-x)^2 + 2(-x) - 9 = 5x^4 + 3x - 2x - 9$, $P(-x)$ has one sign change, therefore there is one possible negative zero. From the graph of $P(x)$ in Figure 67, we see that the actual number of positive and negative zeros are 1 and 1 respectively.

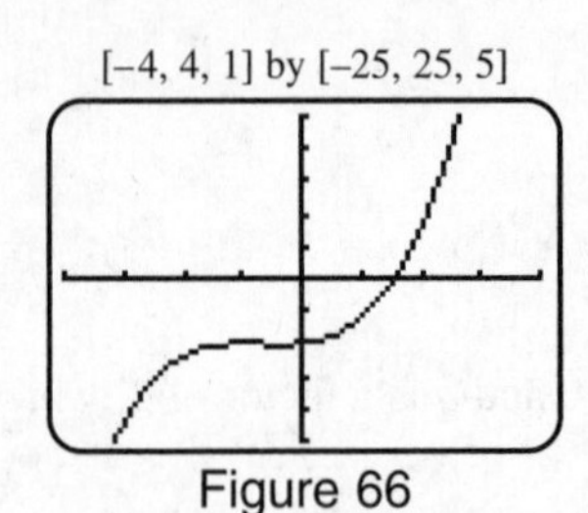

Figure 66

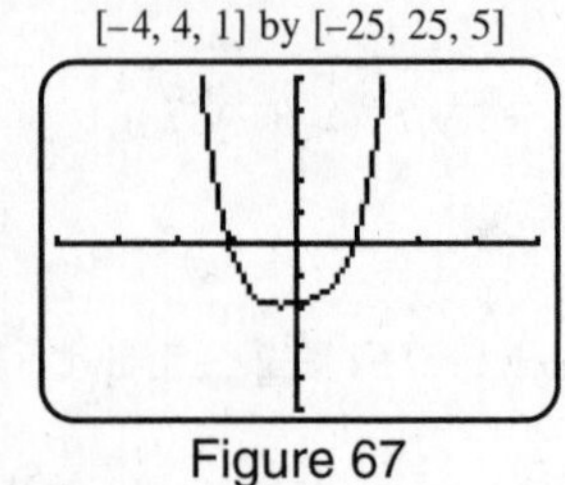

Figure 67

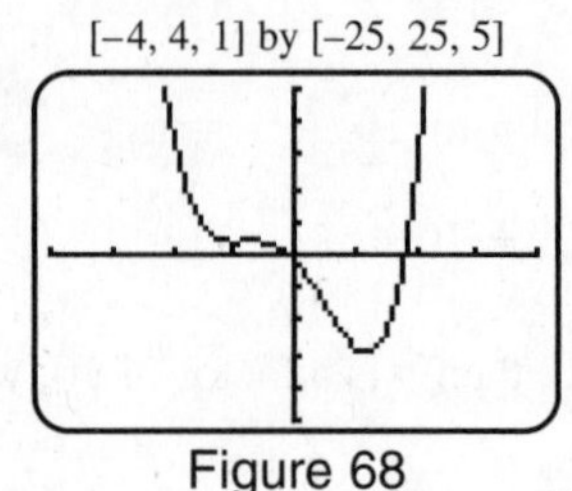

Figure 68

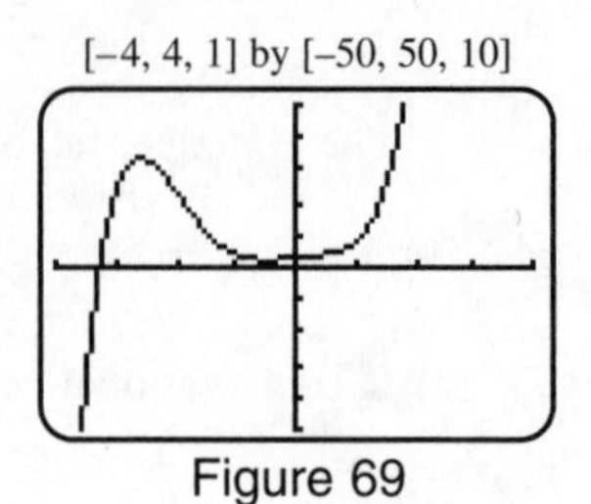

Figure 69

68. $P(x) = 3x^4 + 2x^3 - 8x^2 - 10x - 1$, $P(x)$ has one sign change, therefore there is one possible positive zeros. $P(-x) = 3(-x)^4 + 2(-x)^3 - 8(-x)^2 - 10(-x) - 1 = 3x^4 - 2x^3 - 8x + 10x - 1$, $P(-x)$ has three sign changes, therefore there are 3 or $3 - 2 = 1$ possible negative zeros. From the graph of $P(x)$ in Figure 68, we see that the actual number of positive and negative zeros are 1 and 1 respectively.

69. $P(x) = x^5 + 3x^4 - x^3 + 2x + 3$, $P(x)$ has two sign changes, therefore there are 2 or $2 - 2 = 0$ possible positive zeros. $P(-x) = (-x)^5 + 3(-x)^4 - (-x)^3 + 2(-x) + 3 = -x^5 + 3x + x^3 - 2x + 3$, $P(-x)$ has three sign changes, therefore there are 3 or $3 - 2 = 1$ possible negative zeros. From the graph of $P(x)$ in Figure 69, we see that the actual number of positive and negative zeros are 0 and 1 respectively.

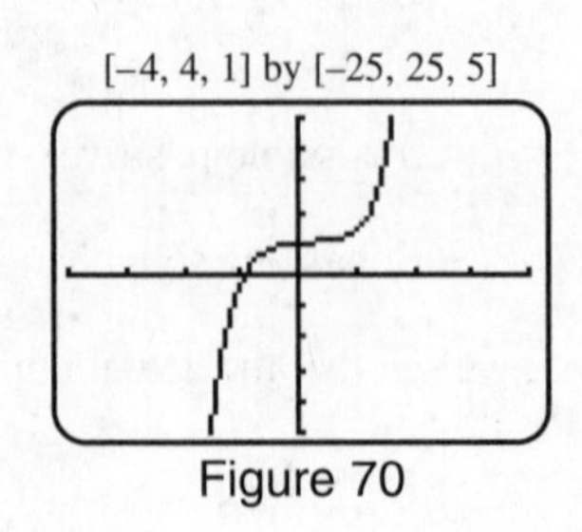

Figure 70

70. $P(x) = 2x^5 - x^4 + x^3 - x^2 + x + 5$, $P(x)$ has four sign changes, therefore there are 4 or $4 - 2 = 2$ or $2 - 2 = 0$ possible positive zeros.
$P(-x) = 2(-x)^5 - (-x)^4 + (-x)^3 - (-x)^2 + (-x) + 5 = -2x^5 - x^4 - x^3 - x^2 - x + 5$, $P(-x)$ has one sign change, therefore there is 1 possible negative zero. From the graph of $P(x)$ in Figure 70, we see that the actual number of positive and negative zeros are 0 and 1 respectively.

71. (a) $f(x) = x^3 + x^2 - 6x = 0 \Rightarrow x(x^2 + x - 6) = x(x + 3)(x - 2) = 0 \Rightarrow x = 0, -3,$ or 2.

    (b) Graph $Y_1$ = X^3 + X^2 − 6X in $[-5, 5, 1]$ by $[-10, 10, 1]$. The $x$-intercepts are –3, 0, and 2.

    (c) Table $Y_1$ = X^3 + X^2 − 6X starting at $x = -4$, incrementing by 1. The zeros or $x$-intercepts are –3, 0, and 2.

72. (a) $f(x) = 2x^2 - 8x + 6 = 0 \Rightarrow (2x - 6)(x - 1) = 0 \Rightarrow x = 3$ or 1.

    (b) Graph $Y_1$ = 2X^2 − 8X + 6 in $[0, 4, 1]$ by $[-5, 5, 1]$. The $x$-intercepts are 1 and 3.

    (c) Table $Y_1$ = 2X^2 − 8X + 6 starting at $x = 0$, incrementing by 1. The zeros or $x$-intercepts are 1 and 3.

73. (a) $f(x) = x^4 - 1 = 0 \Rightarrow x^4 = 1 \Rightarrow x = \pm 1.$

    (b) Graph $Y_1$ = X^4 − 1 in $[-2, 2, 1]$ by $[-10, 10, 1]$. The $x$-intercepts are –1 and 1.

    (c) Table $Y_1$ = X^4 − 1 starting at $x = -2$, incrementing by 1. The zeros or $x$-intercepts are $\pm 1$.

74. (a) $f(x) = x^4 - 5x^2 + 4 = 0 \Rightarrow (x^2 - 1)(x^2 - 4) = (x - 1)(x + 1)(x - 2)(x + 2) = 0 \Rightarrow$ $x = \pm 1$ or $\pm 2$.

    (b) Graph $Y_1$ = X^4 − 5X^2 + 4 in $[-5, 5, 1]$ by $[-5, 5, 1]$. The $x$-intercepts are $\pm 1$ and $\pm 2$.

    (c) Table $Y_1$ = X^4 − 5X^2 + 4 starting at $x = -3$, incrementing by 1. The zeros or $x$-intercepts are $\pm 1$ and $\pm 2$.

75. (a) $f(x) = -x^3 + 4x = 0 \Rightarrow -x(x^2 - 4) = x(x + 2)(x - 2) = 0 \Rightarrow x = 0,$ or $\pm 2$.

    (b) Graph $Y_1$ = −X^3 + 4X in $[-5, 5, 1]$ by $[-5, 5, 1]$. The $x$-intercepts are –2, 0, and 2.

    (c) Table $Y_1$ = −X^3 + 4X starting at $x = -3$, incrementing by 1. The zeros or $x$-intercepts are –2, 0, and 2.

76. (a) $f(x) = 6 - 4x - 2x^2 = 0 \Rightarrow 2x^2 + 4x - 6 = 0 \Rightarrow (2x - 2)(x + 3) = 0 \Rightarrow x = 1,$ or $-3$.

    (b) Graph $Y_1$ = 6 − 4X − 2X^2 in $[-5, 5, 1]$ by $[-10, 10, 1]$. The $x$-intercepts are –3, and 1.

    (c) Table $Y_1$ = 6 − 4X − 2X^2 starting at $x = -4$, incrementing by 1. The zeros or $x$-intercepts are –3, and 1.

77. $x^3 - 25x = 0 \Rightarrow x(x^2 - 25) = 0 \Rightarrow x(x - 5)(x + 5) = 0 \Rightarrow x = 0,$ or $\pm 5$

78. $x^4 - x^3 - 6x^2 = 0 \Rightarrow x^2(x^2 - x - 6) = 0 \Rightarrow x^2(x - 3)(x + 2) = 0 \Rightarrow x = 0, 3,$ or $-2$

79. $x^4 - x^2 = 2x^2 + 4 \Rightarrow x^4 - 3x^2 - 4 = 0 \Rightarrow (x^2 - 4)(x^2 + 1) = 0 \Rightarrow$ $(x - 2)(x + 2)(x^2 + 1) = 0 \Rightarrow x = \pm 2$

80. $x^4 + 5 = 6x^2 \Rightarrow x^4 - 6x^2 + 5 = 0 \Rightarrow (x^2 - 1)(x^2 - 5) = 0 \Rightarrow x = \pm 1$ or $\pm\sqrt{5}$

81. $x^3 - 3x^2 - 18x = 0 \Rightarrow x(x^2 - 3x - 18) = 0 \Rightarrow x(x - 6)(x + 3) = 0 \Rightarrow x = 0, 6,$ or $-3$

82. $x^4 - x^2 = 0 \Rightarrow x^2(x^2 - 1) = 0 \Rightarrow x^2(x + 1)(x - 1) = 0 \Rightarrow x = 0, -1,$ or 1

83. $2x^3 = 4x^2 - 2x \Rightarrow 2x^3 - 4x^2 + 2x = 0 \Rightarrow 2x(x^2 - 2x + 1) = 0 \Rightarrow$ $2x(x - 1)(x - 1) = 0 \Rightarrow x = 0$ or 1

84. $x^3 = x \Rightarrow x^3 - x = 0 \Rightarrow x(x^2 - 1) = 0 \Rightarrow x(x + 1)(x - 1) = 0 \Rightarrow x = 0, -1,$ or 1

85. $12x^3 = 17x^2 + 5x \Rightarrow 12x^3 - 17x^2 - 5x = 0 \Rightarrow x(12x^2 - 17x - 5) = 0 \Rightarrow$ $x(4x + 1)(3x - 5) = 0 \Rightarrow x = 0, -\frac{1}{4},$ or $\frac{5}{3}$

86. $3x^3 + 3x = 10x^2 \Rightarrow 3x^3 - 10x^2 + 3x = 0 \Rightarrow x(3x^2 - 10x + 3) = 0 \Rightarrow x(3x - 1)(x - 3) = 0 \Rightarrow$

$x = 0, \frac{1}{3}$, or 3

87. $9x^4 + 4 = 13x^2 \Rightarrow 9x^4 - 13x^2 + 4 = 0 \Rightarrow (9x^2 - 4)(x^2 - 1) = 0 \Rightarrow x = \pm\frac{2}{3}, x = \pm 1$

88. $4x^4 + 7x^2 - 2 = 0 \Rightarrow (4x^2 - 1)(x^2 + 2) = 0 \Rightarrow x = \pm\frac{1}{2}$

89. $4x^3 + 4x^2 - 3x - 3 = 0 \Rightarrow (4x^3 + 4x^2) - (3x + 3) = 0 \Rightarrow 4x^2(x + 1) - 3(x + 1) = 0 \Rightarrow$

$(4x^2 - 3)(x + 1) = 0$. Set $4x^2 - 3 = 0 \Rightarrow 4x^2 = 3 \Rightarrow x^2 = \frac{3}{4} \Rightarrow x = \pm\frac{\sqrt{3}}{2}$.

The solutions are; $x = -1, \pm\frac{\sqrt{3}}{2}$.

90. $9x^3 + 27x^2 - 2x - 6 = 0 \Rightarrow (9x^3 + 27x^2) - (2x + 6) = 0 \Rightarrow 9x^2(x + 3) - 2(x + 3) = 0 \Rightarrow$

$(9x^2 - 2)(x + 3) = 0$. Set $9x^2 - 2 = 0 \Rightarrow 9x^2 = 2 \Rightarrow x^2 = \frac{2}{9} \Rightarrow x = \pm\frac{\sqrt{2}}{3}$.

The solutions are; $x = -3, \pm\frac{\sqrt{2}}{3}$.

91. $2x^3 + 4 = x(x + 8) \Rightarrow 2x^3 + 4 = x^2 + 8x \Rightarrow 2x^3 - x^2 - 8x + 4 = 0 \Rightarrow$

$(2x^3 - x^2) - (8x - 4) = 0 \Rightarrow x^2(2x - 1) - 4(2x - 1) = 0 \Rightarrow (x^2 - 4)(2x - 1) = 0 \Rightarrow$

$(x + 2)(x - 2)(2x - 1) = 0 \Rightarrow x = -2, 2, \frac{1}{2}$

92. $3x^3 + 18 = x(2x + 27) \Rightarrow 3x^3 + 18 = 2x^2 + 27x \Rightarrow 3x^3 - 2x^2 - 27x + 18 = 0 \Rightarrow$

$(3x^3 - 2x^2) - (27x - 18) = 0 \Rightarrow x^2(3x - 2) - 9(3x - 2) = 0 \Rightarrow (x^2 - 9)(3x - 2) = 0 \Rightarrow$

$(x + 3)(x - 3)(3x - 2) = 0 \Rightarrow x = -3, 3, \frac{2}{3}$

93. $8x^4 - 30x^2 + 27 = 0 \Rightarrow (4x^2 - 9)(2x^2 - 3) = 0 \Rightarrow (2x + 3)(2x - 3)(2x^2 - 3) = 0$.

Set $2x^2 - 3 = 0 \Rightarrow 2x^2 = 3 \Rightarrow x^2 = \frac{3}{2} \Rightarrow x = \pm\sqrt{\frac{3}{2}} \Rightarrow x = \pm\frac{\sqrt{6}}{2}$. The solutions are;

$x = \pm\frac{3}{2}, \pm\frac{\sqrt{6}}{2}$

94. $4x^4 - 21x^2 + 20 = 0 \Rightarrow (4x^2 - 5)(x^2 - 4) = 0 \Rightarrow (4x^2 - 5)(x + 2)(x - 2) = 0$.

Set $4x^2 - 5 = 0 \Rightarrow 4x^2 = 5 \Rightarrow x^2 = \frac{5}{4} \Rightarrow x = \pm\frac{\sqrt{5}}{2}$. The solutions are; $x = \pm 2, \pm\frac{\sqrt{5}}{2}$

95. $x^6 - 19x^3 - 216 = 0 \Rightarrow (x^3 + 8)(x^3 - 27) = 0$. set $x^3 + 8 = 0 \Rightarrow x^3 = -8 \Rightarrow x = -2$.

Also set $x^3 - 27 = 0 \Rightarrow x^3 = 27 \Rightarrow x = 3$. The solutions are; $x = -2, 3$.

96. $x^6 = 7x^3 + 8 \Rightarrow x^6 - 7x^3 - 8 = 0 \Rightarrow (x^3 + 1)(x^3 - 8) = 0$. set $x^3 + 1 = 0 \Rightarrow x^3 = -1 \Rightarrow x = -1$.

Also set $x^3 - 8 = 0 \Rightarrow x^3 = 8 \Rightarrow x = 2$. The solutions are; $x = -1, 2$.

97. The graph of $f(x) = x^3 - 1.1x^2 - 5.9x + 0.7$ is shown in Figure 97. Its zeros are approximately –2.0095, 0.11639, and 2.9931. The solutions are $x \approx -2.01, 0.12,$ or $2.99$.

98. The graph of $f(x) = x^3 + x^2 - 18x + 13$ is shown in Figure 98. Its zeros are approximately –5.0627, 0.78294, and 3.2797. The solutions are $x \approx -5.06, 0.78,$ or $3.28$.

[–10, 10, 1] by [–10, 10, 1]

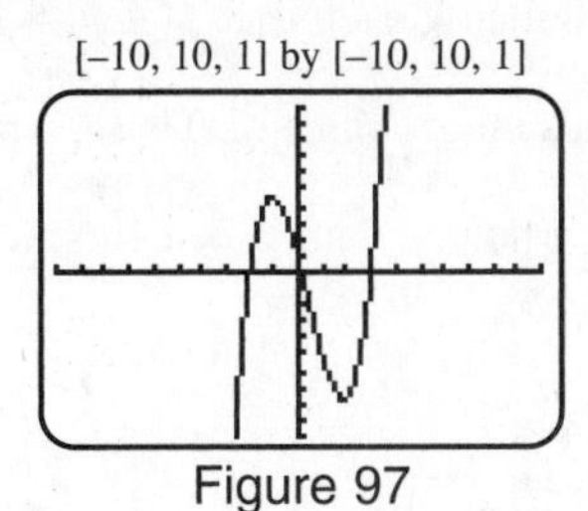

Figure 97

[–10, 10, 1] by [–60, 60, 10]

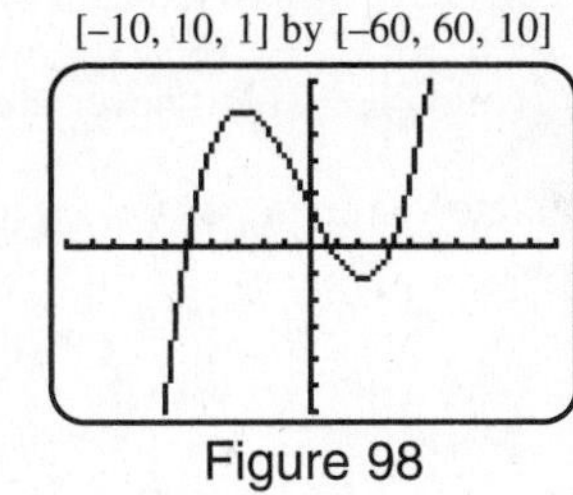

Figure 98

[–10, 10, 1] by [–10, 10, 1]

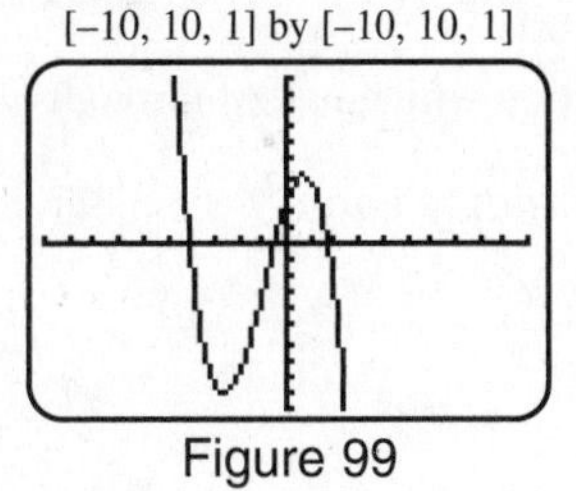

Figure 99

[–5, 15, 1] by [–200, 200, 100]

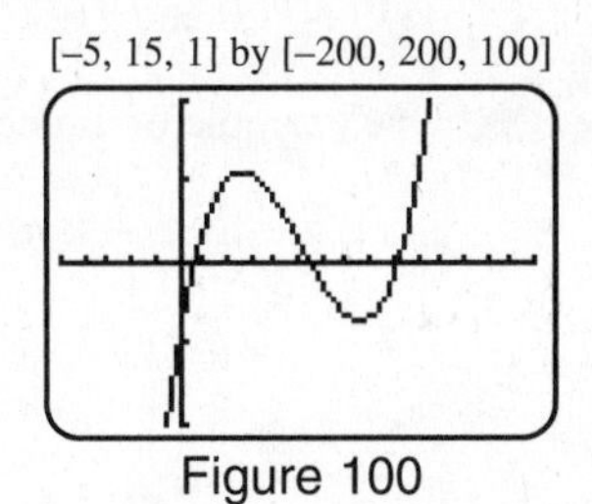

Figure 100

99. The graph of $f(x) = -0.7x^3 - 2x^2 + 4x + 2.5$ is shown in Figure 99. Its zeros are approximately –4.0503, –0.51594, and 1.7091. The solutions are $x \approx -4.05, -0.52,$ or $1.71$.

100. The graph of $f(x) = 3x^3 - 46x^2 + 180x - 99$ is shown in Figure 100. Its zeros are approximately 0.65494, 5.4745, and 9.2039. The solutions are $x \approx 0.65, 5.47,$ or $9.20$.

101. The graph of $f(x) = 2x^4 - 1.5x^3 - 24x^2 - 10x + 13$ is shown in Figure 101. Its zeros are approximately –2.6878, –1.0957, 0.55475, and 3.9787. The solutions are $x \approx -2.69, -1.10, 0.55$ or $3.98$.

[–10, 10, 1] by [–120, 120, 20]

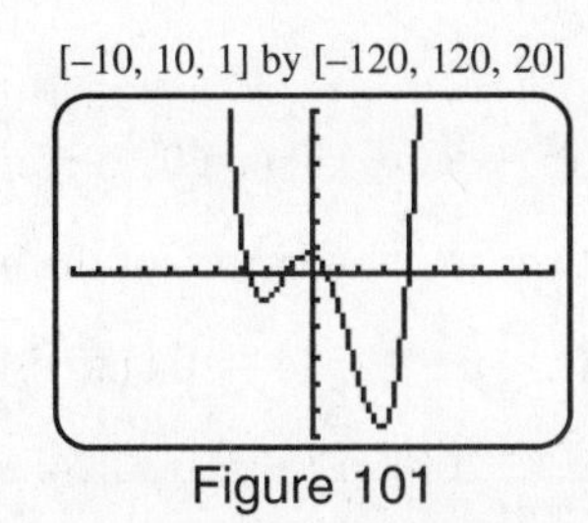

Figure 101

[–10, 10, 1] by [–120, 120, 20]

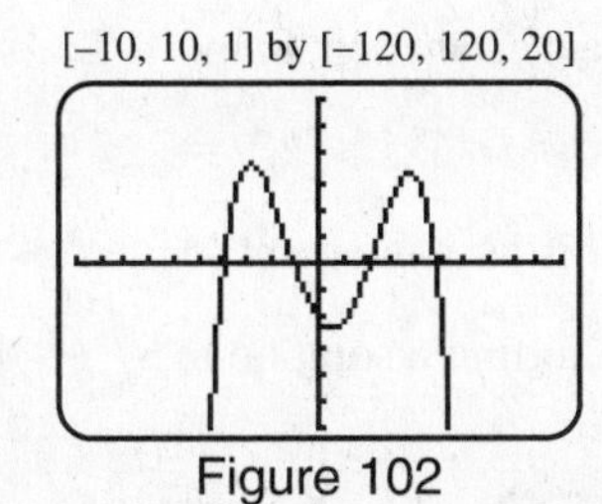

Figure 102

102. The graph of $f(x) = -x^4 + 2x^3 + 20x^2 - 22x - 41$ is shown in Figure 102. Its zeros are approximately –3.8934, –1.0382, 2.0986, and 4.8331. The solutions are $x \approx -3.89, -1.04, 2.10$ or $4.83$.

103. $f(x) = x^2 - 5 \Rightarrow f(2) = 2^2 - 5 = -1$ and $f(3) = 3^2 - 5 = 4$; because $f(2) < 0$ and $f(3) > 0$, by the intermediate value property, there exists an $x$-value between 2 and 3 such that $f(x) = 0$.

104. $f(x) = x^3 - x - 1 \Rightarrow f(1) = 1^3 - 1 - 1 = -1$ and $f(2) = 2^3 - 2 - 1 = 5$; because $f(1) < 0$ and $f(2) > 0$, by the intermediate value property, there exists an $x$-value between 1 and 2 such that $f(x) = 0$.

105. $f(x) = 2x^3 - 1 \Rightarrow f(0) = 2(0)^3 - 1 = -1$ and $f(1) = 2(1)^3 - 1 = 1$; because $f(0) < 0$ and $f(1) > 0$, by the intermediate value property, there exists an $x$-value between 0 and 1 such that $f(x) = 0$.

106. $f(x) = 4x^2 - x - 1 \Rightarrow f(-1) = 4(-1)^2 - (-1) - 1 = 4$ and $f(0) = 4(0)^2 - 0 - 1 = -1$; because $f(-1) > 0$ and $f(0) < 0$, by the intermediate value property, there exists an $x$-value between –1 and 0 such that $f(x) = 0$.

107. $f(x) = x^5 - x^2 + 4 \Rightarrow f(1) = 1^5 - 1^2 + 4 = 4$ and $f(2) = 2^5 - 2^2 + 4 = 32$. Because $f(1) < 20$ and $f(2) > 20$, by the intermediate value property, there exists a number $K$ such that $f(K) = 20$.

108. One example of a function which passes through $(-2, 3)$ and $(1, -2)$ but never takes on the value of 0 is shown in Figure 108. *Answers may vary.* Since the intermediate value property does not hold, $f$ cannot be continuous.

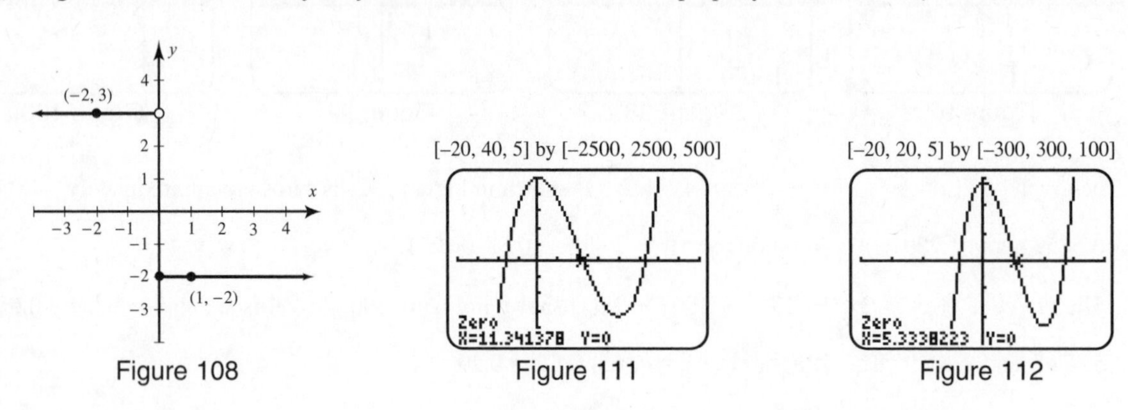


Figure 108 Figure 111 Figure 112

109. $T(x) = x^3 - 6x^2 + 8x$ when $0 \le x \le 4$. Graph $Y_1 = X^3 - 6X^2 + 8X$ in the window $[0, 4, 1]$ by $[-5, 5, 1]$. The zeros are $x = 0$, $x = 2$, and $x = 4$. Since $x = 0, 2$, and 4 correspond to the hours after midnight, then the temperature was 0ºF at 12 am, 2 am and 4 am.

110. $V = lwh \Rightarrow 504 = x(x + 1)(x + 2) \Rightarrow 504 = x^3 + 3x^2 + 2x \Rightarrow x^3 + 3x^2 + 2x - 504 = 0$; a graph of $y = x^3 + 3x^2 + 2x - 504$ indicates that $x = 7$ is an $x$-intercept (or zero); thus, the dimensions of the box are 7 inches by 8 inches by 9 inches. Another way to find a solution to $x^3 + 3x^2 + 2x - 504 = 0$ is to use the rational zero test; the factors of 504 are $\pm1, \pm2, \pm3, \pm4, \pm6, \pm7, \pm8, \pm9, \pm12, \pm14, \pm18, \pm21, \pm24, \pm28, \pm36, \pm42, \pm56, \pm63, \pm72, \pm84, \pm126, \pm168, \pm252$ and $\pm504$; using trial and error, we find that 7 is a zero since $f(7) = 7^3 + 3(7)^2 + 2(7) - 504 = 0$; thus, $x = 7$, and the dimensions of the box again are 7 inches by 8 inches by 9 inches.

111. The graph of $Y_1 = (\pi/3)X^3 - 10\pi X^2 + ((4000\pi)(0.6))/3$ and the smallest positive zero are shown in Figure 111. The ball with a 20-centimeter diameter will sink approximately 11.34 centimeters into the water.

112. We must find the smallest positive zero of $f(x) = 1.0472x^3 - 15.708x^2 + 523.599(0.55)$. The graph of $f$ and this zero are shown in Figure 112. Thus, the ball will sink approximately 5.33 centimeters into the water.

113. $f(x) = x^3 - 66x^2 + 1052x + 652$ and $f(x) = 2500 \Rightarrow 2500 = x^3 - 66x^2 + 1052x + 652 \Rightarrow x^3 - 66x^2 + 1052x - 1848 = 0$; graph $Y_1 = X^3 - 66X^2 + 1052X - 1848$ in the window [0, 45, 5] by [–5000, 5000, 1000]. The zeros are at $x = 2$, $x = 22$, and $x = 42$. Since $x = 1$ corresponds to June 1, there were 2500 birds on approximately June 2, June 22, and July 12.

114. $P(x) = 2x^3 - 18x^2 + 46x$ when $0 \le x \le 6$ and $P(x) = 30$. Graph $Y_1 = 2X\text{^}3 - 18x\text{^}2 + 46X - 30$ in the window $[0, 6, 1]$ by $[-5, 5, 1]$. The zeros are $x = 1$, $x = 3$, and $x = 5$. Since $x = 1, 3$, and 5 correspond to days past May 31, then the insect population was 30 thousand per acre on June 1, June 3, and June 5.

115. (a) Graph $f$ in [–10, 15, 1] by [–70, 70, 10]. It has three zeros of approximately –6.01, 2.15, and 11.7. The approximate complete factored form is $-0.184(x + 6.01)(x - 2.15)(x - 11.7)$.

(b) The zeros represent the months when the average temperature is 0ºF. The zero of –6.01 has no significance since it does not correspond to a month. The zeros of 2.15 and 11.7 mean that in approximately February and November the average temperature in Trout Lake is 0ºF.

116. (a) For March, $x = 3$; $f(3) = 0.0151(3)^4 - 0.438(3)^3 + 3.60(3)^2 - 6.49(3) + 72.5 \approx 74.8$ºF.
For July, $x = 7$; $f(7) = 0.0151(7)^4 - 0.438(7)^3 + 3.60(7)^2 - 6.49(7) + 72.5 \approx 89.5$F.

(b) The graph of $f$ is shown in Figure 116b. The average high temperatures increase from January until July, then they decrease until December..

(c) The graph of $f$ together with the graph of $Y_1 = 80$ is shown in Figure 116c. The intersection points are approximately (4, 80) and (10, 80). This means that the average temperature in Daytona Beach is 80ºF in the months of April and October. This can also be seen if we table $f$ starting at 2 and incrementing by 2.

[0.5, 12.5, 1] by [60, 100, 10]

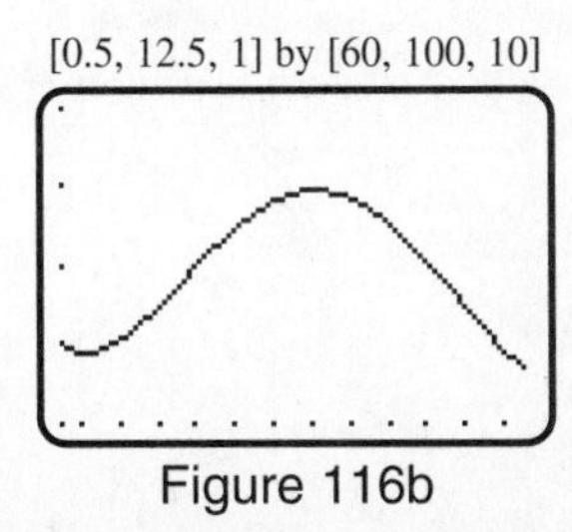

Figure 116b

[0.5, 12.5, 1] by [60, 100, 10]

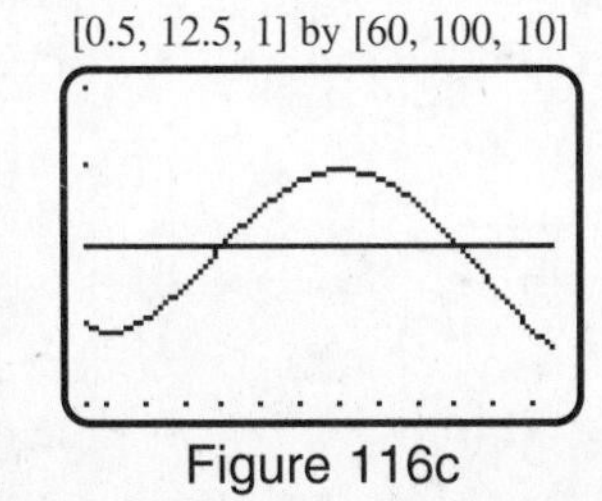

Figure 116c

[0, 70, 10] by [0, 22, 5]

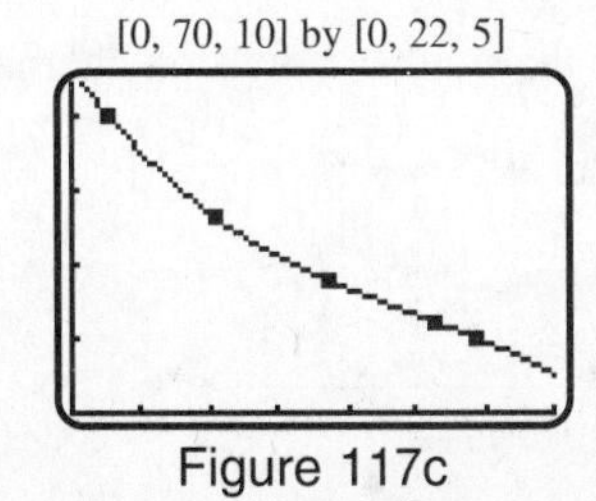

Figure 117c

[0, 70, 10] by [0, 22, 5]

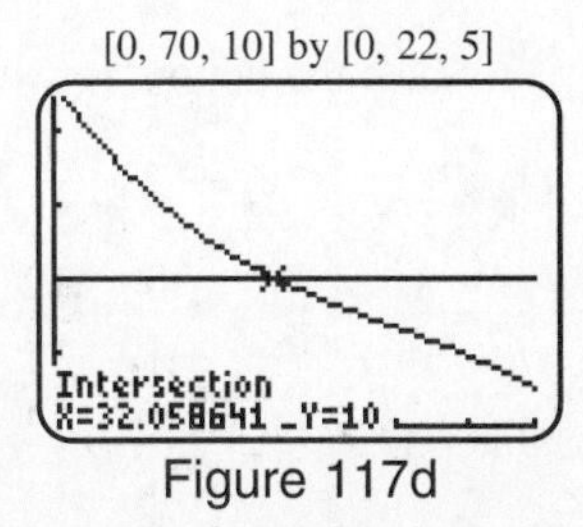


Figure 117d

117. (a) The greater the distance downstream from the plant the less the concentration of copper. This agrees with intuition.

(b) Using the cubic regression function on your calculator we find
$f(x) \approx -0.000068x^3 + 0.0099x^2 - 0.653x + 23$.

(c) See Figure 117c.

(d) We must approximate the distance where the concentration of copper first drops to 10. Graph $Y_1 = C(x)$ and $Y_2 = 10$. The point of intersection is near (32.1, 10) as shown in Figure 117d. Mussels would not be expected to live between the plant and approximately 32.1 miles downstream, that is when $0 \le x < 32.1$ (approximately).

118. (a) We must use the graph to determine where the dog's age is equivalent to being 45 in human years. Mentally visualize the horizontal line $y = 45$. We can see that an age of 45 in humans corresponds to approximately an age of 7 in dog years.

(b) From the graph we see that $f(2) \approx 22, f(6) \approx 41, f(10) \approx 55, f(14) \approx 72, f(18) \approx 90$

(c) Using the quadratic regression function on your calculator
$f(x) \approx -0.001628x^4 + 0.07292x^3 - 1.0912x^2 + 10.21x + 5.4$

(d) Graph $Y_1 = -0.001628X\text{^}4 + 0.07292X\text{^}3 - 1.0912X\text{^}2 + 10.21X + 5.4$ and $Y_2 = 45$ in the window $[0, 10, 1]$ by $[30, 50, 1]$. Use the intersect function on the calculator to find $y \approx 7.15$ when $x = 45$.

## Extended and Discovery Exercise for Section 4.4

1. $P(x) = x^4 - x^3 + 3x^2 - 8x + 8;\ c = 2$

$$\begin{array}{r|rrrrr} 2 & 1 & -1 & 3 & -8 & 8 \\ & & 2 & 2 & 10 & 4 \\ \hline & 1 & 1 & 5 & 2 & 12 \end{array}$$

Since the bottom row of the synthetic division is all non-negative and $c > 0$, $P(x)$ has no real zero greater than 2.

2. $P(x) = 2x^5 - x^4 + 2x^3 - 2x^2 + 4x - 4;\ c = 1$

$$\begin{array}{r|rrrrrr} 1 & 2 & -1 & 2 & -2 & 4 & -4 \\ & & 2 & 1 & 3 & 1 & 5 \\ \hline & 2 & 1 & 3 & 1 & 5 & 1 \end{array}$$

Since the bottom row of the synthetic division is all non-negative and $c > 0$, $P(x)$ has no real zero greater than 1.

3. $P(x) = x^4 + x^3 - x^2 + 3;\ c = -2$

$$\begin{array}{r|rrrrr} -2 & 1 & 1 & -1 & 0 & 3 \\ & & -2 & 2 & -2 & 4 \\ \hline & 1 & -1 & 1 & -2 & 7 \end{array}$$

Since the bottom row of the synthetic division alternates in sign and $c < 0$, $P(x)$ has no real zero less than $-2$.

4. $P(x) = x^5 + 2x^3 - 2x^2 + 5x + 5;\ c = -1$

$$\begin{array}{r|rrrrrr} -1 & 1 & 0 & 2 & -2 & 5 & 5 \\ & & -1 & 1 & -3 & 5 & -10 \\ \hline & 1 & -1 & 3 & -5 & 10 & -5 \end{array}$$

Since the bottom row of the synthetic division alternates in sign and $c < 0$, $P(x)$ has no real zero less than $-1$.

5. $P(x) = 3x^4 + 2x^3 - 4x^2 + x - 1;\ c = 1$

$$\begin{array}{r|rrrrr} 1 & 3 & 2 & -4 & 1 & -1 \\ & & 3 & 5 & 1 & 2 \\ \hline & 3 & 5 & 1 & 2 & 1 \end{array}$$

Since the bottom row of the synthetic division are all non-negative and $c > 0$, $P(x)$ has no real zero greater than 1.

6. $P(x) = 3x^4 + 2x^3 - 4x^2 + x - 1;\ c = -2$

$$\begin{array}{r|rrrrr} -2 & 3 & 2 & -4 & 1 & -1 \\ & & -6 & 8 & -8 & 14 \\ \hline & 3 & -4 & 4 & -7 & 13 \end{array}$$

Since the bottom row of the synthetic division alternates in sign and $c < 0$, $P(x)$ has no real zero less than $-2$.

## Checking Basic Concepts for Sections 4.3 and 4.4

1. $\dfrac{5x^4 - 10x^3 + 5x^2}{5x^2} = \dfrac{5x^4}{5x^2} - \dfrac{10x^3}{5x^2} + \dfrac{5x^2}{5x^2} = x^2 - 2x + 1$

2\. (a)

$$\begin{array}{r}
x^2 + 4 \\
x - 1\overline{)\,x^3 - x^2 + 4x - 4} \\
\underline{x^3 - x^2\phantom{+ 4x - 4}} \\
4x - 4 \\
\underline{4x - 4} \\
0
\end{array}$$

The quotient is $x^2 + 4$.

(b)

$$\begin{array}{r}
x^2 - 2x + 3 \\
2x + 1\overline{)\,2x^3 - 3x^2 + 4x + 4} \\
\underline{2x^3 + \phantom{3}x^2\phantom{+ 4x + 4}} \\
-4x^2 + 4x + 4 \\
\underline{-4x^2 - 2x\phantom{+ 4}} \\
6x + 4 \\
\underline{6x + 3} \\
1
\end{array}$$

The quotient is $x^2 - 2x + 3 + \dfrac{1}{2x + 1}$.

(c)

$$\begin{array}{r}
x^2 - 3x + 2 \\
x^2 + 4\overline{)\,x^4 - 3x^3 + 6x^2 - 13x + 9} \\
\underline{x^4 \phantom{- 3x^3} + 4x^2\phantom{- 13x + 9}} \\
-3x^3 + 2x^2 - 13x + 9 \\
\underline{-3x^3 \phantom{+ 2x^2} - 12x\phantom{+ 9}} \\
2x^2 - \phantom{1}x + 9 \\
\underline{2x^2 \phantom{- x} + 8} \\
-x + 1
\end{array}$$

The quotient is $x^2 - 3x + 2 + \dfrac{-x + 1}{x^2 + 4}$.

3\. Since the graph of the cubic polynomial has zeros $-2$ and 1, the multiplicities of the degree 3 equation is the zero $-2$ is even $\Rightarrow$ 2 and the zero 1 is odd $\Rightarrow$ 1. The factors are $(x + 2)(x + 2)(x - 1)$. To find the leading coefficient use:

$f(0) = 2 \Rightarrow a(0 + 2)(0 + 2)(0 - 1) = 2 \Rightarrow a(2)(2)(-1) = 2 \Rightarrow -4a = 2 \Rightarrow a = -\dfrac{1}{2}$.

The complete factored form is: $f(x) = -\dfrac{1}{2}(x + 2)^2(x - 1)$.

4\. Symbolic: $f(x) = x^3 - 2x^2 - 15x = 0 \Rightarrow x(x^2 - 2x - 15) = x(x - 5)(x + 3) = 0 \Rightarrow$ $x = 0, 5,$ or $-3$.

Graphical: Graph $Y_1$ = X^3 − 2X^2 − 15X in $[-5, 5, 1]$ by $[-40, 20, 5]$. The $x$-intercepts are –3, 0, and 5. See Figure 4a.

Numerical: Table $Y_1$ = X^3 − 2X^2 − 15X starting at $x = -4$, incrementing by 1. By scrolling through the table, we see that the solutions are 0, 5, and –3. See Figure 4b.

[–5, 5, 1] by [–40, 20, 5]

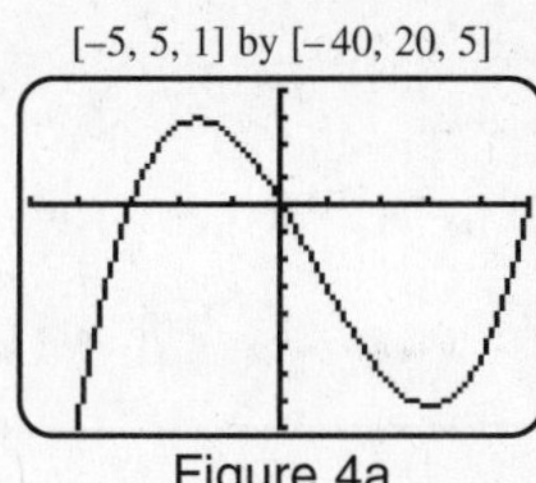

Figure 4a

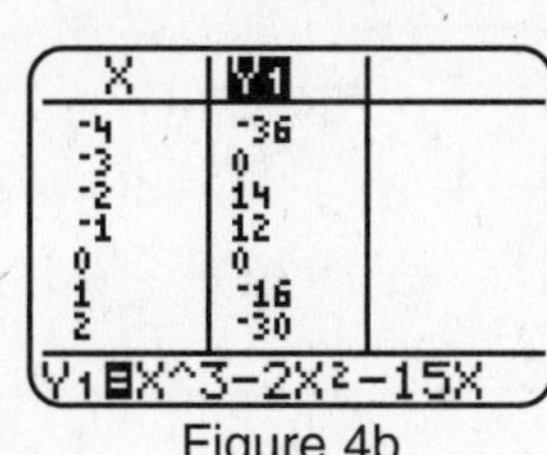


Figure 4b

[–6, 6, 1] by [–150, 150, 20]

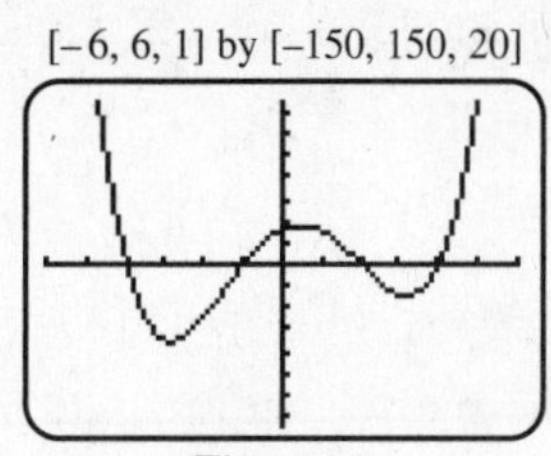

Figure 5

5\. Graph $Y_1$ = X^4 − X^3 − 18X^2 + 16X + 32 in $[-6, 6, 1]$ by $[-150, 150, 20]$. The $x$-intercepts are –4, –1, 2, and 4. See Figure 5. The factored form of $f$ is $f(x) = (x + 4)(x + 1)(x - 2)(x - 4)$.

## 4.5: The Fundamental Theorem of Algebra

1. The graph of $f(x)$ does not intersect the $x$-axis. Therefore, $f$ has no real zeros. Since $f$ is degree 2, there must be two imaginary zeros.
2. The graph of $f(x)$ does not intersect the $x$-axis. Therefore, $f$ has no real zeros. Since $f$ is degree 2, there must be two imaginary zeros.
3. The graph of $f(x)$ intersects the $x$-axis once. Therefore, $f$ has one real zero. Since $f$ is degree 3, there must be two imaginary zeros.
4. The graph of $f(x)$ intersects the $x$-axis three times. Therefore, $f$ has three distinct real zeros. Since $f$ is degree 3, there are no imaginary zeros.
5. The graph of $f(x)$ intersects the $x$-axis twice. Therefore, $f$ has two real zeros. Since $f$ is degree 4, there must be two imaginary zeros.
6. The graph of $f(x)$ does not intersect the $x$-axis. Therefore, $f$ has no real zeros. Since $f$ is degree 4, there must be four imaginary zeros.
7. The graph of $f(x)$ intersects the $x$-axis three times. Therefore, $f$ has three real zeros. Since $f$ is degree 5, there must be two imaginary zeros.
8. The graph of $f(x)$ intersects the $x$-axis once. Therefore, $f$ has one real zero. Since $f$ is degree 5, there must be four imaginary zeros.
9. Degree: 2; leading coefficient: 1; zeros: $6i$ and $-6i$

   (a) $f(x) = (x - 6i)(x + 6i)$

   (b) $(x - 6i)(x + 6i) = x^2 - 36i^2 = x^2 + 36$. Thus, $f(x) = x^2 + 36$.
10. Degree: 3; leading coefficient: 5; zeros: 2, $i$, and $-i$

    (a) $f(x) = 5(x - 2)(x - i)(x + i)$

    (b) $5(x - 2)(x - i)(x + i) = 5(x - 2)(x^2 - i^2) = 5(x - 2)(x^2 + 1) = 5(x^3 + x - 2x^2 - 2) = 5x^3 - 10x^2 + 5x - 10$. Thus, $f(x) = 5x^3 - 10x^2 + 5x - 10$.
11. Degree: 3; leading coefficient: –1; zeros: –1, $2i$, and $-2i$

    (a) $f(x) = -1(x + 1)(x - 2i)(x + 2i)$

    (b) $-1(x + 1)(x - 2i)(x + 2i) = -1(x + 1)(x^2 - 4i^2) = -1(x + 1)(x^2 + 4) = -(x^3 + 4x + x^2 + 4) = -x^3 - x^2 - 4x - 4$. Thus, $f(x) = -x^3 - x^2 - 4x - 4$.
12. Degree: 4; leading coefficient: 3; zeros: –2, 4, $i$, and $-i$

    (a) $f(x) = 3(x + 2)(x - 4)(x - i)(x + i)$

    (b) $3(x + 2)(x - 4)(x - i)(x + i) = 3(x + 2)(x - 4)(x^2 + 1) = 3(x + 2)(x^3 - 4x^2 + x - 4) = 3x^4 - 6x^3 - 21x^2 - 6x - 24$. Thus, $f(x) = 3x^4 - 6x^3 - 21x^2 - 6x - 24$.
13. Degree: 4; leading coefficient: 10; zeros: 1, –1, $3i$, and $-3i$

    (a) $f(x) = 10(x - 1)(x + 1)(x - 3i)(x + 3i)$

    (b) $10(x - 1)(x + 1)(x - 3i)(x + 3i) = 10(x^2 - 1)(x^2 + 9) = 10(x^4 + 8x^2 - 9) = 10x^4 + 80x^2 - 90$. Thus, $f(x) = 10x^4 + 80x^2 - 90$.

14. Degree: 2; leading coefficient: –5; zeros: $1 + i$ and $1 - i$

(a) $f(x) = -5(x - (1 + i))(x - (1 - i))$

(b) $-5(x - (1 + i))(x - (1 - i)) = -5(x^2 - 2x + 2) = -5x^2 + 10x - 10.$

Thus, $f(x) = -5x^2 + 10x - 10.$

15. Degree: 4; leading coefficient: $\frac{1}{2}$; zeros: $-i$ and $2i$

(a) Since $f(x)$ has real coefficients, it must also have a third and fourth zero of $i$ and $-2i$ the conjugate of $-i$ and $2i$. Therefore the complete factored form is: $f(x) = \frac{1}{2}(x + i)(x - i)(x + 2i)(x - 2i)$

(b) $\frac{1}{2}(x + i)(x - i)(x + 2i)(x - 2i) = \frac{1}{2}(x^2 - i^2)(x^2 - 4i^2) = \frac{1}{2}(x^2 + 1)(x^2 + 4) =$

$\frac{1}{2}(x^4 + 4x^2 + x^2 + 4) = \frac{1}{2}x^4 + \frac{5}{2}x^2 + 2.$ Thus, $f(x) = \frac{1}{2}x^4 + \frac{5}{2}x^2 + 2.$

16. Degree: 3; leading coefficient: $-\frac{3}{4}$; zeros: $-3i$ and $\frac{2}{5}$

(a) Since $f(x)$ has real coefficients, it must also have a third zero of $3i$ the conjugate of $-3i$. Therefore the complete factored form is: $f(x) = -\frac{3}{4}\left(x - \frac{2}{5}\right)(x + 3i)(x - 3i)$

(b) $-\frac{3}{4}\left(x - \frac{2}{5}\right)(x + 3i)(x - 3i) = -\frac{3}{4}\left(x - \frac{2}{5}\right)(x^2 - 9i^2) = -\frac{3}{4}\left(x - \frac{2}{5}\right)(x^2 + 9) =$

$-\frac{3}{4}\left(x^3 - \frac{2}{5}x^2 + 9x - \frac{18}{5}\right) = -\frac{3}{4}x^3 + \frac{6}{20}x^2 - \frac{27}{4}x + \frac{54}{20}.$

Thus, $f(x) = -\frac{3}{4}x^3 + \frac{3}{10}x^2 - \frac{27}{4}x + \frac{27}{10}.$

17. Degree: 3; leading coefficient: $-2$; zeros: $1 - i$ and 3

(a) Since $f(x)$ has real coefficients, it must also have a third zero of $1 + i$ the conjugate of $1 - i$. Therefore the complete factored form is: $f(x) = -2(x - (1 + i))(x - (1 - i))(x - 3)$

(b) $-2(x - (1 + i))(x - (1 - i))(x - 3) = -2(x^2 - x + xi - x - xi + 1 - i^2)(x - 3) =$

$-2(x^2 - 2x + 2)(x - 3) = -2(x^3 - 2x^2 + 2x - 3x^2 + 6x - 6) = -2(x^3 - 5x^2 + 8x - 6) =$

$-2x^3 + 10x^2 - 16x + 12.$ Thus, $f(x) = -2x^3 + 10x^2 - 16x + 12.$

18. Degree: 4; leading coefficient: 7; zeros: $2i$ and $3i$

(a) Since $f(x)$ has real coefficients, it must also have a third and fourth zero of $-2i$ and $-3i$ the conjugate of $2i$ and $3i$. Therefore the complete factored form is: $f(x) = 7(x - 2i)(x + 2i)(x - 3i)(x + 3i)$

(b) $7(x - 2i)(x + 2i)(x - 3i)(x + 3i) = 7(x^2 - 4i^2)(x^2 - 9i^2) = 7(x^2 + 4)(x^2 + 9) =$

$7(x^4 + 9x^2 + 4x^2 + 36) = 7x^4 + 91x^2 + 252.$ Thus, $f(x) = 7x^4 + 91x^2 + 252.$

19. First divide:

$$\begin{array}{r|l} & 3x^2 + 75 \\ x - \frac{5}{3} & 3x^3 - 5x^2 + 75x - 125 \\ & \underline{3x^3 - 5x^2} \\ & \qquad 75x - 125 \\ & \qquad \underline{75x - 125} \\ & \qquad\qquad 0 \end{array}$$

Now set $3x^2 + 75 = 0$ and solve. $3x^2 + 75 = 0 \Rightarrow 3x^2 = -75 \Rightarrow x^2 = -25 \Rightarrow x = \pm\sqrt{-25} \Rightarrow$

$x = \pm 5i$. The solutions are $x = \frac{5}{3}, \pm 5i$.

20. If $2i$ is a zero then $-2i$ is also a zero $\Rightarrow (x + 2i)(x - 2i) = x^2 - 4i^2 = x^2 + 4$. Now divide this into the equation:

$$\begin{array}{r|l} & x^2 + 2x + 4 \\ x^2 + 4 & x^4 + 2x^3 + 8x^2 + 8x + 16 \\ & \underline{x^4 \qquad + 4x^2} \\ & \quad 2x^3 + 4x^2 + 8x + 16 \\ & \quad \underline{2x^3 \qquad + 8x} \\ & \qquad 4x^2 \qquad + 16 \\ & \qquad \underline{4x^2 \qquad + 16} \\ & \qquad\qquad 0 \end{array}$$

Then use the quadratic formula to solve $x^2 + 2x + 4$. $\dfrac{-2 \pm \sqrt{4 - 4(1)(4)}}{2(1)} = \dfrac{-2 \pm \sqrt{-12}}{2} =$

$\dfrac{-2 \pm 2\sqrt{-3}}{2} = -1 \pm i\sqrt{3}$. Therefore the solutions are: $x = \pm 2i, -1 \pm i\sqrt{3}$.

21. If $-3i$ is a zero then $3i$ is also a zero $\Rightarrow (x + 3i)(x - 3i) = x^2 - 9i^2 = x^2 + 9$. Now divide this into the equation:

$$\begin{array}{r|l} & 2x^2 - x + 1 \\ x^2 + 9 & 2x^4 - x^3 + 19x^2 - 9x + 9 \\ & \underline{2x^4 \qquad + 18x^2} \\ & \quad -x^3 + x^2 - 9x + 9 \\ & \quad \underline{-x^3 \qquad - 9x} \\ & \qquad x^2 \qquad + 9 \\ & \qquad \underline{x^2 \qquad + 9} \\ & \qquad\qquad 0 \end{array}$$

Then use the quadratic formula to solve $2x^2 - x + 1$. $\dfrac{1 \pm \sqrt{1 - 4(2)(1)}}{2(2)} = \dfrac{1 \pm \sqrt{-7}}{4} =$

$\dfrac{1}{4} \pm \dfrac{i\sqrt{7}}{4}$. Therefore the solutions are: $x = \pm 3i, \dfrac{1}{4} \pm \dfrac{i\sqrt{7}}{4}$.

22. First divide:

$$\begin{array}{r} 7x^2 + 7x + 14 \\ x - \frac{2}{7}\overline{)\,7x^3 + 5x^2 + 12x - 4} \\ \underline{7x^3 - 2x^2} \qquad\qquad \\ 7x^2 + 12x - 4 \\ \underline{7x^2 - 2x} \qquad \\ 14x - 4 \\ \underline{14x - 4} \\ 0 \end{array}$$

Now set $7x^2 + 7x + 14 = 0$ and solve. Using the quadratic formula we get: $\dfrac{-7 \pm \sqrt{49 - 4(7)(14)}}{2(7)} =$

$\dfrac{-7 \pm \sqrt{-343}}{14} = \dfrac{-7 \pm 7i\sqrt{7}}{14} = \dfrac{-1}{2} \pm \dfrac{i\sqrt{7}}{2}$. Therefore the solutions are: $x = \dfrac{2}{7}, \dfrac{-1}{2} \pm \dfrac{i\sqrt{7}}{2}$.

23. $x^2 + 25 = 0 \Rightarrow x^2 = -25 \Rightarrow x = \pm 5i$. Thus, $f(x) = (x - 5i)(x + 5i)$.

24. $x^2 + 11 = 0 \Rightarrow x^2 = -11 \Rightarrow x = \pm i\sqrt{11}$. Thus, $f(x) = (x - i\sqrt{11})(x + i\sqrt{11})$.

25. $3x^3 + 3x = 0 \Rightarrow 3x(x^2 + 1) = 0 \Rightarrow x = 0$ or $\pm i$. Thus, $f(x) = 3(x - 0)(x - i)(x + i)$.

26. $2x^3 + 10x = 0 \Rightarrow 2x(x^2 + 5) = 0 \Rightarrow x = 0$ or $\pm i\sqrt{5}$. Thus, $f(x) = 2(x - 0)(x - i\sqrt{5})(x + i\sqrt{5})$.

27. $x^4 + 5x^2 + 4 = 0 \Rightarrow (x^2 + 1)(x^2 + 4) = 0 \Rightarrow x = \pm i$ or $\pm 2i$.

Thus, $f(x) = (x - i)(x + i)(x - 2i)(x + 2i)$.

28. $x^4 + 4x^2 = 0 \Rightarrow x^2(x^2 + 4) = 0 \Rightarrow x = 0$ or $\pm 2i$. Thus, $f(x) = (x - 0)(x - 0)(x - 2i)(x + 2i)$.

29. The graph of $y = x^3 + 2x^2 + 16x + 32$ is shown in Figure 29. The $x$-intercept appears to be –2. We can use synthetic division to help factor $f$.

$$\begin{array}{r|rrrr} -2 & 1 & 2 & 16 & 32 \\ & & -2 & 0 & -32 \\ \hline & 1 & 0 & 16 & 0 \end{array}$$

$x^3 + 2x^2 + 16x + 32 = (x + 2)(x^2 + 16) = (x + 2)(x + 4i)(x - 4i)$.

Thus, $f(x) = (x + 2)(x + 4i)(x - 4i)$.

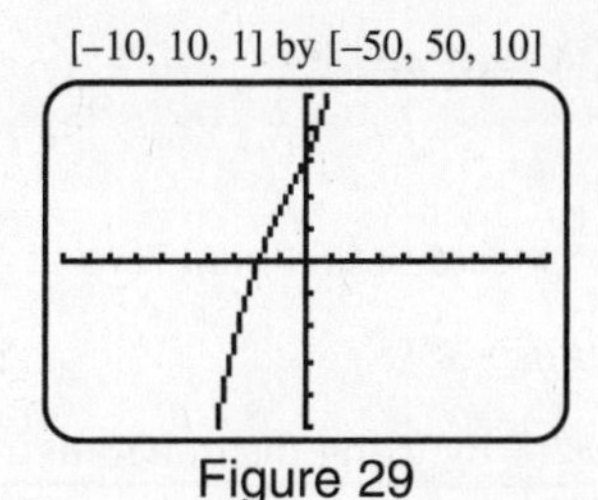


Figure 29

30. The graph of $y = x^4 + 2x^3 + x^2 + 8x - 12$ is shown in Figure 30. The $x$-intercepts appear to be –3 and 1. We can use synthetic division to help factor $f$.

$$\begin{array}{r|rrrrr} 1 & 1 & 2 & 1 & 8 & -12 \\ & & 1 & 3 & 4 & 12 \\ \hline & 1 & 3 & 4 & 12 & 0 \end{array}$$

$x^4 + 2x^3 + x^2 + 8x - 12 = (x - 1)(x^3 + 3x^2 + 4x + 12)$

$$\begin{array}{r|rrrr} -3 & 1 & 3 & 4 & 12 \\ & & -3 & 0 & -12 \\ \hline & 1 & 0 & 4 & 0 \end{array}$$

$x^4 + 2x^3 + x^2 + 8x - 12 = (x - 1)(x^3 + 3x^2 + 4x + 12) = (x - 1)(x + 3)(x^2 + 4) =$ $(x - 1)(x + 3)(x - 2i)(x + 2i)$. Thus, $f(x) = (x - 1)(x + 3)(x - 2i)(x + 2i)$.

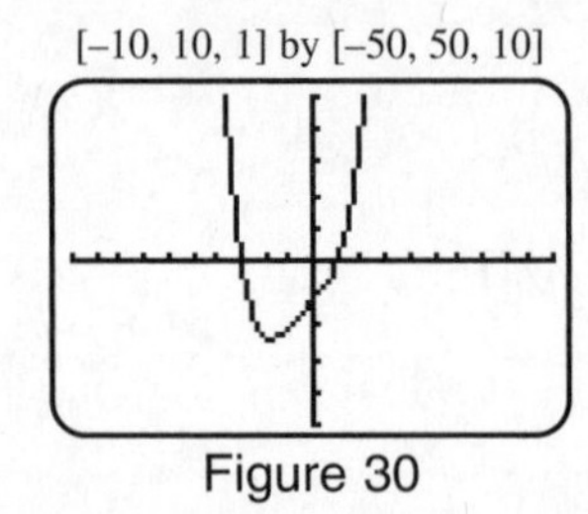

Figure 30

31. $x^3 + x = 0 \Rightarrow x(x^2 + 1) = 0 \Rightarrow x(x + i)(x - i) = 0 \Rightarrow x = 0, \pm i$

32. To solve $2x^3 - x + 1 = 0$, start by graphing $Y_1 = 2X\text{^}3 - X + 1$ in $[-10, 10, 1]$ by $[-10, 10, 1]$ so we locate the rational zero at $x = -1$. Now use synthetic division to help factor $2x^3 - x + 1$.

$$\begin{array}{r|rrrr} -1 & 2 & 0 & -1 & 1 \\ & & -2 & 2 & -1 \\ \hline & 2 & -2 & 1 & 0 \end{array}$$

$2x^3 - x + 1 = (x + 1)(2x^2 - 2x + 1)$

Use the quadratic formula to find the zeros of $2x^2 - 2x + 1$ with $a = 2$, $b = -2$, and $c = 1$.

$$x = \frac{-(-2) \pm \sqrt{(-2)^2 - 4(2)(1)}}{2(2)} = \frac{2 \pm \sqrt{4 - 8}}{4} = \frac{2 \pm \sqrt{-4}}{4} = \frac{2 \pm 2i}{4} = \frac{1}{2} \pm \frac{1}{2}i$$

The solutions are $x = -1, \frac{1}{2} \pm \frac{1}{2}i$.

33. Factor or find the zero of 2 graphically.

$x^3 = 2x^2 - 7x + 14 \Rightarrow x^3 - 2x^2 + 7x - 14 = 0 \Rightarrow x^2(x - 2) + 7(x - 2) = 0 \Rightarrow$ $(x - 2)(x^2 + 7) = 0 \Rightarrow (x - 2)(x + i\sqrt{7})(x - i\sqrt{7}) = 0 \Rightarrow x = 2, \pm i\sqrt{7}$

34. To solve $x^3 - x^2 - x - 2 = 0$, start by graphing $Y_1 = X\text{^}3 - X\text{^}2 - X - 2$ to locate the rational zero at $x = 2$. Now use synthetic division to help factor $x^3 - x^2 - x - 2$ (refer to exercise 32).

$x^3 - x^2 - x - 2 = (x - 2)(x^2 + x + 1)$. We may find the zeros of $x^2 + x + 1$ by using the quadratic formula. The solutions are $x = 2, -\frac{1}{2} \pm \frac{i\sqrt{3}}{2}$.

35. $x^4 + 5x^2 = 0 \Rightarrow x^2(x^2 + 5) = x^2(x + i\sqrt{5})(x - i\sqrt{5}) = 0 \Rightarrow x = 0, \pm i\sqrt{5}$

36. Factor or find the zero of 2 graphically.

$x^4 - 2x^3 + x^2 - 2x = 0 \Rightarrow x^3(x - 2) + x(x - 2) = 0 \Rightarrow (x - 2)(x^3 + x) = 0 \Rightarrow$

$x(x - 2)(x^2 + 1) = 0 \Rightarrow x(x - 2)(x + i)(x - i) = 0 \Rightarrow x = 0, 2, \pm i$

37. $x^4 = x^3 - 4x^2 \Rightarrow x^4 - x^3 + 4x^2 = 0 \Rightarrow x^2(x^2 - x + 4) = 0$

Use the quadratic formula to find the zeros of $x^2 - x + 4$. The solutions are $x = 0, \frac{1}{2} \pm \frac{i\sqrt{15}}{2}$.

38. Factor or find the zero of 1 graphically.

$x^5 + 9x^3 = x^4 + 9x^2 \Rightarrow x^5 - x^4 + 9x^3 - 9x^2 = 0 \Rightarrow x^4(x - 1) + 9x^2(x - 1) = 0 \Rightarrow$

$(x - 1)(x^4 + 9x^2) = 0 \Rightarrow x^2(x - 1)(x^2 + 9) = 0 \Rightarrow x^2(x - 1)(x + 3i)(x - 3i) = 0 \Rightarrow$

$x = 0, 1, \pm 3i$

39. Find the zeros of 1 and 2 using the rational zero test or a graph. See Figures 39a & 39b.

$x^4 + x^3 = 16 - 8x - 6x^2 \Rightarrow x^4 + x^3 + 6x^2 + 8x - 16 = 0$

The graph of $x^4 + x^3 + 6x^2 + 8x - 16$ shows that –2 and 1 are zeros, so $(x + 2)$ and $(x - 1)$ are factors; using synthetic division twice gives the missing factor.

$$\begin{array}{r|rrrrr} -2 & 1 & 1 & 6 & 8 & -16 \\ & & -2 & 2 & -16 & 16 \\ \hline & 1 & -1 & 8 & -8 & 0 \end{array}$$

$$\begin{array}{r|rrrr} 1 & 1 & -1 & 8 & -8 \\ & & 1 & 0 & 8 \\ \hline & 1 & 0 & 8 & 0 \end{array}$$

$x^4 + x^3 + 6x^2 + 8x - 16 = (x + 2)(x - 1)(x^2 + 8) = (x + 2)(x - 1)(x + i\sqrt{8})(x - i\sqrt{8})$

The solutions are $x = -2, 1, \pm i\sqrt{8}$.

[–4, 4, 1] by [–20, 20, 5]

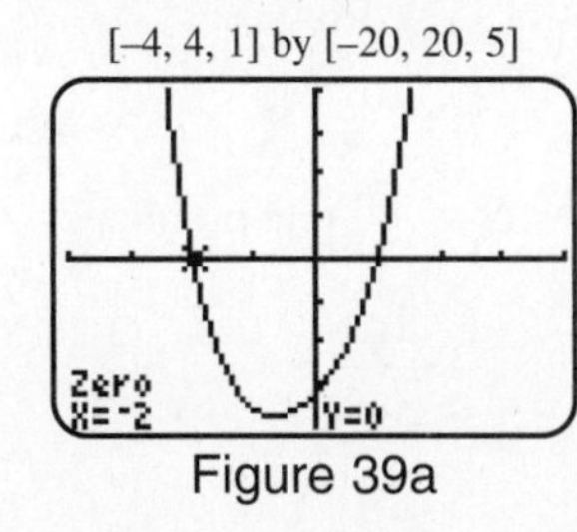

Figure 39a

[–4, 4, 1] by [–20, 20, 5]

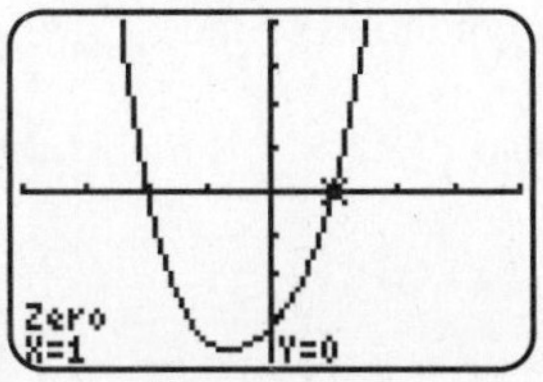

Zero X=1 Y=0

Figure 39b

40. Factor or find the zero of 0 graphically, $x^4 + 2x^2 = x^3 \Rightarrow x^4 - x^3 + 2x^2 = 0 \Rightarrow x^2(x^2 - x + 2) = 0$.

Use the quadratic formula to find the zeros of $x^2 - x + 2$. The solutions are $x = 0, \frac{1}{2} \pm \frac{i\sqrt{7}}{2}$.

41. Find the zero of –2 using the rational zero test or a graph of $y = 3x^3 + 4x^2 - x + 6$. Use synthetic division to factor $3x^3 + 4x^2 - x + 6$.

$$\begin{array}{r|rrrr} -2 & 3 & 4 & -1 & 6 \\ & & -6 & 4 & -6 \\ \hline & 3 & -2 & 3 & 0 \end{array}$$

$3x^3 + 4x^2 - x + 6 = (x + 2)(3x^2 - 2x + 3)$

Use the quadratic formula to find the zeros of $3x^2 - 2x + 3$. The solutions are $x = -2, \frac{1}{3} \pm \frac{i\sqrt{8}}{3}$.

42. Find the zero of –3 using the rational zero test or a graph of $y = 2x^3 + 5x^2 + x + 12$. Use synthetic division to factor $2x^3 + 5x^2 + x + 12$.

$$\begin{array}{r|rrrr} -3 & 2 & 5 & 1 & 12 \\ & & -6 & 3 & -12 \\ \hline & 2 & -1 & 4 & 0 \end{array}$$

$2x^3 + 5x^2 + x + 12 = (x + 3)(2x^2 - x + 4)$

Use the quadratic formula to find the zeros of $2x^2 - x + 4$. The solutions are $x = -3, \frac{1}{4} \pm \frac{i\sqrt{31}}{4}$.

43. $Z = \frac{V}{I} = \frac{50 + 98i}{8 + 5i} = 10 + 6i$

44. $Z = \frac{V}{I} = \frac{30 + 60i}{8 + 6i} = 6 + 3i$

45. $V = IZ = (1 + 2i)(3 - 4i) = 11 + 2i$

46. $V = IZ = \left(\frac{1}{2} + \frac{1}{4}i\right)(8 - 9i) = 6.25 - 2.5i$

47. $I = \frac{V}{Z} = \frac{27 + 17i}{22 - 5i} = 1 + i$

48. $I = \frac{V}{Z} = \frac{10 + 8i}{10 + 5i} = 1.12 + 0.24i$

## 4.6: Rational Functions and Models

1. Yes, since the numerator and denominator are both polynomials. Since $4x - 5 \neq 0$, $D = \left\{x \mid x \neq \frac{5}{4}\right\}$.

2. Yes, since the numerator and denominator are both polynomials. Since $x^2 \neq 0$, $D = \{x \mid x \neq 0\}$.

3. Yes, since $f$ can be written as $f(x) = \frac{x^2 - x - 2}{1}$, and $g(x) = 1$ is a polynomial. $D$ = all real numbers.

4. No, since the denominator is not a polynomial. $D = \{x \mid x > 8\}$

5. No, since the numerator is not a polynomial. $D = \{x \mid x \neq -1\}$

6. Yes, since $f$ can be written as $f(x) = \frac{4 + x}{x}$. Since $x \neq 0$, $D = \{x \mid x \neq 0\}$.

7. Yes, since the numerator and denominator are both polynomials. Since $x^2 + 1 \neq 0$, $D$ = all real numbers.

8. No, since the numerator is not a polynomial. Since $x + 1 \neq 0$, $D = \{x \mid x \neq -1\}$.

9. No, since the numerator is not a polynomial. Since $x^2 + x \neq 0 \Rightarrow x(x + 1) \neq 0$, $D = \{x \mid x \neq -1, x \neq 0\}$.

10. Yes, since the numerator and denominator are both polynomials.

 Since $x^2 - 5 \neq 0$, $D = \{x \mid x \neq -\sqrt{5}, x \neq \sqrt{5}\}$.

11. Yes, since $f$ can be written as $f(x) = \frac{4(x + 1) - 3}{x + 1} \Rightarrow f(x) = \frac{4x + 1}{x + 1}$.

 Since $x + 1 \neq 0$, $D = \{x \mid x \neq -1\}$.

12. Yes, since $f$ can be written as $f(x) = \frac{5x^3 - 4x}{1}$. $D$ = all real numbers.

13. There is a horizontal asymptote of $y = 4$ and a vertical asymptote of $x = 2$; $D = \{x | x \neq 2\}$.

14. There is a horizontal asymptote of $y = 2$ and a vertical asymptote of $x = \pm 4$; $D = \{x | x \neq \pm 4\}$.

15. There is a horizontal asymptote of $y = -4$ and a vertical asymptote of $x = \pm 2$; $D = \{x | x \neq \pm 2\}$.

16. There is a horizontal asymptote of $y = -2$ and a vertical asymptote of $x = -4$; $D = \{x | x \neq -4\}$.

17. There is a horizontal asymptote of $y = 0$ and there is no vertical asymptote; $D =$ all real numbers.

18. There is a horizontal asymptote of $y = 0$ and a vertical asymptote of $x = 0$. Since $x \neq 0$; $D = \{x | x \neq 0\}$.

19. Since the output of $Y_1$ gets closer to 3 as the input $x$ gets larger, it is reasonable to conjecture that the equation for the horizontal asymptote is $y = 3$.

20. Since the output of $Y_1$ gets closer to 5 as the input $x$ gets smaller, it is reasonable to conjecture that the equation for the horizontal asymptote is $y = 5$.

21. Horizontal Asymptotes: The degree of the numerator is equal to the degree of the denominator and the ratio of the leading coefficients is $\frac{4}{2} = 2$. Therefore, $y = 2$ is a horizontal asymptote.

    Vertical Asymptotes: Find the zeros of the denominator, $2x - 6 = 0 \Rightarrow 2x = 6 \Rightarrow x = 3$. Therefore $x = 3$ is a vertical asymptote. (Note that 3 is not a zero of the numerator.)

22. Horizontal Asymptotes: The degree of the numerator is equal to the degree of the denominator and the ratio of the leading coefficients is $\frac{1}{-2} = -\frac{1}{2}$. Therefore, $y = -\frac{1}{2}$ is a horizontal asymptote.

    Vertical Asymptotes: Find the zeros of the denominator, $5 - 2x = 0 \Rightarrow 2x = 5 \Rightarrow x = \frac{5}{2}$. Therefore $x = \frac{5}{2}$ is a vertical asymptote. (Note that $\frac{5}{2}$ is not a zero of the numerator.)

23. Horizontal Asymptotes: The degree of the numerator is less than the degree of the denominator, therefore, the $x$-axis, $y = 0$, is a horizontal asymptote.

    Vertical Asymptotes: Find the zeros of the denominator, $x^2 - 5 = 0 \Rightarrow x^2 = 5 \Rightarrow x = \pm\sqrt{5}$. Therefore $x = \pm\sqrt{5}$ are vertical asymptotes. (Note that $\pm\sqrt{5}$ are not zeros of the numerator.)

24. Horizontal Asymptotes: The degree of the numerator is equal to the degree of the denominator and the ratio of the leading coefficients is $\frac{3}{1} = 3$. Therefore, $y = 3$ is a horizontal asymptote.

    Vertical Asymptotes: Find the zeros of the denominator, $x^2 - 9 = 0 \Rightarrow x^2 = 9 \Rightarrow x = \pm 3$. Therefore $x = \pm 3$ are vertical asymptotes. (Note that $\pm 3$ are not zeros of the numerator.)

25. Horizontal Asymptotes: The degree of the numerator is greater than the degree of the denominator, therefore there is no horizontal asymptote.

    Vertical Asymptotes: Find the zeros of the denominator,

    $x^2 + 3x - 10 = 0 \Rightarrow (x + 5)(x - 2) = 0 \Rightarrow x = -5, 2$. Therefore $x = -5$ and $x = 2$ are the vertical asymptotes. (Note that –5 and 2 are not a zeros of the numerator.)

26. Horizontal Asymptotes: The degree of the numerator is greater than the degree of the denominator, therefore there is no horizontal asymptote.

    Vertical Asymptotes: Find the zeros of the denominator, $x + 2 = 0 \Rightarrow x = -2$.

    Therefore $x = -2$ is a vertical asymptote. (Note that $-2$ is not a zero of the numerator.)

27. Horizontal Asymptotes: The degree of the numerator is equal to the degree of the denominator and the ratio of the leading coefficients is $\frac{1}{2}$. Therefore, $y = \frac{1}{2}$ is a horizontal asymptote.

    Vertical Asymptotes: Find the zeros of the denominator, $(2x - 5)(x + 1) = 0 \Rightarrow x = \frac{5}{2}$ and $x = -1$.

    Therefore $x = \frac{5}{2}$ is a vertical asymptote. (Note that $\frac{5}{2}$ is not a zero of the numerator and $x = -1$ is a zero of the numerator).

28. Horizontal Asymptotes: The degree of the numerator is equal to the degree of the denominator and the ratio of the leading coefficients is $\frac{6}{2} = 3$. Therefore, $y = 3$ is a horizontal asymptote.

    Vertical Asymptotes: Find the zeros of the denominator,

    $2x^2 + x - 6 = 0 \Rightarrow (2x - 3)(x + 2) = 0 \Rightarrow x = \frac{3}{2}, -2$. Therefore $x = -2$ and $x = \frac{3}{2}$ are the vertical asymptotes. (Note that $-2$ and $\frac{3}{2}$ are not a zeros of the numerator.)

29. Horizontal Asymptotes: The degree of the numerator is equal to the degree of the denominator and the ratio of the leading coefficients is $\frac{3}{1} = 3$. Therefore, $y = 3$ is a horizontal asymptote.

    Vertical Asymptotes: Find the zeros of the denominator, $(x + 2)(x - 1) = 0 \Rightarrow x = -2, 1$. Here, only $x = 1$ is a vertical asymptote. (Note that –2 is a zero of the numerator.)

30. Horizontal Asymptotes: The degree of the numerator is less than the degree of the denominator, therefore, the $x$-axis, $y = 0$, is a horizontal asymptote.

    Vertical Asymptotes: Find the zeros of the denominator,

    $x^3 - x = 0 \Rightarrow x(x^2 - 1) = 0 \Rightarrow x(x + 1)(x - 1) = 0 \Rightarrow x = 0, -1, 1$. But $x = 0$ is not a vertical asymptote since 0 is a zero of the numerator and $f(x) = \frac{1}{(x + 1)(x - 1)}$ for $x \neq 0$. Therefore $x = -1$ and $x = 1$ are the vertical asymptotes. (Note that $\pm 1$ are not zeros of the numerator.)

31. Horizontal Asymptotes: The degree of the numerator is greater than the degree of the denominator, therefore there is no horizontal asymptote.

    Vertical Asymptotes: Find the zeros of the denominator, $x + 3 = 0 \Rightarrow x = -3$. But $x = -3$ is not a vertical asymptote since –3 is a zero of the numerator and $f(x) = x - 3$ for $x \neq -3$. There are no vertical asymptotes.

32. Horizontal Asymptotes: The degree of the numerator is greater than the degree of the denominator, therefore there is no horizontal asymptote.

    Vertical Asymptotes: Find the zeros of the denominator, $2x - 1 = 0 \Rightarrow 2x = 1 \Rightarrow x = \frac{1}{2}$.

    But $x = \frac{1}{2}$ is not a vertical asymptote since $\frac{1}{2}$ is a zero of the numerator and $f(x) = x - 1$ for $x \neq \frac{1}{2}$.

    There are no vertical asymptotes.

33. $f(x) = \dfrac{a}{x - 1}$ has a vertical asymptote of $x = 1$. It has a horizontal asymptote of $y = 0$, since the degree of the numerator is less than the degree of the denominator. The best choice is graph *b*.

34. $f(x) = \dfrac{2x + a}{x - 1}$ has a vertical asymptote of $x = 1$ and a horizontal asymptote of $y = 2$, since the degree of the numerator equals the degree of the denominator and the ratio of the leading coefficients is $\dfrac{2}{1}$. The best choice is graph *a*.

35. $f(x) = \dfrac{x - a}{x + 2}$ has a vertical asymptote of $x = -2$ and a horizontal asymptote of $y = 1$, since the degree of the numerator equals the degree of the denominator and the ratio of the leading coefficients is $\dfrac{1}{1}$. The best choice is graph *d*.

36. $f(x) = \dfrac{-2x}{x^2 - a}$ has two vertical asymptotes at $x = \pm\sqrt{a}$ and a horizontal asymptote of $y = 0$, since the degree of the numerator is less than the degree of the denominator. The best choice is graph *c*.

37. One example of a symbolic representation of a rational function with a vertical asymptote of $x = -3$ and a horizontal asymptote of $y = 1$ is $f(x) = \dfrac{x + 1}{x + 3}$. *Answers may vary.*

38. One example of a symbolic representation of a rational function with a vertical asymptote of $x = 4$ and a horizontal asymptote of $y = -3$ is $f(x) = \dfrac{-3x}{x - 4}$. *Answers may vary.*

39. One example of a symbolic representation of a rational function with vertical asymptotes of $x = \pm 3$ and a horizontal asymptote of $y = 0$ is $f(x) = \dfrac{1}{x^2 - 9}$. *Answers may vary.*

40. One example of a symbolic representation of a rational function with vertical asymptotes of $x = -2$ and $x = 4$ and a horizontal asymptote of $y = 5$ is $f(x) = \dfrac{5x^2}{(x + 2)(x - 4)} = \dfrac{5x^2}{x^2 - 2x - 8}$. *Answers may vary.*

41. See Figure 41. Since the degree of the numerator is less than the degree of the denominator, the horizontal asymptote is $y = 0$. To find the vertical asymptote we find the zero of the denominator, $x^2 = 0 \Rightarrow x = 0$.

42. See Figure 42. Since the degree of the numerator is less than the degree of the denominator, the horizontal asymptote is $y = 0$. To find the vertical asymptote we find the zero of the denominator, $x = 0$.

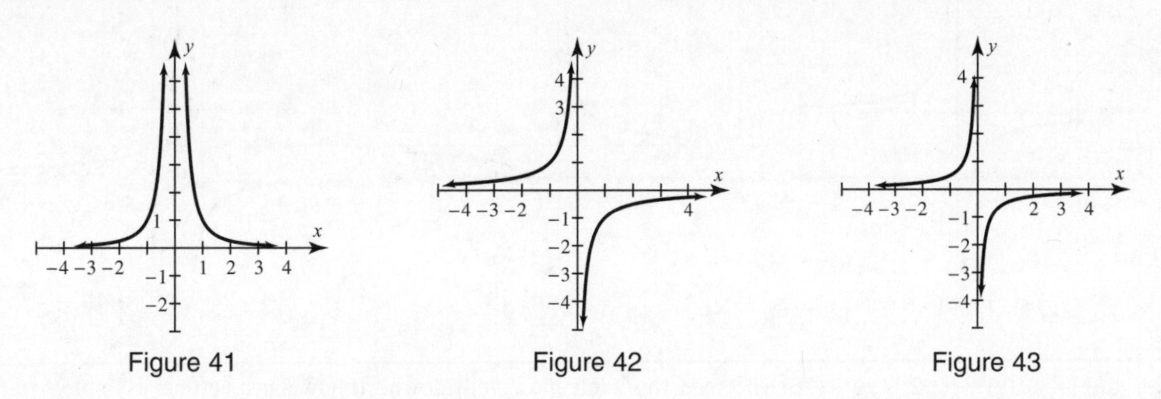

Figure 41 Figure 42 Figure 43

43. See Figure 43. Since the degree of the numerator is less than the degree of the denominator, the horizontal asymptote is $y = 0$. To find the vertical asymptote we find the zero of the denominator, $2x = 0 \Rightarrow x = 0$.

44. See Figure 44. Since the degree of the numerator is less than the degree of the denominator, the horizontal asymptote is $y = 0$. To find the vertical asymptote we find the zero of the denominator, $x^2 = 0 \Rightarrow x = 0$.

45. $g(x) = \dfrac{1}{x-3}$ is $y = \dfrac{1}{x}$ transformed 3 units right $\Rightarrow$ it has a vertical asymptote of $x = 3$. It still has a horizontal asymptote of $y = 0$. See Figure 45. Then $g(x) = f(x-3)$.

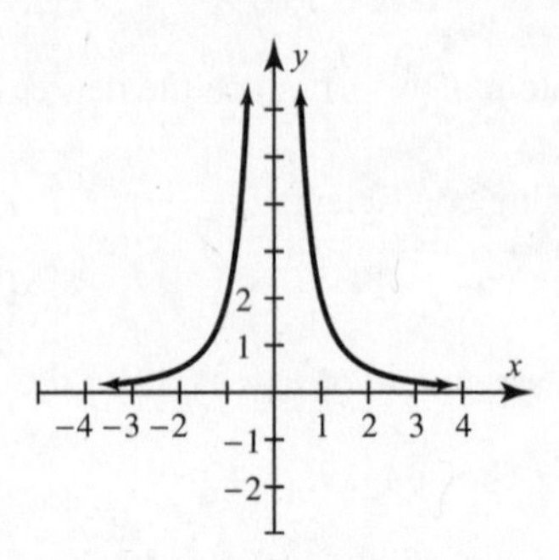

Figure 44

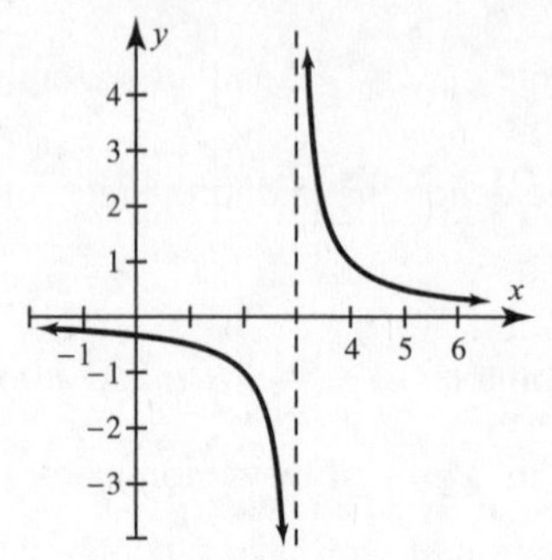

Figure 45

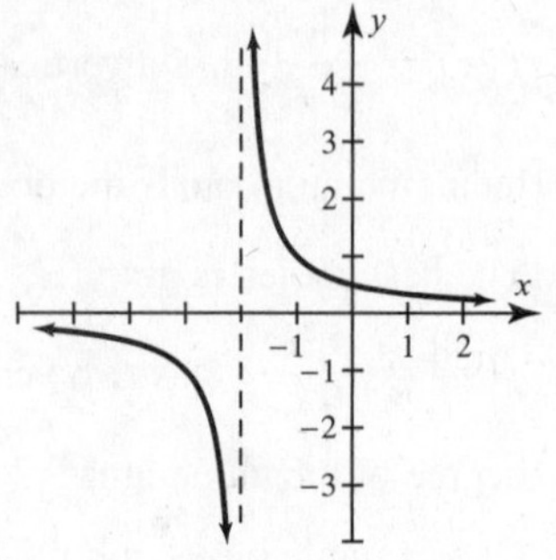

Figure 46

46. $g(x) = \dfrac{1}{x+2}$ is $y = \dfrac{1}{x}$ transformed 2 units left $\Rightarrow$ it has a vertical asymptote of $x = -2$. It still has a horizontal asymptote of $y = 0$. See Figure 46. Then $g(x) = f(x+2)$.

47. $g(x) = \dfrac{1}{x} + 2$ is $y = \dfrac{1}{x}$ transformed 2 units up $\Rightarrow$ it has a horizontal asymptote of $y = 2$. It still has a vertical asymptote of $x = 0$. See Figure 47. Then $g(x) = f(x) + 2$.

48. $g(x) = 1 - \dfrac{2}{x}$ is $y = \dfrac{1}{x}$ transformed by reflecting it across the $x$-axis, then shifting 1 unit up, and vertically stretching by a factor of 2. It now has a horizontal asymptote of $y = 1$. It still has a vertical asymptote of $x = 0$. See Figure 48. Then $g(x) = -2f(x) + 1$.

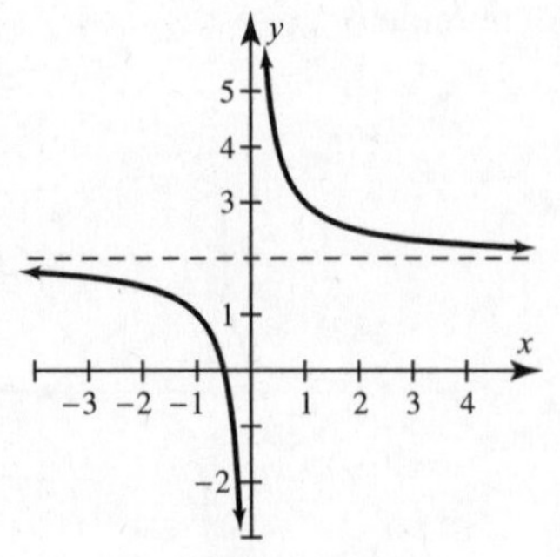

Figure 47

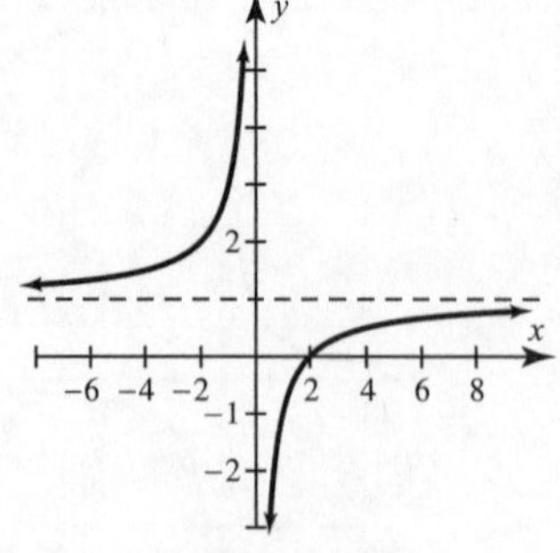

Figure 48

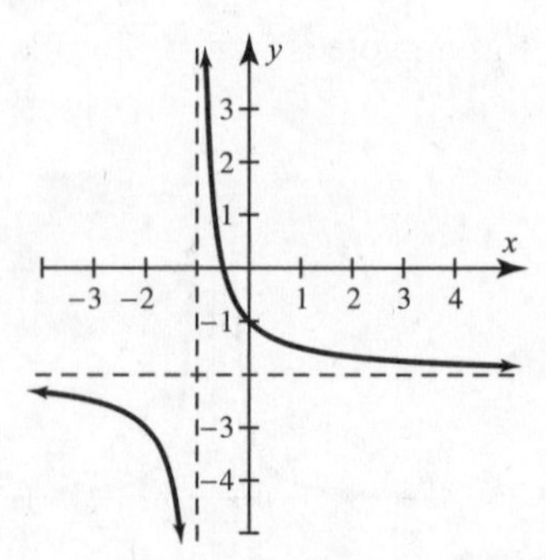

Figure 49

49. $g(x) = \dfrac{1}{x+1} - 2$ is $y = \dfrac{1}{x}$ transformed 1 unit left and 2 units down. It now has a vertical asymptote of $x = -1$, and a horizontal asymptote of $y = -2$. See Figure 49. Then $g(x) = f(x+1) - 2$.

50. $g(x) = \dfrac{1}{x-2} + 1$ is $y = \dfrac{1}{x}$ transformed 2 units right and 1 unit up. It now has a vertical asymptote of $x = 2$, and a horizontal asymptote of $y = 1$. See Figure 50. Then $g(x) = f(x-2) + 1$.

51. $g(x) = -\dfrac{2}{(x-1)^2}$ is $y = \dfrac{1}{x^2}$ transformed by reflecting it across the $x$-axis, then shifting 1 unit right, and vertically stretching by a factor of 2. It now has a vertical asymptote of $x = 1$, and it still has a horizontal asymptote of $y = 0$. See Figure 51. Then $g(x) = -2h(x-1)$.

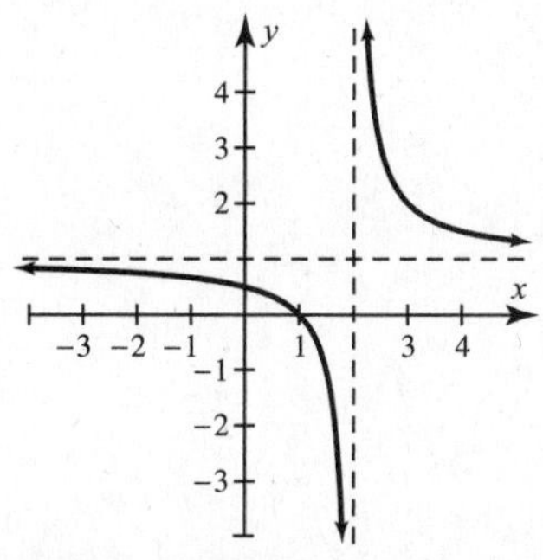
Figure 50

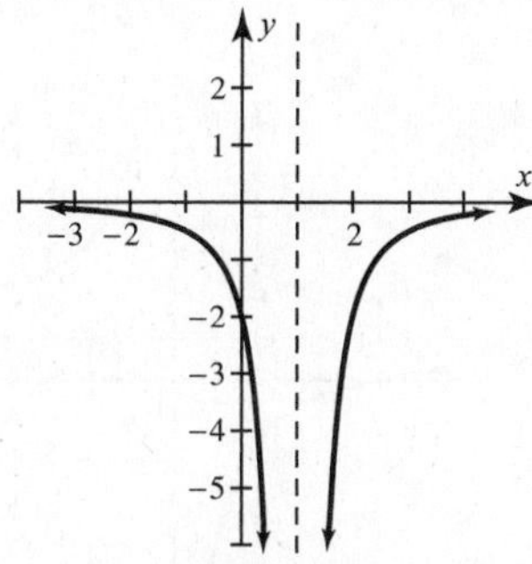
Figure 51

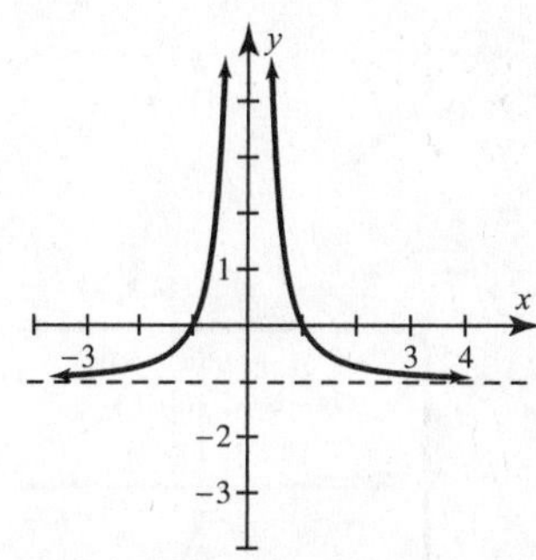
Figure 52

52. $g(x) = \dfrac{1}{x^2} - 1$ is $y = \dfrac{1}{x^2}$ transformed 1 unit down. It still has a vertical asymptote of $x = 0$, and it now has a horizontal asymptote of $y = -1$. See Figure 52. Then $g(x) = h(x) - 1$.

53. $g(x) = \dfrac{1}{(x+1)^2} - 2$ is $y = \dfrac{1}{x^2}$ transformed 1 unit left and 2 units down. It now has a vertical asymptote of $x = -1$, and a horizontal asymptote of $y = -2$. See Figure 53. Then $g(x) = h(x+1) - 2$.

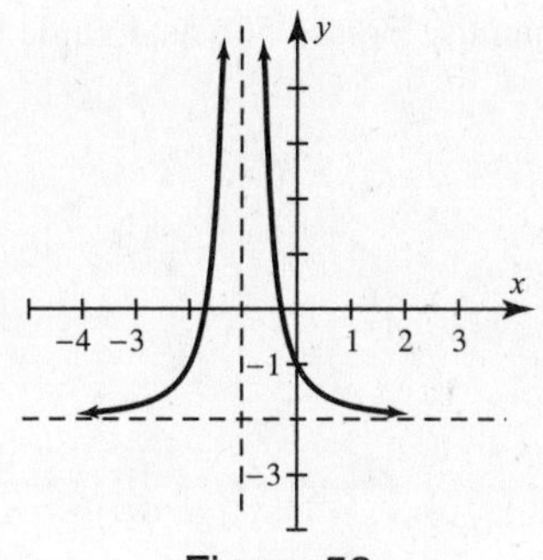
Figure 53

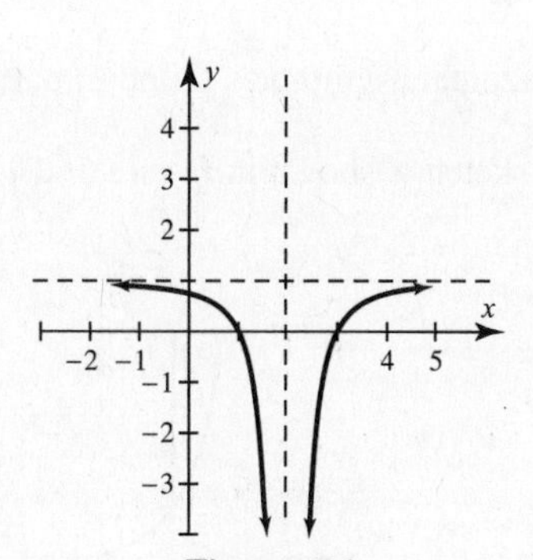
Figure 54

54. $g(x) = 1 - \dfrac{1}{(x-2)^2}$ is $y = \dfrac{1}{x^2}$ transformed by reflecting it across the $x$-axis, then shifting 2 units right, and 1 unit up. It now has a vertical asymptote of $x = 2$, and a horizontal asymptote of $y = 1$. See Figure 54. Then $g(x) = -h(x-2) + 1$.

55. (a) $x - 2 = 0 \Rightarrow x = 2$; $D = \{x | x \neq 2\}$

(b) The graph of $f$ using dot mode is shown in Figure 55b.

(c) Since the degree of the numerator equals the degree of the denominator and the ratio of the leading coefficients is $\frac{1}{1} = 1$, the horizontal asymptote is $y = 1$. There is a vertical asymptote at $x = 2$.

(d) First, sketch the vertical and horizontal asymptotes found in part (c). Then use Figure 55b as a guide to a more complete graph of $f$. The sketch is shown in Figure 55d.

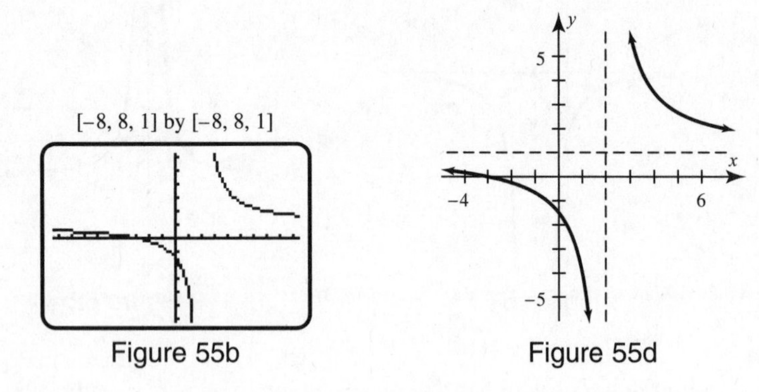


Figure 55b Figure 55d

56. (a) $x + 3 = 0 \Rightarrow x = -3$; $D = \{x | x \neq -3\}$

(b) The graph of $f$ using dot mode is shown in Figure 56b.

(c) Since the degree of the numerator equals the degree of the denominator and the ratio of the leading coefficients is $\frac{-2}{1} = -2$, the horizontal asymptote is $y = -2$. There is a vertical asymptote at $x = -3$.

(d) First, sketch the vertical and horizontal asymptotes found in part (c). Then use Figure 56b as a guide to a more complete graph of $f$. The sketch is shown in Figure 56d.

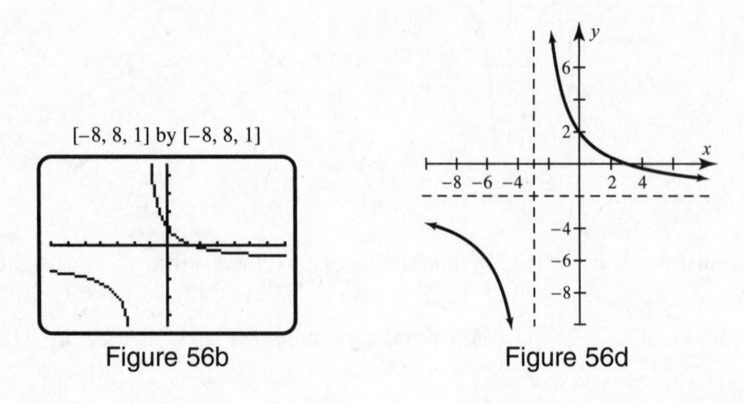


Figure 56b Figure 56d

57. (a) $x^2 - 4 = 0 \Rightarrow x^2 = 4 \Rightarrow x = \pm 2$; $D = \{x \mid x \neq \pm 2\}$

(b) The graph of $f$ using dot mode is shown in Figure 57b.

(c) Since the degree of the numerator is less than the degree of the denominator there is a horizontal asymptote at $y = 0$. There are vertical asymptotes at $x = \pm 2$.

(d) First, sketch the vertical and horizontal asymptotes found in part (c). Then use Figure 57b as a guide to a more complete graph of $f$. The sketch is shown in Figure 57d.

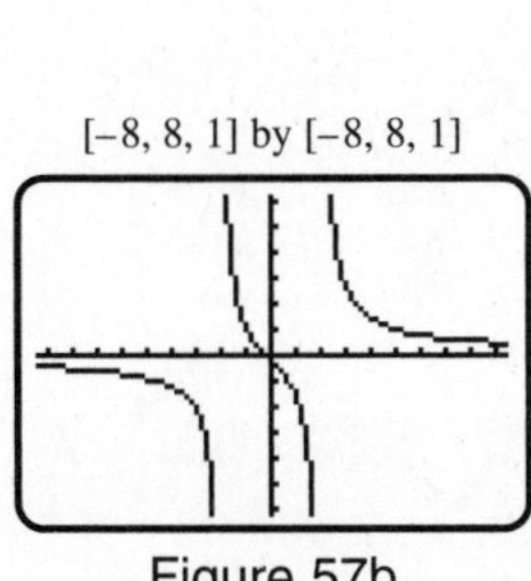

Figure 57b

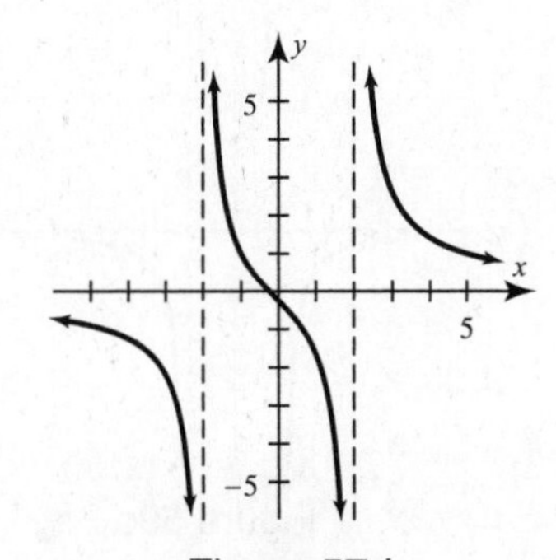

Figure 57d

58. (a) $x^2 - 9 = 0 \Rightarrow x^2 = 9 \Rightarrow x = \pm 3$; $D = \{x \mid x \neq \pm 3\}$

(b) The graph of $f$ using dot mode is shown in Figure 58b.

(c) Since the degree of the numerator equals the degree of the denominator and the ratio of the leading coefficients is $\frac{0.5}{1} = 0.5$, the horizontal asymptote is $y = 0.5$. There are vertical asymptotes at $x = \pm 3$.

(d) First, sketch the vertical and horizontal asymptotes found in part (c). Then use Figure 58b as a guide to a more complete graph of $f$. The sketch is shown in Figure 58d.

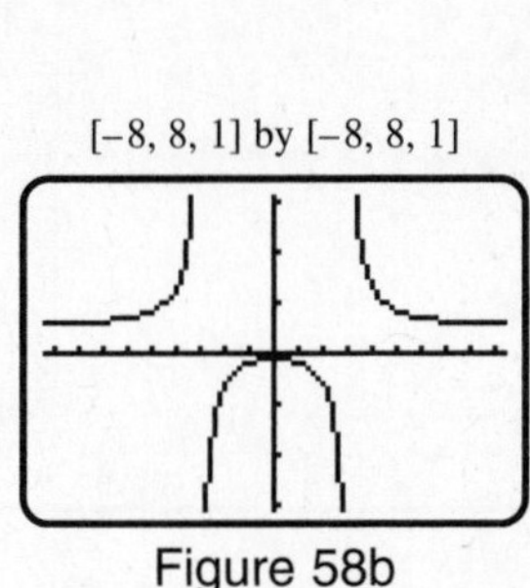

Figure 58b

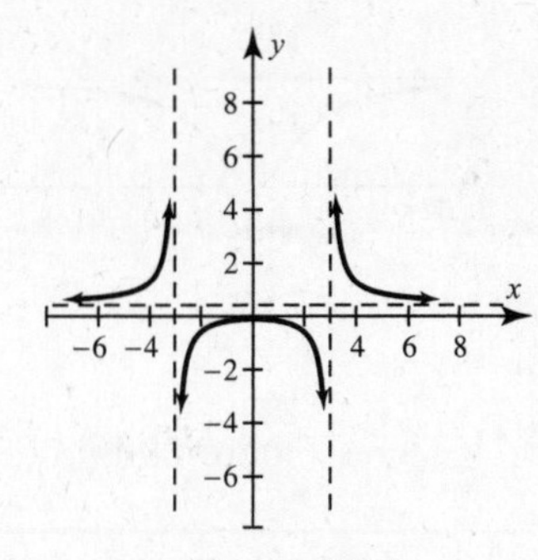

Figure 58d

59. (a) $1 - 0.25x^2 = 0 \Rightarrow 0.25x^2 = 1 \Rightarrow x^2 = 4 \Rightarrow x = \pm 2$; $D = \{x \mid x \neq \pm 2\}$

(b) The graph of $f$ using dot mode is shown in Figure 59b.

(c) Since the degree of the numerator is less than the degree of the denominator there is a horizontal asymptote at $y = 0$. There are vertical asymptotes at $x = \pm 2$.

(d) First, sketch the vertical and horizontal asymptotes found in part (c). Then use Figure 59b as a guide to a more complete graph of $f$. The sketch is shown in Figure 59d.

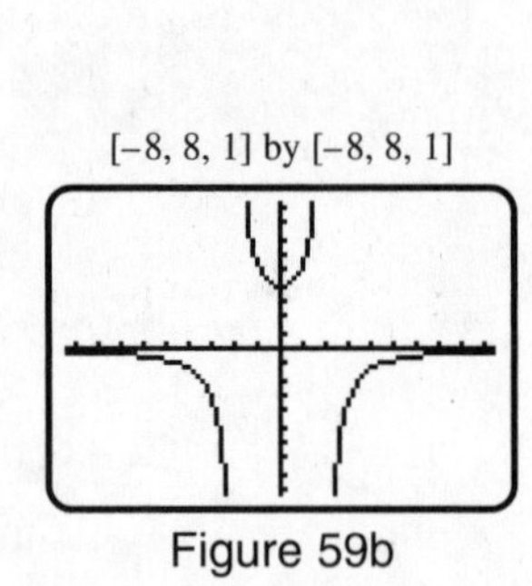

Figure 59b

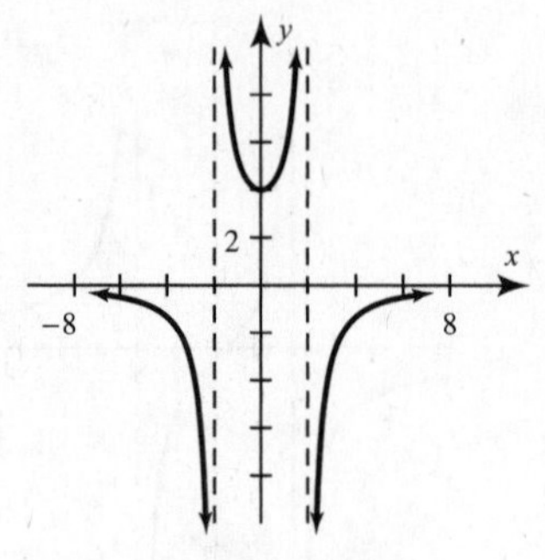

Figure 59d

60. (a) $1 + 0.25x^2 \neq 0$; $D = \{x \mid x \text{ is any real number}\}$

(b) The graph of $f$ using dot mode is shown in Figure 60b.

(c) Since the degree of the numerator equals the degree of the denominator and the ratio of the leading coefficients is $\frac{1}{0.25} = 4$, the horizontal asymptote is $y = 4$. There are no vertical asymptotes.

(d) First, sketch the vertical and horizontal asymptotes found in part (c). Then use Figure 60b as a guide to a more complete graph of $f$. The sketch is shown in Figure 60d.

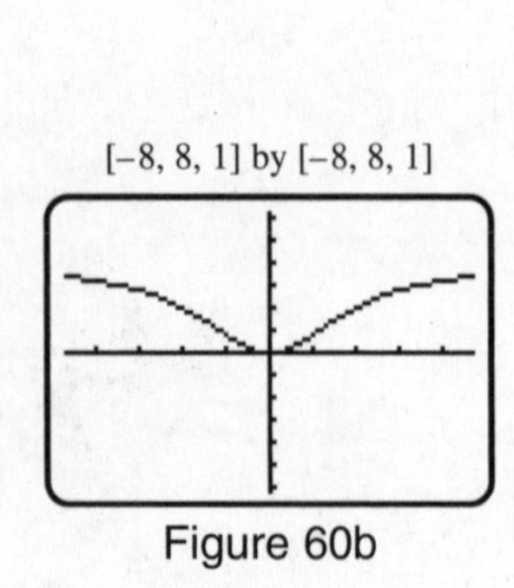

Figure 60b

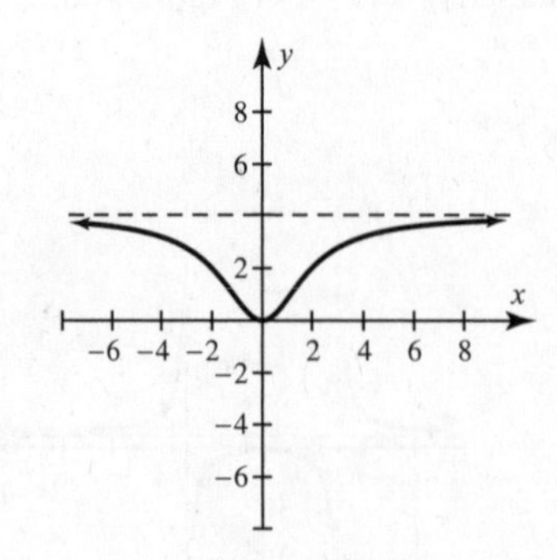

Figure 60d

61. (a) $x - 2 = 0 \Rightarrow x = 2; D = \{x \mid x \neq 2\}$

(b) The graph of $f$ using dot mode is shown in Figure 61b.

(c) Since the degree of the numerator is greater than the degree of the denominator there is no horizontal asymptote. There are no vertical asymptotes. (The numerator equals 2 when $x = 2$).

(d) First, sketch the vertical and horizontal asymptotes found in part (c). Then use Figure 61b as a guide to a more complete graph of $f$. The sketch is shown in Figure 61d.

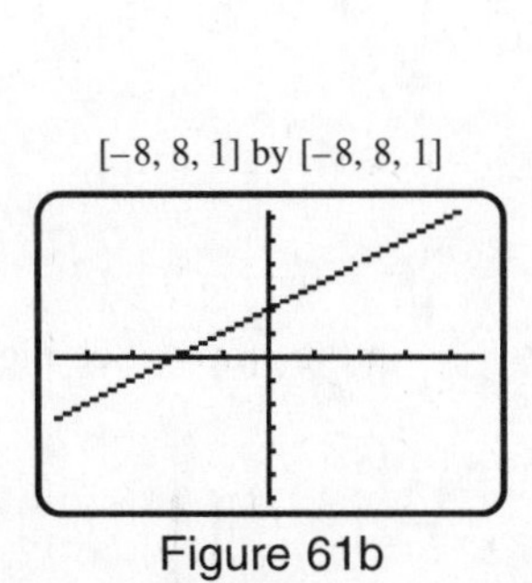

Figure 61b

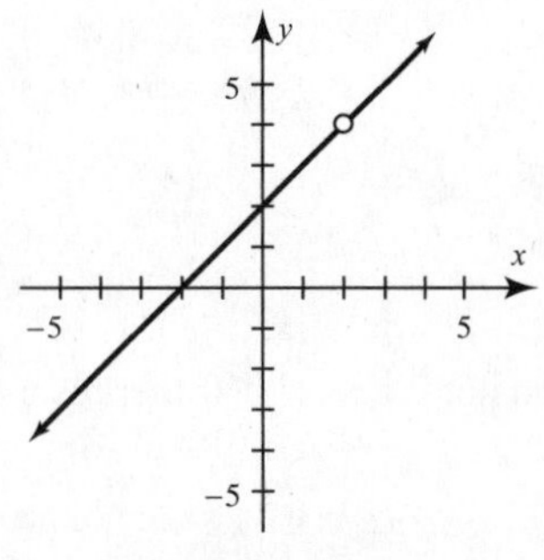

Figure 61d

62. (a) $x^2 - x - 6 = 0 \Rightarrow (x + 2)(x - 3) = 0 \Rightarrow x = -2, 3; D = \{x \mid x \neq -2, 3\}$

(b) The graph of $f$ using dot mode is shown in Figure 62b.

(c) Since the degree of the numerator is less than the degree of the denominator there is a horizontal asymptote at $y = 0$. There are vertical asymptotes at $x = -2$ and $x = 3$.

(d) First, sketch the vertical and horizontal asymptotes found in part (c). Then use Figure 62b as a guide to a more complete graph of $f$. The sketch is shown in Figure 62d.

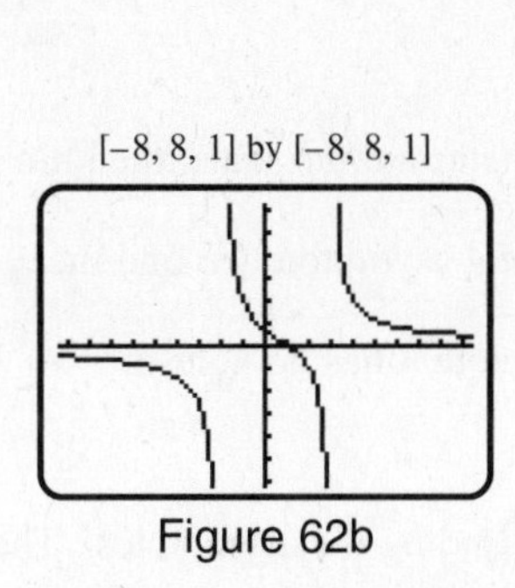

Figure 62b

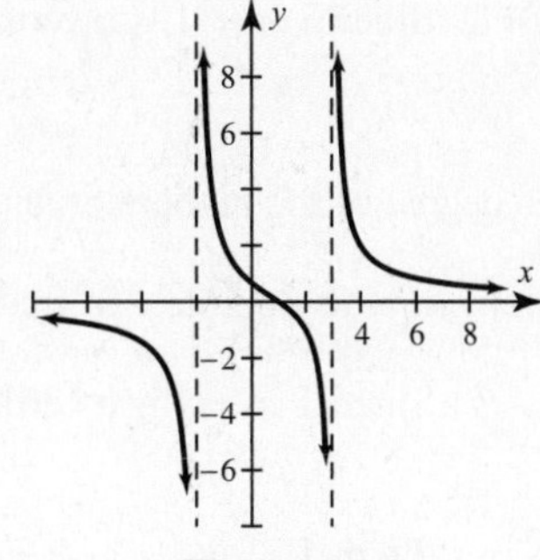

Figure 62d

63. First divide:

$$\begin{array}{r} x-1 \\ x-1\overline{)x^2-2x+1} \\ \underline{x^2-\ \ x} \\ -x+1 \\ \underline{-x+1} \\ 0 \end{array}$$

Now graph $x - 1$; since the denominator $x - 1 \neq 0$ there is a hole at $x = 1$ in the graph. See Figure 63.

64. First divide:

$$\begin{array}{r} 2x+1 \\ 2x+1\overline{)4x^2+4x+1} \\ \underline{4x^2+2x} \\ 2x+1 \\ \underline{2x+1} \\ 0 \end{array}$$

Now graph $2x + 1$; since the denominator $2x + 1 \neq 0$ there is a hole at $x = -\frac{1}{2}$ in the graph. See Figure 64.

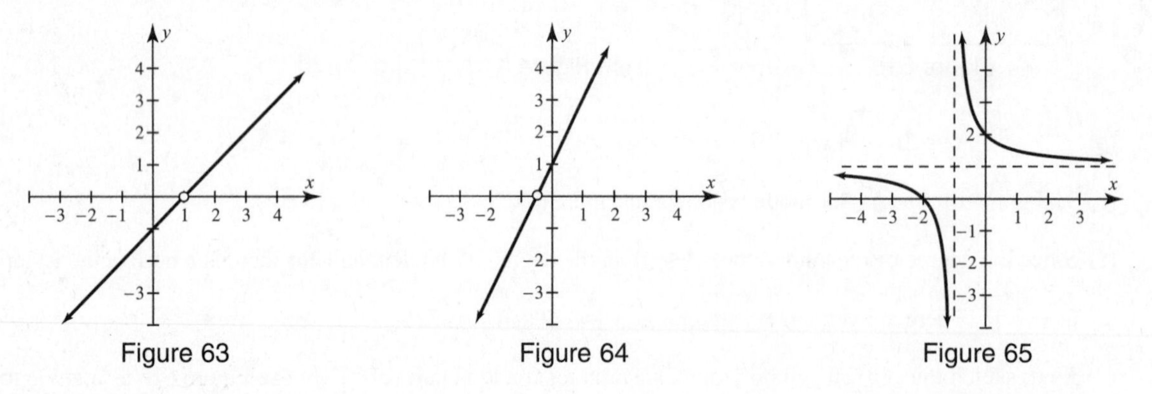

Figure 63 Figure 64 Figure 65

65. First we find the asymptotes. Since the degree of the numerator and denominator are the same, the ratio of the leading coefficients $\frac{1}{1}$ or $y = 1$ is the horizontal asymptote. To find the vertical asymptote we find the zero of the denominator. $x + 1 = 0 \Rightarrow x = -1$. Since $x = -1$ is a vertical asymptote it has no holes.

See Figure 65.

66. First we find the asymptotes. Since the degree of the numerator and denominator are the same, the ratio of the leading coefficients $\frac{2}{1}$ or $y = 2$ is the horizontal asymptote. To find the vertical asymptote we find the zero of the denominator. $x + 1 = 0 \Rightarrow x = -1$. Since $x = -1$ is a vertical asymptote it has no holes.
See Figure 66.

67. First divide: $g(x) = \frac{(2x + 1)(x - 2)}{(x - 2)(x - 2)} = \frac{2x + 1}{x - 2}$. Now graph $\frac{2x + 1}{x - 2}$ by finding it's asymptotes. The ratio of the leading coefficients $\frac{2}{1}$ or $y = 2$ is the horizontal asymptote. To find the vertical asymptote we find the zero of the denominator. $x - 2 = 0 \Rightarrow x = 2$. Since $x = 2$ is an asymptote there are no holes.
See Figure 67.

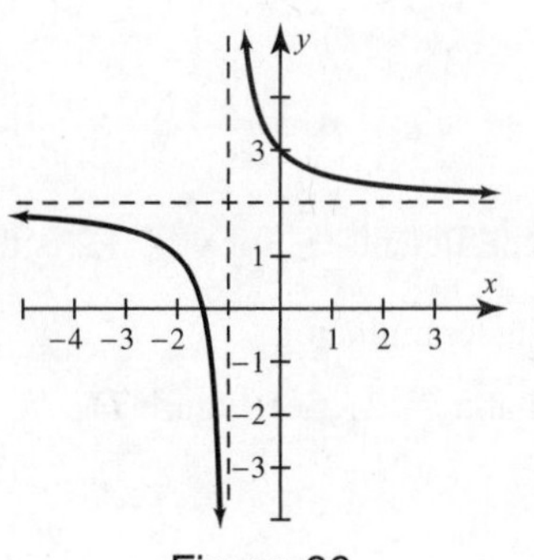

Figure 66

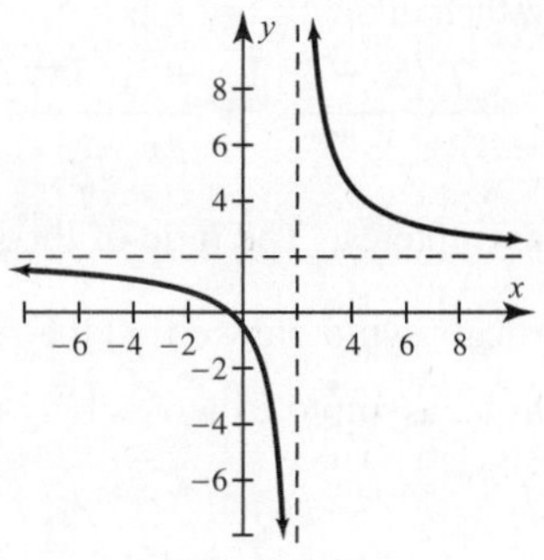

Figure 67

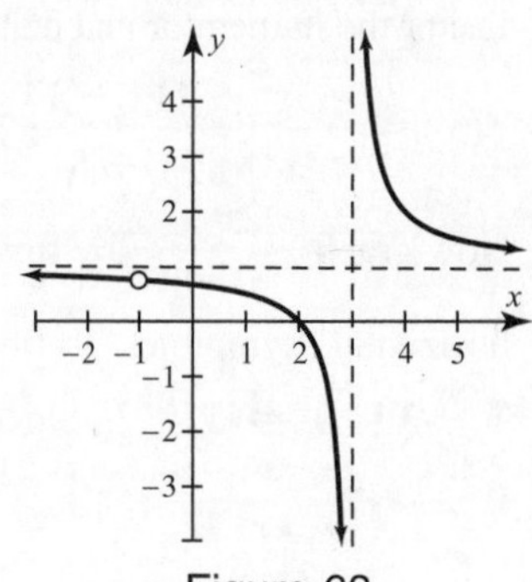

Figure 68

68. First divide: $g(x) = \dfrac{(x-2)(x+1)}{(x-3)(x+1)} = \dfrac{x-2}{x-3}$. Now graph $\dfrac{x-2}{x-3}$ by finding it's asymptotes. The ratio of the leading coefficients $\dfrac{1}{1}$ or $y = 1$ is the horizontal asymptote. To find the vertical asymptote we find the zero of the denominator. $x - 3 = 0 \Rightarrow x = 3$. Since $x = 3$ is an asymptote there is only a hole is at $x = -1$. See Figure 68.

69. Factor the numerator and denominator, then divide: $f(x) = \dfrac{2x^2 + 9x + 9}{2x^2 + 7x + 6} = \dfrac{(2x+3)(x+3)}{(2x+3)(x+2)} = \dfrac{x+3}{x+2}$.

Now graph $\dfrac{x+3}{x+2}$ by finding it's asymptotes. The ratio of the leading coefficients $\dfrac{1}{1}$ or $y = 1$ is the horizontal asymptote. To find the vertical asymptote we find the zero of the denominator. $x + 2 = 0 \Rightarrow x = -2$. Since $x = -2$ is an asymptote there is only a hole is at $2x + 3 = 0$ or $x = \dfrac{-3}{2}$. See Figure 69.

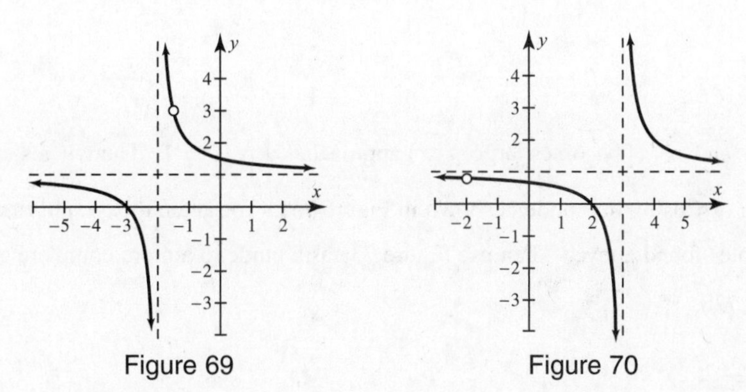

Figure 69 Figure 70

70. Factor the numerator and denominator, then divide: $f(x) = \dfrac{x^2 - 4}{x^2 - x - 6} = \dfrac{(x+2)(x-2)}{(x+2)(x-3)} = \dfrac{x-2}{x-3}$.

Now graph $\dfrac{x-2}{x-3}$ by finding it's asymptotes. The ratio of the leading coefficients $\dfrac{1}{1}$ or $y = 1$ is the horizontal asymptote. To find the vertical asymptote we find the zero of the denominator. $x - 3 = 0 \Rightarrow x = 3$. Since $x = 3$ is an asymptote there is only a hole is at $x = -2$. See Figure 70.

71. Factor the numerator and denominator, then divide:

$$f(x) = \frac{-2x^2 + 11x - 14}{x^2 - 5x + 6} = \frac{(-2x + 7)(x - 2)}{(x - 3)(x - 2)} = \frac{-2x + 7}{x - 3}.$$

Now graph $\frac{-2x + 7}{x - 3}$ by finding it's asymptotes. The ratio of the leading coefficients $\frac{-2}{1}$ or $y = -2$ is the horizontal asymptote. To find the vertical asymptote we find the zero of the denominator. $x - 3 = 0 \Rightarrow x = 3$. Since $x = 3$ is an asymptote there is only a hole is at $x = 2$. See Figure 71.

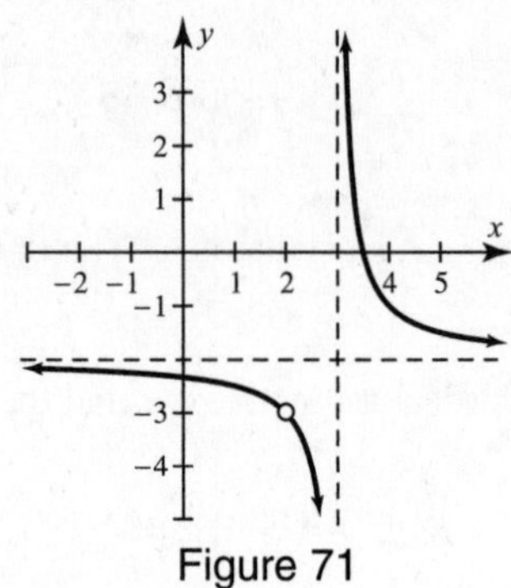

Figure 71

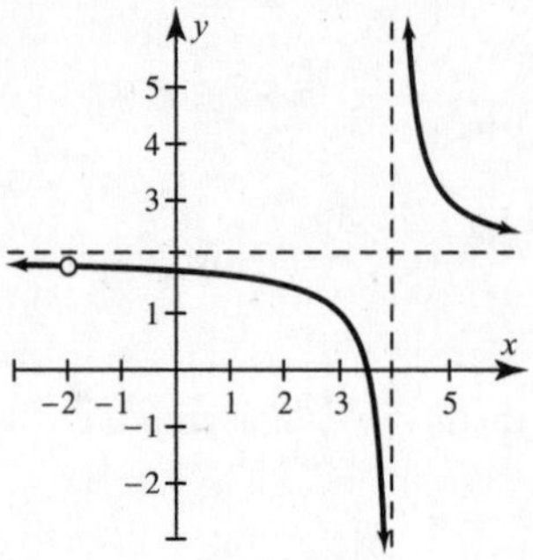

Figure 72

72. Factor the numerator and denominator, then divide: $f(x) = \frac{2x^2 - 3x - 14}{x^2 - 2x - 8} = \frac{(2x - 7)(x + 2)}{(x - 4)(x + 2)} = \frac{2x - 7}{x - 4}$.

Now graph $\frac{2x - 7}{x - 4}$ by finding it's asymptotes. The ratio of the leading coefficients $\frac{2}{1}$ or $y = 2$ is the horizontal asymptote. To find the vertical asymptote we find the zero of the denominator $x - 4 = 0 \Rightarrow x = 4$. Since $x = 4$ is an asymptote there is only a hole is at $x = -2$. See Figure 72.

73. There is a vertical asymptote at $x = -1$ since –1 is a zero of the denominator but is not a zero of the numerator. To find any slant asymptote we will divide the numerator by the denominator using synthetic division:

$$\begin{array}{r|rrr} -1 & 1 & 0 & 1 \\ & & -1 & 1 \\ \hline & 1 & -1 & 2 \end{array}$$

Therefore, $f(x) = x - 1 + \frac{2}{x + 1}$ and as $|x|$ becomes large, $f(x)$ approaches $y = x - 1$. There is a slant asymptote at $y = x - 1$. The graph of $f$ using dot mode is shown in Figure 73a. To sketch this graph, first sketch the vertical and slant asymptotes found above. Then use Figure 73a as a guide to a more complete graph of $f$. The sketch is shown in Figure 73b.

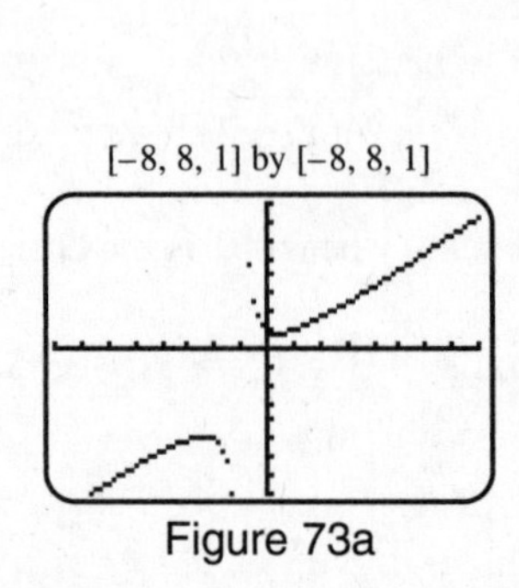

Figure 73a

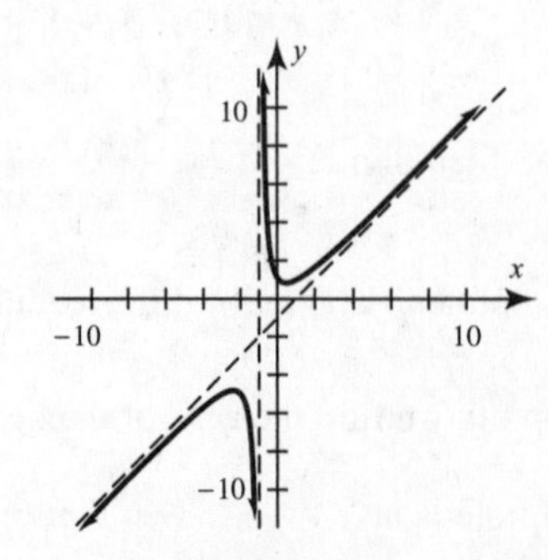

Figure 73b

74. There is a vertical asymptote at $x = 2$ since 2 is a zero of the denominator but is not a zero of the numerator.

To find any slant asymptote we will divide the numerator by the denominator using synthetic division:

$$\begin{array}{r|rrr} 2 & 2 & -5 & -2 \\ & & 4 & -2 \\ \hline & 2 & -1 & -4 \end{array}$$

Therefore, $f(x) = 2x - 1 - \dfrac{4}{x - 2}$ and as $|x|$ becomes large, $f(x)$ approaches $y = 2x - 1$. There is a slant asymptote at $y = 2x - 1$. The graph of $f$ using dot mode is shown in Figure 74a. To sketch this graph, first sketch the vertical and slant asymptotes found above. Then use Figure 74a as a guide to a more complete graph of $f$. The sketch is shown in Figure 74b.

[−8, 8, 1] by [−8, 8, 1]

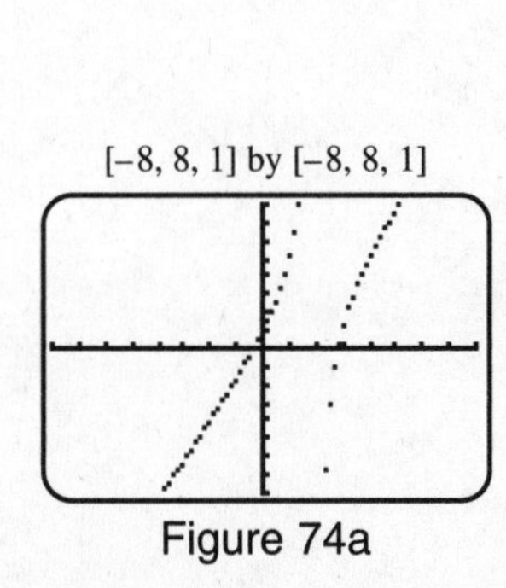

Figure 74a

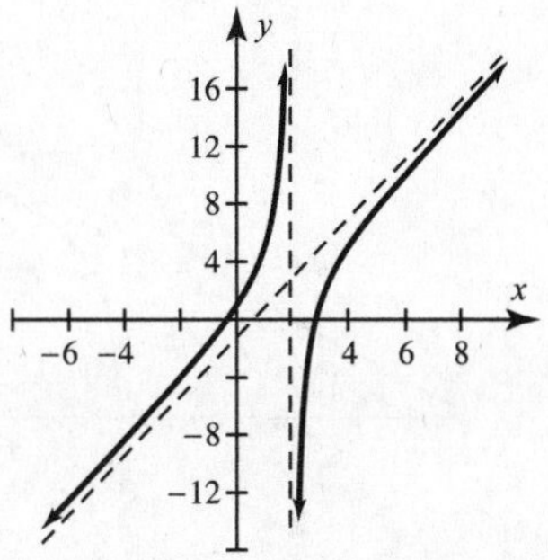

Figure 74b

75. There is a vertical asymptote at $x = -2$ since $-2$ is a zero of the denominator but is not a zero of the numerator.

To find any slant asymptote we will divide the numerator by the denominator using synthetic division:

$$\begin{array}{r|rrr} -2 & 0.5 & -2 & 2 \\ & & -1 & 6 \\ \hline & 0.5 & -3 & 8 \end{array}$$

Therefore, $f(x) = 0.5x - 3 + \dfrac{8}{x + 2}$ and as $|x|$ becomes large, $f(x)$ approaches $y = 0.5x - 3$. There is a slant asymptote at $y = 0.5x - 3$. The graph of $f$ using dot mode is shown in Figure 75a. To sketch this graph, first sketch the vertical and slant asymptotes found above. Then use Figure 75a as a guide to a more complete graph of $f$. The sketch is shown in Figure 75b.

[−14, 14, 2] by [−14, 14, 2]

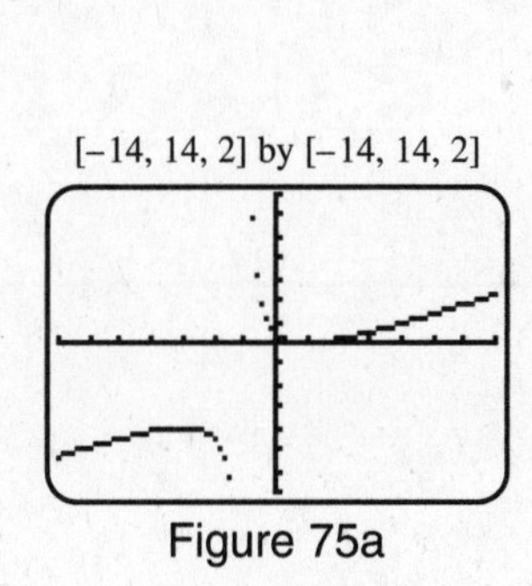

Figure 75a

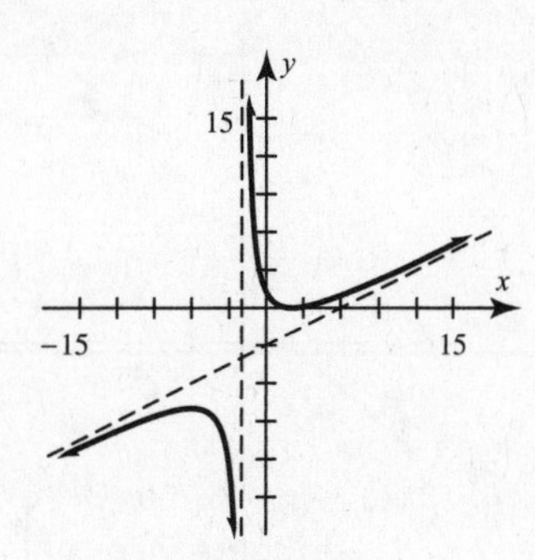


Figure 75b

76. There is a vertical asymptote at $x = 3$ since 3 is a zero of the denominator but is not a zero of the numerator. To find any slant asymptote we will divide the numerator by the denominator using synthetic division:

$$\begin{array}{r|rrr} 3 & 0.5 & 0 & -5 \\ & & 1.5 & 4.5 \\ \hline & 0.5 & 1.5 & -0.5 \end{array}$$

Therefore, $f(x) = 0.5x + 1.5 - \dfrac{0.5}{x-3}$ and as $|x|$ becomes large, $f(x)$ approaches $y = 0.5x + 1.5$. There is a slant asymptote at $y = 0.5x + 1.5$. The graph of $f$ using dot mode is shown in Figure 76a. To sketch this graph, first sketch the vertical and slant asymptotes found above. Then use Figure 76a as a guide to a more complete graph of $f$. The sketch is shown in Figure 76b.

[−5, 10, 1] by [−5, 10, 1]

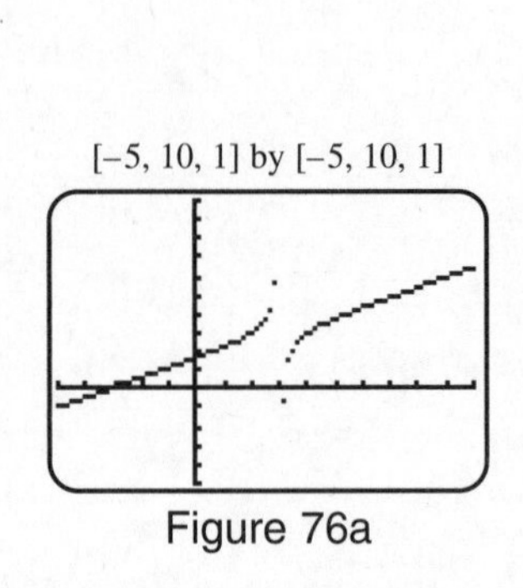

Figure 76a

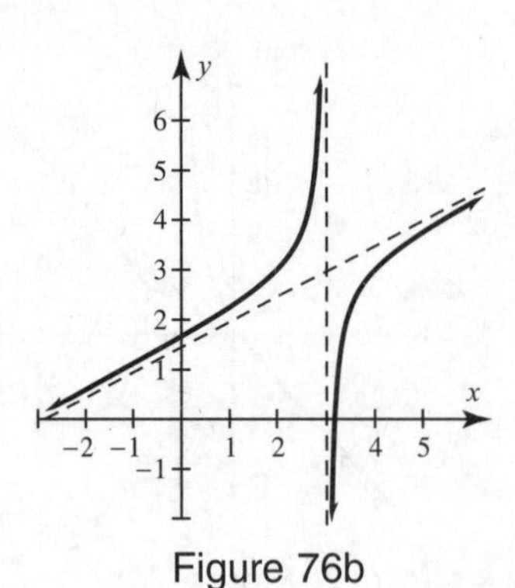


Figure 76b

77. There is a vertical asymptote at $x = 1$ since 1 is a zero of the denominator but is not a zero of the numerator. To find any slant asymptote we will divide the numerator by the denominator using synthetic division:

$$\begin{array}{r|rrr} 1 & 1 & 2 & 1 \\ & & 1 & 3 \\ \hline & 1 & 3 & 4 \end{array}$$

Therefore, $f(x) = x + 3 + \dfrac{4}{x-1}$ and as $|x|$ becomes large, $f(x)$ approaches $y = x + 3$. There is a slant asymptote at $y = x + 3$. The graph of $f$ using dot mode is shown in Figure 77a. To sketch this graph, first sketch the vertical and slant asymptotes found above. Then use Figure 77a as a guide to a more complete graph of $f$. The sketch is shown in Figure 77b.

[−12, 12, 2] by [−20, 20, 4]

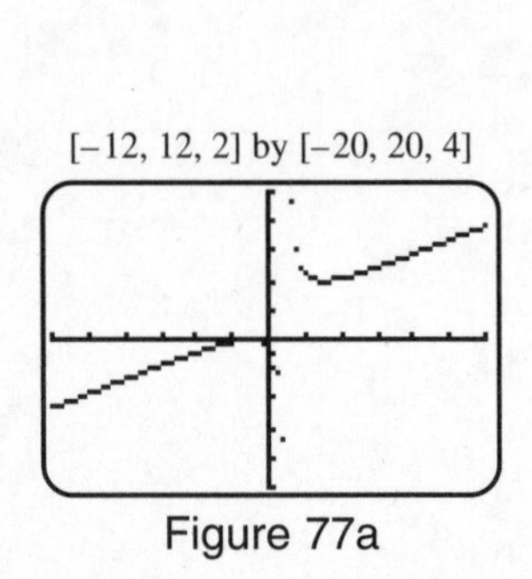

Figure 77a

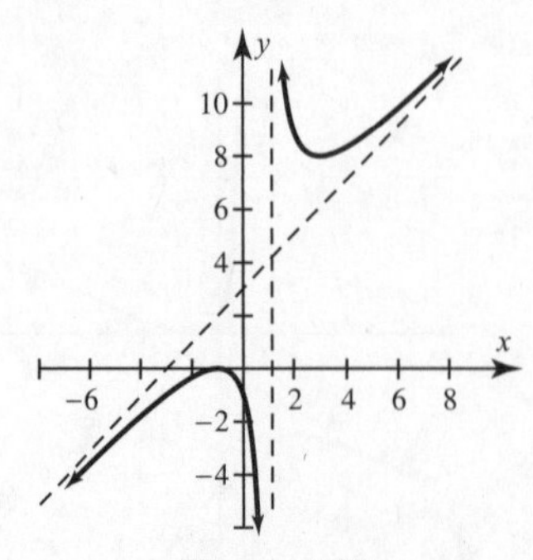


Figure 77b

78. There is a vertical asymptote at $x = 2$ since 2 is a zero of the denominator but is not a zero of the numerator. To find any slant asymptote we will divide the numerator by the denominator using synthetic division:

$$\begin{array}{r|rrr} 2 & 2 & 3 & 1 \\ & & 4 & 14 \\ \hline & 2 & 7 & 15 \end{array}$$

Therefore, $f(x) = 2x + 7 + \dfrac{15}{x - 2}$ and as $|x|$ becomes large, $f(x)$ approaches $y = 2x + 7$. There is a slant asymptote at $y = 2x + 7$. The graph of $f$ using dot mode is shown in Figure 78a. To sketch this graph, first sketch the vertical and slant asymptotes found above. Then use Figure 78a as a guide to a more complete graph of $f$. The sketch is shown in Figure 78b.

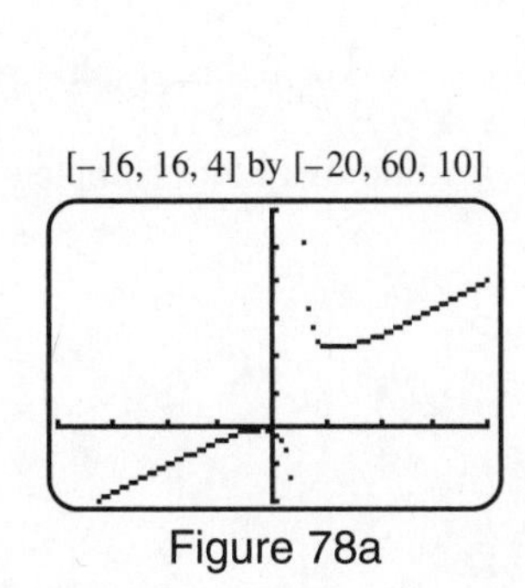


Figure 78a

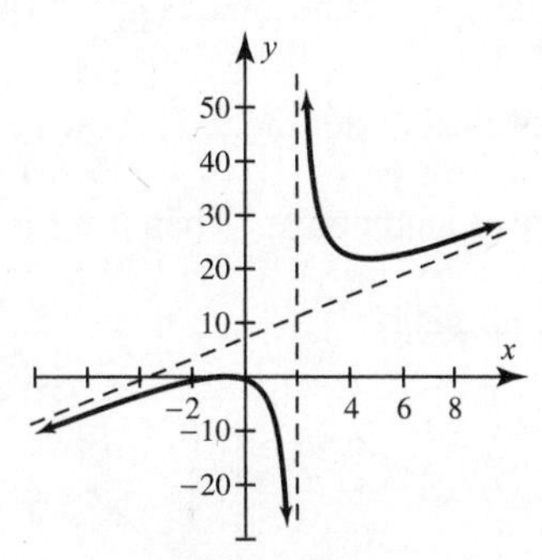


Figure 78b

79. There is a vertical asymptote at $x = \dfrac{1}{2}$ since $\dfrac{1}{2}$ is a zero of the denominator but is not a zero of the numerator. To find any slant asymptote we will divide the numerator by the denominator.

$$\begin{array}{r} 2x + 1 + \frac{1}{2x-1} \\ 2x - 1\overline{)4x^2 + 0x + 0} \\ \underline{4x^2 - 2x} \\ 2x + 0 \\ \underline{2x - 1} \\ 1 \end{array}$$

Therefore, $f(x) = 2x + 1 + \dfrac{1}{2x - 1}$ and as $|x|$ becomes large, $f(x)$ approaches $y = 2x + 1$. There is a slant asymptote at $y = 2x + 1$. The graph of $f$ using dot mode is shown in Figure 79a. To sketch this graph, first sketch the vertical and slant asymptotes found above. Then use Figure 79a as a guide to a more complete graph of $f$. The sketch is shown in Figure 79b.

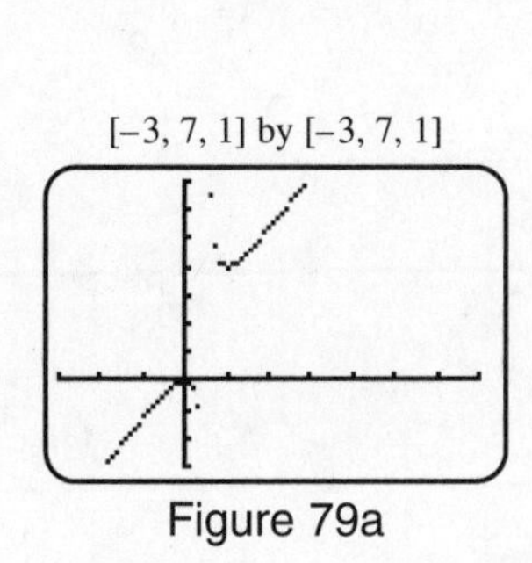


Figure 79a

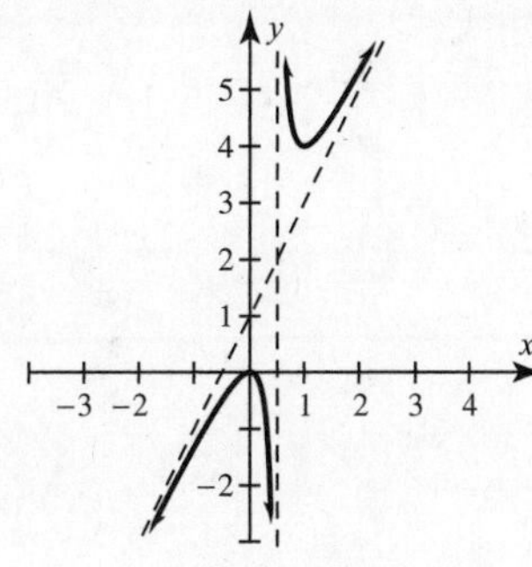


Figure 79b

80. There is a vertical asymptote at $x = \frac{3}{4}$ since $\frac{3}{4}$ is a zero of the denominator but is not a zero of the numerator. To find any slant asymptote we will divide the numerator by the denominator.

$$\begin{array}{r} x + 1 + \frac{1}{4x-3} \\ 4x - 3 \overline{)4x^2 + \phantom{3}x - 2} \\ \underline{4x^2 - 3x\phantom{{}-2}} \\ 4x - 2 \\ \underline{4x - 3} \\ 1 \end{array}$$

Therefore, $f(x) = x + 1 + \frac{1}{4x - 3}$ and as $|x|$ becomes large, $f(x)$ approaches $y = x + 1$. There is a slant asymptote at $y = x + 1$. The graph of $f$ using dot mode is shown in Figure 80a. To sketch this graph, first sketch the vertical and slant asymptotes found above. Then use Figure 80a as a guide to a more complete graph of $f$. The sketch is shown in Figure 80b.

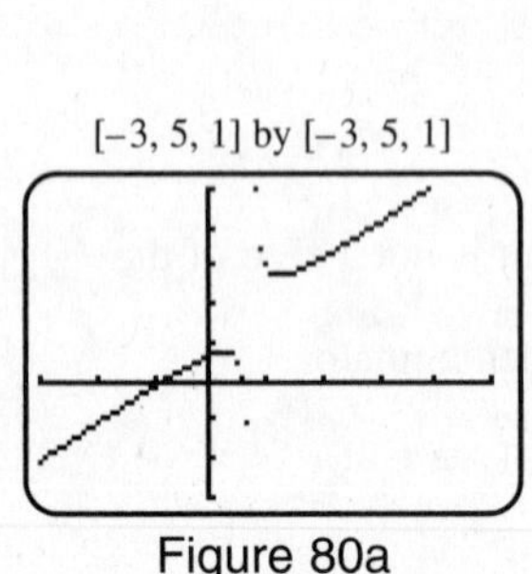


Figure 80a

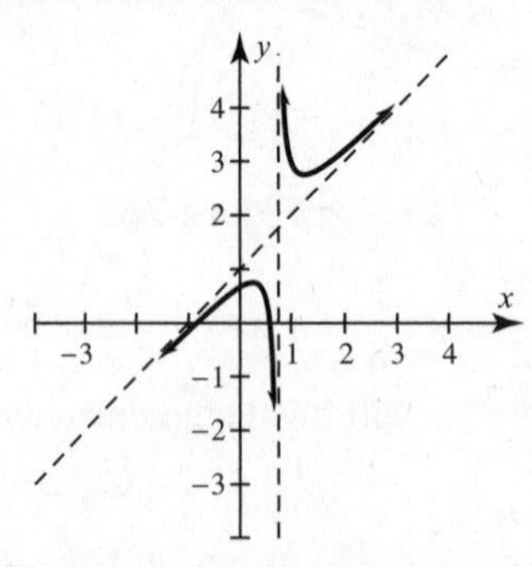


Figure 80b

81. $\frac{4}{x + 2} = -4 \Rightarrow 4 = -4(x + 2) \Rightarrow 4 = -4x - 8 \Rightarrow 12 = -4x \Rightarrow x = -3$

82. $\frac{3}{2x + 1} = -1 \Rightarrow 3 = -1(2x + 1) \Rightarrow 3 = -2x - 1 \Rightarrow 4 = -2x \Rightarrow x = -2$

83. $\frac{x + 1}{x} = 2 \Rightarrow x + 1 = 2x \Rightarrow x = 1$

84. $\frac{2x}{x - 3} = -4 \Rightarrow 2x = -4x + 12 \Rightarrow 6x = 12 \Rightarrow x = 2$

85. $\frac{1 - x}{3x - 1} = -\frac{3}{5} \Rightarrow -3(3x - 1) = 5(1 - x) \Rightarrow -9x + 3 = 5 - 5x \Rightarrow -2 = 4x \Rightarrow x = -\frac{1}{2}$

86. $\frac{3 - 2x}{x + 2} = 12 \Rightarrow 3 - 2x = 12(x + 2) \Rightarrow 3 - 2x = 12x + 24 \Rightarrow -21 = 14x \Rightarrow x = -\frac{3}{2}$

87. $f(x) = \dfrac{2x - 4}{x - 1}$ is in lowest terms.

1) To find the vertical asymptote we find the zero of the denominator, $x - 1 = 0 \Rightarrow x = 1$.

2) Since the degree of the numerator is equal to the degree of the denominator the equation of the horizontal asymptote is $y = \dfrac{2}{1} = 2$.

3) $f(0) = \dfrac{2(0) - 4}{0 - 1} = 4$; $(0, 4)$

4) $\dfrac{2x - 4}{x - 1} = 0 \Rightarrow 2x - 4 = 0 \Rightarrow 2x = 4 \Rightarrow x = 2$; $(2, 0)$

5) $\dfrac{2x - 4}{x - 1} = 2 \Rightarrow 2x - 4 = 2(x - 1) \Rightarrow 2x - 4 = 2x - 2 \Rightarrow 0 = 2 \Rightarrow f$ does not cross the horizontal asymptote.

6) See Figure 87.

7) See Figure 87.

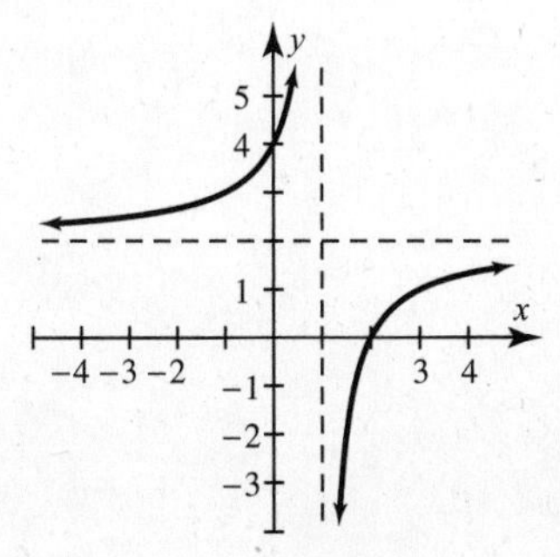

Figure 87

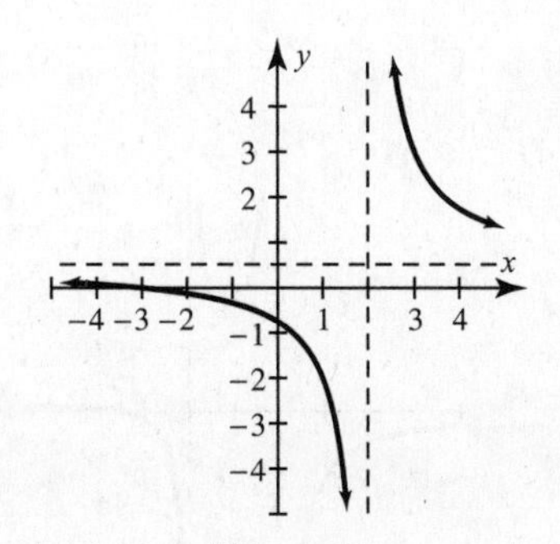

Figure 88

88. $f(x) = \dfrac{x + 3}{2x - 4}$ is in lowest terms.

1) To find the vertical asymptote we find the zero of the denominator, $2x - 4 = 0 \Rightarrow 2x = 4 \Rightarrow x = 2$.

2) Since the degree of the numerator is equal to the degree of the denominator the equation of the horizontal asymptote is $y = \dfrac{1}{2}$.

3) $f(0) = \dfrac{(0) + 3}{2(0) - 4} = -\dfrac{3}{4}$; $\left(0, \dfrac{3}{4}\right)$

4) $\dfrac{x + 3}{2x - 4} = 0 \Rightarrow x + 3 = 0 \Rightarrow x = -3$; $(-3, 0)$

5) $\dfrac{x + 3}{2x - 4} = \dfrac{1}{2} \Rightarrow 2(x + 3) = 2x - 4 \Rightarrow 2x + 6 = 2x - 4 \Rightarrow 6 = -4 \Rightarrow f$ does not cross the horizontal asymptote.

6) See Figure 88.

7) See Figure 88.

89. $f(x) = \dfrac{x^2 - 2x}{x^2 + 6x + 9}$ is in lowest terms.

1) To find the vertical asymptote we find the zero of the denominator, $x^2 + 6x + 9 = 0 \Rightarrow$ $(x + 3)^2 = 0 \Rightarrow x + 3 = 0 \Rightarrow x = -3$.

2) Since the degree of the numerator is equal to the degree of the denominator the equation of the horizontal asymptote is $y = \dfrac{1}{1} = 1$.

3) $f(0) = \dfrac{0^2 - 2(0)}{0^2 + 6(0) + 9} = \dfrac{0}{9} = 0$; $(0, 0)$

4) $\dfrac{x^2 - 2x}{x^2 + 6x + 9} = 0 \Rightarrow x^2 - 2x = 0 \Rightarrow x(x - 2) = 0 \Rightarrow x = 0, x = 2$; $(0, 0), (2, 0)$

5) $\dfrac{x^2 - 2x}{x^2 + 6x + 9} = 1 \Rightarrow x^2 - 2x = x^2 + 6x + 9 \Rightarrow -8x = 9 \Rightarrow x = -\dfrac{9}{8} \Rightarrow f$ crosses the horizontal asymptote at $\left(-\dfrac{9}{8}, 1\right)$

6) See Figure 89.

7) See Figure 89.

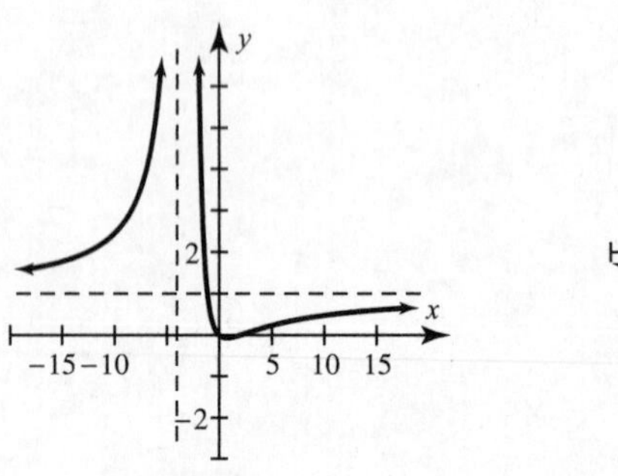

Figure 89

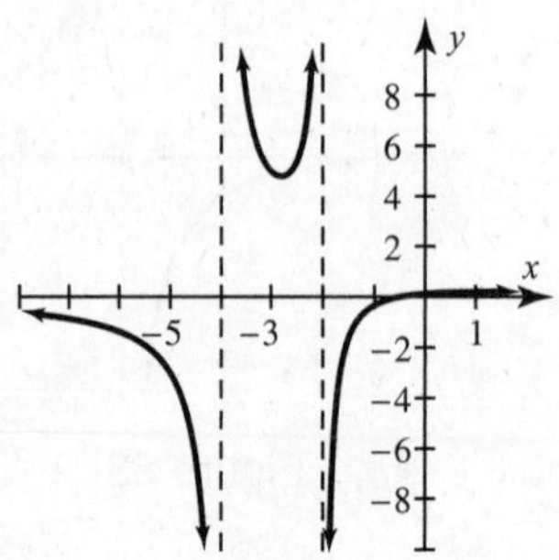

Figure 90

90. $f(x) = \dfrac{2x + 1}{x^2 + 6x + 8}$ is in lowest terms.

1) To find the vertical asymptotes we find the zeros of the denominator, $x^2 + 6x + 8 = 0 \Rightarrow$ $(x + 4)(x + 2) = 0 \Rightarrow x = -4, -2$.

2) Since the degree of the numerator is less than the degree of the denominator the horizontal asymptote is $y = 0$.

3) $f(0) = \dfrac{2(0) + 1}{0^2 + 6(0) + 8} = \dfrac{1}{8} = 0$; $\left(0, \dfrac{1}{8}\right)$

4) $\dfrac{2x + 1}{x^2 + 6x + 8} = 0 \Rightarrow 2x + 1 = 0 \Rightarrow x = -\dfrac{1}{2}$; $\left(-\dfrac{1}{2}, 0\right)$

5) $\dfrac{2x + 1}{x^2 + 6x + 8} = 0 \Rightarrow x = -\dfrac{1}{2} \Rightarrow f$ will cross the horizontal asymptote at $-\dfrac{1}{2}$.

6) See Figure 90.

7) See Figure 90.

91. $f(x) = \dfrac{x^2 + 2x + 1}{x^2 - x - 6}$ is in lowest terms.

1) To find the vertical asymptotes we find the zeros of the denominator, $x^2 - x - 6 = 0 \Rightarrow$ $(x - 3)(x + 2) = 0 \Rightarrow x = 3, -2.$
2) Since the degree of the numerator is equal to the degree of the denominator the equation of the horizontal asymptote is $y = \dfrac{1}{1} = 1.$
3) $f(0) = \dfrac{0^2 + 2(0) + 1}{0^2 - 0 - 6} = -\dfrac{1}{6} = 0;\ \left(0, -\dfrac{1}{6}\right)$
4) $\dfrac{x^2 + 2x + 1}{x^2 - x - 6} = 0 \Rightarrow x^2 + 2x + 1 = 0 \Rightarrow (x + 1)^2 = 0 \Rightarrow x = -1;\ (-1, 0)$
5) $\dfrac{x^2 + 2x + 1}{x^2 - x - 6} = 1 \Rightarrow x^2 + 2x + 1 = x^2 - x - 6 \Rightarrow 3x = -7 \Rightarrow x = -\dfrac{7}{3} \Rightarrow f$ crosses the horizontal asymptote at $-\dfrac{7}{3}.$
6) See Figure 91.
7) See Figure 91.

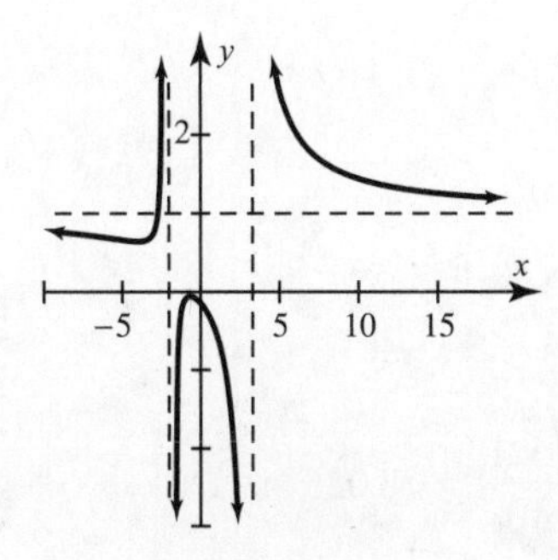


Figure 91

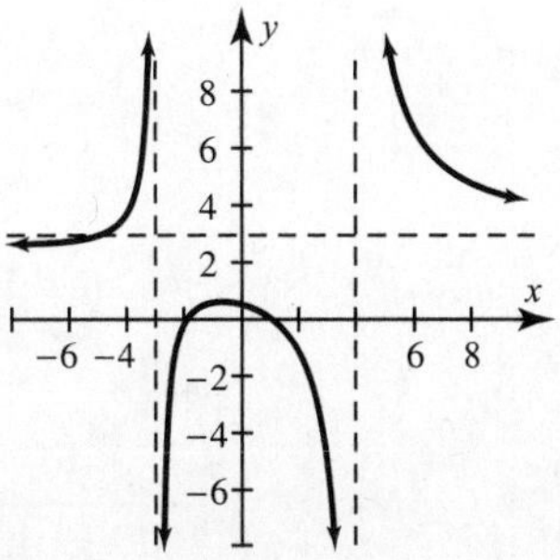

Figure 92

92. $f(x) = \dfrac{3x^2 + 3x - 6}{x^2 - x - 12}$ is in lowest terms.

1) To find the vertical asymptotes we find the zeros of the denominator, $x^2 - x - 12 = 0 \Rightarrow$ $(x - 4)(x + 3) = 0 \Rightarrow x = 4, -3.$
2) Since the degree of the numerator is equal to the degree of the denominator the equation of the horizontal asymptote is $y = \dfrac{3}{1} = 3.$
3) $f(0) = \dfrac{3(0)^2 + 3(0) - 6}{0^2 - 0 - 12} = \dfrac{1}{2} = 0;\ \left(0, \dfrac{1}{2}\right)$
4) $\dfrac{3x^2 + 3x - 6}{x^2 - x - 12} = 0 \Rightarrow 3x^2 + 3x - 6 = 0 \Rightarrow 3(x^2 + x - 2) = 0 \Rightarrow (x + 2)(x - 1) = 0 \Rightarrow$ $x = -2, 1;\ (-2, 0), (1, 0)$
5) $\dfrac{3x^2 + {}^3x - 6}{x^2 - x - 12} = \dfrac{3}{1} \Rightarrow 3(x^2 - x - 12) = 3(x^2 + x - 2) \Rightarrow x^2 - x - 12 = x^2 + x - 2 \Rightarrow$ $-2x = 10 \Rightarrow x = -5 \Rightarrow f$ crosses the horizontal asymptote at $-5.$
6) See Figure 92.
7) See Figure 92.

93. (a) $T(4) = -\frac{1}{4-8} \Rightarrow T(4) = \frac{1}{4} \Rightarrow T(4) = 0.25$; when vehicles leave the ramp at an average rate of 4 vehicles per minute, the wait is 0.25 minutes or 15 seconds.

$T(7.5) = \frac{1}{7.5-8} \Rightarrow T(7.5) = \frac{1}{0.5} \Rightarrow T(7.5) = 2.0$; when vehicles leave the ramp at an average rate of 7.5 vehicles per minute, the wait is 2 minutes.

(b) The wait increases dramatically.

94. (a) From 0 to 5 cars per minute or $D = [0, 5)$.

(b) Finding the zero for the denominator will give us a vertical asymptote. $x - 5 = 0 \Rightarrow x = 5$. See Figure 94.

(c) The wait increases dramatically.

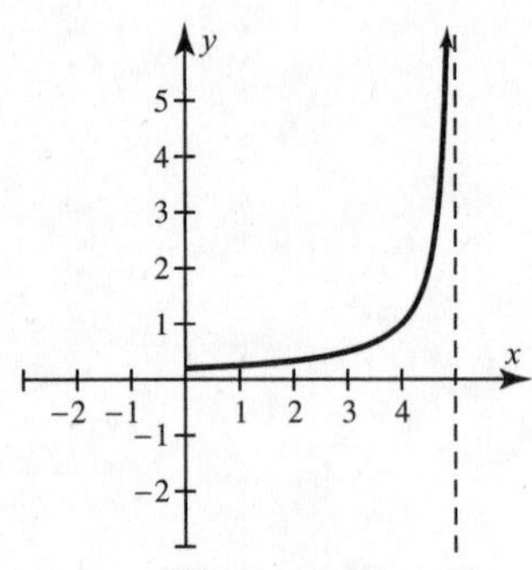


Figure 94

95. (a) $N(20) = \frac{20^2}{1600 - 40(20)} = \frac{400}{800} = \frac{1}{2}$; $N(39) = \frac{39^2}{1600 - 40(39)} = \frac{1521}{40} = 38.025$

(b) The wait increases dramatically.

(c) We find the vertical asymptote by finding the zero of the denominator,

$1600 - 40x = 0 \Rightarrow 1600 = 40x \Rightarrow x = 40$.

96. (a) $N(20) = \frac{20^2}{2500 - 50(20)} = \frac{400}{1500} = \frac{4}{15}$; $N(40) = \frac{40^2}{2500 - 50(40)} = \frac{1600}{500} = 3.2$;

$N(49) = \frac{49^2}{2500 - 50(49)} = \frac{2401}{50} = 48.02$

(b) The length of the line increases dramatically.

(c) We find the vertical asymptote by finding the zero of the denominator,

$2500 - 50x = 0 \Rightarrow 2500 = 50x \Rightarrow x = 50$.

97. (a) Graph $Y_1 = (10X + 1)/(X + 1)$ and $Y_2 = 10$ in [0, 14, 1] by [0, 14, 1]. Since the degree of the numerator and denominator are equal, there is a horizontal asymptote at $y = \frac{10}{1} = 10$. See Figure 97.

(b) The initial population would be $f(0) = 1$ million insects.

(c) After many months the population starts to level off at 10 million.

(d) The horizontal asymptote $y = 10$ represents the limiting population after a very long time.

98. (a) Graph $Y_1 = (X + 10)/(0.5X\^2 + 1)$ in [0, 12, 1] by [0, 12, 1]. Since the degree of the numerator is less than the degree of the denominator, there is a horizontal asymptote at $y = 0$. See Figure 98.

(b) The initial population would be $f(0) = 10$ thousand fish.

(c) The population rapidly declines and after many years, the population tends toward zero.

(d) The horizontal asymptote $y = 0$ represents the limiting population after a very long time. The species is dying out.

[0, 14, 1] by [0, 14, 1]

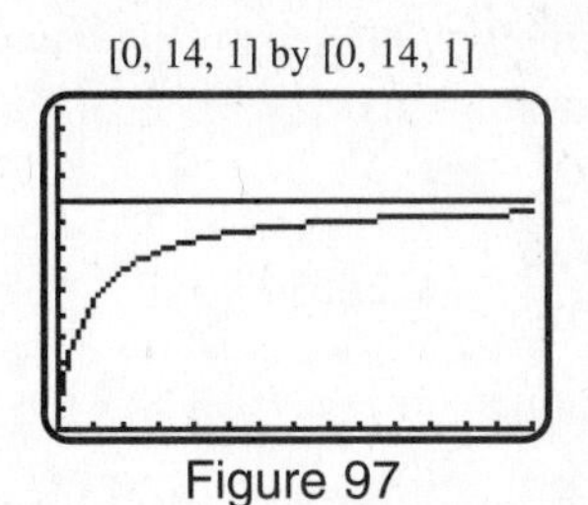

Figure 97

[0, 12, 1] by [0, 12, 1]

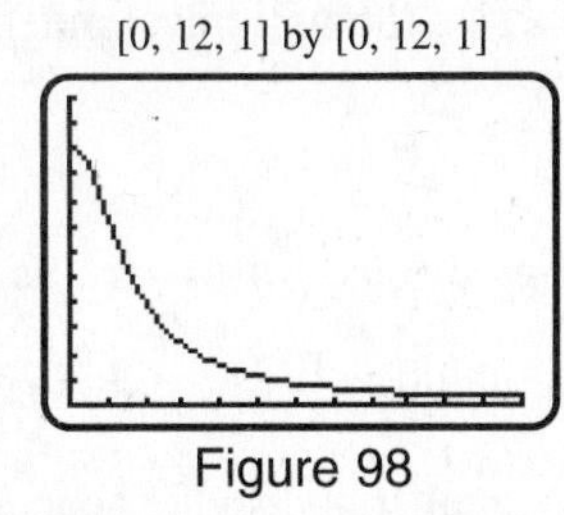

Figure 98

[0, 600, 100] by [0, 50, 5]

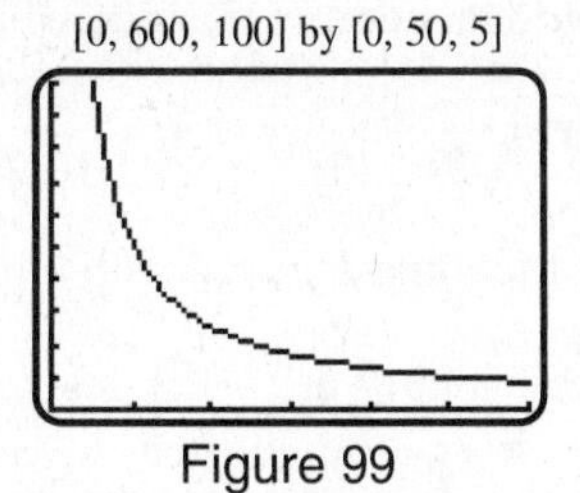

Figure 99

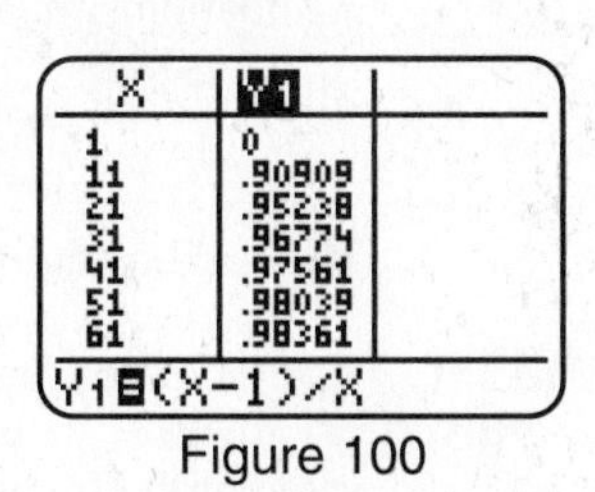


Figure 100

99. (a) $f(x) = \frac{2540}{x} \Rightarrow f(400) = \frac{2540}{400} = 6.35$ inches. A curve designed for 60 mph with a radius of 400 feet should have the outer rail elevated 6.35 inches.

(b) Figure 99 shows the graph of $Y_1 = 2540/X$. This means that a sharper curve must be banked more. As the radius increases, the curve is not as sharp and the elevation of the outer rail decreases.

(c) Since the degree of the numerator is less than the degree of the denominator, the graph of $f(x) = \frac{2540}{x}$ has a horizontal asymptote of $y = 0$. As the radius of the curve increases without bound $(x \to \infty)$, the tracks become straight and no elevation or banking $(y \to 0)$ of the outer rail is necessary.

(d) $f(x) = 12.7 \Rightarrow 12.7 = \frac{2540}{x} \Rightarrow x = \frac{2540}{12.7} = 200$; a radius of 200 feet requires an elevation of 12.7 inches.

100. (a) If there are $x$ balls and only one winning ball, then there are $x - 1$ balls that are not winners. Therefore, the probability of drawing one of these balls is $\frac{x-1}{x}$. The rational function $f$, represented by $f(x) = \frac{x-1}{x}$ computes this probability.

(b) In this example, the domain of $f$ would be $D = \{x \mid x \text{ is a natural number}\}$.

(c) Table $Y_1 = (X - 1)/X$ starting at $x = 1$ and incrementing by 10 as shown in Figure 100. As one continues to increment $x$, $f(x)$ increases but will never exceed 1. This is because the denominator is always one larger than the numerator. As $x$ becomes large, the $f(x)$-values approach 1.

(d) The horizontal asymptote of $f(x) = \frac{x-1}{x}$ is $y = 1$, since the ratio of the leading coefficients is $\frac{1}{1} = 1$. This means that as the number of balls increases without bound, the likelihood of not drawing the winning number becomes certain.

101. (a) At $x = 0$, the denominator of $\frac{2500}{30x}$ is equal to zero, whereas the numerator is nonzero. There is a vertical asymptote at $x = 0$. As the coefficient of friction $x$ becomes smaller and approaches 0, the stopping distance becomes larger and larger without bound. This means that as the road surface becomes very slippery, the distance required to stop becomes very large. If it were possible for the roadway to be covered with glare ice having a coefficient of friction of $x = 0$, then the car would continue indefinitely. A situation similar to this occurs in space where a satellite will travel indefinitely without slowing down.

(b) $340 = \frac{2500}{30x} \Rightarrow x = \frac{2500}{30(340)} \Rightarrow x = \frac{2500}{10{,}200} = \frac{25}{102}$

The coefficient of friction associated with a braking distance of 340 feet is $\frac{25}{102} \approx 0.245$.

102. (a) As $t$ increases, the denominator $t^2 + 1$ gets larger and larger, whereas the numerator is always 5. Thus the value of the fraction $\frac{5}{t^2 + 1}$ becomes smaller and smaller and so the concentration of the drug decreases.

(b) $f(t) = 1.5 \Rightarrow 1.5 = \frac{5}{t^2 + 1} \Rightarrow t^2 + 1 = \frac{5}{1.5} \Rightarrow t^2 = \frac{5}{1.5} - 1 \Rightarrow t = \pm\sqrt{\frac{5}{1.5} - 1} \approx \pm 1.5$

Since time values are positive, the patient should wait for 1.5 hours before taking a second dose.

## Extended and Discovery Exercise for Section 4.6

1. $f(x) = \frac{1}{x}$

$$\frac{f(3) - f(1)}{3 - 1} = \frac{\frac{1}{3} - 1}{2} = -\frac{1}{3}, \quad \frac{f(x + h) - f(x)}{h} = \frac{\frac{1}{x + h} - \frac{1}{x}}{h} = \frac{\frac{x - x - h}{(x + h)(x)}}{h} = \frac{\frac{-h}{x(x + h)}}{h} = -\frac{1}{x(x + h)}$$

2. $f(x) = \frac{1}{x^2}$

$$\frac{f(3) - f(1)}{3 - 1} = \frac{\frac{1}{9} - 1}{2} = -\frac{4}{9},$$

$$\frac{f(x + h) - f(x)}{h} = \frac{\frac{1}{(x + h)^2} - \frac{1}{x^2}}{h} = \frac{\frac{x^2 - (x + h)^2}{x^2(x + h)^2}}{h} = \frac{\frac{x^2 - x^2 - 2xh - h^2}{x^2(x + h)^2}}{h} = \frac{\frac{-2xh - h^2}{x^2(x + h)^2}}{h} = -\frac{2x + h}{x^2(x + h)^2}$$

3. $f(x) = \frac{3}{2x}$

$$\frac{f(3) - f(1)}{3 - 1} = \frac{\frac{3}{6} - \frac{3}{2}}{2} = -\frac{1}{2}, \quad \frac{f(x + h) - f(x)}{h} = \frac{\frac{3}{2(x + h)} - \frac{3}{2x}}{h} = \frac{\frac{3x - 3x - 3h}{2x(x + h)}}{h} =$$

$$\frac{x}{x} \cdot \frac{3}{2(x + h)} - \frac{3}{2x} \cdot \frac{x + h}{x + h} = \frac{3x}{2x(x + h)} - \frac{3(x + h)}{2x(x + h)} = -\frac{3}{2x(x + h)}$$

4. $f(x) = \frac{1}{5 - x}$

$$\frac{f(3) - f(1)}{3 - 1} = \frac{\frac{1}{2} - \frac{1}{4}}{2} = \frac{1}{8},$$

$$\frac{f(x + h) - f(x)}{h} = \frac{\frac{1}{5 - (x + h)} - \frac{1}{5 - x}}{h} = \frac{\frac{5 - x - (5 - x - h)}{(5 - x - h)(5 - x)}}{h} = \frac{\frac{h}{(x - 5)(x - 5 + h)}}{h} = \frac{1}{(x - 5)(x - 5 + h)}$$

## Checking Basic Concepts for Sections 4.5 and 4.6

1. Since the polynomial is quadratic, it can have at most two zeros, which are given as $\pm 4i$. Thus, there no real zeros; since the leading coefficient is 3, $f(x) = 3(x + 4i)(x - 4i) = 3(x^2 + 16) = 3x^2 + 48$.

2. See Figure 2. *Answers may vary.*

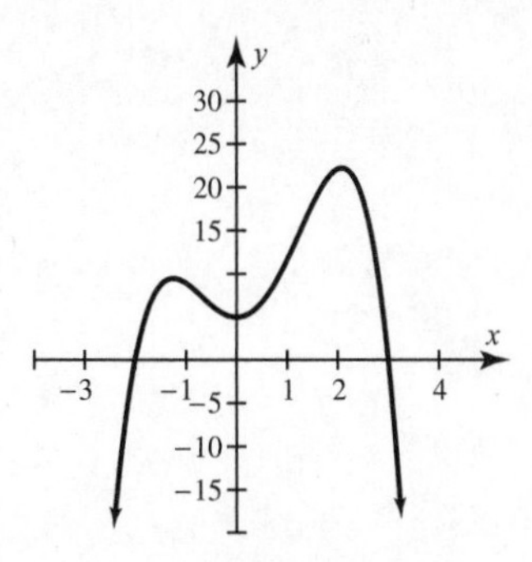


Figure 2

3. Use a graph of $y = x^3 - x^2 + 4x - 4$ or use the rational zero test to find the zero of 1. See Figure 3. The graph indicates that 1 is a zero, so $(x - 1)$ is a factor. Use synthetic division to find the other factor.

$$\begin{array}{r|rrrr} 1 & 1 & -1 & 4 & -4 \\ & & 1 & 0 & 4 \\ \hline & 1 & 0 & 4 & 0 \end{array}$$

$f(x) = (x - 1)(x^2 + 4) = (x - 1)(x + 2i)(x - 2i)$

4. (a) $2x^3 + 45 = 5x^2 - 18x \Rightarrow 2x^3 - 5x^2 + 18x + 45 = 0$

Start by graphing $Y_1 = 2X\text{^}3 - 5X\text{^}2 + 18X + 45$ to locate the rational zero at $x = -\frac{3}{2}$.

Divide $2x^3 - 5x^2 + 18x + 45$ by $x + \frac{3}{2}$.

$$\begin{array}{r} 2x^2 - 8x + 30 \\ x + \tfrac{3}{2}\overline{)2x^3 - 5x^2 + 18x + 45} \\ \underline{2x^3 + 3x^2 \phantom{+ 18x + 45}} \\ -8x^2 + 18x + 45 \\ \underline{-8x^2 - 12x \phantom{+ 45}} \\ 30x + 45 \\ \underline{30x + 45} \\ 0 \end{array}$$

Now use the quadratic formula on $2x^2 - 8x + 30$: $\frac{8 \pm \sqrt{64 - 4(2)(30)}}{2(2)} = \frac{8 \pm \sqrt{-176}}{4} = \frac{8 \pm 4i\sqrt{11}}{4} = 2 \pm i\sqrt{11}$. Therefore the solutions are $x = -\frac{3}{2}, 2 \pm i\sqrt{11}$.

(b) $x^4 + 5x^2 = 36 \Rightarrow x^4 + 5x^2 - 36 = 0 \Rightarrow (x^2 + 9)(x^2 - 4) = 0 \Rightarrow (x^2 + 9)(x + 2)(x - 2) = 0$.

Set $x^2 + 9 = 0 \Rightarrow x^2 = -9 \Rightarrow x = \pm\sqrt{-9} \Rightarrow x = \pm 3i$. Therefore the solutions are: $x = \pm 2, \pm 3i$.

5. (a) The denominator $x - 1 \neq 0 \Rightarrow D\{x | x \neq 1\}$

(b) $f(x) = \frac{1}{x-1} + 2 \Rightarrow f(x) = \frac{1}{x-1} + \frac{2(x-1)}{x-1} \Rightarrow f(x) = \frac{2x-1}{x-1}$. To find the vertical asymptote we find the zero of the denominator. $x - 1 = 0 \Rightarrow x = 1$ is the vertical asymptote. Since the degree of the numerator and denominator is the same, we use the ratio of the leading coefficients $\frac{2}{1} \Rightarrow y = 2$ to find the horizontal asymptote.

(c) See Figure 5.

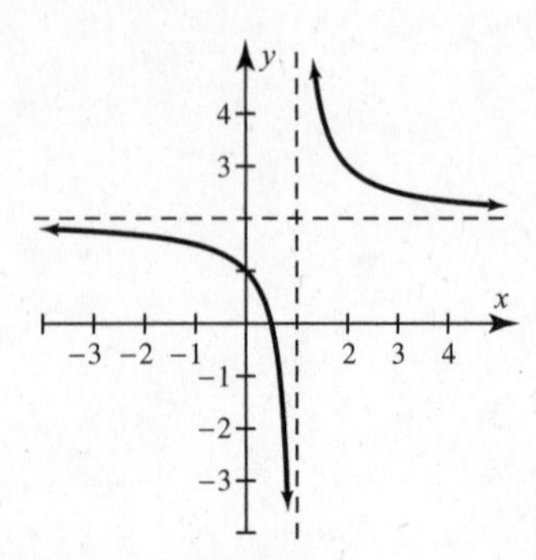


Figure 5

6. Horizontal asymptote: since the degree of the numerator and denominator is the same, we use the ratio of the leading coefficients to find the asymptote. $y = \frac{4}{1} \Rightarrow y = 4$. To find the vertical asymptote we find the zero of the denominator. $x^2 - 4 = 0 \Rightarrow (x + 2)(x - 2) = 0 \Rightarrow x = \pm 2$ are the vertical asymptotes. The domain of $f$ is $D\{x | x \neq -2 \text{ or } x \neq 2\}$.

7. (a) $f(x) = \frac{3x - 1}{2x - 2}$

Since $2x - 2 = 0 \Rightarrow x = 1$, the vertical asymptote is the line $x = 1$. Since the degree of the numerator is equal to the degree of the denominator the equation of the horizontal asymptote is $y = \frac{3}{2}$. See Figure 7a.

(b) $f(x) = \frac{1}{(x+1)^2}$

Since $(x + 1)^2 = 0 \Rightarrow x = -1$, the vertical asymptote is the line $x = -1$. Since the degree of the denominator is greater than the degree of the numerator the equation of the horizontal asymptote is $y = 0$. See Figure 7b.

(c) $f(x) = \frac{x + 2}{x^2 - 4} = \frac{(x + 2)}{(x + 2)(x - 2)} \Rightarrow f(x)$ has a common factor of $(x + 2)$ shows that $f(x)$ has a hole at $x = -2$. Since $x - 2 = 0 \Rightarrow x = 2$, the equation of the vertical asymptote is the line $x = 2$. Since the degree of the numerator is less than the degree of the denominator the equation of the horizontal asymptote is $y = 0$. See Figure 7c.

(d) $f(x) = \frac{(x^2 + 1)}{x^2 - 1}$

Since $x^2 - 1 = 0 \Rightarrow x = \pm 1$, the equations of the vertical asymptotes are the lines $x = \pm 1$. Since the degree of the numerator is equal to the degree of the denominator the equation of the horizontal asymptote is $y = 1$. See Figure 7d.

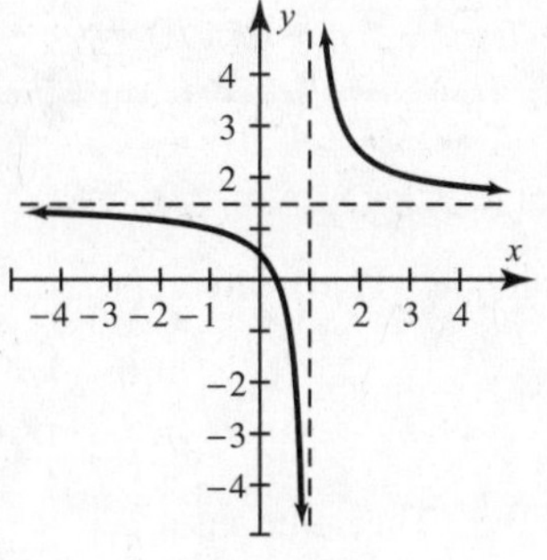

Figure 7a

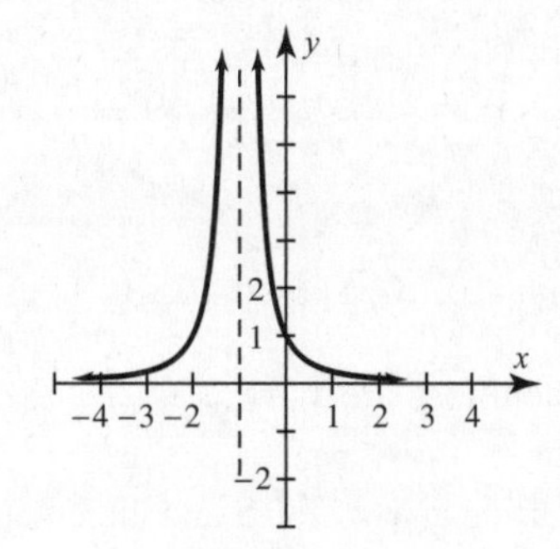

Figure 7b

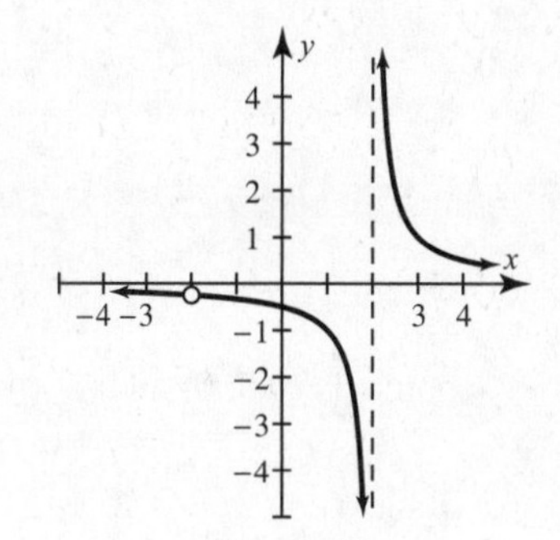

Figure 7c

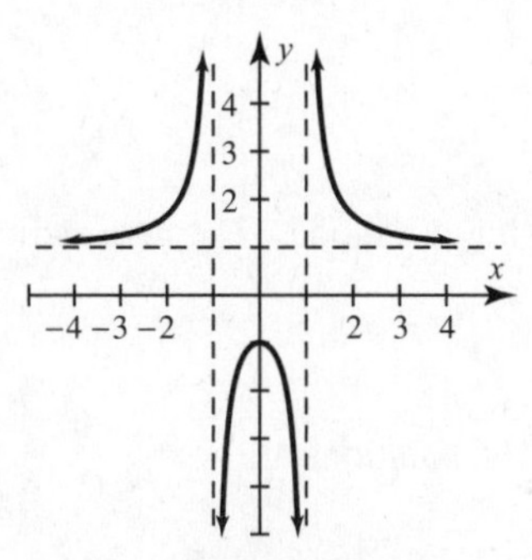

Figure 7d

## 4.7: More Equations and Inequalities

1. (a) $\dfrac{2x}{x + 2} = 6 \Rightarrow 2x = 6(x + 2) \Rightarrow 2x = 6x + 12 \Rightarrow 4x = -12 \Rightarrow x = -3$

   (b) Graph $Y_1 = (2X)/(X + 2)$ and $Y_2 = 6$ in [–10, 10, 1] by [–10, 10, 1] using dot mode. See Figure 1b. The intersection point is (–3, 6). The solution is $x = -3$.

   (c) Table $Y_1 = (2X)/(X + 2)$ starting at $x = -5$ and incrementing by 1. See Figure 1c. The solution is $x = -3$.

[–10, 10, 1] by [–10, 10, 1]

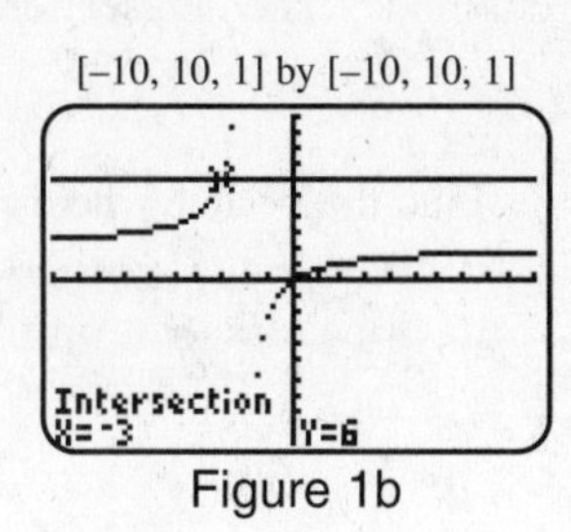

Figure 1b

| X | Y1 |
|---|---|
| -5 | 3.3333 |
| -4 | 4 |
| -3 | 6 |
| -2 | ERROR |
| -1 | -2 |
| 0 | 0 |
| 1 | .66667 |

X=-3

Figure 1c

2. (a) $\dfrac{3x}{2x - 1} = 3 \Rightarrow 3x = 3(2x - 1) \Rightarrow 3x = 6x - 3 \Rightarrow 3x = 3 \Rightarrow x = 1$

   (b) Graph $Y_1 = (3X)/(2X - 1)$ and $Y_2 = 3$ in [–10, 10, 1] by [–10, 10, 1] using dot mode. The intersection point is (1, 3). The solution is $x = 1$.

   (c) Table $Y_1 = (3X)/(2X - 1)$ starting at $x = -1$ and incrementing by 1. The solution is $x = 1$.

3. (a) $2 - \frac{5}{x} + \frac{2}{x^2} = 0 \Rightarrow \frac{2x^2}{x^2} - \frac{5x}{x^2} + \frac{2}{x^2} = 0 \Rightarrow \frac{2x^2 - 5x + 2}{x^2} = 0 \Rightarrow 2x^2 - 5x + 2 = 0 \Rightarrow$

$(2x - 1)(x - 2) = 0 \Rightarrow x = \frac{1}{2}, 2$

(b) Graph $Y_1 = 2 - 5/X + 2/X^2$ in [–10, 10, 1] by [–10, 10, 1] using dot mode. The $x$-intercepts are the points is (0.5, 0) and (2, 0). The solutions are $x = \frac{1}{2}, 2$.

(c) Table $Y_1 = 2 - 5/X + 2/X^2$ starting at $x = -0.5$ and incrementing by 0.5. The solutions are $x = \frac{1}{2}, 2$.

4. (a) $\frac{1}{x^2} + \frac{1}{x} = 2 \Rightarrow \frac{1}{x^2} + \frac{x}{x^2} = 2 \Rightarrow \frac{1 + x}{x^2} = 2 \Rightarrow 1 + x = 2x^2 \Rightarrow 2x^2 - x - 1 = 0 \Rightarrow$

$(2x + 1)(x - 1) = 0 \Rightarrow x = -\frac{1}{2}, 1$

(b) Graph $Y_1 = 1/X^2 + 1/X$ and $Y_2 = 2$ in [–10, 10, 1] by [–10, 10, 1] using dot mode. The intersection points are (–0.5, 2) and (1, 2). The solutions are $x = -\frac{1}{2}, 1$.

(c) Table $Y_1 = 1/X^2 + 1/X$ starting at $x = -1$ and incrementing by 0.5. The solutions are $x = -\frac{1}{2}, 1$.

5. (a) $\frac{1}{x + 1} + \frac{1}{x - 1} = \frac{1}{x^2 - 1} \Rightarrow \frac{x - 1}{x^2 - 1} + \frac{x + 1}{x^2 - 1} = \frac{1}{x^2 - 1} \Rightarrow \frac{2x}{x^2 - 1} = \frac{1}{x^2 - 1} \Rightarrow 2x = 1 \Rightarrow$

$x = \frac{1}{2}$

(b) Graph $Y_1 = 1/(X + 1) + 1/(X - 1)$ and $Y_2 = 1/(X^2 - 1)$ in [–2, 2, 1] by [–5, 5, 1] using dot mode. The intersection point is $\left(\frac{1}{2}, -\frac{4}{3}\right)$. The solution is $x = \frac{1}{2}$.

(c) Table $Y_1 = 1/(X + 1) + 1/(X - 1) - 1/(X^2 - 1)$ starting at $x = -1$ and incrementing by 0.5. Find the $x$-value where $Y_1 = 0$. The solution is $x = \frac{1}{2}$.

6. (a) $\frac{4}{x - 2} = \frac{3}{x - 1} \Rightarrow 4(x - 1) = 3(x - 2) \Rightarrow 4x - 4 = 3x - 6 \Rightarrow x = -2$

(b) Graph $Y_1 = 4/(X - 2)$ and $Y_2 = 3/(X - 1)$ in [–5, 5, 1] by [–5, 5, 1] using dot mode. The intersection point is (–2, –1). The solution is $x = -2$.

(c) Table $Y_1 = 4/(X - 2) - 3/(X - 1)$ starting at $x = -4$ and incrementing by 1. Find the $x$-value where $Y_1 = 0$. The solution is $x = -2$.

7. $\frac{x + 1}{x - 5} = 0 \Rightarrow x + 1 = 0(x - 5) \Rightarrow x + 1 = 0 \Rightarrow x = -1$; Check: $\frac{-1 + 1}{-1 - 5} = \frac{0}{-6} = 0$

8. $\frac{x - 2}{x + 3} = 1 \Rightarrow x - 2 = 1(x + 3) \Rightarrow x - 2 = x + 3 \Rightarrow 0 = 5$; Contradiction: No real solution.

9. $\frac{6(1 - 2x)}{x - 5} = 4 \Rightarrow 6(1 - 2x) = 4(x - 5) \Rightarrow 6 - 12x = 4x - 20 \Rightarrow -16x = -26 \Rightarrow x = \frac{13}{8}$

Check: $\frac{6(1 - 2(\frac{13}{8}))}{\frac{13}{8} - 5} = \frac{6(-\frac{9}{4})}{-\frac{27}{8}} = \frac{-\frac{27}{2}}{-\frac{27}{8}} = -\frac{27}{2} \cdot \left(-\frac{8}{27}\right) = 4$

10. $\frac{2}{5(2x+5)} + 3 = -1 \Rightarrow \frac{2}{10x+25} = -4 \Rightarrow 2 = -4(10x+25) \Rightarrow 2 = -40x - 100 \Rightarrow$

$40x = -102 \Rightarrow x = -2.55$; Check: $\frac{2}{5(2(-2.55)+5)} + 3 = \frac{2}{-0.5} + 3 = -4 + 3 = -1$

11. $\frac{1}{x+2} + \frac{1}{x} = 1 \Rightarrow x + (x+2) = x(x+2) \Rightarrow 2x + 2 = x^2 + 2x \Rightarrow x^2 = 2 \Rightarrow x = \pm\sqrt{2}$

Check: $\frac{1}{\sqrt{2}+2} + \frac{1}{\sqrt{2}} = \frac{\sqrt{2}}{\sqrt{2}(\sqrt{2}+2)} + \frac{\sqrt{2}+2}{\sqrt{2}(\sqrt{2}+2)} = \frac{2\sqrt{2}+2}{2+2\sqrt{2}} = 1$

Check: $\frac{1}{-\sqrt{2}+2} + \frac{1}{\sqrt{2}} = \frac{-\sqrt{2}}{-\sqrt{2}(-\sqrt{2}+2)} + \frac{-\sqrt{2}+2}{-\sqrt{2}(-\sqrt{2}+2)} = \frac{2-2\sqrt{2}}{2-2\sqrt{2}} = 1$

12. $\frac{2x}{x-1} = 5 + \frac{2}{x-1} \Rightarrow 2x = 5(x-1) + 2 \Rightarrow 2x = 5x - 5 + 2 \Rightarrow 3x = 3 \Rightarrow x = 1$; No real solution.

Check: There is no real solution since $x = 1$ is not defined in the original equation.

13. $\frac{1}{x} - \frac{2}{x^2} = 5 \Rightarrow x - 2 = 5x^2 \Rightarrow 5x^2 - x + 2 = 0$; This quadratic equation has no solutions since the discriminant is negative: $(-1)^2 - 4(5)(2) = 1 - 40 = -39 < 0$. No real solution.

14. $\frac{1}{x^2-2} = \frac{1}{x} \Rightarrow x = x^2 - 2 \Rightarrow x^2 - x - 2 = 0 \Rightarrow (x+1)(x-2) = 0 \Rightarrow x = -1, 2$

Check: $\frac{1}{(-1)^2-2} = \frac{1}{-1} \Rightarrow -1 = -1$; Check: $\frac{1}{(2)^2-2} = \frac{1}{2} \Rightarrow \frac{1}{2} = \frac{1}{2}$

15. $\frac{x^3-4x}{x^2+1} = 0 \Rightarrow x^3 - 4x = 0(x^2+1) \Rightarrow x^3 - 4x = 0 \Rightarrow x(x+2)(x-2) = 0 \Rightarrow x = 0, -2, 2$

Check: $\frac{(0)^3-4(0)}{(0)^2+1} = \frac{0}{1} = 0$; Check: $\frac{(-2)^3-4(-2)}{(-2)^2+1} = \frac{0}{5} = 0$; Check: $\frac{(2)^3-4(2)}{(2)^2+1} = \frac{0}{5} = 0$

16. $\frac{1}{x+2} + \frac{1}{x+3} = \frac{2}{x^2+5x+6} \Rightarrow 1(x+3) + 1(x+2) = 2 \Rightarrow 2x + 5 = 2 \Rightarrow 2x = -3 \Rightarrow x = -\frac{3}{2}$

Check: $\frac{1}{-\frac{3}{2}+2} + \frac{1}{-\frac{3}{2}+3} = \frac{2}{(-\frac{3}{2})^2 + 5(-\frac{3}{2}) + 6} \Rightarrow 2 + \frac{2}{3} = \frac{2}{\frac{3}{4}} \Rightarrow \frac{8}{3} = \frac{8}{3}$

17. $\frac{35}{x^2} = \frac{4}{x} + 15 \Rightarrow 35 = 4x + 15x^2 \Rightarrow 15x^2 + 4x - 35 = 0 \Rightarrow (5x-7)(3x+5) = 0 \Rightarrow x = \frac{-5}{3}, \frac{7}{5}$

Check: $\frac{35}{(\frac{-5}{3})^2} = \frac{4}{\frac{-5}{3}} + 15 \Rightarrow \frac{63}{5} = \frac{-12}{5} + \frac{75}{5} \Rightarrow \frac{63}{5} = \frac{63}{5}$;

Check: $\frac{35}{(\frac{7}{5})^2} = \frac{4}{\frac{7}{5}} + 15 \Rightarrow \frac{125}{7} = \frac{20}{7} + \frac{105}{7} \Rightarrow \frac{125}{7} = \frac{125}{7}$

18. $6 - \frac{35}{x} + \frac{36}{x^2} = 0 \Rightarrow 6x^2 - 35x + 36 = 0 \Rightarrow (2x-9)(3x-4) = 0 \Rightarrow x = \frac{4}{3}, \frac{9}{2}$

Check: $6 - \frac{35}{\frac{4}{3}} + \frac{36}{(\frac{4}{3})^2} = 0 \Rightarrow \frac{24}{4} - \frac{105}{4} + \frac{81}{4} = 0 \Rightarrow 0 = 0$;

Check: $6 - \frac{35}{\frac{9}{2}} + \frac{36}{(\frac{9}{2})^2} = 0 \Rightarrow \frac{54}{9} - \frac{70}{9} + \frac{16}{9} = 0 \Rightarrow 0 = 0$

19. $\frac{x+5}{x+2} = \frac{x-4}{x-10} \Rightarrow (x+5)(x-10) = (x-4)(x+2) \Rightarrow x^2 - 5x - 50 = x^2 - 2x - 8 \Rightarrow$

$3x + 42 = 0 \Rightarrow x = -14$; Check: $\frac{(-14)+5}{(-14)+2} = \frac{(-14)-4}{(-14)-10} \Rightarrow \frac{-9}{-12} = \frac{-18}{-24} \Rightarrow \frac{3}{4} = \frac{3}{4}$

20. $\frac{x-1}{x+1}=\frac{x+3}{x-4}\Rightarrow(x-1)(x-4)=(x+1)(x+3)\Rightarrow x^2-5x+4=x^2+4x+3\Rightarrow$

$9x-1=0\Rightarrow x=\frac{1}{9}$; Check: $\frac{(\frac{1}{9})-1}{(\frac{1}{9})+1}=\frac{(\frac{1}{9})+3}{(\frac{1}{9})-4}\Rightarrow\frac{\frac{-8}{9}}{\frac{10}{9}}=\frac{\frac{28}{9}}{\frac{-35}{9}}\Rightarrow-\frac{4}{5}=-\frac{4}{5}$

21. $\frac{1}{x-2}-\frac{2}{x-3}=\frac{-1}{x^2-5x+6}\Rightarrow\frac{1}{x-2}-\frac{2}{x-3}=\frac{-1}{(x-2)(x-3)}\Rightarrow$

$x-3-2(x-2)=-1\Rightarrow-x+1=-1\Rightarrow x=2$; No solution. Check: There is no solution since

$x=2$ is not definrd in the original equation.

22. $\frac{1}{x-1}+\frac{3}{x+1}=\frac{4}{x^2-1}\Rightarrow x+1+3(x-1)=4\Rightarrow x+1+3x-3=4\Rightarrow 4x-6=0\Rightarrow$

$x=\frac{3}{2}$. Check: $\frac{1}{(\frac{3}{2})-1}+\frac{3}{(\frac{3}{2})+1}=\frac{4}{(\frac{3}{2})^2-1}\Rightarrow\frac{1}{\frac{1}{2}}+\frac{3}{\frac{5}{2}}=\frac{4}{\frac{5}{4}}\Rightarrow\frac{10}{5}+\frac{6}{5}=\frac{16}{5}\Rightarrow\frac{16}{5}=\frac{16}{5}$

23. $\frac{2}{x-1}+1=\frac{4}{x^2-1}\Rightarrow\frac{2}{x-1}+1=\frac{4}{(x+1)(x-1)}\Rightarrow 2(x+1)+(x+1)(x-1)=4\Rightarrow$

$2x+2+x^2-1=4\Rightarrow x^2+2x-3=0\Rightarrow(x+3)(x-1)=0\Rightarrow x=-3,1$. Since $x=1$ is not

defined in the original equation $x=-3$. Check: $\frac{2}{-3-1}+1=\frac{4}{(-3)^2-1}\Rightarrow-\frac{1}{2}+1=\frac{4}{8}\Rightarrow\frac{1}{2}=\frac{1}{2}$

24. $\frac{1}{x}+2=\frac{1}{x^2+x}\Rightarrow\frac{1}{x}+2=\frac{1}{x(x+1)}\Rightarrow x+1+2x(x+1)=1\Rightarrow$

$x+1+2x^2+2x=1\Rightarrow 2x^2+3x=0\Rightarrow x(2x+3)=0\Rightarrow x=0,-\frac{3}{2}$. Since $x=0$ is not

defined in the original equation $x=-\frac{3}{2}$. Check: $\frac{1}{-\frac{3}{2}}+2=\frac{1}{(-\frac{3}{2})^2-\frac{3}{2}}\Rightarrow-\frac{2}{3}+2=\frac{1}{\frac{3}{4}}\Rightarrow\frac{4}{3}=\frac{4}{3}$

25. $\frac{1}{x+2}=\frac{4}{4-x^2}-1\Rightarrow\frac{1}{x+2}=\frac{4}{(2+x)(2-x)}-1\Rightarrow 2-x=4-(2+x)(2-x)\Rightarrow$

$2-x=4-(4-x^2)\Rightarrow 2-x=4-4+x^2\Rightarrow x^2+x-2=0\Rightarrow(x+2)(x-1)=0\Rightarrow$

$x=-2,1$. Since $x=-2$ is not defined in the original equation $x=1$.

Check: $\frac{1}{1+2}=\frac{4}{4-(1)^2}-1\Rightarrow\frac{1}{3}=\frac{4}{3}-1\Rightarrow\frac{1}{3}=\frac{1}{3}$

26. $\frac{1}{x-3}+1=\frac{6}{x^2-9}\Rightarrow\frac{1}{x-3}+1=\frac{6}{(x+3)(x-3)}\Rightarrow x+3+(x+3)(x-3)=6\Rightarrow$

$x+3+x^2-9=6\Rightarrow x^2+x-12=0\Rightarrow(x+4)(x-3)=0\Rightarrow x=-4,3$. Since $x=3$ is not

defined in the original equation $x=-4$.

Check: $\frac{1}{-4-3}+1=\frac{6}{(-4)^2-9}\Rightarrow\frac{1}{-7}+1=\frac{6}{16-9}\Rightarrow\frac{6}{7}=\frac{6}{7}$

27. $\frac{1}{x-1}+\frac{1}{x+1}=\frac{2}{x^2-1}\Rightarrow\frac{1}{x-1}+\frac{1}{x+1}=\frac{2}{(x+1)(x-1)}\Rightarrow x+1+x-1=2\Rightarrow$

$2x=2\Rightarrow x=1$. Since $x=1$ is not defined in the original equation, there is no solution to the equation.

28. $\frac{1}{2x+1}+\frac{1}{2x-1}=\frac{2}{4x^2-1}\Rightarrow\frac{1}{2x+1}+\frac{1}{2x-1}=\frac{2}{(2x+1)(2x-1)}\Rightarrow 2x-1+2x+1=2\Rightarrow$

$4x=2\Rightarrow x=\frac{1}{2}$. Since $x=\frac{1}{2}$ is not defined in the original equation there is no solution to this equation.

29. (a) The boundary numbers, the $x$-values for which $f(x) = 0$, are –4, –2, and 2.

    (b) $f(x) > 0$ on the interval for which the graph of $f$ is above the $x$-axis. That is $(-4, -2) \cup (2, \infty)$.

    In set builder notation the intervals are $\{x \mid -4 < x < -2 \text{ or } x > 2\}$.

    (c) $f(x) < 0$ on the interval for which the graph of $f$ is below the $x$-axis. That is $(-\infty, -4) \cup (-2, 2)$.

    In set builder notation the intervals are $\{x \mid x < -4 \text{ or } -2 < x < 2\}$.

30. (a) The boundary numbers, the $x$-values for which $f(x) = 0$, are –2, –1, 1, and 2.

    (b) $f(x) > 0$ on the interval for which the graph of $f$ is above the $x$-axis. That is $(-\infty, -2) \cup (-1, 1) \cup (2, \infty)$.

    In set builder notation the intervals are $\{x \mid x < -2 \text{ or } -1 < x < 1 \text{ or } x > 2\}$.

    (c) $f(x) < 0$ on the interval for which the graph of $f$ is below the $x$-axis. That is $(-2, -1) \cup (1, 2)$.

    In set builder notation the intervals are $\{x \mid -2 < x < -1 \text{ or } 1 < x < 2\}$.

31. (a) The boundary numbers, the $x$-values for which $f(x) = 0$, are –4, –2, 0, and 2.

    (b) $f(x) > 0$ on the interval for which the graph of $f$ is above the $x$-axis. That is $(-4, -2) \cup (0, 2)$.

    In set builder notation the intervals are $\{x \mid -4 < x < -2 \text{ or } 0 < x < 2\}$.

    (c) $f(x) < 0$ on the interval for which the graph of $f$ is below the $x$-axis. That is $(-\infty, -4) \cup (-2, 0) \cup (2, \infty)$.

    In set builder notation the intervals are $\{x \mid x < -4 \text{ or } -2 < x < 0 \text{ or } x > 2\}$.

32. (a) The boundary numbers, the $x$-values for which $f(x) = 0$, are –3 and 1.

    (b) $f(x) > 0$ on the interval for which the graph of $f$ is above the $x$-axis. That is $(-\infty, -3) \cup (-3, 1)$.

    In set builder notation the intervals are $\{x \mid x < -3 \text{ or } -3 < x < 1\}$.

    (c) $f(x) < 0$ on the interval for which the graph of $f$ is below the $x$-axis. That is $(1, \infty)$.

    In set builder notation the interval is $\{x \mid x > 1\}$.

33. (a) The boundary numbers, the $x$-values for which $f(x) = 0$, are –2, 1, and 2.

    (b) $f(x) > 0$ on the interval for which the graph of $f$ is above the $x$-axis. That is $(-\infty, -2) \cup (-2, 1)$.

    In set builder notation the intervals are $\{x \mid x < -2 \text{ or } -2 < x < 1\}$.

    (c) $f(x) < 0$ on the interval for which the graph of $f$ is below the $x$-axis. That is $(1, 2) \cup (2, \infty)$.

    In set builder notation the intervals are $\{x \mid 1 < x < 2 \text{ or } x > 2\}$.

34. (a) The boundary numbers, the $x$-values for which $f(x) = 0$, are –4, –3, –1, 0, and 2.

    (b) $f(x) > 0$ on the interval for which the graph of $f$ is above the $x$-axis. That is $(-4, -3) \cup (-1, 0) \cup (2, \infty)$.

    In set builder notation the intervals are $\{x \mid -4 < x < -3 \text{ or } -1 < x < 0 \text{ or } x > 2\}$.

    (c) $f(x) < 0$ on the interval for which the graph of $f$ is below the $x$-axis. That is $(-\infty, -4) \cup (-3, -1) \cup (0, 2)$.

    In set builder notation the intervals are $\{x \mid x < -4 \text{ or } -3 < x < -1 \text{ or } 0 < x < 2\}$.

35. (a) $f(x)$ is undefined at $x = 0$.

    (b) $f(x) > 0$ on the interval for which the graph of $f$ is above the $x$-axis. That is $(-\infty, 0) \cup (0, \infty)$.

    In set builder notation the intervals are $\{x \mid x < 0 \text{ or } x > 0\}$.

    (c) $f(x) < 0$ on the interval for which the graph of $f$ is below the $x$-axis. There are no solutions.

36. (a) $f(x)$ is undefined at $x = 0$.

(b) $f(x) > 0$ on the interval for which the graph of $f$ is above the $x$-axis. That is $(0, \infty)$

In set builder notation the interval is $\{x \mid x > 0\}$.

(c) $f(x) < 0$ on the interval for which the graph of $f$ is below the $x$-axis. That is $(-\infty, 0)$.

In set builder notation the interval is $\{x \mid x < 0\}$.

37. (a) $f(x)$ is undefined at $x = 1$, $f(x) = 0$ at $x = 0$.

(b) $f(x) > 0$ on the interval for which the graph of $f$ is above the $x$-axis. That is $(-\infty, 0) \cup (1, \infty)$.

In set builder notation the intervals are $\{x \mid x < 0 \text{ or } x > 1\}$.

(c) $f(x) < 0$ on the interval for which the graph of $f$ is below the $x$-axis. That is $(0, 1)$.

In set builder notation the interval is $\{x \mid 0 < x < 1\}$.

38. (a) $f(x)$ is undefined at $x = -2$, $f(x) = 0$ at $x = -1$.

(b) $f(x) > 0$ on the interval for which the graph of $f$ is above the $x$-axis. That is $(-\infty, -2) \cup (-1, \infty)$.

In set builder notation the intervals are $\{x \mid x < -2 \text{ or } x > -1\}$.

(c) $f(x) < 0$ on the interval for which the graph of $f$ is below the $x$-axis. That is $(-2, -1)$.

In set builder notation the interval is $\{x \mid -2 < x < -1\}$.

39. (a) $f(x)$ is undefined at $x = \pm 2$, $f(x) = 0$ at $x = 0$.

(b) $f(x) > 0$ on the interval for which the graph of $f$ is above the $x$-axis. That is $(-\infty, -2) \cup (2, \infty)$.

In set builder notation the intervals are $\{x \mid x < -2 \text{ or } x > 2\}$.

(c) $f(x) < 0$ on the interval for which the graph of $f$ is below the $x$-axis. That is $(-2, 0) \cup (0, 2)$.

In set builder notation the intervals are $\{x \mid -2 < x < 0 \text{ or } 0 < x < 2\}$.

40. (a) $f(x)$ is undefined at $x = \pm 1$, $f(x) = 0$ at $x = 0$.

(b) $f(x) > 0$ on the interval for which the graph of $f$ is above the $x$-axis. That is $(-1, 0) \cup (1, \infty)$.

In set builder notation the intervals are $\{x \mid -1 < x < 0 \text{ or } x > 1\}$.

(c) $f(x) < 0$ on the interval for which the graph of $f$ is below the $x$-axis. That is $(-\infty, -1) \cup (0, 1)$.

In set builder notation the intervals are $\{x \mid x < -1 \text{ or } 0 < x < 1\}$.

41. (a) First find the boundary numbers by solving $x^3 - x = 0$.

$x^3 - x = 0 \Rightarrow x(x^2 - 1) = 0 \Rightarrow x(x + 1)(x - 1) = 0 \Rightarrow x = 0, -1, \text{or } 1$

The boundary values divide the number line into four intervals. Choose a test value from each of these intervals and evaluate $x^3 - x$ for these values. See Figure 41a. The solution is $(-1, 0) \cup (1, \infty)$.

In set builder notation the intervals are $\{x \mid -1 < x < 0 \text{ or } x > 1\}$.

(b) Graph $Y_1 = X^3 - X$ as shown in Figure 41b. The $x$-intercepts are –1, 0, and 1. The graph is above the $x$-axis on the interval $(-1, 0) \cup (1, \infty)$.

| Interval | Test Value $x$ | $x^3 - x$ | Positive or Negative? |
|---|---|---|---|
| $(-\infty, -1)$ | $-2$ | $-6$ | Negative |
| $(-1, 0)$ | $-0.5$ | $0.375$ | Positive |
| $(0, 1)$ | $0.5$ | $-0.375$ | Negative |
| $(1, \infty)$ | $2$ | $6$ | Positive |

Figure 41a

[−3, 3, 0.5] by [−3, 3, 0.5]

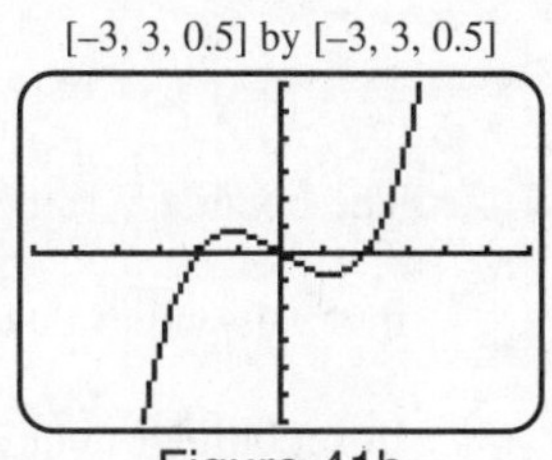

Figure 41b

42. (a) First write the inequality as $8x^3 - 27 < 0$. Then find the boundary numbers by solving $8x^3 - 27 = 0$.

$$8x^3 - 27 = 0 \Rightarrow 8x^3 = 27 \Rightarrow x^3 = \frac{27}{8} \Rightarrow x = \frac{3}{2} = 1.5$$

The boundary value divides the number line into two intervals. Choose a test value from each of these intervals and evaluate $8x^3 - 27$ for these values. See Figure 42a. The solution is $(-\infty, 1.5)$.

In set builder notation the interval is $\{x \mid x < 1.5\}$.

(b) Graph $Y_1 = 8X^\wedge3 - 27$ as shown in Figure 42b. The $x$-intercept is 1.5. The graph is below the $x$-axis on the interval $(-\infty, 1.5)$.

| Interval | Test Value $x$ | $8x^3 - 27$ | Positive or Negative? |
|---|---|---|---|
| $(-\infty, 1.5)$ | $0$ | $-27$ | Negative |
| $(1.5, \infty)$ | $2$ | $37$ | Positive |

Figure 42a

[0, 3, 0.5] by [−40, 40, 5]

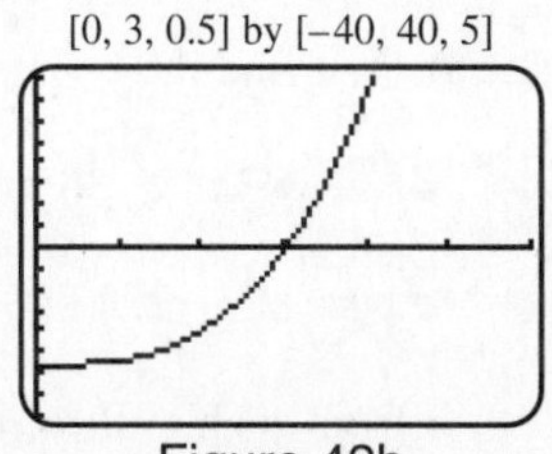

Figure 42b

43. (a) Write the inequality as $x^3 + x^2 - 2x \geq 0$. Then find the boundary numbers by solving $x^3 + x^2 - 2x = 0$.

$$x^3 + x^2 - 2x = 0 \Rightarrow x(x^2 + x - 2) = 0 \Rightarrow x(x + 2)(x - 1) = 0 \Rightarrow x = 0, -2, \text{ or } 1$$

The boundary values divide the number line into four intervals. Choose a test value from each of these intervals and evaluate $x^3 + x^2 - 2x$ for these values. See Figure 43a. The solution is $[-2, 0] \cup [1, \infty)$.

In set builder notation the intervals are $\{x \mid -2 \leq x \leq 0 \text{ or } x \geq 1\}$.

(b) Graph $Y_1 = X^\wedge3 + X^\wedge2 - 2X$ as shown in Figure 43b. The $x$-intercepts are –1, 0, and 1. The graph intersects or is above the $x$-axis on the interval $[-2, 0] \cup [1, \infty)$.

| Interval | Test Value $x$ | $x^3 + x^2 - 2x$ | Positive or Negative? |
|---|---|---|---|
| $(-\infty, -2)$ | $-3$ | $-12$ | Negative |
| $(-2, 0)$ | $-1$ | $2$ | Positive |
| $(0, 1)$ | $0.5$ | $-0.625$ | Negative |
| $(1, \infty)$ | $2$ | $8$ | Positive |

Figure 43a

[−3, 3, 1] by [−5, 5, 1]

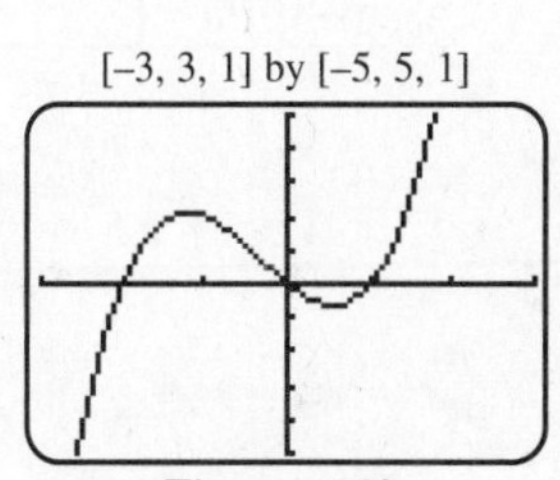

Figure 43b

44. (a) Write the inequality as $2x^3 - 3x^2 - 5x \le 0$. Then find the boundary numbers by solving $2x^3 - 3x^2 - 5x = 0$.

$2x^3 - 3x^2 - 5x = 0 \Rightarrow x(2x^2 - 3x - 5) = 0 \Rightarrow x(2x - 5)(x + 1) = 0 \Rightarrow x = -1, 0$, or $2.5$

The boundary values divide the number line into four intervals. Choose a test value from each of these intervals and evaluate $2x^3 - 3x^2 - 5x$ for these values. See Figure 44a. The solution is $(-\infty, -1] \cup [0, 2.5]$. In set builder notation the intervals are $\{x \mid x \le -1 \text{ or } 0 \le x \le 2.5\}$.

(b) Graph $Y_1 = 2X\text{^}3 - 3X\text{^}2 - 5X$ as shown in Figure 44b. The $x$-intercepts are –1, 0, and 2.5. The graph intersects or is below the $x$-axis on the interval $(-\infty, -1] \cup [0, 2.5]$.

| Interval | Test Value $x$ | $2x^3 - 3x^2 - 5x$ | Positive or Negative? |
|---|---|---|---|
| $(-\infty, -1)$ | –2 | –18 | Negative |
| $(-1, 0)$ | $-0.5$ | 1.5 | Positive |
| $(0, 2.5)$ | 1 | $-6$ | Negative |
| $(2.5, \infty)$ | 3 | 12 | Positive |

Figure 44a

[–4, 4, 0.5] by [–10, 5, 1]

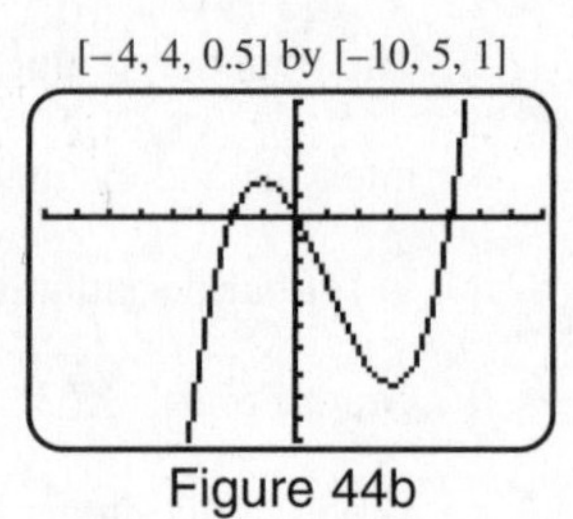

Figure 44b

45. (a) First find the boundary numbers by solving $x^4 - 13x^2 + 36 = 0$.

$x^4 - 13x^2 + 36 = 0 \Rightarrow (x^2 - 4)(x^2 - 9) = 0 \Rightarrow (x + 2)(x - 2)(x + 3)(x - 3) \Rightarrow$

$x = -3, -2, 2$ or $3$ The boundary values divide the number line into five intervals. Choose a test value from each of these intervals and evaluate $x^4 - 13x^2 + 36$ for these values. See Figure 45a. The solution is $(-3, -2) \cup (2, 3)$. In set builder notation the intervals are $\{x \mid -3 < x < -2 \text{ or } 2 < x < 3\}$.

(b) Graph $Y_1 = X\text{^}4 - 13X\text{^}2 + 36$ as shown in Figure 45b. The $x$-intercepts are –3, –2, 2 and 3. The graph is below the $x$-axis on the interval $(-3, -2) \cup (2, 3)$.

| Interval | Test Value $x$ | $x^4 - 13x^2 + 36$ | Positive or Negative? |
|---|---|---|---|
| $(-\infty, -3)$ | $-4$ | 84 | Positive |
| $(-3, -2)$ | $-2.5$ | $-6.1875$ | Negative |
| $(-2, 2)$ | 0 | 36 | Positive |
| $(2, 3)$ | 2.5 | $-6.1875$ | Negative |
| $(3, \infty)$ | 4 | 84 | Positive |

Figure 45a

[–5, 5, 1] by [–10, 100, 10]

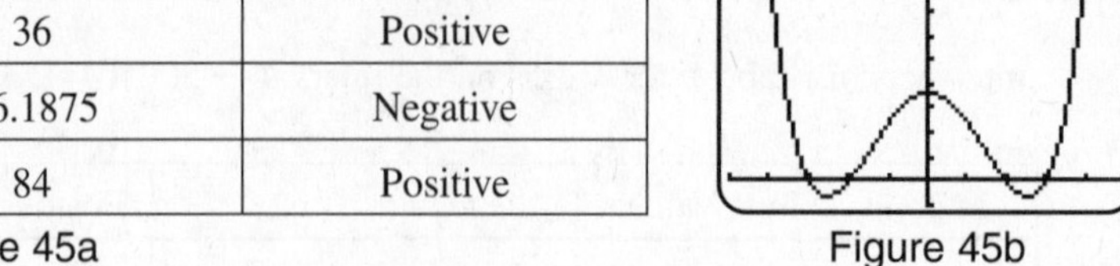

Figure 45b

46. (a) First find the boundary numbers by solving $4x^4 - 5x^2 - 9 = 0$.

$4x^4 - 5x^2 - 9 = 0 \Rightarrow (4x^2 - 9)(x^2 + 1) = 0 \Rightarrow (2x + 3)(2x - 3)(x^2 + 1) = 0 \Rightarrow$

$x = -1.5$ or $1.5$ The boundary values divide the number line into three intervals. Choose a test value from each of these intervals and evaluate $4x^4 - 5x^2 - 9$ for these values. See Figure 46a. The solution is $(-\infty, -1.5] \cup [1.5, \infty)$. In set builder notation the intervals are $\{x \mid x \leq -1.5 \text{ or } x \geq 1.5\}$.

(b) Graph $Y_1 = 4X^\wedge 4 - 5X^\wedge 2 - 9$ as shown in Figure 46b. The $x$-intercepts are –1.5 and 1.5. The graph intersects or is above the $x$-axis on the interval $(-\infty, -1.5] \cup [1.5, \infty)$.

| Interval | Test Value $x$ | $4x^4 - 5x^2 - 9$ | Positive or Negative? |
|---|---|---|---|
| $(-\infty, -1.5)$ | –2 | 35 | Positive |
| $(-1.5, 1.5)$ | 0 | –9 | Negative |
| $(1.5, \infty)$ | 2 | 35 | Positive |

Figure 46a

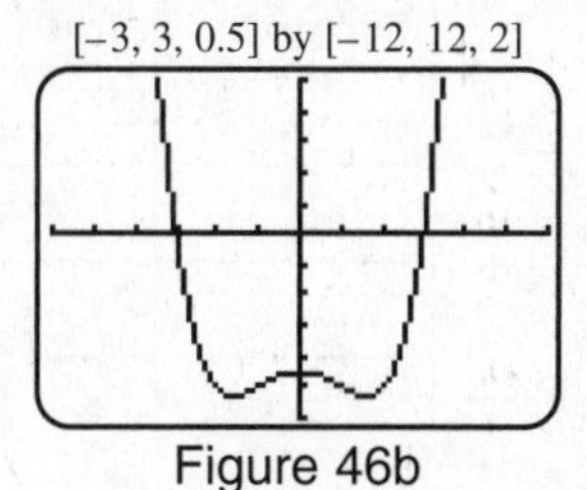


Figure 46b

47. Write the inequality as $7x^4 - 14x^2 \geq 0$. Then find the boundary numbers by solving $7x^4 - 14x^2 = 0$. $7x^4 - 14x^2 = 0 \Rightarrow 7x^2(x^2 - 2) = 0 \Rightarrow x = 0$ or $\pm\sqrt{2}$. The boundary values divide the number line into four intervals. Choose a test value from each of these intervals and evaluate $7x^4 - 14x^2$ for these values. See Figure 47. The solution is $(-\infty, -\sqrt{2}) \cup (\sqrt{2}, \infty)$. In set builder notation the intervals are $\{x \mid x < -\sqrt{2} \text{ or } x > \sqrt{2}\}$.

| Interval | Test Value $x$ | $7x^4 - 14x^2$ | Positive or Negative? |
|---|---|---|---|
| $(-\infty, -\sqrt{2})$ | –2 | 56 | Positive |
| $(-\sqrt{2}, 0)$ | –1 | –7 | Negative |
| $(0, \sqrt{2})$ | 1 | –7 | Negative |
| $(\sqrt{2}, \infty)$ | 2 | 56 | Positive |

Figure 47

48. Write the inequality as $3x^4 - 4x^2 - 7 < 0$. Then find the boundary numbers by solving $3x^4 - 4x^2 - 7 = 0$.

$3x^4 - 4x^2 - 7 = 0 \Rightarrow (3x^2 - 7)(x^2 + 1) = 0 \Rightarrow x = \pm\sqrt{\frac{7}{3}}$

The boundary values divide the number line into three intervals. Choose a test value from each of these intervals and evaluate $3x^4 - 4x^2 - 7$ for these values. See Figure 48. The solution is $\left(-\sqrt{\frac{7}{3}}, \sqrt{\frac{7}{3}}\right)$.

In set builder notation the interval is $\left\{x \mid -\sqrt{\frac{7}{3}} < x < \sqrt{\frac{7}{3}}\right\}$.

| Interval | Test Value $x$ | $3x^4 - 4x^2 - 7$ | Positive or Negative? |
|---|---|---|---|
| $(-\infty, -\sqrt{\frac{7}{3}})$ | –2 | 25 | Positive |
| $(-\sqrt{\frac{7}{3}}, \sqrt{\frac{7}{3}})$ | 0 | –7 | Negative |
| $(\sqrt{\frac{7}{3}}, \infty)$ | 2 | 25 | Positive |

Figure 48

49. First find the boundary numbers by solving $(x - 1)(x - 2)(x + 2) = 0$.

$(x - 1)(x - 2)(x + 2) = 0 \Rightarrow x = -2, 1 \text{ or } 2$

The boundary values divide the number line into four intervals. Choose a test value from each of these intervals and evaluate $(x - 1)(x - 2)(x + 2)$ for these values. See Figure 49. The solution is $[-2, 1] \cup [2, \infty)$.

In set builder notation the intervals are $\{x \mid 2 \leq x \leq 1 \text{ or } x \geq 2\}$.

| Interval | Test Value $x$ | $(x - 1)(x - 2)(x + 2)$ | Positive or Negative? |
|---|---|---|---|
| $(-\infty, -2)$ | $-3$ | $-20$ | Negative |
| $(-2, 1)$ | 0 | 4 | Positive |
| $(1, 2)$ | 1.5 | $-0.875$ | Negative |
| $(2, \infty)$ | 3 | 10 | Positive |

Figure 49

50. First find the boundary numbers by solving $-(x + 1)^2(x - 2) = 0$.

$-(x + 1)^2(x - 2) = 0 \Rightarrow x = -1$ or 2. The boundary values divide the number line into three intervals.

Choose a test value from each of these intervals and evaluate $-(x + 1)^2(x - 2)$ for these values.

See Figure 50. The solution is $(-\infty, 2]$. In set builder notation the interval is $\{x \mid x \leq 2\}$.

| Interval | Test Value $x$ | $-(x + 1)^2(x - 2)$ | Positive or Negative? |
|---|---|---|---|
| $(-\infty, -1)$ | $-2$ | 4 | Positive |
| $(-1, 2)$ | 0 | 2 | Positive |
| $(2, \infty)$ | 3 | $-16$ | Negative |

Figure 50

51. Write the inequality as $2x^4 + 2x^3 - 12x^2 \leq 0$. Find the boundary numbers by solving $2x^4 + 2x^3 - 12x^2 = 0$.

$2x^4 + 2x^3 - 12x^2 = 0 \Rightarrow 2x^2(x^2 + x - 6) = 0 \Rightarrow 2x^2(x + 3)(x - 2) = 0 \Rightarrow x = -3, 0 \text{ or } 2$

The boundary values divide the number line into four intervals. Choose a test value from each of these intervals and evaluate $2x^4 + 2x^3 - 12x^2$ for these values. See Figure 51. The solution is $[-3, 2]$.

In set builder notation the interval is $\{x \mid -3 \leq x \leq 2\}$.

| Interval | Test Value $x$ | $2x^4 + 2x^3 - 12x^2$ | Positive or Negative? |
|---|---|---|---|
| $(-\infty, -3)$ | $-4$ | 192 | Positive |
| $(-3, 0)$ | $-1$ | $-12$ | Negative |
| $(0, 2)$ | 1 | $-8$ | Negative |
| $(2, \infty)$ | 3 | 108 | Positive |

Figure 51

52. First find the boundary numbers by solving $x^3 + 6x^2 + 9x = 0$.

$x^3 + 6x^2 + 9x = 0 \Rightarrow x(x^2 + 6x + 9) = 0 \Rightarrow x(x + 3)^2 = 0 \Rightarrow x = -3 \text{ or } 0$

The boundary values divide the number line into three intervals. Choose a test value from each of these intervals and evaluate $x^3 + 6x^2 + 9x$ for these values. See Figure 52. The solution is $(0, \infty)$.

In set builder notation the interval is $\{x \mid x > 0\}$.

| Interval | Test Value $x$ | $x^3 + 6x^2 + 9x$ | Positive or Negative? |
|---|---|---|---|
| $(-\infty, -3)$ | $-4$ | $-4$ | Negative |
| $(-3, 0)$ | $-1$ | $-4$ | Negative |
| $(0, \infty)$ | 1 | 16 | Positive |

Figure 52

53. Write the inequality as $x^3 - 7x^2 + 14x - 8 \le 0$.

Then Graph $Y_1 = X\text{^}3 - 7X\text{^}2 + 14X - 8$ as shown in Figure 53. The $x$-intercepts are 1, 2, and 4.

The graph intersects or is below the $x$-axis on the interval $(-\infty, 1] \cup [2, 4]$. In set builder notation the intervals are $\{x \mid x \le 1 \text{ or } 2 \le x \le 4\}$.

54. Write the inequality as $2x^3 + 3x^2 - 3x - 2 < 0$.

Then Graph $Y_1 = 2X\text{^}3 + 3X\text{^}2 - 3X - 2$ as shown in Figure 54. The $x$-intercepts are $-2$, $-0.5$, and 1.

The graph is below the $x$-axis on the interval $(-\infty, -2) \cup (-0.5, 1)$. In set builder notation the intervals are $\left\{x \mid x < -2 \text{ or } -\frac{1}{2} < x < 1\right\}$.

[-2, 5, 1] by [-10, 10, 1]

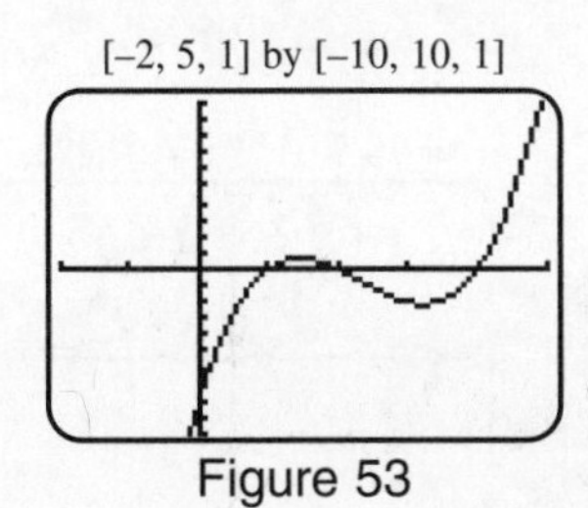

Figure 53

[-4, 4, 1] by [-5, 5, 1]  [-4, 4, 1] by [-5, 5, 1]

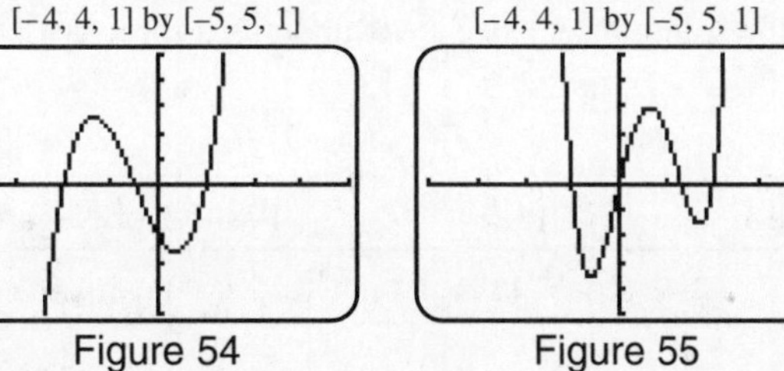

Figure 54  Figure 55

[-2, 8, 1] by [-500, 200, 50]

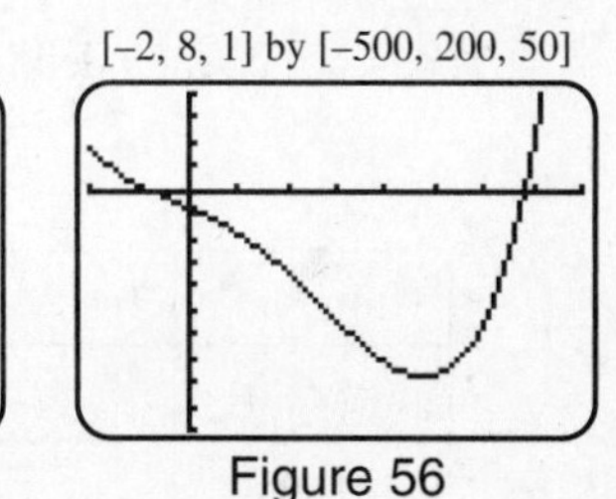

Figure 56

55. Graph $Y_1 = 3X\text{^}4 - 7X\text{^}3 - 2X\text{^}2 + 8X$ as shown in Figure 55. The $x$-intercepts are $-1$, 0, $\frac{4}{3}$ and 2.

The graph is above the $x$-axis on the interval $(-\infty, -1) \cup \left(0, \frac{4}{3}\right) \cup (2, \infty)$. In set builder notation the intervals are $\left\{x \mid x < -1 \text{ or } 0 < x < \frac{4}{3} \text{ or } x > 2\right\}$.

56. Write the inequality as $x^4 - 5x^3 - 5x^2 - 45x - 36 \le 0$.

Then Graph $Y_1 = X\text{^}4 - 5X\text{^}3 - 5X\text{^}2 - 45X - 36$ as shown in Figure 56.

The $x$-intercepts are approximately $-0.8047$ and $6.8159$. The graph intersects or is below the $x$-axis on the interval $[-0.8047, 6.8159]$, approximately. In set builder notation the interval is $\{x \mid -0.8047 \le x \le 6.8159\}$.

57. (a) Find the zeros of the numerator and the denominator.

Numerator: No zero; Denominator: $x = 0$

This boundary number divides the number line into two intervals. Choose a test value from each of these intervals and evaluate $\frac{1}{x}$ for these values. See Figure 57a. The solution is $(-\infty, 0)$. In set builder notation the interval is $\{x \mid x < 0\}$.

(b) Graph $Y_1 = 1/X$ as shown in Figure 57b. The graph has a vertical asymptote at $x = 0$ and no $x$-intercepts. The graph is below the $x$-axis on the interval $(-\infty, 0)$.

| Interval | Test Value $x$ | $1/x$ | Positive or Negative? |
|---|---|---|---|
| $(-\infty, 0)$ | –1 | –1 | Negative |
| $(0, \infty)$ | 1 | 1 | Positive |

Figure 57a

[–4, 4, 1] by [–2, 2, 0.5]

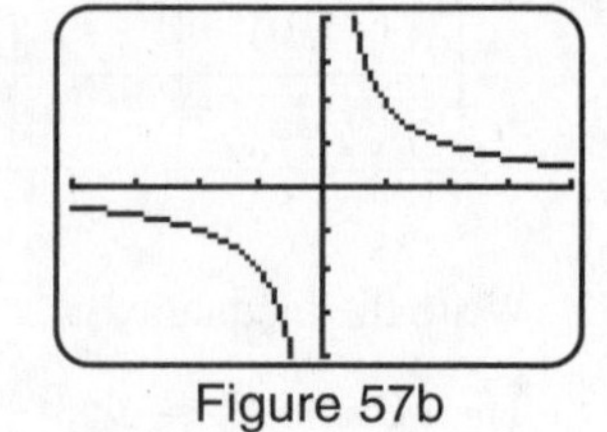

Figure 57b

58. (a) Find the zeros of the numerator and the denominator.

Numerator: No zero; Denominator: $x^2 = 0 \Rightarrow x = 0$

This boundary number divides the number line into two intervals. Choose a test value from each of these intervals and evaluate $\frac{1}{x^2}$ for these values. See Figure 58a. The solution is $(-\infty, 0) \cup (0, \infty)$. In set builder notation the intervals are $\{x \mid x < 0 \text{ or } x > 0\}$.

(b) Graph $Y_1 = 1/X$^2 as shown in Figure 58b. The graph has a vertical asymptote at $x = 0$ and no $x$-intercepts. The graph is above the $x$-axis on the interval $(-\infty, 0) \cup (0, \infty)$. Note that the value $x = 0$ can not be included in the solution set since $\frac{1}{x^2}$ is undefined for $x = 0$.

| Interval | Test Value $x$ | $1/x^2$ | Positive or Negative? |
|---|---|---|---|
| $(-\infty, 0)$ | –1 | 1 | Positive |
| $(0, \infty)$ | 1 | 1 | Positive |

Figure 58a

[–4, 4, 1] by [–2, 2, 0.5]

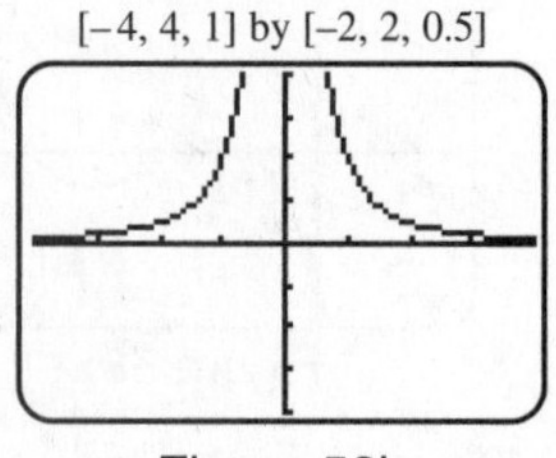

Figure 58b

59. (a) Find the zeros of the numerator and the denominator.

Numerator: No zero; Denominator: $x + 3 = 0 \Rightarrow x = -3$

This boundary number divides the number line into two intervals. Choose a test value from each of these intervals and evaluate $\frac{4}{x + 3}$ for these values. See Figure 59a. The solution is $(-3, \infty)$. In set builder notation the interval is $\{x \mid x > -3\}$.

(b) Graph $Y_1 = 4/(X + 3)$ using dot mode as shown in Figure 59b. The graph has a vertical asymptote at $x = -3$ and no $x$-intercepts. The graph is above the $x$-axis on the interval $(-3, \infty)$. Note that the value $x = -3$ can not be included in the solution set since $\frac{4}{x + 3}$ is undefined for $x = -3$.

| Interval | Test Value $x$ | $4/(x + 3)$ | Positive or Negative? |
|---|---|---|---|
| $(-\infty, -3)$ | $-4$ | $-4$ | Negative |
| $(-3, \infty)$ | 1 | 1 | Positive |

Figure 59a

[−6, 1, 1] by [−4, 4, 1]

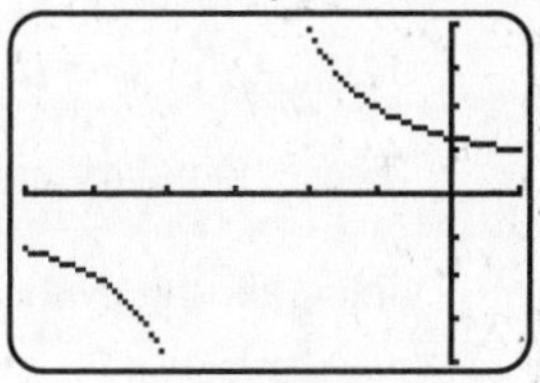

Figure 59b

60. (a) Find the zeros of the numerator and the denominator.

Numerator: $x - 1 = 0 \Rightarrow x = 1$; Denominator: $x + 1 = 0 \Rightarrow x = -1$

These boundary numbers divide the number line into three intervals. Choose a test value from each of these intervals and evaluate $\dfrac{x - 1}{x + 1}$ for these values. See Figure 60a. The solution is $(-1, 1)$. In set builder notation the interval is $\{x \mid -1 < x < 1\}$.

(b) Graph $Y_1 = (X - 1)/(X + 1)$ using dot mode as shown in Figure 60b. The graph has a vertical asymptote at $x = -1$ and an $x$-intercept at $x = 1$. The graph is below the $x$-axis on the interval $(-1, 1)$.

| Interval | Test Value $x$ | $(x - 1)/(x + 1)$ | Positive or Negative? |
|---|---|---|---|
| $(-\infty, -1)$ | $-2$ | 3 | Positive |
| $(-1, 1)$ | 0 | $-1$ | Negative |
| $(1, \infty)$ | 3 | 0.5 | Positive |

Figure 60a

[−4, 4, 1] by [−4, 4, 1]

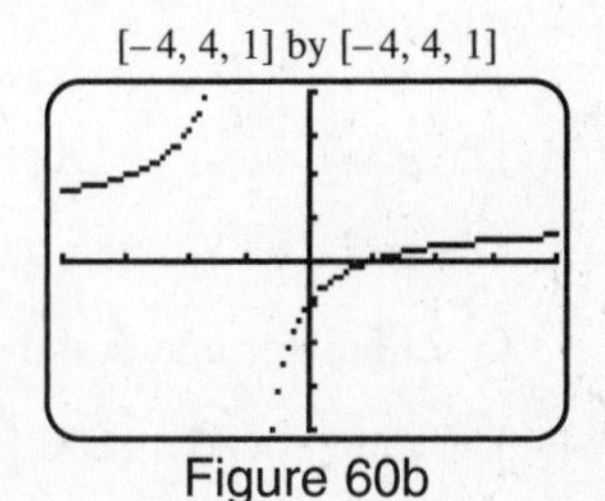

Figure 60b

61. (a) Find the zeros of the numerator and the denominator.

Numerator: No zero; Denominator: $x^2 - 4 = 0 \Rightarrow x = \pm 2$

These boundary numbers divide the number line into three intervals. Choose a test value from each of these intervals and evaluate $\dfrac{5}{x^2 - 4}$ for these values. See Figure 61a. The solution is $(-2, 2)$. In set builder notation the interval is $\{x \mid -2 < x < 2\}$.

(b) Graph $Y_1 = 5/(X\text{^}2 - 4)$ using dot mode as shown in Figure 61b. The graph has vertical asymptotes at $x = \pm 2$ and no $x$-intercepts. The graph is below the $x$-axis on the interval $(-2, 2)$.

| Interval | Test Value $x$ | $5/(x^2 - 4)$ | Positive or Negative? |
|---|---|---|---|
| $(-\infty, -2)$ | $-3$ | 1 | Positive |
| $(-2, 2)$ | 0 | $-1.25$ | Negative |
| $(2, \infty)$ | 3 | 1 | Positive |

Figure 61a

[−4, 4, 1] by [−4, 4, 1]

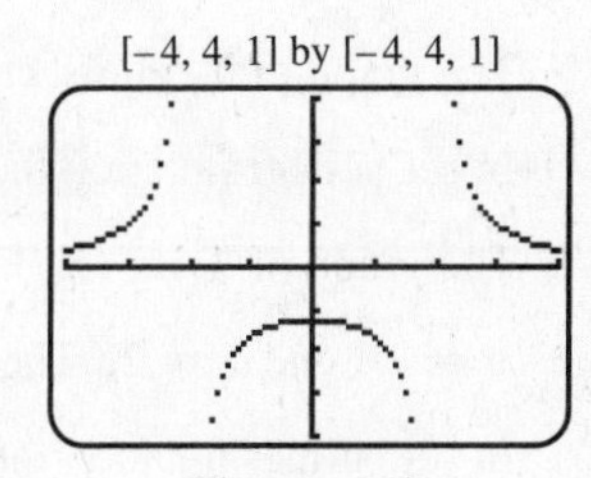

Figure 61b

62. (a) Find the zeros of the numerator and the denominator.

Numerator: $x = 0$; Denominator: $x^2 - 1 = 0 \Rightarrow x = \pm 1$

These boundary numbers divide the number line into four intervals. Choose a test value from each of these intervals and evaluate $\dfrac{x}{x^2 - 1}$ for these values. See Figure 62a. The solution is $(-1, 0] \cup (1, \infty)$. In set builder notation the intervals are $\{x \mid -1 < x \le 0 \text{ or } x > 1\}$.

(b) Graph $Y_1 = X/(X\text{^}2 - 1)$ using dot mode as shown in Figure 62b. The graph has vertical asymptotes at $x = \pm 1$ and an $x$-intercepts at $x = 0$. The graph intersects or is above the $x$-axis on the interval $(-1, 0] \cup (1, \infty)$. Note that neither 1 nor –1 can be included in the solution set since $\dfrac{x}{x^2 - 1}$ is undefined for these values.

| Interval | Test Value $x$ | $x/(x^2 - 1)$ | Positive or Negative? |
|---|---|---|---|
| $(-\infty, -1)$ | -3 | $-0.375$ | Negative |
| $(-1, 0)$ | $-0.6$ | 0.9375 | Positive |
| $(0, 1)$ | 0.6 | $-0.9375$ | Negative |
| $(1, \infty)$ | 3 | 0.375 | Positive |

Figure 62a

[–4, 4, 1] by [–4, 4, 1]

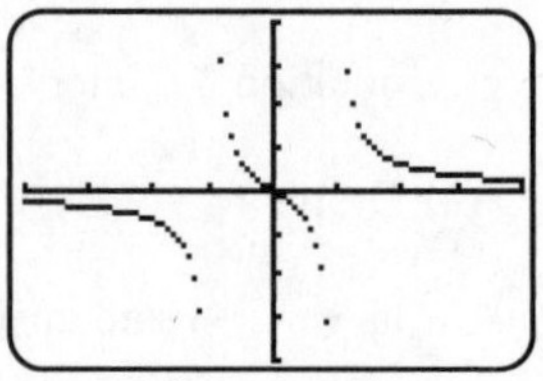

Figure 62b

63. The graph of $Y_1 = (X + 1)\text{^}2/(X - 2)$ has a vertical asymptote at $x = 2$ and an $x$-intercept at $x = -1$. The graph of $Y_1$ intersects or is below the $x$-axis on the interval $(-\infty, 2)$. Note that 2 can not be included. In set builder notation the interval is $\{x \mid x > 2\}$.

64. The graph of $Y_1 = 2X/(X - 2)\text{^}2$ has a vertical asymptote at $x = 2$ and an $x$-intercept at $x = 0$. The graph of $Y_1$ is above the $x$-axis on the interval $(0, 2) \cup (2, \infty)$. In set builder notation the intervals are $\{x \mid 0 < x < 2 \text{ or } x > 2\}$.

65. The graph of $Y_1 = (3 - 2X)/(1 + X)$ has a vertical asymptote at $x = -1$ and an $x$-intercept at $x = \dfrac{3}{2}$. The graph of $Y_1$ is below the $x$-axis on the interval $(-\infty, -1) \cup \left(\dfrac{3}{2}, \infty\right)$. In set builder notation the intervals are $\left\{x \mid x < -1 \text{ or } x > \dfrac{3}{2}\right\}$.

66. First, rewrite the inequality:

$$\frac{x + 1}{4 - 2x} \ge 1 \Rightarrow \frac{x + 1}{4 - 2x} - 1 \ge 0 \Rightarrow \frac{x + 1 - 4 + 2x}{4 - 2x} \ge 0 \Rightarrow \frac{3x - 3}{4 - 2x} \ge 0 \Rightarrow \frac{3(x - 1)}{-2(x - 2)} \ge 0$$

The graph of $Y_1 = 3(X - 1)/(-2(X - 2))$ has a vertical asymptote at $x = 2$ and an $x$-intercept at $x = 1$. The graph of $Y_1$ intersects or is above the $x$-axis on the interval $[1, 2)$. Note that 2 can not be included. In set builder notation the interval is $\{x \mid 1 \le x < 2\}$.

67. The graph of $Y_1 = (X + 1)(X - 2)/(X + 3)$ has a vertical asymptote of at $x = -3$ and $x$-intercepts at $x = -1$ and $x = 2$. The graph of $Y_1$ is below the $x$-axis on the interval $(-\infty, -3) \cup (-1, 2)$. In set builder notation the intervals are $\{x \mid x < -3 \text{ or } -1 < x < 2\}$.

68. The graph of $Y_1 = X(X - 3)/(X + 2)$ has a vertical asymptote of at $x = -2$ and $x$-intercepts at $x = 0$ and $x = 3$. The graph of $Y_1$ is on or above the $x$-axis on the interval $(-2, 0] \cup [3, \infty)$.

    In set builder notation the intervals are $\{x \mid -2 < x \le 0 \text{ or } x \ge 3\}$.

69. The graph of $Y_1 = 2X - 5/((X + 1)(X - 1))$ has vertical asymptotes at $x = -1$ and $x = 1$ and an $x$-intercept at $x = \frac{5}{2}$. The graph of $Y_1$ is on or above the $x$-axis on the interval $(-1, 1) \cup \left[\frac{5}{2}, \infty\right)$.

    In set builder notation the intervals are $\left\{x \mid -1 < x < 1 \text{ or } x \ge \frac{5}{2}\right\}$.

70. The graph of $Y_1 = (5 - X)/((X - 2)(X + 1))$has vertical asymptotes at $x = -1$ and $x = 2$ and an $x$-intercept at $x = 5$. The graph of $Y_1$ is below the $x$-axis on the interval $(-1, 2) \cup (5, \infty)$.

    In set builder notation the interval is $\{x \mid -1 < x < 2 \text{ or } x > 5\}$.

71. First, rewrite the inequality:

$$\frac{1}{x-3} \le \frac{5}{x-3} \Rightarrow \frac{1}{x-3} - \frac{5}{x-3} \le 0 \Rightarrow \frac{-4}{x-3} \le 0$$

    The graph of $Y_1 = -4/(X - 3)$ has a vertical asymptote at $x = 3$ and no $x$-intercept.

    The graph of $Y_1$ intersects or is below the $x$-axis on the interval $(3, \infty)$. Note that 3 can not be included.

    In set builder notation the interval is $\{x \mid x > 3\}$.

72. First, rewrite the inequality:

$$\frac{3}{2-x} > \frac{x}{2+x} \Rightarrow \frac{3}{2-x} - \frac{x}{2+x} > 0 \Rightarrow \frac{3(2+x) - x(2-x)}{(2-x)(2+x)} > 0 \Rightarrow \frac{x^2 + x + 6}{(2-x)(2+x)} > 0$$

    The graph of $Y_1 = (X\text{^}2 + X + 6)/((2 - X)(2 + X))$ has vertical asymptotes at $x = \pm 2$ and no $x$-intercept.

    The graph of $Y_1$ is above the $x$-axis on the interval $(-2, 2)$.

    In set builder notation the intervals are $\{x \mid -2 < x < 2\}$.

73. First, rewrite the inequality:

$$2 - \frac{5}{x} + \frac{2}{x^2} \ge 0 \Rightarrow \frac{2x^2 - 5x + 2}{x^2} \ge 0 \Rightarrow \frac{(2x-1)(x-2)}{x^2} \ge 0$$

    The graph of $Y_1 = (2X - 1)(X - 2)/X\text{^}2$ has a vertical asymptote at $x = 0$ and $x$-intercepts $x = \frac{1}{2}$ and $x = 2$. The graph of $Y_1$ intersects or is above the $x$-axis on the interval $(-\infty, 0) \cup \left(0, \frac{1}{2}\right] \cup [2, \infty)$.

    In set builder notation the intervals are $\left\{x \mid x < 2 \text{ or } 0 < x \le \frac{1}{2} \text{ or } x \ge 2\right\}$.

74. First, rewrite the inequality:

$$\frac{1}{x-1}+\frac{1}{x+1}>\frac{3}{4}\Rightarrow\frac{1}{x-1}+\frac{1}{x+1}-\frac{3}{4}>0\Rightarrow\frac{4(x+1)+4(x-1)-3(x^2-1)}{4(x-1)(x+1)}>0\Rightarrow$$

$$\frac{8x-3x^2+3}{4(x-1)(x+1)}>0\Rightarrow\frac{-(3x^2-8x-3)}{4(x-1)(x+1)}>0\Rightarrow\frac{-(3x+1)(x-3)}{4(x-1)(x+1)}>0$$

The graph of $Y_1 = -(3X + 1)(X - 3)/(4(X - 1)(X + 1))$ has vertical asymptotes at $x = \pm 1$ and $x$-intercepts $x = -\frac{1}{3}$ and $x = 3$. The graph of $Y_1$ is above the $x$-axis on the interval $\left(-1, -\frac{1}{3}\right) \cup (1, 3)$.

In set builder notation the intervals are $\left\{x \mid -1 < x < -\frac{1}{3} \text{ or } 1 < x < 3\right\}$.

75. First, rewrite the inequality:

$$\frac{1}{x}\leq\frac{2}{x+2}\Rightarrow\frac{1}{x}-\frac{2}{x+2}\leq 0\Rightarrow\frac{x+2-2x}{x(x+2)}\leq 0\Rightarrow\frac{2-x}{x(x+2)}\leq 0.$$ The graph of

$Y_1 = (2 - X)/((X( + 2))$has vertical asymptotes at $x = 0$ and$x = -2$, and $x$-intercept of $x = 2$. The graph of $Y_1$ is below the $x$-axis on the interval $(-2, 0) \cup [2, \infty)$. In set builder notation the intervals are $\left\{x \mid -2 < x < 0 \text{ or } x \geq 2\right\}$.

76. First, rewrite the inequality:

$$\frac{1}{x+1}<\frac{1}{x}+1\Rightarrow\frac{1}{x+1}<\frac{1+x}{x}\Rightarrow\frac{1}{x+1}-\frac{1+x}{x}<0\Rightarrow\frac{x-(1+x)(1+x)}{x(x+1)}<0\Rightarrow$$

$$\frac{x-(1+2x+x^2)}{x(x+1)}<0\Rightarrow\frac{x-1-2x-x^2}{x(x+1)}<0\Rightarrow\frac{-x^2-x-1}{x(x+1)}<0.$$ The graph of

$Y_1 = -X^2 - X - 1/X(X + 1)$ has vertical asymptotes of $x = 0$ and $x = -1$. $Y_1$ is below the $x$-axis on the interval $(-\infty, -1) \cup (0, \infty)$.

77. (a) Since 15 seconds equals 0.25 minute, graph $Y_1 = (X - 5)/(X^2 - 10X)$ and $Y_2 = 0.25$ as shown in Figure 77. The intersection point is near (12.4, 0.25). The gate should admit 12.4 cars per minute on average to keep the wait less than 15 seconds. Note: The reason the answer is greater than 10 cars per minute is because cars are arriving randomly. For some minutes, more than 10 vehicles might arrive at the gate.

(b) $\frac{12.4}{5} = 2.48$ or 3 parking attendants must be on duty to keep the average wait less than 15 seconds.

[10, 15, 1] by [0, 1, 0.1]

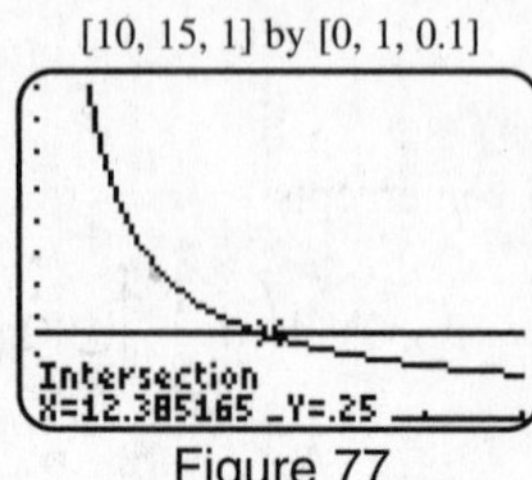


Figure 77

[0, 1, 0.1] by [0, 4, 1]

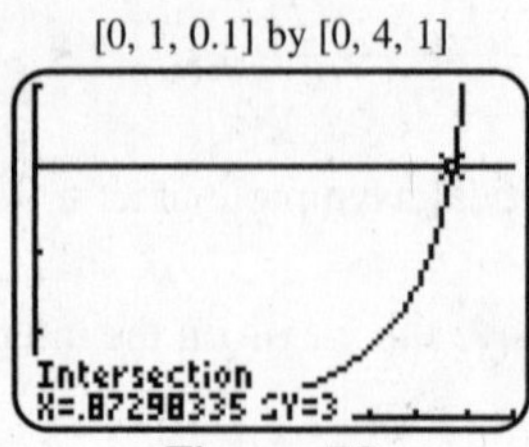


Figure 78

78. We must determine when $f(x) = \frac{x^2}{2 - 2x} = 3$. Graph $Y_1 = X^2/(2 - 2X)$ and $Y_2 = 3$ as shown in Figure 78. The graphs intersect near (0.87, 3). A traffic intensity of $x \approx 0.87$ causes the average length of a line to be 3 cars.

79. Let $y$ = height, $x$ = width, and $2x$ = length of the box. To relate the variables, we use the volume formula for a box and the fact that $V = 196$ cubic inches. $V = (2x)xy = 2x^2y \Rightarrow y = \dfrac{V}{2x^2} = \dfrac{196}{2x^2} = \dfrac{98}{x^2}$.

The surface area of the box is the sum of the areas of the 6 rectangular sides. We are given that $A = 280\text{ in}^2$.

$A = 2(x \cdot y) + 2(2x \cdot y) + 2(x \cdot 2x) \Rightarrow A = 6xy + 4x^2 = 280$; and since $y = \dfrac{98}{x^2}$ we get the equation

$6x\left(\dfrac{98}{x^2}\right) + 4x^2 = 280 \Rightarrow \dfrac{588}{x} + 4x^2 = 280.$

Figures 79a and 79b show the intersection points when graphing $Y_1 = 588/X + 4X\text{^}2$ and $Y_2 = 280$.

There are two possible solutions (in inches):

width = 7, length = 14, height = $\dfrac{98}{7^2} = 2$ or width $\approx 2.266$, length $\approx 4.532$, height $\approx \dfrac{98}{2.266^2} \approx 19.086$.

[0, 10, 2] by [100, 400, 20]

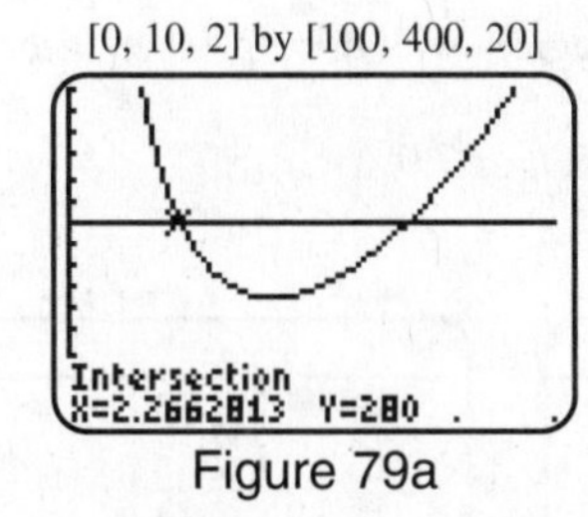

Figure 79a

[0, 10, 2] by [100, 400, 20]

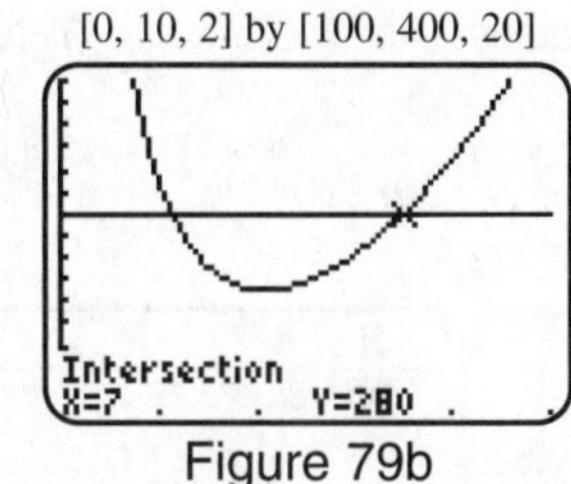

Figure 79b

[0, 10, 1] by [0, 500, 100]

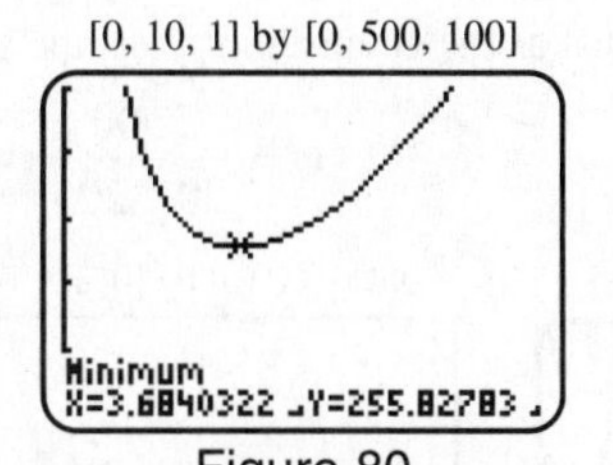

Figure 80

80. (a) $V = \pi r^2 h$

(b) $S(r)$ = top area + bottom area + side area $\Rightarrow S(r) = \pi r^2 + \pi r^2 + \pi^2 rh \Rightarrow S(r) = 2\pi r^2 + 2\pi rh$

Since the volume is $100\pi$, we can solve for $h$. $100\pi = \pi r^2 h \Rightarrow 100 = r^2 h \Rightarrow h = \dfrac{100}{r^2}$.

Therefore, the surface area in terms of $r$ is $S(r) = 2\pi r^2 + 2\pi r \dfrac{100}{r^2} \Rightarrow S(r) = 2\pi r^2 + \dfrac{200\pi}{r}$;

$S(2) = 108\pi \approx 339.3\text{ cm}^2$; when the radius is 2 cm, the surface area is $108\text{ cm}^2$.

(c) Graph the equation: $S(r) = 2\pi r^2 + \dfrac{200\pi}{r}$. The minimum surface area is when

$r \approx 3.7$ cm $\Rightarrow h = \dfrac{100}{(3.7)^2}$ or $h \approx 7.4$ cm. The dimensions are $r \approx 3.7$ cm, $h = 7.4$ cm. See Figure 80.

81. (a) $V = L \cdot W \cdot H \Rightarrow V = x \cdot x \cdot h \Rightarrow 108 = x^2 h \Rightarrow \dfrac{108}{x^2} = h$. The surface area $A(x) = x^2 + 4xh \Rightarrow$

$A(x) = x^2 + 4x\left(\dfrac{108}{x^2}\right) \Rightarrow A(x) = \left(x^2 + \dfrac{432}{x}\right)$. This finds surface area in square inches. To find

square feet we must divide by 144 (the number of square inches in a square foot) $\Rightarrow$

$A(x) = \left(x^2 + \dfrac{432}{x}\right) \div 144 \Rightarrow A(x) = \dfrac{x^2}{144} + \dfrac{3}{x}.$

(b) $C = 0.10\left(\dfrac{x^2}{144} + \dfrac{3}{x}\right)$

(c) Graph the equation: $C = 0.10\left(\dfrac{x^2}{144} + \dfrac{3}{x}\right)$. The minimum cost is when $x \approx 6 \Rightarrow h = \dfrac{108}{(6)^2} \Rightarrow h = 3.$

The dimensions are $6 \times 6 \times 3$ inches.

82. (a) The graph of $C$ is shown in Figure 82a. As $x$ approaches 100% the cost of the program increases without bound. That is, 100% participation in the recycling program is impossible to achieve.

(b) The cost of 75% participation is $C(75) = \dfrac{1.2(75)}{100 - 75} = 3.6$, which represents $3,600,000.

(c) We must determine $x$ such that $C(x) = 5$. Graph $Y_1 = 1.2X/(100 - X)$ and $Y_2 = 5$. The graphs intersect near the point (80.6, 5). See Figure 82c. Thus, if the city spends 5 million dollars on the recycling project, approximately 81% participation can be expected.

83. (a) $D(0.05) = \dfrac{2500}{30(0.3 + 0.05)} \approx 238$

The braking distance far a car traveling at 50 mph on a 5% uphill grade is about 238 feet.

(b) Table $Y_1 = 2500/(30(0.3 + X))$ starting at $x = 0$ and incrementing by 0.05 as shown in Figure 83.

The table indicates that as the grade $x$ increases, the braking distance decreases. This agrees with driving experience.

(c) $220 = \dfrac{2500}{30(0.3 + x)} \Rightarrow 0.3 + x = \dfrac{2500}{30(220)} \Rightarrow x = \dfrac{2500}{30(220)} - 0.3 \approx 0.079$, or 7.9%

[0, 100, 10] by [0, 10, 1]

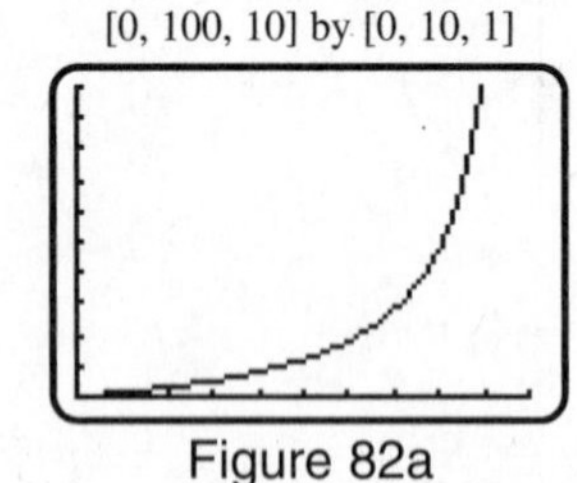

Figure 82a

[0, 100, 10] by [0, 10, 1]

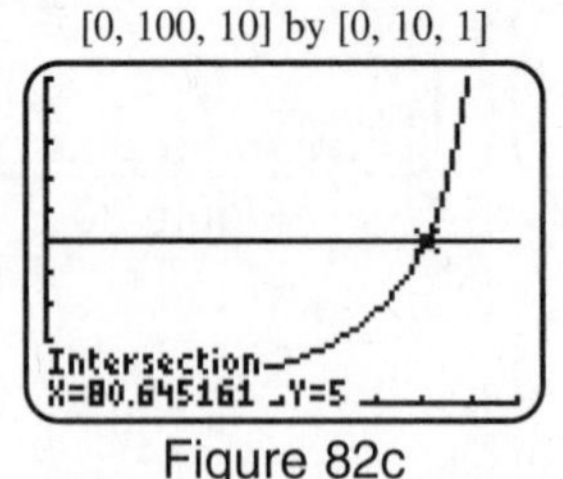


Figure 82c

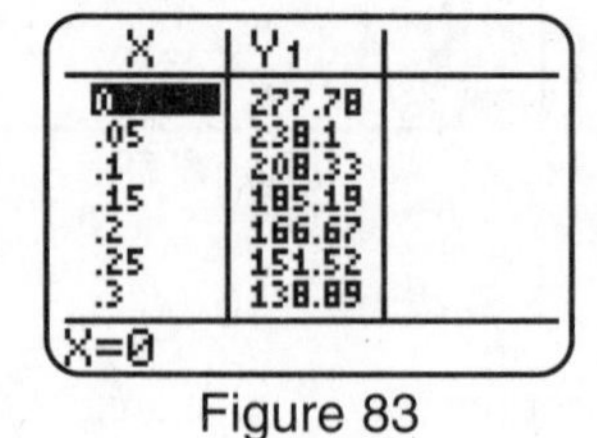

| X | $Y_1$ |
|---|---|
| 0 | 277.78 |
| .05 | 238.1 |
| .1 | 208.33 |
| .15 | 185.19 |
| .2 | 166.67 |
| .25 | 151.52 |
| .3 | 138.89 |

X=0

Figure 83

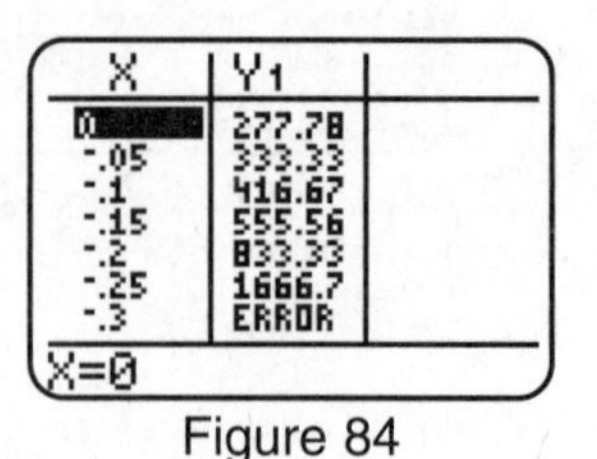

| X | $Y_1$ |
|---|---|
| 0 | 277.78 |
| -.05 | 333.33 |
| -.1 | 416.67 |
| -.15 | 555.56 |
| -.2 | 833.33 |
| -.25 | 1666.7 |
| -.3 | ERROR |

X=0

Figure 84

84. (a) $D(-0.1) = \dfrac{2500}{30(0.3 - 0.1)} \approx 417$

The braking distance far a car traveling at 50 mph on a 10% downhill grade is about 417 feet.

(b) Table $Y_1 = 2500/(30(0.3 + X))$ starting at $x = 0$ and incrementing by $-0.05$ as shown in Figure 84. The table indicates that as the grade $x$ decreases (becomes steeper downhill), the braking distance increases. This agrees with driving experience.

(c) There is a vertical asymptote at $x = -0.3$. As the grade decreases toward $-0.3$, the stopping distance increases without bound. At $x = -0.3$ the hill is so steep that there is not enough traction on the wet pavement to stop. According to this model, traveling on wet pavement at 50 mph on a grade of –30%, a car will slide down the hill rather than stop.

(d) $350 = \dfrac{2500}{30(0.3 + x)} \Rightarrow 0.3 + x = \dfrac{2500}{30(350)} \Rightarrow x = \dfrac{2500}{30(350)} - 0.3 \approx -0.062$, or 6.2% downhill.

85. (a) Graph $Y_1 = X\text{^}2/(1600 - 40X)$ and $Y_2 = 8$ (not shown). The graphs intersect approximately at (36, 8). The graph of $Y_1$ is equal to or is below the graph of $Y_2$ when $x \le 36$ (approximately).

(b) The average line length is less than or equal to 8 cars when the average arrival rate is 36 cars per hour or less.

86. (a) $5 \le \dfrac{1}{3 - x} \le 10 \Rightarrow \dfrac{1}{5} \ge 3 - x \ge \dfrac{1}{10} \Rightarrow 0.2 \ge 3 - x \ge 0.1 \Rightarrow -2.8 \ge -x \ge -2.9 \Rightarrow$

$2.8 \le x \le 2.9$

(b) As long as the number of vehicles leaving the ramp stays between 2.8 and 2.9 vehicles per minute, the waiting time for a car trying to exit will be between 5 minutes and 10 minutes.

87. (a) The graph of $D(x) = \dfrac{120}{x}$ increases as $x$ decreases, which means the braking distance increases as the coefficient of friction becomes smaller.

(b) $\dfrac{120}{x} \geq 400 \Rightarrow \dfrac{120}{400} \geq x \Rightarrow 0.3 \geq x$; the braking distance is 400 feet or more when $0 < x \leq 0.3$.

88. Graph $Y_1 = 0.0145X^4 - 0.426X^3 + 3.53X^2 - 6.22X + 72$ and $Y_2 = 75$. The graph of $Y_1$ intersects and is above the graph of $Y_2$ when $3.04 \leq x \leq 11.2$ (approximately). See Figures 88a & 88b. The monthly average high temperature is 75°F or more from March until November.

[1, 12, 1] by [60, 100, 5]

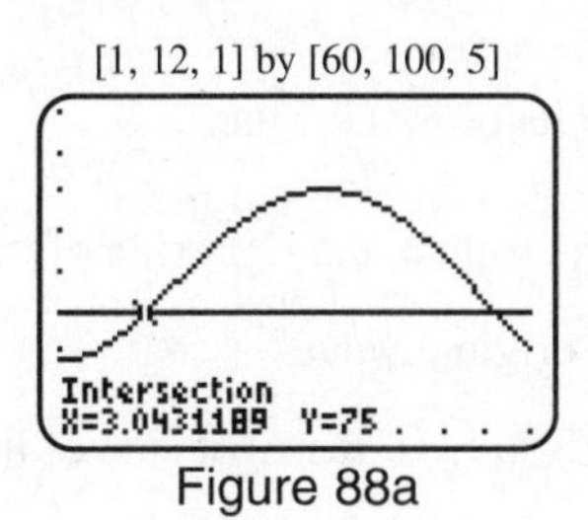


Figure 88a

[1, 12, 1] by [60, 100, 5]

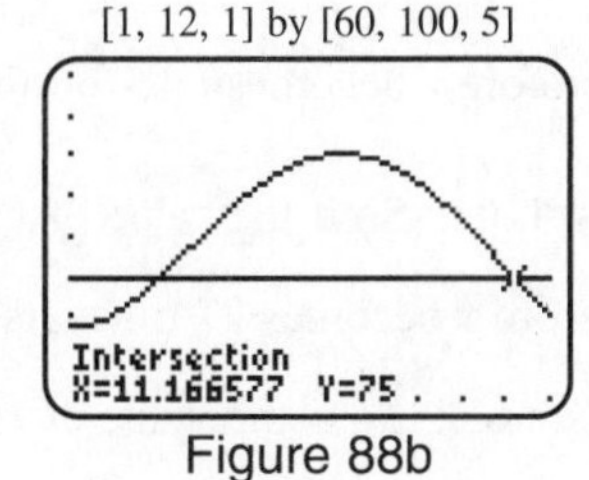


Figure 88b

[2, 7, 0.5] by [200, 500, 100]

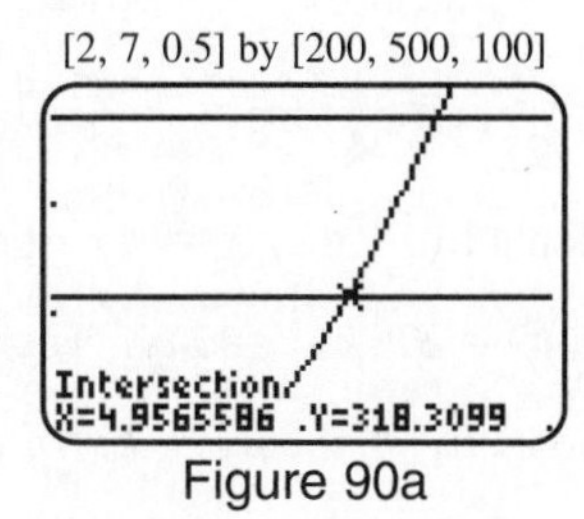


Figure 90a

[2, 7, 0.5] by [200, 500, 100]

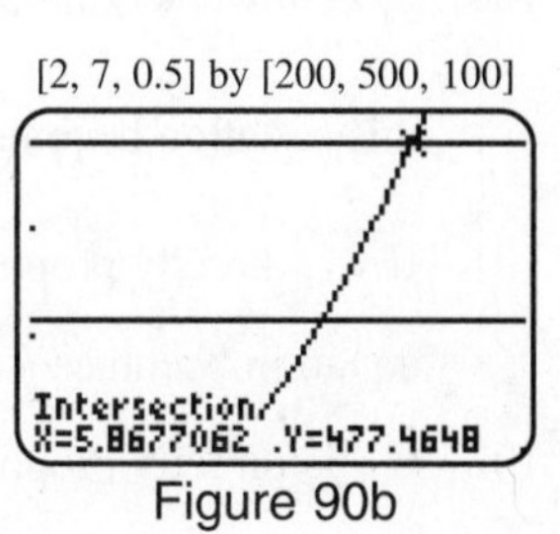


Figure 90b

89. The volume of a cube is $V = x^3$, where $x$ is the length of a side.

$212.8 \leq V \leq 213.2 \Rightarrow 212.8 \leq x^3 \leq 213.2 \Rightarrow \sqrt[3]{212.8} \leq x \leq \sqrt[3]{213.2}$ inches.

This is approximately $5.97022 \leq x \leq 5.97396$ inches.

90. The volume of a cylinder is $V = r^2h$. For the given aluminum can, $h = r + 8$.

If $1000 < V < 1500$ cubic centimeters, then

$1000 < \pi r^2(r + 8) < 1500 \Rightarrow \dfrac{1000}{\pi} < r^3 + 8r^2 < \dfrac{1500}{\pi} \Rightarrow 318.3099 < r^3 + 8r^2 < 4.77.4648$

Graph $Y_1 = X^3 + 8X^2$, $Y_2 = 318.3099$ and $Y_3 = 477.4648$ and find the intersection points as shown in Figures 90a & 90b. The graph of $Y_1$ is on or between the graphs of $Y_2$ and $Y_3$ when $4.96 \leq x \leq 5.87$ so the volume of the aluminum can is between 1000 and 1500 cubic centimeters when $4.96 \leq r \leq 5.87$ cm (approximately).

91. If $y = \dfrac{k}{x}$ and $y = 2$ when $x = 3$, then $2 = \dfrac{k}{3} \Rightarrow k = 6$.

92. If $y = \dfrac{k}{x^2}$ and $y = \dfrac{1}{4}$ when $x = 8$, then $\dfrac{1}{4} = \dfrac{k}{64} \Rightarrow 4k = 64 \Rightarrow k = 16$.

93. If $y = kx^3$ and $y = 64$ when $x = 2$, then $64 = k(8) \Rightarrow 8k = 64 \Rightarrow k = 8$.

94. If $y = kx^{3/2}$ and $y = 96$ when $x = 16$, then $96 = k(16)^{3/2} \Rightarrow 96 = 64k \Rightarrow k = \dfrac{96}{64} = \dfrac{3}{2}$.

95. If $T = kx^{3/2}$ and $T = 20$ when $x = 4$, then $20 = k(4)^{3/2} \Rightarrow 20 = 8k \Rightarrow k = 2.5$.

The variation equation becomes $T = 2.5x^{3/2}$. When $x = 16$, $T = 2.5(16)^{3/2} = 2.5(64) = 160$.

96. If $y = kx^2$ and $y = 10.8$ when $x = 3$, then $10.8 = k(3)^2 \Rightarrow 9k = 10.8 \Rightarrow k = 1.2$.

The variation equation becomes $y = 1.2x^2$. When $x = 1.5$, $y = 1.2(1.5)^2 = 2.7$.

97. If $y = \dfrac{k}{x}$ and $y = 5$ when $x = 6$, then $5 = \dfrac{k}{6} \Rightarrow k = 30$.

The variation equation becomes $y = \dfrac{30}{x}$. When $x = 15$, $y = \dfrac{30}{15} = 2$.

98. If $z = \frac{k}{t^3}$ and $z = 0.08$ when $t = 5$, then $0.08 = \frac{k}{5^3} \Rightarrow 0.08 = \frac{k}{125} \Rightarrow k = 0.08(125) = 10$.

The variation equation becomes $z = \frac{10}{t^3}$. When $t = 2$, $z = \frac{10}{2^3} = \frac{10}{8} = 1.25$.

99. If $y$ is inversely proportional to $x$, then $y = \frac{k}{x}$ must hold. So if the value of $x$ is doubled, the right side of this equation becomes $\frac{k}{2x} = \frac{1}{2} \cdot \frac{k}{x} = \frac{1}{2}y$. Therefore $y$ becomes half its original value.

100. If $y$ is inversely proportional to $x^2$, then $y = \frac{k}{x^2}$ must hold. So if the value of $x$ is doubled, the right side of this equation becomes $\frac{k}{(2x)^2} = \frac{1}{4} \cdot \frac{k}{x^2} = \frac{1}{4}y$. Therefore $y$ becomes one-fourth its original value.

101. If $y$ is directly proportional to $x^3$, then $y = kx^3$ must hold. So if the value of $x$ is tripled, the right side of this equation becomes $k(3x)^3 = 27 \cdot kx^3 = 27y$. Therefore $y$ becomes 27 times its original value.

102. If $y$ is directly proportional to $x^2$, then $y = kx^2$ must hold. So if the value of $x$ is halved, the right side of this equation becomes $k\left(\frac{1}{2}x\right)^2 = \frac{1}{4} \cdot kx^2 = \frac{1}{4}y$. Therefore $y$ becomes one-fourth its original value.

103. Since $y = kx^n$, we know that $k = \frac{y}{x^n}$ where $k$ is a constant. Using trial and error, let $n = 1$ while calculating various values for $k$ using $x$- and $y$-values from the table. For example, when $x = 2$ and $y = 2$, the value of $k$ is 1. But for $x = 4$ and $y = 8$, the value of $k$ is 2. Since the value of $k$ did not remain constant we know that the value of $n$ is not 1. Repeat this process for $n = 2$. For each $x$ and $y$ pair in the table, the value of $k$ is 0.5. Therefore $k = 0.5$ and $n = 2$.

104. Since $y = kx^n$, we know that $k = \frac{y}{x^n}$ where $k$ is a constant. Using trial and error, let $n = 1$ while calculating various values for $k$ using $x$- and $y$-values from the table. For example, when $x = 3$ and $y = 32.4$, the value of $k$ is 10.8. But for $x = 5$ and $y = 150$, the value of $k$ is 30. Since the value of $k$ did not remain constant we know that the value of $n$ is not 1. Repeat this process for $n = 3$. For each $x$ and $y$ pair in the table, the value of $k$ is 1.2. Therefore $k = 1.2$ and $n = 3$.

105. Since $y = \frac{k}{x^n}$, we know that $k = yx^n$ where $k$ is a constant. Using trial and error, let $n = 1$ while calculating various values for $k$ using $x$- and $y$-values from the table. For example, when $x = 2$ and $y = 1.5$, the value of $k$ is 3. And for $x = 3$ and $y = 1$, the value of $k$ is also 3. Since the value of $k$ remained constant we know that the value of $n$ is 1. For each $x$ and $y$ pair in the table, the value of $k$ is 3. Therefore $k = 3$ and $n = 1$.

106. Since $y = \frac{k}{x^n}$, we know that $k = yx^n$ where $k$ is a constant. Using trial and error, let $n = 1$ while calculating various values for $k$ using $x$- and $y$-values from the table. For example, when $x = 2$ and $y = 9$, the value of $k$ is 18. But for $x = 6$ and $y = 1$, the value of $k$ is 6. Since the value of $k$ did not remain constant we know that the value of $n$ is not 1. Repeat this process for $n = 2$. For each $x$ and $y$ pair in the table, the value of $k$ is 36. Therefore $k = 36$ and $n = 2$.

107. If $y$ is directly proportional to $x^{1.25}$, then $y = kx^{1.25}$ must hold. Given that $y = 1.9$ when $x = 1.1$, we may calculate the value of $k = \frac{y}{x^{1.25}} = \frac{1.9}{1.1^{1.25}} \approx 1.69$. The variation equation can be written as $y \approx 1.69x^{1.25}$. When a fiddler crab has claws weighing 0.75 grams, its body weight will be $y \approx 1.69(0.75)^{1.25} \approx 1.18$ grams.

108. Let $W =$ the weight of the object, and let $d =$ the distance the object is from the center of the earth. If $W$ is inversely proportional to $d^2$, then $W = \frac{k}{d^2}$ must hold. Given that $W = 160$ when $d = 4000$, we may calculate the value of $k = Wd^2 = 160(4000)^2 = 2.56 \times 10^9$. The variation equation is $W = \frac{2.56 \times 10^9}{d^2}$. When the distance from the center of the earth is $4000 + 8000 = 12{,}000$ miles, $W = \frac{2.56 \times 10^9}{12{,}000^2} \approx 17.8$ pounds.

109. Let $I =$ the intensity of the light, and let $d =$ the distance from a star to the earth. If $I$ is inversely proportional to $d^2$, then $I = \frac{k}{d^2}$ must hold. Suppose a ground-based telescope can see a star with intensity $I_g$. Then the Hubble Telescope can see stars of intensity $\frac{1}{50} \cdot I_g = \frac{1}{50} \cdot \frac{k}{d^2} = \frac{k}{(d\sqrt{50})^2}$. That is, the Hubble Telescope can see $\sqrt{50} \approx 7$ times as far as ground-based telescopes.

110. Since the volume is directly proportional to the square of the radius, halving the radius will reduce the volume by a factor of $0.5^2 = 0.25$. Hence, a cylinder with radius 5 inches (half of 10) will have a volume of $0.25(200 \text{ cubic inches}) = 50$ cubic inches.

111. Since the resistance varies inversely as the square of the diameter of the wire, increasing the diameter of the wire by a factor of 1.5 will decrease the resistance by a factor of $\frac{1}{1.5^2} = \frac{4}{9}$. Hence, a 25 foot wire with a diameter of 3 millimeters (1.5 times 2 millimeters) will have a resistance of $\frac{4}{9}(0.5 \text{ ohm}) = \frac{2}{9}$ ohm.

112. Since the strength is directly proportional to the square of the thickness, we have $1000 = k(3.5)^2 \Rightarrow k \approx 81.633$. Thus, strength $= 81.633(12)^2 \approx 11{,}755$.

113. In this exercise $F = \frac{K\sqrt{T}}{L}$. If both T and L are doubled, $\frac{K\sqrt{2T}}{2L} = \frac{\sqrt{2}}{2} \cdot \frac{K\sqrt{T}}{L} = \frac{\sqrt{2}}{2} F$. Therefore $F$ decreases by a factor of $\frac{\sqrt{2}}{2}$.

114. If $T$ is quadrupled, $\frac{K\sqrt{4T}}{L} = \sqrt{4} \cdot \frac{K\sqrt{T}}{L} = 2 \cdot \frac{K\sqrt{T}}{L} = 2F$. If $L$ is divided by Z, $\frac{K\sqrt{T}}{\frac{1}{2}L} = 2\frac{K\sqrt{T}}{L} = 2F$. Therefore you can either quadruple the tension or halve the length.

## 4.8: Power Functions and Radical Equations

1. $8^{2/3} = (8^{1/3})^2 = 2^2 = 4$

2. $-16^{3/2} = -(16^{1/2})^3 = -(\sqrt{16}\,)^3 = -4^3 = -64$

3. $16^{-3/4} = (16^{1/4})^{-3} = (2\,)^{-3} = \frac{1}{2^3} = \frac{1}{8}$

4. $25^{-3/2} = (25^{1/2})^{-3} = (5\ )^{-3} = \dfrac{1}{5^3} = \dfrac{1}{125}$

5. $-81^{0.5} = -81^{1/2} = -\sqrt{81} = -9$

6. $32^{1/5} = \sqrt[3]{32} = 2$

7. $(9^{3/4})^2 = 9^{3/2} = (\sqrt{9}\ )^3 = 3^3 = 27$

8. $(4^{-1/2})^{-4} = 4^2 = 16$

9. $\dfrac{8^{5/6}}{8^{1/2}} = 8^{5/6-1/2} = 8^{1/3} = 2$

10. $\dfrac{4^{-1/2}}{4^{3/2}} = 4^{-1/2-3/2} = 4^{-2} = \dfrac{1}{16}$

11. $27^{5/6} \cdot 27^{-1/6} = 27^{5/6+(-1/6)} = 27^{2/3} = \sqrt[3]{27^2} = 3^2 = 9$

12. $16^{2/3} \cdot 16^{-1/6} = 16^{2/3+(-1/6)} = 16^{1/2} = \sqrt{16} = 4$

13. $(-27)^{-5/3} = \dfrac{1}{(-27)^{5/3}} = \dfrac{1}{\sqrt[3]{(-27)^5}} = \dfrac{1}{(-3)^5} = -\dfrac{1}{243}$

14. $(-32)^{-3/5} = \dfrac{1}{(-32)^{3/5}} = \dfrac{1}{\sqrt[5]{(-32)^3}} = \dfrac{1}{(-2)^3} = -\dfrac{1}{8}$

15. $(0.5^{-2})^2 = \left(\dfrac{1}{2}\right)^{-4} = 2^4 = 16$

16. $(2^{-2})^{-3/2} = 2^3 = 8$

17. $\left(\dfrac{2}{3}\right)^{-2} = \left(\dfrac{3}{2}\right)^2 = \dfrac{9}{4}$

18. $(8^{-1/3} + 27^{-1/3})^2 = \left(\dfrac{1}{8^{1/3}} + \dfrac{1}{27^{1/3}}\right)^2 = \left(\dfrac{1}{\sqrt[3]{8}} + \dfrac{1}{\sqrt[3]{27}}\right)^2 = \left(\dfrac{1}{2} + \dfrac{1}{3}\right)^2 = \left(\dfrac{5}{6}\right)^2 = \dfrac{25}{36}$

19. $\sqrt{2x} = (2x)^{1/2}$

20. $\sqrt{x+1} = (x+1)^{1/2}$

21. $\sqrt[3]{z^5} = z^{5/3}$

22. $\sqrt[5]{x^2} = x^{2/5}$

23. $(\sqrt[4]{y}\ )^{-3} = (y^{1/4})^{-3} = y^{-3/4} = \dfrac{1}{y^{3/4}}$

24. $(\sqrt[3]{y^2}\ )^{-5} = (y^{2/3})^{-5} = y^{-10/3} = \dfrac{1}{y^{10/3}}$

25. $\sqrt{x} \cdot \sqrt[3]{x} = x^{1/2} \cdot x^{1/3} = x^{1/2+1/3} = x^{5/6}$

26. $(\sqrt[5]{z}\ )^{-3} = (z^{1/5})^{-3} = z^{-3/5} = \dfrac{1}{z^{3/5}}$

27. $\sqrt{y \cdot \sqrt{y}} = (y \cdot y^{1/2})^{1/2} = (y^{3/2})^{1/2} = y^{3/4}$

28. $\dfrac{\sqrt[3]{x}}{\sqrt{x}} = \dfrac{x^{1/3}}{x^{1/2}} = x^{1/3-1/2} = x^{-1/6} = \dfrac{1}{x^{1/6}}$

29. $a^{-3/4}b^{1/2} = \dfrac{b^{1/2}}{a^{3/4}} = \dfrac{\sqrt{b}}{\sqrt[4]{a^3}}$

30. $a^{-2/3}b^{3/5} = \dfrac{b^{3/5}}{a^{2/3}} = \dfrac{\sqrt[5]{b^3}}{\sqrt[3]{a^2}}$

31. $(a^{1/2} + b^{1/2})^{1/2} = \sqrt{\sqrt{a} + \sqrt{b}}$

32. $(a^{3/4} - b^{3/2})^{1/3} = \sqrt[3]{\sqrt[4]{a^3} - \sqrt{b^3}}$

33. $\sqrt{x+2} = x - 4 \Rightarrow x + 2 = x^2 - 8x + 16 \Rightarrow x^2 - 9x + 14 = 0 \Rightarrow (x-2)(x-7) = 0 \Rightarrow$

$x = 2$ or 7.

Check: $\sqrt{2+2} = 2 \neq 2 - 4$ (not a solution); $\sqrt{7+2} = 3 = 7 - 4$. The only solution is $x = 7$.

34. $\sqrt{2x+1} = 13 \Rightarrow 2x + 1 = 169 \Rightarrow 2x = 168 \Rightarrow x = 84$; Check: $\sqrt{2(84)+1} = \sqrt{169} = 13$

35. $\sqrt{3x+7} = 3x + 5 \Rightarrow 3x + 7 = 9x^2 + 30x + 25 \Rightarrow 9x^2 + 27x + 18 = 0 \Rightarrow 9(x^2 + 3x + 2) = 0 \Rightarrow$

$9(x+2)(x+1) = 0 \Rightarrow x = -2$ or $-1$

Check: $\sqrt{3(-2)+7} \neq 3(-2) + 5$ (not a solution); $\sqrt{3(-1)+7} = 2 = 3(-1) + 5$. The only solution is $x = -1$.

36. $\sqrt{1-x} = x + 5 \Rightarrow 1 - x = (x+5)^2 \Rightarrow 1 - x = x^2 + 10x + 25 \Rightarrow x^2 + 11x + 24 = 0 \Rightarrow$

$(x+8)(x+3) = 0 \Rightarrow x = -8$ or $-3$

Check: $\sqrt{1-(-8)} \neq -8 + 5$ (not a solution); $\sqrt{1-(-3)} = 2 = -3 + 5$. The only solution is $x = -3$.

37. $\sqrt{5x-6} = x \Rightarrow 5x - 6 = x^2 \Rightarrow x^2 - 5x + 6 = 0 \Rightarrow (x-2)(x-3) = 0 \Rightarrow x = 2$ or 3

Check: $\sqrt{5(2)-6} = 2$; $\sqrt{5(3)-6} = 3$

38. $x - 5 = \sqrt{5x-1} \Rightarrow (x-5)^2 = 5x - 1 \Rightarrow x^2 - 10x + 25 = 5x - 1 \Rightarrow x^2 - 15x + 26 = 0 \Rightarrow$

$(x-13)(x-2) = 0 \Rightarrow x = 13$ or 2

Check: $13 - 5 = 8 = \sqrt{5(13)-1}$; $2 - 5 = -3 \neq \sqrt{5(2)-1}$ (not a solution). The only solution is $x = 13$.

39. $\sqrt{x+5} + 1 = x \Rightarrow \sqrt{x+5} = x - 1 \Rightarrow x + 5 = (x-1)^2 \Rightarrow x + 5 = x^2 - 2x + 1 \Rightarrow$

$x^2 - 3x - 4 = 0 \Rightarrow (x-4)(x+1) = 0 \Rightarrow x = -1$ or $x = 4$

Check: $\sqrt{-1+5} + 1 = -1 \Rightarrow \sqrt{4} + 1 = -1 \Rightarrow 3 \neq -1$ (not a solution).

Check: $\sqrt{4+5} + 1 = 4 \Rightarrow \sqrt{9} + 1 = 4 \Rightarrow 4 = 4$. The only solution is $x = 4$.

40. $\sqrt{4-3x} = x + 8 \Rightarrow 4 - 3x = (x+8)^2 \Rightarrow 4 - 3x = x^2 + 16x + 64 \Rightarrow x^2 + 19x + 60 = 0 \Rightarrow$

$(x+15)(x+4) = 0 \Rightarrow x = -15$ or $x = -4$

Check: $\sqrt{4-3(-15)} = -15 + 8 \Rightarrow \sqrt{49} = -7 \Rightarrow 7 \neq -7$ (not a solution).

Check: $\sqrt{4-3(-4)} = -4 + 8 \Rightarrow \sqrt{16} = 4 \Rightarrow 4 = 4$. The only solution is $x = -4$.

41. $\sqrt{x+1} + 3 = \sqrt{3x+4} \Rightarrow (\sqrt{x+1} + 3)^2 = 3x + 4 \Rightarrow x + 1 + 6\sqrt{x+1} + 9 = 3x + 4 \Rightarrow$

$6\sqrt{x+1} = 2x - 6 \Rightarrow 3\sqrt{x+1} = x - 3 \Rightarrow (3\sqrt{x+1})^2 = (x-3)^2 \Rightarrow$

$9(x+1) = x^2 - 6x + 9 \Rightarrow x^2 - 15x = 0 \Rightarrow x(x-15) = 0 \Rightarrow x = 0$ or 15

Check: $\sqrt{(0)+1} + 3 \neq \sqrt{3(0)+4}$ (not a solution); $\sqrt{(15)+1} + 3 = 7 = \sqrt{3(15)+4}$.

The only solution is $x = 15$.

42. $\sqrt{x} = \sqrt{x-5} + 1 \Rightarrow x = (\sqrt{x-5} + 1)^2 \Rightarrow x = x - 5 + 2\sqrt{x-5} + 1 \Rightarrow 4 = 2\sqrt{x-5} \Rightarrow$

$2 = \sqrt{x-5} \Rightarrow 4 = x - 5 \Rightarrow x = 9$ Check: $\sqrt{9} = 3 = \sqrt{9-5} + 1$

43. $\sqrt{2x} - \sqrt{x+1} = 1 \Rightarrow \sqrt{2x} = 1 + \sqrt{x+1} \Rightarrow 2x = (1 + \sqrt{x+1})^2 \Rightarrow$

$2x = 1 + 2\sqrt{x+1} + x + 1 \Rightarrow x - 2 = 2\sqrt{x+1} \Rightarrow x^2 - 4x + 4 = 4(x+1) \Rightarrow$

$x^2 - 4x + 4 = 4x + 4 \Rightarrow x^2 - 8x = 0 \Rightarrow x(x-8) = 0 \Rightarrow x = 0$ or 8.

Check: $\sqrt{2(0)} - \sqrt{0+1} = 1 \Rightarrow \sqrt{0} - \sqrt{1} = 1 \Rightarrow -1 = 1$ (not a solution);

$\sqrt{2(8)} - \sqrt{8+1} = 1 \Rightarrow \sqrt{16} - \sqrt{9} = 1 \Rightarrow 4 - 3 = 1 \Rightarrow 1 = 1$ The only solution is 8.

44. $\sqrt{2x-4} + 2 = \sqrt{3x+4} \Rightarrow (\sqrt{2x-4} + 2)^2 = 3x + 4 \Rightarrow 2x - 4 + 4\sqrt{2x-4} + 4 = 3x + 4 \Rightarrow$

$4\sqrt{2x-4} = x + 4 \Rightarrow 16(2x-4) = (x+4)^2 \Rightarrow 32x - 64 = x^2 + 8x + 16 \Rightarrow$

$x^2 - 24x + 80 = 0 \Rightarrow (x-20)(x-4) = 0 \Rightarrow x = 4$ or $x = 20$

Check: $\sqrt{2(4)-4} + 2 = \sqrt{3(4)+4} \Rightarrow \sqrt{4} + 2 = \sqrt{16} \Rightarrow 4 = 4.$

Check: $\sqrt{2(20)-4} + 2 = \sqrt{3(20)+4} \Rightarrow \sqrt{36} + 2 = \sqrt{64} \Rightarrow 8 = 8.$ The solution is $x = 4, 20$.

45. $\sqrt[3]{z+1} = -3 \Rightarrow z + 1 = (-3)^3 \Rightarrow z + 1 = -27 \Rightarrow z = -28$

Check: $\sqrt[3]{-28-1} = \sqrt[3]{-27} = -3$

46. $\sqrt[3]{z} + 5 = 4 \Rightarrow \sqrt[3]{z} = -1 \Rightarrow z = (-1)^3 \Rightarrow z = -1$

Check: $\sqrt[3]{-1} + 5 = -1 + 5 = 4$

47. $\sqrt[3]{x+1} = \sqrt[3]{2x-1} \Rightarrow x + 1 = 2x - 1 \Rightarrow x = 2$

Check: $\sqrt[3]{2+1} = \sqrt[3]{3} = \sqrt[3]{2(2)-1}$

48. $\sqrt[3]{2x^2+1} = \sqrt[3]{1-x} \Rightarrow 2x^2 + 1 = 1 - x \Rightarrow 2x^2 + x = 0 \Rightarrow x(2x+1) = 0 \Rightarrow x = 0$ or $-\frac{1}{2}$

Check: $\sqrt[3]{2(0)^2+1} = \sqrt[3]{1} = \sqrt[3]{1-0}$; $\sqrt[3]{2(-\frac{1}{2})^2+1} = \sqrt[3]{\frac{3}{2}} = \sqrt[3]{1-(\frac{1}{2})}$

49. $\sqrt[4]{x-2} + 4 = 20 \Rightarrow \sqrt[4]{x-2} = 16 \Rightarrow x - 2 = (16)^4 \Rightarrow x - 2 = 65{,}536 \Rightarrow x = 65{,}538$

Check: $\sqrt[4]{65{,}538-2} + 4 = 20 \Rightarrow \sqrt[4]{65{,}536} + 4 = 20 \Rightarrow 20 = 20$

50. $\sqrt[4]{2x+3} = \sqrt{x+1} \Rightarrow 2x + 3 = (x+1)^2 \Rightarrow 2x + 3 = x^2 + 2x + 1 \Rightarrow x^2 - 2 = 0 \Rightarrow$

$x^2 = 2 \Rightarrow x = \pm\sqrt{2}$. Then $-\sqrt{2}$ does not check.

Check: $\sqrt[4]{2(\sqrt{2})+3} = \sqrt{\sqrt{2}+1} \Rightarrow 2\sqrt{2} + 3 = (\sqrt{2}+1)^2 \Rightarrow 2\sqrt{2} + 3 = 2 + 2\sqrt{2} + 1 \Rightarrow$

$3 = 3$

51. $f(x) = x^{3/2} - x^{1/2} \Rightarrow f(50) = 50^{3/2} - 50^{1/2} \approx 346.48$

52. $f(x) = x^{5/4} - x^{-3/4} \Rightarrow f(7) = 7^{5/4} - 7^{-3/4} \approx 11.15$

53. The graph of $f(x) = x^a$ is increasing, since $a > 0$. However, since $a < b$ its graph increases more slowly than the graph of $f(x) = x^b$. The best choice is graph $b$.

54. The graph of $f(x) = x^b$ is increasing, since $b > 1$. However, since $b > a$ its graph increases more rapidly than the graph of $f(x) = x^a$. The best choice is graph $a$.

55. Shift the graph of $f(x) = \sqrt{x}$ up 1 unit to get the graph of $f(x) = \sqrt{x} + 1$. See Figure 55.

56. Shift the graph of $f(x) = \sqrt[3]{x}$ to the right 1 unit to get the graph of $f(x) = \sqrt[3]{x - 1}$. See Figure 56.

57. Shift the graph of $f(x) = x^{2/3}$ down 1 unit to get the graph of $f(x) = x^{2/3} - 1$. See Figure 57.

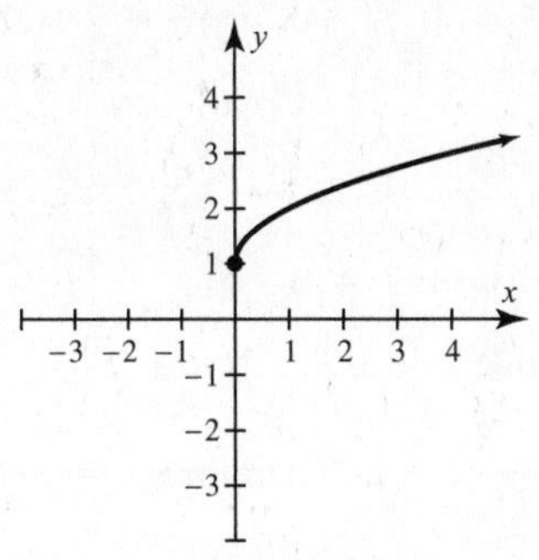

Figure 55

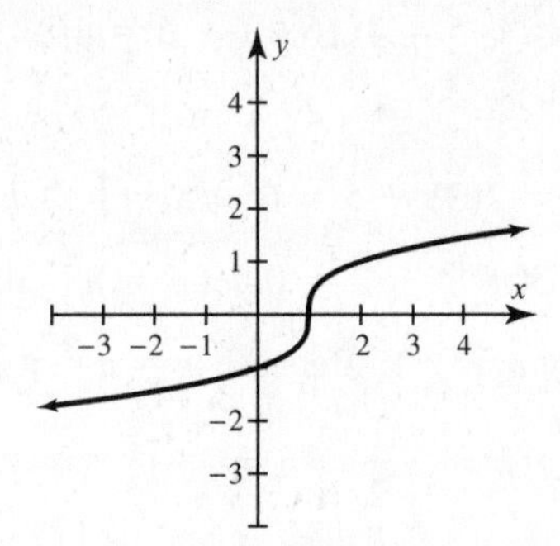

Figure 56

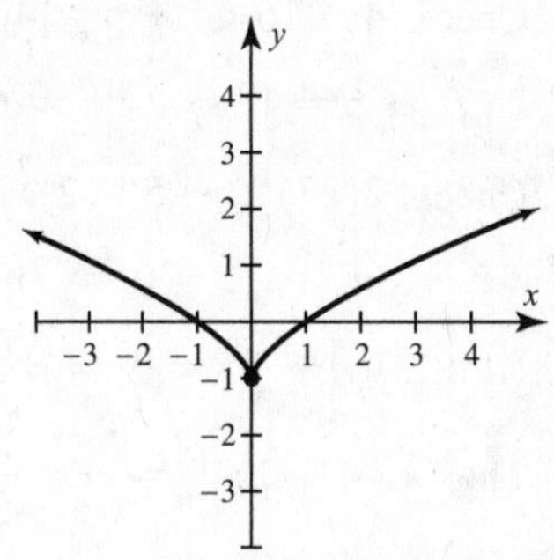

Figure 57

58. Shift the graph of $f(x) = \sqrt{x}$ to the right 1 unit to get the graph of $f(x) = \sqrt{x - 1}$. See Figure 58.

59. Shift the graph of $f(x) = \sqrt{x}$ left 2 units and down 1 unit to get the graph of $f(x) = \sqrt{x + 2} - 1$.

See Figure 59.

60. Shift the graph of $f(x) = x^{2/3}$ to the right 1 unit to get the graph of $f(x) = (x - 1)^{2/3}$. See Figure 60.

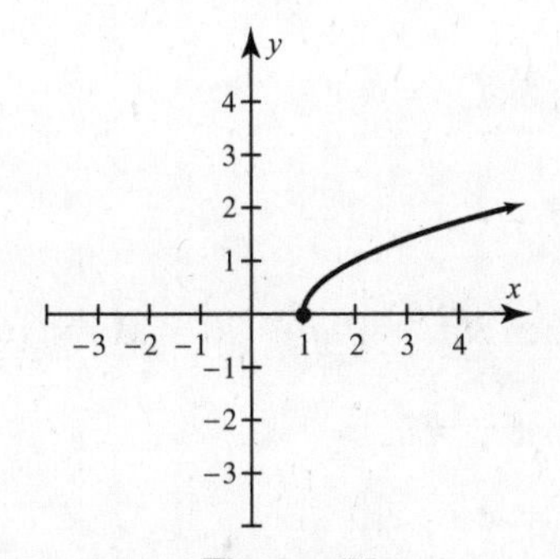

Figure 58

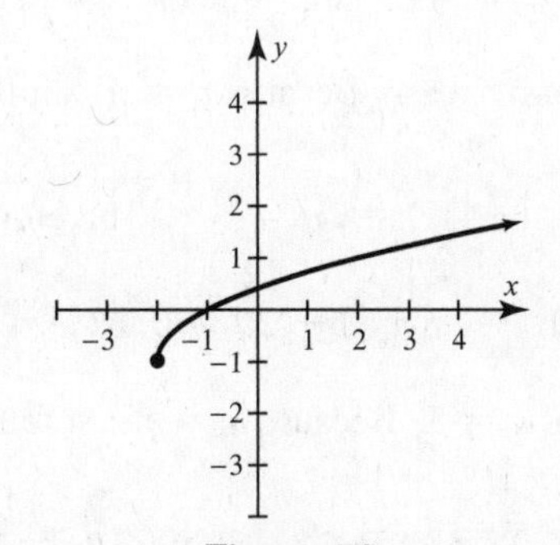

Figure 59

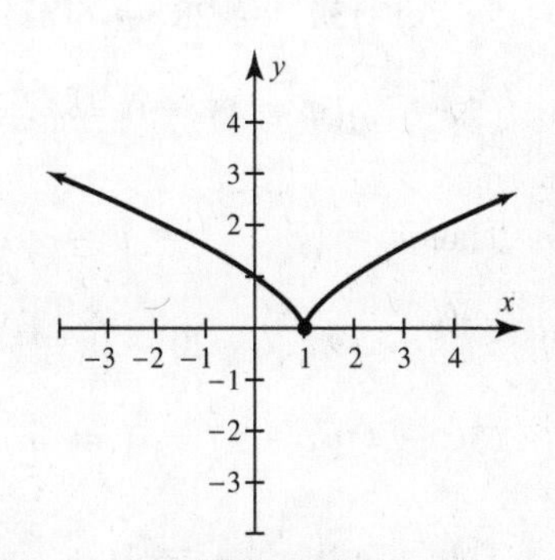

Figure 60

61. $x^3 = 8 \Rightarrow x = \sqrt[3]{8} \Rightarrow x = 2$; Check: $2^3 = 8$

62. $x^4 = \dfrac{1}{81} \Rightarrow x = \sqrt[4]{\dfrac{1}{81}} \Rightarrow x = \pm\dfrac{1}{3}$; Check: $\left(\pm\dfrac{1}{3}\right)^4 = \dfrac{1}{81}$

63. $x^{1/4} = 3 \Rightarrow x = 3^4 \Rightarrow x = 81$; Check: $81^{1/4} = \sqrt[4]{81} = 3$

64. $x^{1/3} = \dfrac{1}{5} \Rightarrow x = \left(\dfrac{1}{5}\right)^3 \Rightarrow x = \dfrac{1}{125}$; Check: $\left(\dfrac{1}{125}\right)^{1/3} = \dfrac{1}{5}$

65. $x^{2/5} = 4 \Rightarrow (x^{2/5})^{5/2} = 4^{5/2} \Rightarrow x = (\sqrt{4})^5 \Rightarrow x = (\pm 2)^5 \Rightarrow x = \pm 32$

Check: $(\pm 32)^{2/5} = (\sqrt[5]{\pm 32})^2 = (\pm 2)^2 = 4$

66. $x^{2/3} = 16 \Rightarrow (x^{2/3})^{3/2} = 16^{3/2} \Rightarrow x = (\sqrt{16})^3 \Rightarrow x = (\pm 4)^3 \Rightarrow x = \pm 64$

Check: $(\pm 64)^{2/3} = (\sqrt[3]{\pm 64})^2 = (\pm 4)^2 = 16$

67. $2(x^{1/5} - 2) = 0 \Rightarrow x^{1/5} - 2 = 0 \Rightarrow x^{1/5} = 2 \Rightarrow (x^{1/5})^5 = 2^5 \Rightarrow x = 32$

Check: $2(32^{1/5} - 2) = 2(2 - 2) = 2(0) = 0$

68. $x^{1/2} + x^{1/2} = 8 \Rightarrow 2x^{1/2} = 8 \Rightarrow x^{1/2} = 4 \Rightarrow (x^{1/2})^2 = 4^2 \Rightarrow x = 16$

Check: $16^{1/2} + 16^{1/2} = \sqrt{16} + \sqrt{16} = 4 + 4 = 8$

69. $4x^{3/2} + 5 = 21 \Rightarrow 4x^{3/2} = 16 \Rightarrow x^{3/2} = 4 \Rightarrow (x^{3/2})^{2/3} = 4^{2/3} \Rightarrow x = \sqrt[3]{4^2} \Rightarrow x = \sqrt[3]{16}$

Check: $4(\sqrt[3]{16})^{3/2} + 5 = 4(16^{1/3})^{3/2} + 5 = 4(16^{1/2}) + 5 = 4(\sqrt{16}\,) + 5 = 4(4) + 5 = 16 + 5 = 21$

70. $2x^{1/3} - 5 = 1 \Rightarrow 2x^{1/3} = 6 \Rightarrow x^{1/3} = 3 \Rightarrow (x^{1/3})^3 = 3^3 \Rightarrow x = 27$

Check: $2(27)^{1/3} - 5 = 2\sqrt[3]{27} - 5 = 2(3) - 5 = 6 - 5 = 1$

71. $n^{-2} + 3n^{-1} + 2 = 0 \Rightarrow (n^{-1})^2 + 3(n^{-1}) + 2 = 0$, let $u = n^{-1}$, then $u^2 + 3u + 2 = 0 \Rightarrow$

$(u + 2)(u + 1) = 0 \Rightarrow u = -2$ or $u = -1$. Because $u = n^{-1}$, it follows that $n = u^{-1}$.

Thus $n = (-2)^{-1} \Rightarrow n = \dfrac{1}{(-2)} \Rightarrow n = -\dfrac{1}{2}$ or $n = (-1)^{-1} \Rightarrow n = \dfrac{1}{(-1)} = -1$. Therefore, $n = -1, -\dfrac{1}{2}$.

72. $2n^{-2} - n^{-1} = 3 \Rightarrow 2n^{-2} - n^{-1} - 3 = 0 \Rightarrow 2(n^{-1})^2 - (n^{-1}) - 3 = 0$, let $u = n^{-1}$,

then $2u^2 - u - 3 = 0 \Rightarrow (2u - 3)(u + 1) = 0 \Rightarrow u = -1$ or $u = \dfrac{3}{2}$.

Because $u = n^{-1}$, it follows that $n = u^{-1}$.

Thus $n = (-1)^{-1} \Rightarrow n = \dfrac{1}{(-1)} \Rightarrow n = -1$ or $n = \left(\dfrac{3}{2}\right)^{-1} \Rightarrow n = \dfrac{1}{\left(\frac{3}{2}\right)} \Rightarrow n = \dfrac{2}{3}$. Therefore, $n = -1, \dfrac{2}{3}$.

73. $5n^{-2} + 13n^{-1} = 28 \Rightarrow 5(n^{-1})^2 + 13(n^{-1}) - 28 = 0$, let $u = n^{-1}$, then $5u^2 + 13u - 28 = 0 \Rightarrow$

$(5u - 7)(u + 4) = 0 \Rightarrow u = \dfrac{7}{5}$ or $u = -4$. Because $u = n^{-1}$, it follows that $n = u^{-1}$.

Thus $n = \left(\dfrac{7}{5}\right)^{-1} \Rightarrow n = \dfrac{5}{7}$ or $n = (-4)^{-1} \Rightarrow n = -\dfrac{1}{4}$. Therefore, $n = -\dfrac{1}{4}, \dfrac{5}{7}$.

74. $3n^{-2} - 19n^{-1} + 20 = 0 \Rightarrow 3(n^{-1})^2 - 19(n^{-1}) + 20 = 0$, let $u = n^{-1}$, then $3u^2 - 19u + 20 = 0 \Rightarrow$

$(3u - 4)(u - 5) = 0 \Rightarrow u = \dfrac{4}{3}$ or $u = 5$. Because $u = n^{-1}$, it follows that $n = u^{-1}$.

Thus $n = \left(\dfrac{4}{3}\right)^{-1} \Rightarrow n = \dfrac{3}{4}$ or $n = 5 \Rightarrow n = \dfrac{1}{5}$. Therefore, $n = \dfrac{1}{5}, \dfrac{3}{4}$.

75. $x^{2/3} - x^{1/3} - 6 = 0 \Rightarrow (x^{1/3})^2 - x^{1/3} - 6 = 0$, let $u = x^{1/3}$, then $u^2 - u - 6 = 0 \Rightarrow$

$(u - 3)(u + 2) = 0 \Rightarrow u = -2$ or $u = 3$. Because $u = x^{1/3}$, it follows that $x = u^3$.

Thus $x = (-2)^3 \Rightarrow x = -8$ or $x = 3^3 \Rightarrow x = 27$. Therefore, $x = -8, 27$.

76. $x^{2/3} + 9x^{1/3} + 14 = 0 \Rightarrow (x^{1/3})^2 + 9(x^{1/3}) + 14 = 0$, let $u = x^{1/3}$, then $u^2 + 9u + 14 = 0 \Rightarrow$

$(u + 7)(u + 2) = 0 \Rightarrow u = -7$ or $u = -2$. Because $u = x^{1/3}$, it follows that $x = u^3$.

Thus $x = (-7)^3 \Rightarrow x = -343$ or $x = (-2)^3 \Rightarrow x = -8$. Therefore, $x = -343, -8$.

77. $6x^{2/3} - 11x^{1/3} + 4 = 0 \Rightarrow 6(x^{1/3})^2 - 11(x^{1/3}) + 4 = 0$, let $u = x^{1/3}$, then $6u^2 - 11u + 4 = 0$.

Using the quadratic formula to solve we get: $u = \dfrac{11 \pm \sqrt{121 - 4(6)(4)}}{2(6)} = \dfrac{11 \pm \sqrt{25}}{12} = \dfrac{11 \pm 5}{12} \Rightarrow$

$u = \dfrac{16}{12} \Rightarrow u = \dfrac{4}{3}$ or $u = \dfrac{6}{12} \Rightarrow u = \dfrac{1}{2}$. Because $u = x^{1/3}$, it follows that $x = u^3$.

Thus $x = \left(\dfrac{4}{3}\right)^3 \Rightarrow x = \dfrac{64}{27}$ or $x = \left(\dfrac{1}{2}\right)^3 \Rightarrow x = \dfrac{1}{8}$. Therefore, $x = \dfrac{1}{8}, \dfrac{64}{27}$.

78. $10x^{2/3} + 29x^{1/3} + 10 = 0 \Rightarrow 10(x^{1/3})^2 + 29(x^{1/3}) + 10 = 0$, let $u = x^{1/3}$, then $10u^2 + 29u + 10 = 0$.

Using the quadratic formula to solve we get: $u = \dfrac{-29 \pm \sqrt{841 - 4(10)(10)}}{2(10)} = \dfrac{-29 \pm \sqrt{441}}{20} =$

$\dfrac{-29 \pm 21}{20} \Rightarrow u = \dfrac{-5}{2}$ or $\Rightarrow u = \dfrac{-2}{5}$. Because $u = x^{1/3}$, it follows that $x = u^3$.

Thus $x = \left(\dfrac{-5}{2}\right)^3 \Rightarrow x = \dfrac{-125}{8}$ or $x = \left(\dfrac{-2}{5}\right)^3 \Rightarrow x = \dfrac{-8}{125}$. Therefore, $x = \dfrac{-125}{8}, \dfrac{-8}{125}$.

79. $x^{3/4} - x^{1/2} - x^{1/4} + 1 = 0 \Rightarrow (x^{1/4})^3 - (x^{1/4})^2 - (x^{1/4}) + 1 = 0$, let $u = x^{1/4}$,

then $u^3 - u^2 - u + 1 = 0 \Rightarrow (u^3 - u^2) - (u - 1) = 0 \Rightarrow u^2(u - 1) - 1(u - 1) = 0 \Rightarrow$

$(u^2 - 1)(u - 1) = 0 \Rightarrow (u + 1)(u - 1)(u - 1) = 0 \Rightarrow u = -1$ or $u = 1$.

Because $u = x^{1/4}$ it follows that $x = u^4$.

Thus $x = (-1)^4 \Rightarrow x = 1$ or $x = (1)^4 \Rightarrow x = 1$. Therefore, $x = 1$.

80. $x^{3/4} - 2x^{1/2} - 4x^{1/4} + 8 = 0 \Rightarrow (x^{1/4})^3 - 2(x^{1/4})^2 - 4(x^{1/4}) + 8 = 0$, let $u = x^{1/4}$, then

$u^3 - 2u^2 - 4u + 8 = 0 \Rightarrow (u^3 - 2u^2) - (4u - 8) = 0 \Rightarrow u^2(u - 2) - 4(u - 2) = 0 \Rightarrow$

$(u^2 - 4)(u - 2) = 0 \Rightarrow (u + 2)(u - 2)(u - 2) = 0 \Rightarrow u = -2$ or $u = 2$. Because $u = x^{1/4}$

it follows that $x = u^4$. Thus $x = (-2)^4 \Rightarrow x = 16$ or $x = (2)^4 \Rightarrow x = 16$. Therefore, $x = 16$.

81. $x^{-2/3} - 2x^{-1/3} - 3 = 0 \Rightarrow (x^{-1/3})^2 - 2x^{-1/3} - 3 = 0$, let $u = x^{-1/3}$, then $u^2 - 2u - 3 = 0 \Rightarrow$

$(u - 3)(u + 1) = 0 \Rightarrow u = 3$ or $-1$. Because $u = x^{-1/3}$ it follows that $x = u^{-3}$.

Thus $x = 3^{-3} = \dfrac{1}{27}, x = -1^{-3} = -1$.

82. $6x^{-2/3} - 13x^{-1/3} - 5 = 0 \Rightarrow 6(x^{-1/3})^2 - 13x^{-1/3} - 5 = 0$, let $u = x^{-1/3}$, then $6u^2 - 13u - 5 = 0 \Rightarrow$

$(3u + 1)(2u - 5) = 0 \Rightarrow u = -\dfrac{1}{3}$ or $\dfrac{5}{2}$; Because $u = x^{-1/3}$ it follows that $x = u^{-3}$.

$x = \left(-\dfrac{1}{3}\right)^{-3} = -27, x = \left(\dfrac{5}{2}\right)^{-3} = \dfrac{8}{125}$.

83. Average rate of change $= \dfrac{s(\frac{9}{2}) - s(\frac{1}{2})}{\frac{9}{2} - \frac{1}{2}} = \dfrac{\sqrt{96(\frac{9}{2})} - \sqrt{96(\frac{1}{2})}}{4} = \dfrac{\sqrt{432} - \sqrt{48}}{4} \approx 3.5$. The average speed over the time interval is about 3.5 mph.

84. Average rate of change $= \dfrac{s(\frac{9}{2}) - s(\frac{1}{2})}{\frac{9}{2} - \frac{1}{2}} = \dfrac{3(\frac{9}{2})^{3/4} - 3(\frac{1}{2})^{3/4}}{4} \approx 1.9$ The average speed over the time interval is about 1.9 mph.

85. $S(w) = 3 \Rightarrow 1.27w^{2/3} = 3 \Rightarrow w^{2/3} = \dfrac{3}{1.27} \Rightarrow w = \left(\dfrac{3}{1.27}\right)^{3/2} \Rightarrow w \approx 3.63$

The bird weighs about 3.63 pounds

86. $L = 2.43W^{0.3326} \Rightarrow L = 2.43(5.2)^{0.3326} \Rightarrow L \approx 4.2$; The wingspan of the bird is about 4.2 feet.

87. $f(15) = 15^{1.5} \approx 58.1$; The planet would take about 58.1 years to orbit the sun.

88. $f(x) = 200 \Rightarrow x^{1.5} = 200 \Rightarrow x^{3/2} = 200 \Rightarrow x = 200^{2/3} \Rightarrow x \approx 34.2$;

The average distance of the planet is about 34 times farther from the sun than Earth.

89. (a) Following the hint, $f(1) = a(1)^b = 1960 \Rightarrow a = 1960$

(b) Plot the four data points (0.5, 4500), (1, 1960), (2, 850), and (3, 525) together with $f(x) = 1960x^b$ for different values of $b$. Through trial and error, a value of $b \approx -1.2$ can be found. Figure 89 shows a graph of $Y_1 = 1960X\text{^}(-1.2)$ along with the data.

(c) $f(x) = 1960x^{-1.2} \Rightarrow f(4) = 1960(4)^{-1.2} \approx 371$. This means that if the zinc ion concentration in the water reaches 371 milligrams per liter, the rainbow trout will live only 4 minutes on average.

[0, 5, 1] by [0, 5000, 1000]

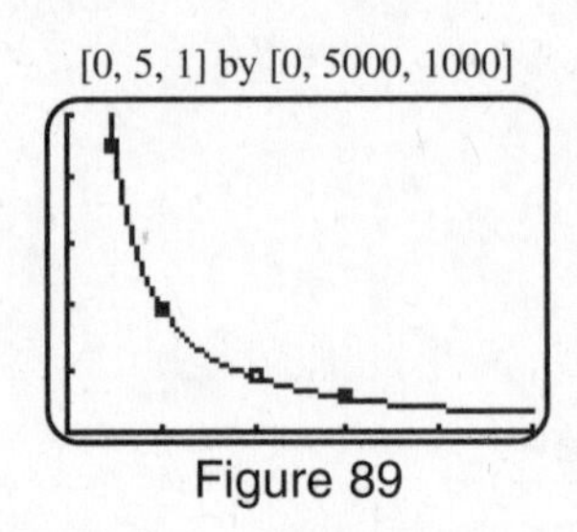

Figure 89

[0, 2000, 200] by [0, 20, 2]

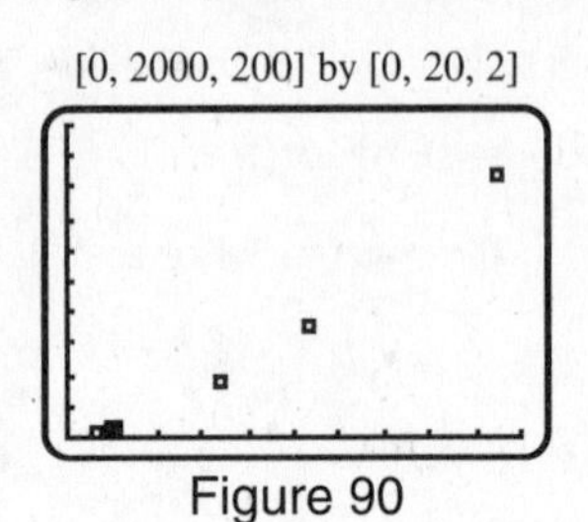

Figure 90

90. (a) See Figure 90.

(b) Using the power regession function on the graphing calculator we see that $f(x) \approx 0.0002x^{1.5}$. $b \approx 1.5$.

(c) $f(x) = 0.0002(422)^{1.5} \approx 1.73$ days. The approximation is very close to the actual value of 1.77 days. The estimate involved interpolation.

91. (a) $f(2) = 0.445(2)^{1.25} \approx 1.06$ grams

(b) We must solve the equation $0.445x^{1.25} = 0.5$ for $x$. Graph $Y_1 = 0.445X\text{^}1.25$ and $Y_2 = 0.5$. Their graphs intersect near (1.1, 0.5). See Figure 91. When the claw weighs 0.5 grams, the crab weighs about 1.1 grams.

(c) $0.445x^{1.25} = 0.5 \Rightarrow 0.445x^{5/4} = 0.5 \Rightarrow x^{5/4} = \dfrac{0.5}{0.445} \Rightarrow x = \left(\dfrac{0.5}{0.445}\right)^{4/5} \Rightarrow x \approx 1.1$ grams

[0, 2, 0.2] by [0, 1, 0.2]

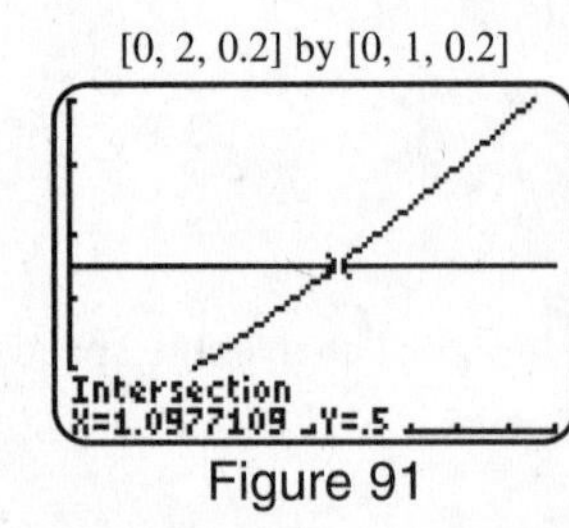


Figure 91

[1, 9, 1] by [0, 6, 1]

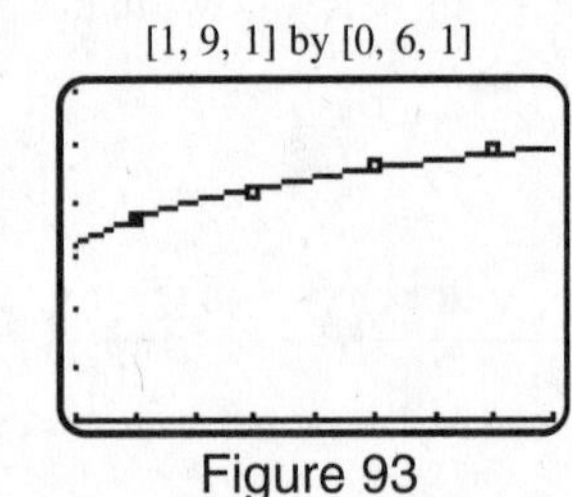

Figure 93

[0, 15, 3] by [0, 150, 25]

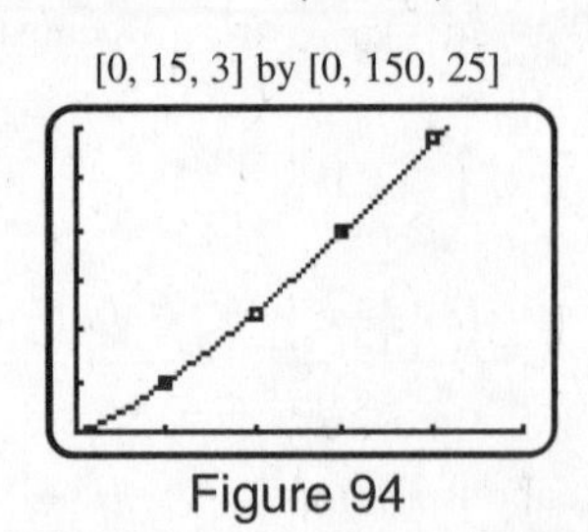

Figure 94

92. (a) $f(68) = 152 \Rightarrow a(68)^{1.7} = 152 \Rightarrow a = \dfrac{152}{68^{1.7}} \Rightarrow a \approx 0.11657$; $f(66) = 0.11657(66)^{1.7} \approx 144$ pounds

(b) $f(68) = 137 \Rightarrow a(68)^{1.7} = 137 \Rightarrow a = \dfrac{137}{68^{1.7}} \Rightarrow a \approx 0.10506$; $f(70) = 0.10506(70)^{1.7} \approx 144$ pounds

93. Use the power regression feature of your graphing calculator to find the values of $a$ and $b$ in the equation $f(x) = ax^b$. For this exercise, $a \approx 3.20$ and $b \approx 0.20$.

The graph of $Y_1 = 3.20X\text{^}0.20$ is shown together with the data in Figure 93.

94. Use the power regression feature of your graphing calculator to find the values of $a$ and $b$ in the equation $f(x) = ax^b$. For this exercise, $a \approx 5.71$ and $b \approx 1.30$.

The graph of $Y_1 = 5.71X\text{^}1.30$ is shown together with the data in Figure 94.

95. (a) Using the power regression function on the graphing calculator we see that $f(x) \approx 0.005192x^{1.7902}$.

*Answers may vary.*

(b) The year 2012 is 32 years after 1980. $f(32) \approx 0.005192(32)^{1.7902} \approx 2.6$ million. The estimate involved extrapolation.

(c) See Figure 95. We can see from the graph of $f(x)$ that the number of employees reached 1.million in about 1999.

[0, 40, 2] by [0, 3, 1]

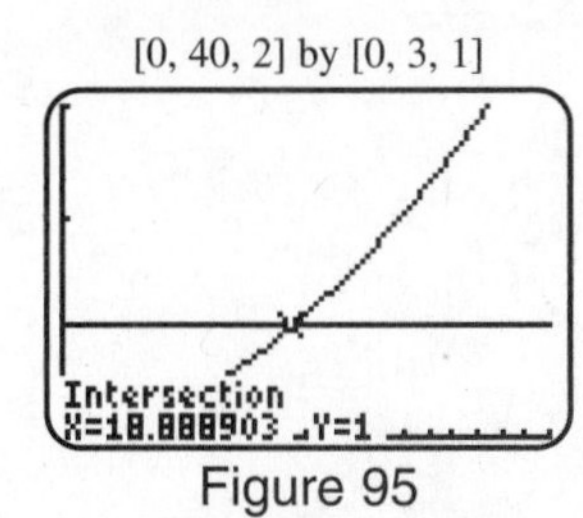


Figure 95

[0, 12, 1] by [0, 50,000, 5000]

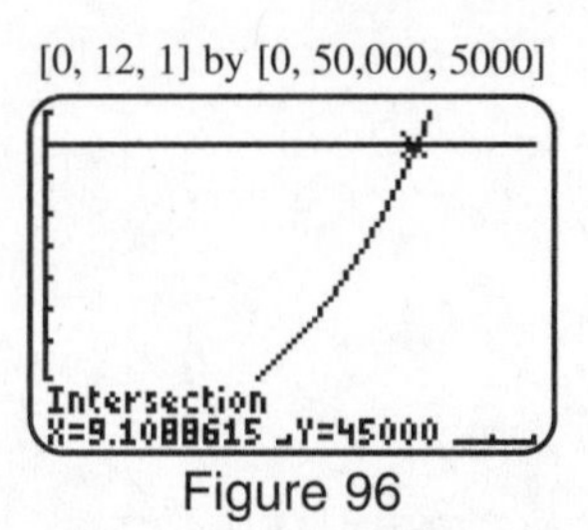


Figure 96

96. (a) Using the power regression function on the graphing calculator we see that $f(x) \approx 101.56x^{2.7583}$.

*Answers may vary.*

(b) The year 2006 is 11 years since 1995. $f(11) \approx 101.56(11)^{2.7583} \approx 75{,}720$. The result used extrapolation.

(c) See Figure 96. We can see from the graph of $f(x)$ that the number of releases first surpassed 45,000 sometime in 2004.

97. Use the power regression feature of your graphing calculator to find the values of $a$ and $b$ in the equation $f(x) = ax^b$. For this exercise, $a \approx 874.54$ and $b \approx -0.49789$.

98. $f(60) = 874.54(60)^{-0.49789} \approx 114$ bpm and $f(4000) = 874.54(4000)^{-0.49789} \approx 14$ bpm

A 60-pound dog has a pulse rate of about 114 bpm and a 2-ton whale has a pulse rate of about 14 bpm.

## Extended and Discovery Exercise for Section 4.8

1. The graph of an odd root function is always increasing; the function is negative for $x < 0$, positive for $x > 0$, and zero at $x = 0$.

2. The graph of an even root function is always increasing; the function is defined only for $x \geq 0$, and is zero at $x = 0$.

3. The graph of a power function in which the exponent is a negative odd integer has the $y$-axis as a vertical asymptote and the $x$-axis as a horizontal asymptote; the function is undefined at $x = 0$; the function is decreasing on $(-\infty, 0)$ and on $(0, \infty)$. The function is symmetric with respect to the origin.

4. The graph of a power function in which the exponent is a negative even integer has the $y$-axis as a vertical asymptote and the $x$-axis as a horizontal asymptote; the function is undefined at $x = 0$; the function is increasing on $(-\infty, 0)$ and decreasing on $(0, \infty)$. The function is symmetric with respect to the $y$-axis.

5. $\dfrac{f(x+h)-f(x)}{h}=\dfrac{\sqrt{x+h}-\sqrt{x}}{h}=\dfrac{\sqrt{x+h}-\sqrt{x}}{h}\cdot\dfrac{\sqrt{x+h}+\sqrt{x}}{\sqrt{x+h}+\sqrt{x}}=\dfrac{x+h-x}{h(\sqrt{x+h}+\sqrt{x})}=$
$\dfrac{1}{\sqrt{x+h}+\sqrt{x}}$

6. $\dfrac{f(x+h)-f(x)}{h}=\dfrac{\frac{1}{x+h}-\frac{1}{x}}{h}=\dfrac{1}{x+h}\cdot\dfrac{1}{h}-\dfrac{1}{x}\cdot\dfrac{1}{h}=\dfrac{1}{h^2+xh}-\dfrac{1}{xh}=\dfrac{xh}{xh(h^2+xh)}-\dfrac{h^2+xh}{xh(h^2+xh)}=$
$-\dfrac{h^2}{xh(h^2+xh)}=-\dfrac{h^2}{xh^2(h+x)}=-\dfrac{1}{x(x+h)}=-\dfrac{1}{x^2+xh}$

7. $\dfrac{x^{-2/3}+x^{1/3}}{x}=\dfrac{x^{-2/3}(1+x)}{x}=\dfrac{1+x}{x^{2/3}(x)}=\dfrac{1+x}{x^{5/3}}$

8. $\dfrac{x^{1/4}-x^{-3/4}}{x}=\dfrac{x^{-3/4}(x-1)}{x}=\dfrac{x-1}{x^{3/4}(x)}=\dfrac{x-1}{x^{7/4}}$

9. $\dfrac{\frac{2}{3}(x+1)x^{-1/3}-x^{2/3}}{(x+1)^2}=\dfrac{x^{-1/3}[\frac{2}{3}x+\frac{2}{3}-x]}{(x+1)^2}=\dfrac{-\frac{1}{3}x+\frac{2}{3}}{x^{1/3}(x+1)^2}=\dfrac{\frac{-x+2}{3}}{x^{1/3}(x+1)^2}=\dfrac{2-x}{3x^{1/3}(x+1)^2}$

10. $\dfrac{(x^2+1)^{1/2}-\frac{1}{2}x(x^2+1)^{-1/2}(2x)}{x^2+1}=\dfrac{(x^2+1)^{-1/2}[x^2+1-x^2]}{x^2+1}=\dfrac{1}{(x^2+1)^{1/2}(x^2+1)}=\dfrac{1}{(x^2+1)^{3/2}}$

## Checking Basic Concepts for Sections 4.7 and 4.8

1. (a) $\dfrac{3x-1}{1-x}=1\Rightarrow 3x-1=1-x\Rightarrow 4x=2\Rightarrow x=\dfrac{1}{2}$; Check: $\dfrac{3(\frac{1}{2})-1}{1-(\frac{1}{2})}=1\Rightarrow\dfrac{\frac{1}{2}}{\frac{1}{2}}=1\Rightarrow 1=1$

(b) $3+\dfrac{8}{x}=\dfrac{35}{x^2}\Rightarrow 3x^2+8x=35\Rightarrow 3x^2+8x-35=0\Rightarrow(3x-7)(x+5)=0\Rightarrow x=-5,\dfrac{7}{3}$

Check: $3+\dfrac{8}{(-5)}=\dfrac{35}{(-5)^2}\Rightarrow 3-\dfrac{8}{5}=\dfrac{35}{25}\Rightarrow\dfrac{75}{25}-\dfrac{40}{25}=\dfrac{35}{25}\Rightarrow\dfrac{35}{25}=\dfrac{35}{25}$

Check: $3+\dfrac{8}{(\frac{7}{3})}=\dfrac{35}{(\frac{7}{3})^2}\Rightarrow 3+\dfrac{24}{7}=\dfrac{45}{7}\Rightarrow\dfrac{21}{7}+\dfrac{24}{7}=\dfrac{45}{7}\Rightarrow\dfrac{45}{7}=\dfrac{45}{7}$

(c) $\dfrac{1}{x-1}-\dfrac{1}{3(x+2)}=\dfrac{1}{(x+2)(x-1)}\Rightarrow 3(x+2)-(x-1)=3\Rightarrow 3x+6-x+1=3\Rightarrow$

$2x=-4\Rightarrow x=-2$; Check: $\dfrac{1}{(-2)-1}-\dfrac{1}{3(-2+2)}=\dfrac{1}{(-2+2)(-2-1)}\Rightarrow\dfrac{1}{-3}-\dfrac{1}{0}=\dfrac{1}{0}$

Since $-2$ is not defined in the original equation there is no solution.

2. First find the boundary numbers by solving $2x^3+x^2-6x=0$.

$2x^3+x^2-6x=0\Rightarrow x(2x^2+x-6)=0\Rightarrow x(2x-3)(x+2)=0\Rightarrow x=-2, 0$ or $1.5$;

In set builder notation the interval is $\left\{x\,|\,x<-2 \text{ or } 0<x<\dfrac{3}{2}\right\}$.

3. The graph of $Y_1=(X\wedge 2-1)/(X+2)$ has a vertical asymptote at $x=-2$ and $x$-intercepts at $x=\pm1$.

The graph of $Y_1$ intersects or is above the $x$-axis on the interval $(-2,-1]\cup[1,\infty)$.

In set builder notation the interval is $\{x\,|\,-2<x\le-1 \text{ or } x\ge 1\}$.

4. $y = \frac{k}{x^3} \Rightarrow 150 = \frac{k}{(\frac{1}{5})^3} \Rightarrow k = 1.2;\ y = \frac{1.2}{x^3} \Rightarrow y = \frac{1.2}{(\frac{1}{2})^3} \Rightarrow y = 9.6$

5. (a) $-4^{3/2} = -(\sqrt{4}\ )^3 = -(2)^3 = -8$

(b) $(8^{-2})^{1/3} = 8^{-2/3} = \frac{1}{8^{2/3}} = \frac{1}{(\sqrt[3]{8})^2} = \frac{1}{2^2} = \frac{1}{4}$

(c) $\sqrt[3]{27^2} = (\sqrt[3]{27})^2 = 3^2 = 9$

6. $4x^{3/2} - 3 = 29 \Rightarrow 4x^{3/2} = 32 \Rightarrow x^{3/2} = 8 \Rightarrow x = 8^{2/3} \Rightarrow x = (\sqrt[3]{8})^2 \Rightarrow x = 2^2 \Rightarrow x = 4$

7. $\sqrt{5x - 4} = x - 2 \Rightarrow 5x - 4 = x^2 - 4x + 4 \Rightarrow x^2 - 9x + 8 = 0 \Rightarrow (x - 1)(x - 8) = 0 \Rightarrow$

$x = 1$ or $8$

Check: $\sqrt{5(1) - 4} \neq 1 - 2$ (not a solution); $\sqrt{5(8) - 4} = 6 = 8 - 2$. The only solution is $x = 8$.

8. (a) $n^{-2} + 6n^{-1} = 16 \Rightarrow (n^{-1})^2 + 6(n^{-1}) - 16 = 0$, let $u = n^{-1}$, then $u^2 + 6u - 16 = 0 \Rightarrow$

$(u + 8)(u - 2) = 0 \Rightarrow u = -8$ or $u = 2$. Because $u = n^{-1}$, it follows that $n = u^{-1}$.

Thus $n = (-8)^{-1} \Rightarrow n = -\frac{1}{8} \Rightarrow$ or $n = (2)^{-1} \Rightarrow n = \frac{1}{2}$. Therefore, $n = -\frac{1}{8}, \frac{1}{2}$.

(b) $2x^{2/3} + 5x^{1/3} - 12 = 0 \Rightarrow 2(x^{1/3})^2 + 5(x^{1/3}) - 12 = 0$, let $u = x^{1/3}$, then $2u^2 + 5u - 12 = 0 \Rightarrow$

$(2u - 3)(u + 4) = 0 \Rightarrow u = -4$ or $u = \frac{3}{2}$. Because $u = x^{1/3}$, it follows that $x = u^3$.

Thus $x = (-4)^3 \Rightarrow x = -64$ or $x = \left(\frac{3}{2}\right)^3 \Rightarrow x = \frac{27}{8}$. Therefore, $x = -64, \frac{27}{8}$.

9. Use the power regression feature of your graphing calculator to find the values of $a$ and $b$ in the equation

$f(x) = ax^b$. For this exercise, $a = 2$ and $b = 0.5$. That is, $f(x) = 2x^{1/2}$ or $f(x) = 2\sqrt{x}$ .

## Chapter 4 Review Exercises

1. First put in standard order:

$f(x) = -7x^3 - 2x^2 + x + 4$, now the degree is: 3, and the leading coefficient is: $-7$.

2. (a) There are local minima of –4.5 and –0.5. There is a local maximum of 0.

(b) The absolute minimum is –4.5. There is no absolute maximum.

3. (a) There is a local minimum of –2. There is a local maximum of 4.

(b) There is neither an absolute minimum nor an absolute maximum.

4. (a) The graph of $Y_1 = -0.25X^4 + 0.67X^3 + 9.5X^2 - 20X - 50$ is shown in Figure 4. Two local maxima and one local minimum occur on this graph. Local maxima are associated with the points near (–3.996, 75.12) and (5.007, 15.00), while a local minimum corresponds to the point (0.9995, –60.08). Thus, $f$ has two local maxima of approximately 75.12 and 15, and a local minimum of about –60.08.

   (b) The graph of $f$ has an absolute maximum of approximately 75.12 and no absolute minimum.

   (c) Tracing the graph of $f$ from left to right, the $y$-values increase when $-\infty < x \leq -3.996$, decrease when $-3.996 \leq x \leq 0.9995$, increase for $0.9995 \leq x \leq 5.007$, and then decrease for $5.007 \leq x < \infty$. In interval notation $f$ increases on $(-\infty, -3.996] \cup [0.9995, 5.007]$ and decreases on $[-3.996, 0.9995] \cup [5.007, \infty)$. All value have been rounded to four significant digits.

5. The graph of $f(x) = x^4 + 2x^3 - 9x^2 - 2x + 20$ is shown in Figure 5. There are two local minima, one local maximum and two $x$-intercepts.

[–10, 10, 1] by [–150, 150, 50]

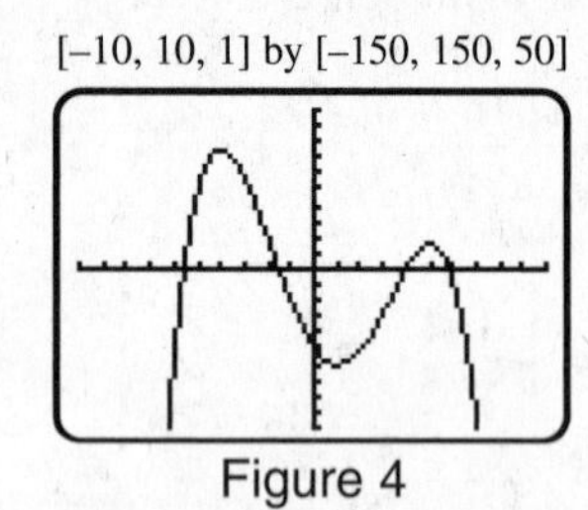

Figure 4

[–10, 10, 1] by [–100, 100, 10]

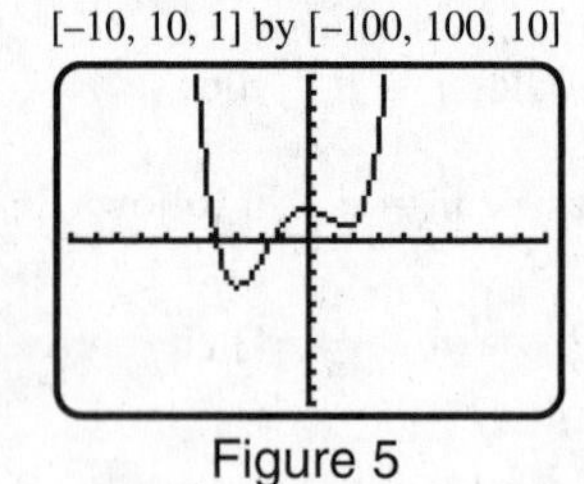

Figure 5

[–3, 7, 1] by [–5, 5, 1]

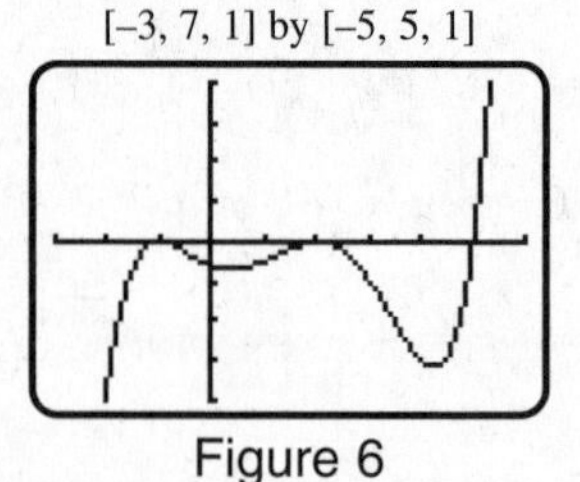

Figure 6

6. The graph of $f(x) = 0.03x^5 - 0.21x^4 + 0.21x^3 + 0.57x^2 - 0.48x + 0.6$ is shown in Figure 6. There are turning points near (–1, 0), (0.379, –0.693), (2, 0), and (4.22, –3.14).

7. $f(x) = 2x^6 - 5x^4 - x^2 \Rightarrow f$ is even since each power of $x$ is even.

8. $f(x) = -5x^3 - 18 \Rightarrow f$ is neither odd nor even. It is not even since it contains an odd power of $x$ and it is not odd since $f(0) \neq 0$.

9. $f(x) = 7x^5 + 3x^3 - x \Rightarrow f$ is odd since each power of $x$ is odd.

10. $f(x) = \dfrac{1}{1 + x^2} \Rightarrow f$ is even since replacing $x$ with $-x$ does not change the resulting value of $f(x)$.

11. $f$ is odd since $f(-x) = -f(x)$ for all $x$-values in the table.

12. $f$ is even since $f(-x) = f(x)$ for all $x$-values in the table.

13. See Figure 13. *Answers may vary.*

14. See Figure 14. *Answers may vary.*

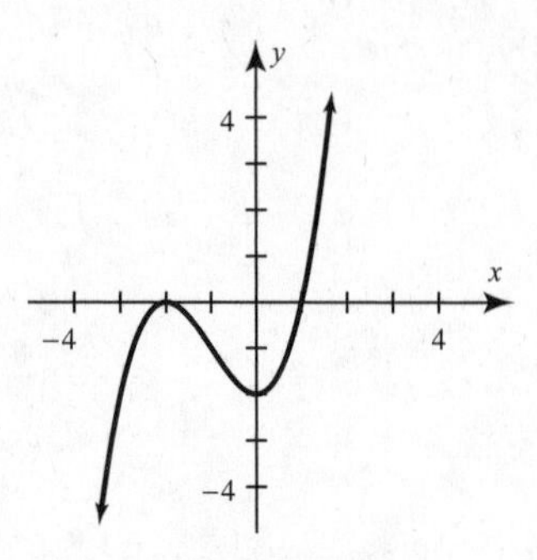


Figure 13

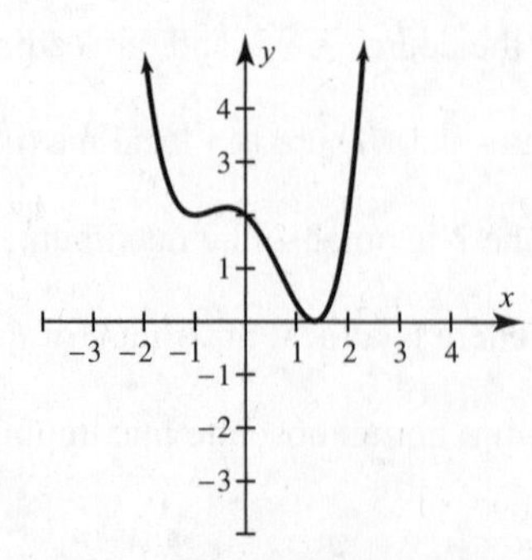


Figure 14

15. (a) 2 turning points; 3 $x$-intercepts at: $x \approx -2, 0, 1$.

    (b) This is a an odd degreed function going down to the right $\Rightarrow$ negative.

    (c) Since it has 2 turning points, it is a minimum of 3rd degree.

16. (a) 3 turning points; 3 $x$-intercepts at: $x \approx -2, -1, 1$.

    (b) This is an even degreed function going up at each end $\Rightarrow$ positive.

    (c) Since it has 3 turning points, it's minimum degree is 4.

17. A negative cubic function $\Rightarrow$ up on the left end and down on the right end;

    $f(x) \to \infty$ as $x \to -\infty$; $f(x) \to -\infty$ as $x \to \infty$.

18. A negative quadratic function $\Rightarrow$ down on both ends; $f(x) \to -\infty$ as $x \to -\infty$; $f(x) \to -\infty$ as $x \to \infty$.

19. $f(-2) = (-2)^3 + 1 \Rightarrow f(-2) = -7 \Rightarrow (-2, -7)$ and $f(-1) = (-1)^3 + 1 \Rightarrow f(-1) = 0 \Rightarrow (-1, 0)$.

    To find the average rate of change we use: $\dfrac{y_2 - y_1}{x_2 - x_1} \Rightarrow \dfrac{0 - (-7)}{(-1) - (-2)} \Rightarrow \dfrac{7}{1} \Rightarrow 7$

20. $\dfrac{g(x + h) - g(x)}{h} = \dfrac{4(x + h)^3 - 4x^3}{h} = \dfrac{4(x^3 + 3x^2h + 3xh^2 + h^3) - 4x^3}{h} =$

    $\dfrac{4x^3 + 12x^2h + 12xh^2 + 4h^3 - 4x^3}{h} = 12x^2 + 12xh + 4h^2$

21. (a) The graph of $f$ has of two different pieces: $y = 2x$ when $0 \le x < 2$ and $y = 8 - x^2$ when $2 \le x \le 4$.

    The graph is shown in Figure 21. The graph of $f$ is continuous.

    (b) To evaluate $f(1)$ we must use the first piece of the function: $f(1) = 2(1) = 2$

    To evaluate $f(3)$ we must use the second piece of the function: $f(3) = 8 - (3)^2 = 8 - 9 = -1$

    (c) We must solve the equation $f(x) = 2$ for each piece of the piecewise-defined function $f$.

    $2x = 2 \Rightarrow x = 1$ and $8 - x^2 = 2 \Rightarrow x^2 = 6 \Rightarrow x = \pm\sqrt{6}$

    Since $x = -\sqrt{6}$ is not in the domain of $f$, the solutions are $x = 1$ or $\sqrt{6}$.

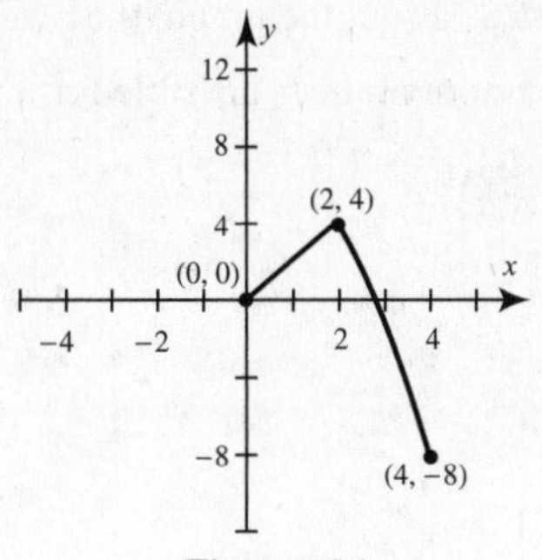


Figure 21

22. Since $g$ is a polynomial function with only odd powers on the variable $x$, the function is odd and therefore has origin symmetry.

23. $\dfrac{14x^3 - 21x^2 - 7x}{7x} = 2x^2 - 3x - 1$

24.
$$
\begin{array}{r}
2x^2 - 5x + 6 \\
x + 2\overline{)2x^3 - x^2 - 4x + 1} \\
\underline{2x^3 + 4x^2} \qquad\qquad \\
-5x^2 - 4x + 1 \\
\underline{-5x^2 - 10x} \quad\; \\
6x + 1 \\
\underline{6x + 12} \\
-11
\end{array}
$$

Therefore the quotient is: $2x^2 - 5x + 6 + \dfrac{-11}{x + 2}$

25.
$$
\begin{array}{r}
2x^2 - 3x + 1 \\
2x + 3\overline{)4^3 \qquad - 7x + 4} \\
\underline{4x^3 + 6x^2} \qquad\qquad \\
-6x^2 - 7x + 4 \\
\underline{-6x^2 - 9x} \quad\; \\
2x + 4 \\
\underline{2x + 3} \\
1
\end{array}
$$

Therefore the quotient is: $2x^2 - 3x + 1 + \dfrac{1}{2x + 3}$

26.
$$
\begin{array}{r}
3x - 5 \\
x^2 + 4\overline{)3x^3 - 5x^2 + 13x - 18} \\
\underline{3x^3 \qquad + 12x} \quad\; \\
-5x^2 + x - 18 \\
\underline{-5x^2 \qquad - 20} \\
x + 2
\end{array}
$$

Therefore the quotient is: $3x - 5 + \dfrac{x + 2}{x^2 + 4}$

27. Since the leading coefficient of $f(x)$ is $\frac{1}{2}$ and the degree of the polynomial is 3, all of the zeros are given, thus: $f(x) = \frac{1}{2}(x - 1)(x - 2)(x - 3)$.

28. The graph of $Y_1 = X\text{^}4 + 2X\text{^}3 - 13X\text{^}2 - 14X + 24$ is shown in Figure 28. From the graph, the $x$-intercepts of $f$ are located at $-4, -2, 1$, and 3. Four $x$-intercepts is the maximum number possible for a quartic polynomial. The leading coefficient is $a_n = 1$. Thus $f(x) = (x + 4)(x + 2)(x - 1)(x - 3)$.

[-5, 5, 1] by [-35, 35, 5]

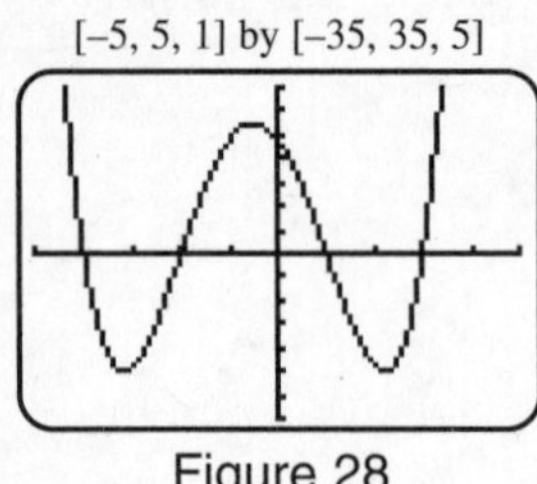

Figure 28

[-5, 5, 1] by [-20, 50, 5]

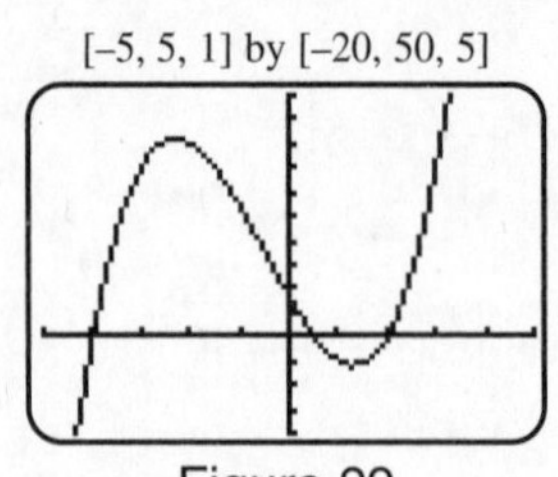

Figure 29

29. The graph of $Y_1 = 2X\text{^}3 + 3X\text{^}2 - 18X + 8$ is shown in Figure 29. From the graph, the $x$-intercepts of $f$ are located at $-4, \frac{1}{2}$, and 2. Three $x$-intercepts is the maximum number possible for a cubic polynomial. The leading coefficient is $a_n = 2$. Thus $f(x) = 2(x + 4)\left(x - \frac{1}{2}\right)(x - 2)$.

30. $f(x) = (x + 2)^2(x - 2)^3$ has a leading coefficient of 1. Other leading coefficients are possible.

31. The graph has $x$-intercepts or zeros of $x = -2, 1, 3 \Rightarrow$ it has factors $(x + 2)(x - 1)(x - 3)$.

    Since $f(0) = 3$ we can solve for the leading coefficient $a$ by setting $a(0 + 2)(0 - 1)(0 - 3) = 3$ and solving $\Rightarrow a(2)(-1)(-3) = 3 \Rightarrow 6a = 3 \Rightarrow a = \frac{1}{2}$.

    The complete factored form is: $f(x) = \frac{1}{2}(x + 2)(x - 1)(x - 3)$.

32. (a) Once

    (b) Twice

    (c) Three times

33. By the rational zeros test, any rational zero of $2x^3 + x^2 - 13x + 6$ must be one of the following: $\pm 6, \pm 3, \pm 2, \pm 1, \pm\frac{3}{2}, \pm\frac{1}{2}$. By evaluating $f$ at each of these values we find that the three rational zeros are $-3, \frac{1}{2}$, and 2.

34. By the rational zeros test, any rational zero of $x^3 + x^2 - 11x - 11$ must be one of the following: $\pm 11, \pm 1$. By evaluating $f$ at each of these values we find that the only rational zeros is –1. The best way to find the complete factored form of $f$ is to factor it by grouping.

35. $9x = 3x^3 \Rightarrow 3x^3 - 9x = 0 \Rightarrow 3x(x^2 - 3) = 0 \Rightarrow x = 0, \pm\sqrt{3}$

36. $x^3 - x^2 - 6x = 0 \Rightarrow x(x^2 - x - 6) = 0 \Rightarrow x(x - 3)(x + 2) = 0 \Rightarrow x = -2, 0, 3$

37. $x^4 - 3x^2 + 2 = 0 \Rightarrow (x^2 - 1)(x^2 - 2) = 0 \Rightarrow (x + 1)(x - 1)(x^2 - 2) = 0 \Rightarrow x = \pm 1, \pm\sqrt{2}$

38. $2x^3 + x^2 = 6x + 3 \Rightarrow 2x^3 + x^2 - 6x - 3 = 0 \Rightarrow (2x^3 + x^2) - (6x + 3) = 0 \Rightarrow$
    $x^2(2x + 1) - 3(2x + 1) = 0 \Rightarrow (x^2 - 3)(2x + 1) = 0 \Rightarrow x = -\frac{1}{2}, \pm\sqrt{3}$

39. The $x$-intercepts on the graph of $Y_1 = X\text{^}3 - 3X + 1$ are approximately $-1.88$, 0.35 and 1.53. See Figure 39.

[–10, 10, 1] by [–10, 10, 1]

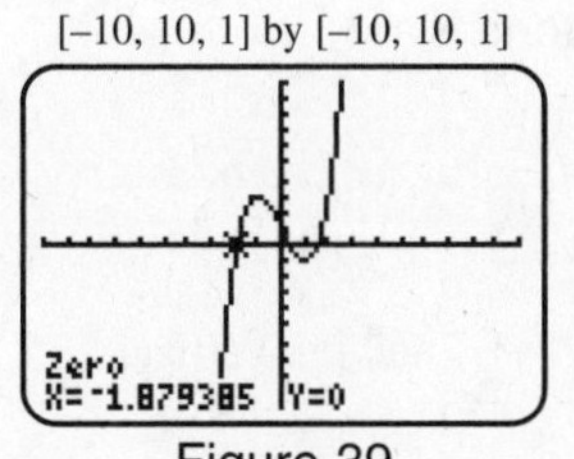


Figure 39

[–10, 10, 1] by [–10, 10, 1]

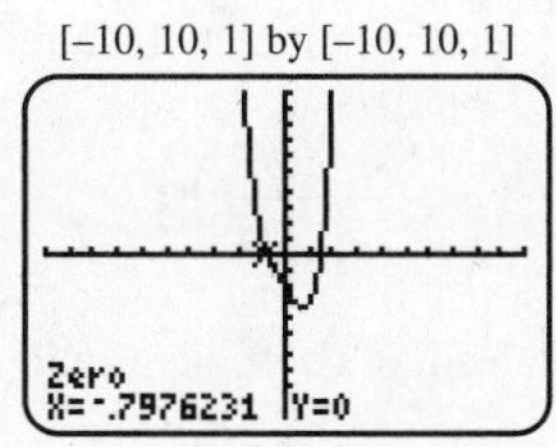


Figure 40

40. The $x$-intercepts on the graph of $Y_1 = X\text{^}4 - 2X - 2$ are approximately $-0.80$ and 1.49. See Figure 40.

41. $(2 - 2i) + (-3 + 2i) = (2 + (-3)) + (-2 + 2)i = -1$

42. $(-5 + 4i) - (-3 - 4i) = (-5 + 3) + (4 + 4)i = -2 + 8i$

43. $(3 + 2i)^2 = (3 + 2i)(3 + 2i) = 9 + 12i + 4i^2 = 9 + 12i - 4 = 5 + 12i$

44. $\frac{3 + i}{1 + i} \cdot \frac{1 - i}{1 - i} = \frac{3 - 3i + i - i^2}{1 - i^2} = \frac{4 - 2i}{2} = 2 - i$

45. $x^3 + x = 0 \Rightarrow x(x^2 + 1) = 0 \Rightarrow x = 0$ or $x = \pm i$

46. $x^4 + 3x^2 + 2 = 0 \Rightarrow (x^2 + 1)(x^2 + 2) = 0 \Rightarrow x = \pm i$ or $x = \pm i\sqrt{2}$

47. Graph $Y_1 = X^3 - 3X^2 + 3X - 9$ in [–5, 5, 1] by [–25, 25, 5] (not shown). Its graph crosses the $x$-axis once. Therefore, $f$ has one real zero. Since $f$ is degree 3, there must be two imaginary zeros.

48. $f(x) = 4(x - 1)(x - 3i)(x + 3i)$; the expanded form is $f(x) = 4x^3 - 4x^2 + 36x - 36$.

49. The easiest way to factor a polynomial is to determine its zeros. Then, we can find its complete factorization. If one graphs $f(x) = 2x^2 + 4$, it does not intersect the $x$-axis. Therefore, there are no real zeros. However, the Fundamental Theorem of Algebra tells us that it must have complex zeros. These can be found by solving for $x$. $2x^2 + 4 = 0 \Rightarrow 2x^2 = -4 \Rightarrow x^2 = -2 \Rightarrow x = \pm\sqrt{-2} \Rightarrow x = \pm i\sqrt{2}$

Since $a_n = 2$, the complete factorization is

$f(x) = 2(x - i\sqrt{2})(x - (-i\sqrt{2})) = 2(x - i\sqrt{2})(x + i\sqrt{2})$.

50. A quadratic equation has 4 solutions, since it has 2 $x$-intercepts it has 2 real solutions and then must have 2 imaginary solutions. Setting $2x^4 - x^2 - 1 = 0$ and solving will find them. $2x^4 - x^2 - 1 = 0 \Rightarrow$

$(2x^2 + 1)(x^2 - 1) = 0 \Rightarrow (2x^2 + 1)(x + 1)(x - 1) = 0 \Rightarrow x = \pm 1, \pm\sqrt{-\frac{1}{2}} \Rightarrow x = \pm 1, \pm\frac{i\sqrt{2}}{2}$.

51. If $i$ is a zero then $-i$ is also a zero $\Rightarrow (x + i)(x - i)$ or $x^2 + 1$ is a factor. By polynomial long division:

$$\begin{array}{r}
x^2 + x + 1 \\
x^2 + 1 \overline{)\, x^4 + x^3 + 2x^2 + x + 1} \\
\underline{x^4 \qquad + x^2 \qquad\qquad} \\
x^3 + x^2 + x + 1 \\
\underline{x^3 \qquad + x \qquad} \\
x^2 \qquad + 1 \\
\underline{x^2 \qquad + 1} \\
0
\end{array}$$

Solve for $x^2 + x + 1 = 0$ using the quadratic formula: $x = \frac{-1 \pm \sqrt{1 - 4(1)(1)}}{2(1)} = \frac{-1 \pm \sqrt{-3}}{2} =$

$-\frac{1}{2} \pm \frac{i\sqrt{3}}{2}$. Therefore the zeros are $\pm i, -\frac{1}{2} \pm \frac{i\sqrt{3}}{2}$ and the complete factored form is:

$f(x) = (x + i)(x - i)\left(x - \left(-\frac{1}{2} + \frac{i\sqrt{3}}{2}\right)\right)\left(x - \left(-\frac{1}{2} - \frac{i\sqrt{3}}{2}\right)\right)$

52. The $D\left\{x \mid x \neq -\frac{4}{5}\right\}$; the horizontal asymptote is the leading coefficient ratio $y = \frac{3}{5}$, and the vertical asymptote is the zero of the denominator $x = -\frac{4}{5}$.

53. Horizontal asymptote: since the degree of the numerator and denominator is the same the horizontal asymptote is the leading coefficient ratio $y = \frac{2}{3}$. Vertical asymptotes: they can be found by finding the zero's of the denominator that are not zeros of the numerator

$\Rightarrow$ solve: $3x^2 + 8x - 3 \Rightarrow (3x - 1)(x + 3) = 0 \Rightarrow x = -3, \frac{1}{3}$. However, $x = -3$ is not a vertical asymptote because $-3$ is a zero of the numerator.

The horizontal asymptote is $y = \frac{2}{3}$ and the vertical asymptote is $x = \frac{1}{3}$.

54. (a) $x^2 - 4 = 0 \Rightarrow x^2 = 4 \Rightarrow x = \pm 2; D = \{x \mid x \neq \pm 2\}$

(b) Since the degree of the numerator equals the degree of the denominator and the ratio of the leading coefficients is $\frac{2}{1} = 2$, the horizontal asymptote is $y = 2$. There are vertical asymptotes at $x = \pm 2$.

(c) The graph of $f$ using dot mode is shown in Figure 54c.

(d) First, sketch the vertical and horizontal asymptotes found in part (c). Then use Figure 54a as a guide to a more complete graph of $f$. The sketch is shown in Figure 54d.

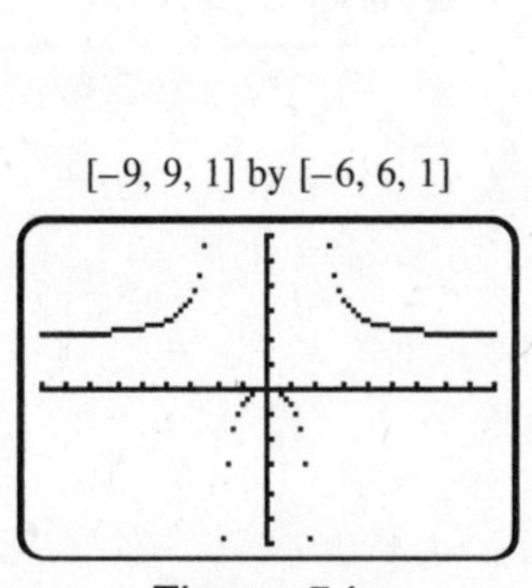


Figure 54c

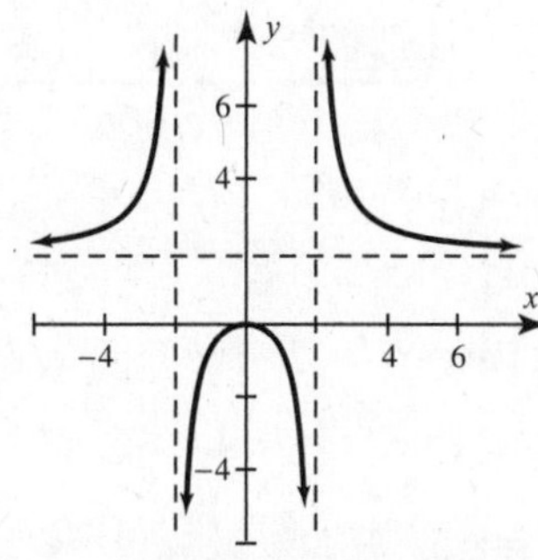


Figure 54d

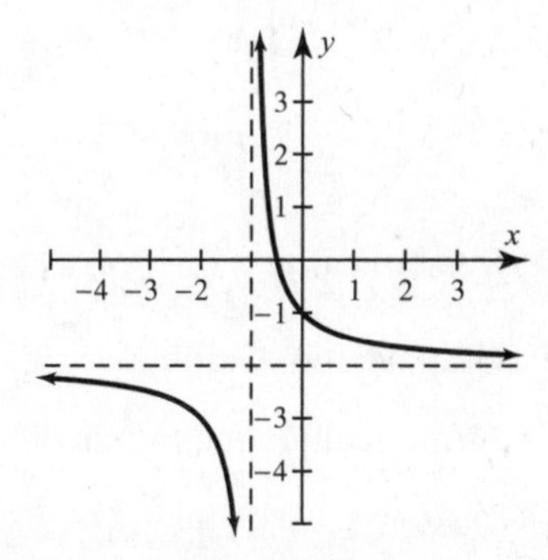


Figure 55

55. $g(x)$ is the function $f(x) = \frac{1}{x}$ shifted 1 left and 2 down. See Figure 55.

56. $g(x) = \frac{x}{x - 1}$ is like the function $f(x) = \frac{1}{x}$ with a horizontal asymptote of $y = 1$ and a vertical asymptote of $x = 1$. See Figure 56.

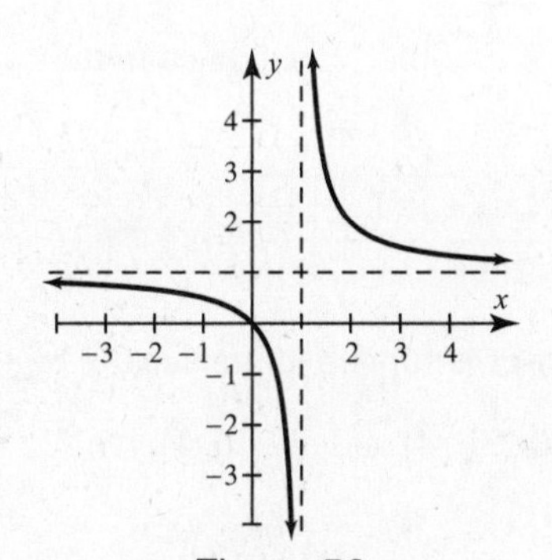


Figure 56

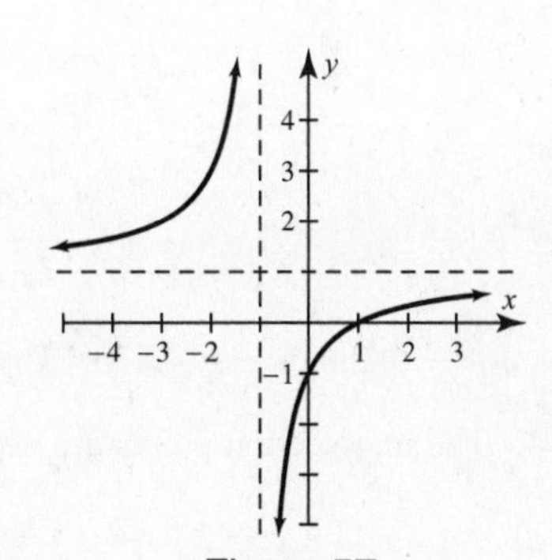


Figure 57

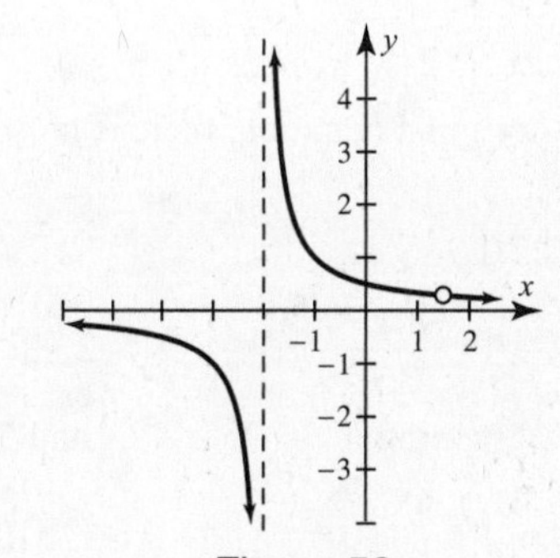


Figure 58

57. $g(x) = \frac{x^2 - 1}{x^2 + 2x + 1} \Rightarrow g(x) = \frac{(x + 1)(x - 1)}{(x + 1)(x + 1)} \Rightarrow g(x) = \frac{(x - 1)}{(x + 1)} \Rightarrow g(x) = \frac{x - 1}{x + 1}$. This is similar to $f(x) = \frac{1}{x}$ with a horizontal asymptote of $y = 1$ and a vertical asymptote of $x = -1$. See Figure 57.

58. $g(x) = \frac{2x - 3}{2x^2 + x - 6} \Rightarrow g(x) = \frac{2x - 3}{(2x - 3)(x + 2)} \Rightarrow g(x) = \frac{1}{x + 2}$, which is the graph of $f(x) = \frac{1}{x}$ shifted 2 units left. See Figure 58.

59. One example of a function that has a vertical asymptote at $x = -2$ and a horizontal asymptote at $y = 2$ is shown in Figure 59.

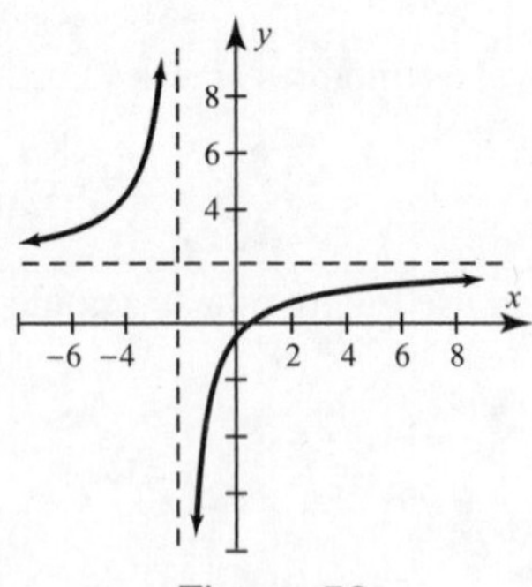


Figure 59

[−9.4, 9.4, 1] by [−6.2, 6.2, 1]

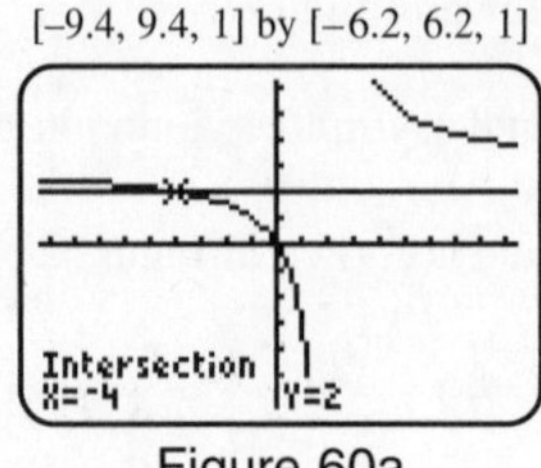


Figure 60a

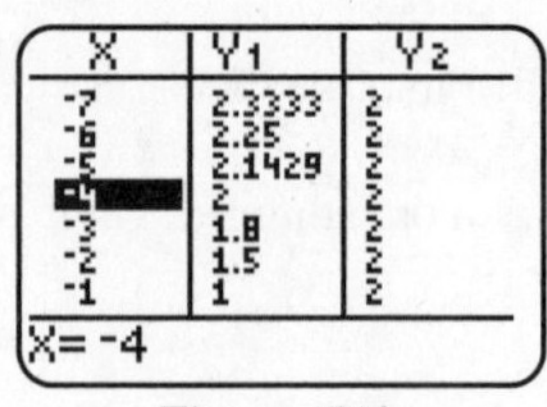


Figure 60b

60. Symbolically: $\dfrac{3x}{x-2} = 2 \Rightarrow 3x = 2(x-2) \Rightarrow 3x = 2x - 4 \Rightarrow x = -4.$

Graphically: Graph $Y_1 = 3X/(X-2)$ and $Y_2 = 2$. See Figure 60a. From the graph, $x = -4$.

Numerically: See Figure 60b. From the table, $x = -4$.

61. $\dfrac{5x+1}{x+3} = 3 \Rightarrow 5x + 1 = 3(x+3) \Rightarrow 5x + 1 = 3x + 9 \Rightarrow 2x = 8 \Rightarrow x = 4$

This answer is supported graphically by graphing $Y_1 = (5X+1)/(X+3)$ and $Y_2 = 3$. The intersection point is $(4, 3)$. Making a table of $Y_1$ starting at 0 and incrementing by 1 will support this result numerically.

62. $\dfrac{1}{x} - \dfrac{1}{x^2} + 2 = 0 \Rightarrow x - 1 + 2x^2 = 0 \Rightarrow 2x^2 + x - 1 = 0 \Rightarrow (2x-1)(x+1) = 0 \Rightarrow x = \dfrac{1}{2}$ or $-1$

This answer is supported graphically by graphing $Y_1 = 1/X - 1/X^\wedge 2 + 2$. The $x$-intercepts are $-1$ and $0.5$. Making a table of $Y_1$ starting at $-2$ and incrementing by 0.5 will support this result numerically.

63. $\dfrac{1}{x+2} + \dfrac{1}{x-2} = \dfrac{4}{x^2-4} \Rightarrow x - 2 + x + 2 = 4 \Rightarrow 2x - 4 \Rightarrow x = 2.$ Since 2 is defined in the original equation, there is no solution.

64. $x - \dfrac{1}{x} = 4 \Rightarrow x^2 - 1 = 4x \Rightarrow x^2 - 4x - 1 = 0 \Rightarrow x = \dfrac{4 \pm \sqrt{(-4)^2 - 4(1)(-1)}}{2(1)} \Rightarrow$

$x = \dfrac{4 \pm \sqrt{20}}{2} \Rightarrow x = 2 \pm \sqrt{5}$ or $x \approx -0.236$ or $x \approx 4.236$; This answer is supported graphically by graphing $Y_1 = X - 1/X$ and $Y_2 = 4$. The intersection points are near $(-0.236, 4)$ and $(4.236, 4)$.

65. $\dfrac{x+5}{x-2} = \dfrac{x-1}{x+1} \Rightarrow (x+5)(x+1) = (x-1)(x-2) \Rightarrow x^2 + 6x + 5 = x^2 - 3x + 2 \Rightarrow$

$9x = -3 \Rightarrow x = -\dfrac{1}{3}$; Check: $\dfrac{-\frac{1}{3}+5}{-\frac{1}{3}-2} = \dfrac{-\frac{1}{3}-1}{-\frac{1}{3}+1} \Rightarrow \dfrac{\frac{14}{3}}{-\frac{7}{3}} = \dfrac{-\frac{4}{3}}{\frac{2}{3}} \Rightarrow -2 = -2$

66. $\dfrac{2x-5}{3x+1} = 5 \Rightarrow 2x - 5 = 5(3x+1) \Rightarrow 2x - 5 = 15x + 5 \Rightarrow 13x = -10 \Rightarrow x = \dfrac{-10}{13}$

Check: $\dfrac{2(\frac{-10}{13}) - 5}{3(\frac{-10}{13}) + 1} = 5 \Rightarrow \dfrac{\frac{-20}{13} - 5}{\frac{-30}{13} + 1} = 5 \Rightarrow \dfrac{\frac{-85}{13}}{\frac{-17}{13}} = 5 \Rightarrow 5 = 5$

67. (a) $(-\infty, -4) \cup (-2, 3)$; In set builder notation the interval is $\{x \mid x < -4 \text{ or } -2 < x < 3\}$.

(b) $(-4, -2) \cup (3, \infty)$; In set builder notation the interval is $\{x \mid -4 < x < -2 \text{ or } x > 3\}$.

68. (a) $(-\infty, -2) \cup (2, \infty)$; In set builder notation the interval is $\{x \mid x < -2 \text{ or } x > 2\}$.

(b) $(-2, 0) \cup (0, 2)$; In set builder notation the interval is $\{x \mid -2 < x < 0 \text{ or } 0 < x < 2\}$.

69. Find the boundary numbers by solving $x^3 + x^2 - 6x = 0$.

$x^3 + x^2 - 6x = 0 \Rightarrow x(x^2 + x - 6) = 0 \Rightarrow x(x + 3)(x - 2) = 0 \Rightarrow x = -3, 0 \text{ or } 2.$

The boundary values divide the number line into four intervals. Choose a test value from each of these intervals and evaluate $x^3 + x^2 - 6x$ for these values. See Figure 69. The solution is $(-3, 0) \cup (2, \infty)$; In set builder notation the interval is $\{x \mid -3 < x < 0 \text{ or } x > 2\}$.

| Interval | Test Value $x$ | $x^3 + x^2 - 6x$ | Positive or Negative? |
|---|---|---|---|
| $(-\infty, -3)$ | $-4$ | $-24$ | Negative |
| $(-3, 0)$ | $-1$ | 6 | Positive |
| $(0, 2)$ | 1 | $-4$ | Negative |
| $(2, \infty)$ | 3 | 18 | Positive |

Figure 69

70. Write the inequality as $x^4 - 5x^2 + 4 < 0$.

Then Graph $Y_1 = X\text{^}4 - 5X\text{^}2 + 4$ as shown in Figure 70. The $x$-intercepts are $-2, -1, 1$, and 2.

The graph is below the $x$-axis on the interval $(-2, -1) \cup (1, 2)$; In set builder notation the interval is $\{x \mid -2 < x < -1 \text{ or } 1 < x < 2\}$

71. Graph $Y_1 = (2X - 1)/(X + 2)$ using dot mode as shown in Figure 71. The graph has a vertical asymptote at $x = -2$ and an $x$-intercept at $x = \frac{1}{2}$. The graph is above the $x$-axis on the interval $(-\infty, -2) \cup \left(\frac{1}{2}, \infty\right)$;

In set builder notation the interval is $\left\{x \mid x < -2 \text{ or } x > \frac{1}{2}\right\}$

[-4, 4, 1] by [-5, 5, 1]

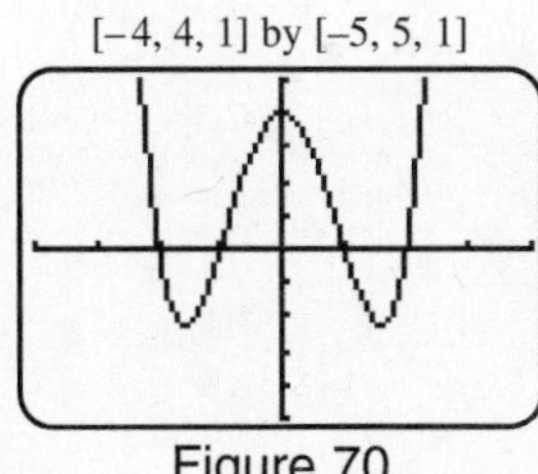

Figure 70

[-8, 4, 2] by [-5, 5, 1]

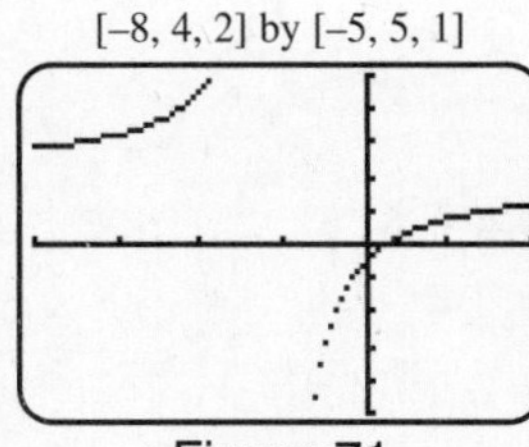

Figure 71

[-5, 5, 1] by [-5, 5, 1]

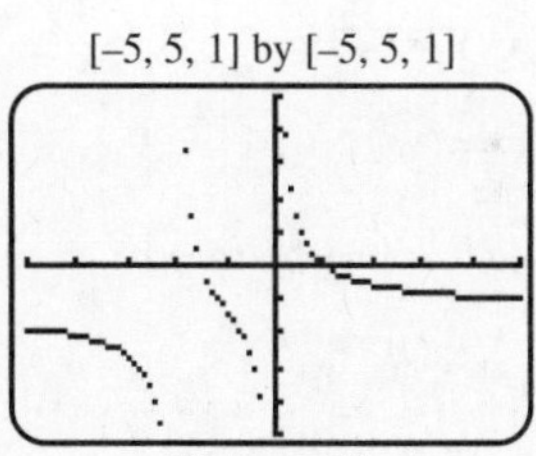

Figure 72

72. First, rewrite the inequality:

$$\frac{1}{x} + \frac{1}{x+2} \le \frac{4}{3} \Rightarrow \frac{1}{x} + \frac{1}{x+2} - \frac{4}{3} \le 0 \Rightarrow \frac{3(x+2) + 3x - 4x(x+2)}{3x(x+2)} \le 0 \Rightarrow$$

$\frac{-4x^2 - 2x + 6}{3x(x+2)} \le 0$. Graph $Y_1 = (-\,4X\text{^}2 - 2X + 6)/(3X(X + 2))$ using dot mode as shown in Figure 72. The graph has vertical asymptotes at $x = -2$ and $x = 0$ and $x$-intercepts $x = -1.5$ and $x = 1$. The graph of $Y_1$ intersects or is below the $x$-axis on the interval $(-\infty, -2) \cup [-1.5, 0) \cup [1, \infty)$. In set builder notation the interval is $\{x \mid x < -2 \text{ or } -1.5 \le x < 0 \text{ or } x \ge 1\}$

73. $(36^{3/4})^2 = 36^{3/2} = (\sqrt{36}\,)^3 = 6^3 = 216$

74. $(9^{-3/2})^{-2} = 9^3 = 729$

75. $(2^{-3/2} \cdot 2^{1/2})^{-3} = (2^{-3/2+1/2})^{-3} = (2^{-1})^{-3} = 2^3 = 8$

76. $\left(\dfrac{4}{9}\right)^{-3/2} = \left(\dfrac{9}{4}\right)^{3/2} = \left(\sqrt{\dfrac{9}{4}}\right)^3 = \left(\dfrac{3}{2}\right)^3 = \dfrac{27}{8}$

77. $\sqrt[3]{x^4} = x^{4/3}$

78. $(\sqrt[4]{z})^{-1/2} = (z^{1/4})^{-1/2} = z^{-1/8} = \dfrac{1}{z^{1/8}}$

79. $\sqrt[3]{y \cdot \sqrt{y}} = (y \cdot y^{1/2})^{1/3} = (y^{3/2})^{1/3} = y^{1/2}$

80. $\sqrt{x} \cdot \sqrt[3]{x^2} \cdot \sqrt[4]{x^3} = x^{1/2} \cdot x^{2/3} \cdot x^{3/4} = x^{1/2+2/3+3/4} = x^{23/12}$

81. $D = \{x \mid x \geq 0\}$; $f(3) = 3^{5/2} \approx 15.59$

82. $D = \{x \mid x \neq 0\}$; $f(3) = 3^{-2/3} \approx 0.48$

83. $x^5 = 1024 \Rightarrow x = \sqrt[5]{1024} = 4$ Check: $4^5 = 1024$

84. $x^{1/3} = 4 \Rightarrow x = 4^3 = 64$ Check: $64^{1/3} = 4$

85. $\sqrt{x - 2} = x - 4 \Rightarrow x - 2 = (x - 4)^2 \Rightarrow x - 2 = x^2 - 8x + 16 \Rightarrow x^2 - 9x + 18 = 0 \Rightarrow$
$(x - 6)(x - 3) = 0 \Rightarrow x = 3$ or $6$
Check: $\sqrt{3 - 2} \neq 3 - 4$ (not a solution); $\sqrt{6 - 2} = 2 = 6 - 4$. The only solution is $x = 6$.

86. $x^{3/2} = 27 \Rightarrow x = 27^{2/3} = 9$ Check: $9^{3/2} = 27$

87. $2x^{1/4} + 3 = 6 \Rightarrow 2x^{1/4} = 3 \Rightarrow x^{1/4} = \dfrac{3}{2} \Rightarrow x = \left(\dfrac{3}{2}\right)^4 \Rightarrow x = \dfrac{81}{16}$
Check: $2\left(\dfrac{81}{16}\right)^{1/4} + 3 = 2\left(\dfrac{3}{2}\right) + 3 = 3 + 3 = 6$

88. $\sqrt{x - 2} = 14 - x \Rightarrow x - 2 = (14 - x)^2 \Rightarrow x - 2 = 196 - 28x + x^2 \Rightarrow x^2 - 29x + 198 = 0 \Rightarrow$
$(x - 18)(x - 11) = 0 \Rightarrow x = 18$ or $11$
Check: $\sqrt{18 - 2} \neq 14 - 18$ (not a solution); $\sqrt{11 - 2} = 3 = 14 - 11$. The only solution is $x = 11$.

89. $\sqrt[3]{2x - 3} + 1 = 4 \Rightarrow \sqrt[3]{2x - 3} = 3 \Rightarrow 2x - 3 = 3^3 \Rightarrow 2x - 3 = 27 \Rightarrow 2x = 30 \Rightarrow x = 15$
Check: $\sqrt[3]{2(15) - 3} + 1 = \sqrt[3]{27} + 1 = 3 + 1 = 4$

90. $x^{1/3} + 3x^{1/3} = -2 \Rightarrow 4x^{1/3} = -2 \Rightarrow x^{1/3} = -\dfrac{1}{2} \Rightarrow x = \left(-\dfrac{1}{2}\right)^3 \Rightarrow x = -\dfrac{1}{8}$
Check: $\left(-\dfrac{1}{8}\right)^{1/3} + 3\left(-\dfrac{1}{8}\right)^{1/3} = -\dfrac{1}{2} - \dfrac{3}{2} = -\dfrac{4}{2} = -2$

91. $2n^{-2} - 5n^{-1} = 3 \Rightarrow 2(n^{-1})^2 - 5(n^{-1}) = 3$, let $u = n^{-1}$, then $2u^2 - 5u - 3 = 0 \Rightarrow$
$(2u + 1)(u - 3) = 0 \Rightarrow u = -\dfrac{1}{2}, 3$. If $u = n^{-1}$, then it follows that $n = u^{-1}$, thus $n = \left(-\dfrac{1}{2}\right)^{-1} \Rightarrow$
$n = -2$ or $n = (3)^{-1} \Rightarrow n = \dfrac{1}{3}$
Check: $2(-2)^{-2} - 5(-2)^{-1} = 3 \Rightarrow 2\left(\dfrac{1}{4}\right) - 5\left(-\dfrac{1}{2}\right) = 3 \Rightarrow \dfrac{1}{2} + \dfrac{5}{2} = 3 \Rightarrow 3 = 3$
Check: $2\left(\dfrac{1}{3}\right)^{-2} - 5\left(\dfrac{1}{3}\right)^{-1} = 3 \Rightarrow 2(9) - 5(3) = 3 \Rightarrow 18 - 15 = 3 \Rightarrow 3 = 3$
The solution are: $n = -2, \dfrac{1}{3}$.

92. $m^{-3} + 2m^{-2} + m^{-1} = 0 \Rightarrow (m^{-1})^3 + 2(m^{-1})^2 + (m^{-1}) = 0$, let $u = m^{-1}$, then $u^3 + 2u^2 + u = 0 \Rightarrow$

$u(u^2 + 2u + 1) = 0 \Rightarrow u(u + 1)(u + 1) = 0 \Rightarrow u = -1, 0$. If $u = m^{-1}$, then it follows that $m = u^{-1}$,

thus $m = (-1)^{-1} \Rightarrow m = -1$ or $m = (0)^{-1} \Rightarrow m = \frac{1}{0}$, which is undefined.

Check: $(-1)^{-3} + 2(-1)^{-2} + (-1)^{-1} = 0 \Rightarrow -1 + 2 + (-1) = 0 \Rightarrow 0 = 0$. The solution is: $m = -1$.

93. $k^{2/3} - 4k^{1/3} - 5 = 0 \Rightarrow (k^{1/3})^2 - 4(k^{1/3}) - 5 = 0$, let $u = k^{1/3}$, then $u^2 - 4u - 5 = 0 \Rightarrow$

$(u - 5)(u + 1) = 0 \Rightarrow u = -1, 5$. If $u = k^{1/3}$, then it follows that $k = u^3$, thus $k = (-1)^3 \Rightarrow$

$k = -1$ or $k = (5)^3 \Rightarrow k = 125$.

Check: $(-1)^{2/3} - 4(-1)^{1/3} - 5 = 0 \Rightarrow 1 - (-4) - 5 = 0 \Rightarrow 0 = 0$

Check: $(125)^{2/3} - 4(125)^{1/3} - 5 = 0 \Rightarrow 25 - 4(5) - 5 = 0 \Rightarrow 0 = 0$. The solutions are: $k = -1, 125$.

94. $x^{3/4} - 16x^{1/4} = 0 \Rightarrow (x^{1/4})^3 - 16(x^{1/4}) = 0$, let $u = x^{1/4}$, then $u^3 - 16u = 0 \Rightarrow u(u^2 - 16) = 0 \Rightarrow$

$u(u + 4)(u - 4) = 0 \Rightarrow u = -4, 0, 4$. If $u = x^{1/4}$, then it follows that $x = u^4$, thus $x = (-4)^4 \Rightarrow$

$x = 256$ or $x = (0)^4 \Rightarrow x = 0$ or $x = (4)^4 \Rightarrow x = 256$.

Check: $(0)^{3/4} - 16(0)^{1/4} = 0 \Rightarrow 0 - 0 = 0 \Rightarrow 0 = 0$.

Check: $(256)^{3/4} - 16(256)^{1/4} = 0 \Rightarrow 64 - 16(4) = 0 \Rightarrow 0 = 0$. The solutions are: $x = 0, 256$.

95. $\sqrt{x + 1} + 1 = \sqrt{2x} \Rightarrow (\sqrt{x + 1} + 1)^2 = 2x \Rightarrow x + 1 + 2\sqrt{x + 1} + 1 = 2x \Rightarrow$

$2\sqrt{x + 1} = x - 2 \Rightarrow 4(x + 1) = x^2 - 4x + 4 \Rightarrow 4x + 4 = x^2 - 4x + 4 \Rightarrow x^2 - 8x = 0 \Rightarrow$

$x(x - 8) = 0 \Rightarrow x = 0, 8$.

Check: $\sqrt{0 + 1} + 1 = \sqrt{2(0)} \Rightarrow 1 + 1 = 0 \Rightarrow 2 \neq 0 \Rightarrow 0$ is not a solution.

Check: $\sqrt{8 + 1} + 1 = \sqrt{2(8)} \Rightarrow 4 = 4$. The solution is: $x = 8$.

96. $\sqrt{x - 2} = 5 - \sqrt{x + 3} \Rightarrow (\sqrt{x - 2}\,)^2 = (5 - \sqrt{x + 3})^2 \Rightarrow x - 2 = 25 - 10\sqrt{x + 3} + x + 3 \Rightarrow$

$-30 = -10\sqrt{x + 3} \Rightarrow 900 = 100(x + 3) \Rightarrow 9 = x + 3 \Rightarrow x = 6$.

Check: $\sqrt{6 - 2} = 5 - \sqrt{6 + 3} \Rightarrow \sqrt{4} = 5 - \sqrt{9} \Rightarrow 2 = 5 - 3 \Rightarrow 2 = 2$. The solution is: $x = 6$.

97. (a) Dog: $f(24) = 1607(24)^{-0.75} \approx 148$ bpm; Person: $f(66) = 1607(66)^{-0.75} \approx 69$ bpm

(b) We must approximate the length of an animal with a heart rate of 400 bpm. To do this, solve the equation $f\,x) = 400$ or $1607x^{-0.75} = 400$ bpm.

$$1607x^{-0.75} = 400 \Rightarrow x^{-0.75} = \frac{400}{1607} \Rightarrow x^{0.75} = \frac{1607}{400} \Rightarrow x^{3/4} = \frac{1607}{400} \Rightarrow x = \left(\frac{1607}{400}\right)^{4/3} \approx 6.4$$

A six-inch animal such as a large bird or smaller rodent might have a heart rate of 400 bpm.

98. (a) $T(2) = \frac{1}{4-2} = \frac{1}{2}$; if vehicles leave the ramp randomly at the rate of 2 vehicles per minute, the average time spent waiting in line and paying the attendant is 30 seconds.

(b) See Figure 98.

(c) The waiting time increases as $x$ increases from 0 to 4.

(d) $T(x) = 5 \Rightarrow \frac{1}{4-x} = 5 \Rightarrow 1 = 5(4-x) \Rightarrow 1 = 20 - 5x \Rightarrow 5x = 19 \Rightarrow x = \frac{19}{5} \approx 3.8$

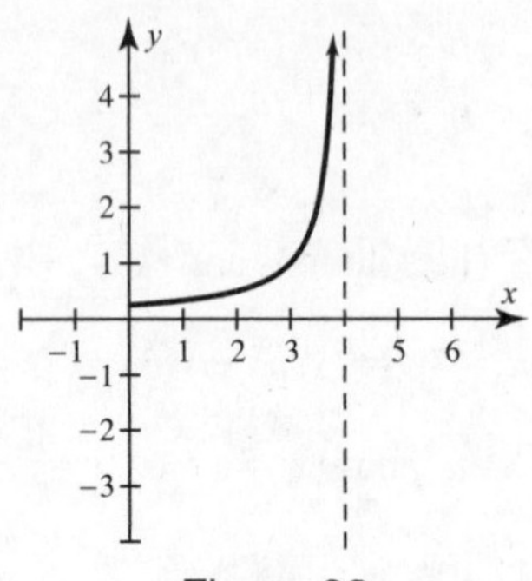

Figure 98

[0, 13, 1] by [0, 100, 10]

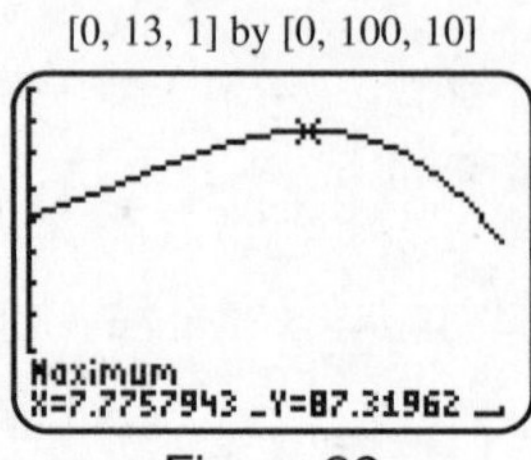


Figure 99

[0, 8, 1] by [0, 500, 100]

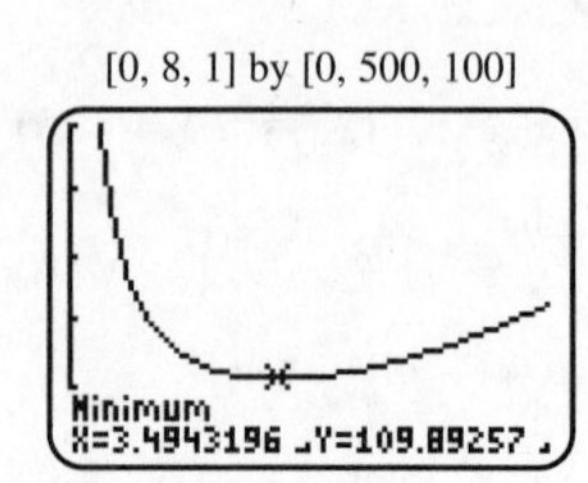


Figure 100

99. (a) May is $T(5) \Rightarrow T(5) = -0.064(5)^3 + 0.56(5)^2 + 2.9(5) + 61 \Rightarrow$

$T(5) = -8 + 14 + 14.5 + 61 \Rightarrow T(5) = 81.5$. The temperature in May is 81.5°F.

(b) Graph the function. See Figure 99. From the graph the ocean reaches a maximum temperature of about 87.3°F in July.

100. Let $x$ = width, then length = $3x$. If $V = l \cdot w \cdot h$ then $96 = 3x \cdot x \cdot h \Rightarrow 96 = 3x^2h$ and $h = \frac{96}{3x^2} \Rightarrow$

$h = \frac{32}{x^2}$. The surface area of the box is: $s(x) = l \cdot w + 2lh + 2wh$ or

$$s(x) = (3x)(x) + 2(3x)\left(\frac{32}{x^2}\right) + 2(x)\left(\frac{32}{x^2}\right) \Rightarrow s(x) = 3x^2 + \frac{192}{x} + \frac{64}{x} \Rightarrow s(x) = 3x^2 + \frac{256}{x}.$$

Graph the equation, See Figure 100. The minimum value for $x$ is: $x = 3.5$.

Therefore: width = 3.5 inches, length = 3(3.5) = 10.5 inches, and height $= \frac{32}{(3.5)^2} \approx 2.6$ inches.

The box is: $10.5 \times 3.5 \times 2.6$ inches.

101. Since the time is directly proportional to the square root of the height, the equation $t = k\sqrt{h}$ must hold. If it takes 1 second to drop 16 feet then $1 = k\sqrt{16} \Rightarrow k = 0.25$. Therefore, from a height of 256 feet the object will take $t = 0.25\sqrt{256} = 4$ seconds to strike the ground.

102. (a) Using power regression with the given data gives $a \approx 1.8342$ and $b \approx -0.4839$. Thus

$f(x) \approx 1.8342x^{-0.4839}$.

(b) $f(3) \approx 1.8342(3)^{-0.4839} \approx 1.08$; the elephant's stepping frequency would be about 1.08 steps per second.

## Extended and Discovery Exercise for Chapter 4

1. (a) See Figure 1.

   (b) The velocity of the bike rider is 20 ft/sec at 10 seconds.

| $f(t) = t^2$ | $t_1 = 10$<br>$t_2 = 11$ | $t_1 = 10$<br>$t_2 = 10.1$ | $t_1 = 10$<br>$t_2 = 10.01$ | $t_1 = 10$<br>$t_2 = 10.001$ |
|---|---|---|---|---|
| average velocity (ft/sec) | 21 | 20.1 | 20.01 | 20.001 |

Figure 1

2. (a) See Figure 2.

   (b) The velocity of the bike rider is 0.25 ft/sec at 4 seconds.

| $f(t) = \sqrt{t}$ | $t_1 = 4$<br>$t_2 = 5$ | $t_1 = 4$<br>$t_2 = 4.1$ | $t_1 = 4$<br>$t_2 = 4.01$ | $t_1 = 4$<br>$t_2 = 4.001$ |
|---|---|---|---|---|
| average velocity (ft/sec) | 0.236 | 0.248 | 0.2498 | 0.24998 |

Figure 2

3. (a) $\dfrac{f(a+h)-f(a)}{h} = \dfrac{5(a+h)-5a}{h} = \dfrac{5a+5h-5a}{h} = \dfrac{5h}{h} = 5$

   (b) Since 5 is a constant, the instantaneous velocity is 5 as $h$ approaches 0.

   (c) At $a = 5, 10,$ and 15 the instantaneous velocity is 5.

4. (a) $\dfrac{f(a+h)-f(a)}{h} = \dfrac{(a+h)^2+2(a+h)-(a^2+2a)}{h} = \dfrac{a^2+2ah+h^2+2a+2h-a^2-2a}{h} =$

   $\dfrac{2ah+h^2+2h}{h} = \dfrac{h(2a+h+2)}{h} = 2a+h+2$

   (b) $2a + h + 2$ approaches $2a + 2$ as $h$ approaches 0. The instantaneous velocity is given by $2a + 2$.

   (c) At $a = 5, 2a + 2 = 12$; at $a = 10, 2a + 2 = 22$; at $a = 15, 2a + 2 = 32$

5. (a) $\dfrac{f(a+h)-f(a)}{h} = \dfrac{\frac{200}{a+h}-\frac{200}{a}}{h} = \dfrac{200a-200a-200h}{a(a+h)}\cdot\dfrac{1}{h} = \dfrac{-200h}{a(a+h)}\cdot\dfrac{1}{h} = -\dfrac{200}{a(a+h)}$

   (b) $-\dfrac{200}{a(a+h)}$ approaches $-\dfrac{200}{a^2}$ as $h$ approaches 0. The instantaneous velocity is given by $-\dfrac{200}{a^2}$.

   (c) At $a = 5, -\dfrac{200}{a^2} = -8$; at $a = 10, -\dfrac{200}{a^2} = -2$; at $a = 15, -\dfrac{200}{a^2} = -\dfrac{8}{9}$

6. (a) $\dfrac{f(a+h)-f(a)}{h} = \dfrac{(a+h)^3-a^3}{h} = \dfrac{a^3+3a^2h+3ah^2+h^3-a^3}{h} = \dfrac{3a^2h+3ah^2+h^3}{h} =$

   $\dfrac{h(3a^2+3ah+h^2)}{h} = 3a^2+3ah+h^2$

   (b) $3a^2 + 3ah + h^2$ approaches $3a^2$ as $h$ approaches 0. The instantaneous velocity is given by $3a^2$.

   (c) At $a = 5, 3a^2 = 75$; at $a = 10, 3a^2 = 300$; at $a = 15, 3a^2 = 675$

7. (a) $\dfrac{f(a+h)-f(a)}{h} = \dfrac{\sqrt{a+h}-\sqrt{a}}{h} = \dfrac{\sqrt{a+h}-\sqrt{a}}{h} \cdot \dfrac{\sqrt{a+h}+\sqrt{a}}{\sqrt{a+h}+\sqrt{a}} = \dfrac{(a+h)-a}{h(\sqrt{a+h}+\sqrt{a})} =$

$\dfrac{h}{h(\sqrt{a+h}+\sqrt{a})} = \dfrac{1}{\sqrt{a+h}+\sqrt{a}}$

(b) $\dfrac{1}{\sqrt{a+h}+\sqrt{a}}$ approaches $\dfrac{1}{2\sqrt{a}}$ as $h$ approaches 0. The instantaneous velocity is given by $\dfrac{1}{2\sqrt{a}}$.

(c) At $a = 5$, $\dfrac{1}{2\sqrt{a}} = \dfrac{1}{2\sqrt{5}} \approx 0.224$; at $a = 10$, $\dfrac{1}{2\sqrt{a}} = \dfrac{1}{2\sqrt{10}} \approx 0.158$;

at $a = 15$, $\dfrac{1}{2\sqrt{a}} = \dfrac{1}{2\sqrt{15}} \approx 0.129$

8. (a) See Figures 8a-d.

(b) Neither the graph of the linear function nor the graph of its average rate of change have any turning points.

(c) For any linear function, the graph of it average rate of change is a constant function whose value is equal to the slope of the graph of the linear function.

[−10, 10, 1] by [−10, 10, 1]

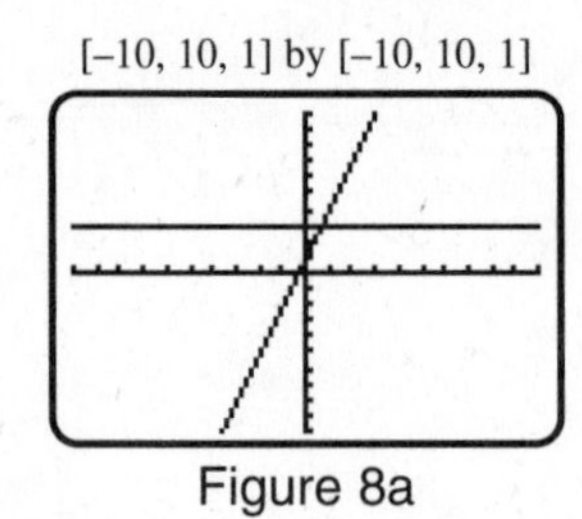

Figure 8a

[−10, 10, 1] by [−10, 10, 1]

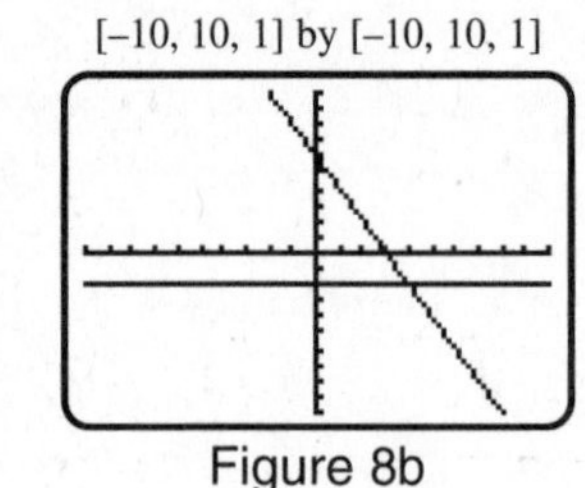

Figure 8b

[−10, 10, 1] by [−10, 10, 1]

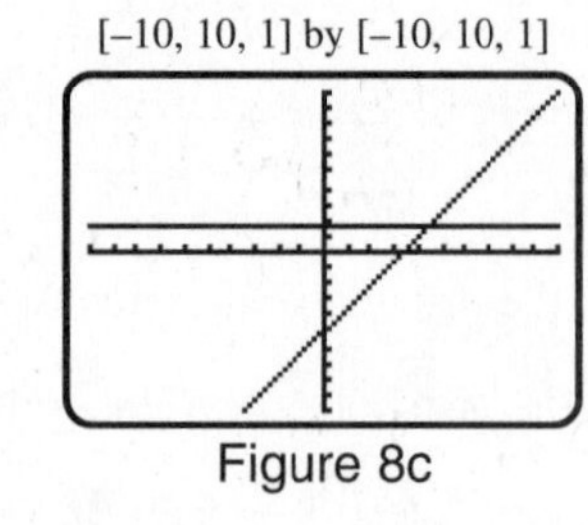

Figure 8c

[−10, 10, 1] by [−10, 10, 1]

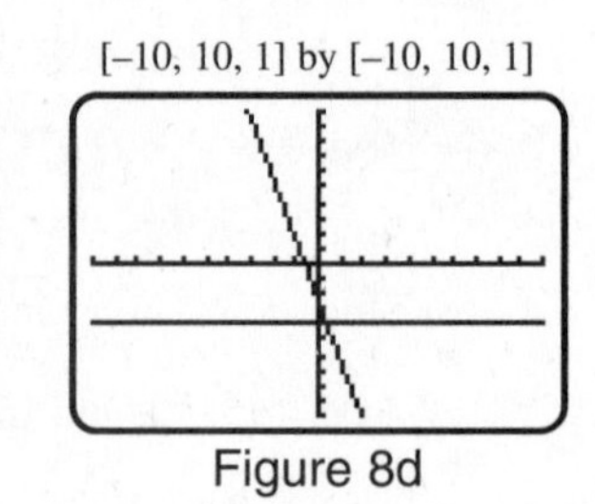

Figure 8d

9. (a) See Figures 9a-d.

(b) The graph of each quadratic function has one turning point, whereas the graph of its average rate of change has no turning points.

(c) For any quadratic function, the graph of its average rate of change is a linear function. If the leading coefficient of the quadratic function is negative, the slope of the corresponding linear function is negative. If the leading coefficient of the quadratic function is positive, then the slope of the corresponding linear function is positive.

[−10, 10, 1] by [−10, 10, 1]

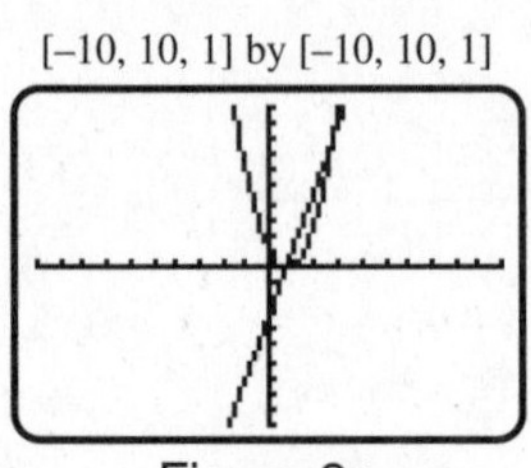

Figure 9a

[−10, 10, 1] by [−10, 10, 1]

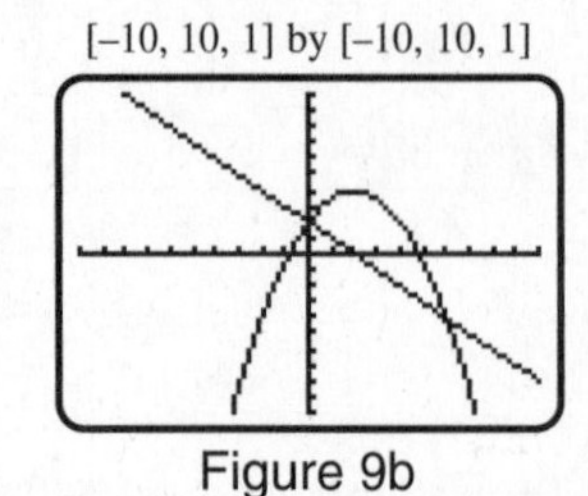

Figure 9b

[−10, 10, 1] by [−10, 10, 1]

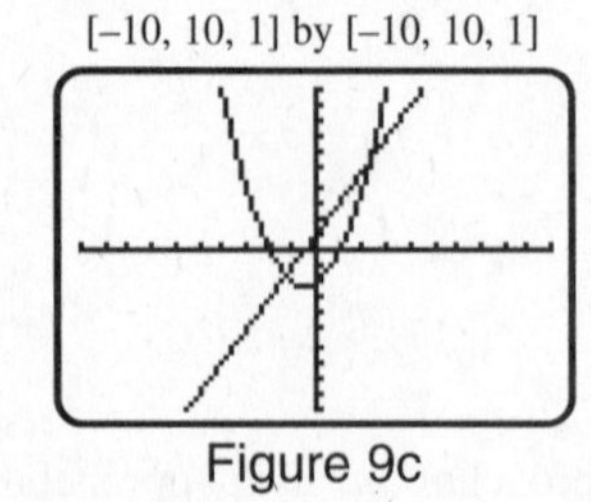

Figure 9c

[−10, 10, 1] by [−10, 10, 1]

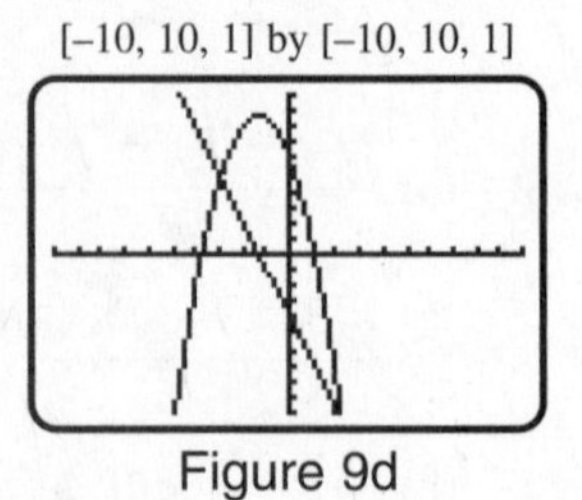

Figure 9d

10. (a) See Figures 10a-d.

    (b) The graph of each cubic function has two turning points or none, whereas the graph of its average rate of change has one turning point.

    (c) For any cubic function, the graph of its average rate of change is a quadratic function. The leading coefficient of the cubic function and the leading coefficient of its average rate of change have the same sign.

[−10, 10, 1] by [−10, 10, 1]

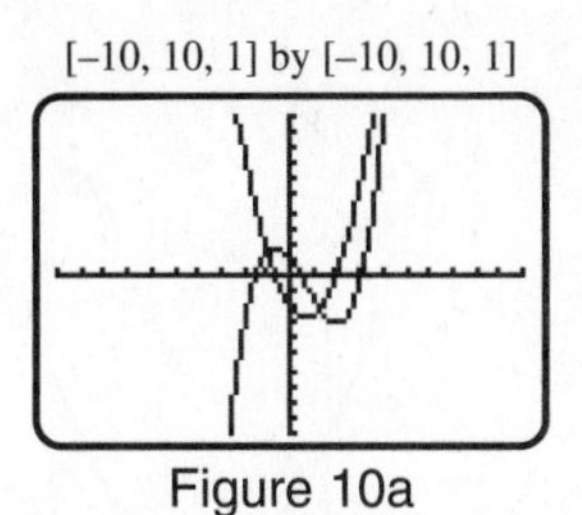

Figure 10a

[−10, 10, 1] by [−10, 10, 1]

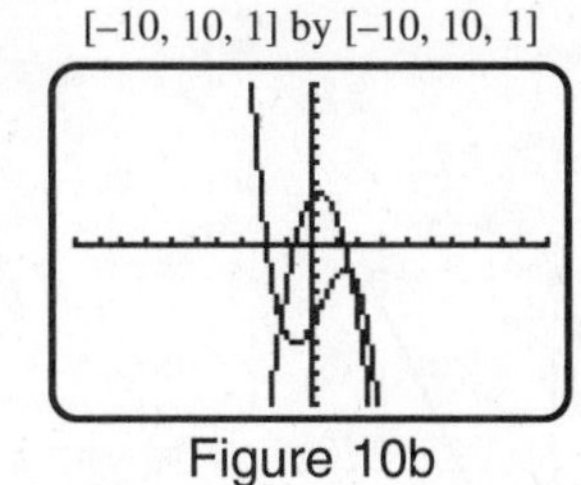

Figure 10b

[−10, 10, 1] by [−10, 10, 1]

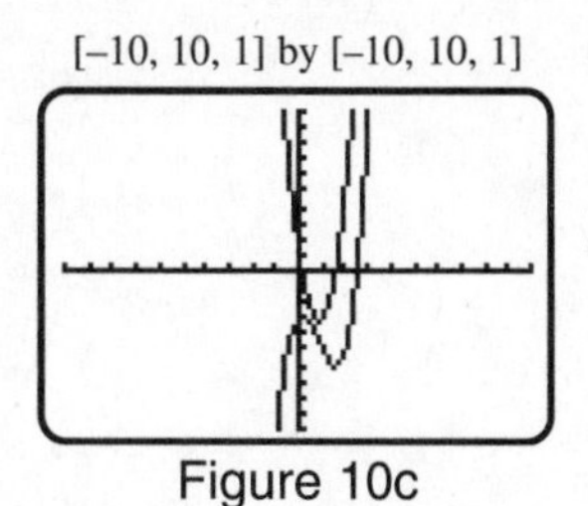

Figure 10c

[−10, 10, 1] by [−10, 10, 1]

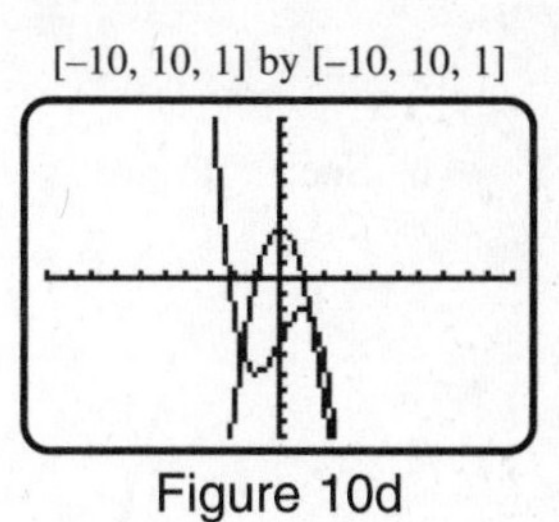

Figure 10d

11. (a) See Figures 11a-c.

    (b) The graph of each quartic function has one or three turning points, whereas the graph of its average rate of change has two turning point.

    (c) For any quartic function, the graph of its average rate of change is a cubic function. The leading coefficient of the quartic function and the leading coefficient of its average rate of change have the same sign.

[−10, 10, 1] by [−10, 10, 1]

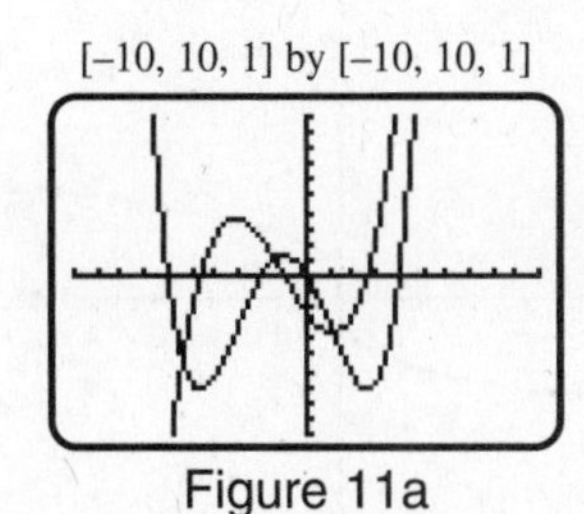

Figure 11a

[−10, 10, 1] by [−10, 10, 1]

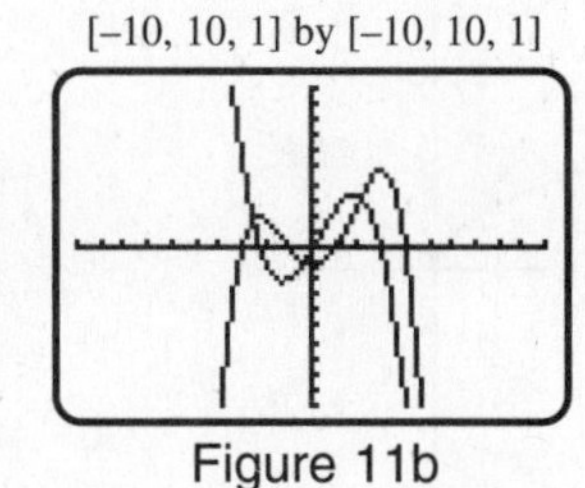

Figure 11b

[−10, 10, 1] by [−10, 10, 1]

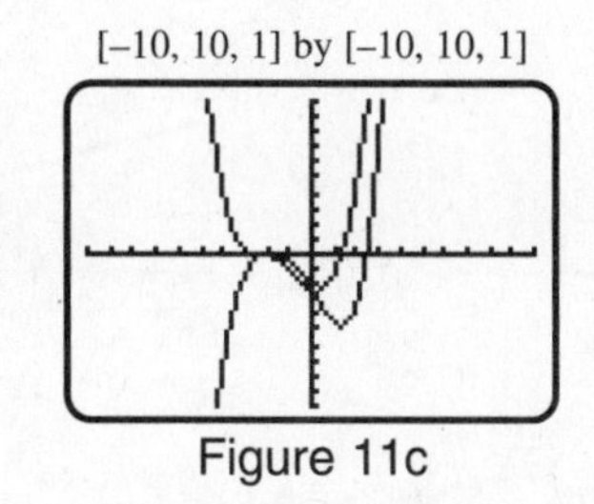

Figure 11c

## Chapters 1-4 Cumulative Review Exercises

1. Percent change is: $\dfrac{\text{change}}{\text{original quantity}} = \dfrac{54 - 45}{45} = \dfrac{9}{45} = 0.20$. Therefore a 20% change.

2. Move the decimal point two places to the right, $0.065 = 6.5 \times 10^{-2}$.

   Move the decimal point five places to the right, $7.88 \times 10^5 = 788{,}000$.

3. (a) $D = \{-3, -1, 0, 1\}$; $R = \{4, -2, 5\}$

   (b) No, all input must have unique outputs and $-1$ has an output of $-2$ and 5.

4. Using the distance formula: $D = \sqrt{(x_2 - x_1)^2 + (y_2 - y_1)^2}$ we get:

   $D = \sqrt{(3 - (-1))^2 + (-9 - 4)^2} \Rightarrow D = \sqrt{16 + 169} \Rightarrow D = \sqrt{185}$

5. $D = \{x \mid -2 \le x \le 2\}$; $R = \{x \mid 0 \le x \le 3\}$

6. (a) See Figure 6a.

   (b) See Figure 6b.

   (c) See Figure 6c.

   (d) See Figure 6d.

   (e) See Figure 6e.

   (f) See Figure 6f.

   (g) See Figure 6g.

   (h) See Figure 6h.

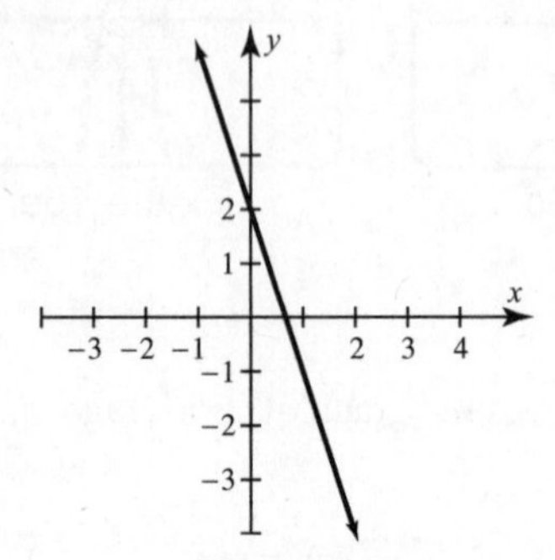

Figure 6a

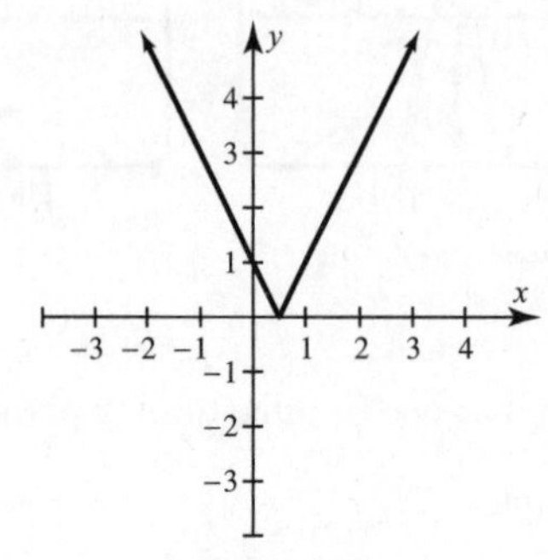

Figure 6b

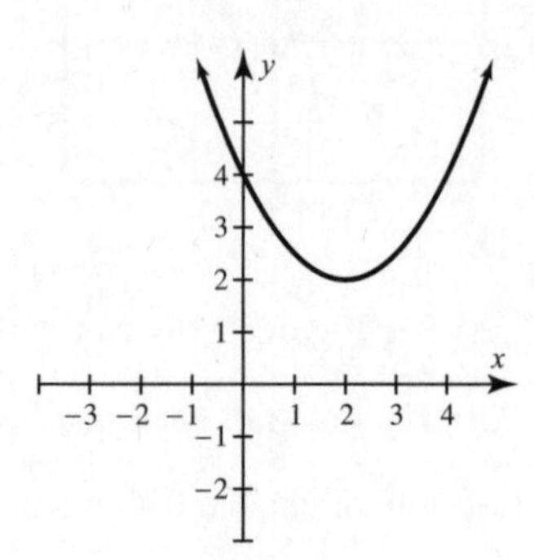

Figure 6c

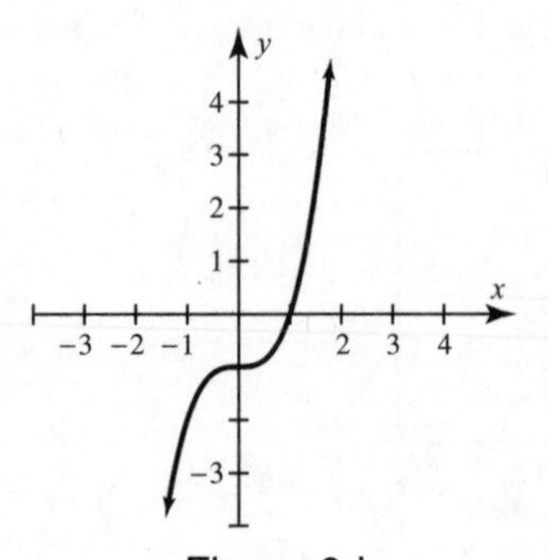

Figure 6d

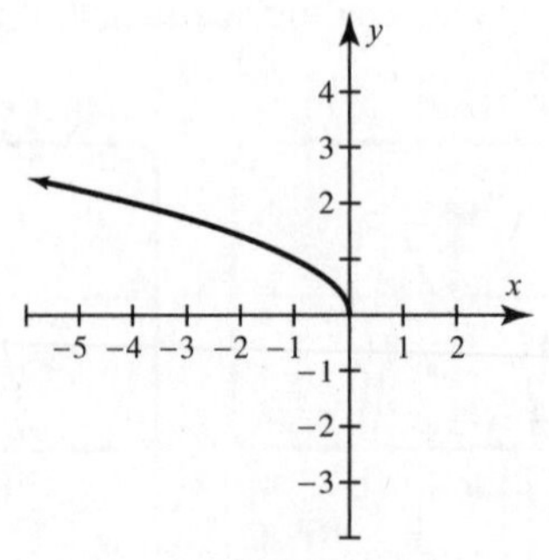

Figure 6e

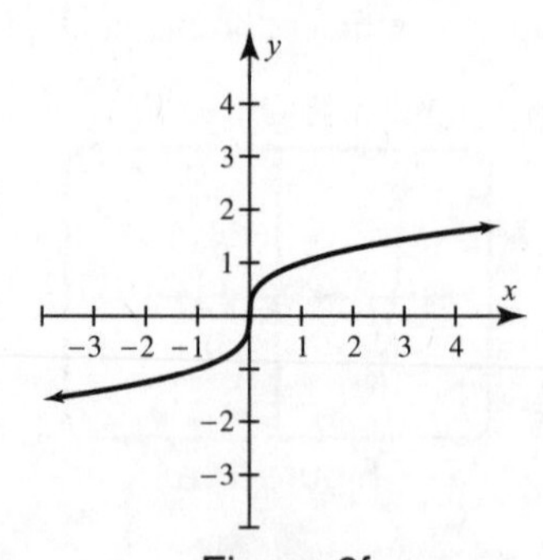

Figure 6f

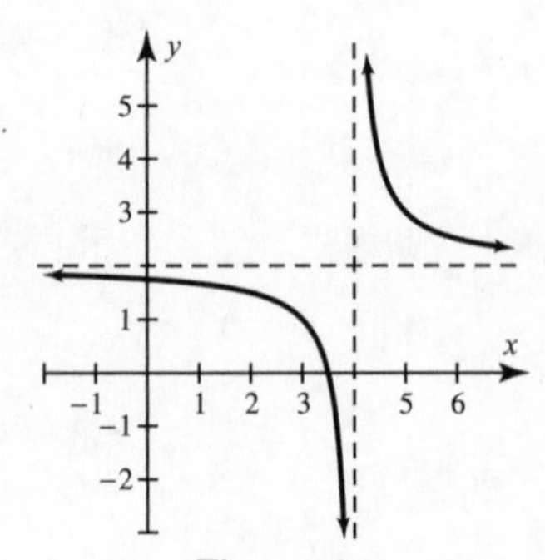

Figure 6g

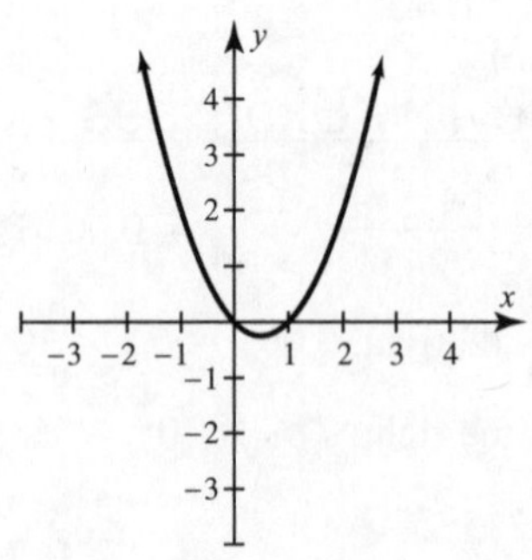

Figure 6h

7. (a) $D = \{x \mid x \leq -2 \text{ or } x \geq 2\}$, all numbers between $-2$ and 2 give the unreal solutions, square roots of negative numbers.

   (b) $f(2) = \sqrt{(2)^2 - 4} \Rightarrow f(2) = \sqrt{0} \Rightarrow f(2) = 0$

8. (a) Determinator cannot $= 0 \Rightarrow$ we find $3x^2 + 11x - 4 = 0 \Rightarrow (3x-1)(x+4) = 0 \Rightarrow x \neq -4, \frac{1}{3}$.

$D = \left\{x \mid x \neq -4 \text{ or } x \neq \frac{1}{3}\right\}$

(b) $f(2) = \dfrac{2(2)-3}{3(2)^2 + 11(2) - 4} \Rightarrow f(2) = \dfrac{1}{12 + 22 - 4} \Rightarrow f(2) = \dfrac{1}{30}$

9. $c(x) = 0.25x + 200$; $c(2000) = 0.25(2000) + 200 \Rightarrow c(2000) = 700$. The monthly cost of driving and maintaining a car driven 2000 miles is \$700.

10. (a) The graph intersects $(0, 1)$ and $(3, 0)$. The slope $= \dfrac{0-1}{3-0} = \dfrac{-1}{3} \Rightarrow m = -\dfrac{1}{3}$. The $y$-intercept is:1, and the $x$-intercept is: 3.

(b) Using slope intercept form: $f(x) = -\dfrac{1}{3}x + 1$

(c) $f(-3) = \dfrac{-1}{3}(-3) + 1 \Rightarrow f(-3) = 2$. When $x = -3, y = 2$ thus $f(-3) = 2$.

(d) $0 = \dfrac{-1}{3}(x) + 1 \Rightarrow \dfrac{-1}{3}x = -1 \Rightarrow x = 3$

11. $f(-3) = (-3)^3 - (-3) \Rightarrow f(-3) = -24$ or $(-3, -24)$; $f(-2) = (-2)^3 - (-2) \Rightarrow$

$f(-2) = -6$ or $(-2, -6)$. The average rate of change $= \dfrac{-6 - (-24)}{-2 - (-3)} = \dfrac{18}{1} = 18$.

12. $\dfrac{f(x+h) - f(x)}{h} = \dfrac{(x+h)^2 + 6(x+h) - (x^2 + 6x)}{h} = \dfrac{x^2 + 2xh + h^2 + 6x + 6h - x^2 - 6x}{h} =$

$\dfrac{2xh + h^2 + 6h}{h} = 2x + h + 6$

13. Slope $= \dfrac{(-4) - 5}{3 - (-2)} = \dfrac{-9}{5}$. Using point slope form $y = m(x - x_1) + y$ and point $(-2, 5)$ we get:

$y = \dfrac{-9}{5}(x+2) + 5 \Rightarrow y = \dfrac{-9}{5}x - \dfrac{18}{5} + 5 \Rightarrow y = \dfrac{-9}{5}x + \dfrac{7}{5}$

14. First convert $3x - 4y = 12$ to slope-intercept form. $3x - 4y = 12 \Rightarrow -4y = -3x + 12 \Rightarrow$

$y = \dfrac{3}{4}x - 3 \Rightarrow$ the slope is $\dfrac{3}{4}$. Then the slope of a line perpendicular to this is $-\dfrac{4}{3}$. Now use point-slope form $y = m(x - x_1) + y$, point $(-1, 4)$ and slope $-\dfrac{4}{3}$. We get $y = -\dfrac{4}{3}(x+1) + 4 \Rightarrow$

$y = -\dfrac{4}{3}x - \dfrac{4}{3} + 4 \Rightarrow y = -\dfrac{4}{3}x + \dfrac{8}{3}$

15. All lines parallel to the $x$-axis have 0 slope and will have graphs of $y =$ (the $y$-coordinate) $\Rightarrow y = -5$.

16. For the $x$-intercept $y = 0 \Rightarrow 5x - 4(0) = 10 \Rightarrow 5x = 10 \Rightarrow x = 2$. The $x$-intercept is $(2, 0)$ or 2. For the $y$-intercept $x = 0 \Rightarrow 5(0) - 4y = 10 \Rightarrow -4y = 10 \Rightarrow y = -\frac{5}{2}$. The $y$-intercept is $\left(0, -\frac{5}{2}\right)$ or $-\frac{5}{2}$. The graph is shown in Figure 16.

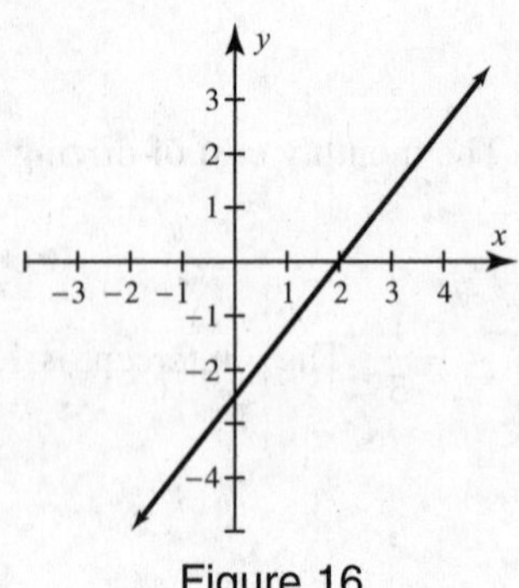

Figure 16

[–10, 10, 1] by [–10, 10, 1]

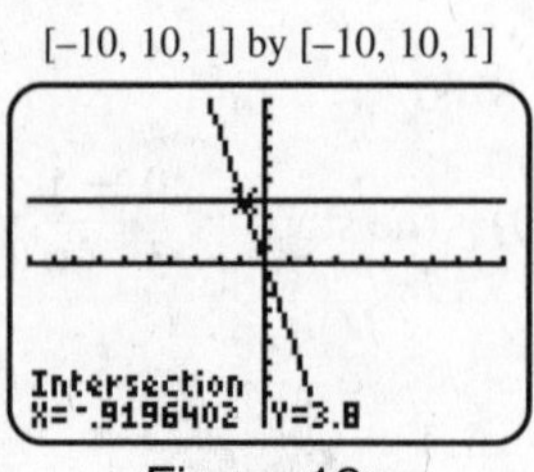

Figure 18a

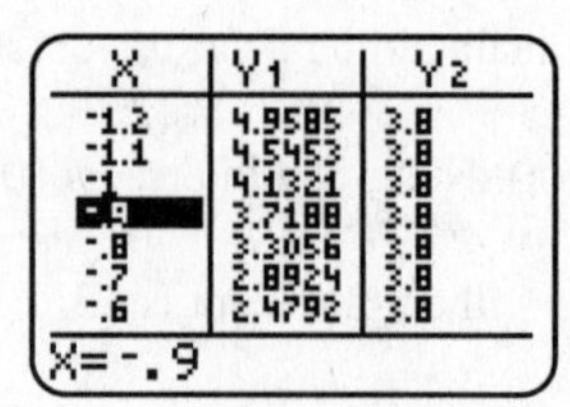

| X | Y1 | Y2 |
|---|---|---|
| -1.2 | 4.9585 | 3.8 |
| -1.1 | 4.5453 | 3.8 |
| -1 | 4.1321 | 3.8 |
|  | 3.7188 | 3.8 |
| -.8 | 3.3056 | 3.8 |
| -.7 | 2.8924 | 3.8 |
| -.6 | 2.4792 | 3.8 |

X=-.9

Figure 18b

17. Each radio costs \$15 to manufacture. The fixed cost for this company to produce radios is \$2000.

18. $-2.4x - 2.1 = \sqrt{3}x + 1.7 \Rightarrow -2.4x - \sqrt{3}x = 3.8$. Graph $Y_1 = -2.4X - \sqrt{3}X$ and $Y_2 = 3.8$. See Figure 18a. $y = 3.8$ at $x = -0.9$. Make a table of $Y_1 = -2.4X - \sqrt{3}$ from $x = -1.2$ to $x = -0.5$ by 0.1 units. See Figure 18b. $y = 3.8$ at $x = -0.9$.

19. $-3(2 - 3x) - (-x - 1) = 1 \Rightarrow -6 + 9x + x + 1 = 1 \Rightarrow 10x - 5 = 1 \Rightarrow 10x = 6 \Rightarrow x = \frac{3}{5}$

20. $\frac{5 - 3x}{6} = \frac{x - (3 - 4x)}{2} = 5 - 3x = 3(x - (3 - 4x)) \Rightarrow 5 - 3x = 3(x - 3 + 4x) \Rightarrow$
$5 - 3x = 3x - 9 + 12x \Rightarrow -18x = -14 \Rightarrow x = \frac{7}{9}$

21. $|3x - 4| + 1 = 5 \Rightarrow |3x - 4| = 4 \Rightarrow 3x - 4 = 4 \Rightarrow 3x = 8 \Rightarrow x = \frac{8}{3}$ or
$3x - 4 = -4 \Rightarrow 3x = 0 \Rightarrow x = 0$. Therefore $x = 0, \frac{8}{3}$.

22. $x^3 + 5 = 5x^2 + x \Rightarrow x^3 - 5x^2 - x + 5 = 0 \Rightarrow (x^3 - 5x^2) - (x - 5) = 0 \Rightarrow$
$x^2(x - 5) - (x - 5) = 0 \Rightarrow (x^2 - 1)(x - 5) = 0 \Rightarrow (x + 1)(x - 1)(x - 5) = 0 \Rightarrow x = \pm 1, 5$

23. $7x^2 + 9x = 10 \Rightarrow 7x^2 + 9x - 10 = 0 \Rightarrow (7x - 5)(x + 2) = 0 \Rightarrow x = -2, \frac{5}{7}$

24. $2x^2 + x + 2 = 0$. Using the quadratic formula we get: $\frac{-1 \pm \sqrt{1 - 4(2)(2)}}{2(2)} = \frac{-1 \pm \sqrt{-15}}{4} =$
$-\frac{1}{4} \pm \frac{i\sqrt{15}}{4}$

25. $2x^3 + 4x^2 = 6x \Rightarrow 2x^3 + 4x^2 - 6x = 0 \Rightarrow 2x(x^2 + 2x - 3) = 0 \Rightarrow 2x(x + 3)(x - 1) = 0 \Rightarrow$
$x = -3, 0, 1$

26. $x^4 + 9 = 10x^2 \Rightarrow x^4 - 10x^2 + 9 = 0 \Rightarrow (x^2 - 9)(x^2 - 1) = 0 \Rightarrow$
$(x + 3)(x - 3)(x + 1)(x - 1) = 0 \Rightarrow x = -3, -1, 1, 3$

27. $3x^{2/3} + 5x^{1/3} - 2 = 0 \Rightarrow 3(x^{1/3})^2 + 5(x^{1/3}) - 2 = 0$. Let $u = x^{1/3}$, then $3u^2 + 5u - 2 = 0 \Rightarrow$ $(3u - 1)(u + 2) = 0 \Rightarrow u = -2, \frac{1}{3}$, If $u = x^{1/3}$ then it follows $x = u^3$, thus $x = (-2)^3 \Rightarrow x = -8$ or $x = \left(\frac{1}{3}\right)^3 \Rightarrow x = \frac{1}{27}$. Therefore $x = -8, \frac{1}{27}$

28. $\sqrt{5 + 2x} + 4 = x + 5 \Rightarrow \sqrt{5 + 2x} = x + 1 \Rightarrow 5 + 2x = (x + 1)^2 \Rightarrow 5 + 2x = x^2 + 2x + 1 \Rightarrow$ $x^2 - 4 = 0 \Rightarrow (x + 2)(x - 2) = 0 \Rightarrow x = \pm 2$

Check: $\sqrt{5 + 2(-2)} + 4 = -2 + 5 \Rightarrow \sqrt{1} + 4 = -2 + 5 \Rightarrow 5 = 3 \Rightarrow -2$ is not a solution.

Check: $\sqrt{5 + 2(2)} + 4 = 2 + 5 \Rightarrow \sqrt{9} + 4 = 7 \Rightarrow 7 = 7 \Rightarrow 2$ is a solution.

29. $\frac{2x - 3}{5 - x} = \frac{4x - 3}{1 - 2x} \Rightarrow (2x - 3)(1 - 2x) = (4x - 3)(5 - x) \Rightarrow$ $2x - 4x^2 - 3 + 6x = 20x - 4x^2 - 15 + 3x \Rightarrow 15x = 12 \Rightarrow x = \frac{4}{5}$

30. $\sqrt[3]{x - 4} - 1 = 3 \Rightarrow \sqrt[3]{x - 4} = 4 \Rightarrow x - 4 = 4^3 \Rightarrow x - 4 = 64 \Rightarrow x = 68$

31. $\frac{1}{2}x - (4 - x) + 1 = \frac{3}{2}x - 5 \Rightarrow \frac{1}{2}x - 4 + x + 1 = \frac{3}{2}x - 5 \Rightarrow \frac{3}{2}x - 3 = \frac{3}{2}x - 5 \Rightarrow$ $-3 = -5$, since this is false the equation has no solutions and is a contradiction.

32. See Figure 32. Because there is a jump, $f$ is not continuous; $f(1) = 1 - (1)^2 \Rightarrow f(1) = 0$

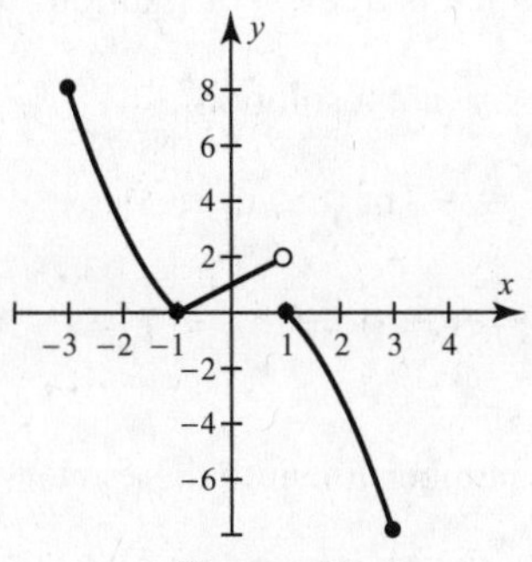

Figure 32

33. $-\frac{1}{3}x - (1 + x) > \frac{2}{3}x \Rightarrow -\frac{1}{3}x - 1 - x > \frac{2}{3}x \Rightarrow -\frac{4}{3}x - 1 > \frac{2}{3}x \Rightarrow -2x > 1 \Rightarrow x < -\frac{1}{2} \Rightarrow$ $\left(-\infty, -\frac{1}{2}\right)$; In set builder notation the interval is $\left\{x \mid x < -\frac{1}{2}\right\}$.

34. $-4 \le 4x - 6 < \frac{5}{2} \Rightarrow 2 \le 4x < \frac{17}{2} \Rightarrow \frac{1}{2} \le x < \frac{17}{8} \Rightarrow \left[\frac{1}{2}, \frac{17}{8}\right)$; In set builder notation the interval is $\left\{x \mid \frac{1}{2} \le x < \frac{17}{8}\right\}$.

35. The solutions to $|5x - 7| \ge 3$ satisfy $x \le s_1$ or $x \ge s_2$ where $s_1$ and $s_2$ are the solutions to $|5x - 7| = 3$.

$|5x - 7| = 3$ is equivalent to $5x - 7 = -3 \Rightarrow x = \frac{4}{5}$ and $5x - 7 = 3 \Rightarrow x = 2$.

The interval is $\left(-\infty, \frac{4}{5}\right] \cup [2, \infty)$; In set builder notation the interval is $\left\{x \mid x \le \frac{4}{5} \text{ or } x \ge 2\right\}$.

36. For $5x^2 + 13x - 6 < 0$, first set $5x^2 + 13x - 6 = 0 \Rightarrow (5x - 2)(x + 3) = 0 \Rightarrow x = -3, \frac{2}{5}$. These boundary numbers separate the number line into these intervals: $(-\infty, -3)$, $\left(-3, \frac{2}{5}\right)$, and $\left(\frac{2}{5}, \infty\right)$. Checking an $x$ value in each interval we get for $x = -5$, $5(-5)^2 + 13(-5) - 6 < 0 \Rightarrow 125 + (-65) - 6 < 0 \Rightarrow 54 < 0$, which is false $\Rightarrow$ not a solution; for $x = 0$, $5(0)^2 + 13(0) - 6 < 0 \Rightarrow -6 < 0$, which is true $\Rightarrow$ a solution; for $x = 1$, $5(1)^2 + 13(1) - 6 < 0 \Rightarrow 12 < 0$, which is false $\Rightarrow$ not a solution. Therefore $\left(-3, \frac{2}{5}\right)$. In set builder notation the interval is $\left\{x \mid -3 < x < \frac{2}{5}\right\}$.

37. For $x^3 - 9x \le 0$, first set $x^3 - 9x = 0 \Rightarrow x(x^2 - 9) = 0 \Rightarrow x(x + 3)(x - 3) = 0 \Rightarrow x = -3, 0, 3$. These boundary numbers separate the number line into these intervals: $(-\infty, -3)$, $(-3, 0)$, $(0, 3)$ and $(3, \infty)$. Checking an $x$ value in each interval we get:

for $x = -5$, $(-5)^3 - 9(-5) \le 0 \Rightarrow -125 + 45 \le 0 \Rightarrow -80 \le 0$, which is true $\Rightarrow$ a solution;

for $x = -1$, $(-1)^3 - 9(-1) \le 0 \Rightarrow -1 + 9 \le 0 \Rightarrow 8 \le 0$, which is false $\Rightarrow$ not a solution; for $x = 1$, $(1)^3 - 9(1) \le 0 \Rightarrow 1 - 9 \le 0 \Rightarrow -8 \le 0$, which is true $\Rightarrow$ a solution.

for $x = 5$, $(5)^3 - 9(5) \le 0 \Rightarrow 125 - 45 \le 0 \Rightarrow 80 \le 0$, which is false $\Rightarrow$ not a solution.

Therefore $(-\infty, -3] \cup [0, 3]$. In set builder notation the intervals are $\{x \mid x \le -3 \text{ or } 0 \le x \le 3\}$.

38. For $\frac{4x - 3}{x + 2} > 0$, first set the numerator and denominator equal to zero. $4x - 3 = 0 \Rightarrow 4x = 3 \Rightarrow x = \frac{3}{4}$ and $x + 2 = 0 \Rightarrow x = -2$. These boundary numbers separate the number line into these intervals: $(-\infty, -2)$, $\left(-2, \frac{3}{4}\right)$, and $\left(\frac{3}{4}, \infty\right)$. Checking an $x$ value in each interval we get: for $-3$, $\frac{4(-3) - 3}{(-3) + 2} > 0 \Rightarrow \frac{-15}{-1} > 0 \Rightarrow 15 > 0$, which is true $\Rightarrow$ a solution; for $0$, $\frac{4(0) - 3}{0 + 2} > 0 \Rightarrow \frac{-3}{2} > 0$, which is false $\Rightarrow$ a not solution; for $1$, $\frac{4(1) - 3}{1 + 2} > 0 \Rightarrow \frac{1}{3} > 0$, which is true $\Rightarrow$ a solution. Therefore $(-\infty, -2) \cup \left(\frac{3}{4}, \infty\right)$.

In set builder notation the intervals are $\left\{x \mid x < -2 \text{ or } x > \frac{3}{4}\right\}$.

39. (a) $x = -3, -1, 1, 2$

(b) $(-\infty, -3) \cup (-1, 1) \cup (2, \infty)$; In set builder notation the intervals are $\{x \mid x < -3 \text{ or } -1 < x < 1 \text{ or } x > 2\}$.

(c) $[-3, -1] \cup [1, 2]$; In set builder notation the intervals are $\{x \mid -3 \le x \le -1 \text{ or } 1 \le x \le 2\}$.

40. $f(x) = 2x^2 - 4x + 1 \Rightarrow y = 2x^2 - 4x + 1 \Rightarrow y - 1 = 2x^2 - 4x \Rightarrow y - 1 = 2(x^2 - 2x) \Rightarrow$
$y + 1 = 2(x^2 - 2x + 1) \Rightarrow y + 1 = 2(x - 1)^2 \Rightarrow y = 2(x - 1)^2 - 1 \Rightarrow f(x) = 2(x - 1)^2 - 1$

41. $f(x) = -\frac{1}{2}x^2 + 3x - 2 \Rightarrow y = -\frac{1}{2}x^2 + 3x - 2 \Rightarrow y + 2 = -\frac{1}{2}x^2 + 3x \Rightarrow$

$y + 2 = -\frac{1}{2}\,(x^2 - 6x) \Rightarrow$

$y + 2 - \frac{9}{2} = -\frac{1}{2}(x^2 - 6x + 9) \Rightarrow y - \frac{5}{2} = -\frac{1}{2}(x - 3)^2 \Rightarrow$

$y = -\frac{1}{2}(x - 3)^2 + \frac{5}{2} \Rightarrow f(x) = -\frac{1}{2}\,(x - 3)^2 + \frac{5}{2} \Rightarrow$ the vertex is $\left(3, \frac{5}{2}\right)$.

42. $x^2 - 3x = 1 \Rightarrow x^2 - 3x + \frac{9}{4} = 1 + \frac{9}{4}\left(x - \frac{3}{2}\right)^2 = \frac{13}{4} \Rightarrow x - \frac{3}{2} = \pm\sqrt{\frac{13}{4}} \Rightarrow$

$x = \frac{3}{2} \pm \frac{\sqrt{13}}{2}$ or $x = \frac{3 \pm \sqrt{13}}{2}$

43. (a) Shift $f(x)$ 2 units left and 1 unit down. See Figure 43a.

(b) Multiply the $y$-coordinate of each point by $-2$ and plot. The new graph will open up. See Figure 43b.

(c) Shift $f(x)$ up one unit and reflect across the $y$-axis. See Figure 43c.

(d) Multiply the $x$-coordinate of each point by 2 and plot. See Figure 43d.

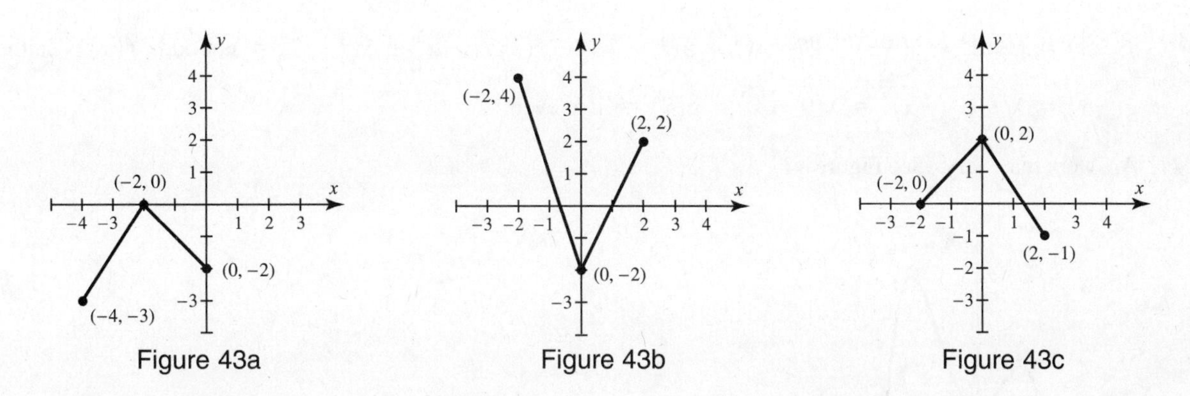


Figure 43a Figure 43b Figure 43c

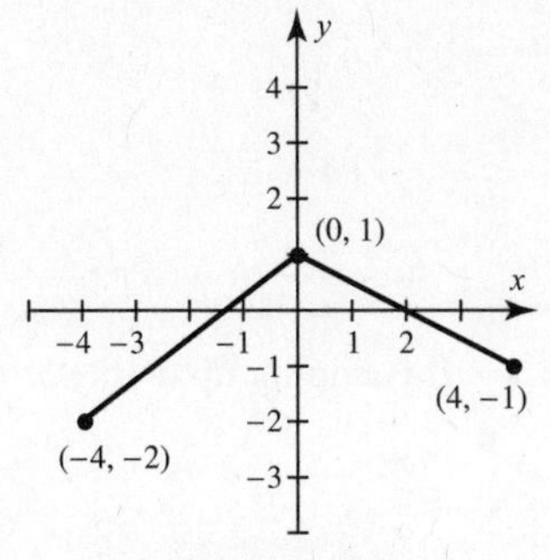


Figure 43d

44. Take the graph of $y = \sqrt{x}$ and shift it one unit left and vertically stretch by a factor of 2. See Figure 44.

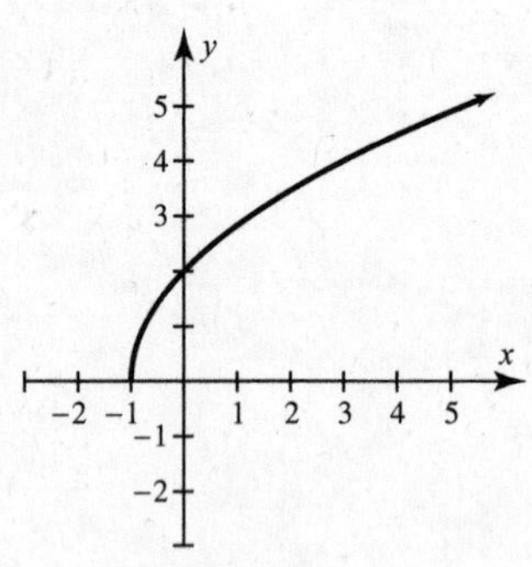


Figure 44

45. (a) It is increasing: $(-\infty, -2]$ and $[1, \infty)$; it is decreasing: $[-2, 1]$. In set builder notation the intervals are $\{x \mid x \le -2 \text{ or } x \ge 1\}$ and $\{x \mid -2 \le x \le 1\}$.

(b) The zeros are approximately $x = -3.3, 0$ and $1.8$.

(c) The turning points are: $(-2, 3)$ and $(1, -1)$.

(d) It has local extrema, maximum: 3, and minimum: $-1$.

46. $f(-x) = (-x)^4 - 5(-x)^3 - 7 = x^4 + 5x^3 - 7 \ne f(x) \Rightarrow$ not even.

$f(-x) = (-x)^4 - 5(-x)^3 - 7 = x^4 + 5x^3 - 7 \ne -f(x) = -x^4 + 5x^3 - 7 \Rightarrow$ not odd. $f(x)$ is neither.

$g(-x) = \sqrt{9 - (-x)^2} = \sqrt{9 - x^2} = g(x) \Rightarrow$ it is even.

47. Answers may vary. See Figure 47.

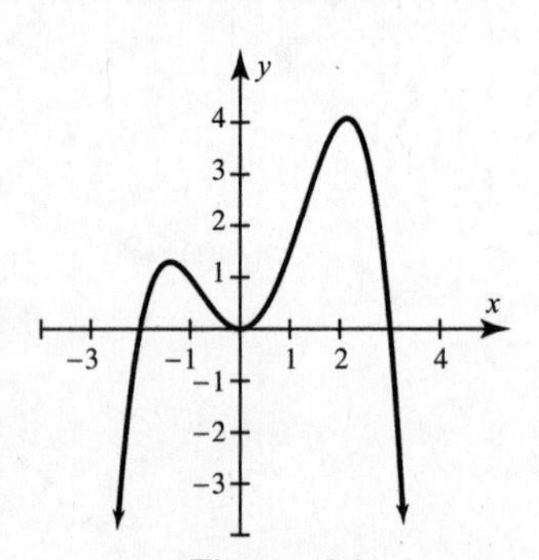


Figure 47

48. Since $f(x) = 4 + 3x - x^3$ is a $f(x) = x^3$ graph reflected across the $x$-axis $\Rightarrow$ it is ending up on the left and down on the right.

49. (a)

$$\begin{array}{rl} & a - 2 + \frac{12}{4a^2} \\ 4a^2 & \overline{)4a^3 - 8a^2 + 12} \\ & \underline{4a^3} \\ & -8a^2 + 12 \\ & \underline{-8a^2} \\ & 12 \end{array}$$

Therefore the quotient is: $a - 2 + \dfrac{3}{a^2}$

(b)

$$\begin{array}{rl} & 2x^2 + 2x - 2 + \frac{-1}{x-1} \\ x - 1 & \overline{)2x^3 \qquad - 4x + 1} \\ & \underline{2x^3 - 2x^2} \\ & 2x^2 - 4x + 1 \\ & \underline{2x^2 - 2x} \\ & -2x + 1 \\ & \underline{-2x + 2} \\ & -1 \end{array}$$

Therefore the quotient is: $2x^2 + 2x - 2 + \dfrac{-1}{x - 1}$

(c)

$$\begin{array}{rl} & x^2 + 2x - 3 + \frac{x+4}{x^2+2} \\ x^2 + 2 & \overline{)x^4 + 2x^3 - x^2 + 5x - 2} \\ & \underline{x^4 \qquad + 2x^2} \\ & 2x^3 - 3x^2 + 5x - 2 \\ & \underline{2x^3 \qquad + 4x} \\ & -3x^2 + x - 2 \\ & \underline{-3x^2 \qquad - 6} \\ & x + 4 \end{array}$$

Therefore the quotient is: $x^2 + 2x - 3 + \dfrac{x + 4}{x^2 + 2}$

50. $f(x) = -5x(x + 1)(x - 2)$

51. $f(x) = 4(x + 3)(x - 1)^2(x - 4)^3$

52. $f(x) = \dfrac{1}{2}(x + 2)(x - i)(x + i)(x - 2i)(x + 2i) = \dfrac{1}{2}x^5 + x^4 + \dfrac{5}{2}x^3 + 5x^2 + 2x + 4$

53. $2x^3 - x^2 - 6x + 3 = (2x^3 - x^2) - (6x - 3) = x^2(2x - 1) - 3(2x - 1) = (x^2 - 3)(2x - 1) =$

$(x + \sqrt{3})(x - \sqrt{3})(2x - 1) \Rightarrow f(x) = (x + \sqrt{3})(x - \sqrt{3})(2x - 1) \Rightarrow$

the complete factored form is: $f(x) = 2(x + \sqrt{3})(x - \sqrt{3})\left(x - \dfrac{1}{2}\right)$

54. The zeros are: $x = -2, -1$, and $1 \Rightarrow$ we have factors $(x + 2)(x + 1)(x - 1)$. Now to find the leading coefficient we solve for $f(0) = 4 \Rightarrow a(0 + 2)(0 + 1)(0 - 1) = 4 \Rightarrow a(2)(1)(-1) = 4 \Rightarrow -2a = 4 \Rightarrow$ $a = -2$. Therefore the complete factored form is: $f(x) = -2(x + 2)(x + 1)(x - 1)$.

55. $\dfrac{3 + 4i}{1 - i} \cdot \dfrac{1 + i}{1 + i} = \dfrac{3 + 3i + 4i + 4i^2}{1 - (i)^2} = \dfrac{3 + 7i + 4(-1)}{1 - (-1)} = \dfrac{-1 + 7i}{2}$ or $\dfrac{-1}{2} + \dfrac{7i}{2}$

56. $x^4 - 25 = 0 \Rightarrow (x^2 - 5)(x^2 + 5) = 0 \Rightarrow x = \pm\sqrt{5}$ or $x = \pm\sqrt{-5} \Rightarrow x = \pm\sqrt{5}, \pm i\sqrt{5}$

57. For the domain the denominator cannot equal zero $\Rightarrow$ set $x^2 - 3x - 4 = 0 \Rightarrow (x + 1)(x - 4) = 0$.

Then $D = \{x \mid x \neq -1, x \neq 4\}$. Since the degree of the numerator is less then the degree of the denominator the horizontal asymptote is $y = 0$. The vertical asymptotes are values when the demoninator equals 0 $\Rightarrow$ the vertical asymptotes are: $x = -1, x = 4$.

58. $\sqrt[3]{x^5} = x^{5/3}$; $8^{5/3} = \sqrt[3]{8^5} = (\sqrt[3]{8})^5 = 2^5 = 32$

59. For $m_1$ use $(0, 0)$ and $(2, 40{,}000) \Rightarrow \dfrac{40{,}000 - 0}{2 - 0} \Rightarrow \dfrac{40{,}000}{2} \Rightarrow m_1 = 20{,}000$; the pool is being filled at a rate of 20,000 gallons per hour.

For $m_2$ use $(2, 40{,}000)$ and $(3, 50{,}000) \Rightarrow \dfrac{50{,}000 - 40{,}000}{3 - 2} \Rightarrow \dfrac{10{,}000}{1} \Rightarrow m_2 = 10{,}000$; now the pool is being filled at a rate of 10,000 gallons per hour.

For $m_3$ use $(3, 50{,}000)$ and $(4, 50{,}000) \Rightarrow \dfrac{50{,}000 - 50{,}000}{4 - 3} \Rightarrow \dfrac{0}{1} \Rightarrow m_3 = 0$; the amount of water in the pool is remaining constant.

For $m_4$ use $(4, 50{,}000)$ and $(6, 20{,}000) \Rightarrow \dfrac{20{,}000 - 50{,}000}{6 - 4} \Rightarrow \dfrac{-30{,}000}{2} \Rightarrow m_4 = -15{,}000$; the pool is being drained at a rate of 15,000 gallons per hour.

60. After 0.5 hours the first runner is $8(0.5) - 2$ or 2 miles south of where the second runner starts. After 0.5 hours the second runner is $7(0.5)$ or 3.5 miles west of where they started. Using $(0, 2)$ as the new location of the first runner and $(-3.5, 0)$ as the new location of the second runner and the distance formula we get:

$d = \sqrt{(-3.5 - 0)^2 + (0 - 2)^2} \Rightarrow d = \sqrt{12.25 + 4} \Rightarrow d = \sqrt{16.25} \Rightarrow d = 4.0$ miles.

61. $D(0) = 4(0)^2 = 0 \Rightarrow (0, 0)$; $D(2) = 4(2)^2 = 16 \Rightarrow (2, 16)$; $D(4) = 4(4)^2 = 64 \Rightarrow (4, 64)$

The average rate of change from 0 to 2 is: $\dfrac{16 - 0}{2 - 0} = \dfrac{16}{2} = 8$.

The average rate of change from 2 to 4 is: $\dfrac{64 - 16}{4 - 2} = \dfrac{48}{2} = 24$.

Between 0 and 2 seconds, the car travels at an average rate of 8 feet per second. Between 2 and 4 seconds, the car travels at an average rate of 24 feet per second.

62. The first person can paint $\dfrac{1}{10}x$ job per hour, the second $\dfrac{1}{8}x$ job per hour $\Rightarrow$ together they can do one paint job in: $\dfrac{1}{10}x + \dfrac{1}{8}x = 1$. $\dfrac{1}{10}x + \dfrac{1}{8}x = 1 \Rightarrow \dfrac{8}{80}x + \dfrac{10}{80}x = 1 \Rightarrow \dfrac{18}{80}x = 1 \Rightarrow x = \dfrac{80}{18} \Rightarrow x = \dfrac{40}{9}$ or $x = 4.44$ hours.

63. $0.35(2) + 0.12x = 0.20(x + 2) \Rightarrow 0.70 + 0.12x = 0.20x + 0.40 \Rightarrow 0.30 = 0.08x \Rightarrow x = 3.75$ liters

64. (a) If $(1990, 250)$ and $(2000, 280)$ then the average rate of change is: $\dfrac{280 - 250}{2000 - 1990} = \dfrac{30}{10} = 3$.

Then, $P(t) = 3(t - 1990) + 250$ or $P(t) = 3t - 5720$.

(b) $300 = 3(t - 1990) + 250 \Rightarrow 50 = 3t - 5970 \Rightarrow 3t = 6020 \Rightarrow t = 2006.7 \Rightarrow 2007$ or late 2006.

65. Graph $R(x) = x(800 - x)$ with $x$ by the 100's from 0 to 800. See Figure 65. The maximum revenue is made when 400 toy figures are sold.

[0, 1000, 100] by [0, 200,000, 20,000]

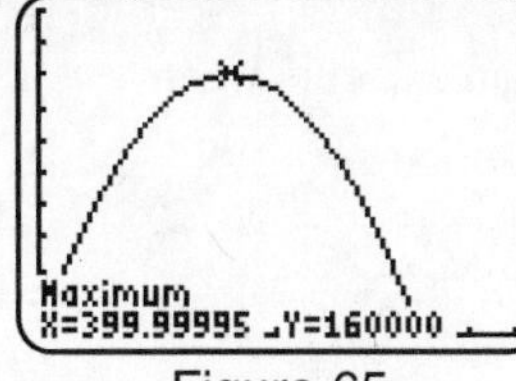


Figure 65

[0, 300, 100] by [0, 50,000, 10,000]

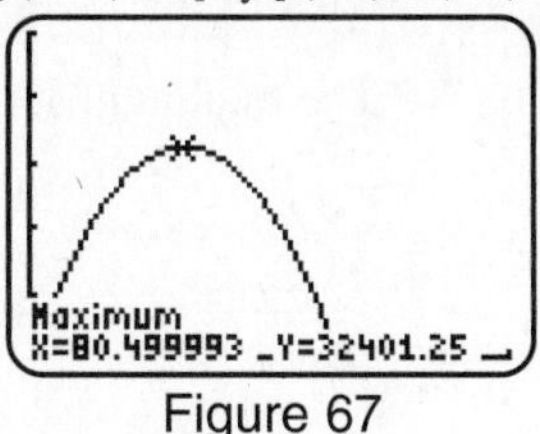


Figure 67

[0, 12, 2] by [0, 90, 10]

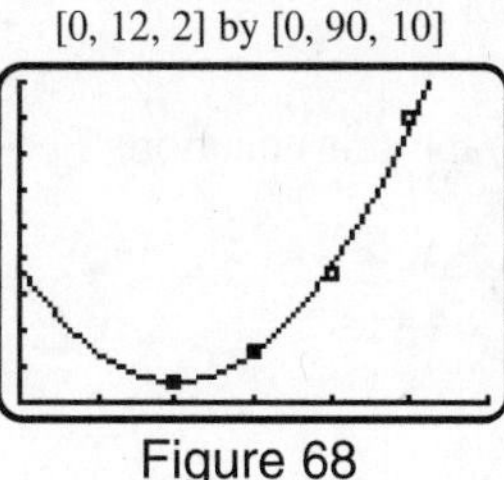

Figure 68

[1997, 2003, 1] by [0, 20, 2]

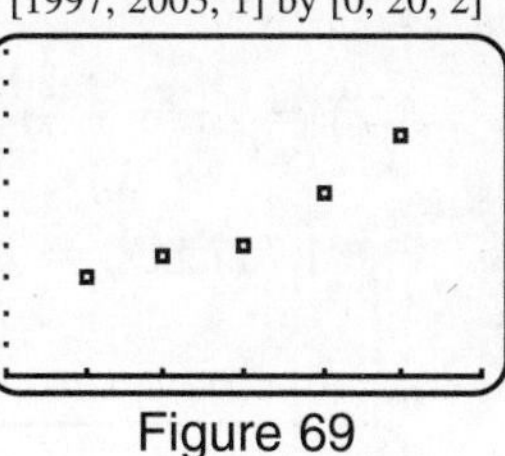

Figure 69

66. If the dimension of the rectangular sheet of metal is: $x$ by $x + 6$, then the dimensions of the sides of the box are $x - 4$ by $x + 2$ and the $h = 2 \Rightarrow 2(x - 4)(x + 2) = 270 \Rightarrow 2(x^2 - 2x - 8) = 270 \Rightarrow$ $2x^2 - 4x - 16 = 270 \Rightarrow 2x^2 - 4x - 286 = 0 \Rightarrow 2(x^2 - 2x - 143) = 0 \Rightarrow$ $2(x + 11)(x - 13) = 0 \Rightarrow x = -11, 13$. Since length cannot be negative the dimensions of the sheet of metal are: 13 by 19 inches.

67. (a) $C(t) = t(805 - 5t)$

(b) $C(t) = 17{,}000 \Rightarrow 17{,}000 = t(805 - 5t) \Rightarrow 17{,}000 = 805t - 5t^2 \Rightarrow 5t^2 - 805t + 17{,}000 = 0 \Rightarrow$ $5(t^2 - 161t + 3400) = 0 \Rightarrow 5(t - 25)(t - 136) = 0 \Rightarrow t = 25, 136$. The cost is \$17,000 when either 25 or 136 tickets are purchased.

(c) Graph $C(t) = t(805 - 5t)$. See Figure 67. The maximum cost of \$32,400 is reached at 80 to 81 tickets are sold.

68. Using the lowest values $x = 4$ and $y = 6$ as the vertex of the parabola we get: $f(x) = a(x - 4)^2 + 6$. Using the graph, see Figure 68, and trial and error, $a \approx 2$ produces a reasonable fit for the data $\Rightarrow$ $f(x) = 2(x - 4)^2 + 6$.

69. (a) Using the lowest values $x = 1998$ and $y = 6.1$ as the vertex of the parabola we get: $f(x) = a(x - 1998)^2 + 6.1$. Using the graph, see Figure 69, and trial and error, $a \approx 0.5$ produces a reasonable fit for the data $\Rightarrow f(x) = 0.5(x - 1998)^2 + 6.1$. *Answers may vary.*

(b) $f(2004) = 0.5(2004 - 1998)^2 + 6.1 \Rightarrow f(2004) = 0.5(6)^2 + 6.1 \Rightarrow f(2004) = 0.5(36) + 6.1 \Rightarrow$ $f(2004) = 24.1\%$. *Answers may vary.*

70. (a) Using the lowest values $x = 1961$ and $y = 13$ as the vertex of the parabola we get: $f(x) = a(x - 1961)^2 + 13$. Using the graph, see Figure 70, and trial and error, $a \approx 0.01$ produces a reasonable fit for the data $\Rightarrow f(x) = 0.01(x - 1961)^2 + 13$.

(b) $40 = 0.01(x - 1961)^2 + 13 \Rightarrow 27 = 0.01(x - 1961)^2 \Rightarrow 2700 = (x - 1961)^2 \Rightarrow$ $\sqrt{2700} = x - 1961 \Rightarrow 51.96 = x - 1961 \Rightarrow 2013 \approx x$, slightly later than the experts prediction of 2009.

[1955, 2005, 5] by [0, 35, 5]

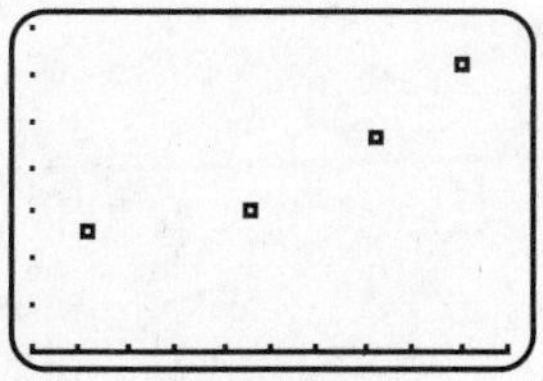

Figure 70

71. Since volume of a cylinder is: $V = \pi r^2 h$. Then $10\pi = \pi r^2 h \Rightarrow h = \frac{10}{r^2}$.

The surface area of the can is: $S(r) = 2\pi r^2 + 2\pi rh \Rightarrow S(r) = 2\pi r^2 + 2\pi r \cdot \frac{10}{r^2} \Rightarrow$

$S(r) = 2\pi r^2 + \frac{20\pi}{r}$. Graph this equation. See Figure 71. The minimum surface area occurs when

$r \approx 1.7$ inches $\Rightarrow$ then $h = \frac{10}{(1.7)^2}$ or $h \approx 3.5$ inches.

[0, 5, 1] by [0, 100, 10]

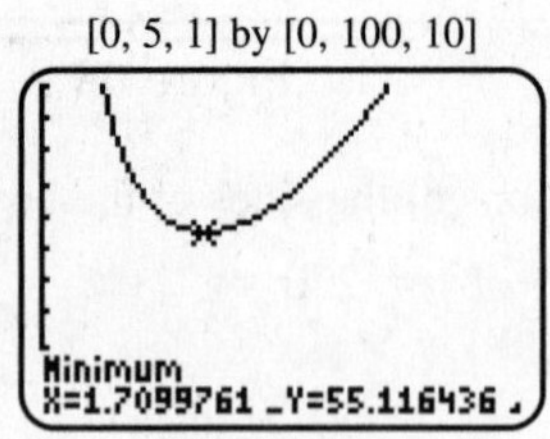


Figure 71

# Chapter 5: Exponential and Logarithmic Functions

## 5.1: Combining Functions

1. $(f + g)(3) = f(3) + g(3) = 2 + 5 = 7$
2. $(g \circ f)(3) = g(f(3)) = g(2) = 5$
3. $(fg)(x) = f(x)g(x) = (x^2)(4x) = 4x^3$
4. $(f \circ g)(x) = f(g(x)) = f(4x) = (4x)^2 = 16x^2$
5. $(g \circ f)(x) = g(f(x))$. Therefore, $(g \circ f)(x)$ calculates the cost of $x$ square yards of carpet.
6. $(g \circ f)(x) = g(f(x))$. Therefore, $(g \circ f)(x)$ converts the number of hours into the number of years.
7. (a) $f(3) = 2(3) - 3 = 3$ and $g(3) = 1 - 3^2 = -8$. Thus, $(f + g)(3) = f(3) + g(3) = 3 + (-8) = -5$.

   (b) $f(-1) = 2(-1) - 3 = -5$ and $g(-1) = 1 - (-1)^2 = 0$.

   Thus, $(f - g)(-1) = f(-1) - g(-1) = -5 - 0 = -5$.

   (c) $f(0) = 2(0) - 3 = -3$ and $g(0) = 1 - 0^2 = 1$. Thus, $(fg)(0) = f(0) \cdot g(0) = (-3)(1) = -3$.

   (d) $f(2) = 2(2) - 3 = 1$ and $g(2) = 1 - 2^2 = -3$. Thus, $(f/g)(2) = \dfrac{f(2)}{g(2)} = \dfrac{1}{-3} = -\dfrac{1}{3}$.
8. (a) $g(-2) = -2 + 3 = 1$. Thus, $(g + g)(-2) = g(-2) + g(-2) = 1 + 1 = 2$.

   (b) $f(0) = 4(0) - 0^3 = 0$ and $g(0) = 0 + 3 = 3$. Thus, $(f - g)(0) = f(0) - g(0) = 0 - 3 = -3$.

   (c) $f(1) = 4(1) - 1^3 = 3$ and $g(1) = 1 + 3 = 4$. Thus, $(gf)(1) = g(1) \cdot f(1) = (4)(3) = 12$.

   (d) $f(-3) = 4(-3) - (-3)^3 = 15$ and $g(-3) = -3 + 3 = 0$. Thus, $(g/f)(-3) = \dfrac{g(-3)}{f(-3)} = \dfrac{0}{15} = 0$.
9. (a) $f(2) = 2(2) + 1 = 5$ and $g(2) = \dfrac{1}{2}$. Thus, $(f + g)(2) = f(2) + g(2) = 5 + \dfrac{1}{2} = \dfrac{11}{2}$.

   (b) $f\left(\dfrac{1}{2}\right) = 2\left(\dfrac{1}{2}\right) + 1 = 2$ and $g\left(\dfrac{1}{2}\right) = \dfrac{1}{\frac{1}{2}} = 2$. Thus, $(f - g)\left(\dfrac{1}{2}\right) = f\left(\dfrac{1}{2}\right) - g\left(\dfrac{1}{2}\right) = 2 - 2 = 0$.

   (c) $f(4) = 2(4) + 1 = 9$ and $g(4) = \dfrac{1}{4}$. Thus, $(fg)(4) = f(4) \cdot g(4) = (9)\left(\dfrac{1}{4}\right) = \dfrac{9}{4}$.

   (d) $f(0) = 2(0) + 1 = 1$ and $g(0) = \dfrac{1}{0} \Rightarrow$ undefined. Thus, $(f/g)(0) \Rightarrow$ undefined.
10. (a) $f(-8) = \sqrt[3]{(-8)^2} = 4$ and $g(-8) = |-8 - 3| = 11$.

    Thus, $(f + g)(-8) = f(-8) + g(-8) = 4 + 11 = 15$.

    (b) $f(-1) = \sqrt[3]{(-1)^2} = 1$ and $g(-1) = |-1 - 3| = 4$.

    Thus, $(f - g)(-1) = f(-1) + g(-1) = 1 - 4 = -3$.

    (c) $f(0) = \sqrt[3]{(0)^2} = 0$ and $g(0) = |0 - 3| = 3$. Thus, $(fg)(0) = f(0) \cdot g(0) = (0)(3) = 0$.

    (d) $f(27) = \sqrt[3]{(27)^2} = 9$ and $g(27) = |27 - 3| = 24$. Thus, $(f/g)(27) = \dfrac{f(27)}{g(27)} = \dfrac{9}{24} = \dfrac{3}{8}$.
11. (a) $(f + g)(x) = f(x) + g(x) = 2x + x^2$; Domain: all real numbers.

    (b) $(f - g)(x) = f(x) - g(x) = 2x - x^2$; Domain: all real numbers.

    (c) $(fg)(x) = f(x) \cdot g(x) = (2x)(x^2) = 2x^3$; Domain: all real numbers.

    (d) $(f/g)(x) = \dfrac{f(x)}{g(x)} = \dfrac{2x}{x^2} = \dfrac{2}{x}$; Domain: $\{x \mid x \neq 0\}$.

12. (a) $(f + g)(x) = f(x) + g(x) = (1 - 4x) + (3x + 1) = -x + 2$; Domain: all real numbers.

(b) $(f - g)(x) = f(x) - g(x) = (1 - 4x) - (3x + 1) = -7x$; Domain: all real numbers.

(c) $(fg)(x) = f(x) \cdot g(x) = (1 - 4x)(3x + 1) = -12x^2 - x + 1$; Domain: all real numbers.

(d) $(f/g)(x) = \dfrac{f(x)}{g(x)} = \dfrac{1 - 4x}{3x + 1}$; Domain: $\left\{x \mid x \neq -\dfrac{1}{3}\right\}$.

13. (a) $(f + g)(x) = f(x) + g(x) = (x^2 - 1) + (x^2 + 1) = 2x^2$; Domain: all real numbers.

(b) $(f - g)(x) = f(x) - g(x) = (x^2 - 1) - (x^2 + 1) = -2$; Domain: all real numbers.

(c) $(fg)(x) = f(x) \cdot g(x) = (x^2 - 1)(x^2 + 1) = x^4 - 1$; Domain: all real numbers.

(d) $(f/g)(x) = \dfrac{f(x)}{g(x)} = \dfrac{x^2 - 1}{x^2 + 1}$; Domain: all real numbers.

14. (a) $(f + g)(x) = f(x) + g(x) = (4x^3 - 8x^2) + (4x^2) = 4x^3 - 4x^2$; Domain: all real numbers.

(b) $(f - g)(x) = f(x) - g(x) = (4x^3 - 8x^2) - (4x^2) = 4x^3 - 12x^2$; Domain: all real numbers.

(c) $(fg)(x) = f(x) \cdot g(x) = (4x^3 - 8x^2)(4x^2) = 16x^5 - 32x^4$; Domain: all real numbers.

(d) $(f/g)(x) = \dfrac{f(x)}{g(x)} = \dfrac{4x^3 - 8x^2}{4x^2} = x - 2$; Domain: $\{x \mid x \neq 0\}$.

15. (a) $(f + g)(x) = f(x) + g(x) = (x - \sqrt{x - 1}) + (x + \sqrt{x - 1}) = 2x$; Domain: $\{x \mid x \geq 1\}$.

(b) $(f - g)(x) = f(x) - g(x) = (x - \sqrt{x - 1}) - (x + \sqrt{x - 1}) = -2\sqrt{x - 1}$; Domain: $\{x \mid x \geq 1\}$.

(c) $(fg)(x) = f(x) \cdot g(x) = (x - \sqrt{x - 1})(x + \sqrt{x - 1}) = x^2 - (x - 1) = x^2 - x + 1$;

Domain: $\{x \mid x \geq 1\}$.

(d) $(f/g)(x) = \dfrac{f(x)}{g(x)} = \dfrac{x - \sqrt{x - 1}}{x + \sqrt{x - 1}}$; Domain: $\{x \mid x \geq 1\}$.

16. (a) $(f + g)(x) = f(x) + g(x) = (3 + \sqrt{2x + 9}) + (3 - \sqrt{2x + 9}) = 6$; Domain: $\left\{x \mid x \geq -\dfrac{9}{2}\right\}$.

(b) $(f - g)(x) = f(x) - g(x) = (3 + \sqrt{2x + 9}) - (3 - \sqrt{2x + 9}) = 2\sqrt{2x + 9}$;

Domain: $\left\{x \mid x \geq -\dfrac{9}{2}\right\}$.

(c) $(fg)(x) = f(x) \cdot g(x) = (3 + \sqrt{2x + 9})(3 - \sqrt{2x + 9}) =$

$9 - 3\sqrt{2x + 9} + 3\sqrt{2x + 9} - (2x + 9) = 9 - 2x - 9 = -2x$; Domain: $\left\{x \mid x \geq -\dfrac{9}{2}\right\}$.

(d) $(f/g)(x) = \dfrac{f(x)}{g(x)} = \dfrac{3 + \sqrt{2x + 9}}{3 - \sqrt{2x + 9}}$; Domain: $\left\{x \mid x \geq -\dfrac{9}{2} \text{ and } x \neq 0\right\}$.

17. (a) $(f + g)(x) = f(x) + g(x) = (\sqrt{x} - 1) + (\sqrt{x} + 1) = 2\sqrt{x}$; Domain: $\{x \mid x \geq 0\}$.

(b) $(f - g)(x) = f(x) - g(x) = (\sqrt{x} - 1) - (\sqrt{x} + 1) = -2$; Domain: $\{x \mid x \geq 0\}$.

(c) $(fg)(x) = f(x) \cdot g(x) = (\sqrt{x} - 1)(\sqrt{x} + 1) = x - 1$; Domain: $\{x \mid x \geq 0\}$.

(d) $(f/g)(x) = \dfrac{f(x)}{g(x)} = \dfrac{\sqrt{x} - 1}{\sqrt{x} + 1}$; Domain: $\{x \mid x \geq 0\}$.

18. (a) $(f + g)(x) = f(x) + g(x) = \sqrt{1 - x} + x^3$; Domain: $\{x \mid x \leq 1\}$.

(b) $(f - g)(x) = f(x) - g(x) = \sqrt{1 - x} - x^3$; Domain: $\{x \mid x \leq 1\}$.

(c) $(fg)(x) = f(x) \cdot g(x) = (\sqrt{1 - x})(x^3) = x^3\sqrt{1 - x}$; Domain: $\{x \mid x \leq 1\}$.

(d) $(f/g)(x) = \dfrac{f(x)}{g(x)} = \dfrac{\sqrt{1 - x}}{x^3}$; Domain: $\{x \mid x \leq 1 \text{ and } x \neq 0\}$.

19. (a) $(f + g)(x) = f(x) + g(x) = \frac{1}{x+1} + \frac{3}{x+1} = \frac{4}{x+1}$; Domain: $\{x | x \neq -1\}$.

(b) $(f - g)(x) = f(x) - g(x) = \frac{1}{x+1} - \frac{3}{x+1} = -\frac{2}{x+1}$; Domain: $\{x | x \neq -1\}$.

(c) $(fg)(x) = f(x) \cdot g(x) = \left(\frac{1}{x+1}\right)\left(\frac{3}{x+1}\right) = \frac{3}{(x+1)^2}$; Domain: $\{x | x \neq -1\}$.

(d) $(f/g)(x) = \frac{f(x)}{g(x)} = \frac{\frac{1}{x+1}}{\frac{3}{x+1}} = \frac{1}{x+1} \cdot \frac{x+1}{3} = \frac{1}{3}$; Domain: $\{x | x \neq -1\}$.

20. (a) $(f + g)(x) = f(x) + g(x) = \sqrt{x} + 3$; Domain: $\{x | x \geq 0\}$.

(b) $(f - g)(x) = f(x) - g(x) = \sqrt{x} - 3$; Domain: $\{x | x \geq 0\}$.

(c) $(fg)(x) = f(x) \cdot g(x) = (\sqrt{x})(3) = 3\sqrt{x}$; Domain: $\{x | x \geq 0\}$.

(d) $(f/g)(x) = \frac{f(x)}{g(x)} = \frac{\sqrt{x}}{3}$; Domain: $\{x | x \geq 0\}$.

21. (a) $(f + g)(x) = f(x) + g(x) = \frac{1}{2x-4} + \frac{x}{2x-4} = \frac{1+x}{2x-4}$; Domain: $\{x | x \neq 2\}$.

(b) $(f - g)(x) = f(x) - g(x) = \frac{1}{2x-4} - \frac{x}{2x-4} = \frac{1-x}{2x-4}$; Domain: $\{x | x \neq 2\}$.

(c) $(fg)(x) = f(x) \cdot g(x) = \left(\frac{1}{2x-4}\right)\left(\frac{x}{2x-4}\right) = \frac{x}{(2x-4)^2}$; Domain: $\{x | x \neq 2\}$.

(d) $(f/g)(x) = \frac{f(x)}{g(x)} = \frac{\frac{1}{2x-4}}{\frac{x}{2x-4}} = \frac{1}{2x-4} \cdot \frac{2x-4}{x} = \frac{1}{x}$; Domain: $\{x | x \neq 0 \text{ and } x \neq 2\}$.

22. (a) $(f + g)(x) = f(x) + g(x) = \frac{1}{x} + x^3 = \frac{1+x^4}{x}$; Domain: $\{x | x \neq 0\}$.

(b) $(f - g)(x) = f(x) - g(x) = \frac{1}{x} - x^3 = \frac{1-x^4}{x}$; Domain: $\{x | x \neq 0\}$.

(c) $(fg)(x) = f(x) \cdot g(x) = \left(\frac{1}{x}\right)(x^3) = x^2$; Domain: $\{x | x \neq 0\}$.

(d) $(f/g)(x) = \frac{f(x)}{g(x)} = \frac{\frac{1}{x}}{x^3} = \frac{1}{x} \cdot \frac{1}{x^3} = \frac{1}{x^4}$; Domain: $\{x | x \neq 0\}$.

23. (a) $(f + g)(x) = f(x) + g(x) = (x^2 - 1) + (|x+1|) = x^2 - 1 + |x+1|$; Domain: all real numbers.

(b) $(f - g)(x) = f(x) - g(x) = (x^2 - 1) - (|x+1|) = x^2 - 1 - |x+1|$; Domain: all real numbers.

(c) $(fg)(x) = f(x) \cdot g(x) = (x^2 - 1)(|x+1|) = (x^2 - 1)(|x+1|)$; Domain: all real numbers.

(d) $(f/g)(x) = \frac{f(x)}{g(x)} = \frac{x^2 - 1}{|x+1|}$; Domain: $\{x | x \neq -1\}$.

24. (a) $(f + g)(x) = f(x) + g(x) = |2x - 1| + |2x + 1|$; Domain: all real numbers.

(b) $(f - g)(x) = f(x) - g(x) = |2x - 1| - |2x + 1|$; Domain: all real numbers.

(c) $(fg)(x) = f(x) \cdot g(x) = (|2x - 1|)(|2x + 1|) = |4x^2 - 1|$; Domain: all real numbers.

(d) $(f/g)(x) = \frac{f(x)}{g(x)} = \frac{|2x - 1|}{|2x + 1|}$; Domain: $\left\{x \middle| x \neq -\frac{1}{2}\right\}$.

25. (a) $(f+g)(x) = f(x) + g(x) = \dfrac{(x-1)(x-2)}{x+1} + \dfrac{(x+1)(x-1)}{x-2} =$

$\dfrac{(x-1)(x-2)(x-2)}{(x+1)(x-2)} + \dfrac{(x-1)(x+1)(x+1)}{(x+1)(x-2)} =$

$\dfrac{(x-1)(x^2-4x+4)}{(x+1)(x-2)} + \dfrac{(x-1)(x^2+2x+1)}{(x+1)(x-2)} = \dfrac{(x-1)(2x^2-2x+5)}{(x+1)(x-2)};$

Domain: $\{x \mid x \neq -1, x \neq 2\}$

(b) $(f-g)(x) = f(x) - g(x) = \dfrac{(x-1)(x-2)}{x+1} - \dfrac{(x+1)(x-1)}{x-2} =$

$\dfrac{(x-1)(x-2)(x-2)}{(x+1)(x-2)} - \dfrac{(x-1)(x+1)(x+1)}{(x+1)(x-2)} =$

$\dfrac{(x-1)(x^2-4x+4)}{(x+1)(x-2)} - \dfrac{(x-1)(x^2+2x+1)}{(x+1)(x-2)} = \dfrac{(x-1)(-6x+3)}{(x+1)(x-2)} = \dfrac{-3(x-1)(2x-1)}{(x+1)(x-2)};$

Domain: $\{x \mid x \neq -1, x \neq 2\}$

(c) $(fg)(x) = f(x) \cdot g(x) = \dfrac{(x-1)(x-2)}{x+1} \cdot \dfrac{(x+1)(x-1)}{x-2} =$

$\dfrac{(x-2)(x-1)(x+1)(x-1)}{(x+1)(x-2)} = (x-1)(x-1) = (x-1)^2$; Domain: $\{x \mid x \neq -1, x \neq 2\}$

(d) $(f/g)(x) = \dfrac{f(x)}{g(x)} = \dfrac{(x-2)(x-1)}{x+1} \div \dfrac{(x+1)(x-1)}{x-2} = \dfrac{(x-2)(x-1)}{x+1} \cdot \dfrac{x-2}{(x+1)(x-1)} =$

$\dfrac{(x-2)^2}{(x+1)^2}$; Domain: $\{x \mid x \neq 1, x \neq -1 \text{ and } x \neq 2\}$

26. (a) $(f+g)(x) = f(x) + g(x) = \left(\dfrac{4x-2}{x+2}\right) + \left(\dfrac{2x-1}{3x+6}\right) = \dfrac{3}{3} \cdot \left(\dfrac{4x-2}{x+2}\right) + \left(\dfrac{2x-1}{3x+6}\right) =$

$\dfrac{12x-6}{3x+6} + \dfrac{2x-1}{3x+6} = \dfrac{14x-7}{3x+6} = \dfrac{7(2x-1)}{3(x+2)}$; Domain: $\{x \mid x \neq -2\}$

(b) $(f-g)(x) = f(x) - g(x) = \left(\dfrac{4x-2}{x+2}\right) - \left(\dfrac{2x-1}{3x+6}\right) = \dfrac{3}{3} \cdot \left(\dfrac{4x-2}{x+2}\right) - \left(\dfrac{2x-1}{3x+6}\right) =$

$\dfrac{12x-6}{3x+6} - \dfrac{2x-1}{3x+6} = \dfrac{10x-5}{3x+6} = \dfrac{5(2x-1)}{3(x+2)}$; Domain: $\{x \mid x \neq -2\}$

(c) $(fg)(x) = f(x) \cdot g(x) = \left(\dfrac{4x-2}{x+2}\right)\left(\dfrac{2x-1}{3x+6}\right) = \dfrac{2(2x-1)}{(x+2)} \cdot \dfrac{(2x-1)}{3(x+2)} = \dfrac{2(2x-1)^2}{3(x+2)^2};$

Domain: $\{x \mid x \neq -2\}$

(d) $(f/g)(x) = \dfrac{f(x)}{g(x)} = \dfrac{4x-2}{x+2} \div \dfrac{2x-1}{3x+6} = \dfrac{2(2x-1)}{x+2} \cdot \dfrac{3(x+2)}{(2x-1)} = 6;$

Domain: $\left\{x \mid x \neq -2 \text{ and } x \neq \dfrac{1}{2}\right\}$

27. (a) $(f+g)(x) = f(x) + g(x) = \dfrac{2}{(x+1)(x-1)} + \dfrac{(x+1)}{(x-1)(x-1)} =$

$\dfrac{2(x-1)}{(x+1)(x-1)^2} + \dfrac{(x+1)^2}{(x+1)(x-1)^2} = \dfrac{2x-2}{(x+1)(x-1)^2} + \dfrac{x^2+2x+1}{(x+1)(x-1)^2} = \dfrac{x^2+4x-1}{(x+1)(x-1)^2};$

Domain: $\{x \mid x \neq -1, x \neq 1\}$

(b) $(f-g)(x) = f(x) - g(x) = \dfrac{2}{(x+1)(x-1)} - \dfrac{(x+1)}{(x-1)(x-1)} =$

$\dfrac{2(x-1)}{(x+1)(x-1)^2} - \dfrac{(x+1)^2}{(x+1)(x-1)} = \dfrac{2x-2}{(x+1)(x-1)^2} - \dfrac{x^2+2x+1}{(x+1)(x-1)^2} = \dfrac{-x^2-3}{(x+1)(x-1)^2};$

Domain: $\{x \mid x \neq -1, x \neq 1\}$

(c) $(fg)(x) = f(x) \cdot g(x) = \dfrac{2}{(x+1)(x-1)} \cdot \dfrac{(x+1)}{(x-1)(x-1)} = \dfrac{2}{(x-1)^3}$; Domain: $\{x \mid x \neq -1, x \neq 1\}$

(d) $(f/g)(x) = f(x) \div g(x) = \dfrac{2}{(x+1)(x-1)} \div \dfrac{(x+1)}{(x-1)(x-1)} =$

$\dfrac{2}{(x+1)(x-1)} \cdot \dfrac{(x-1)(x-1)}{(x+1)} = \dfrac{2(x-1)}{(x+1)^2}$; Domain: $\{x \mid x \neq -1, x \neq 1\}$

28. (a) $(f+g)(x) = f(x) + g(x) = \left(\dfrac{1}{x+2}\right) + \left(\dfrac{x^2+x-2}{1}\right) = \left(\dfrac{1}{x+2}\right) + \dfrac{x+2}{x+2} \cdot \left(\dfrac{x^2+x-2}{1}\right) =$

$\left(\dfrac{1}{x+2}\right) + \left(\dfrac{x^3+3x^2-4}{x+2}\right) = \dfrac{x^3+3x^2-3}{x+2}$; Domain: $\{x \mid x \neq -2\}$

(b) $(f-g)(x) = f(x) - g(x) = \left(\dfrac{1}{x+2}\right) - \left(\dfrac{x^2+x-2}{1}\right) = \left(\dfrac{1}{x+2}\right) - \dfrac{x+2}{x+2} \cdot \left(\dfrac{x^2+x-2}{1}\right) =$

$\left(\dfrac{1}{x+2}\right) - \left(\dfrac{x^3+3x^2-4}{x+2}\right) = \dfrac{-x^3-3x^2+5}{x+2}$; Domain: $\{x \mid x \neq -2\}$

(c) $(fg)(x) = f(x) \cdot g(x) = \left(\dfrac{1}{x+2}\right)\left(\dfrac{x^2+x-2}{1}\right) = \dfrac{x^2+x-2}{x+2} = \dfrac{(x+2)(x-1)}{x+2} = x-1;$

Domain: $\{x \mid x \neq -2\}$

(d) $(f/g)(x) = f(x) \div g(x) = \left(\dfrac{1}{x+2}\right) \div \left(\dfrac{x^2+x-2}{1}\right) = \left(\dfrac{1}{x+2}\right)\left(\dfrac{1}{x^2+x-2}\right) =$

$\left(\dfrac{1}{x+2}\right)\left(\dfrac{1}{(x+2)(x-1)}\right) = \dfrac{1}{(x-1)(x+2)^2}$; Domain: $\{x \mid x \neq -2, x \neq 1\}$

29. (a) $(f+g)(x) = f(x) + g(x) = (x^{5/2} - x^{3/2}) + (x^{1/2}) = x^{5/2} - x^{3/2} + x^{1/2} = x^{1/2}(x^2 - x + 1);$

Domain: $\{x \mid x \geq 0\}$

(b) $(f-g)(x) = f(x) - g(x) = (x^{5/2} - x^{3/2}) - (x^{1/2}) = x^{5/2} - x^{3/2} - x^{1/2} = x^{1/2}(x^2 - x - 1);$

Domain: $\{x \mid x \geq 0\}$

(c) $(fg)(x) = f(x) \cdot g(x) = (x^{5/2} - x^{3/2})(x^{1/2}) = x^3 - x^2 = x^2(x-1)$; Domain: $\{x \mid x \geq 0\}$

(d) $(f/g)(x) = f(x) \div g(x) = \left(\dfrac{x^{5/2} - x^{3/2}}{x^{1/2}}\right) = x^2 - x = x(x-1)$; Domain: $\{x \mid x > 0\}$

30. (a) $(f+g)(x) = f(x) + g(x) = (x^{2/3} - 2x^{1/3} + 1) + (x^{1/3} - 1) = x^{2/3} - x^{1/3}$;

Domain: All real numbers.

(b) $(f-g)(x) = f(x) - g(x) = (x^{2/3} - 2x^{1/3} + 1) - (x^{1/3} - 1) = x^{2/3} - 3x^{1/3} + 2$;

Domain: All real numbers.

(c) $(fg)(x) = f(x) \cdot g(x) = (x^{2/3} - 2x^{1/3} + 1)(x^{1/3} - 1) = x - 2x^{2/3} + x^{1/3} - x^{2/3} + 2x^{1/3} - 1 =$
$x - 3x^{2/3} + 3x^{1/3} - 1$ or $(x^{1/3} - 1)^3$; Domain: All real numbers.

(d) $(f/g)(x) = f(x) \div g(x) = \left(\dfrac{x^{2/3} - 2x^{1/3} + 1}{x^{1/3} - 1}\right) \Rightarrow$

$$\begin{array}{r}
x^{1/3} - 1 \phantom{+ 1} \\
x^{1/3} - 1 \enclose{longdiv}{x^{2/3} - 2x^{1/3} + 1} \\
\underline{x^{2/3} - x^{1/3} \phantom{+ 1}} \\
-x^{1/3} + 1 \\
\underline{-x^{1/3} + 1} \\
0
\end{array}$$

$\Rightarrow x^{1/3} - 1$; Domain: $\{x \mid x \neq 1\}$

31. (a) From the graph $f(2) = 4$ and $g(2) = -2$. Thus, $(f+g)(2) = f(2) + g(2) = 4 + (-2) = 2$.

(b) From the graph $f(1) = 1$ and $g(1) = -3$. Thus, $(f-g)(1) = f(1) - g(1) = 1 - (-3) = 4$.

(c) From the graph $f(0) = 0$ and $g(0) = -4$. Thus, $(fg)(0) = f(0) \cdot g(0) = (0)(-4) = 0$.

(d) From the graph $f(1) = 1$ and $g(1) = -3$. Thus, $(f/g)(1) = \dfrac{f(1)}{g(1)} = \dfrac{1}{-3} = -\dfrac{1}{3}$.

32. (a) From the graph $f(1) = -3$ and $g(1) = 1$. Thus, $(f+g)(1) = f(1) + g(1) = -3 + 1 = -2$.

(b) From the graph $f(0) = -2$ and $g(0) = 0$. Thus, $(f-g)(0) = f(0) - g(0) = -2 - 0 = -2$.

(c) From the graph $f(-1) = -3$ and $g(-1) = -1$. Thus, $(fg)(-1) = f(-1) \cdot g(-1) = (-3)(-1) = 3$.

(d) From the graph $f(1) = -3$ and $g(1) = 1$. Thus, $(f/g)(1) = \dfrac{f(1)}{g(1)} = \dfrac{-3}{1} = -3$.

33. (a) From the graph $f(0) = 0$ and $g(0) = 2$. Thus, $(f+g)(0) = f(0) + g(0) = 0 + 2 = 2$.

(b) From the graph $f(-1) = -2$ and $g(-1) = 1$. Thus, $(f-g)(-1) = f(-1) - g(-1) = -2 - 1 = -3$.

(c) From the graph $f(1) = 2$ and $g(1) = 1$. Thus, $(fg)(1) = f(1) \cdot g(1) = (2)(1) = 2$.

(d) From the graph $f(2) = 4$ and $g(2) = -2$. Thus, $(f/g)(2) = \dfrac{f(2)}{g(2)} = \dfrac{4}{-2} = -2$.

34. (a) From the graph $f(-1) = 0$ and $g(-1) = 3$. Thus, $(f+g)(-1) = f(-1) + g(-1) = 0 + 3 = 3$.

(b) From the graph $f(-2) = -1$ and $g(-2) = 4$. Thus, $(f-g)(-2) = f(-2) - g(-2) = -1 - 4 = -5$.

(c) From the graph $f(0) = 1$ and $g(0) = 2$. Thus, $(fg)(0) = f(0) \cdot g(0) = (1)(2) = 2$.

(d) From the graph $f(2) = 3$ and $g(2) = 0$. Thus, $(f/g)(2) = \dfrac{f(2)}{g(2)} = \dfrac{3}{0} \Rightarrow$ undefined.

35. (a) $(f+g)(-1) = f(-1) + g(-1) = -3 + -2 = -5$.

(b) $(g-f)(0) = g(0) - f(0) = 3 - 5 = -2$.

(c) $(gf)(2) = g(2) \cdot f(2) = 0 \cdot 1 = 0$.

(d) $(f/g)(2) = \dfrac{f(2)}{g(2)} = \dfrac{1}{0} \Rightarrow$ undefined.

36. (a) $(f + g)(-1) = f(-1) + g(-1) = 4 + 2 = 6.$

(b) $(g - f)(0) = g(0) - f(0) = 0 - 1 = -1.$

(c) $(gf)(2) = g(2) \cdot f(2) = 1 \cdot 3 = 3.$

(d) $(f/g)(2) = \dfrac{f(2)}{g(2)} = \dfrac{3}{1} = 3.$

37. (a) $(f + g)(2) = f(2) + g(2) = 7 + (-2) = 5$

(b) $(f - g)(4) = f(4) - g(4) = 10 - 5 = 5$

(c) $(fg)(-2) = f(-2) \cdot g(-2) = (0)(6) = 0$

(d) $(f/g)(0) = \dfrac{f(0)}{g(0)} = \dfrac{5}{0} \Rightarrow$ undefined

38. (a) $(f + g)(2) = f(2) + g(2) = 5 + 4 = 9$

(b) $(f - g)(4) = f(4) - g(4) = 0 - 0 = 0$

(c) $(fg)(-2) = f(-2) \cdot g(-2) = (-4)(2) = -8$

(d) $(f/g)(0) = \dfrac{f(0)}{g(0)} = \dfrac{8}{-1} = -8$

39. For example: $(f - g)(2) = f(2) - g(2) = 7 - (-2) = 9$. See Figure 39. A dash (—) indicates that the value of the function is undefined.

| $x$ | $-2$ | 0 | 2 | 4 |
|---|---|---|---|---|
| $(f + g)(x)$ | 6 | 5 | 5 | 15 |
| $(f - g)(x)$ | $-6$ | 5 | 9 | 5 |
| $(fg)(x)$ | 0 | 0 | $-14$ | 50 |
| $(f/g)(x)$ | 0 | — | $-3.5$ | 2 |

Figure 39

| $x$ | $-2$ | 0 | 2 | 4 |
|---|---|---|---|---|
| $(f + g)(x)$ | $-2$ | 7 | 9 | 0 |
| $(f - g)(x)$ | $-6$ | 9 | 1 | 0 |
| $(fg)(x)$ | $-8$ | $-8$ | 20 | 0 |
| $(f/g)(x)$ | $-2$ | $-8$ | 1.25 | — |

Figure 40

40. For example: $(f - g)(2) = f(2) - g(2) = 5 - 4 = 1$. See Figure 40. A dash (—) indicates that the value of the function is undefined.

41. (a) $g(x) = 2x + 1 \Rightarrow g(-3) = 2(-3) + 1 \Rightarrow g(-3) = -5$

(b) $g(x) = 2x + 1 \Rightarrow g(b) = 2(b) + 1 \Rightarrow g(b) = 2b + 1$

(c) $g(x) = 2x + 1 \Rightarrow g(x^3) = 2(x^3) + 1 \Rightarrow g(x^3) = 2x^3 + 1$

(d) $g(x) = 2x + 1 \Rightarrow g(2x - 3) = 2(2x - 3) + 1 \Rightarrow g(2x - 3) = 4x - 6 + 1 \Rightarrow$

$g(2x - 3) = 4x - 5$

42. (a) $g(x) = 5 - \dfrac{1}{2}x \Rightarrow g(-3) = 5 - \dfrac{1}{2}(-3) \Rightarrow g(-3) = \dfrac{10}{2} + \dfrac{3}{2} \Rightarrow g(-3) = \dfrac{13}{2}$

(b) $g(x) = 5 - \dfrac{1}{2}x \Rightarrow g(b) = 5 - \dfrac{1}{2}(b) \Rightarrow g(b) = 5 - \dfrac{b}{2}$

(c) $g(x) = 5 - \dfrac{1}{2}x \Rightarrow g(x^3) = 5 - \dfrac{1}{2}(x^3) \Rightarrow g(x^3) = 5 - \dfrac{x^3}{2}$

(d) $g(x) = 5 - \dfrac{1}{2}x \Rightarrow g(2x - 3) = 5 - \dfrac{1}{2}(2x - 3) \Rightarrow g(2x - 3) = \dfrac{10}{2} - \dfrac{2x - 3}{2} \Rightarrow$

$g(2x - 3) = \dfrac{13}{2} - x$

43. (a) $g(x) = 2(x + 3)^2 - 4 \Rightarrow g(-3) = 2((-3) + 3)^2 - 4 \Rightarrow g(-3) = 2(0) - 4 \Rightarrow g(-3) = -4$

(b) $g(x) = 2(x + 3)^2 - 4 \Rightarrow g(b) = 2((b) + 3)^2 - 4 \Rightarrow g(b) = 2(b + 3)^2 - 4$

(c) $g(x) = 2(x + 3)^2 - 4 \Rightarrow g(x^3) = 2((x^3) + 3)^2 - 4 \Rightarrow g(x^3) = 2(x^3 + 3)^2 - 4$

(d) $g(x) = 2(x + 3)^2 - 4 \Rightarrow g(2x - 3) = 2((2x - 3) + 3)^2 - 4 \Rightarrow g(2x - 3) = 2(2x)^2 - 4 \Rightarrow$

$g(2x - 3) = 2(4x^2) - 4 \Rightarrow g(2x - 3) = 8x^2 - 4$

44. (a) $g(x) = -(x - 1)^2 \Rightarrow g(-3) = -((-3) - 1)^2 \Rightarrow g(-3) = -(-4)^2 \Rightarrow g(-3) = -16$

(b) $g(x) = -(x - 1)^2 \Rightarrow g(b) = -((b) - 1)^2 \Rightarrow g(b) = -(b - 1)^2$

(c) $g(x) = -(x - 1)^2 \Rightarrow g(x^3) = -((x^3) - 1)^2 \Rightarrow g(x^3) = -(x^3 - 1)^2$

(d) $g(x) = -(x - 1)^2 \Rightarrow g(2x - 3) = -((2x - 3) - 1)^2 \Rightarrow g(2x - 3) = -(2x - 4)^2 \Rightarrow$

$g(2x - 3) = -4x^2 + 16x - 16 \Rightarrow g(2x - 3) = -4(x^2 - 4x + 4) \Rightarrow g(2x - 3) = -4(x - 2)^2$

45. (a) $g(x) = \frac{1}{2}x^2 + 3x - 1 \Rightarrow g(-3) = \frac{1}{2}(-3)^2 + 3(-3) - 1 \Rightarrow g(-3) = \frac{9}{2} - 9 - 1 \Rightarrow$

$g(-3) = \frac{9}{2} - \frac{20}{2} \Rightarrow g(-3) = -\frac{11}{2}$

(b) $g(x) = \frac{1}{2}x^2 + 3x - 1 \Rightarrow g(b) = \frac{1}{2}(b)^2 + 3(b) - 1 \Rightarrow g(b) = \frac{1}{2}b^2 + 3b - 1$

(c) $g(x) = \frac{1}{2}x^2 + 3x - 1 \Rightarrow g(x^3) = \frac{1}{2}(x^3)^2 + 3(x^3) - 1 \Rightarrow g(x^3) = \frac{1}{2}x^6 + 3x^3 - 1$

(d) $g(x) = \frac{1}{2}x^2 + 3x - 1 \Rightarrow g(2x - 3) = \frac{1}{2}(2x - 3)^2 + 3(2x - 3) - 1 \Rightarrow$

$g(2x - 3) = \frac{4x^2 - 12x + 9}{2} + 6x - 9 - 1 \Rightarrow g(2x - 3) = 2x^2 - 6x + \frac{9}{2} + 6x - \frac{20}{2} \Rightarrow$

$g(2x - 3) = 2x^2 - \frac{11}{2}$

46. (a) $g(x) = 2x^2 - x - 9 \Rightarrow g(-3) = 2(-3)^2 - (-3) - 9 \Rightarrow g(-3) = 18 + 3 - 9 \Rightarrow g(-3) = 12$

(b) $g(x) = 2x^2 - x - 9 \Rightarrow g(b) = 2(b)^2 - (b) - 9 \Rightarrow g(b) = 2b^2 - b - 9$

(c) $g(x) = 2x^2 - x - 9 \Rightarrow g(x^3) = 2(x^3)^2 - (x^3) - 9 \Rightarrow g(x^3) = 2x^6 - x^3 - 9$

(d) $g(x) = 2x^2 - x - 9 \Rightarrow g(2x - 3) = 2(2x - 3)^2 - (2x - 3) - 9 \Rightarrow$

$g(2x - 3) = 2(4x^2 - 12x + 9) - (2x - 3) - 9 \Rightarrow$

$g(2x - 3) = 8x^2 - 24x + 18 - 2x + 3 - 9 \Rightarrow g(2x - 3) = 8x^2 - 26x + 12$

47. (a) $g(x) = \sqrt{x + 4} \Rightarrow g(-3) = \sqrt{(-3) + 4} \Rightarrow g(-3) = \sqrt{1} \Rightarrow g(-3) = 1$

(b) $g(x) = \sqrt{x + 4} \Rightarrow g(b) = \sqrt{(b) + 4} \Rightarrow g(b) = \sqrt{b + 4}$

(c) $g(x) = \sqrt{x + 4} \Rightarrow g(x^3) = \sqrt{(x^3) + 4} \Rightarrow g(x^3) = \sqrt{x^3 + 4}$

(d) $g(x) = \sqrt{x + 4} \Rightarrow g(2x - 3) = \sqrt{(2x - 3) + 4} \Rightarrow g(2x - 3) = \sqrt{2x + 1}$

48. (a) $g(x) = \sqrt{2 - x} \Rightarrow g(-3) = \sqrt{2 - (-3)} \Rightarrow g(-3) = \sqrt{5}$

(b) $g(x) = \sqrt{2 - x} \Rightarrow g(b) = \sqrt{2 - (b)} \Rightarrow g(b) = \sqrt{2 - b}$

(c) $g(x) = \sqrt{2 - x} \Rightarrow g(x^3) = \sqrt{2 - (x^3)} \Rightarrow g(x^3) = \sqrt{2 - x^3}$

(d) $g(x) = \sqrt{2 - x} \Rightarrow g(2x - 3) = \sqrt{2 - (2x - 3)} \Rightarrow g(2x - 3) = \sqrt{5 - 2x}$

49. (a) $g(x) = |3x - 1| + 4 \Rightarrow g(-3) = |3(-3) - 1| + 4 \Rightarrow g(-3) = |-10| + 4 \Rightarrow g(-3) = 14$

(b) $g(x) = |3x - 1| + 4 \Rightarrow g(b) = |3(b) - 1| + 4 \Rightarrow g(b) = |3b - 1| + 4$

(c) $g(x) = |3x - 1| + 4 \Rightarrow g(x^3) = |3(x^3) - 1| + 4 \Rightarrow g(x^3) = |3x^3 - 1| + 4$

(d) $g(x) = |3x - 1| + 4 \Rightarrow g(2x - 3) = |3(2x - 3) - 1| + 4 \Rightarrow g(2x - 3) = |6x - 10| + 4$

50. (a) $g(x) = 2|1 - x| - 7 \Rightarrow g(-3) = 2|1 - (-3)| - 7 \Rightarrow g(-3) = 2|4| - 7 \Rightarrow g(-3) = 8 - 7 \Rightarrow$
$g(-3) = 1$

(b) $g(x) = 2|1 - x| - 7 \Rightarrow g(b) = 2|1 - (b)| - 7 \Rightarrow g(b) = 2|1 - b| - 7$

(c) $g(x) = 2|1 - x| - 7 \Rightarrow g(x^3) = 2|1 - (x^3)| - 7 \Rightarrow g(x^3) = 2|1 - x^3| - 7$

(d) $g(x) = 2|1 - x| - 7 \Rightarrow g(2x - 3) = 2|1 - (2x - 3)| - 7 \Rightarrow g(2x - 3) = 2|4 - 2x| - 7$

51. (a) $g(x) = \dfrac{4x}{x + 3} \Rightarrow g(-3) = \dfrac{4(-3)}{(-3) + 3} \Rightarrow g(-3) = \dfrac{-12}{0} \Rightarrow g(-3) = \text{undefined}$

(b) $g(x) = \dfrac{4x}{x + 3} \Rightarrow g(b) = \dfrac{4(b)}{b + 3} \Rightarrow g(b) = \dfrac{4b}{b + 3}$

(c) $g(x) = \dfrac{4x}{x + 3} \Rightarrow g(x^3) = \dfrac{4(x^3)}{x^3 + 3} \Rightarrow g(x^3) = \dfrac{4x^3}{x^3 + 3}$

(d) $g(x) = \dfrac{4x}{x + 3} \Rightarrow g(2x - 3) = \dfrac{4(2x - 3)}{(2x - 3) + 3} \Rightarrow g(2x - 3) = \dfrac{8x - 12}{2x} \Rightarrow$
$g(2x - 3) = \dfrac{4x - 6}{x} \Rightarrow g(2x - 3) = \dfrac{2(2x - 3)}{x}$

52. (a) $g(x) = \dfrac{x + 3}{2} \Rightarrow g(-3) = \dfrac{(-3) + 3}{2} \Rightarrow g(-3) = 0$

(b) $g(x) = \dfrac{x + 3}{2} \Rightarrow g(b) = \dfrac{(b) + 3}{2} \Rightarrow g(-3) = \dfrac{b + 3}{2}$

(c) $g(x) = \dfrac{x + 3}{2} \Rightarrow g(x^3) = \dfrac{(x^3) + 3}{2} \Rightarrow g(x^3) = \dfrac{x^3 + 3}{2}$

(d) $g(x) = \dfrac{x + 3}{2} \Rightarrow g(2x - 3) = \dfrac{(2x - 3) + 3}{2} \Rightarrow g(2x - 3) = \dfrac{2x}{2} \Rightarrow g(2x - 3) = x$

53. (a) $(f \circ g)(2) = f(g(2)) = f(2^2) = f(4) = \sqrt{4 + 5} = \sqrt{9} = 3$

(b) $(g \circ f)(-1) = g(f(-1)) = g(\sqrt{-1 + 5}) = g(2) = 2^2 = 4$

54. (a) $(f \circ g)(1) = f(g(1)) = f(2(1)^2 + (1) + 1) = f(4) = |4^2 - 4| = |12| = 12$

(b) $(g \circ f)(-3) = g(f(-3)) = g(|(-3)^2 - 4|) = g(5) = 2(5)^2 + (5) + 1 = 56$

55. (a) $(f \circ g)(-4) = f(g(-4)) = f(|-4|) = f(4) = 5(4) - 2 = 18$

(b) $(g \circ f)(5) = g(f(5)) = g(5(5) - 2) = g(23) = |23| = 23$

56. (a) $(f \circ g)(3) = f(g(3)) = f(5) = \dfrac{1}{5 - 4} = \dfrac{1}{1} = 1$

(b) $(g \circ f)(8) = g(f(8)) = g\left(\dfrac{1}{8 - 4}\right) = g\left(\dfrac{1}{4}\right) = 5$

57. (a) $(f \circ g)(x) = f(g(x)) = f(x^2 + 3x - 1) = (x^2 + 3x - 1)^3$; $D$: all real numbers

(b) $(g \circ f)(x) = g(f(x)) = g(x^3) = (x^3)^2 + 3(x^3) - 1 = x^6 + 3x^3 - 1$; $D$: all real numbers

(c) $(f \circ f)(x) = f(f(x)) = f(x^3) = (x^3)^3 = x^9$; $D$: all real numbers

58. (a) $(f \circ g)(x) = f(g(x)) = f\left(\frac{1}{x^2}\right) = 2 - \frac{1}{x^2}$; $D = \{x \mid x \neq 0\}$

(b) $(g \circ f)(x) = g(f(x)) = g(2 - x) = \frac{1}{(2 - x)^2}$; $D = \{x \mid x \neq 2\}$

(c) $(f \circ f)(x) = f(f(x)) = f(2 - x) = 2 - (2 - x) = x$; $D$: all real numbers

59. (a) $(f \circ g)(x) = f(g(x)) = f(x^4 + x^2 - 3x - 4) = x^4 + x^2 - 3x - 2$; $D$: all real numbers

(b) $(g \circ f)(x) = g(f(x)) = g(x + 2) = (x + 2)^4 + (x + 2)^2 - 3(x + 2) - 4$; $D$: all real numbers

(c) $(f \circ f)(x) = f(f(x)) = f(x + 2) = (x + 2) + 2 = x + 4$; $D$: all real numbers

60. (a) $(f \circ g)(x) = f(g(x)) = f(\sqrt{1 - x}\,) = (\sqrt{1 - x}\,)^2 = 1 - x$; $D = \{x \mid x \leq 1\}$

(b) $(g \circ f)(x) = g(f(x)) = g(x^2) = \sqrt{1 - x^2}$; $D = \{x \mid -1 \leq x \leq 1\}$

(c) $(f \circ f)(x) = f(f(x)) = f(x^2) = (x^2)^2 = x^4$; $D$: all real numbers

61. (a) $(f \circ g)(x) = f(g(x)) = f(x^3) = 2 - 3x^3$; $D$: all real numbers

(b) $(g \circ f)(x) = g(f(x)) = g(2 - 3x) = (2 - 3x)^3$; $D$: all real numbers

(c) $(f \circ f)(x) = f(f(x)) = f(2 - 3x) = 2 - 3(2 - 3x) = 9x - 4$; $D$: all real numbers

62. (a) $(f \circ g)(x) = f(g(x)) = f(1 - x^2) = \sqrt{1 - x^2}$; $D = \{x \mid -1 \leq x \leq 1\}$

(b) $(g \circ f)(x) = g(f(x)) = g(\sqrt{x}) = 1 - (\sqrt{x})^2 = 1 - x$; $D = \{x \mid x \geq 0\}$

(c) $(f \circ f)(x) = f(f(x)) = f(\sqrt{x}) = \sqrt{\sqrt{x}} = \sqrt[4]{x}$; $D = \{x \mid x \geq 0\}$

63. (a) $(f \circ g)(x) = f(g(x)) = f(5x) = \frac{1}{5x + 1}$; $D = \left\{x \mid x \neq -\frac{1}{5}\right\}$

(b) $(g \circ f)(x) = g(f(x)) = g\left(\frac{1}{x + 1}\right) = 5\left(\frac{1}{x + 1}\right) = \frac{5}{x + 1}$; $D = \{x \mid x \neq -1\}$

(c) $(f \circ f)(x) = f(f(x)) = f\left(\frac{1}{x + 1}\right) = \frac{1}{\frac{1}{x + 1} + 1} = \frac{1}{\frac{1 + x + 1}{x + 1}} = \frac{x + 1}{x + 2}$;

$D = \{x \mid x \neq -1 \text{ and } x \neq -2\}$

64. (a) $(f \circ g)(x) = f(g(x)) = f\left(\frac{2}{x - 1}\right) = \frac{1}{3(\frac{2}{x - 1})} = \frac{x - 1}{6}$; $D = \{x \mid x \neq 1\}$

(b) $(g \circ f)(x) = g(f(x)) = g\left(\frac{1}{3x}\right) = \frac{2}{\frac{1}{3x} - 1} = \frac{2}{\frac{1 - 3x}{3x}} = \frac{6x}{1 - 3x}$; $D = \left\{x \mid x \neq 0 \text{ and } x \neq \frac{1}{3}\right\}$

(c) $(f \circ f)(x) = f(f(x)) = f\left(\frac{1}{3x}\right) = \frac{1}{3(\frac{1}{3x})} = \frac{1}{\frac{1}{x}} = x$; $D = \{x \mid x \neq 0\}$

65. (a) $(f \circ g)(x) = f(g(x)) = f(\sqrt{4 - x^2}) = \sqrt{4 - x^2} + 4$; $D = \{x \mid -2 \leq x \leq 2\}$

(b) $(g \circ f)(x) = g(f(x)) = g(x + 4) = \sqrt{4 - (x + 4)^2}$; $D = \{x \mid -6 \leq x \leq -2\}$

(c) $(f \circ f)(x) = f(f(x)) = f(x + 4) = (x + 4) + 4 = x + 8$; $D$: all real numbers

66. (a) $(f \circ g)(x) = f(g(x)) = f(4x^3 - 5x^2) = 2(4x^3 - 5x^2) + 1 = 8x^3 - 10x^2 + 1$; $D$: all real numbers

(b) $(g \circ f)(x) = g(f(x)) = g(2x + 1) = 4(2x + 1)^3 - 5(2x + 1)^2 = 32x^3 + 28x^2 + 4x - 1$;

$D$: all reals

(c) $(f \circ f)(x) = f(f(x)) = f(2x + 1) = 2(2x + 1) + 1 = 4x + 3$; $D$: all real numbers

67. (a) $(f \circ g)(x) = f(g(x)) = f(3x) = \sqrt{3x - 1}$ ; $D = \left\{x \mid x \geq \frac{1}{3}\right\}$

(b) $(g \circ f)(x) = g(f(x)) = g(\sqrt{x - 1}\,) = 3\sqrt{x - 1}$ ; $D = \{x \mid x \geq 1\}$

(c) $(f \circ f)(x) = f(f(x)) = f(\sqrt{x - 1}\,) = \sqrt{\sqrt{x - 1} - 1}; D = \{x \mid x \geq 2\}$

68. (a) $(f \circ g)(x) = f(g(x)) = f(2x + 3) = \dfrac{(2x + 3) - 3}{2} = \dfrac{2x + 0}{2} = x$; $D$: all real numbers

(b) $(g \circ f)(x) = g(f(x)) = g\left(\dfrac{x - 3}{2}\right) = 2\left(\dfrac{x - 3}{2}\right) + 3 = x - 3 + 3 = x$; $D$: all real numbers

(c) $(f \circ\ )(x) = f(f(x)) = f\left(\dfrac{x - 3}{2}\right) = \dfrac{\frac{x - 3}{2} - 3}{2} = \dfrac{\frac{x - 3}{2} - \frac{6}{2}}{2} = \dfrac{\frac{x - 9}{2}}{2} = \dfrac{x - 9}{2} \cdot \dfrac{1}{2} = \dfrac{x - 9}{4}$;

$D$: all real numbers

69. (a) $(f \circ g)(x) = f(g(x)) = f\left(\dfrac{1 - x}{5}\right) = 1 - 5\left(\dfrac{1 - x}{5}\right) = 1 - (1 - x) = x$; $D$: all real numbers

(b) $(g \circ f)(x) = g(f(x)) = g(1 - 5x) = \dfrac{1 - (1 - 5x)}{5} = \dfrac{5x}{5} = x$; $D$: all real numbers

(c) $(f \circ f)(x) = f(f(x)) = f(1 - 5x) = 1 - 5(1 - 5x) = 1 - 5 + 25x = 25x - 4$;

$D$: all real numbers

70. (a) $(f \circ g)(x) = f(g(x)) = f(x^3 + 1\,) = \sqrt[3]{(x^3 + 1) - 1} = \sqrt[3]{x^2 + 1 - 1} = x$; $D$: all real numbers

(b) $(g \circ f)(x) = g(f(x)) = g(\sqrt[3]{x - 1}) = (\sqrt[3]{x - 1})^3 + 1 = x - 1 + 1 = x$; $D$: all real numbers

(c) $(f \circ f)(x) = f(f(x)) = f(\sqrt[3]{x - 1}) = \sqrt[3]{\sqrt[3]{x - 1} - 1}$; $D$: all real numbers

71. (a) $(f \circ g)(x) = f(g(x)) = f\left(\dfrac{1}{kx}\right) = \dfrac{1}{k(\frac{1}{kx})} = \dfrac{1}{\frac{1}{x}} = x$; $D$: $\{x \mid x \neq 0\}$

(b) $(g \circ f)(x) = g(f(x)) = g\left(\dfrac{1}{kx}\right) = \dfrac{1}{k(\frac{1}{kx})} = \dfrac{1}{\frac{1}{x}} = x$; $D$: $\{x \mid x \neq 0\}$

(c) $(f \circ f)(x) = f(f(x)) = f\left(\dfrac{1}{kx}\right) = \dfrac{1}{k(\frac{1}{kx})} = \dfrac{1}{\frac{1}{x}} = x$; $D$: $\{x \mid x \neq 0\}$

72. (a) $(f \circ g)(x) = f(g(x)) = f(\sqrt{ax}\,) = a(\sqrt{ax}\,)^2 = a \cdot ax = a^2x$; $D$: $\{x \mid x \geq 0\}$

(b) $(g \circ f)(x) = g(f(x)) = g(ax^2) = \sqrt{a(ax^2)} = \sqrt{a^2x^2} = |ax|$; $D$: all real numbers

(c) $(f \circ f)(x) = f(f(x)) = f(ax^2) = a(ax^2)^2 = a \cdot a^2 \cdot x^4 = a^3x^4$; $D$: all real numbers

73. (a) $(f \circ g)(4) = f(g(4)) = f(0) = -4$

(b) $(g \circ f)(3) = g(f(3)) = g(2) = 2$

(c) $(f \circ f)(2) = f(f(2)) = f(0) = -4$

74. (a) $(f \circ g)(2) = f(g(2)) = f(-2) = -4$

(b) $(g \circ g)(0) = g(g(0)) = g(2) = -2$

(c) $(g \circ f)(4) = g(f(4)) = g(2) = -2$

75. (a) $(f \circ g)(1) = f(g(1)) = f(2) = -3$

(b) $(g \circ f)(-2) = g(f(-2)) = g(-3) = -2$

(c) $(g \circ g)(-2) = g(g(-2)) = g(-1) = 0$

76. (a) $(f \circ g)(-2) = f(g(-2)) = f(4) = 2$

(b) $(g \circ f)(1) = g(f(1)) = g(1) = 1$

(c) $(f \circ f)(0) = f(f(0)) = f(0) = 0$

77. (a) $(g \circ f)(1) = g(f(1)) = g(4) = 5$

(b) $(f \circ g)(4) = f(g(4)) = f(5) \Rightarrow$ undefined

(c) $(f \circ f)(3) = f(f(3)) = f(1) = 4$

78. (a) $(g \circ f)(1) = g(f(1)) = g(2) = 4$

(b) $(f \circ g)(4) = f(g(4)) \Rightarrow$ undefined, since $g(4)$ is undefined

(c) $(f \circ f)(3) = f(f(3)) = f(6) = 7$

79. $g(3) = 4;\ f(4) = 2$

80. $g(6) = 7;\ f(7) = 0$

81. $h(x) = \sqrt{x-2} \Rightarrow g(x) = \sqrt{x}$ and $f(x) = x - 2$. *Answers may vary.*

82. $h(x) = (x+2)^4 \Rightarrow g(x) = x^4$ and $f(x) = x + 2$. *Answers may vary.*

83. $h(x) = \dfrac{1}{x+2} \Rightarrow g(x) = \dfrac{1}{x}$ and $f(x) = x + 2$. *Answers may vary.*

84. $h(x) = 5(x+2)^2 - 4 \Rightarrow g(x) = 5x^2 - 4$ and $f(x) = x + 2$. *Answers may vary.*

85. $h(x) = 4(2x+1)^3 \Rightarrow g(x) = 4x^3$ and $f(x) = 2x + 1$. *Answers may vary.*

86. $h(x) = \sqrt[3]{x^2+1} \Rightarrow g(x) = \sqrt[3]{x}$ and $f(x) = x^2 + 1$. *Answers may vary.*

87. $h(x) = (x^3-1)^2 \Rightarrow g(x) = x^2$ and $f(x) = x^3 - 1$. *Answers may vary.*

88. $h(x) = 4(x-5)^{-2} \Rightarrow g(x) = 4x^{-2}$ and $f(x) = x - 5$. *Answers may vary.*

89. $h(x) = -4|x+2| - 3 \Rightarrow g(x) = -4|x| - 3$ and $f(x) = x + 2$. *Answers may vary.*

90. $h(x) = 5\sqrt{x-1} \Rightarrow g(x) = 5\sqrt{x}$ and $f(x) = x - 1$. *Answers may vary.*

91. $h(x) = \dfrac{1}{(x-1)^2} \Rightarrow g(x) = \dfrac{1}{x^2}$ and $f(x) = x - 1$. *Answers may vary.*

92. $h(x) = \dfrac{2}{x^2-x+1} \Rightarrow g(x) = \dfrac{2}{x}$ and $f(x) = x^2 - x + 1$. *Answers may vary.*

93. $h(x) = x^{3/4} - x^{1/4} \Rightarrow g(x) = x^3 - x$ and $f(x) = x^{1/4}$. *Answers may vary.*

94. $h(x) = x^{2/3} - 5x^{1/3} + 4 \Rightarrow g(x) = x^2 - 5x + 4$ and $f(x) = x^{1/3}$. *Answers may vary.*

95. The cost function would not change but the revenue function would be $R(x) = 15x$. Therefore,

$P(x) = R(x) - C(x) = 15x - (2x + 2000) = 13x - 2000;\ P(3000) = 13(3000) - 2000 = \$37{,}000$

96. (a) $C(x) = 1.5x + 150{,}000$

(b) $R(x) = 6.5x;\ R(8000) = 6.5(8000) = \$52{,}000$

(c) $P(x) = R(x) - C(x) = 6.5x - (1.5x + 150{,}000) = 5x - 150{,}000$

$P(40{,}000) = 5(40{,}000) - 150{,}000 = \$50{,}000$

(d) $R(x) = C(x) \Rightarrow 6.5x = 1.5x + 150{,}000 \Rightarrow 5x = 150{,}000 \Rightarrow x = 30{,}000$

To break even, 30,000 videos must be sold.

97. (a) $I(x) = 36x$

(b) $C(x) = 2.54x$

(c) $F(x) = (C \circ I)(x)$

(d) $F(x) = 36(2.54x) = 91.44x$

98. (a) $Q(x) = 4x$

(b) $C(x) = 4x$

(c) $T(x) = 16x$

(d) $F(x) = (T \circ C \circ Q)(x)$

(e) $F(x) = 4(4(16x)) = 256x$

99. (a) In Example 1, the reaction distance for a reaction time of 2.5 seconds was $\frac{11}{3}x$.

The reaction distance for a driver with a reaction time of 1.25 seconds would be half. Thus, $f(x) = \frac{11}{6}x$.

(b) $d(x) = f(x) + g(x) = \frac{11}{6}x + \frac{1}{9}x^2$

(c) $d(60) = \frac{11}{6}(60) + \frac{1}{9}(60)^2 = 510$; this car requires 510 feet to stop at 60 mph.

100. (a) The formula $s(x) = r(x) + b(x) = \frac{11}{5}x + \frac{1}{11}x^2$ is the stopping distance when driving at $x$ miles per hour. $s(55) = \frac{11}{5}(55) + \frac{1}{11}(55)^2 = 121 + 275 = 396$ feet.

(b) See Figure 100b. For a given x-value, the y-value for 5 can be found by adding the corresponding $y$-values for $r$ and $b$.

(c) See Figure 100c. $r(x) = \frac{11}{5}x$, $r(11) = \frac{11}{5}(11) = 24.2$, $r(22) = \frac{11}{5}(22) = 24.2$,

$r(33) = \frac{11}{5}(33) = 72.6$, $r(44) = \frac{11}{5}(44) = 96.8$, $r(55) = \frac{11}{5}(55) = 121$

$b(x) = \frac{1}{11}(x)^2$, $b(11) = \frac{11^2}{11} = 11$, $b(22) = \frac{22^2}{11} = 44$, $b(33) = \frac{33^2}{11} = 99$, $b(44) = \frac{44^2}{11} = 176$,

$b(55) = \frac{55^2}{11} = 275$

$s(x) = r(x) + b(x)$, $s(11) = r(11) + b(11) = 35.2$, $s(22) = r(22) + b(22) = 92.4$,

$s(33) = r(33) + b(33) = 171.6$, $s(44) = r(44) + b(44) = 272.8$, $s(55) = r(55) + b(55) = 396$

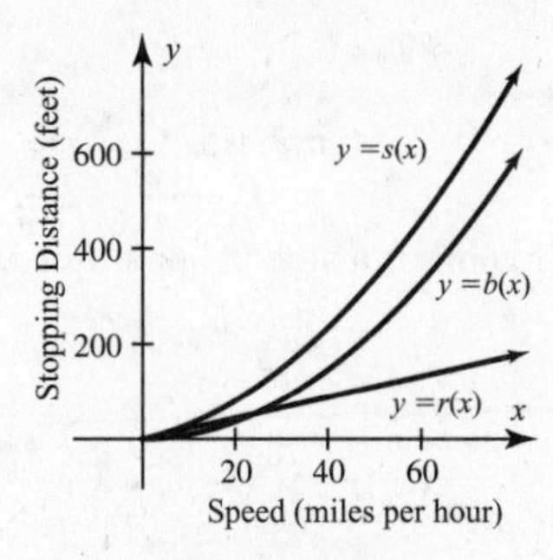

Figure 100b

| Speed | 11 | 22 | 33 | 44 | 55 |
|---|---|---|---|---|---|
| $r(x)$ | 24.2 | 48.4 | 72.6 | 96.8 | 121 |
| $b(x)$ | 11 | 44 | 99 | 176 | 275 |
| $s(x)$ | 35.2 | 92.4 | 171.6 | 272.8 | 396 |

Figure 100c

101. (a) $(g \circ f)(1) = g(f(1)) = g(1.5) = 5.25$;

A 1% decrease in the ozone layer could result in a 5.25% increase in skin cancer.

(b) $(f \circ g)(21) = f(g(21))$, but $g(21)$ is not given by the table. So $(f \circ g)(21)$ is not possible using these tables.

102. (a) Since $f(0) = 0$ and $f(1) = 1.5$, it follows that the slope of the graph of $f$ is $\frac{1.5 - 0}{1 - 0} = 1.5 \Rightarrow f(x) = 1.5x$.

Similarly, $g(0) = 0$ and $g(1.5) = 5.25 \Rightarrow m = \frac{5.25 - 0}{1.5} = 3.5$ and so $g(x) = 3.5x$.

(b) $(g \circ f)(x) = g(f(x)) = g(1.5x) = 3.5(1.5x) = 5.25x$

(c) $(g \circ f)(3.5) = 5.25(3.5) = 18.375$;

A 3.5% decrease in the ozone layer could result in an 18.4% increase in skin cancer.

103. (a) $(g \circ f)(1975) = g(f(1975)) = g(3) = 4.5\%$

(b) $(g \circ f)(x)$ computes the percent increase in peak demand during year $x$.

104. (a) $(g \circ f)(1980) = g(f(1980)) = g(3.5) \approx 5$; In 1980 the average nighttime temperature had risen about 3.5°C since 1948, which resulted in a 5% increase in peak-demand for electricity.

(b) $(f \circ g)(3)$ is meaningless because the range of $g$ is not the same as the domain of $f$.

105. (a) $(g \circ f)(1960) = g(f(1960)) = g(0.11(1960 - 1948)) = g(1.32) = 1.5(1.32) = 1.98$

In 1960 the temperature had risen 1.32°C which resulted in a 1.98% increase in peak-demand for electricity.

(b) $(g \circ f)(x) = g(f(x)) = g(0.11(x - 1948)) = 1.5(0.11(x - 1948)) = 0.165(x - 1948)$

(c) $f$, $g$, and $f \circ g$ are all linear functions.

106. (a) When $x = 2$, the amount of water in the pool is approximately 4000 cubic feet. Using 4000 as input into function $g$, we can estimate that $g(4000) \approx 30{,}000$ gallons.

(b) $(g \circ f)(x)$ computes the gallons of water contained in the pool after $x$ days.

107. (a) $(g \circ f)(2) = g(f(2)) = g(77) \approx 25°\text{C}$. After 2 hours the temperature is about 25°C.

*Answers may vary.*

(b) $(g \circ f)(x)$ computes the Celsius temperature after $x$ hours.

108. The radius of the circular wave at the end of $t$ seconds would be $6t$ inches.

$C = 2\pi r \Rightarrow C(t) = 2\pi(6t) = 12\pi t$

109. $A = \pi r^2 \Rightarrow A(t) = \pi(6t)^2 = 36\pi t^2$

110. $S = \pi r\sqrt{r^2 + h^2}$ and $h = 2r \Rightarrow S = \pi r\sqrt{r^2 + (2r)^2} \Rightarrow S = \pi r\sqrt{5r^2} \Rightarrow S = \pi r^2\sqrt{5}$

111. (a) For $A(s) = \frac{\sqrt{3}}{4}s^2$, $A(4s) = \frac{\sqrt{3}}{4}(4s)^2 = 16\frac{\sqrt{3}}{4}s^2 = 16A(s)$; if the length of a side is quadrupled, the area increases by a factor of 16.

(b) For $A(s) = \frac{\sqrt{3}}{4}s^2$, $A(s + 2) = \frac{\sqrt{3}}{4}(s + 2)^2 = \frac{\sqrt{3}}{4}(s^2 + 4s + 4) = \frac{\sqrt{3}}{4}s^2 + \sqrt{3}s + \sqrt{3} =$ $A(s) + \sqrt{3}(s + 1)$; if the length of a side increases by 2, the area increases by $\sqrt{3}(s + 1)$.

112. (a) $A(r) = 4\pi r^2$; $A(r + h) = 4\pi(r + h)^2 = 4\pi(r^2 + 2rh + h^2) = 4\pi r^2 + 8\pi rh + 4\pi h^2 \Rightarrow$

$A(r + h) - Ar = 4\pi r^2 + 8\pi rh + 4\pi h^2 - 4\pi r^2 = 8\pi rh + 4\pi h^2$; it represents the difference in surface area when the radius increases from $r$ to $r + h$.

(b) $8\pi(3)(0.1) + 4\pi(0.1)^2 = 2.4\pi + 0.04\pi = 2.44\pi$; $8\pi(6)(0.1) + 4\pi(0.1)^2 = 4.8\pi + 0.04\pi = 4.84\pi$

(c) It depends on the value of $r$.

113. (a) $(c + o)(1970) = c(1970) + o(1970) = 32.4 + 17.6 = 50$

(b) $(c + o)(x)$ computes the total coal and oil $SO_2$ emissions in the year $x$.

(c) A tabular representation of $(c + o)(x)$ is given in Figure 113.

| $x$ | 1860 | 1900 | 1940 | 1970 | 2000 |
|---|---|---|---|---|---|
| $(C + O)(x)$ | 2.4 | 12.8 | 26.5 | 50.0 | 78.0 |

Figure 113

| $x$ | 1860 | 1900 | 1940 | 1970 | 2000 |
|---|---|---|---|---|---|
| $h(x)$ | — | 63 | 10.52 | 1.84 | 2.39 |

Figure 114

114. The values of $h(x)$ can be computed as follows: $h(1900) = \dfrac{f(1900)}{g(1900)} = \dfrac{12.6}{0.2} = 63$. The other values are found in a similar manner. See Figure 114. The function $h$ computes the ratio of coal $SO_2$ emissions to oil $SO_2$ emissions. It provides a measure of which source causes the most pollution. Since the ratio is always greater than 1, coal causes the most $SO_2$ emissions. The ratio of coal emissions to oil emissions decreased dramatically from 1900 to 1970, then increased slightly.

115. (a) To find the total emissions we must add the developed and developing countries' emissions for each year. The resulting table is shown in Figure 115.

(b) $h(x) = f(x) + g(x)$

| $x$ | 1990 | 2000 | 2010 | 2020 | 2030 |
|---|---|---|---|---|---|
| $h(x)$ | 32 | 35.5 | 39 | 42.5 | 46 |

Figure 115

116. A graphical solution can be found by adding the corresponding $y$-values. For example, when $x = 1990$, $f(1990) \approx 27$ and $g(1990) \approx 5$, so $h(1990) \approx 27 + 5 = 32$. Since $f$ and $g$ appear to be linear functions, their sum will also be linear. A graph of $h = f + g$, together with $f$ and $g$ is shown in Figure 116.

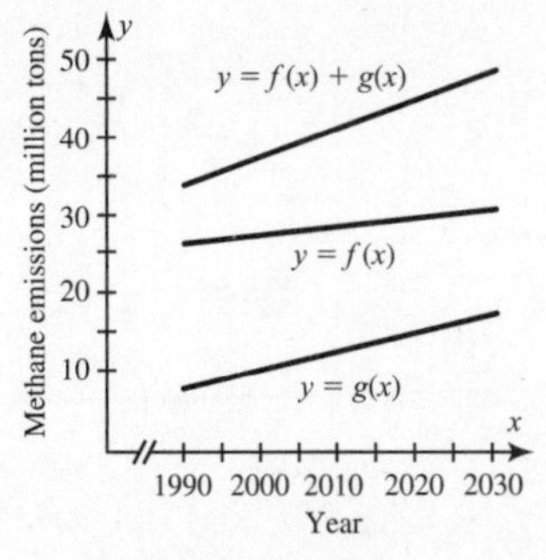


Figure 116

117. $h(x) = f(x) + g(x) = (0.1x - 172) + (0.25x - 492.5) = 0.35x - 664.5$

118. $h(x) = \dfrac{1900(x - 1982)^2 + 619}{3200(x - 1982)^2 + 1586}$; the graph of $h$ is shown in Figure 118a.

By tracing this graph, we find that the ratio of AIDS deaths to cases remained near 0.6 from 1986 to 1994. This means that approximately 60% of the people who contracted AIDS have died.

[1982, 1994, 2] by [0, 1, 0.1]

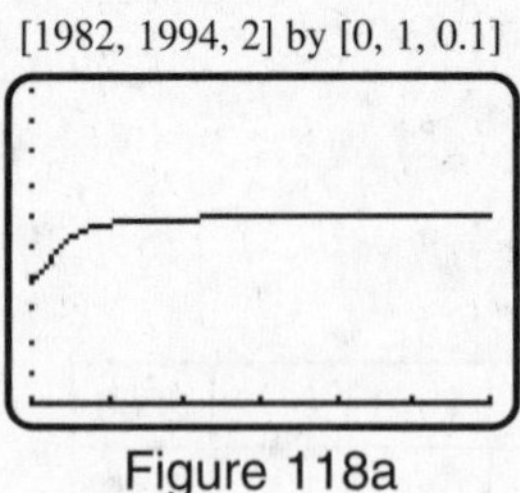

Figure 118a

119. (a) $P(h_0) = mph_0 = \frac{1}{2}m \cdot 2gh_0 = \frac{1}{2}m(\sqrt{2gh_0})^2 = \frac{1}{2}m(V_f) = K(V_f)$

(b) The potential energy of the ball before it is dropped is equal to the kinetic energy of the ball when it lands.

120. $S = 4\pi r^2 \Rightarrow r^2 = \frac{S}{4\pi} \Rightarrow r = \sqrt{\frac{S}{4\pi}}$; $V = \frac{4}{3}\pi r^3 \Rightarrow V = \frac{4}{3}\pi\left(\sqrt{\frac{S}{4\pi}}\right)^3 \Rightarrow V = \frac{4}{3}\pi\left(\frac{S}{4\pi}\right)^{3/2}$

121. Let $f(x) = ax + b$ and $g(x) = cx + d$. Then $f(x) + g(x) = (ax + b) + (cx + d) = (a + c)x + (b + d)$, which is linear.

122. Let $f(x)$ and $g(x)$ be odd functions. Then $f(-x) = -f(x)$ and $g(-x) = -g(x)$.
Thus $(g \circ f)(-x) = g(f(-x)) = g(-f(x)) = -g(f(x)) = -(g \circ f)(x)$. That is, $(g \circ f)(x)$ is an odd function.

123. (a) $f(x) = k$ and $g(x) = ax + b$. Thus, $(f \circ g)(x) = f(g(x)) = f(ax + b) = k$; $f \circ g$ is a constant function.

(b) $f(x) = k$ and $g(x) = ax + b$. Thus, $(g \circ f)(x) = g(f(x)) = g(k) = ak + b$; $g \circ f$ is a constant function.

124. $(g \circ f)(x) = g(f(x)) = g(ax + b) = c(ax + b) + d = cax + cb + d = cax + (cb + d)$.
The slope of the graph of $y = cax + (cb + d)$ is $ca$.

## 5.2: Inverse Functions and Their Representations

1. Closing a window.
2. Climbing down a ladder.
3. Closing a book, standing up, and walking out of the classroom.
4. Turning off the lights and closing the door.
5. Subtract 2 from $x$; $x + 2$ and $x - 2$
6. Divide $x$ by 5; $5x$ and $\frac{x}{5}$

7. Divide $x$ by 3 and add 2; $3(x - 2)$ and $\frac{x}{3} + 2$

8. Subtract 10 from $x$ and then multiply the result by 20; $\frac{x}{20} + 10$ and $20(x - 10)$

9. Subtract 1 from $x$ and cube the result; $\sqrt[3]{x} + 1$ and $(x - 1)^3$

10. Subtract 3 from $x$ and divide the result by –2; $-2x + 3$ and $\frac{x - 3}{-2}$

11. Take the reciprocal of $x$; $\frac{1}{x}$ and $\frac{1}{x}$

12. Square the number $x$; $\sqrt{x}$ and $x^2$

13. Since a horizontal line will intersect the graph at most once, $f$ is one-to-one.

14. Since a horizontal line will intersect the graph three times, $f$ is not one-to-one.

15. Since a horizontal line will intersect the graph two times, $f$ is not one-to-one.

16. Since a horizontal line will intersect the graph at most once, $f$ is one-to-one.

17. Since a horizontal line will intersect the graph two times, $f$ is not one-to-one.

18. Since a horizontal line will intersect the graph six times, $f$ is not one-to-one.

19. Since $f(2) = 3$ and $f(3) = 3$, different inputs result in the same output. Therefore $f$ is not one-to-one. Does not have an inverse.

20. Since different inputs always result in different outputs, $f$ is one-to-one. Does have an inverse.

21. Since different inputs always result in different outputs, $f$ is one-to-one. Does have an inverse.

22. Since $f(-2) = 4$ and $f(2) = 4$, different inputs result in the same output. Therefore $f$ is not one-to-one. Does not have an inverse.

23. Since the graph of $f$ is a line sloping upward from left to right, a horizontal line can intersect it at most once. Therefore, $f$ is one-to-one.

24. Since the graph of $f$ is a parabola, a horizontal line can intersect it more than once. Therefore, $f$ is not one-to-one.

25. Since the graph of $f$ is a parabola, a horizontal line can intersect it more than once. Therefore, $f$ is not one-to-one.

26. Since the graph of $f$ is a line sloping downward from left to right, a horizontal line can intersect it at most once. Therefore $f$ is one-to-one.

27. Since the graph of $f$ is a parabola, a horizontal line can intersect it more than once. Therefore, $f$ is not one-to-one.

28. Since the graph of $f$ is a V-shape, a horizontal line can intersect it more than once. Therefore, $f$ is not one-to-one.

29. Since the graph of $f$ is a V-shape, a horizontal line can intersect it more than once. Therefore, $f$ is not one-to-one.

30. Since the graph of $f$ is always increasing, a horizontal line can intersect it at most once. Therefore, $f$ is one-to-one.

31. Since the graph of $f$ is both increasing and decreasing, a horizontal line can intersect it more than once. Therefore, $f$ is not one-to-one.

32. Since the graph of $f$ is decreasing and negative when $x < 0$ and it is decreasing and positive when $x > 0$, a horizontal line can intersect it at most once. Therefore, $f$ is one-to-one.

33. Since the graph of $f$ is both increasing and decreasing, a horizontal line can intersect it more than once. Therefore, $f$ is not one-to-one.

34. Since the graph of $f$ is both increasing and decreasing, a horizontal line can intersect it more than once. Therefore, $f$ is not one-to-one.

35. Since the graph of $f$ is a line sloping upward from left to right, a horizontal line can intersect it at most once. Therefore $f$ is one-to-one.

36. Since the graph of $f$ is both increasing and decreasing, a horizontal line can intersect more than once. Therefore $f$ is not one-to-one.

37. Since the person goes up and down, there would be several times when the person attained a particular height above the ground. A one-to-one function would not model this situation.

38. Since more people are acquiring AIDS each year, the cumulative number of cases is increasing. A horizontal line would intersect a graph of AIDS cases at most once. A one-to-one function would model this situation.

39. Since the population of the United States increased each of these years, a horizontal line would intersect a graph of this population at most once. A one-to-one function would model this situation.

40. Since the stone goes up and down, there could be two different time when it was at a particular height. A one-to-one function would not model this situation.

41. The inverse operation of taking the cube root of $x$ is cubing $x$. Therefore, $f^{-1}(x) = x^3$.

42. The inverse operation of multiplying by 2 is dividing by 2. Therefore, $f^{-1}(x) = \frac{x}{2}$.

43. The inverse operations of multiplying by –2 and adding 10 are subtracting 10 and dividing by $-2$. Therefore, $f^{-1}(x) = \frac{x - 10}{-2} = -\frac{1}{2}x + 5$.

44. The inverse operations of cubing a number and adding 2 are subtracting 2 and taking the cube root of the result. Therefore, $f^{-1}(x) = \sqrt[3]{x - 2}$.

45. The inverse operations of multiplying by 3 and subtracting 1 are adding 1 and dividing by 3. Therefore, $f^{-1}(x) = \frac{x + 1}{3}$.

46. The inverse operations of subtracting 1 and dividing by 2 are multiplying by 2 and adding 1. Therefore, $f^{-1}(x) = 2x + 1$.

47. The inverse operations of cubing a number, multiplying by 2 and subtracting 5 are adding 5, dividing by 2 and taking the cube root of the result. Therefore, $f^{-1}(x) = \sqrt[3]{\frac{x + 5}{2}}$.

48. The inverse operations of cubing a number, multiplying by $-\frac{1}{2}$ and adding 1 are subtracting 1, dividing by $-\frac{1}{2}$ (or multiplying by –2) and taking the cube root of the result. Therefore, $f^{-1}(x) = \sqrt[3]{-2(x - 1)} = \sqrt[3]{2(1 - x)}$.

49. The inverse operations of squaring a number and subtracting 1 are adding 1 and taking the square root. Therefore, $f^{-1}(x) = \sqrt{x + 1}$.

50. The inverse operations of adding 2 and squaring the result are taking the square root and subtracting 2.

Since the domain of $f$ is $x \leq -2$ we use the negative square root. Therefore, $f^{-1}(x) = -\sqrt{x} - 2, x \geq 0$.

51. The inverse operations of multiplying by 2 and taking the reciprocal are taking the reciprocal and dividing by 2.

Therefore, $f^{-1}(x) = \frac{1}{x} \div 2 = \frac{1}{2x}$.

52. The inverse operations of taking the square root, taking the reciprocal and multiplying by 2 are dividing by 2 taking the reciprocal and squaring the result. Therefore, $f^{-1}(x) = \left(\frac{1}{\frac{x}{2}}\right)^2 = \left(\frac{2}{x}\right)^2 = \frac{4}{x^2}$ for $x > 0$.

53. The inverse operations of multiplying by $-5$, adding 4, multiplying by $\frac{1}{2}$, and adding 1 are subtracting 1, dividing by $\frac{1}{2}$ (or multipying by 2), subtracting 4, and dividing by $-5 \Rightarrow$

$f^{-1}(x) = \frac{2(x-1)-4}{-5} = \frac{2x-6}{-5} = -\frac{2(x-3)}{5}$.

54. The inverse operations of multiplying by 2, subtracting 4, multiplying by $-\frac{3}{4}$, and adding 6 are subtracting 6, dividing by $-\frac{3}{4}\left(\text{or multiplying by } -\frac{4}{3}\right)$, adding 4, and dividing by 2 $\Rightarrow$

$f^{-1}(x) = \frac{-\frac{4}{3}(x-6)+4}{2} = \frac{-\frac{4}{3}x+8+4}{2} = -\frac{2}{3}x + 6$ or $f^{-1}(x) = 6 - \frac{2}{3}x$.

55. $y = \frac{x}{x+2} \Rightarrow y(x+2) = x \Rightarrow xy + 2y = x \Rightarrow 2y = x - xy \Rightarrow 2y = x(1-y) \Rightarrow x = \frac{2y}{1-y} \Rightarrow$

$f^{-1}(x) = \frac{2x}{1-x} \Rightarrow f^{-1}(x) = -\frac{2x}{x-1}$

56. $y = \frac{3x}{x-1} \Rightarrow y(x-1) = 3x \Rightarrow xy - y = 3x \Rightarrow -y = 3x - xy \Rightarrow -y = x(3-y) \Rightarrow$

$x = \frac{-y}{3-y} \Rightarrow f^{-1}(x) = \frac{x}{x-3}$

57. $y = \frac{2x+1}{x-1} \Rightarrow y(x-1) = 2x+1 \Rightarrow xy - y = 2x + 1 \Rightarrow xy - 2x = y + 1 \Rightarrow$

$x(y-2) = y + 1 \Rightarrow x = \frac{y+1}{y-2} \Rightarrow f^{-1}(x) = \frac{x+1}{x-2}$

58. $y = \frac{1-x}{3x+1} \Rightarrow y(3x+1) = 1 - x \Rightarrow 3xy + y = 1 - x \Rightarrow 3xy + x = 1 - y \Rightarrow$

$x(3y+1) = 1 - y \Rightarrow x = \frac{1-y}{3y+1} \Rightarrow f^{-1}(x) = -\frac{x-1}{3x+1}$

59. $y = \frac{1}{x} - 3 \Rightarrow y + 3 = \frac{1}{x} \Rightarrow x = \frac{1}{y+3} \Rightarrow f^{-1}(x) = \frac{1}{x+3}$

60. $y = \frac{1}{x+5} + 2 \Rightarrow y - 2 = \frac{1}{x+5} \Rightarrow \frac{1}{y-2} = x + 5 \Rightarrow x = \frac{1}{y-2} - 5 \Rightarrow f^{-1}(x) = \frac{1}{x-2} - 5$

61. $y = \frac{1}{x^3-1} \Rightarrow \frac{1}{y} = x^3 - 1 \Rightarrow \frac{1}{y} + 1 = x^3 \Rightarrow \frac{1}{y} + \frac{y}{y} = x^3 \Rightarrow \frac{y+1}{y} = x^3 \Rightarrow f^{-1}(x) = \sqrt[3]{\frac{x+1}{x}}$

62. $y = \dfrac{2}{2 - x^3} \Rightarrow y(2 - x^3) = 2 \Rightarrow 2y - x^3y = 2 \Rightarrow -x^3y = 2 - 2y \Rightarrow x^3 = \dfrac{2 - 2y}{-y} \Rightarrow$

$x = \sqrt[3]{\dfrac{2y - 2}{y}} \Rightarrow f^{-1}(x) = \sqrt[3]{\dfrac{2(x - 1)}{x}}$

63. $y = 4 - x^2, x \geq 0 \Rightarrow x^2 = 4 - y \Rightarrow x = \sqrt{4 - y}$; therefore $f^{-1}(x) = \sqrt{4 - x}$

64. $y = 2(x + 3)^2, x \geq -3 \Rightarrow \dfrac{y}{2} = (x + 3)^2 \Rightarrow \sqrt{\dfrac{y}{2}} = x + 3 \Rightarrow x = \sqrt{\dfrac{y}{2}} - 3;$

therefore $f^{-1}(x) = \sqrt{\dfrac{x}{2}} - 3$

65. $y = (x - 2)^2 + 4, x \geq 2 \Rightarrow y - 4 = (x - 2)^2 \Rightarrow \sqrt{y - 4} = x - 2 \Rightarrow x = \sqrt{y - 4} + 2;$

therefore $f^{-1}(x) = \sqrt{x - 4} + 2$.

66. $y = x^4 - 1, x \geq 0 \Rightarrow y + 1 = x^4 \Rightarrow x = \sqrt[4]{y + 1}$; therefore $f^{-1}(x) = \sqrt[4]{x + 1}$

67. $y = x^{2/3} + 1, x \geq 0 \Rightarrow x^{2/3} = y - 1 \Rightarrow x = (y - 1)^{3/2}; \Rightarrow f^{-1}(x) = (x - 1)^{3/2}$

68. $y = 2(x + 3)^{2/3}, x \geq -3 \Rightarrow \dfrac{y}{2} = (x + 3)\dfrac{2}{3} \Rightarrow \left(\dfrac{y}{2}\right)^{3/2} = x + 3 \Rightarrow \left(\dfrac{y}{2}\right)^{3/2} - 3 = x \Rightarrow$

$f^{-1}(x) = \left(\dfrac{x}{2}\right)^{3/2} - 3$

69. $y = \sqrt{9 - 2x^2}, -\dfrac{3}{12} \leq x \leq \dfrac{3}{\sqrt{2}} \Rightarrow y^2 = 9 - 2x^2 \Rightarrow y^2 - 9 = -2x^2 \Rightarrow \dfrac{9 - y^2}{2} = x^2 \Rightarrow$

$\sqrt{\dfrac{9 - y^2}{2}} = x; \Rightarrow f^{-1}(x) = \sqrt{\dfrac{9 - x^2}{2}}$

70. $y = \sqrt{25 - x^2}, -5 \leq x \leq 5 \Rightarrow y^2 = 25 - x^2 \Rightarrow y^2 - 25 = -x^2 \Rightarrow 25 - y^2 = x^2 \Rightarrow$

$\sqrt{25 - y^2} = x;\ f^{-1}(x) = \sqrt{25 - x^2}$

71. $y = 5x - 15 \Rightarrow y + 15 = 5x \Rightarrow \dfrac{y + 15}{5} = x \Rightarrow f^{-1}(x) = \dfrac{x + 15}{5}$; $D$ and $R$ are all real numbers.

72. $y = (x + 3)^2, x \geq -3 \Rightarrow \sqrt{y} = x + 3 \Rightarrow \sqrt{y} - 3 = x \Rightarrow f^{-1}(x) = \sqrt{x} - 3;$

$D = \{x | x \geq 0\}$ and $R = \{y | y \geq -3\}$

73. $y = \sqrt[3]{x - 5} \Rightarrow y^3 = x - 5 \Rightarrow y^3 + 5 = x \Rightarrow f^{-1}(x) = x^3 + 5$; $D$ and $R$ are all real numbers

74. $y = 6 - 7x \Rightarrow y - 6 = -7x \Rightarrow -\dfrac{y - 6}{7} = x \Rightarrow f^{-1}(x) = -\dfrac{x - 6}{7}$; $D$ and $R$ are all real numbers.

75. $y = \dfrac{x - 5}{4} \Rightarrow 4y = x - 5 \Rightarrow 4y + 5 = x \Rightarrow f^{-1}(x) = 4x + 5$; $D$ and $R$ are all real numbers.

76. $y = \dfrac{x + 2}{9} \Rightarrow 9y = x + 2 \Rightarrow 9y - 2 = x \Rightarrow f^{-1}(x) = 9x - 2$; $D$ and $R$ are all real numbers.

77. $y = \sqrt{x - 5}, x \geq 5 \Rightarrow y^2 = x - 5 \Rightarrow y^2 + 5 = x \Rightarrow f^{-1}(x) = x^2 + 5;$

$D = \{x | x \geq 0\}$ and $R = \{y | y \geq 5\}$

78. $y = \sqrt{5 - 2x}, x \leq \dfrac{5}{2} \Rightarrow y^2 = 5 - 2x \Rightarrow y^2 - 5 = -2x \Rightarrow \dfrac{y^2 - 5}{-2} = x \Rightarrow f^{-1}(x) = -\dfrac{x^2 - 5}{2};$

$D = \{x | x \geq 0\}$ and $R = \left\{y | y \leq \dfrac{5}{2}\right\}$

79. $y = \frac{1}{x+3} \Rightarrow \frac{1}{y} = x + 3 \Rightarrow \frac{1}{y} - 3 = x \Rightarrow f^{-1}(x) = \frac{1}{x} - 3$; $D = \{x \mid x \neq 0\}$ and $D = \{y \mid y \neq -3\}$

80. $y = \frac{2}{x-1} \Rightarrow \frac{2}{y} = x - 1 \Rightarrow \frac{2}{y} + 1 = x \Rightarrow f^{-1}(x) = \frac{2}{x} + 1$; $D = \{x \mid x \neq 0\}$ and $D = \{y \mid y \neq 1\}$

81. $y = 2x^3 \Rightarrow \frac{y}{2} = x^3 \Rightarrow \sqrt[3]{\frac{y}{2}} = x \Rightarrow f^{-1}(x) = \sqrt[3]{\frac{x}{2}}$; $D$ and $R$ are all real numbers.

82. $y = 1 - 4x^3 \Rightarrow y - 1 = -4x^3 \Rightarrow \frac{y-1}{-4} = x^3 \Rightarrow \sqrt[3]{\frac{y-1}{-4}} = x \Rightarrow \sqrt[3]{\frac{1-y}{4}} = x \Rightarrow$

$f^{-1}(x) = \sqrt[3]{\frac{1-x}{4}}$; $D$ and $R$ are all real numbers.

83. $y = x^2, x \geq 0 \Rightarrow \sqrt{y} = x \Rightarrow f^{-1}(x) = \sqrt{x}$; $D = \{x \mid x \geq 0\}$ and $D = \{y \mid y \geq 0\}$

84. $y = \sqrt[3]{1-x} \Rightarrow y^3 = 1 - x \Rightarrow x = 1 - y^3 \Rightarrow f^{-1}(x) = 1 - x^3$; $D$ and $R$ are all real numbers.

85. The domain and range of $f$ are $D = \{1, 2, 3\}$ and $R = \{5, 7, 9\}$. Interchange these to get the domain and range of $f^{-1}$; $D = \{5, 7, 9\}$ and $R = \{1, 2, 3\}$. See Figure 85.

| $x$ | 5 | 7 | 9 |
|---|---|---|---|
| $f^{-1}(x)$ | 1 | 2 | 3 |

Figure 85

| $x$ | 0 | 1 | 2 |
|---|---|---|---|
| $f^{-1}(x)$ | 1 | 10 | 100 |

Figure 86

86. The domain and range of $f$ are $D = \{1, 10, 100\}$ and $R = \{0, 1, 2\}$. Interchange these to get the domain and range of $f^{-1}$; $D = \{0, 1, 2\}$ and $R = \{1, 10, 100\}$. See Figure 86.

87. The domain and range of $f$ are $D = \{0, 2, 4\}$ and $R = \{0, 4, 16\}$. Interchange these to get the domain and range of $f^{-1}$; $D = \{0, 4, 16\}$ and $R = \{0, 2, 4\}$. See Figure 87.

| $x$ | 0 | 4 | 16 |
|---|---|---|---|
| $f^{-1}(x)$ | 0 | 2 | 4 |

Figure 87

| $x$ | 1 | 2 | 4 |
|---|---|---|---|
| $f^{-1}(x)$ | 0 | 1 | 2 |

Figure 88

88. The domain and range of $f$ are $D = \{0, 1, 2\}$ and $R = \{1, 2, 4\}$. Interchange these to get the domain and range of $f^{-1}$; $D = \{1, 2, 4\}$ and $R = \{0, 1, 2\}$. See Figure 88.

89. Since $f$ multiplies $x$ by 4, $f^{-1}$ divides $x$ by 4. See Figure 89.

| $x$ | 0 | 2 | 4 | 6 |
|---|---|---|---|---|
| $f^{-1}(x)$ | 0 | $\frac{1}{2}$ | 1 | $\frac{3}{2}$ |

Figure 89

| $x$ | −8 | −1 | 8 | 27 |
|---|---|---|---|---|
| $f^{-1}(x)$ | −2 | −1 | 2 | 3 |

Figure 90

90. Since $f$ cubes $x$, $f^{-1}$ takes the cube root of $x$. See Figure 90.

91. $f(1) = 3 \Rightarrow f^{-1}(3) = 1$

92. $f(2) = 5 \Rightarrow f^{-1}(5) = 2$

93. $g(3) = 4 \Rightarrow g^{-1}(4) = 3$

94. $g(-1) = 0 \Rightarrow g^{-1}(0) = -1$

95. $(f \circ g^{-1})(1) = f(g^{-1}(1)) = f(2) = 5$. Note that $g(2) = 1 \Rightarrow g^{-1}(1) = 2$.

96. $(g^{-1} \circ g^{-1})(2) = g^{-1}(g^{-1}(2)) = g^{-1}(1) = 2$. Note that $g(1) = 2 \Rightarrow g^{-1}(2) = 1$ and $g(2) = 1 \Rightarrow$ $g^{-1}(1) = 2$.

97. $(g \circ f^{-1})(5) = g(f^{-1}(5)) = g(2) = 1$. Note that $f(2) = 5 \Rightarrow f^{-1}(5) = 2$.

98. $(f^{-1} \circ g)(4) = f^{-1}(g(4)) = f^{-1}(5) = 2$. Note that $f(2) = 5 \Rightarrow f^{-1}(5) = 2$.

99. (a) $f(1) \approx \$110$

(b) $f^{-1}(110) \approx 1$ year

(c) $f^{-1}(160) \approx 5$ years

The function $f^{-1}$ computes the number of years it takes for this savings account to accumulate $x$ dollars.

100. (a) $f(4) \approx 90°\text{C}$

(b) $f^{-1}(90) \approx 4$ minutes

(c) $f^{-1}(80) \approx 8.5$ minutes

The function $f^{-1}$ computes the number of minutes it takes for the water to cool to a temperature of $x$ degrees Celsius.

101. (a) $f(-1) = 2$

(b) $f^{-1}(-2) = 3$

(c) $f^{-1}(0) = 1$

(d) $(f^{-1} \circ f)(3) = f^{-1}(f(3)) = f^{-1}(-2) = 3$

102. (a) $f(1) = 1$

(b) $f^{-1}(1) = 1$

(c) $f^{-1}(4) = 3$

(d) $(f \circ f^{-1})(2.5) = f(f^{-1}(2.5)) = 2.5$

103. (a) $f(4) = 4$

(b) $f^{-1}(0) = 0$

(c) $f^{-1}(6) = 9$

(d) $(f^{-1} \circ f)(4) = f^{-1}(f(4)) = f^{-1}(4) = 4$

104. (a) $f(1) = 0$

(b) $f^{-1}(-1) = 0$

(c) $f^{-1}(3) = 2$

(d) $(f \circ f^{-1})(1) = f(f^{-1}(1)) = f(0) = 1$

105. The graph of $f$ passes through the points (–2, –4) and (1, 2). Thus, the graph of $f^{-1}$ passes through the points (–4, –2) and (2, 1). Plot these points and sketch the reflection of $f$ in the line $y = x$ to obtain the graph of $f^{-1}$. Notice that since the graph of $f$ is a line, its reflection will also be a line. See Figure 105.

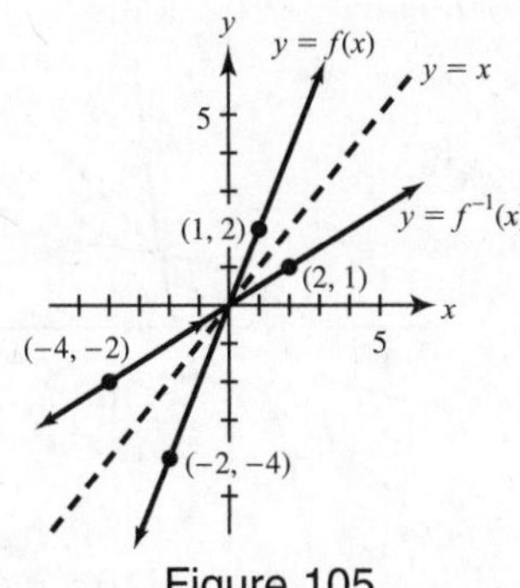

Figure 105

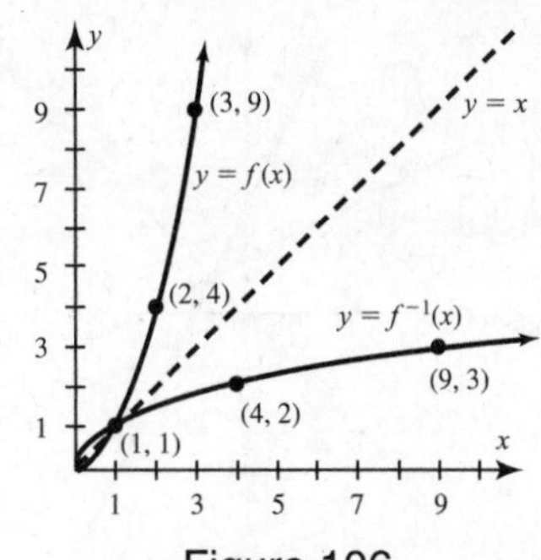

Figure 106

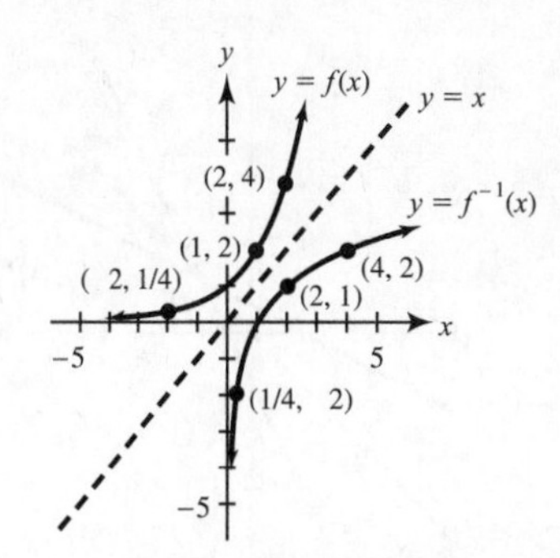

Figure 107

106. The graph of $f$ passes through the points (1, 1), (2, 4) and (3, 9). Thus, the graph of $f^{-1}$ passes through the points (1, 1), (4, 2) and (9, 3). Plot these points and sketch the reflection of $f$ in the line $y = x$ to obtain the graph of $f^{-1}$. See Figure 106.

107. The graph of $f$ passes through the points $\left(-2, \frac{1}{4}\right)$, (0, 1), (1, 2) and (2, 4). Thus, the graph of $f^{-1}$ passes through the points $\left(\frac{1}{4}, -2\right)$, (1, 0), (2, 1) and (4, 2). Plot these points and sketch the reflection of $f$ in the line $y = x$ to obtain the graph of $f^{-1}$. See Figure 107.

108. The graph of $f$ passes through the points (–6, –4), (–4, 0) and (–2, 4). Thus, the graph of $f^{-1}$ passes through the points (–4, –6), (0, –4) and (4, –2). Plot these points and sketch the reflection of $f$ in the line $y = x$ to obtain the graph of $f^{-1}$. See Figure 108.

109. The graph of $f$ passes through the points (–3, –2), (–1, 1) and (2, 2). Thus, the graph of $f^{-1}$ passes through the points (–2, –3), (1, –1) and (2, 2). Plot these points and sketch the reflection of $f$ in the line $y = x$ to obtain the graph of $f^{-1}$. See Figure 109.

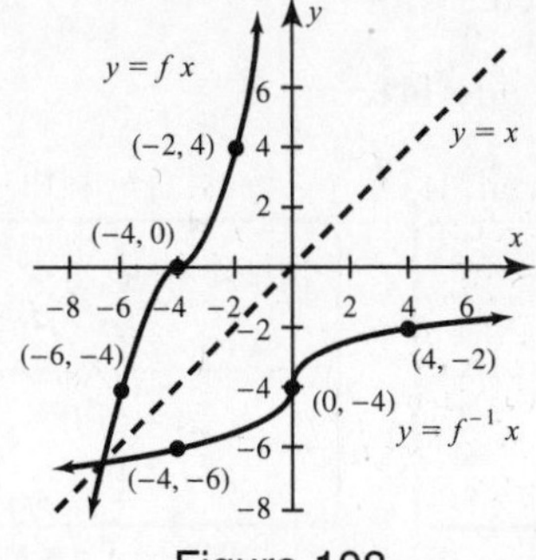

Figure 108

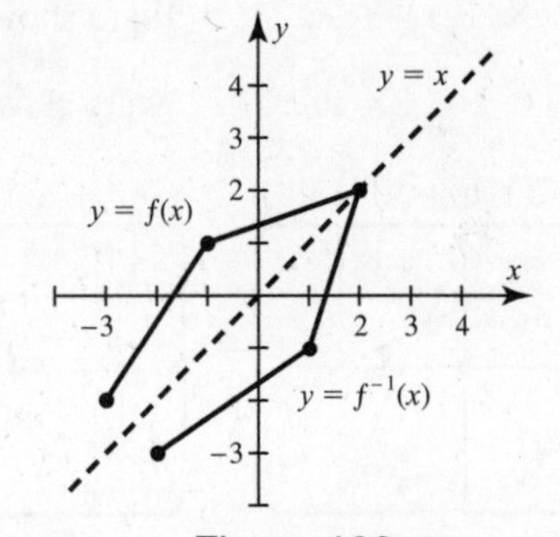

Figure 109

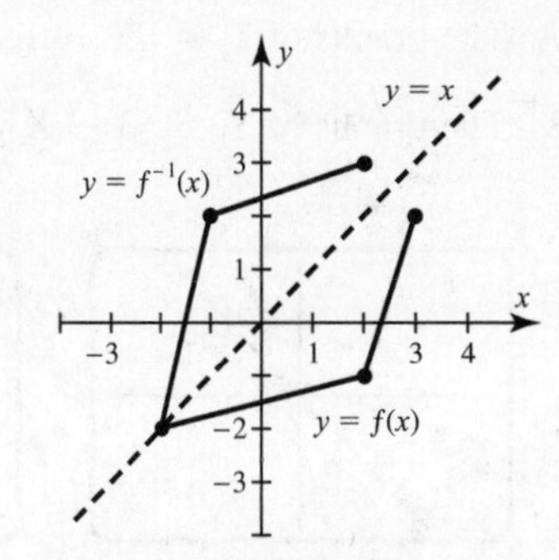

Figure 110

110. The graph of $f$ passes through the points (–2, –2), (2, –1) and (3, 2). Thus, the graph of $f^{-1}$ passes through the points (–2, –2), (–1, 2) and (2, 3). Plot these points and sketch the reflection of $f$ in the line $y = x$ to obtain the graph of $f^{-1}$. See Figure 110.

111. The graphs of $y = 2x - 1$, $y = \dfrac{x + 1}{2}$, and $y = x$ are shown in Figure 111.

112. The graphs of $y = -\dfrac{1}{2}x + 1$, $y = -2x + 2$, and $y = x$ are shown in Figure 112.

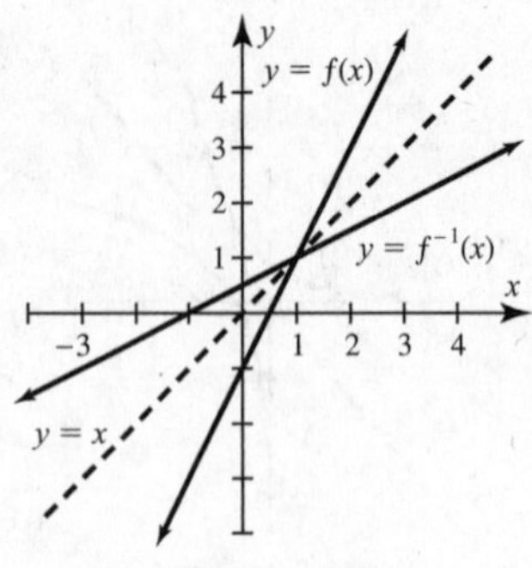


Figure 111

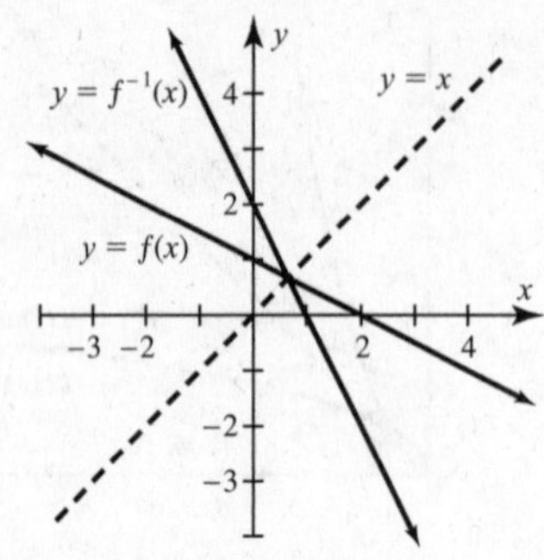


Figure 112

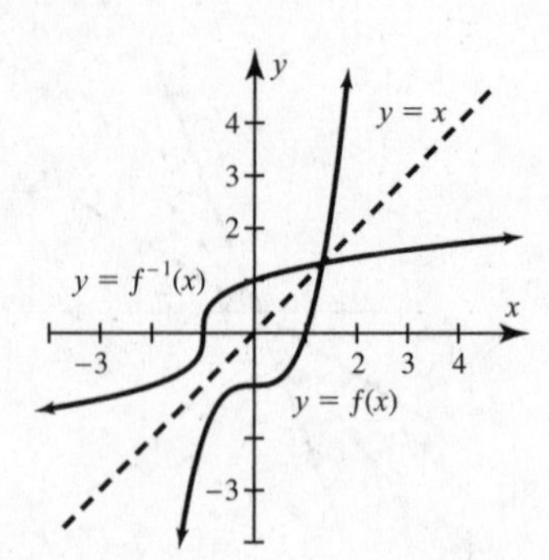


Figure 113

113. The graphs of $y = x^3 - 1$, $y = \sqrt[3]{x + 1}$, and $y = x$ are shown in Figure 113.

114. The graphs of $y = \sqrt[3]{x - 1}$, $y = x^3 + 1$, and $y = x$ are shown in Figure 114.

115. The graphs of $y = (x + 1)^2$, $y = \sqrt{x} - 1$, and $y = x$ are shown in Figure 115.

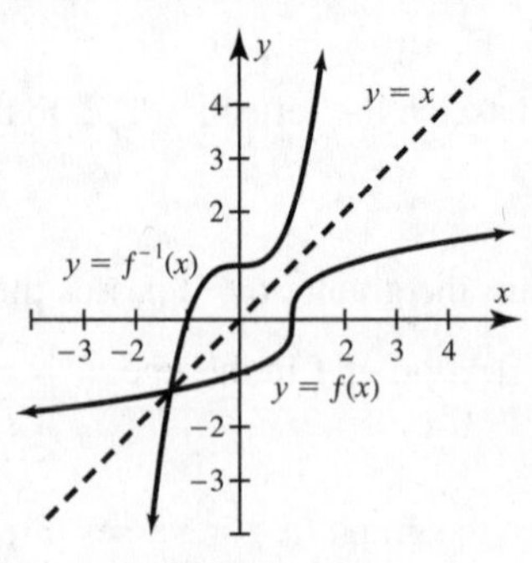


Figure 114

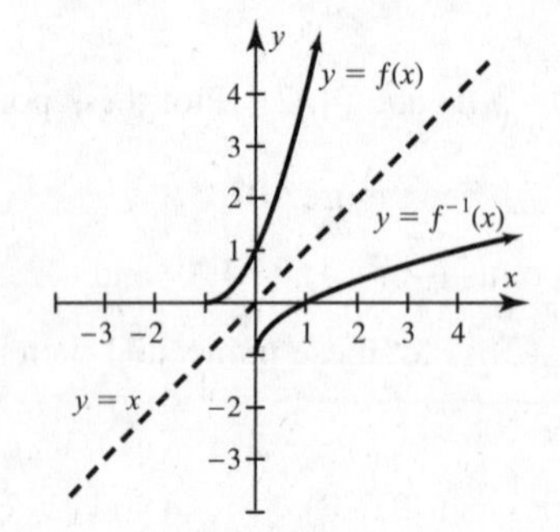


Figure 115

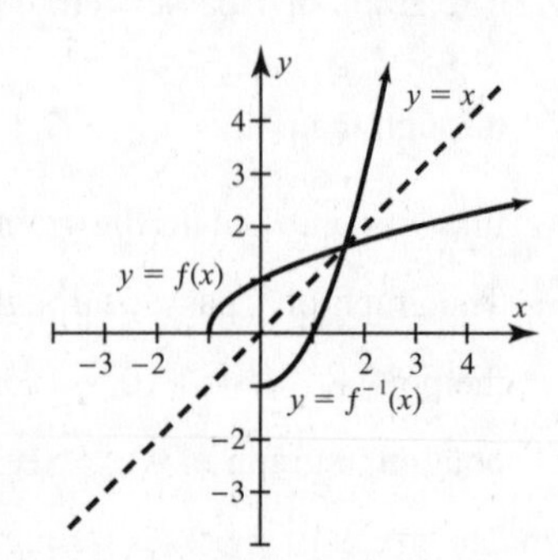


Figure 116

116. The graphs of $y = \sqrt{x + 1}$, $y = x^2 - 1$ where $x \geq 0$, and $y = x$ are shown in Figure 116.

117. The graphs of $Y_1 = 3X - 1$, $Y_2 = (X + 1)/3$ and $Y_3 = X$ are shown in Figure 117.

118. The graphs of $Y_1 = (3 - X)/2$, $Y_2 = 3 - 2X$ and $Y_3 = X$ are shown in Figure 118.

[−4.7, 4.7, 1] by [−3.1, 3.1, 1]

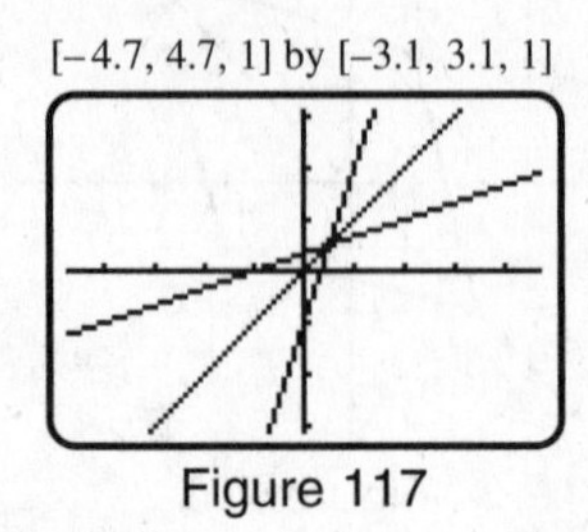

Figure 117

[−4.7, 4.7, 1] by [−3.1, 3.1, 1]

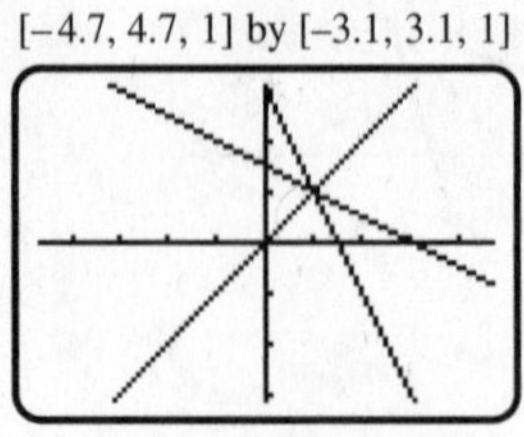

Figure 118

[−4.7, 4.7, 1] by [−3.1, 3.1, 1]

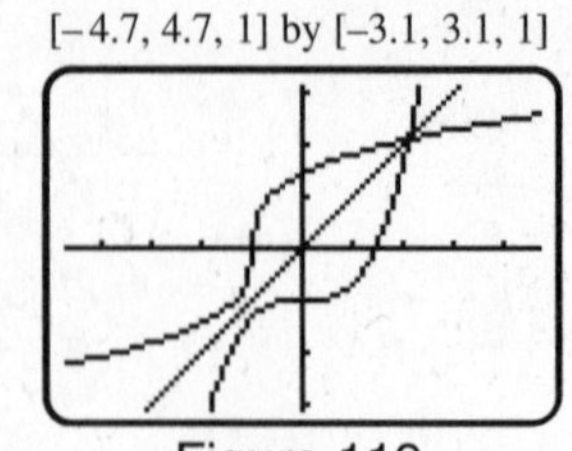

Figure 119

[−4.7, 4.7, 1] by [−3.1, 3.1, 1]

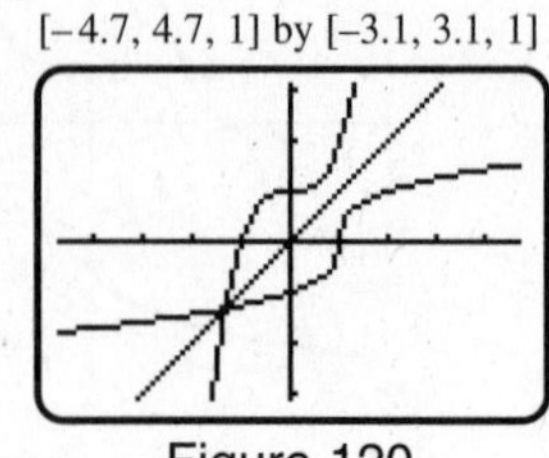

Figure 120

119. The graphs of $Y_1 = X^3/3 - 1$, $Y_2 = \sqrt[3]{(3X + 3)}$ and $Y_3 = X$ are shown in Figure 119.

120. The graphs of $Y_1 = \sqrt[3]{(X - 1)}$, $Y_2 = X^3 + 1$ and $Y_3 = X$ are shown in Figure 120.

121. (a) Since each volume value is the result of exactly one radius value, $V$ represents a one-to-one function.

(b) The inverse of $V$ computes the radius $r$ of a sphere with volume $V$.

(c) $V = \frac{4}{3}\pi r^3 \Rightarrow r^3 = \frac{3V}{4\pi} \Rightarrow r = \sqrt[3]{\frac{3V}{4\pi}}$

(d) No; if $V$ and $r$ were interchanged, then $r$ would represent the volume and $V$ would represent the radius.

122. (a) $F = \frac{9}{5}C + 32 \Rightarrow \frac{9}{5}C = F - 32 \Rightarrow C = \frac{5}{9}(F - 32) \Rightarrow f^{-1}(C) = \frac{5}{9}(C - 32)$

The function $f^{-1}(C)$ converts a Fahrenheit temperature to an equivalent Celsius temperature.

(b) No if $C$ and $F$ were interchanged, $C$ would represent the Fahrenheit temperature and $F$ would represent the Celsius temperature.

(c) $f^{-1}(68) = \frac{5}{9}(68 - 32) = \frac{5}{9}(36) = 20$; a temperature of 68°F is equivalent to 20°C.

123. (a) $W = \frac{25}{7}(70) - \frac{800}{7} = \frac{950}{7} \approx 135.7$ pounds

(b) Yes, since no weight value corresponds to more than one height value.

(c) $W = \frac{25}{7}h - \frac{800}{7} \Rightarrow \frac{25}{7}h = W + \frac{800}{7} \Rightarrow h = \frac{7}{25}\left(W + \frac{800}{7}\right) = \frac{7}{25}W + 32 \Rightarrow W^{-1} = \frac{7}{25}W + 32$

(d) $W^{-1}(150) = \frac{7}{25}(150) + 32 \Rightarrow W^{-1}(150) = 74$; the maximum recommended height for a person weighing 150 pounds is 74 inches.

(e) The inverse computes the maximum recommended height of a person with a given weight.

124. (a) $y = x^{3/2} \Rightarrow y^{2/3} = (x^{3/2})^{2/3} \Rightarrow x = y^{2/3} \Rightarrow T^{-1}(x) = x^{2/3}, x \geq 0$

(b) The inverse of $T$ calculates how many times farther from the sun a planet is than Earth, if it takes $x$ years to orbit the sun.

125. (a) $(F \circ Y)(2) = F(Y(2)) = F(3520) = 10{,}560$. $(F \circ Y)(2)$ computes the number of feet in 2 miles.

(b) $F^{-1}(26{,}400) = 8800$. $F^{-1}$ converts feet to yards. There are 8800 yards in 26,400 feet.

(c) $(Y^{-1} \circ F^{-1})(21{,}120) = Y^{-1}(F^{-1}(21{,}120)) = Y^{-1}(7040) = 4$. $(Y^{-1} \circ F^{-1})(21{,}120)$ computes the number of miles in 21,120 feet.

126. (a) Since $F$ converts yards to feet, it multiplies the input $x$ by 3. Thus $F(x) = 3x$. Similarly, $Y$ converts miles to yards, it multiplies the input $x$ by 1760. Thus $Y(x) = 1760x$. The composition function is given by $(F \circ Y)(x) = F(Y(x)) = F(1760x) = 3(1760x) = 5280x$. $F \circ Y$ converts miles to feet.

(b) First find the inverse functions for $F$ and $Y$.

$y = 3x \Rightarrow x = \frac{y}{3} \Rightarrow F^{-1}(x) = \frac{x}{3}$ and $y = 1760x \Rightarrow x = \frac{y}{1760} \Rightarrow F^{-1}(x) = \frac{x}{1760}$

Then $(Y^{-1} \circ F^{-1})(x) = Y^{-1}(F^{-1}(x)) = Y^{-1}\left(\frac{x}{3}\right) = \frac{x}{5280}$. $(Y^{-1} \circ F^{-1})(x)$ computes the number of miles in $x$ feet.

127. (a) $(Q \circ C)(96) = Q(C(96)) = Q(6) = 1.5$. $(Q \circ C)(96)$ computes the number of quarts in 96 tablespoons.

(b) $Q^{-1}(2) = 8$. $Q^{-1}$ converts quarts into cups. There are 8 cups in 2 quarts.

(c) $(C^{-1} \circ Q^{-1})(1.5) = C^{-1}(Q^{-1}(1.5)) = C^{-1}(6) = 96$. $(C^{-1} \circ Q^{-1})(1.5)$ computes the number of tablespoons in 1.5 quarts.

128. (a) Since $C$ converts tablespoons to cups, it divides the input $x$ by 16. Thus $C(x) = \frac{x}{16}$. Similarly, $Q$ converts cups into quarts, it divides the input $x$ by 4. Thus $Q(x) = \frac{x}{4}$. The composition function is given by

$(Q \circ C)(x) = Q(C(x)) = Q\left(\frac{x}{16}\right) = \frac{\frac{x}{16}}{4} = \frac{x}{64}$. $Q \circ C$ converts tablespoons to quarts.

(b) First find the inverse functions for $C$ and $Q$.

$y = \frac{x}{16} \Rightarrow x = 16y \Rightarrow C^{-1}(x) = 16x$ and $y = \frac{x}{4} \Rightarrow x = 4y \Rightarrow C^{-1}(x) = 4x$

Then $(C^{-1} \circ Q^{-1})(x) = C^{-1}(Q^{-1}(x)) = C^{-1}(4x) = 16(4x) = 64x$. $(C^{-1} \circ Q^{-1})(x)$ computes the number of tablespoons in $x$ quarts.

129. (a) $f(x) = 0.06(x - 1930) + 62.5 \Rightarrow f(1930) = 0.06(1930 - 1930) + 62.5 = 62.5$ and $f(1980) = 0.06(1980 - 1930) + 62.5 = 65.5$. In 1930 there was cloud cover 62.5% of the time, whereas in 1980 it increased to 65.5%. It increased by 3%.

(b) $f^{-1}$ computes the year when the cloud cover was $x$ percent.

(c) $f(1930) = 62.5 \Rightarrow f^{-1}(62.5) = 1930$. Similarly, $f(1980) = 65.5 \Rightarrow f^{-1}(65.5) = 1980$.

(d) Using the technique shown in Example 6, we can find $f^{-1}(x)$.

$y = 0.06(x - 1930) + 62.5 \Rightarrow y - 62.5 = 0.06(x - 1930)\frac{y - 62.5}{0.06} = x - 1930 \Rightarrow$

$1930 + \frac{y - 62.5}{0.06} = x \Rightarrow f^{-1}(x) = 1930 + \frac{x - 62.5}{0.06}$ or $f^{-1}(x) = \frac{50}{3}(x - 62.5) + 1930$

130. (a) Since different inputs always produce different outputs, the function is one-to-one.

(b) Since $R$ is one-to-one, $R^{-1}$ exists. A tabular representation of $R^{-1}$ is given in Figure 130. $R^{-1}$ computes the year when the rise in sea level is predicted to be $t$ centimeters.

| $t$ | 0 | 1 | 18 | 44 | 66 |
|---|---|---|---|---|---|
| $R^{-1}(t)$ | 1990 | 2000 | 2030 | 2070 | 2100 |

Figure 130

## Extended and Discovery Exercises for Section 5.2

1. (a) $f^{-1}$ computes the elapsed time in seconds when the rocket was $x$ feet above the ground.

(b) The solution to the equation $f(x) = 5000$ is the time in seconds when the rocket was 5000 feet above the ground.

(c) Evaluate $f^{-1}(5000)$.

2. The graph of $f^{-1}$ is a reflection of the graph of $f$ across the line $y = x$. The reflection of any point in quadrant I across the line $y = x$ is located in quadrant I and the reflection af any point in quadrant II across the line $y = x$ is located in quadrant IV. That is, $f^{-1}$ lies in quadrants I and IV.

## Checking Basic Concepts for Sections 5.1 and 5.2

1. (a) $(f + g)(1) = f(1) + g(1) = -1 + 2 = 1$
   (b) $(f - g)(-1) = f(-1) - g(-1) = 1 - (-2) = 3$
   (c) $(fg)(0) = f(0) \cdot g(0) = (-2)(-1) = 2$
   (d) $(f/g)(2) = \dfrac{f(2)}{g(2)} = \dfrac{2}{0} \Rightarrow$ undefined
   (e) $(f \circ g)(2) = f(g(2)) = f(0) = -2$
   (f) $(g \circ f)(-2) = g(f(-2)) = g(0) = -1$
2. (a) $(f + g)(1) = f(1) + g(1)$, from the graph $f(1) = 2$ and $g(1) = -2 \Rightarrow$
   $f(1) + g(1) = 2 + (-2) = 0$
   (b) $(g - f)(0) = g(0) - f(0)$, from the graph $g(0) = -1$ and $f(0) = 1 \Rightarrow$
   $g(0) - f(0) = -1 - (-1) = -2$
   (c) $(fg)(2) = f(2) \cdot g(2)$, from the graph $f(2) = 3$ and $g(2) = (-1) \Rightarrow f(2) \cdot g(2) = 3 \cdot (-1) = -3$
   (d) $(g/f)(-1) = g(-1)/f(-1)$, from the graph $g(-1) = 2$ and $f(-1) = 0 \Rightarrow$
   $g(-1)/f(-1) = \dfrac{2}{0} =$ undefined
   (e) $(f \circ g)(2) = f(g(2))$ from the graph $g(2) = -1 \Rightarrow f(g(2)) = f(-1)$. From the graph $f(-1) = 0$.
   (f) $(g \circ f)(1) = g(f(1))$ from the graph $f(1) = 2 \Rightarrow g(f(2)) = g(2)$. From the graph $g(2) = -1$.
3. (a) $(f + g)(x) = f(x) + g(x) = (x^2 + 3x - 2) + (3x - 1) = x^2 + 6x - 3$
   (b) $(f/g)(x) = \dfrac{f(x)}{g(x)} = \dfrac{x^2 + 3x - 2}{3x - 1}, x \neq \dfrac{1}{3}$
   (c) $(f \circ g)(x) = f(g(x)) = f(3x - 1) = (3x - 1)^2 + 3(3x - 1) - 2 = 9x^2 + 3x - 4$
4. $y = 5 - 2x \Rightarrow 2x = 5 - y \Rightarrow x = \dfrac{5 - y}{2} \Rightarrow f^{-1}(x) = \dfrac{5 - x}{2}$
5. (a) All horizontal lines intersect once $\Rightarrow$ yes; yes; $y = x + 1 \Rightarrow y - 1 = x$, therefore $f^{-1}(x) = x - 1$.
   (b) A parabola $\Rightarrow$ no; no.
6. The graph of $y = \sqrt[3]{x}$, $y = x^3$ and $y = x$ are shown in Figure 6.

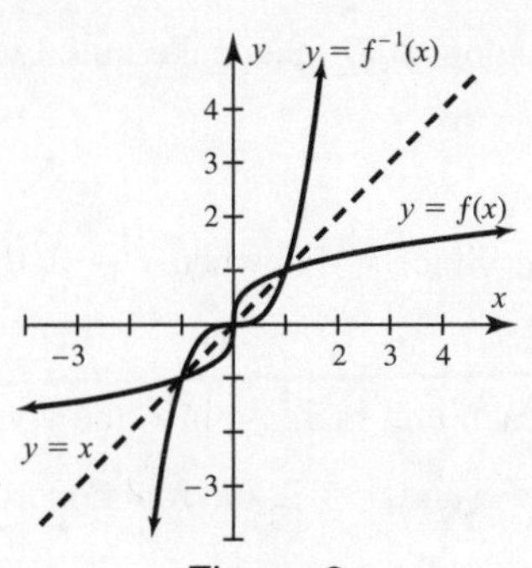


Figure 6

7. (a) Since $f(0) = -2$, then $f^{-1}(-2) = 0$.

(b) $(f^{-1} \circ g)(1) \Rightarrow f^{-1}(g(1)) \Rightarrow f^{-1}(2) = 2$

8. (a) Since $f(1) = 2$, then $f^{-1}(2) = 1$.

(b) $(f^{-1} \circ g)(0) \Rightarrow f^{-1}(g(0)) \Rightarrow f^{-1}(-1) = -2$

## 5.3: Exponential Functions and Models

1. $2^{-3} = \frac{1}{2^3} = \frac{1}{8}$

2. $(-3)^{-2} = \frac{1}{(-3)^2} = \frac{1}{9}$

3. $3(4)^{1/2} = 3\sqrt{4} = 3(2) = 6$

4. $5\left(\frac{1}{2}\right)^{-3} = 5\left(\frac{2}{1}\right)^3 = 5(8) = 40$

5. $-2(27)^{2/3} = -2(\sqrt[3]{27})^2 = -2(3)^2 = -2(9) = -18$

6. $-4\,(8)^{-2/3} = -4\left(\frac{1}{8^{2/3}}\right) = -4\left(\frac{1}{(\sqrt[3]{8})^2}\right) = -4\left(\frac{1}{2^2}\right) = -4\left(\frac{1}{4}\right) = \frac{-4}{4} = -1$

7. $4^{1/6}4^{1/3} = 4^{1/6+1/3} = 4^{1/2} = \sqrt{4} = 2$

8. $\frac{9^{5/6}}{9^{1/3}} = 9^{5/6-1/3} = 9^{1/2} = \sqrt{9} = 3$

9. $e^xe^x = e^{x+x} = e^{2x}$

10. $e^{3x}e^{1+x} = e^{3x+(1+x)} = e^{4x+1}$

11. $3^0 = 1$

12. $5\left(\frac{3}{4}\right)^0 = 5(1) = 5$

13. $(5^{101})^{1/101} = 5^1 = 5$

14. $(8^{27})^{1/27} = 8^1 = 8$

15. For each unit increase in $x$, the $y$-values decrease by 1.2, so the data is linear. Since $y = 2$ when $x = 0$, the function $f(x) = -1.2x + 2$ can model the data.

16. For each unit increase in $x$, the $y$-values are multiplied by 4, so the data is exponential. Since the initial value is $C = 2$ and $a = 4$, the function $f(x) = 2(4^x)$ can model the data.

17. For each unit increase in $x$, the $y$-values are multiplied by $\frac{1}{2}$, so the data is exponential. Since the initial value is $C = 8$ and $a = \frac{1}{2}$, the function $f(x) = 8\left(\frac{1}{2}\right)^x$ can model the data.

18. For each unit increase in $x$, the $y$-values increase by 2.5, so the data is linear. Since $y = 8$ when $x = 0$, the function $f(x) = 2.5x + 8$ can model the data.

19. For each 2-unit increase in $x$, the $y$-values are multiplied by 4. That is, for each unit increase in $x$, the $y$-values are multiplied by 2, so the data is exponential. Since the initial value is $C = 5$ and $a = 2$, the function $f(x) = 5(2^x)$ can model the data.

20. For each 10-unit increase in $x$, the $y$-values increase by 2, so the data is linear. Since $y = 25$ when $x = 0$, the function $f(x) = 0.2x + 25$ can model the data.

21. For each 1-year increase, the salary is multiplied by 1.08 to get the new salary. This is an example of exponential growth; $C = \$40{,}000$ and $a = 1.08 \Rightarrow f(n) = 40{,}000(1.08)^{n-1}$, where $n = 1, 2, 3, \ldots$.

22. For each 1-year increase, the salary is increased by \$5000 to get the new salary. This is an example of linear growth; $f(n) = 5000n + 35{,}000$, where $n = 1, 2, 3, \ldots$.

23. For $x > 4$, $f(x) > g(x)$; for example $f(10) = 1024$ whereas $g(10) = 100$. That is, $f(x) = 2^x$ becomes larger.

24. $f(x) = 4 + 3(x), f(0) = 4, f(10) = 34.$ $g(x) = 4(3^x), g(0) = 4, g(10) = 236{,}196.$
Therefore, $g(x)$ becomes larger for $0 \leq x \leq 10$.

25. $f(x) = 2x + 1, f(0) = 1, f(10) = 21.$ $g(x) = 2^{-x}, g(0) = 2, g(10) = 9.76 \times 10^{-4}.$
Therefore, $f(x)$ becomes larger for $0 \leq x \leq 10$.

26. In the first option, each amount increases by 2¢ for each week, so the growth is linear. Since there are 52 weeks in a year, the total amount paid at the end of a year would be only about 1¢ + 52(2¢) = 1¢ + 104¢ = \$1.05. It would not be a good idea to accept this offer. In the second option, the amount is multiplied by 2 for each week, so the growth is exponential. The total amount paid at the end of the year would be $1¢(2¢)^{51}$. This is about \$22,517,998,136,900. It would be an extremely good idea to accept this offer.

27. $f(0) = 5 \Rightarrow C = 5$ and $a = 1.5$

28. $f(1) = 3$ and $a = \frac{3}{4} \Rightarrow f(0) = 3 \div \frac{3}{4} = 3 \cdot \frac{4}{3} = 4; C = 4$ and $a = \frac{3}{4}$

29. $f(0) = 10$ and $f(1) = 20 \Rightarrow C = 10$ and $a = \frac{20}{10} = 2$

30. $f(0) = 7$ and $f(-1) = 1 \Rightarrow C = 7$ and $a = \frac{7}{1} = 7$

31. $f(1) = 9$ and $f(2) = 27 \Rightarrow a = \frac{27}{9} = 3; C = f(0) = 9 \div 3 = 3$

32. $f(-1) = \frac{1}{4} \Rightarrow Ca^{-1} = \frac{1}{4} \Rightarrow \frac{C}{a} = \frac{1}{4} \Rightarrow C = \frac{a}{4};\ f(1) = 4 \Rightarrow Ca^1 = 4 \Rightarrow C = \frac{4}{a}$
Thus $\frac{a}{4} = \frac{4}{a} \Rightarrow a^2 = 16 \Rightarrow a = 4$; then $C = 1$.

33. $f(-2) = \frac{9}{2}$ and $f(2) = \frac{1}{18} \Rightarrow Ca^{-2} = \frac{9}{2} \Rightarrow \frac{C}{a^2} = \frac{9}{2} \Rightarrow C = \frac{9a^2}{2};\ Ca^2 = \frac{1}{18} \Rightarrow C = \frac{1}{18a^2}$ thus
$\frac{1}{18a^2} = \frac{9a^2}{2} \Rightarrow 162a^4 = 2 \Rightarrow a^4 = \frac{1}{81} \Rightarrow a = \frac{1}{3}$; then $C = \frac{1}{18(\frac{1}{3})^2} \Rightarrow C = \frac{1}{18(\frac{1}{9})} \Rightarrow C = \frac{1}{2}$.

34. $f(-2) = \frac{3}{4}$ and $f(2) = 12 \Rightarrow Ca^{-2} = \frac{3}{4} \Rightarrow \frac{C}{a^2} = \frac{3}{4} \Rightarrow C = \frac{3a^2}{4};\ Ca^2 = 12 \Rightarrow C = \frac{12}{a^2}$, thus
$\frac{3a^2}{4} = \frac{12}{a^2} \Rightarrow 3a^4 = 48 \Rightarrow a^4 = 16 \Rightarrow a = 2$; if $a = 2$ then $C = \frac{3(4)}{4} = 3$.

35. $C = 5000, a = 2$; $x$ represents time in hours

36. $C = 15{,}000$, $a = 3$; $x$ represents time in decades

37. $C = 200{,}000$, $a = 0.95$; $x$ represents the number of years after 2000

38. $C = 6000$, $a = 0.5$; $x$ represents time in years

39. $f(9.5) = 30(0.9)^{9.5} \approx 11$; the tire's pressure is about 11 pounds per square inch after 9.5 minutes.

40. The population in 2007 was about $38(1.016)^5 \approx 41{,}100{,}000$.

41. $f(x) = 4e^{-1.2x} \Rightarrow f(-2.4) = 4e^{-1.2(-2.4)} = 4e^{2.88} \approx 71.2571$

42. $f(x) = -2.1e^{-0.71x} \Rightarrow f(1.9) = -2.1e^{-0.71(1.9)} = -2.1e^{-1.349} \approx -0.5449$

43. $f(x) = \dfrac{e^x - e^{-x}}{2} \Rightarrow f(-0.7) = \dfrac{e^{-0.7} - e^{0.7}}{2} \approx -0.7586$

44. $f(x) = 4(e^{-0.3x} - e^{-0.6x}) \Rightarrow f(1.6) = 4(e^{-0.3(1.6)} - e^{-0.6(1.6)}) = 4(e^{-0.48} - e^{-0.96}) \approx 0.9436$

45. See Figure 45.

46. See Figure 46.

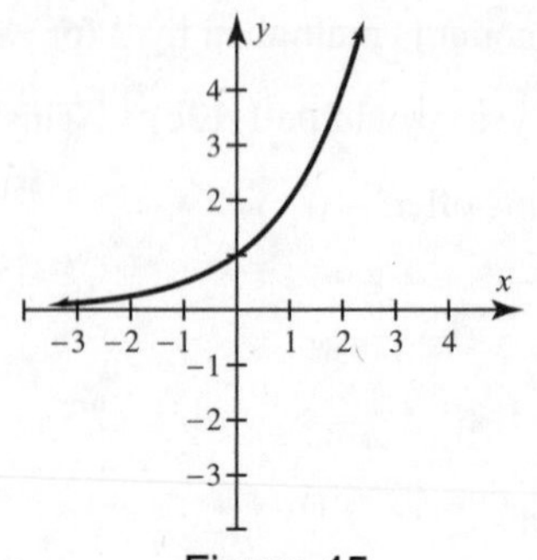

Figure 45

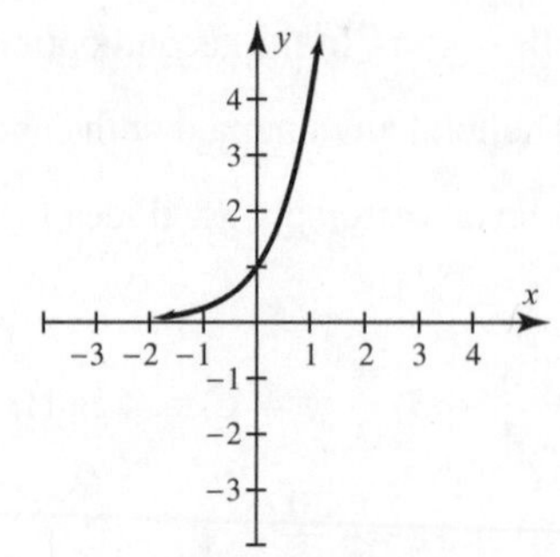

Figure 46

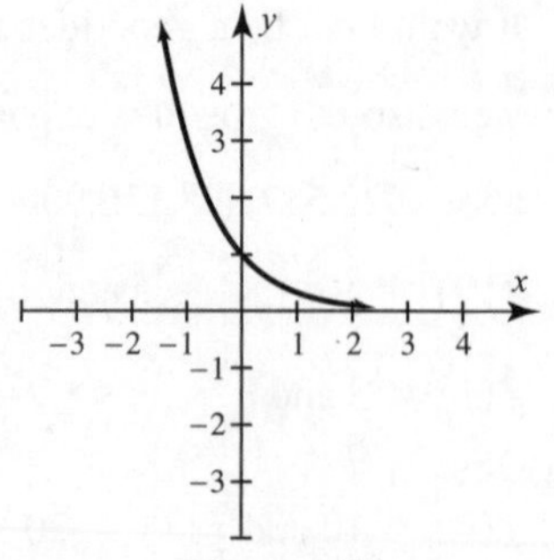

Figure 47

47. See Figure 47.

48. See Figure 48.

49. See Figure 49.

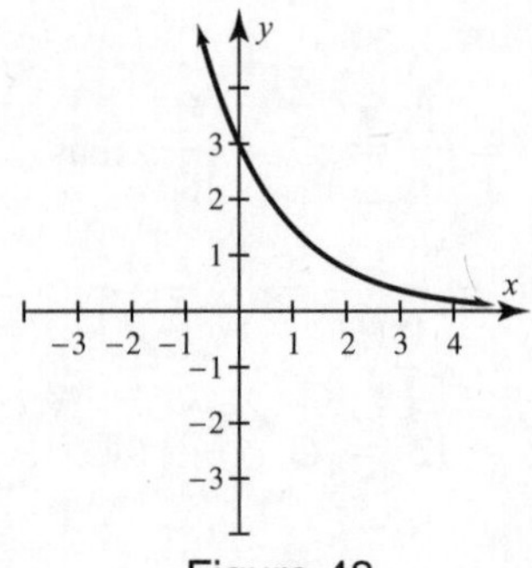

Figure 48

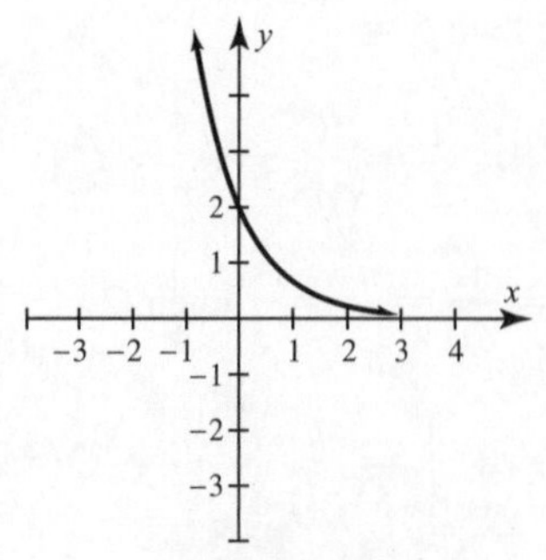

Figure 49

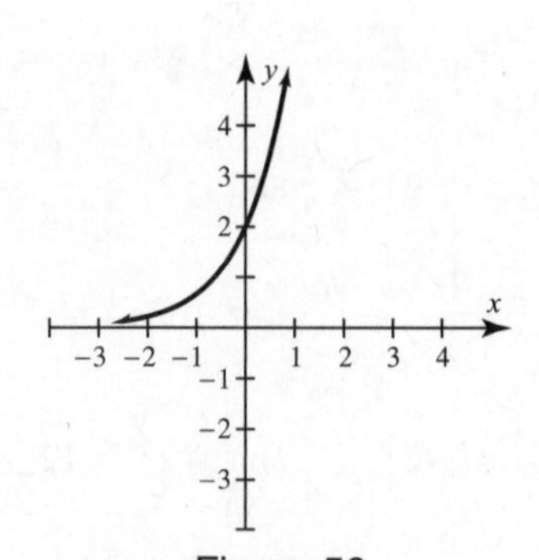

Figure 50

50. See Figure 50.

51. See Figure 51.

52. See Figure 52.

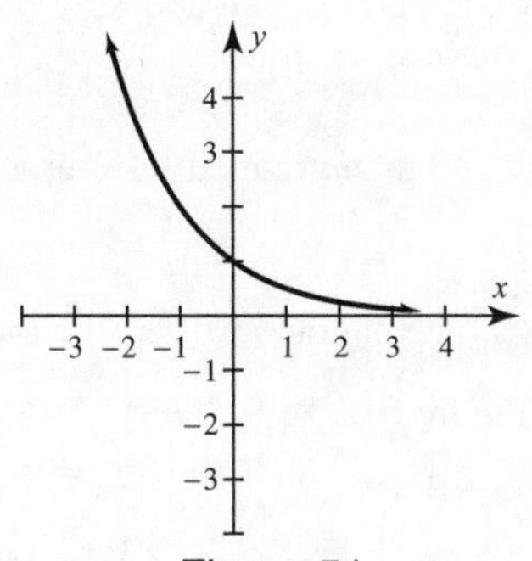

Figure 51

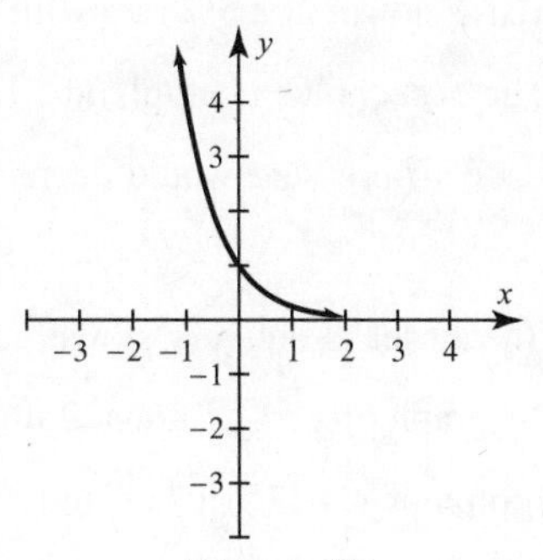

Figure 52

53. Since $y = 1$ when $x = 0$, $C = 1$ and so $y = a^x$.

Since $y = 4$ when $x = -2$, $4 = a^{-2} \Rightarrow \frac{1}{a^2} = 4 \Rightarrow a^2 = \frac{1}{4} \Rightarrow a = \frac{1}{2}$. That is $C = 1$ and $a = \frac{1}{2}$.

54. Since $y = 3$ when $x = 0$, $C = 3$ and so $y = 3a^x$.

Since $y = 6$ when $x = 1$, $6 = 3a^1 \Rightarrow a = 2$. That is $C = 3$ and $a = 2$.

55. Since $y = \frac{1}{2}$ when $x = 0$, $C = \frac{1}{2}$ and so $y = \frac{1}{2}a^x$.

Since $y = 8$ when $x = 2$, $8 = \frac{1}{2}a^2 \Rightarrow a^2 = 16 \Rightarrow a = 4$. That is $C = \frac{1}{2}$ and $a = 4$.

56. Since $y = 3$ when $x = 0$, $C = 3$ and so $y = 3a^x$.

Since $y = 1$ when $x = 1$, $1 = 3a^1 \Rightarrow a = \frac{1}{3}$. That is $C = 3$ and $a = \frac{1}{3}$.

57. (a) $D$: $(-\infty, \infty)$; $R$: $(0, \infty)$

(b) Decreasing, as $x$ increases $\left(\frac{1}{8}\right)^x$ decreases.

(c) $y = 0$ as $x$ increases, $7\left(\frac{1}{8}\right)^x$ gets closer and closer to 0.

(d) $y$-intercept: 7; no $x$-intercept.

(e) All horizontal lines intersect once $\Rightarrow$ yes; yes.

58. (a) $D$: $(-\infty, \infty)$; $R$: $(0, \infty)$

(b) Increasing, as $x$ increases, $e^x$ increases.

(c) $y = 0$, as $x$ decreases, $e^x$ gets closer and closer to zero.

(d) $y$-intercept: 1; no $x$-intercept because it has a $y = 0$ asymptote.

(e) No horizontal line intersects the graph more than once $\Rightarrow$ yes; yes.

59. (i) The graph of $y = e^x$ increases faster than the graph of $y = 1.5^x$. The best choice is graph b.

(ii) The graph of $y = 3^{-x}$ decreases faster than the graph of $y = 0.99^x$. The best choice is graph d.

(iii) The graph of $y = 1.5^x$ increases slower than the graph of $y = e^x$. The best choice is graph a.

(iv) The graph of $y = 0.99^x$ is almost a horizontal line since $y = 1^x$ is horizontal. The best choice is graph c.

60. (i) The amount of money would increase faster at a 10% rate with continuous compounding than at a 5% rate with annual compounding. The best choice is graph b.

(ii) The amount of money would increase slower at a 5% rate with annual compounding than at a 10% rate with continuous compounding. The best choice is graph d.

(iii) If a car tire has a large hole in it, the air pressure would decrease rapidly and then gradually decrease. The best choice is graph a.

(iv) If a car tire has a tiny hole in it, the air leaks out very slowly. The best choice is graph c.

61. (a) To graph $y = 2^x - 2$, translate the graph of $y = 2^x$ down 2 units. See Figure 61a.

(b) To graph $y = 2^{x-1}$, translate the graph of $y = 2^x$ right 1 unit. See Figure 61b.

(c) To graph $y = 2^{-x}$, reflect the graph of $y = 2^x$ about the $y$-axis. See Figure 61c.

(d) To graph $y = -2^x$, reflect the graph of $y = 2^x$ about the $x$-axis. See Figure 61d.

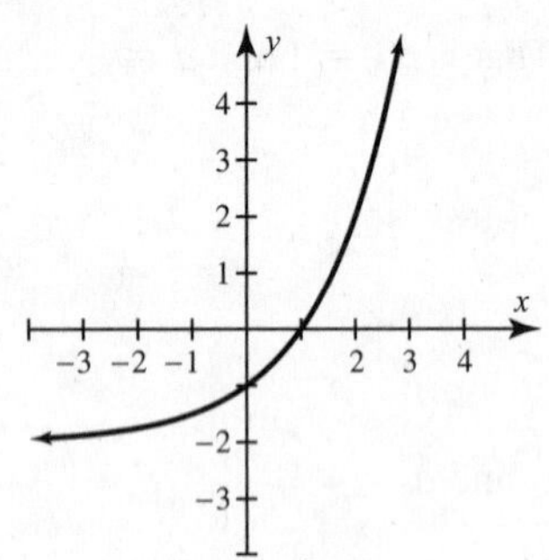

Figure 61a

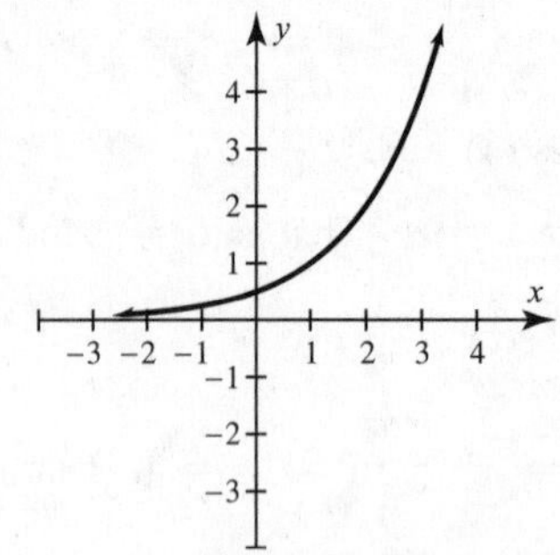

Figure 61b

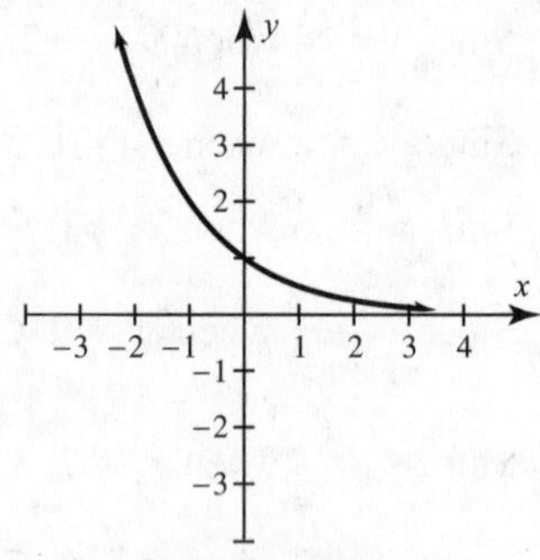

Figure 61c

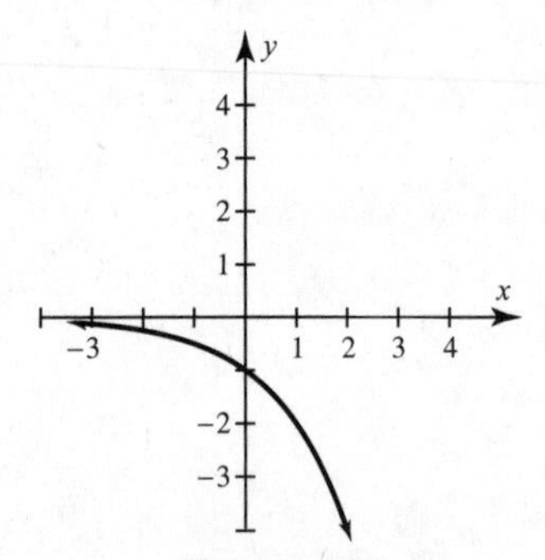

Figure 61d

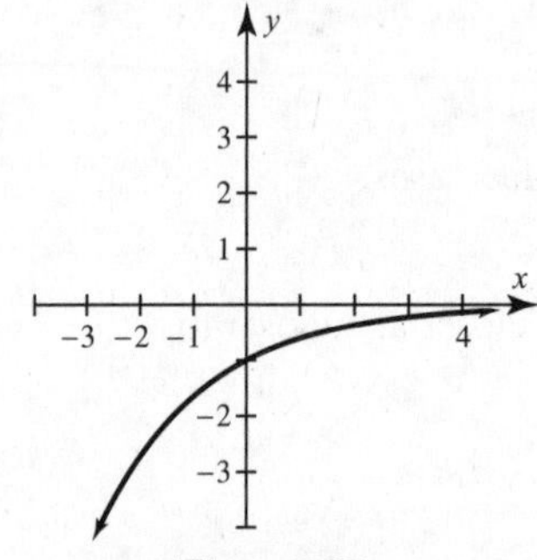

Figure 62a

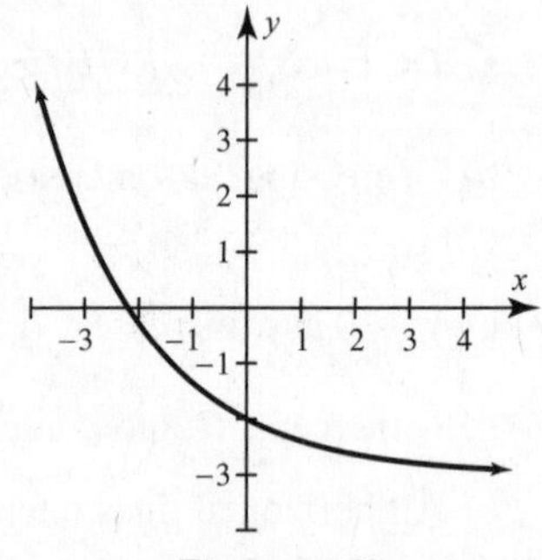

Figure 62b

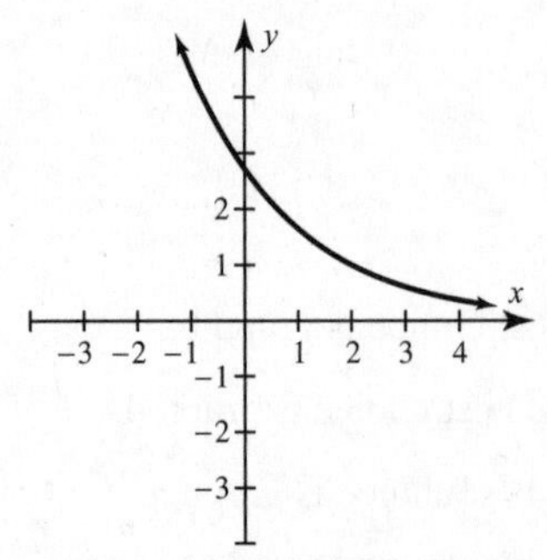

Figure 62c

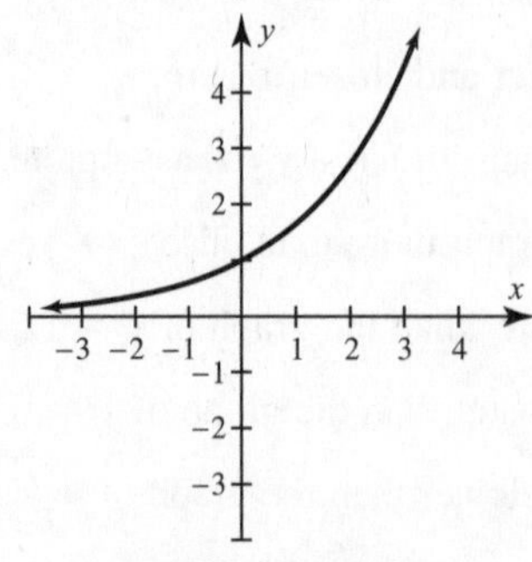

Figure 62d

62. (a) To graph $y = -e^{-0.5x}$, reflect the graph of $y = e^{-0.5x}$ about the $x$-axis. See Figure 62a.

(b) To graph $y = e^{-0.5x} - 3$, translate the graph of $y = e^{-0.5x}$ down 3 units. See Figure 62b.

(c) To graph $y = e^{-0.5(x-2)}$, translate the graph of $y = e^{-0.5x}$ right 2 units. See Figure 62c.

(d) To graph $y = e^{0.5x}$, reflect the graph of $y = e^{-0.5x}$ about the $y$-axis. See Figure 62d.

63. $A_n = A_0(1 + r)^n \Rightarrow A_5 = 600(1 + 0.07)^5 \approx \$841.53$

64. $A_n = A_0\left(1 + \frac{r}{m}\right)^{mn} \Rightarrow A_{10} = 2300\left(1 + \frac{0.11}{2}\right)^{2(10)} \approx \$6710.84$

65. $A_n = A_0\left(1 + \frac{r}{m}\right)^{mn} \Rightarrow A_{20} = 950\left(1 + \frac{0.03}{365}\right)^{365(20)} \approx \$1730.97$

66. $A_n = A_0\left(1 + \frac{r}{m}\right)^{mn} \Rightarrow A_2 = 3300\left(1 + \frac{0.08}{4}\right)^{4(2)} \approx \$3866.48$

67. $A_n = A_0 e^{rn} \Rightarrow A_8 = 2000e^{0.10(8)} \approx \$4451.08$

68. $A_n = A_0 e^{rn} \Rightarrow A_{50} = 100e^{0.19(50)} \approx \$1{,}335{,}972.68$

69. $A_n = A_0\left(1 + \frac{r}{m}\right)^{mn} \Rightarrow A_{2.5} = 1600\left(1 + \frac{0.104}{12}\right)^{12(2.5)} \approx \$2072.76$

70. $A_n = A_0(1 + r)^n \Rightarrow A_5 = 2000(1 + 0.087)^5 \approx \$3035.13$

71. $A_{20} = 2000\left(1 + \frac{0.10}{12}\right)^{12(20)} \approx \$14{,}656.15$; $A_{20} = 2000\left(1 + \frac{0.13}{12}\right)^{12(20)} \approx \$26{,}553.58$

A 13% interest rate results in considerably more interest than a 10% interest rate.

72. $A_5 = 90{,}000(1 + 0.15)^5 \approx \$181{,}022.15$

73. $A_{10} = 8000(1 + 0.06)^{10} \approx \$14{,}326.78$

74. Let $A_0$ represent the initial investment. Then the investment is doubled when $A_n = 2A_0$.

$A_n = A_0(1 + 0.12)^n \Rightarrow 2A_0 = A_0(1.12)^n \Rightarrow (1.12)^n = 2$; Graph $Y_1 = 1.12$^X and $Y_2 = 2$. See Figure 74a. At 12% compounded annually, it takes about 6 years for an investment to double its value.

$A_n = A_0(1 + 0.06)^n \Rightarrow 2A_0 = A_0(1.06)^n \Rightarrow (1.06)^n = 2$; Graph $Y_1 = 1.06$^X and $Y_2 = 2$. See Figure 74b. At 6% compounded annually, it takes about 12 years for an investment to double its value.

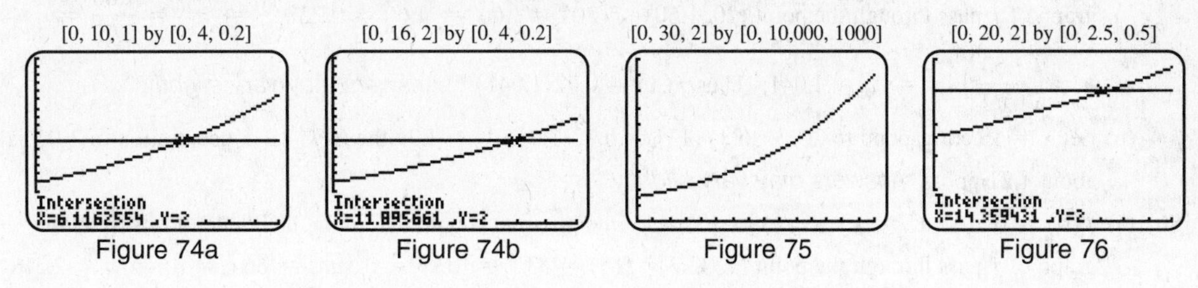

Figure 74a Figure 74b Figure 75 Figure 76

75. (a) $P = 1500, r = 0.06$ and $t = 30 \Rightarrow A = Pe^{rt} \Rightarrow A = 1500e^{0.06(30)} \approx 9074.47$

(b) During the last 10 years. See Figure 75.

76. (a) $P = 1.3$ million, $r = 0.03$ and $t = 10 \Rightarrow A = Pe^{rt} \Rightarrow A = 1.3e^{0.03(10)} \approx 1.75$ million

(b) 2014; See Figure 76.

77. $A_n = A_o(1 + r)^n \Rightarrow A_{30} = 340(1 + 0.0454)^{30} \approx 1288.11$ billion or 1.288 trillion.

78. $A_n = A_0(1 + r)^n \Rightarrow A_{30} = 340(1 + 0.0654)^{30} \approx 2274.36$ billion or 2.274 trillion or approximately 76% more than at the 4.54% interest rate. Long term, the national debt is very sensitive to interest rates. A small change in interest rate (+2%) can affect the debt dramatically (+76%) over a long period of time.

79. $A_{10} = 50\left[\dfrac{(1 + \frac{0.08}{26})^{260} - 1}{\frac{0.08}{26}}\right] \approx \$19{,}870.65$

80. Since the worker has 45 years to work, we must solve the equation:

$$x\left[\frac{(1 + \frac{0.10}{26})^{26(45)} - 1}{\frac{0.10}{26}}\right] = 1{,}000{,}000 \Rightarrow x = 1{,}000{,}000\left[\frac{\frac{0.10}{26}}{(1 + \frac{0.10}{26})^{26(45)} - 1}\right] \approx \$43.59.$$

The 20-year-old worker should deposit $43.59 each two-week pay period.

81. $A(x) = Pe^{rt} \Rightarrow 0.85 = e^{5r} \Rightarrow \ln(0.85) = 5r \Rightarrow r = \dfrac{\ln(0.85)}{5} \approx -0.0325 \Rightarrow A(x) = Pe^{-0.0325x}$

$P$ is the initial value.

82. $A(x) = Pe^{rt} \Rightarrow 3P = Pe^{r(15)} \Rightarrow 3 = e^{15r} \Rightarrow \ln(3) = 15r \Rightarrow r = \dfrac{\ln(3)}{15} \approx 0.0732 \Rightarrow A(x) = Pe^{0.0732x}$

83. (a) The number of *E. coli* was modeled by $N(x) = N_0\,e^{0.014x}$, where $x$ is in minutes and $N_0 = 500{,}000$. Since 3 hours is 180 minutes, $N(180) = 500{,}000e^{0.014(180)} \approx 6{,}214{,}000$ bacteria per milliter.

(b) Solve the equation $500{,}000\ e^{0.014x} = 10{,}000{,}000$. Graph $Y_1 = 500000e$^(0.014X) and $Y_2 = 10E6$ as shown in Figure 83. The point of intersection is near (214, 10,000,000). Thus, there will be 10 million *E. coli* after about 214 minutes, or about 3.6 hours.

[0, 300, 100] by [0, 20,000,000, 5,000,000]

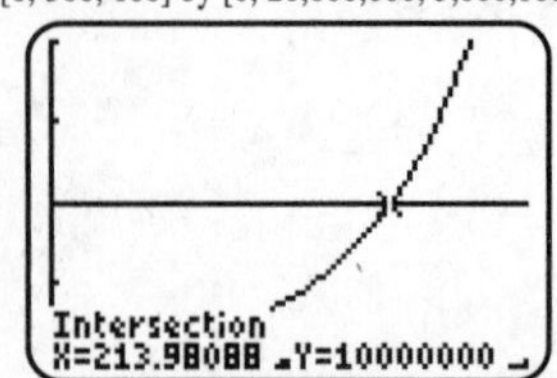


Figure 83

84. (a) $A = A_0e^{-rt} \Rightarrow A = 2e^{-0.2(3.5)} \approx 0.99$; the drug concentration after 3.5 hours is about 0.99 milligrams.

(b) $1.5 = 2e^{-0.2t} \Rightarrow 0.75 = e^{-0.2t} \Rightarrow \ln(0.75) = -0.2t \Rightarrow t = \dfrac{\ln(0.75)}{-0.2} \approx 1.44$hr.

85. (a) $f(0) = 0.72 \Rightarrow C \approx 0.72$, so $f(x) = 0.72a^x$. One possible way to determine the value of $a$ is to let the graph of $f$ pass through the point (20, 1.60). $f(20) = 1.60 \Rightarrow 1.60 = 0.72a^{20} \Rightarrow a^{20} = \dfrac{1.60}{0.72} \Rightarrow$ $a = \left(\dfrac{1.60}{0.72}\right)^{1/20} \Rightarrow a \approx 1.041$; Thus $f(x) = 0.72(1.041)^x$. *Answers may vary slightly.*

(b) Let $x = 13$ correspond to 2013, so ; $f(13) = 0.72(1.041)^{13} \approx 1.21$ the CFC-12 concentration in 2013 is about 1.21 ppb. *Answers may vary slightly.*

86. (a) $f(0) = 0.5 \Rightarrow C = 0.5$, so $f(x) = 0.5a^x$. One possible way to determine the value of $a$ is to let the graph of $f$ pass through the point (5, 33.3). $f(5) = 33.3 \Rightarrow 33.3 = 0.5a^5 \Rightarrow 66.6 = a^5 \Rightarrow a \approx 2.316$. Thus $f(x) = 0.5(2.316)^x$. *Answers may vary slightly.*

(b) $f(6.2) = 0.5(2.316)^{6.2} \approx 91.3$ billion per liter. *Answers may vary slightly.*

87. (a) $p(x) = 1 - e^{-5x/6} \Rightarrow p(3) = 1 - e^{-5(3)/6} \Rightarrow p(3) = 1 - e^{-15/6} \approx 0.92$, or 92%

(b) Find $x$ when $p(x) = 0.5$. That is, solve $0.5 = 1 - e^{-5x/6}$ for $x$.

Graph $Y_1 = 0.5$ and $Y_2 = 1 - e$^(−5X/6) as shown in Figure 87. There is a 50-50 chance of at least one car entering the intersection during an interval of about 0.83 minutes.

88. (a) $P(2) = 1 - e^{-0.1144(2)} \approx 0.20$ and $P(20) = 1 - e^{-0.1144(20)} \approx 0.90$. There is a 20% chance that at least one tree will be located within a circle having a radius of 2 feet, and there is a 90% chance of at least one tree being located within a circle with a radius of 20 feet.

(b) The graph of $P$ is shown in Figure 88. The larger the circle in the forest, the more likely it is to contain a tree. It is not very likely that a circle with a radius of 1-foot would contain a tree since trees do not grow that densely. However, there is an excellent chance that a circle with a radius of 100 feet contains at least one tree. Otherwise, it would be more of a clearing than a forest.

(c) Graph $Y_1 = 1 - e$^$(-0.1144X)$ and $Y_2 = 0.5$. The graphs intersect near (6.06, 0.5). Thus, a circle with a radius of approximately 6.1 feet will have a 50-50 chance of containing at least one tree.

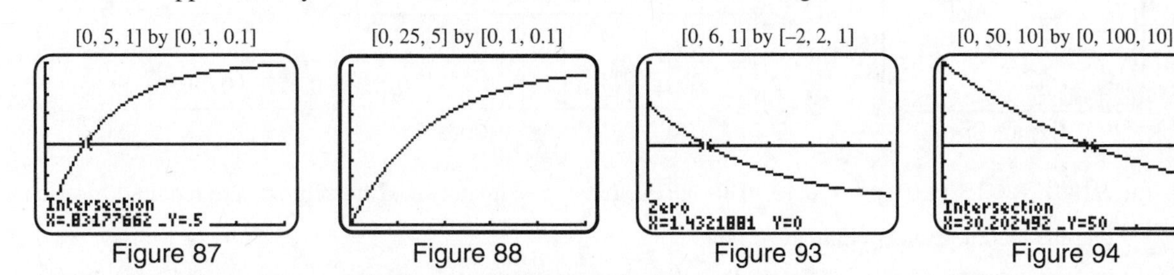

Figure 87 Figure 88 Figure 93 Figure 94

89. To find the age of the fossil solve $0.10 = 1\left(\frac{1}{2}\right)^{x/5700}$. Graph $Y_1 = 0.10$ and $Y_2 = 0.5$^$(X/5700)$. The graphs intersect near (18934.99, 0.1), so the fossil is about 18,935 years old.

90. To find the age of the fossil solve the equation $0.2 = \left(\frac{1}{2}\right)^{x/5700}$.

Graph $Y_1 = 0.2$ and $Y_2 = 0.5$^$(X/5700)$. The graphs intersect near the point (13234.99, 0.2), so the fossil is about 13,235 years old.

91. $P = 1\left(\frac{1}{2}\right)^{x/1600} \Rightarrow P = 1\left(\frac{1}{2}\right)^{3000/1600} \Rightarrow P \approx 0.273$, or 27.3%

92. $P = 1\left(\frac{1}{2}\right)^{x/28} \Rightarrow P = 1\left(\frac{1}{2}\right)^{50/28} \Rightarrow P \approx 0.29$, or 29%

93. (a) Since the initial amount is 2.5 ppm, $C = 2.5$. Since 30% of the chlorine dissipates each day, 70% remains. So, $a = 0.7$.

(b) $f(2) = 2.5(0.7)^2 = 1.225$ parts per million.

(c) Chlorine will need to be added after the level drops to 1.5 parts per million. Therefore, we must solve the equation $2.5(0.7)^x = 1.5 \Rightarrow 2.5(0.7)^x - 1.5 = 0$. Graph $Y_1 = 2.5(0.7)$^$X - 1.5$ and determine any $x$-intercepts or zeros. There is one zero located at $x \approx 1.4$ as shown in Figure 93. If the chlorine level should not drop below 1.5 parts per million, chlorine should be added before the middle of the second day.

94. (a) $A(x) = 100e^{-0.02295x} \Rightarrow A(50) = 100e^{-0.02295(50)} \approx 31.7$ milligrams. Since the original sample contained 100 milligrams, the half-life would be the time required for the sample to disintegrate into 50 milligrams. Since 31.7 is less than this, the half-life must be less than 50 years.

(b) Graph $Y_1 = 100e$^$(-0.02295X)$ and $Y_2 = 50$ as shown in Figure 94. The graphs intersect near (30.2, 50). Therefore, the half-life of cesium is approximately 30.2 years.

95. (a) Using the exponential regression function on your calculator we find $W = 18.29(1.279)^x$.

(b) $W = 18.29(1.279)^9 \approx 168$ thousand pounds.

(c) Solve by graphing $Y_1 = 18.29(1.279)$^X and $Y_2 = 242$. The minimum thickness is about 10.5 inches. See Figure 95.

96. (a) Let $f$ compute the percentage of contaminants passing through $x$ inches of the filter. the percentage passing through 1 inch is 10%, through 2 inches is 10% of 10% or 1%, through 3 inches is 10% of 1% or 0.1%, and so on. See Figure 96. The function is $f(x) = 100(0.1^x)$.

(b) $f(2.3) = 100(0.1)^{2.3} \approx 0.5\%$

[0, 12, 1] by [0, 300, 50]

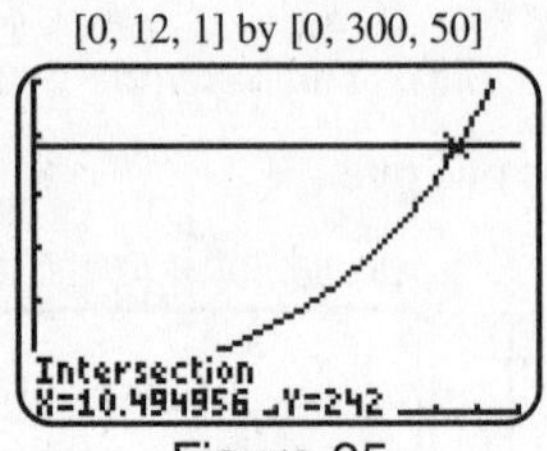


Figure 95

| $x$ | 1 | 2 | 3 | 4 | 5 |
|---|---|---|---|---|---|
| $f(x)$ | 10% | 1% | 0.1% | 0.01% | 0.001% |

Figure 96

97. (a) $H(30) = 0.157(1.033)^{30} \approx 0.42$. This means that approximately 0.42 horsepower are required for each ton that the locomotive is pulling at 30 mph.

(b) To pull a 5000-ton train at 30 mph, approximately a $0.42(5000) = 2100$ horsepower engine is needed.

(c) $\frac{2100}{1350} \approx 1.56$. This value must be rounded up. Two locomotives having 1350 horsepower would move a 5000-ton train at 30 mph.

98. (a) $S(t) = 100(0.999993)^{t^5} \Rightarrow S(4) = 100(0.999993)^{1024} \approx 99.3$ and $S(15) = 100(0.999993)^{759{,}375} \approx 0.49$

After 4 years approximately 99% of the reindeer are still alive, while after 15 years only about 0.5% are still alive. Evidently a 15 year-old reindeer is quite old.

(b) Graph $Y_1 = 100(0.999993)$^(X^5) as shown in Figure 98. Initially the graph is essentially horizontal at 100. This means that during the first 5 years, very few reindeer die. Then the graph begins to decrease very rapidly, until at 13 years, only about 7% are still alive. After 13 years the graph begins to level off slightly. This means that a few reindeer live to an old age.; Yes, $y = 100$ and $y = 0$; percentage cannot be larger than 100 nor smaller than 0.

[0, 15, 5] by [0, 110, 10]

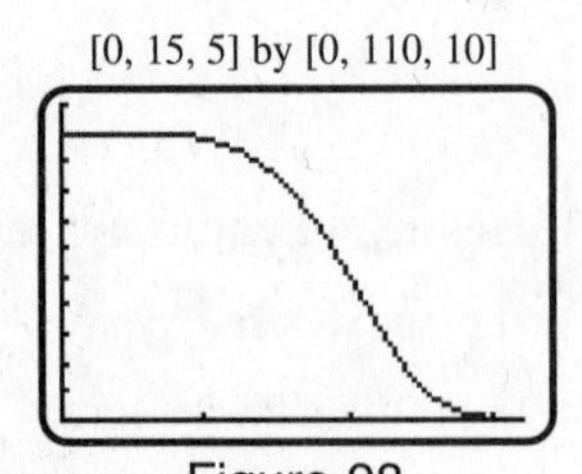

Figure 98

## Extended and Discovery Exercises for Section 5.3

1. $P = A(1 + r/n)^{-nt} \Rightarrow P = \dfrac{A}{(1 + r/n)^{nt}} \Rightarrow A = P(1 + r/n)^{nt}$

2. $P = 30{,}000(1 + 0.075/4)^{-4(12.5)} = 11{,}850.5953$; The present value should be \$11,850.60.

3. $P = 15{,}000(1 + 0.05/12)^{-12(3)} = 12{,}914.64367$; The present value should be \$12,914.64.

4. $40{,}000 = Pe^{0.06(6)} \Rightarrow \dfrac{40{,}000}{e^{0.36}} = P \Rightarrow P \approx \$27{,}907.05$

5. (a) $x = 0 \Rightarrow e^0 = 1 \Rightarrow e^{0+0.001} = 1.0010005 \Rightarrow \dfrac{1 + 1.0010005}{2} \approx 1.0005$

   (b) $e^0 = 1$

   (c) They are very similar.

6. (a) $x = -2 \Rightarrow e^{-2} = 0.13533 \Rightarrow e^{-2+0.001} = 0.13547 \Rightarrow \dfrac{0.13533 + 0.13547}{2} \approx 0.13540$

   (b) $e^{-2} \approx 0.1353$

   (c) They are very similar.

7. (a) $x = -0.5 \Rightarrow e^{-0.5} = 0.6065 \Rightarrow e^{-0.5+0.001} = 0.6071 \Rightarrow \dfrac{0.6065 + 0.6071}{2} \approx 0.6068$

   (b) $e^{-0.5} \approx 0.6065$

   (c) They are very similar.

8. (a) $x = 1.5 \Rightarrow e^{1.5} = 4.4817 \Rightarrow e^{1.5+0.001} = 4.4862 \Rightarrow \dfrac{4.4817 + 4.4862}{2} \approx 4.4839$

   (b) $e^{1.5} = 4.4817$

   (c) They are very similar.

9. The average rate of change near $x$ and the value of the function at $x$ are approximately equal.

10. $e^k$; the slope of a secant line over a small interval near $k$ is approximately $e^k$. That is, this slope is approximately equal to the $y$-value on the graph of $y = e^x$.

## 5.4: Logarithmic Functions and Models

1. See Figure 1.

| $x$ | $10^0$ | $10^4$ | $10^{-8}$ | $10^{1.26}$ |
|---|---|---|---|---|
| $\log x$ | 0 | 4 | -8 | 1.26 |

Figure 1

| $x$ | $10^{-2}$ | $10^{-\pi}$ | $10^5$ | $10^{7.89}$ |
|---|---|---|---|---|
| $\log x$ | $-2$ | $-\pi$ | 5 | 7.89 |

Figure 2

2. See Figure 2.

3. (a) $\log(-3)$ is undefined

   (b) $\log \dfrac{1}{100} = \log \dfrac{1}{10^2} = \log 1^{-2} = -2$

   (c) $\log \sqrt{0.1} = \log 10^{-1/2} = -\dfrac{1}{2}$

   (d) $\log 5^0 = 0$

4. (a) $\log 10{,}000 = \log 10^4 = 4$

   (b) $\log(-\pi)$ is undefined

   (c) $\log \sqrt{0.001} = \log 10^{-3/2} = -\dfrac{3}{2}$

   (d) $\log 8^0 = 0$

5. (a) $\log 10 = \log 10^1 = 1$

   (b) $\log 10{,}000 = \log 10^4 = 4$

   (c) $20 \log 0.1 = 20 \log 10^{-1} = 20(-1) = -20$

   (d) $\log 10 + \log 0.001 = \log 10^1 + \log 10^{-3} = 1 + (-3) = -2$

6. (a) $\log 100 = \log 10^2 = 2$

   (b) $\log 1{,}000{,}000 = \log 10^6 = 6$

   (c) $5 \log 0.01 = 5 \log 10^{-2} = 5(-2) = -10$

   (d) $\log 0.1 - \log 1000 = \log 10^{-1} - \log 10^3 = -1 - 3 = -4$

7. (a) $2 \log 0.1 + 4 = 2 \log 10^{-1} + 4 = 2(-1) + 4 = -2 + 4 = 2$

   (b) $\log 10^{1/2} = \frac{1}{2}$

   (c) $3 \log 100 - \log 1000 = 3 \log 10^2 - \log 10^3 = 3(2) - 3 = 6 - 3 = 3$

   (d) $\log(-10)$ is undefined

8. (a) $\log(-4)$ is undefined

   (b) $\log 1 = \log 10^0 = 0$

   (c) $\log 0$ is undefined

   (d) $-6 \log 100 = -6 \log 10^2 = -6(2) = -12$

9. (a) Since $10^1 \le 79 \le 10^2$, $\log 10^1 \le \log 79 \le \log 10^2 \Rightarrow 1 \le \log 79 \le 2 \Rightarrow n = 1$; $\log 79 \approx 1.898$

   (b) Since $10^2 \le 500 \le 10^3$, $\log 10^2 \le \log 500 \le \log 10^3 \Rightarrow 2 \le \log 500 \le 3 \Rightarrow n = 2$; $\log 500 \approx 2.699$

   (c) Since $10^0 \le 5 \le 10^1$, $\log 10^0 \le \log 5 \le \log 10^1 \Rightarrow 0 \le \log 5 \le 1 \Rightarrow n = 0$; $\log 5 \approx 0.6990$

   (d) Since $10^{-1} \le 0.5 \le 10^0$, $\log 10^{-1} \le \log 0.5 \le \log 10^0 \Rightarrow -1 \le \log 0.5 \le 0 \Rightarrow n = -1$;
   $\log 0.5 \approx -0.3010$

10. (a) Since $10^1 \le 63 \le 10^2$, $\log 10^1 \le \log 63 \le \log 10^2 \Rightarrow 1 \le \log 63 \le 2 \Rightarrow n = 1$; $\log 63 \approx 1.799$

    (b) Since $10^3 \le 5000 \le 10^4$, $\log 10^3 \le \log 5000 \le \log 10^4 \Rightarrow 3 \le \log 5000 \le 4 \Rightarrow n = 3$;
    $\log 5000 \approx 3.699$

    (c) Since $10^0 \le 9 \le 10^1$, $\log 10^0 \le \log 9 \le \log 10^1 \Rightarrow 0 \le \log 9 \le 1 \Rightarrow n = 0$; $\log 9 \approx 0.954$

    (d) Since $10^{-2} \le 0.04 \le 10^{-1}$, $\log 10^{-2} \le \log 0.04 \le \log 10^{-1} \Rightarrow -2 \le \log 0.04 \le \Rightarrow 1 \Rightarrow n = -2$;
    $\log 0.04 \approx -1.398$

11. (a) $\frac{3}{2}$ since $\sqrt{1000} = 1000^{1/2} = (10^3)^{1/2} = 10^{3/2}$

    (b) $\frac{1}{3}$ since $\log \sqrt[3]{10} = \log 10^{1/3}$

    (c) $\log \sqrt[5]{0.1} = \log (10^{-1})^{1/5} = \log (10)^{-1/5} = -\frac{1}{5}$

    (d) $\log \sqrt{0.01} = \log (10^{-2})^{1/2} = \log 10^{-1} = -1$

12. (a) $\log \sqrt{100{,}000} = \log (10^5)^{1/2} = \log 10^{5/2} = \frac{5}{2}$

    (b) $\log \sqrt[3]{100} = \log (10^2)^{1/3} = \log 10^{2/3} = \frac{2}{3}$

    (c) $2 \log \sqrt{0.1} = 2 \log (10^{-1})^{1/2} = 2 \log 10^{-1/2} = 2\left(-\frac{1}{2}\right) = -1$

    (d) $10 \log \sqrt[3]{10} = 10 \log 10^{1/3} = 10\left(\frac{1}{3}\right) = \frac{10}{3}$

13. The input to a logarithmic function must be positive. Thus, any element of the domain of $f$ must satisfy $x + 3 > 0$, or equivalently, $x > -3$. Thus $D$: $(-3, \infty)$, or $\{x \mid x > -3\}$.

14. The input to a logarithmic function must be positive. Thus, any element of the domain of $f$ must satisfy $2x - 4 > 0$, or equivalently, $x > 2$. Thus $D$: $(2, \infty)$, or $\{x \mid x > 2\}$.

15. The input to a logarithmic function must be positive. Thus, any element of the domain of $f$ must satisfy $x^2 - 1 > 0 \Rightarrow x^2 > 1 \Rightarrow x < -1$ or $x > 1$ Thus $D$: $(-\infty, -1) \cup (1, \infty)$, or $\{x \mid x < -1, \text{ or } x > 1\}$.

16. The input to a logarithmic function must be positive. Thus, any element of the domain of $f$ must satisfy $4 - x^2 > 0 \Rightarrow -x^2 > -4 \Rightarrow x^2 < 4 \Rightarrow x > -2$ and $x < 2$. Thus $D$: $(-2, 2)$, or $\{x \mid -2 < x < 2\}$.

17. The input to a logarithmic function must be positive. Thus, any element of the domain of $f$ must satisfy $4^x > 0 \Rightarrow x$ can be any real number. Thus $D$: $(-\infty, \infty)$, or $\{x \mid -\infty < x < \infty\}$.

18. The input to a logarithmic function must be positive. Thus, any element of the domain of $f$ must satisfy $5^x - 25 > 0 \Rightarrow 5^x > 25 \Rightarrow x > 2$. Thus $D$: $(2, \infty)$, or $\{x \mid x > 2\}$.

19. The input to a logarithmic function must be positive. Thus, any element of the domain of $f$ must satisfy $\sqrt{3 - x} - 1 > 0 \Rightarrow \sqrt{3 - x} > 1 \Rightarrow x < 2$. Thus $D$: $(-\infty, 2)$, or $\{x \mid x < 2\}$.

20. The input to a logarithmic function must be positive. Thus, any element of the domain of $f$ must satisfy $4 - \sqrt{2 - x} > 0 \Rightarrow -\sqrt{2 - x} > -4 \Rightarrow \sqrt{2 - x} < 4 \Rightarrow x > -14$ and $x \leq 2$. Thus $D$: $(-14, 2]$, or $\{x \mid -14 < x \leq 2\}$.

21. $\log_8 8^{-5.7} = -5.7$

22. $\log_4 4^{-1.23} = -1.23$

23. $7^{\log_7 2x} = 2x$ for $x > 0$

24. $6^{\log_6 (x+1)} = x + 1$ for $x > -1$

25. $\log_{1/3} \left(\frac{1}{3}\right)^{64} = 64$

26. $\log_{0.4} \left(\frac{2}{5}\right)^{-3} = -3$

27. $\ln e^{-4} = -4$

28. $2^{\log_2 k} = k$

29. $\log_5 5^{\pi} = \pi$

30. $\log_6 6^9 = 9$

31. $3^{\log_3 (x-1)} = x - 1$, for $x > 1$

32. $8^{\log_8 (\pi+1)} = \pi + 1$

33. $\log_2 64 = \log_2 2^6 = 6$

34. $\log_2 \frac{1}{4} = \log_2 2^{-2} = -2$

35. $\log_4 2 = \log_4 \sqrt{4} = \log_4 4^{1/2} = \frac{1}{2}$

36. $\log_3 9 = \log_3 3^2 = 2$

37. $\ln e^{-3} = -3$

38. $\ln e = \log_e e^1 = 1$

39. $\log_8 64 = \log_8 8^2 = 2$

40. $\ln \sqrt[3]{e} = \ln e^{1/3} = \dfrac{1}{3}$

41. $\log_{1/2}\left(\dfrac{1}{4}\right) = \log_{1/2}\left(\dfrac{1}{2}\right)^2 = 2$

42. $\log_{1/3}\left(\dfrac{1}{27}\right) = \log_{1/3}\left(\dfrac{1}{3}\right)^3 = 3$

43. $\log_{1/6} 36 = \log_{1/6}\left(\dfrac{1}{6}\right)^{-2} = -2$

44. $\log_{1/4} 64 = \log_{1/4}\left(\dfrac{1}{4}\right)^{-3} = -3$

45. $\log_a \dfrac{1}{a} = \log_a a^{-1} = -1$

46. $\log_a (a^2 \cdot a^3) = \log_a a^5 = 5$

47. $\log_5 5^0 = 0$

48. $\ln \sqrt{e} = \ln e^{1/2} = \dfrac{1}{2}$

49. $\log_2 \dfrac{1}{16} = \log_2 2^{-4} = -4$

50. $\log_8 8^k = k$

51. See Figure 51.

52. See Figure 52.

| $x$ | 6 | 7 | 21 |
|---|---|---|---|
| $f(x)$ | 0 | 2 | 8 |

Figure 51

| $x$ | $\frac{1}{18}$ | $\frac{3}{2}$ | $\frac{9}{2}$ |
|---|---|---|---|
| $f(x)$ | $-4$ | 2 | 4 |

Figure 52

53. (a) $10^x = 0.01 \Rightarrow \log 10^{-2} = x \Rightarrow x = -2$

(b) $10^x = 7 \Rightarrow \log 7 = x \Rightarrow x \approx 0.85$

(c) $10^x = -4 \Rightarrow \log(-4) = x \Rightarrow$ no solution

54. (a) $10^x = 1{,}000 \Rightarrow \log 10^3 = x \Rightarrow x = 3$

(b) $10^x = 5 \Rightarrow \log(5) = x \Rightarrow x \approx 0.70$

(c) $10^x = -2 \Rightarrow \log(-2) = x \Rightarrow$ no solution

55. (a) $4^x = \dfrac{1}{16} \Rightarrow 4^x = 4^{-2} \Rightarrow x = -2$

(b) $e^x = 2 \Rightarrow \ln(2) = x \Rightarrow x \approx 0.69$

(c) $5^x = 125 \Rightarrow 5^x = 5^3 \Rightarrow x = 3$

56. (a) $2^x = 9 \Rightarrow \log_2(9) = x \Rightarrow x = \dfrac{\log 9}{\log(2)} \approx 3.17$

(b) $10^x = \dfrac{1}{1000} \Rightarrow 10^x = 10^{-3} \Rightarrow x = -3$

(c) $e^x = 8 \Rightarrow \ln(8) = x \Rightarrow x \approx 2.08$

57. (a) $9^x = 1 \Rightarrow 9^x = 9^0 \Rightarrow x = 0$

(b) $10^x = \sqrt{10} \Rightarrow 10^x = 10^{1/2} \Rightarrow x = \dfrac{1}{2}$

(c) $4^x = \sqrt[3]{4} \Rightarrow 4^x = 4^{1/3} \Rightarrow x = \dfrac{1}{3}$

58. (a) $2^x = \sqrt{8} \Rightarrow 2^x = (2^3)^{1/2} \Rightarrow 2x = 2^{3/2} \Rightarrow x = \dfrac{3}{2}$

(b) $7^x = 1 \Rightarrow 7^x = 7^0 \Rightarrow x = 0$

(c) $e^x = \sqrt[3]{e} \Rightarrow e^x = e^{1/3} \Rightarrow x = \dfrac{1}{3}$

59. $e^{-x} = 3 \Rightarrow \ln e^{-x} = \ln 3 \Rightarrow -x = \ln 3 \Rightarrow x = -\ln 3 \approx -1.10$

60. $e^{-x} = \dfrac{1}{2} \Rightarrow \ln e^{-x} = \ln\dfrac{1}{2} \Rightarrow -x = \ln\dfrac{1}{2} \Rightarrow x = -\ln\dfrac{1}{2} \approx 0.69$

61. $10^x - 5 = 95 \Rightarrow 10^x = 100 \Rightarrow 10^x = 10^2 \Rightarrow x = 2$

62. $2 \cdot 10^x = 66 \Rightarrow 10^x = 33 \Rightarrow \log 10^x = \log 33 \Rightarrow x = \log 33 \approx 1.52$

63. $10^{3x} = 100 \Rightarrow 10^{3x} = 10^2 \Rightarrow 3x = 2 \Rightarrow x = \dfrac{2}{3} \approx 0.67$

64. $4 \cdot 10^{2x} + 1 = 21 \Rightarrow 10^{2x} = 5 \Rightarrow \log 10^{2x} = \log 5 \Rightarrow 2x = \log 5 \Rightarrow x = \dfrac{\log 5}{2} \approx 0.35$

65. $5(10^{4x}) = 65 \Rightarrow 10^{4x} = 13 \Rightarrow \log(13) = 4x \Rightarrow x = \dfrac{\log(13)}{4} \approx 0.28$

66. $3(10^{x-2}) = 72 \Rightarrow 10^{x-2} = 24 \Rightarrow \log(24) = x - 2 \Rightarrow x = \log(24) + 2 \approx 3.38$

67. $4(3^x) - 3 = 13 \Rightarrow 4(3^x) = 16 \Rightarrow 3^x = 4 \Rightarrow \log_3(4) = \dfrac{\log(4)}{\log(3)} \approx 1.26$

68. $5(7^x) + 3 = 83 \Rightarrow 5(7^x) = 80 \Rightarrow 7^x = 16 \Rightarrow \log_7(16) = \dfrac{\log(16)}{\log(7)} \approx 1.42$

69. $e^x + 1 = 24 \Rightarrow e^x = 23 \Rightarrow \ln e^x = \ln 23 \Rightarrow x = \ln 23 \approx 3.14$

70 $1 - 2e^x = -5 \Rightarrow 2e^x = 6 \Rightarrow e^x = 3 \Rightarrow \ln e^x = \ln 3 \Rightarrow x = \ln 3 \approx 1.10$

71. $2^x + 1 = 15 \Rightarrow 2^x = 14 \Rightarrow \log_2 2^x = \log_2 14 \Rightarrow x = \log_2 14$ or $x \approx 3.81$

72. $3 \cdot 5^x = 125 \Rightarrow 5^x = \dfrac{125}{3} \Rightarrow \log_5 5^x = \log_5\left(\dfrac{125}{3}\right) \Rightarrow x = \log_5\left(\dfrac{125}{3}\right) \approx 2.32$

73. $5e^x + 2 = 20 \Rightarrow 5e^x = 18 \Rightarrow e^x = \dfrac{18}{5} \Rightarrow \ln e^x = \ln\dfrac{18}{5} \Rightarrow x = \ln\left(\dfrac{18}{5}\right) \approx 1.28$

74 $6 - 2e^{3x} = -10 \Rightarrow -2e^{3x} = -16 \Rightarrow e^{3x} = 8 \Rightarrow e^x = \sqrt[3]{8} \Rightarrow e^x = 2 \Rightarrow \ln e^x = \ln 2 \Rightarrow$

$x = \ln 2 \approx 0.69$

75. $8 - 3(2)^{0.5x} = -40 \Rightarrow -3(2)^{0.5x} = -48 \Rightarrow 2^{0.5x} = 16 \Rightarrow 2^{0.5x} = 2^4 \Rightarrow 0.5x = 4 \Rightarrow x = \dfrac{4}{0.5} \Rightarrow$

$x = 8$

76. $2(3)^{-2x} + 5 = 167 \Rightarrow 2(3)^{-2x} = 162 \Rightarrow 3^{-2x} = 81 \Rightarrow 3^{-2x} = 3^4 \Rightarrow -2x = 4 \Rightarrow x = \frac{4}{-2} \Rightarrow x = -2$

77. (a) $\log x = 2 \Rightarrow 10^2 = x \Rightarrow x = 100$

(b) $\log x = -3 \Rightarrow 10^{-3} = x \Rightarrow x = \frac{1}{1000}$

(c) $\log x = 1.2 \Rightarrow 10^{1.2} = x \Rightarrow x \approx 15.8489$

78. (a) $\log x = 1 \Rightarrow 10^1 = x \Rightarrow x = 10$

(b) $\log x = -4 \Rightarrow 10^{-4} = x \Rightarrow x = \frac{1}{10{,}000}$

(c) $\log x = 0.3 \Rightarrow 10^{0.3} = x \Rightarrow x \approx 1.9953$

79. (a) $\log_2 x = 6 \Rightarrow x = 2^6 = x \Rightarrow 64$

(b) $\log_3 x = -2 \Rightarrow x = 3^{-2} = x \Rightarrow \frac{1}{9}$

(c) $\ln x = 2 \Rightarrow x = e^2 \Rightarrow x \approx 7.3891$

80. (a) $\log_4 x = 2 \Rightarrow x = 4^2 = x \Rightarrow 16$

(b) $\log_8 x = -1 \Rightarrow x = 8^{-1} = x \Rightarrow \frac{1}{8}$

(c) $\ln x = -2 \Rightarrow x = e^{-2} \Rightarrow x \approx 0.1353$

81. $\log_2 x = 1.2 \Rightarrow 2^{\log_2 x} = 2^{1.2} \Rightarrow x = 2^{1.2} \approx 2.2974$

82. $\log_4 x = 3.7 \Rightarrow 4^{\log_4 x} = 4^{3.7} \Rightarrow x = 4^{3.7} \approx 168.8970$

83. $5 \log_7 (2x) = 10 \Rightarrow \log_7 (2x) = 2 \Rightarrow 2x = 7^2 \Rightarrow 2x = 49 \Rightarrow x = \frac{49}{2}$

84. $2 \log_4 x = 3.4 \Rightarrow \log_4 x = 1.7 \Rightarrow x = 4^{1.7} \Rightarrow x \approx 10.5561$

85. $2 \log x = 6 \Rightarrow \log x = 3 \Rightarrow 10^{\log x} = 10^3 \Rightarrow x = 10^3 = 1000$

86. $\log 4x = 2 \Rightarrow 10^{\log 4x} = 10^2 \Rightarrow 4x = 100 \Rightarrow x = 25$

87. $2 \log 5x = 4 \Rightarrow \log 5x = 2 \Rightarrow 10^{\log 5x} = 10^2 \Rightarrow 5x = 100 \Rightarrow x = 20$

88. $6 - \log x = 3 \Rightarrow \log x = 3 \Rightarrow 10^{\log x} = 10^3 \Rightarrow x = 10^3 = 1000$

89. $4 \ln x = 3 \Rightarrow \ln x = \frac{3}{4} \Rightarrow e^{\ln x} = e^{3/4} \Rightarrow x = e^{3/4} \approx 2.1170$

90. $\ln 5x = 8 \Rightarrow e^{\ln 5x} = e^8 \Rightarrow 5x = e^8 \Rightarrow x = \frac{e^8}{5} \approx 596.1916$

91. $5 \ln x - 1 = 6 \Rightarrow 5 \ln x = 7 \Rightarrow \ln x = \frac{7}{5} \Rightarrow e^{\ln x} = e^{7/5} \Rightarrow x = e^{7/5} \approx 4.0552$

92. $2 \ln 3x = 8 \Rightarrow \ln 3x = 4 \Rightarrow e^{\ln 3x} = e^4 \Rightarrow 3x = e^4 \Rightarrow x = \frac{e^4}{3} \approx 18.1994$

93. $4 \log_2 x = 16 \Rightarrow \log_2 x = 4 \Rightarrow 2^{\log_2 x} = 2^4 \Rightarrow x = 2^4 = 16$

94. $\log_3 5x = 10 \Rightarrow 3^{\log_3 5x} = 3^{10} \Rightarrow 5x = 3^{10} \Rightarrow x = \frac{3^{10}}{5} = 11{,}809.8$

95. $5 \ln (2x) + 6 = 12 \Rightarrow 5 \ln (2x) = 6 \Rightarrow \ln (2x) = \frac{6}{5} \Rightarrow e^{\ln 2x} = e^{6/5} \Rightarrow 2x = e^{6/5} \Rightarrow$

$x = \frac{e^{6/5}}{2} \approx 1.6601$

96. $16 - 4\ln 3x = 2 \Rightarrow -4\ln 3x = -14 \Rightarrow \ln 3x = \dfrac{7}{2} \Rightarrow e^{\ln 3x} = e^{7/2} \Rightarrow 3x = e^{7/2} \Rightarrow$

$x = \dfrac{e^{7/2}}{3} \approx 11.0385$

97. $9 - 3\log_4 2x = 3 \Rightarrow -3\log_4 2x = -6 \Rightarrow \log_4 2x = 2 \Rightarrow 4^{\log_4 2x} = 4^2 \Rightarrow 2x = 16 \Rightarrow x = 8$

98. $7\log_6(4x) + 5 = -2 \Rightarrow 7\log_6(4x) = -7 \Rightarrow \log_6(4x) = -1 \Rightarrow 6^{\log_6(4x)} = 6^{-1} \Rightarrow 4x = \dfrac{1}{6} \Rightarrow$

$x = \dfrac{1}{24}$

99. $f(x) = a + b\log x$ and $f(1) = 5 \Rightarrow 5 = a + b\log 1 \Rightarrow 5 = a + b(0) \Rightarrow a = 5$

$f(x) = 5 + b\log x$ and $f(10) = 7 \Rightarrow 7 = 5 + b\log 10 \Rightarrow 7 = 5 + b(1) \Rightarrow b = 2$

The function is $f(x) = 5 + 2\log x$.

100. $f(x) = a + b\log_2 x$ and $f(1) = 3.1 \Rightarrow 3.1 = a + b\log_2 1 \Rightarrow 3.1 = a + b(0) \Rightarrow a = 3.1$

$f(x) = 3.1 + b\log_2 x$ and $f(2) = 6 \Rightarrow 6 = 3.1 + b\log_2 2 \Rightarrow 6 = 3.1 + b(1) \Rightarrow b = 2.9$

The function is $f(x) = 3.1 + 2.9\log_2 x$.

101. Since $f(x) = e^x$, $f^{-1}(x) = \ln x$. See Figure 101.

102. Since $f(x) = \log_4 x$, $f^{-1}(x) = 4^x$. See Figure 102.

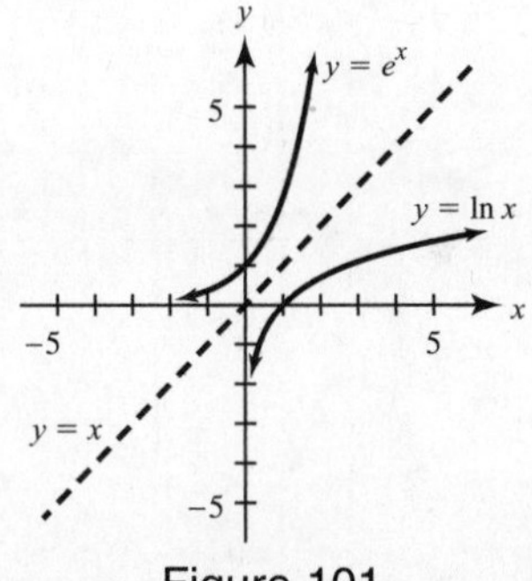


Figure 101

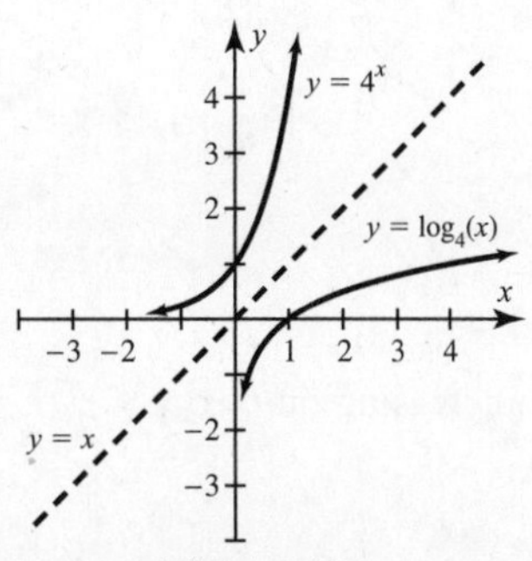


Figure 102

103. See Figure 103.

104. See Figure 104.

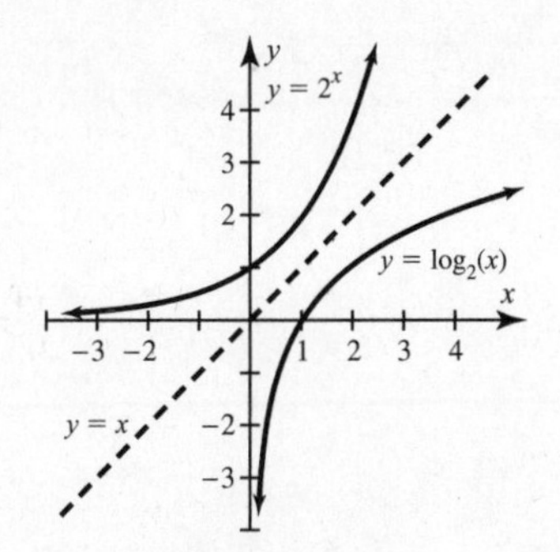


Figure 103

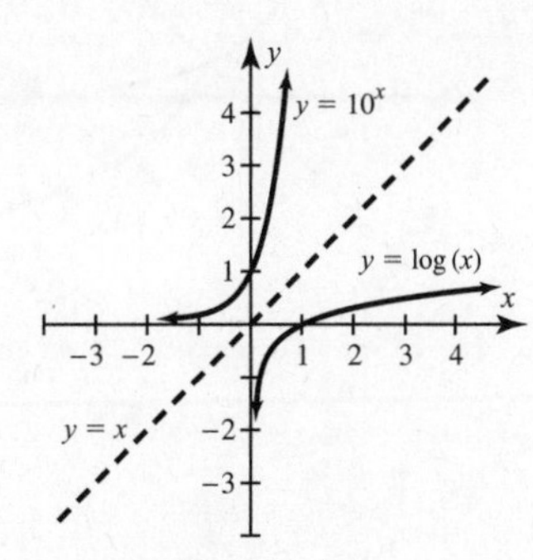


Figure 104

105. The graph is shown in Figure 105. $D = \{x \mid x > -1\}$

106. The graph is shown in Figure 106. $D = \{x \mid x > 3\}$

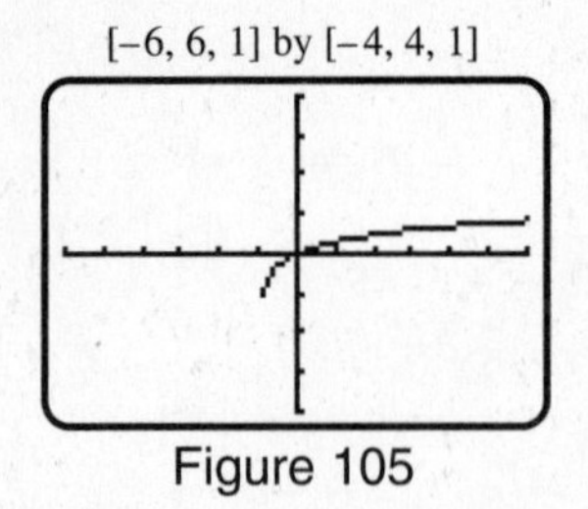

Figure 105

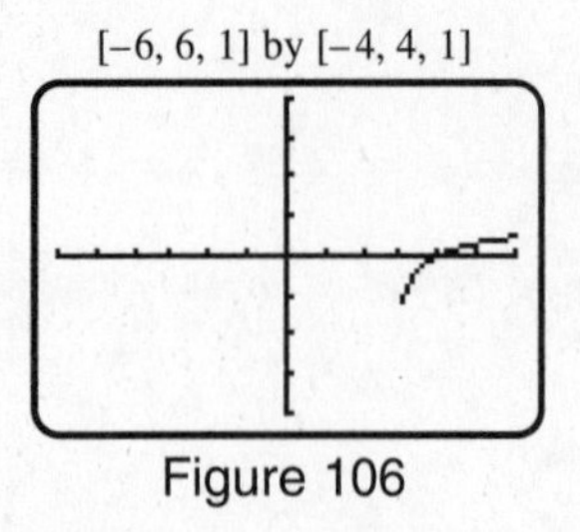

Figure 106

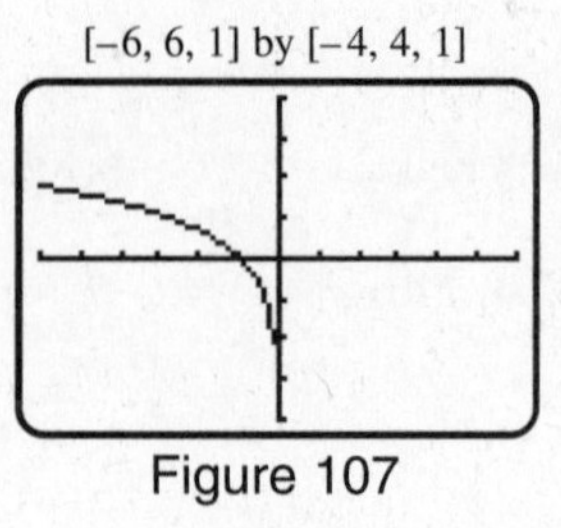

Figure 107

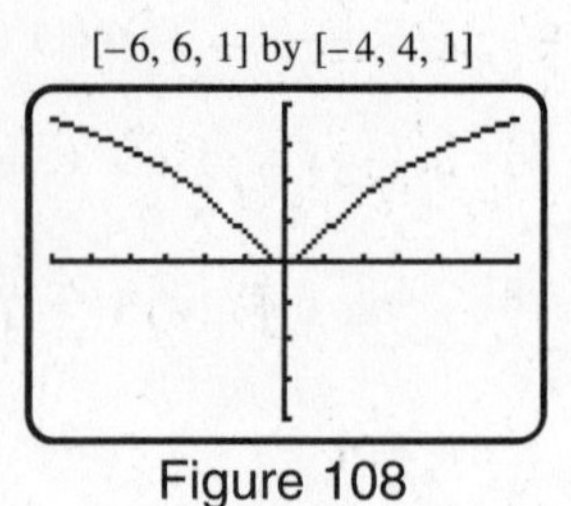

Figure 108

107. The graph is shown in Figure 107. $D = \{x \mid x < 0\}$

108. The graph is shown in Figure 108. $D =$ all real numbers

109. Decreasing. See Figure 109.

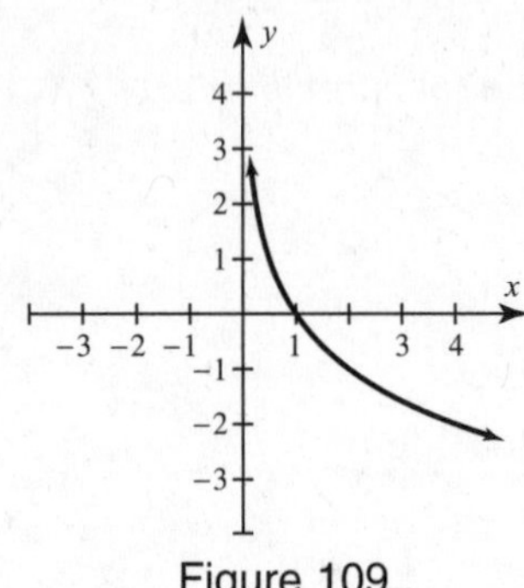
Figure 109

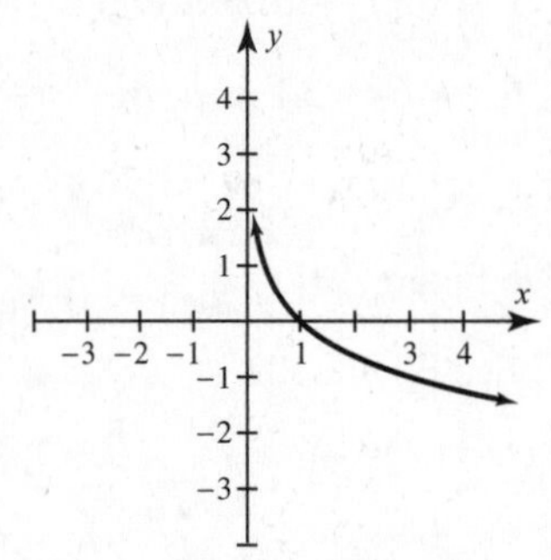
Figure 110

110. Decreasing. See Figure 110.

111. (a) See Figure 111.

(b) $f$ is increasing on $(0, \infty)$; $f^{-1}$ is increasing on $(-\infty, \infty)$.

112. (a) See Figure 112.

(b) $f$ is decreasing on $(0, \infty)$; $f^{-1}$ is decreasing on $(-\infty, \infty)$.

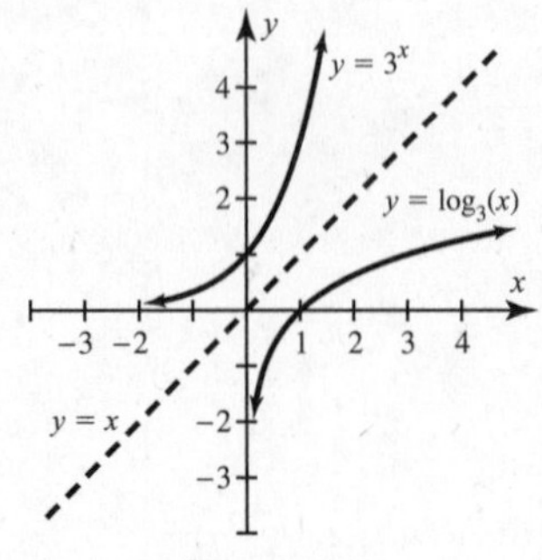

Figure 111

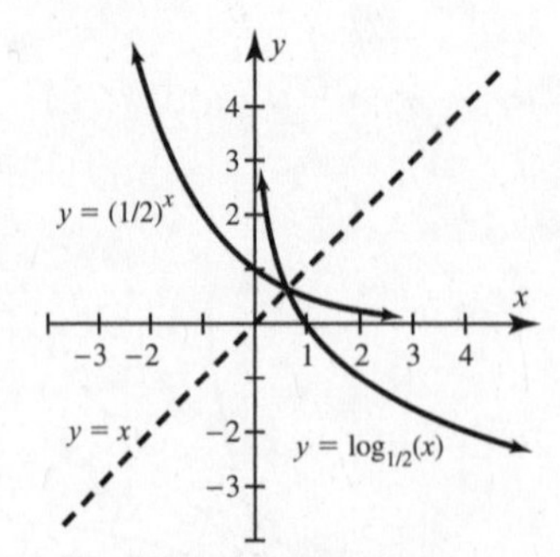

Figure 112

113. (a) $7^{4x} = 4 \Rightarrow \log_7 4 = 4x$

(b) $e^x = 7 \Rightarrow \ln(7) = x$

(c) $c^x = b \Rightarrow \log_c(b) = x$

114. (a) $5^{2x} = 9 \Rightarrow \log_5(9) = 2x$

(b) $b^x = a \Rightarrow \log_b(a) = x$

(c) $d^{2x} = b \Rightarrow \log_d(b) = 2x$

115. (a) $\log_8(x) = 3 \Rightarrow x = 8^3$

(b) $\log_9(2 + x) = 5 \Rightarrow 2 + x = 9^5$

(c) $\log_k b = c \Rightarrow b = k^c$

116. (a) $\log(x) = 4 \Rightarrow x = 10^4$

(b) $\log(8x) = 7 \Rightarrow 8x = e^7$

(c) $\log_a(x) = b \Rightarrow x = a^b$

117. $D(x) = 10\log(10^{16}x),\ x = 10^{-11/2} \Rightarrow D(10^{-11/2}) = 10\log(10^{16}(10^{-11/2})) \Rightarrow 10\log(10^{21/2}) \Rightarrow$
$10\left(\dfrac{21}{2}\right) \Rightarrow$ 105 decibels.

118. $10\log(10^{16}x) + 15 = 10\log(10^{16}x) + \log 10^{15} = 10\log(10^{16}x) + 10\log 10^{1.5} =$
$10[\log(10^{16}x) + \log 10^{1.5}] = 10\log(10^{16}10^{1.5}x)$; That is, the intensity increases by a factor of $10^{1.5}$, or approximately 31.6.

119. $f(x) = a + b\log x$ and $f(1) = 7 \Rightarrow 7 = a + b\log 1 \Rightarrow 7 = a + b(0) \Rightarrow a = 7$
$f(x) = 7 + b\log x$ and $f(10) = 11 \Rightarrow 11 = 7 + b\log 10 \Rightarrow 11 = 7 + b(1) \Rightarrow b = 4$
The function that models the given data is $f(x) = 7 + 4\log x$.
$f(x) = 16 \Rightarrow 16 = 7 + 4\log x \Rightarrow 9 = 4\log x \Rightarrow \log x = \dfrac{9}{4} \Rightarrow 10^{\log x} = 10^{9/4} \Rightarrow$
$x = 10^{9/4} \approx 178$. The island would be about 178 square kilometers.

120. $f(x) = a + b\log x$ and $f(10) = 500 \Rightarrow 500 = a + b\log 10 \Rightarrow 500 = a + b(1) \Rightarrow a + b = 500$
$f(100) = 800 \Rightarrow 800 = a + b\log 100 \Rightarrow 800 = a + b(2) \Rightarrow a + 2b = 800$
Solving the equations for $a$ gives $a = 500 - b$ and $a = 800 - 2b$, thus
$500 - b = 800 - 2b \Rightarrow b = 300$. Since $a + b = 500$ and $b = 300$, $a + 300 = 500 \Rightarrow a = 200$.
The function that models the given data is $f(x) = 200 + 300\log x$.
$f(x) = 1200 \Rightarrow 1200 = 200 + 300\log x \Rightarrow 1000 = 300\log x \Rightarrow \log x = \dfrac{10}{3} \Rightarrow$
$10^{\log x} = 10^{10/3} \Rightarrow x = 10^{10/3} \approx 2154$. The acreage would be about 2154 acres.

121. (a) $f(x) = Ca^x$ and $f(0) = 3 \Rightarrow 3 = Ca^0 \Rightarrow 3 = C(1) \Rightarrow C = 3$
$f(x) = 3a^x$ and $f(1) = 6 \Rightarrow 6 = 3a^1 \Rightarrow 2 = a^1 \Rightarrow a = 2$; thus $f(x) = 3(2^x)$ models the data.

(b) $f(x) = 16 \Rightarrow 16 = 3(2^x) \Rightarrow 2^x = \dfrac{16}{3}$. Graph $Y_1 = 2$^X and $Y_2 = 16/3$ in [0, 5, 1] by [4, 20, 5].
The graphs (not shown) intersect near (2.41, 5.33), so there were 16 million bacteria after about 2.4 days.

122. (a) $f(x) = Ca^x$ and $f(0) = 100 \Rightarrow 100 = Ca^0 \Rightarrow 100 = C(1) \Rightarrow C = 100$
$f(x) = 100a^x$ and $f(5) = 300 \Rightarrow 300 = 100a^5 \Rightarrow 3 = a^5 \Rightarrow a = \sqrt[5]{3}$
Thus $f(x) = 100(3^{1/5})^x$ or $f(x) = 100(3^{x/5})$ models the data.

(b) $f(x) = 2000 \Rightarrow 2000 = 100(3^{x/5}) \Rightarrow 3^{x/5} = 20$
Graph $Y_1 = 3$^(X/5) and $Y_2 = 20$ in the window [0, 16, 2] by [0, 25, 5]. The graphs (not shown) intersect near thepoint (13.634, 20), so the account contained $2000 after about 13.63 years.

123. (a) The graph of $L$ is shown in Figure 123. It is an increasing function. The implication is that heavier planes generally require longer runways.

(b) Since the weight is measured in 1000-pound units, start by evaluating $L(10)$ and $L(100)$.

$L(10) = 3 \log 10 = 3$ and $L(100) = 3 \log 100 = 6$. Thus, a 10,000-pound plane requires approximately 3000 feet of runway, whereas as 100,000-pound plane requires approximately 6000 feet. The distance does not increase by a factor of 10.

(c) If the weight increases tenfold, the runway length increases by 3000 feet.

[0, 50, 10] by [0, 6, 1]

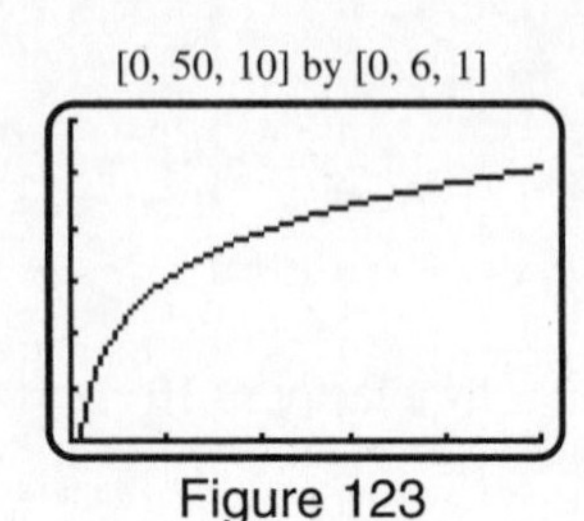

Figure 123

124. $L(x) = 5 \Rightarrow 5 = 3 \log x \Rightarrow \log x = \dfrac{5}{3} \Rightarrow 10^{\log x} = 10^{5/3} \Rightarrow x = 10^{5/3} \approx 46.4$

Since the weight is measured in thousands of pounds, the maximum weight of a plane taking off from a 5000-ft runway is about 46,400 pounds.

125. (a) $\text{pH} = -\log(x) \Rightarrow \text{pH} = -\log(10^{-4.7}) \Rightarrow \text{pH} = -(-4.7) = 4.7$

(b) $-\log(x) = 8.2 \Rightarrow \log(x) = -8.2 \Rightarrow 10^{\log(x)} = 10^{-8.2} \Rightarrow x = 10^{-8.2}$. Since $\dfrac{10^{-4.7}}{10^{-8.2}} = 10^{3.5}$ the hydrogen concentration in the rainwater is $10^{3.5} \approx 3162$ times greater than it is in seawater.

126. (a) Since the pH is computed by $f(x) = -\log x$ where $x$ is the hydrogen ion concentration, we must solve $-\log x = 4.92 \Rightarrow \log x = -4.92 \Rightarrow 10^{\log x} = 10^{-4.92} \Rightarrow x = 10^{-4.92} \approx 0.000012$.

(b) Since the pH is computed by $f(x) = -\log x$ where $x$ is the hydrogen ion concentration, we must solve $-\log x = 3.9 \Rightarrow \log x = -3.9 \Rightarrow 10^{\log x} = 10^{-3.9} \Rightarrow x = 10^{-3.9} \approx 0.000126$.

127. (a) Since $I_0 = 1$, $R(x) = 6.0 \Rightarrow \log x = 6.0 \Rightarrow 10^{\log x} = 10^{6.0} \Rightarrow x = 10^6 = 1{,}000{,}000$

Similarly $R(x) = 8.0 \Rightarrow \log x = 8.0 \Rightarrow 10^{\log x} = 10^{8.0} \Rightarrow x = 10^8 = 100{,}000{,}000$

(b) $\dfrac{10^8}{10^6} = 10^{8-6} = 10^2 = 100$. The Indonesian earthquake was 100 times more intense (powerful) than the Yugoslovian earthquake.

128. The Richter number $R$ increases to $R + 3$. If $x$ is increasing by a factor of $10^K$, then R increases to $(R + K)$.

129. (a) $f(x) = 0.48 \ln(x + 1) + 27 \Rightarrow f(0) = 0.48 \ln(0 + 1) + 27 = 0.48 \ln 1 + 27 = 0.48(0) + 27 = 27$ and $f(100) = 0.48 \ln(100 + 1) + 27 \approx 29.2$ inches. At the center, or eye, of the hurricane the pressure is 27 inches of mercury, while 100 miles from the eye the air pressure has risen to 29.2 inches of mercury.

(b) Graph $Y_1 = 0.48 \ln(X + 1) + 27$ as shown in Figure 129. At first, the air pressure rises rapidly as one moves away from the eye. Then, the air pressure starts to level off and does not increase significantly for distances greater than 200 miles.

(c) $f(x) = 28 \Rightarrow 28 = 0.48 \ln(x + 1) + 27 \Rightarrow \ln(x + 1) = \dfrac{1}{0.48} \Rightarrow e^{\ln(x+1)} = e^{1/0.48} \Rightarrow x + 1 = e^{1/0.48} \Rightarrow x = e^{1/0.48} - 1 \approx 7.03$; the air pressure is 28 inches of mercury about 7 miles from the eye of the hurricane.

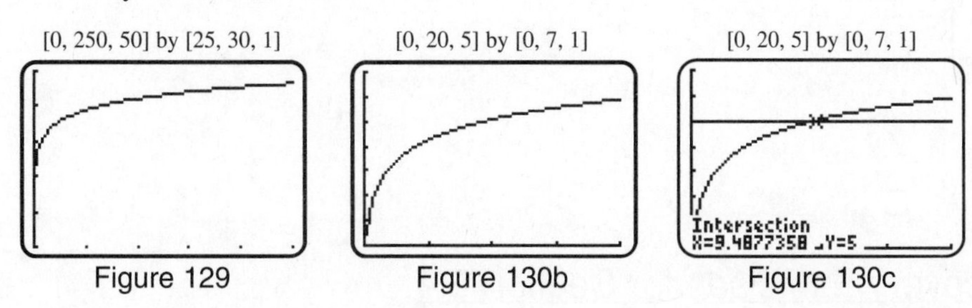

Figure 129 Figure 130b Figure 130c

130. (a) $f(x) = 1.2 \ln x + 2.3 \Rightarrow f(5) = 1.2 \ln 5 + 2.3 \approx 4.2$. At 5 meters above the ground the wind speed is approximately 4.2 meters per second.

(b) Graph $Y_1 = 1.2 \ln(X) + 2.3$ in [0, 20, 5] by [0, 7, 1]. See Figure 130b. At first the wind speed increases rapidly with increased height. About 10 meters up, the wind speed starts to level off.

(c) Graph $Y_1 = 1.2 \ln(X) + 2.3$ and $Y_2 = 5$ in [0, 20, 5] by [0, 7, 1]. See Figure 130c. The graphs intersect near the point (9.48, 5). Thus, the wind speed is 5 meters per second about 9.5 meters above the ground.

131. (a) $T(x) = 20 + 80e^{-x} \Rightarrow T(1) = 20 + 80e^{-1} \approx 49.4$; the temperature is about 49.4°C after 1 hour.

(b) $T(x) = 60 \Rightarrow 60 = 20 + 80e^{-x} \Rightarrow 40 = 80e^{-x} \Rightarrow e^{-x} = \dfrac{1}{2} \Rightarrow \ln e^{-x} = \ln\left(\dfrac{1}{2}\right) \Rightarrow -x = \ln\left(\dfrac{1}{2}\right) \Rightarrow x = -\ln\left(\dfrac{1}{2}\right) \approx 0.693$; the water took about 0.69 hours, or 41.4 minutes to cool to 60°C.

132. (a) $T(x) = 20 - 15(10)^{-0.05x} \Rightarrow T(5) = 20 - 15(10)^{-0.05(5)} = 20 - 15(10)^{-0.25} \approx 11.56$;

After 5 minutes, the temperature of the soda is about 12°C.

(b) $T(x) = 15 \Rightarrow 15 = 20 - 15(10)^{-0.05x} \Rightarrow -5 = -15(10)^{-0.05x} \Rightarrow 10^{-0.05x} = \dfrac{1}{3} \Rightarrow$

$\log 10^{-0.05x} = \log\left(\dfrac{1}{3}\right) \Rightarrow -0.05x = \log\left(\dfrac{1}{3}\right) \Rightarrow x = -\dfrac{\log\left(\frac{1}{3}\right)}{0.05} \approx 9.54$

The temperature of the soda is 15°C after about 9.5 minutes.

133. (a) $f(x) = e^{-x/3} \Rightarrow f(5) = e^{-5/3} \approx 0.189$

The probability that no car enters the intersection during a 5-minute period is about 0.189 or 18.9%.

(b) $f(x) = 0.30 \Rightarrow 0.30 = e^{-x/3} \Rightarrow \ln e^{-x/3} = \ln 0.3 \Rightarrow -\dfrac{x}{3} = \ln 0.3 \Rightarrow x = -3 \ln 0.3 \approx 3.6$

The probability that no car enters the intersection will be 30% during a period of about 3.6 minutes.

134. (a) $P(x) = 4.88e^{0.0133x}$ and $P(x) = 5.4 \Rightarrow 5.4 = 4.88e^{0.0133x} \Rightarrow e^{0.0133x} = \dfrac{5.4}{4.88} \Rightarrow$

$$\ln e^{0.0133x} = \ln\left(\frac{5.4}{4.88}\right) \Rightarrow 0.0133x = \ln\left(\frac{5.4}{4.88}\right) \Rightarrow x = \frac{\ln\left(\frac{5.4}{4.88}\right)}{0.0133} \approx 7.61$$

Since $x = 0$ corresponds to 1990, the population of Tennessee was 5.4 million in 1998.

(b) Graph $Y_1 = 4.88\ e$^(0.0133X) and $Y_2 = 5.4$ in [0, 10, 1] by [4, 6, 1]. See Figure 134. The graphs intersect near the point (7.613, 5.4). Thus, $x \approx 7.61$ and the population was 5.4 million in 1998.

[0, 10, 1] by [4, 6, 1]

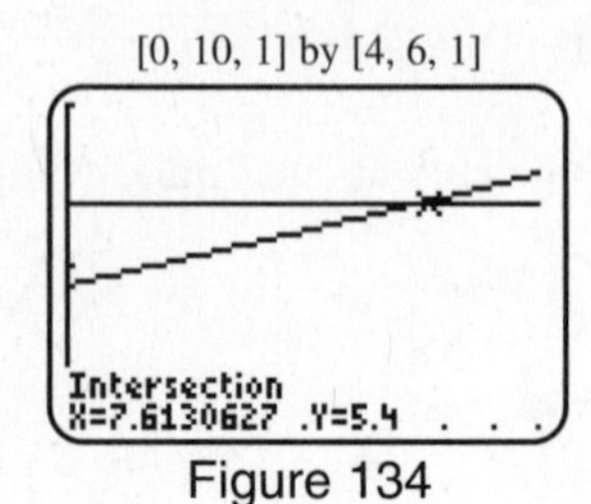


Figure 134

## Extended and Discovery Exercises for Section 5.4

1. (a) If $x = 1$ then $\ln(1) = 0$ and if $x = 1.001$ then $\ln(1.001) = 0.0009995 \Rightarrow$

(1, 0) and (1.001, 0.0009995), the average rate of change is $\dfrac{0.0009995 - 0}{1.001 - 1} \approx 1.00$.

(b) If $x = 2$ then $\ln(2) = 0.693147$ and if $x = 2.001$ then $\ln(2.001) = 0.693647 \Rightarrow$

(2, 0.693147) and (2.001, 0.693647), the average rate of change is $\dfrac{0.693647 - 0.693147}{2.001 - 2} \approx 0.50$.

(c) If $x = 3$ then $\ln(3) = 1.098612$ and if $x = 3.001$ then $\ln(3.001) = 1.098946 \Rightarrow$

(3, 1.098612) and (3.001, 1.098946), the average rate of change is $\dfrac{1.098946 - 1.098612}{3.001 - 2} \approx 0.33$.

(d) If $x = 4$ then $\ln(4) = 1.386294$ and if $x = 4.001$ then $\ln(4.001) = 1.386544 \Rightarrow$

(4, 1.386294) and (4.001, 1.386544), the average rate of change is $\dfrac{1.386544 - 1.386294}{4.001 - 4} \approx 0.25$.

2. The average rate of change near $x$ is the reciprocal of $x$. That is, the average rate of change near $x$ is $\dfrac{1}{x}$.

3. (a) At day 0 the concentration was 1000 and after 6 days it was 1,000,000. Therefore, $f(0) = 1000$ and $f(6) = 1{,}000{,}000$. From 0 to 6 the average rate of change is $\dfrac{f(6) - f(0)}{6 - 0} = \dfrac{10^6 - 10^3}{6} = 166{,}500$.

(b) Let $N_1 = 1000$, $x_1 = 0$, $N_2 = 1{,}000{,}000$, and $x_2 = 6$. The specific growth rate is given by

$$r = \frac{\log 10^6 - \log 10^3}{6 - 0} = \frac{6 - 3}{6 - 0} = \frac{3}{6} = 0.5$$

(c) The specific growth rate is a smaller, more convenient number to use.

4. (a) $T(C(x)) = 6.5 \ln\left(\frac{364(1.005)^x}{280}\right) = 6.5 \ln(1.3 \cdot 1.005^x)$; $T(100) = 6.5 \ln\left(\frac{364(1.005)^{100}}{280}\right) \approx 4.95$

This model predicts an average global temperature increase of about 5°F in the year 2100.

(b) Graph $Y_1 = 364(1.005)$^X in [0, 200, 50] by [0, 1000, 100] and $Y_2 = 6.5 \ln(364(1.005)$^X/280) in [0, 200, 50] by [0, 10, 1]. The graph of $Y_1$ is exponential while the graph of $Y_2$ appears linear over this time interval. See Figures 4a and 4b.

(c) $C$ is an exponential function and $T$ is approximately linear over the same time period. While the carbon dioxide levels in the atmosphere increase exponentially, the average global temperature rises at nearly a constant rate each year.

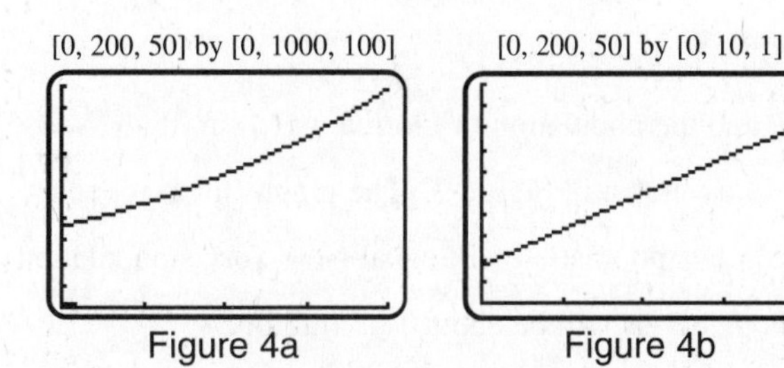

Figure 4a Figure 4b

## Checking Basic Concepts for Sections 5.3 and 5.4

1. $A = 1200\left(1 + \frac{0.095}{12}\right)^{12(4)} \approx 1752.12$; After four years the account balance will be \$1752.12. If compounding continuously, the account balance will be $A = 1200e^{0.095(4)} \approx \$1754.74$.

2. $f(x) = Ca^x$ and $f(0) = 4 \Rightarrow 4 = Ca^0 \Rightarrow 4 = C(1) \Rightarrow C = 4$

$f(x) = 4a^x$ and $f(1) = 2 \Rightarrow 2 = 4a^1 \Rightarrow \frac{1}{2} = a^1 \Rightarrow a = \frac{1}{2}$; thus $f(x) = 4\left(\frac{1}{2}\right)^x$ models the data.

3. $\log_2 15$ represents the power of 2 resulting in 15. That is, $2^{\log_2 15} = 15$ by definition. There is no integer $k$ such that $2^k = 15$, so $\log_2 15$ does not equal an integer. Since $2^4 = 16$, the value of $\log_2 15$ is slightly less than 4.

4. (a) $\log_6 36 = \log_6 6^2 = 2$

(b) $\log \sqrt{10} + \log 0.01 = \log 10^{1/2} + \log 10^{-2} = \frac{1}{2} + (-2) = -\frac{3}{2} = -1.5$

(c) $\ln \frac{1}{e^2} = \ln e^{-2} = -2$

5. (a) $e^x = 5 \Rightarrow \ln e^x = \ln 5 \Rightarrow x = \ln 5 \approx 1.609$

(b) $10^x = 25 \Rightarrow \log 10^x = \log 25 \Rightarrow x = \log 25 \approx 1.398$

(c) $\log x = 1.5 \Rightarrow 10^{\log x} = 10^{1.5} \Rightarrow x = 10^{1.5} \approx 31.623$

6. (a) $2e^x + 1 = 25 \Rightarrow 2e^x = 24 \Rightarrow e^x = 12 \Rightarrow \ln e^x = \ln 12 \Rightarrow x = \ln 12 \approx 2.485$

   This can be graphically supported using the intersection method by graphing $Y_1 = 2e$^X + 1 and $Y_2 = 25$. The intersection is near (2.485, 25).

   (b) $\log 2x = 2.3 \Rightarrow 10^{\log 2x} = 10^{2.3} \Rightarrow 2x = 10^{2.3} \Rightarrow x = \dfrac{10^{2.3}}{2} \approx 99.763$

   This can be graphically supported using the intersection method by graphing $Y_1 = \log(2X)$ and $Y_2 = 2.3$. The intersection is near (99.763, 2.3).

   (c) $\log x^2 = 1 \Rightarrow 10^{\log x^2} = 10^1 \Rightarrow x^2 = 10 \Rightarrow x = \pm\sqrt{10} \approx \pm 3.162$

   This can be graphically supported using the intersection method by graphing $Y_1 = \log$ (X^2) and $Y_2 = 1$. The intersection points are near (–3.162, 1) and (3.162, 1).

7. (a) Let $x = 0$ in $f(x) = 18.2e^{0.001x} \Rightarrow f(0) = 18.2e^{0.001(0)} = 18.2e^0 = 18.2(1) = 18.2$

   Let $x = 0$ in $g(x) = 14e^{0.0168x} \Rightarrow g(0) = 14e^{0.0168(0)} = 14e^0 = 14(1) = 14$

   In 1994 the population in New York was 18.2 million and the population in Florida was 14 million.

   (b) Graph $Y_1 = 18.2e$^(0.001X) and $Y_1 = 14e$^(0.0168X) as shown in Figure 7. The graphs intersect near the point (16.6, 18.5). According to these models, Florida's population will equal New York's population by approximately the year 2011. At that time, both populations will be about 18.5 million.

[0, 25, 5] by [13, 22, 1]

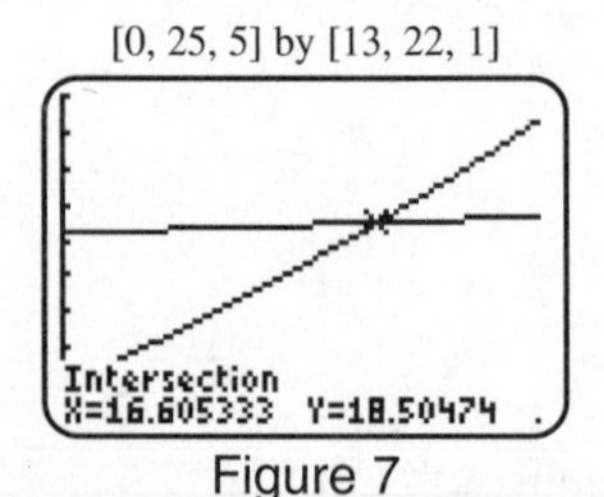


Figure 7

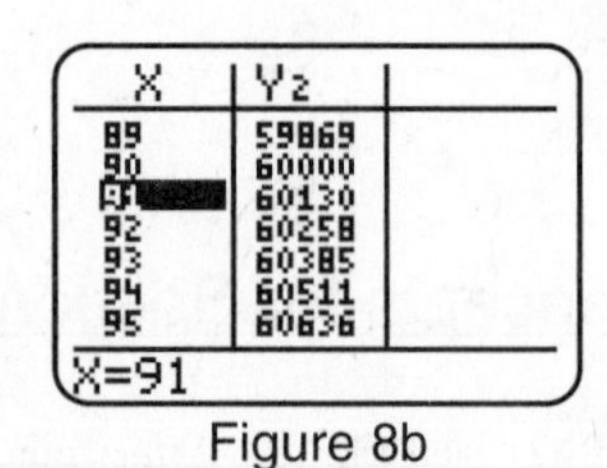


Figure 8a

| X | Y2 |
|---|---|
| 89 | 59869 |
| 90 | 60000 |
| 91 | 60130 |
| 92 | 60258 |
| 93 | 60385 |
| 94 | 60511 |
| 95 | 60636 |

X=91

Figure 8b

8. (a) Table $Y_1 = 30000(1.1$^X) starting at $x = 5$ and incrementing by 1. The person's salary first exceeds \$60,000 after 8 years of experience. See Figure 8a.

   (b) Table $Y_1 = 30000 \log(10 + X)$ starting at $x = 89$ and incrementing by 1. The person's salary first exceeds \$60,000 after 91 years of experience. Exponential growth is preferable. See Figure 8b.

## 5.5: Properties of Logarithms

1. $\log 4 + \log 7 \approx 1.447$; $\log 28 \approx 1.447$; $\log 4 + \log 7 = \log 28 = \log(4 \cdot 7)$; Property 2
2. $\ln 12 + \ln 5 \approx 4.094$; $\ln 60 \approx 4.094$; $\ln 12 + \ln 5 = \ln 60 = \ln(12 \cdot 5)$; Property 2
3. $\ln 72 - \ln 8 \approx 2.197$; $\ln 9 \approx 2.197$; $\ln 72 - \ln 8 = \ln 9 = \ln\left(\dfrac{72}{8}\right)$; Property 3
4. $3 \log 4 \approx 1.806$; $\log 4^3 \approx 1.806$; $3 \log 4 = \log 4^3$; Property 4
5. $10 \log 2 \approx 3.010$; $\log 1024 \approx 3.010$; $10 \log 2 = \log 1024 = \log 2^{10}$; Property 4
6. $\log_2 100 - \log_2 20 \approx 2.322$; $\log_2 5 \approx 2.322$; $\log_2 100 - \log_2 20 = \log_2 5 = \log_2\left(\dfrac{100}{20}\right)$; Property 3

7. $\log_2 ab = \log_2 a + \log_2 b$

8. $\ln 3x = \ln 3 + \ln x$

9. $\ln 7a^4 = \ln 7 + 4 \ln a$

10. $\log \dfrac{a^3}{3} = 3 \log a - \log 3$

11. $\log \dfrac{6}{z} = \log 6 - \log z$

12. $\ln \dfrac{xy}{z} = \ln xy - \ln z = \ln x + \ln y - \ln z$

13. $\log \dfrac{x^2}{3} = \log x^2 - \log 3 = 2 \log x - \log 3$

14. $\log 3x^6 = \log 3 + \log x^6 = \log 3 + 6 \log x$

15. $\ln \dfrac{2x^7}{3k} = \ln 2x^7 - \ln 3k = \ln 2 + \ln x^7 - (\ln 3 + \ln k) = \ln 2 + 7 \ln x - \ln 3 - \ln k$

16. $\ln \dfrac{kx^3}{5} = \ln kx^3 - \ln 5 = \ln k + \ln x^3 - \ln 5 = \ln k + 3 \ln x - \ln 5$

17. $\log_2 4k^2x^3 = \log_2 4k^2 + \log_2 x^3 = \log_2 4 + \log_2 k^2 + \log_2 x^3 = 2 + 2 \log_2 k + 3 \log_2 x$

18. $\log \dfrac{5kx^2}{11} = \log 5kx^2 - \log 11 = \log 5 + \log k + 2 \log x - \log 11$

19. $\log_5 \dfrac{25x^3}{y^4} = \log_5 25x^3 - \log_5 y^4 = 2 + 3 \log_5 x - 4 \log_5 y$

20. $\log_2 \dfrac{32}{xy^2} = \log_2 32 - \log_2 xy^2 = 5 - (\log_2 x + 2 \log_2 y) = 5 - \log_2 x - 2 \log_2 y$

21. $\ln \dfrac{x^4}{y^2\sqrt{z^3}} = \ln (x^4) - (\ln y^2 + \ln (z^{3/2})) = 4 \ln (x) - 2 \ln (y) - \dfrac{3}{2} \ln (z)$

22. $\ln \dfrac{x\sqrt[3]{y^2}}{z^6} = \ln (x) + (\ln (y^{2/3}) - \ln (z^6)) = \ln (x) + \dfrac{2}{3} \ln (y) - 6 \ln (z)$

23. $\log_4 0.25(x + 2)^3 = \log_4 0.25 + \log_4 (x + 2)^3 = -1 + 3 \log_4 (x + 2)$

24. $\log 0.001(a - b)^{-3} = \log 0.001 + \log (a - b)^{-3} = -3 + -3 \log (a - b) = -3 - 3 \log (a - b)$

25. $\log_5 \dfrac{x^3}{(x - 4)^4} = \log_5 x^3 - \log_5 (x - 4)^4 = 3 \log_5 x - 4 \log_5 (x - 4)$

26. $\log_8 \dfrac{(3x - 2)^2}{x^2 + 1} = \log_8 (3x - 2)^2 - \log_8 (x^2 + 1) = 2 \log_8 (3x - 2) - \log_8 (x^2 + 1)$

27. $\log_2 \dfrac{\sqrt{x}}{z^2} = \log_2 \sqrt{x} - \log_2 z^2 = \log_2 x^{1/2} - \log_2 z^2 = \dfrac{1}{2} \log_2 x - 2 \log_2 z$

28. $\log \sqrt{\dfrac{xy^2}{z}} = \log \left(\dfrac{xy^2}{z}\right)^{1/2} = \dfrac{1}{2} \log \left(\dfrac{xy^2}{z}\right) = \dfrac{1}{2} [\log x + 2 \log y - \log z] = \dfrac{1}{2} \log x + \log y - \dfrac{1}{2} \log z$

29. $\ln \sqrt[3]{\dfrac{2x + 6}{(x + 1)^5}} = \ln \left(\dfrac{2x + 6}{(x + 1)^5}\right)^{1/3} = \dfrac{1}{3} [\ln (2x + 6) - 5 \ln (x + 1)] = \dfrac{1}{3} \ln (2x + 6) - \dfrac{5}{3} \ln (x + 1)$

30. $\log \dfrac{\sqrt{x^2 + 4}}{\sqrt[3]{x - 1}} = \log (x^2 + 4)^{1/2} - \log (x - 1)^{1/3} = \dfrac{1}{2} \log (x^2 + 4) - \dfrac{1}{3} \log (x - 1)$

31. $\log_2 \dfrac{\sqrt[3]{x^2 - 1}}{\sqrt{1 + x^2}} = \log_2 \sqrt[3]{x^2 - 1} - \log_2 \sqrt{1 + x^2} = \log_2 (x^2 - 1)^{1/3} - \log_2 (1 + x^2)^{1/2} =$

$\dfrac{1}{3} \log_2 (x^2 - 1) - \dfrac{1}{2} \log_2 (1 + x^2)$

32. $\log_8 \sqrt[3]{\dfrac{x + y^2}{2z + 1}} = \log_8 \left(\dfrac{x + y^2}{2z + 1}\right)^{1/3} = \dfrac{1}{3} [\log_8 (x + y^2) - \log_8 (2z + 1)] =$

$\dfrac{1}{3} \log_8 (x + y^2) - \dfrac{1}{3} \log_8 (2z + 1)$

33. $\log 2 + \log 3 = \log (2 \cdot 3) = \log 6$

34. $\log \sqrt{2} + \log \sqrt[3]{2} = \log (2^{1/2} \cdot 2^{1/3}) = \log 2^{5/6} = \dfrac{5}{6} \log 2$

35. $\ln \sqrt{5} - \ln 25 = \ln \left(\dfrac{5^{1/2}}{5^2}\right) = \ln 5^{-3/2} = -\dfrac{3}{2} \ln 5$

36. $\ln 33 - \ln 11 = \ln \left(\dfrac{33}{11}\right) = \ln 3$

37. $\log 20 + \log \dfrac{1}{10} = \log (20)\left(\dfrac{1}{10}\right) = \log \dfrac{20}{10} = \log 2$

38. $\log_2 24 + \log_2 \dfrac{1}{48} = \log_2 (24)\left(\dfrac{1}{48}\right) = \log_2 \dfrac{24}{48} = \log_2 \dfrac{1}{2} = -1$

39. $\log 4 + \log 3 - \log 2 = \log \dfrac{4(3)}{2} = \log \dfrac{12}{2} = \log 6$

40. $\log_3 5 - \log_3 10 - \log_3 \dfrac{1}{2} = \log_3 \left(\dfrac{\frac{5}{10}}{\frac{1}{2}}\right) = \log_3 \left(\dfrac{5}{10}\right)\left(\dfrac{2}{1}\right) = \log_3 \dfrac{10}{10} = \log_3 1 = 0$

41. $\log_7 5 + \log_7 k^2 = \log_7 (5)(k^2) = \log_7 5k^2$

42. $\log_6 45 + \log_6 b^3 = \log_6 (45)(b^3) = \log_6 45b^3$

43. $\ln x^6 - \ln x^3 = \ln \dfrac{x^6}{x^3} = \ln x^{6-3} = \ln x^3$

44. $\log 10x^5 - \log 5x = \log \dfrac{10x^5}{5x} = \log 2x^{5-1} = \log 2x^4$

45. $\log \sqrt{x} + \log x^2 - \log x = \log \left(\dfrac{x^{1/2} \cdot x^2}{x}\right) = \log x^{3/2} = \dfrac{3}{2} \log x$

46. $\log \sqrt[4]{x} + \log x^4 - \log x^2 = \log \left(\dfrac{x^{1/4} \cdot x^4}{x^2}\right) = \log x^{9/4} = \dfrac{9}{4} \log x$

47. $3 \ln (x) - \dfrac{3}{2} \ln (y) + 4 \ln (z) = \ln (x^3) - \ln (\sqrt{y^3}) + \ln (z^2) = \ln \left(\dfrac{x^3 z^4}{\sqrt{y^3}}\right)$

48. $\dfrac{2}{3} \ln (y) - 4 \ln (x) - \dfrac{1}{2} \ln (z) = \ln (\sqrt[3]{y^2}) - \ln (x^4) - \ln (\sqrt{z}) = \ln \left(\dfrac{\sqrt[3]{y^2}}{x^4 \sqrt{z}}\right)$

49. $\ln \dfrac{1}{e^2} + \ln 2e = \ln \left(\dfrac{1}{e^2} \cdot 2e\right) = \ln \dfrac{2}{e}$

50. $\ln 4e^3 - \ln 2e^2 = \ln \left(\dfrac{4e^3}{2e^2}\right) = \ln 2e$

51. $2 \ln x - 4 \ln y + \frac{1}{2} \ln z = \ln x^2 - \ln y^4 + \ln z^{1/2} = \ln \frac{x^2}{y^4} + \ln \sqrt{z} = \ln \frac{x^2\sqrt{z}}{y^4}$

52. $\frac{1}{3} \log_5 (x + 1) + \frac{1}{3} \log_5 (x - 1) = \frac{1}{3} [\log_5 (x + 1) + \log_5 (x - 1)] = \frac{1}{3} \log_5 (x + 1)(x - 1) =$

$\log_5 (x^2 - 1)^{1/3} = \log_5 \sqrt[3]{x^2 - 1}$

53. $\log 4 - \log x + 7 \log \sqrt{x} = \log \frac{4}{x} + \log (\sqrt{x})^7 = \log \left(\frac{4x^{7/2}}{x}\right) = \log 4x^{5/2} = \log 4\sqrt{x^5}$

54. $\ln 3e - \ln \frac{1}{4e} = \ln \left(\frac{3e}{\frac{1}{4e}}\right) = \ln (3e \cdot 4e) = \ln 12e^2$

55. $2 \log (x^2 - 1) + 4 \log (x - 2) - \frac{1}{2} \log y = \log (x^2 - 1)^2 + \log (x - 2)^4 - \log y^{1/2} =$

$\log \frac{(x^2 - 1)^2(x - 2)^4}{\sqrt{y}}$

56. $\log_3 x + \log_3 \sqrt{x + 3} - \frac{1}{3} \log_3 (x - 4) = \log_3 x\sqrt{x + 3} - \log_3 (x - 4)^{1/3} = \log_3 \frac{x\sqrt{x + 3}}{\sqrt[3]{x - 4}}$

57. (a) Table $Y_1 = \log (3X) + \log (2X)$ and $Y_2 = \log (6X\wedge 2)$ starting at $x = 1$, incrementing by 1.

See Figure 57. From the table we see that $Y_1 = Y_2$, so $f(x) = g(x)$.

(b) By property 2: $\log 3x + \log 2x = \log (3x \cdot 2x) = \log 6x^2$

58. (a) Table $Y_1 = \ln (3X) - \ln (2X)$ and $Y_2 = \ln (X)$ starting at $x = 1$, incrementing by 1. See Figure 58.

From the table we see that $Y_1 \neq Y_2$, so $f(x) \neq g(x)$.

(b) Not possible.

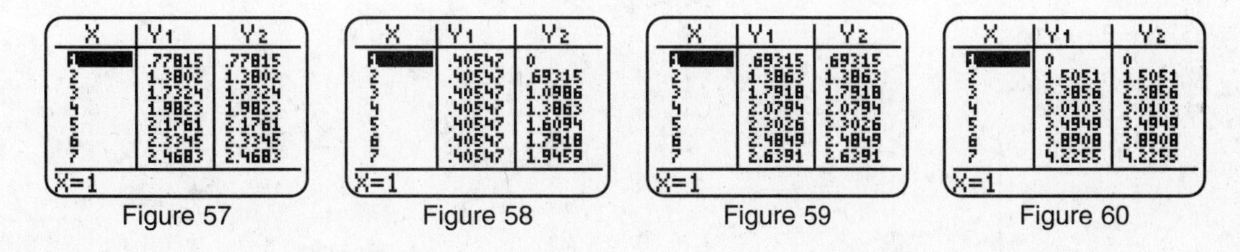

| X | Y1 | Y2 |
|---|---|---|
| 1 | .77815 | .77815 |
| 2 | 1.3802 | 1.3802 |
| 3 | 1.7324 | 1.7324 |
| 4 | 1.9823 | 1.9823 |
| 5 | 2.1761 | 2.1761 |
| 6 | 2.3345 | 2.3345 |
| 7 | 2.4683 | 2.4683 |

X=1

Figure 57

| X | Y1 | Y2 |
|---|---|---|
| 1 | .40547 | 0 |
| 2 | .40547 | .69315 |
| 3 | .40547 | 1.0986 |
| 4 | .40547 | 1.3863 |
| 5 | .40547 | 1.6094 |
| 6 | .40547 | 1.7918 |
| 7 | .40547 | 1.9459 |

X=1

Figure 58

| X | Y1 | Y2 |
|---|---|---|
| 1 | .69315 | .69315 |
| 2 | 1.3863 | 1.3863 |
| 3 | 1.7918 | 1.7918 |
| 4 | 2.0794 | 2.0794 |
| 5 | 2.3026 | 2.3026 |
| 6 | 2.4849 | 2.4849 |
| 7 | 2.6391 | 2.6391 |

X=1

Figure 59

| X | Y1 | Y2 |
|---|---|---|
| 1 | 0 | 0 |
| 2 | 1.5051 | 1.5051 |
| 3 | 2.3856 | 2.3856 |
| 4 | 3.0103 | 3.0103 |
| 5 | 3.4949 | 3.4949 |
| 6 | 3.8908 | 3.8908 |
| 7 | 4.2255 | 4.2255 |

X=1

Figure 60

59. (a) Table $Y_1 = \ln (2X\wedge 2) - \ln (X)$ and $Y_2 = \ln (2X)$ starting at $x = 1$, incrementing by 1. See Figure 59.

From the table we see that $Y_1 = Y_2$, so $f(x) = g(x)$.

(b) By property 3: $\ln 2x^2 - \ln x = \ln \left(\frac{2x^2}{x}\right) = \ln 2x$

60. (a) Table $Y_1 = \log (X\wedge 2) + \log (X\wedge 3)$ and $Y_2 = 5 \log (X)$ starting at $x = 1$, incrementing by 1.

See Figure 60. From the table we see that $Y_1 = Y_2$, so $f(x) = g(x)$.

(b) By property 4: $\log x^2 + \log x^3 = 2 \log x + 3 \log x = 5 \log x$

61. (a) Table $Y_1 = \ln(X\text{^}4) - \ln(X\text{^}2)$ and $Y_2 = 2\ln(X)$ starting at $x = 1$, incrementing by 1. See Figure 61.

From the table we see that $Y_1 = Y_2$, so $f(x) = g(x)$.

(b) By property 4: $\ln x^4 - \ln x^2 = 4\ln x - 2\ln x = 2\ln x$

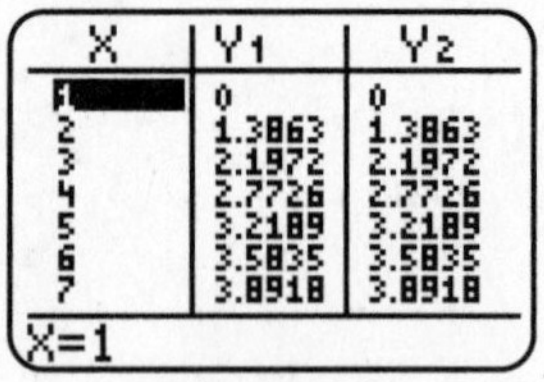

| X | Y1 | Y2 |
|---|---|---|
| 1 | 0 | 0 |
| 2 | 1.3863 | 1.3863 |
| 3 | 2.1972 | 2.1972 |
| 4 | 2.7726 | 2.7726 |
| 5 | 3.2189 | 3.2189 |
| 6 | 3.5835 | 3.5835 |
| 7 | 3.8918 | 3.8918 |

X=1

Figure 61

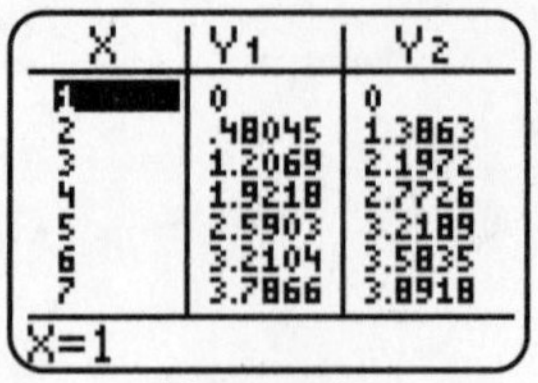

| X | Y1 | Y2 |
|---|---|---|
| 1 | 0 | 0 |
| 2 | .48045 | 1.3863 |
| 3 | 1.2069 | 2.1972 |
| 4 | 1.9218 | 2.7726 |
| 5 | 2.5903 | 3.2189 |
| 6 | 3.2104 | 3.5835 |
| 7 | 3.7866 | 3.8918 |

X=1

Figure 62

62. (a) Table $Y_1 = (\ln(X))\text{^}2$ and $Y_2 = 2\ln(X)$ starting at $x = 1$, incrementing by 1. See Figure 62.

From the table we see that $Y_1 \neq Y_2$, so $f(x) \neq g(x)$.

(b) Not possible.

63. See Figure 63.

64. See Figure 64.

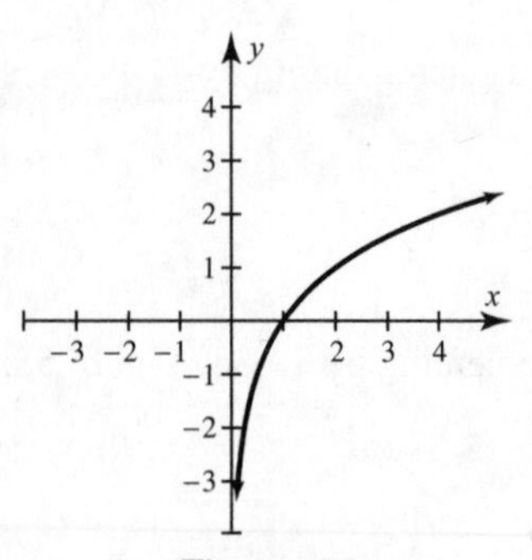

Figure 63

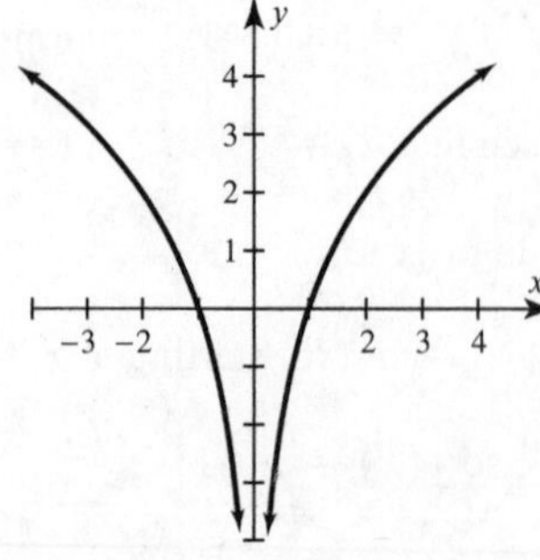

Figure 64

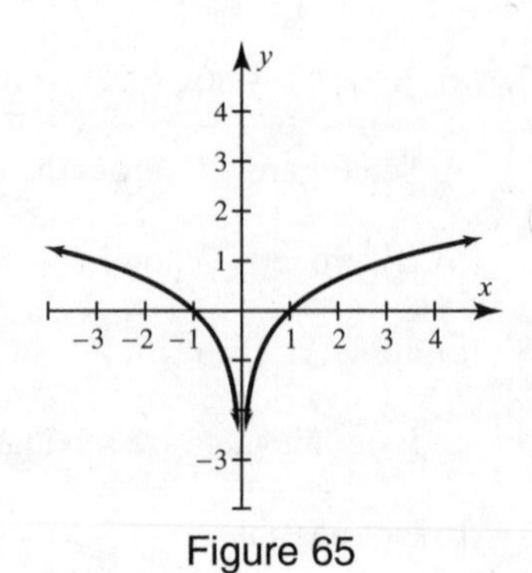

Figure 65

65. See Figure 65.

66. See Figure 66.

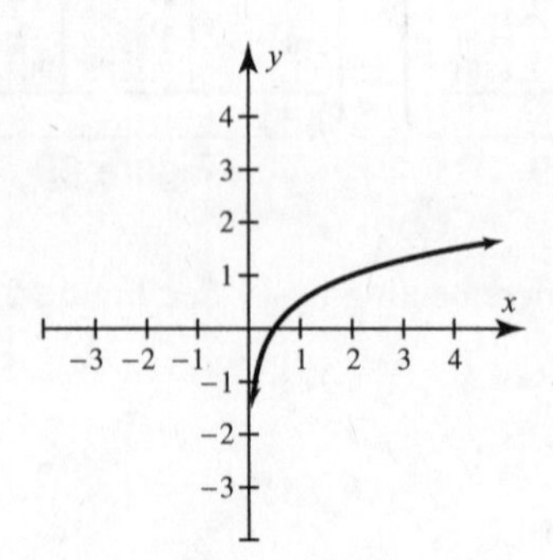

Figure 66

67. $\log_2 25 = \dfrac{\log 25}{\log 2} \approx 4.644$

68. $\log_3 67 = \dfrac{\log 67}{\log 3} \approx 3.827$

69. $\log_5 130 = \dfrac{\log 130}{\log 5} \approx 3.024$

70. $\log_6 0.77 = \dfrac{\log 0.77}{\log 6} \approx -0.146$

71. $\log_2 5 + \log_2 7 = \dfrac{\log 5}{\log 2} + \dfrac{\log 7}{\log 2} \approx 5.129$

72. $\log_9 85 + \log_7 17 = \dfrac{\log 85}{\log 9} + \dfrac{\log 17}{\log 7} \approx 3.478$

73. $\sqrt{\log_4 46} = \sqrt{\dfrac{\log 46}{\log 4}} \approx 1.662$

74. $2 \log_5 15 + \sqrt[3]{\log_3 67} = 2\left(\dfrac{\log 15}{\log 5}\right) + \sqrt[3]{\dfrac{\log 67}{\log 3}} \approx 4.929$

75. $\dfrac{\log_2 12}{\log_2 3} = \dfrac{\frac{\log 12}{\log 2}}{\frac{\log 3}{\log 2}} = \dfrac{\log 12}{\log 2} \cdot \dfrac{\log 2}{\log 3} = \dfrac{\log 12}{\log 3} \approx 2.262$

76. $\dfrac{\log_7 125}{\log_7 25} = \dfrac{\frac{\log 125}{\log 7}}{\frac{\log 25}{\log 7}} = \dfrac{\log 125}{\log 7} \cdot \dfrac{\log 7}{\log 25} = \dfrac{\log 125}{\log 25} = 1.5$

77. Graph $Y_1 = \log(X\text{^}3 + X\text{^}2 + 1)/\log 2$ and $Y_2 = 7$ in [0, 10, 2] by [0, 10, 2]. The graphs intersect near the point (4.714, 7), so the solution to $\log_2(x^3 + x^2 + 1) = 7$ is $x \approx 4.714$.

78. Graph $Y_1 = \log(1 + X\text{^}2 + 2X\text{^}4)/\log 3$ and $Y_2 = 4$ in [–10, 10, 2] by [0, 10, 2]. The graphs intersect near the points (–2.466, 4) and (2.466, 4), so the solutions to $\log_3(1 + x^2 + 2x^4) = 4$ are $x \approx \pm 2.466$.

79. Graph $Y_1 = \log(X\text{^}2 + 1)/\log 2$ and $Y_2 = 5 - \log(X\text{^}4 + 1)/\log 3$ in [–5, 5, 2] by [–5, 10, 2]. The graphs intersect near the points (–2.035, 2.362) and (2.035, 2.362), so the solutions to the equation $\log_2(x^2 + 1) = 5 - \log_3(x^4 + 1)$ are $x \approx \pm 2.035$.

80. Graph $Y_1 = \ln(X\text{^}2 + 2)$ and $Y_2 = \log(10 - X\text{^}2)/\log 2$ in [–5, 5, 2] by [–5, 10, 2]. The graphs intersect near the points (–2.415, 2.059) and (2.415, 2.059), so the solutions to the equation $\ln(x^2 + 2) = \log_2(10 - x^2)$ are $x \approx \pm 2.415$.

81. Change base 10 to base $e$: $L(x) = 3 \log x = \dfrac{3 \cdot \ln x}{\ln 10}$;

$L(50) = 3 \log 50 \approx 5.097$ and $L(50) = \dfrac{3 \ln 50}{\ln 10} \approx 5.097$. Yes, the answers agree.

82. $y = bx^a \Rightarrow \log y = \log(bx^a) \Rightarrow \log y = \log b + \log x^a \Rightarrow \log y = \log b + a \log x$

83. $f(x) = 160 + 10 \log x \Rightarrow f(10x) = 160 + 10 \log(10x) = 160 + 10(\log 10 + \log x) =$ $160 + 10(1 + \log x) = 160 + 10 + 10 \log x = 160 + 10 \log x + 10$, thus $f(10x) = f(x) + 10$. In other words, the decibel level increases by 10 decibels.

84. Change base 10 to base $e$: $f(x) = 160 + 10 \log x = 160 + \dfrac{10 \ln x}{\ln 10}$

$f(5 \times 10^{-8}) = 160 + 10 \log(5 \times 10^{-8}) \approx 86.99$ and $f(5 \times 10^{-8}) = 160 + \dfrac{10 \ln(5 \times 10^{-8})}{\ln 10} \approx 86.99$

Yes, the answers are the same.

85. $\ln I - \ln I_0 = -kx \Rightarrow \ln I = \ln I_0 - kx \Rightarrow e^{\ln I} = e^{\ln I_0 - kx} \Rightarrow e^{\ln I} = e^{\ln I_0} \cdot e^{-kx} \Rightarrow I = I_0 e^{-kx}$

86. $A = Ca^x \Rightarrow \log A = \log(Ca^x) \Rightarrow \log A = \log C + \log a^x \Rightarrow \log A = \log C + x \log a \Rightarrow$

$x \log a = \log A - \log C \Rightarrow x = \dfrac{\log A - \log C}{\log a}$

87. (a) $P = 34e^{0.013x} \Rightarrow \dfrac{P}{34} = e^{0.013x} \Rightarrow \ln\left(\dfrac{P}{34}\right) = 0.013x \Rightarrow x = \dfrac{1}{0.013}\ln\left(\dfrac{P}{34}\right)$

(b) $x = \dfrac{\ln\left(\frac{38}{34}\right)}{0.013} \approx 8.6$. The population is expected to reach 38 million during 2009.

88. (a) $P = 8e^{0.023x} \Rightarrow \dfrac{P}{8} = e^{0.023x} \Rightarrow \ln\left(\dfrac{P}{8}\right) = 0.023x \Rightarrow x = \dfrac{1}{0.023}\ln\left(\dfrac{P}{8}\right)$

(b) $x = \dfrac{\ln\left(\frac{10}{8}\right)}{0.023} \approx 9.7$. The population is expected to reach 10 million during 2010.

89. $A = Pe^{rt} \Rightarrow \dfrac{A}{P} = e^{rt} \Rightarrow \ln\dfrac{A}{P} = \ln e^{rt} \Rightarrow \ln\dfrac{A}{P} = rt \Rightarrow \dfrac{\ln\frac{A}{P}}{r} = t \Rightarrow t = \dfrac{\ln\frac{A}{P}}{r}$

90. $P = P_0 e^{r(t-t_0)} + 5 \Rightarrow P - 5 = P_0 e^{r(t-t_0)} \Rightarrow \dfrac{P-5}{P_0} = e^{r(t-t_0)} \Rightarrow \ln\dfrac{P-5}{P_0} = \ln e^{r(t-t_0)} \Rightarrow$

$\ln\dfrac{P-5}{P_0} = r(t - t_0) \Rightarrow \dfrac{\ln\frac{P-5}{P_0}}{r} = t - t_0 \Rightarrow \dfrac{\ln\frac{P-5}{P_0}}{r} + t_0 = t$

91. $\log 1 + 2\log 2 + 3\log 3 + 4\log 4 + 5\log 5 = \log 1 + \log 2^2 + \log 3^3 + \log 4^4 + \log 5^5 =$

$\log(1 \cdot 2^2 \cdot 3^3 \cdot 4^4 \cdot 5^5) = \log 86{,}400{,}000$

92. $\log_2(x + \sqrt{x^2 - 4}) + \log_2(x - \sqrt{x^2 - 4}) = 2 \Rightarrow \log_2((x + \sqrt{x^2 - 4})(x - \sqrt{x^2 - 4})) = 2 \Rightarrow$

$\log_2(x^2 - x^2 + 4) = 2 \Rightarrow \log_2 4 = 2 \Rightarrow \log_2 2^2 = 2 \Rightarrow 2 = 2;\ [2, \infty)$

## 5.6: Exponential and Logarithmic Equations

1. (a) The graphs appear to intersect near the point (2, 7.5). Thus, the solution is $x \approx 2$.

   (b) $f(x) = g(x) \Rightarrow e^x = 7.5 \Rightarrow \ln e^x = \ln 7.5 \Rightarrow x = \ln 7.5$ about 2.015

2. (a) The graphs appear to intersect near the point (0.7, 0.5). Thus, the solution is $x \approx 0.7$.

   (b) $f(x) = g(x) \Rightarrow 0.1(10^x) = 0.5 \Rightarrow 10^x = 5 \Rightarrow \log 10^x = \log 5 \Rightarrow x = \log 5$ about 0.699

3. (a) The graphs appear to intersect near the point (2, 2.5). Thus, the solution is $x \approx 2$.

   (b) $f(x) = g(x) \Rightarrow 10^{0.2x} = 2.5 \Rightarrow \log 10^{0.2x} = \log 2.5 \Rightarrow 0.2x = \log 2.5 \Rightarrow x = \dfrac{\log 2.5}{0.2}$ about 1.990

4. (a) The graphs appear to intersect near the point (–1, 2). Thus, the solution is $x \approx -1$.

   (b) $f(x) = g(x) \Rightarrow e^{-0.7x} = 2 \Rightarrow \ln e^{-0.7x} = \ln 2 \Rightarrow -0.7x = \ln 2 \Rightarrow x = \dfrac{\ln 2}{-0.7}$ about $-0.990$

5. $4e^x = 5 \Rightarrow e^x = \dfrac{5}{4} \Rightarrow \ln e^x = \ln\dfrac{5}{4} \Rightarrow x = \ln\dfrac{5}{4} \approx 0.2231$

6. $2e^{-x} = 8 \Rightarrow e^{-x} = 4 \Rightarrow \ln e^{-x} = \ln 4 \Rightarrow -x = \ln 4 \Rightarrow x = -\ln 4 \approx -1.386$

7. $2(10^x) + 5 = 45 \Rightarrow 2(10^x) = 40 \Rightarrow 10^x = 20 \Rightarrow \log 10^x = \log 20 \Rightarrow x = \log 20 \approx 1.301$

8. $100 - 5(10^x) = 7 \Rightarrow 5(10^x) = 93 \Rightarrow 10^x = \dfrac{93}{5} \Rightarrow \log 10^x = \log \dfrac{93}{5} \Rightarrow x = \log \dfrac{93}{5} \approx 1.270$

9. $2.5e^{-1.2x} = 1 \Rightarrow e^{-1.2x} = \dfrac{1}{2.5} \Rightarrow \ln e^{-1.2x} = \ln \dfrac{1}{2.5} \Rightarrow -1.2x = \ln \dfrac{1}{2.5} \Rightarrow x = \dfrac{\ln \frac{1}{2.5}}{-1.2} \approx 0.7636$

10. $9.5e^{0.005x} = 19 \Rightarrow e^{0.005x} = 2 \Rightarrow \ln e^{0.005x} = \ln 2 \Rightarrow 0.005x = \ln 2 \Rightarrow x = \dfrac{\ln 2}{0.005} \approx 138.6$

11. $1.2(0.9^x) = 0.6 \Rightarrow 0.9^x = 0.5 \Rightarrow \ln 0.9^x = \ln 0.5 \Rightarrow x \ln 0.9 = \ln 0.5 \Rightarrow x = \dfrac{\ln 0.5}{\ln 0.9} \approx 6.579$

12. $0.05(1.15^x) = 5 \Rightarrow 1.15^x = 100 \Rightarrow \log 1.15^x = \log 100 \Rightarrow x \log 1.15 = 2 \Rightarrow x = \dfrac{2}{\log 1.15} \approx 32.95$

13. $4(1.1^{x-1}) = 16 \Rightarrow 1.1^{x-1} = 4 \Rightarrow \ln 1.1^{x-1} = \ln 4 \Rightarrow (x - 1) \ln 1.1 = \ln 4 \Rightarrow x - 1 = \dfrac{\ln 4}{\ln 1.1} \Rightarrow$

$x = \dfrac{\ln 4}{\ln 1.1} + 1 \approx 15.55$

14. $3(2^{x-2}) = 99 \Rightarrow 2^{x-2} = 33 \Rightarrow \ln 2^{x-2} = \ln 33 \Rightarrow (x - 2) \ln 2 = \ln 33 \Rightarrow x - 2 = \dfrac{\ln 33}{\ln 2} \Rightarrow$

$x = \dfrac{\ln 33}{\ln 2} + 2 \approx 7.044$

15. $5(1.2)^{3x-2} + 94 = 100 \Rightarrow 5(1.2)^{3x-2} = 6 \Rightarrow (1.2)^{3x-2} = 1.2 \Rightarrow \ln 1.2^{3x-2} = \ln 1.2 \Rightarrow$

$(3x - 2) \ln 1.2 = \ln 1.2 \Rightarrow 3x - 2 = \dfrac{\ln 1.2}{\ln 1.2} \Rightarrow 3x - 2 = 1 \Rightarrow 3x = 3 \Rightarrow x = 1$

16. $1.4(2)^{x+3} = 2.8 \Rightarrow 2^{x+3} = \dfrac{2.8}{1.4} \Rightarrow 2^{x+3} = 2 \Rightarrow \ln 2^{x+3} = \ln 2 \Rightarrow$

$(x + 3) \ln 2 = \ln 2 \Rightarrow x + 3 = \dfrac{\ln 2}{\ln 2} \Rightarrow x + 3 = 1 \Rightarrow x = -2$

17. $5^{3x} = 5^{1-2x} \Rightarrow \log_5 5^{3x} = \log_5 5^{1-2x} \Rightarrow 3x = 1 - 2x \Rightarrow 5x = 1 \Rightarrow x = \dfrac{1}{5}$

18. $7^{x^2} = 7^{4x-3} \Rightarrow \log_7 7^{x^2} = \log_7 7^{4x-3} \Rightarrow x^2 = 4x - 3 \Rightarrow x^2 - 4x + 3 = 0 \Rightarrow (x - 3)(x - 1) = 0;$

$x = 1, 3$

19. $10^{x^2} = 10^{3x-2} \Rightarrow \log 10^{x^2} = \log 10^{3x-2} \Rightarrow x^2 = 3x - 2 \Rightarrow x^2 - 3x + 2 = 0 \Rightarrow$

$(x - 1)(x - 2) = 0 \Rightarrow x = 1$ or $x = 2$

20. $e^{2x} = e^{5x-3} \Rightarrow \ln e^{2x} = \ln e^{5x-3} \Rightarrow 2x = 5x - 3 \Rightarrow 3x = 3 \Rightarrow x = 1$

21. No solution since no power of $\dfrac{1}{5}$ will result in a negative value.

22. No solution since no power of 2 will result in a negative value.

23. $\left(\dfrac{2}{5}\right)^{x-2} = \dfrac{1}{3} \Rightarrow \log\left(\dfrac{2}{5}\right)^{x-2} = \log\left(\dfrac{1}{3}\right) \Rightarrow (x - 2)\log\left(\dfrac{2}{5}\right) = \log\left(\dfrac{1}{3}\right) \Rightarrow x - 2 = \dfrac{\log\left(\frac{1}{3}\right)}{\log\left(\frac{2}{5}\right)} \Rightarrow$

$x = 2 + \dfrac{\log\left(\frac{1}{3}\right)}{\log\left(\frac{2}{5}\right)} \approx 3.199$

24. $\left(\dfrac{3}{2}\right)^{x+1} = \dfrac{7}{3} \Rightarrow \log\left(\dfrac{3}{2}\right)^{x+1} = \log\left(\dfrac{7}{3}\right) \Rightarrow (x + 1)\log\left(\dfrac{3}{2}\right) = \log\left(\dfrac{7}{3}\right) \Rightarrow x + 1 = \dfrac{\log\left(\frac{7}{3}\right)}{\log\left(\frac{3}{2}\right)} \Rightarrow$

$x = \dfrac{\log\left(\frac{7}{3}\right)}{\log\left(\frac{3}{2}\right)} - 1 \approx 1.090$

25. $4^{x-1} = 3^{2x} \Rightarrow \log 4^{x-1} = \log 3^{2x} \Rightarrow (x-1)\log 4 = 2x \log 3 \Rightarrow x \log 4 - \log 4 = 2x \log 3 \Rightarrow$

$x \log 4 - 2x \log 3 = \log 4 \Rightarrow x(\log 4 - 2\log 3) = \log 4 \Rightarrow x = \dfrac{\log 4}{\log 4 - 2\log 3} \approx -1.710$

26. $3^{1-2x} = e^{0.5x} \Rightarrow \ln 3^{1-2x} = \ln e^{0.5x} \Rightarrow (1-2x)\ln 3 = 0.5x \Rightarrow \ln 3 - 2x \ln 3 = 0.5x \Rightarrow$

$\ln 3 = 0.5x + 2x \ln 3 = \ln 3 \Rightarrow x(0.5 + 2\ln 3) \Rightarrow x = \dfrac{\ln 3}{0.5 + 2\ln 3} \approx 0.407$

27. $e^{x-3} = 2^{3x} \Rightarrow \ln e^{x-3} = \ln 2^{3x} \Rightarrow x - 3 = 3x \ln 2 \Rightarrow -3 = -x + 3x \ln 2 \Rightarrow$

$3 = x - 3x \ln 2 \Rightarrow 3 = x(1 - 3\ln 2) \Rightarrow x = \dfrac{3}{1 - 3\ln 2} \Rightarrow x = \dfrac{3}{1 - \ln 8} \Rightarrow x \approx -2.779$

28. $6^{x+1} = 4^{2x-1} \Rightarrow \log 6^{x+1} = \log 4^{2x-1} \Rightarrow (x+1)\log 6 = (2x-1)\log 4 \Rightarrow$

$x \log 6 + \log 6 = 2x \log 4 - \log 4 \Rightarrow x \log 6 - 2x \log 4 = -\log 4 - \log 6 \Rightarrow$

$x(\log 6 - 2\log 4) = -\log 4 - \log 6 \Rightarrow x = \dfrac{-\log 4 - \log 6}{\log 6 - 2\log 4} \Rightarrow x \approx 3.240$

29. $3(1.4)^x - 4 = 60 \Rightarrow 3(1.4)^x = 64 \Rightarrow 1.4^x = \dfrac{64}{3} \Rightarrow \log 1.4^x = \log \dfrac{64}{3} \Rightarrow x \log 1.4 = \log \dfrac{64}{3} \Rightarrow$

$x = \dfrac{\log \frac{64}{3}}{\log 1.4} \approx 9.095$

30. $2(1.05)^x + 3 = 10 \Rightarrow 2(1.05)^x = 7 \Rightarrow 1.05^x = \dfrac{7}{2} \Rightarrow \log 1.05^x = \log \dfrac{7}{2} \Rightarrow x \log 1.05 = \log \dfrac{7}{2} \Rightarrow$

$x = \dfrac{\log \frac{7}{2}}{\log 1.05} \approx 25.677$

31. $5(1.015)^{x-1980} = 8 \Rightarrow 1.015^{x-1980} = \dfrac{8}{5} \Rightarrow \log 1.015^{x-1980} = \log \dfrac{8}{5} \Rightarrow (x - 1980)\log 1.015 = \log \dfrac{8}{5} \Rightarrow$

$x \log 1.015 - 1980 \log 1.015 = \log \dfrac{8}{5} \Rightarrow x \log 1.015 = \log \dfrac{8}{5} + 1980 \log 1.015 \Rightarrow$

$x = \dfrac{\log \frac{8}{5} + 1980 \log 1.015}{\log 1.015} = \dfrac{\log \frac{8}{5}}{\log 1.015} + 1980 \approx 2012$

32. $30 - 3(0.75)^{x-1} = 29 \Rightarrow 3(0.75)^{x-1} = 1 \Rightarrow 0.75^{x-1} = \dfrac{1}{3} \Rightarrow \log 0.75^{x-1} = \log \dfrac{1}{3} \Rightarrow$

$(x-1)\log 0.75 = \log \dfrac{1}{3} \Rightarrow x \log 0.75 - \log 0.75 = \log \dfrac{1}{3} \Rightarrow x \log 0.75 = \log \dfrac{1}{3} + \log 0.75 \Rightarrow$

$x = \dfrac{\log \frac{1}{3} + \log 0.75}{\log 0.75} = \dfrac{\log \frac{1}{3}}{\log 0.75} + 1 \approx 4.819$

33. $4\left(\dfrac{3}{4}\right)^{x+1} = \dfrac{1}{81}\left(\dfrac{3}{2}\right)^{5+x} \Rightarrow 324\left(\dfrac{3}{4}\right)^{x+1} = \left(\dfrac{3}{2}\right)^{5+x} \Rightarrow \ln\left[324\left(\dfrac{3}{4}\right)^{x+1}\right] = \ln\left(\dfrac{3}{2}\right)^{5+x} \Rightarrow$

$\ln 324 + \ln\left(\dfrac{3}{4}\right)^{x+1} = \ln\left(\dfrac{3}{2}\right)^{5+x} \Rightarrow \ln 324 + (x+1)\ln\dfrac{3}{4} = (5+x)\ln\dfrac{3}{2} \Rightarrow$

$\ln 324 + x\ln\dfrac{3}{4} + \ln\dfrac{3}{4} = 5\ln\dfrac{3}{2} + x\ln\dfrac{3}{2} \Rightarrow x\ln\dfrac{3}{4} - x\ln\dfrac{3}{2} = 5\ln\dfrac{3}{2} - \ln 324 - \ln\dfrac{3}{4} \Rightarrow$

$x\left(\ln\dfrac{3}{4} - \ln\dfrac{3}{2}\right) = 5\ln\dfrac{3}{2} - \ln 324 - \ln\dfrac{3}{4} \Rightarrow x = \dfrac{5\ln\frac{3}{2} - \ln 324 - \ln\frac{3}{4}}{\ln\frac{3}{4} - \ln\frac{3}{2}} \Rightarrow x = 5$

34. $5\left(\frac{2}{5}\right)^{x+1} = \frac{1}{125}\left(\frac{4}{5}\right)^{x-3} \Rightarrow 625\left(\frac{2}{5}\right)^{x+1} = \left(\frac{4}{5}\right)^{x-3} \Rightarrow \ln\left[625\left(\frac{2}{5}\right)^{x+1}\right] = \ln\left(\frac{4}{5}\right)^{x-3} \Rightarrow$

$\ln 625 + \ln\left(\frac{2}{5}\right)^{x+1} = \ln\left(\frac{4}{5}\right)^{x-3} \Rightarrow \ln 625 + (x+1)\ln\frac{2}{5} = (x-3)\ln\frac{4}{5} \Rightarrow$

$\ln 625 + x\ln\frac{2}{5} + \ln\frac{2}{5} = x\ln\frac{4}{5} - 3\ln\frac{4}{5} \Rightarrow x\ln\frac{2}{5} - x\ln\frac{4}{5} = -\ln 625 - \ln\frac{2}{5} - 3\ln\frac{4}{5} \Rightarrow$

$x\left(\ln\frac{2}{5} - \ln\frac{4}{5}\right) = -\left(\ln 625 + \ln\frac{2}{5} + 3\ln\frac{4}{5}\right) \Rightarrow x = \frac{-(\ln 625 + \ln\frac{2}{5} + 3\ln\frac{4}{5})}{\ln\frac{2}{5} - \ln\frac{4}{5}} \Rightarrow x = 7$

35. $3\log x = 2 \Rightarrow \log x = \frac{2}{3} \Rightarrow 10^{\log x} = 10^{2/3} \Rightarrow x = 10^{2/3} \approx 4.642$

36. $5\ln x = 10 \Rightarrow \ln x = 2 \Rightarrow e^{\ln x} = e^2 \Rightarrow x = e^2 \approx 7.389$

37. $\ln 2x = 5 \Rightarrow e^{\ln 2x} = e^5 \Rightarrow 2x = e^5 \Rightarrow x = \frac{e^5}{2} \approx 74.207$

38. $\ln 4x = 1.5 \Rightarrow e^{\ln 4x} = e^{1.5} \Rightarrow 4x = e^{1.5} \Rightarrow x = \frac{e^{1.5}}{4} \approx 1.120$

39. $\log 2x^2 = 2 \Rightarrow 10^{\log 2x^2} = 10^2 \Rightarrow 2x^2 = 100 \Rightarrow x^2 = 50 \Rightarrow x = \pm\sqrt{50} \approx \pm 7.071$

40. $\log(2-x) = 0.5 \Rightarrow 10^{\log(2-x)} = 10^{0.5} \Rightarrow 2 - x = \sqrt{10} \Rightarrow x = 2 - \sqrt{10} \approx -1.162$

41. $\log_2(3x-2) = 4 \Rightarrow 2^{\log_2(3x-2)} = 2^4 \Rightarrow 3x - 2 = 16 \Rightarrow 3x = 18 \Rightarrow x = 6$

42. $\log_3(1-x) = 1 \Rightarrow 3^{\log_3(1-x)} = 3^1 \Rightarrow 1 - x = 3 \Rightarrow -x = 2 \Rightarrow x = -2$

43. $\log_5(8-3x) = 3 \Rightarrow 5^{\log_5(8-3x)} = 5^3 \Rightarrow 8 - 3x = 125 \Rightarrow -3x = 117 \Rightarrow x = -39$

44. $\log_6(2x+4) = 2 \Rightarrow 6^{\log_6(2x+4)} = 6^2 \Rightarrow 2x + 4 = 36 \Rightarrow 2x = 32 \Rightarrow x = 16$

45. $160 + 10\log x = 50 \Rightarrow 10\log x = -110 \Rightarrow \log x = -11 \Rightarrow 10^{\log x} = 10^{-11} \Rightarrow x = 10^{-11}$

46. $160 + 10\log x = 120 \Rightarrow 10\log x = -40 \Rightarrow \log x = -4 \Rightarrow 10^{\log x} = 10^{-4} \Rightarrow x = 10^{-4}$

47. $\ln x + \ln x^2 = 3 \Rightarrow \ln x + 2\ln x = 3 \Rightarrow 3\ln x = 3 \Rightarrow \ln x = 1 \Rightarrow e^{\ln x} = e^1 \Rightarrow x = e \approx 2.718$

48. $\log x^5 = 4 + 3\log x \Rightarrow 5\log x = 4 + 3\log x \Rightarrow 2\log x = 4 \Rightarrow \log x = 2 \Rightarrow 10^{\log x} = 10^2 \Rightarrow$

$x = 100$

49. $2\log_2 x = 4.2 \Rightarrow \log_2 x = 2.1 \Rightarrow 2^{\log_2 x} = 2^{2.1} \Rightarrow x = 2^{2.1} \approx 4.287$

50. $3\log_2(3x) = 1 \Rightarrow \log_2(3x) = \frac{1}{3} \Rightarrow 2^{\log_2(3x)} = 2^{1/3} \Rightarrow 3x = \sqrt[3]{2} \Rightarrow x = \frac{\sqrt[3]{2}}{3} \approx 0.42$

51. $\log x + \log 2x = 2 \Rightarrow \log(x \cdot 2x) = 2 \Rightarrow \log 2x^2 = 2 \Rightarrow 10^{\log 2x^2} = 10^2 \Rightarrow 2x^2 = 100 \Rightarrow$

$x^2 = 50 \Rightarrow x = \pm\sqrt{50}$. When $x = -\sqrt{50} < 0$, $\log x$ is undefined. Therefore, the only solution is

$x = \sqrt{50} \approx 7.071$.

52. $\ln 2x + \ln 3x = \ln 6 \Rightarrow \ln(2x \cdot 3x) = \ln 6 \Rightarrow \ln 6x^2 = \ln 6 \Rightarrow e^{\ln 6x^2} = e^{\ln 6} \Rightarrow 6x^2 = 6 \Rightarrow$

$x^2 = 1 \Rightarrow x = \pm 1$. When $x = -1 < 0$, both $\log 2x$ and $\log 3x$ are undefined. Therefore, the only solution is

$x = 1$.

53. $\log(2-3x) = 3 \Rightarrow 10^3 = 2 - 3x \Rightarrow 1000 = 2 - 3x \Rightarrow 998 = -3x \Rightarrow x = -\frac{998}{3}$

54. $\log(x^2+1) = 2 \Rightarrow 10^2 = x^2 + 1 \Rightarrow 100 = x^2 + 1 \Rightarrow x^2 = 99 \Rightarrow x = \pm\sqrt{99} = \pm 3\sqrt{11} \approx 9.950$

55. $\ln(x) + \ln(3x - 1) = \ln(10) \Rightarrow \ln(x(3x - 1)) = \ln(10) \Rightarrow \ln(3x^2 - x) = \ln(10) \Rightarrow$
$3x^2 - x = 10 \Rightarrow 3x^2 - x - 10 = 0 \Rightarrow (3x + 5)(x - 2) = 0 \Rightarrow 3x + 5 = 0$ or $x - 2 = 0 \Rightarrow$
$x = -\frac{5}{3}$ or $x = 2$. When $x = -\frac{5}{3}$, both $\ln(3x - 1)$ and $\ln(x)$ are undefined, therefore the only solution is $x = 2$.

56. $\log x + \log(2x + 5) = \log 7 \Rightarrow \log(x(2x + 5)) = \log 7 \Rightarrow \log(2x^2 + 5x) = \log 7 \Rightarrow$
$10^{\log(2x^2+5x)} = 10^{\log 7} \Rightarrow 2x^2 + 5x = 7 \Rightarrow 2x^2 + 5x - 7 = 0 \Rightarrow (2x + 7)(x - 1) = 0 \Rightarrow$
$x = -\frac{7}{2}$ or $x = 1$. When $x = -\frac{7}{2}$ both $\log x$ and $\log(2x + 5)$ are undefined. The only solution is $x = 1$.

57. $2\ln x = \ln(2x + 1) \Rightarrow \ln x^2 = \ln(2x + 1) \Rightarrow e^{\ln x^2} = e^{\ln(2x+1)} \Rightarrow x^2 = 2x + 1 \Rightarrow$
$x^2 - 2x - 1 = 0 \Rightarrow x = \dfrac{2 \pm \sqrt{2^2 - 4(1)(-1)}}{2(1)} = \dfrac{2 \pm \sqrt{8}}{2} = \dfrac{2 \pm 2\sqrt{2}}{2} = 1 \pm \sqrt{2} \Rightarrow$
$x = 1 + \sqrt{2}$ or $x = 1 - \sqrt{2}$.
When $x = 1 - \sqrt{2} \approx -0.414$, $\ln x$ is undefined. The only solution is $x = 1 + \sqrt{2}$.

58. $\log(x^2 + 3) = 2\log(x + 1) \Rightarrow \log(x^2 + 3) = \log(x + 1)^2 \Rightarrow 10^{\log(x^2+3)} = 10^{\log(x+1)^2} \Rightarrow$
$x^2 + 3 = (x + 1)^2 \Rightarrow x^2 + 3 = x^2 + 2x + 1 \Rightarrow 2x = 2 \Rightarrow x = 1$

59. $\log(x + 1) + \log(x - 1) = \log 3 \Rightarrow \log[(x + 1)(x - 1)] = \log 3 \Rightarrow \log(x^2 - 1) = \log 3 \Rightarrow$
$10^{\log(x^2-1)} = 10^{\log 3} \Rightarrow x^2 - 1 = 3 \Rightarrow x^2 = 4 \Rightarrow x = -2$ or $x = 2$
When $x = -2$ both $\log(x - 1)$ and $\log(x + 1)$ are undefined. The only solution is $x = 2$.

60. $\ln(x^2 - 4) - \ln(x + 2) = \ln(3 - x) \Rightarrow \ln\dfrac{(x + 2)(x - 2)}{x + 2} = \ln(3 - x) \Rightarrow$
$\ln(x - 2) = \ln(3 - x) \Rightarrow e^{\ln(x-2)} = e^{\ln(3-x)} \Rightarrow x - 2 = 3 - x \Rightarrow 2x = 5 \Rightarrow x = \frac{5}{2}$

61. $\log_2 2x = 4 - \log_2(x + 2) \Rightarrow \log_2 2x + \log_2(x + 2) = 4 \Rightarrow \log_2[2x(x + 2)] = 4 \Rightarrow$
$\log_2(2x^2 + 4x) = 4 \Rightarrow 2^{\log_2(2x^2+4x)} = 4 \Rightarrow 2x^2 + 4x - 16 = 0 \Rightarrow 2(x^2 + 2x - 8) = 0 \Rightarrow$
$2(x + 4)(x - 2) = 0 \Rightarrow x = -4, x = 2$, since we cannot take the log of a negative number, $x = 2$.

62. $\log_3 x + \log_3(x + 2) = \log_3 24 \Rightarrow \log_3(x)(x + 2) = \log_3 24 \Rightarrow \log_3(x^2 + 2x) = \log_3 24 \Rightarrow$
$3^{\log_3(x^2+2x)} = 3^{\log_3 24} \Rightarrow x^2 + 2x = 24 \Rightarrow x^2 + 2x - 24 = 0 \Rightarrow (x + 6)(x - 4) = 0,$
since we cannot take the log of a negative number, $x = 4$.

63. $\log_5(x + 1) + \log_5(x - 1) = \log_5 15 \Rightarrow \log_5(x + 1)(x - 1) = \log_5 15 \Rightarrow$
$\log_5(x^2 - 1) = \log_5 15 \Rightarrow 5^{\log_5(x^2-1)} = 5^{\log_5 15} \Rightarrow x^2 - 1 = 15 \Rightarrow x^2 - 16 = 0 \Rightarrow$
$(x + 4)(x - 4) = 0$, since we cannot take the log of a negative number, $x = 4$.

64. $\log_7 4x - \log_7(x + 3) = \log_7 x \Rightarrow \log_7\dfrac{4x}{x + 3} = \log_7 x \Rightarrow \dfrac{4x}{x + 3} = x \Rightarrow x(x + 3) = 4x \Rightarrow$
$x^2 + 3x = 4x \Rightarrow x^2 - x = 0 \Rightarrow x(x - 1) = 0$, since we cannot take the log of zero, $x = 1$.

65. Graph $Y_1 = 2X + e$^(X) and $Y_2 = 2$ as shown in Figure 65.
The graphs intersect near the point (0.31, 2), so the solution to $2x + e^x = 2$ is $x \approx 0.31$.

66. Graph $Y_1 = Xe$^(X) $- 1$ as shown in Figure 66.
The graph intersects the $x$-axis near the point (0.57, 0), so the solution to $xe^x - 1 = 0$ is $x \approx 0.57$.

[–5, 5, 1] by [–5, 5, 1]

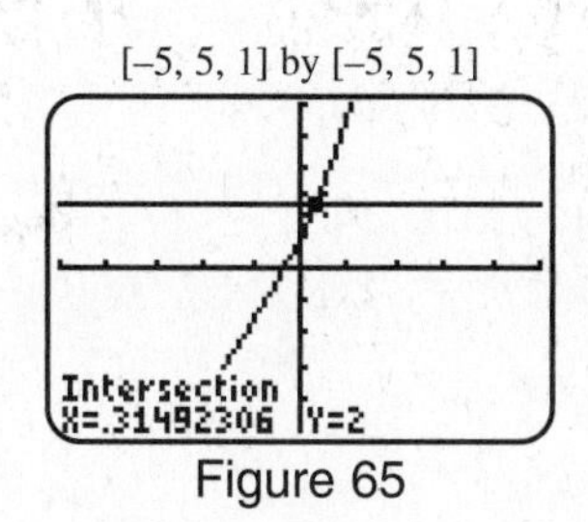

Figure 65

[–5, 5, 1] by [–5, 5, 1]

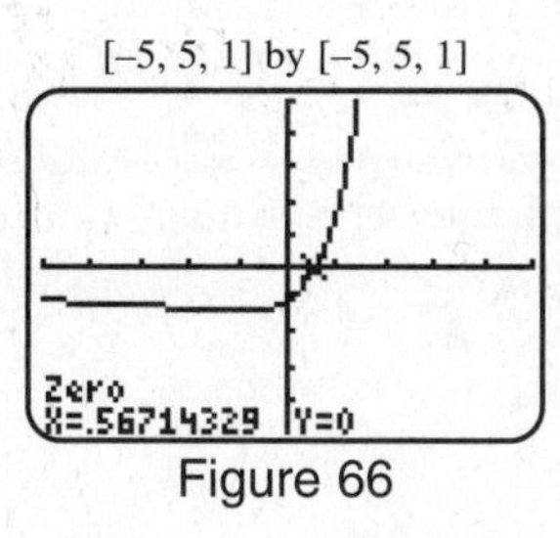

Figure 66

[–5, 5, 1] by [–5, 5, 1]

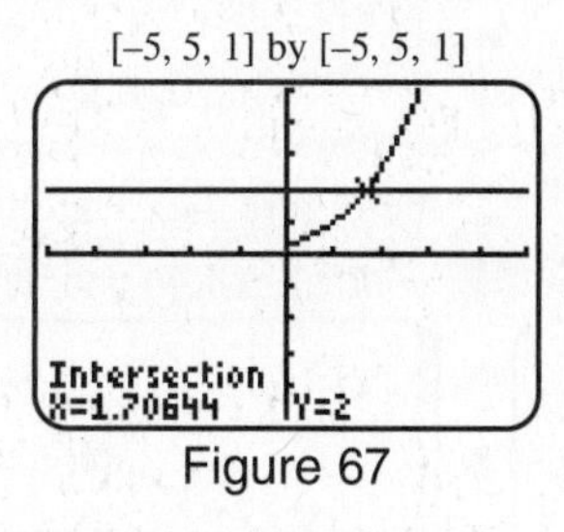

Figure 67

[–5, 5, 1] by [–5, 5, 1]

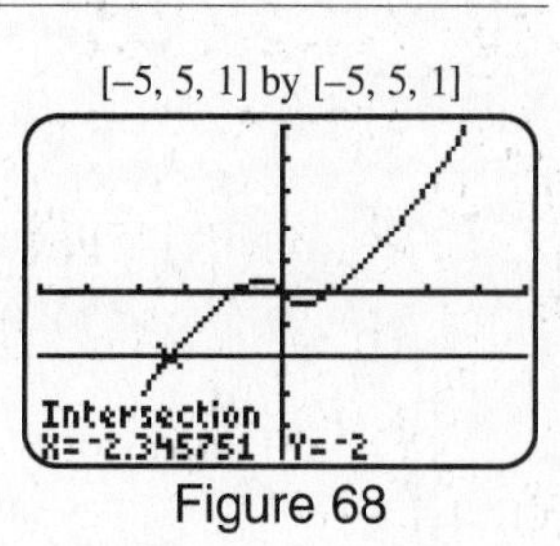

Figure 68

67. Graph $Y_1 = X\text{^}2 + X \ln(X)$ and $Y_2 = 2$ as shown in Figure 67.

The graphs intersect near the point (1.71, 2), so the solution to $x^2 - x \ln x = 2$ is $x \approx 1.71$.

68. Graph $Y_1 = X \ln(\text{abs}(X))$ and $Y_2 = -2$ as shown in Figure 68.

The graphs intersect near the point (–2.35, –2), so the solution to $x \ln|x| = -2$ is $x \approx -2.35$.

69. Graph $Y_1 = Xe\text{^}(-X) + \ln(X)$ and $Y_2 = 1$ as shown in Figure 69.

The graphs intersect near the point (2.10, 2), so the solution to $xe^{-x} + \ln x = 1$ is $x \approx 2.10$.

70. Graph $Y_1 = 2\text{^}(X - 2)$ and $Y_2 = \log(X\text{^}4)$ as shown in Figures 70a, 70b and 70c.

The graphs intersect near the points (–1.07, 0.12), (1.50, 0.71), and (2.88, 1.84), so the solutions to $2^{x-2} = \log x^4$ are $x \approx -1.07$, $x \approx 1.50$, or $x \approx 2.88$.

[–5, 5, 1] by [–5, 5, 1]

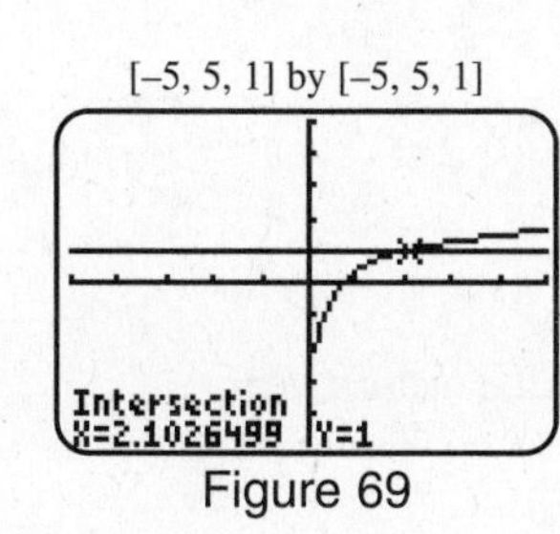

Figure 69

[–2, 5, 1] by [–3, 3, 1]

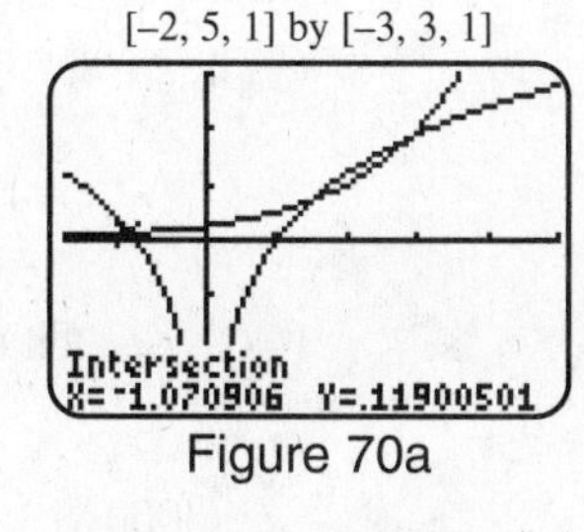

Figure 70a

[–2, 5, 1] by [–3, 3, 1]

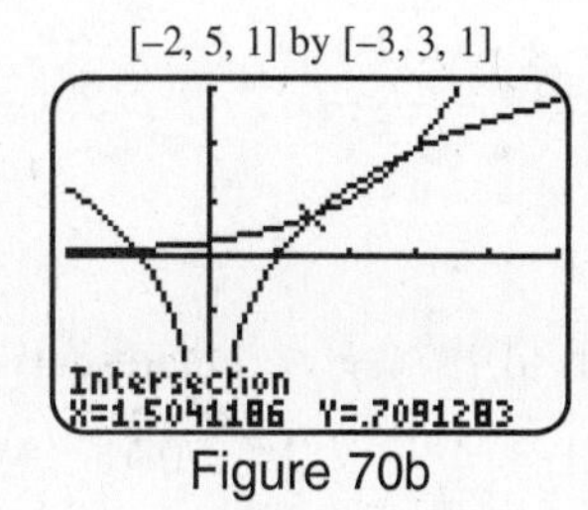

Figure 70b

[–2, 5, 1] by [–3, 3, 1]

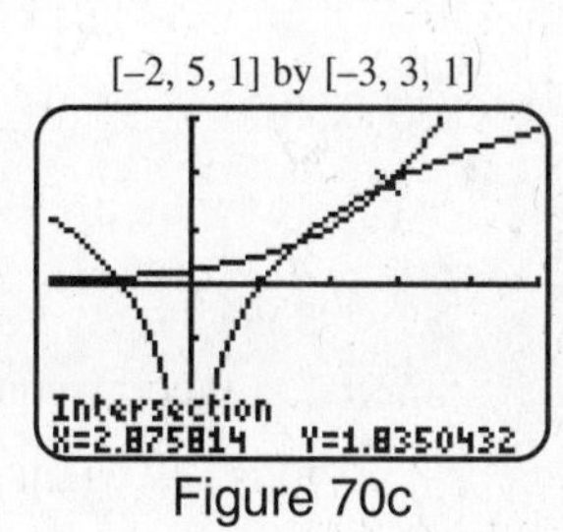

Figure 70c

71. $4 = 3(1.017)^{x-1960} \Rightarrow \frac{4}{3} = (1.017)^{x-1960} \Rightarrow \ln\left(\frac{4}{3}\right) = \ln(1.017)^{x-1960} \Rightarrow$

$\ln\left(\frac{4}{3}\right) = (x - 1960)\ln(1.017) \Rightarrow \frac{\ln\left(\frac{4}{3}\right)}{\ln(1.017)} = x - 1960 \Rightarrow x = 1960 + \frac{\ln\left(\frac{4}{3}\right)}{\ln(1.017)} \Rightarrow x = 1977$

72. (a) $P(x) = 3.7(1.035)^{x-1990}$

(b) $P(x) = 3.7(1.035)^{2005-1990} \Rightarrow P(x) = 3.7(1.035)^{15} \Rightarrow P(x) = 6.2$ million

73. $250 = 1000e^{-0.12x} \Rightarrow 0.25 = e^{-0.12x} \Rightarrow \ln(0.25) = -0.12x \Rightarrow x = \frac{\ln(0.25)}{-0.12} \approx 11.55$ ft. Graph

$Y_1 = 250$ and $Y_2 = 1000e^{-0.12x}$, See Figure 73. The graph intersects at approximately (11.55, 250).

[0, 15, 1] by [0, 1000, 100]

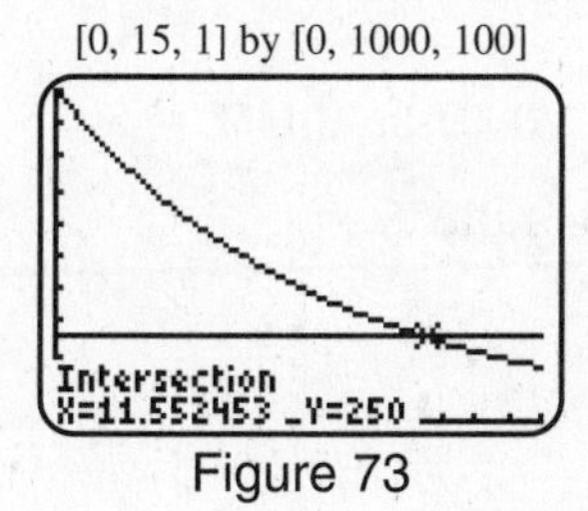

Figure 73

74. $5 = 500e^{-0.2x} \Rightarrow 0.01 = e^{-0.2x} \Rightarrow \ln(0.01) = -0.2x \Rightarrow x = \dfrac{\ln(0.01)}{-0.2} \approx 23.03$ ft. Graph

$Y_1 = 5$ and $Y_2 = 500e^{-0.2x}$, see Figure 74. The graph intersects at approximately (23.03, 5).

[0, 30, 5] by [0, 50, 5]

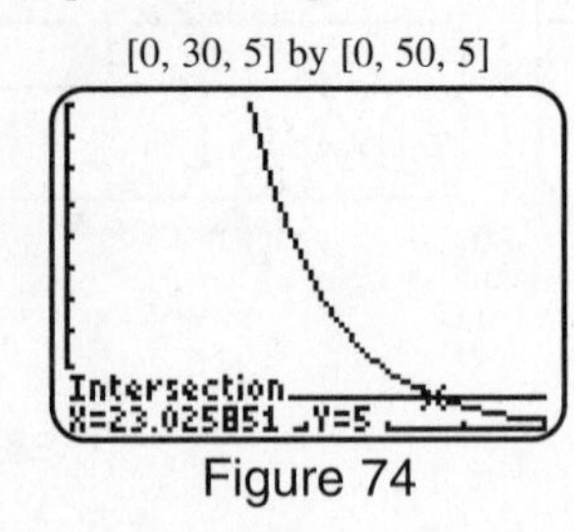


Figure 74

[0, 10, 1] by [0, 150, 10]

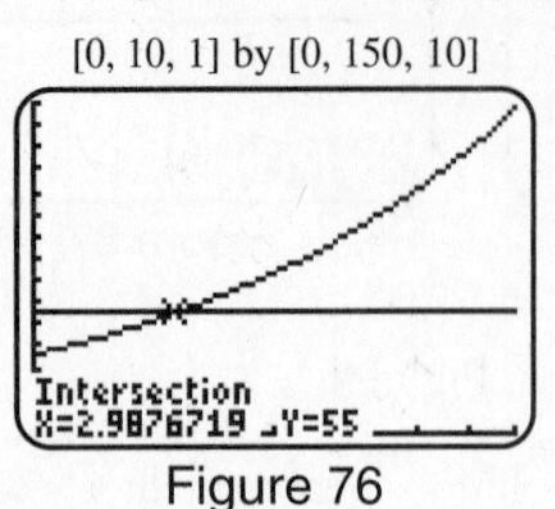


Figure 76

75. $0.5e^{0.014t} = 25 \Rightarrow e^{0.014t} = 50 \Rightarrow 0.014t = \ln 50 \Rightarrow t = \dfrac{\ln 50}{0.014} \approx 279.4$ min

76. (a) We must solve the equation $f(x) = 55$.

$$36.2\,e^{0.14x} = 55 \Rightarrow e^{0.14x} = \frac{55}{36.2} \Rightarrow \ln e^{0.14x} = \ln\frac{55}{36.2} \Rightarrow 0.14x = \ln\frac{55}{36.2} \Rightarrow x = \frac{\ln\frac{55}{36.2}}{0.14} \approx 2.99$$

Since $x = 0$ corresponds to 1987, $x \approx 3$ represents $1987 + 3 = 1990$, rounded to the nearest year.

(b) Graph $Y_1 = 36.2e\text{^}(0.14X)$ and $Y_2 = 55$ as shown in Figure 76. The graphs intersect near (3, 55).

Therefore, Christmas credit card spending was approximately \$55 billion in 1990.

77. We must solve the equation $f(x) = 95$.

$$230(0.881)^x = 95 \Rightarrow 0.881^x = \frac{95}{230} \Rightarrow \log 0.881^x = \log\frac{95}{230} \Rightarrow x\log 0.881 = \log\frac{95}{230}$$

$$x = \frac{\log\frac{95}{230}}{\log 0.881} \approx 7$$

Since $x = 0$ corresponds to 1974, $x \approx 7$ represents $1974 + 7 = 1981$, rounded to the nearest year.

78. (a) $F(2005) = 2340(1.124)^{2005-1988} \approx 17070$

(b) $30{,}000 = 2340(1.124)^{x-1988} \Rightarrow \dfrac{30{,}000}{2340} = 1.124^{x-1988} \Rightarrow \ln\left(\dfrac{30{,}000}{2340}\right) = \ln(1.124)^{x-1988} \Rightarrow$

$$\ln\left(\frac{30{,}000}{2340}\right) = (x - 1988)(\ln(1.124)) \Rightarrow \frac{\ln\left(\frac{30{,}000}{2340}\right)}{\ln(1.124)} = x - 1998 \Rightarrow$$

$$x = \frac{\ln\left(\frac{30{,}000}{2340}\right)}{\ln(1.124)} + 1998 \approx 2009.82 \Rightarrow 2010$$

79. (a) $P(x) = Ca^{x-2000} \Rightarrow P(2000) = Ca^{2000-2000} \Rightarrow 1 - Ca^0 \Rightarrow C = 1$, so $P(x) = a^{x-2000}$

$P(2025) = a^{2025-2000} \Rightarrow 1.4 = a^{25} \Rightarrow a = 1.4^{1/25} \approx 1.01355$

(b) $P(x) = (1.01355)^{x-2000} \Rightarrow P(2010) = (1.01355)^{10} \approx 1.144$;

in 2010 the population if India will be about1.14 billion.

(c) $P(x) = 1.5 \Rightarrow 1.01355^{x-2000} = 1.5 \Rightarrow \ln 1.01355^{x-2000} = \ln 1.5 \Rightarrow (x - 2000)\ln 1.01355 = \ln 1.5 \Rightarrow$

$x\ln 1.01355 - 2000\ln 1.01355 = \ln 1.5 \Rightarrow x\ln 1.01355 = \ln 1.5 + 2000\ln 1.01355 \Rightarrow$

$$x = \frac{\ln 1.5 + 2000\ln 1.01355}{\ln 1.01355} = \frac{\ln 1.5}{\ln 1.01355} + 2000 \approx 2030.13;$$

India's population might reach 1.5 billion in 2030.

80. (a) $P(x) = Ca^{x-2007} \Rightarrow P(2007) = Ca^{2007-2007} \Rightarrow 164 = Ca^0 \Rightarrow C = 164$, so $P(x) = 164a^{x-2007}$

$$P(2025) = 164a^{2025-2007} \Rightarrow 250 = 164a^{18} \Rightarrow \left(\frac{250}{164}\right) = a^{18} \Rightarrow a = \left(\frac{250}{164}\right)^{1/18} \approx 1.0237$$

(b) $P(2015) = 164(1.0237)^{2015-2007} \approx 197.8$ million. The predicted value is low by about 6 million.

(c) $212 = 164(1.0237)^{x-2007} \Rightarrow \frac{212}{164} = (1.0237)^{x-2007} \Rightarrow \ln\left(\frac{212}{164}\right) = \ln(1.0237)^{x-2007} \Rightarrow$

$$\ln\left(\frac{212}{164}\right) = (x-2007)\ln(1.0237) \Rightarrow \frac{\ln\left(\frac{212}{164}\right)}{\ln(1.0237)} = x - 2007 \Rightarrow$$

$$x = 2007 + \frac{\ln\left(\frac{212}{164}\right)}{\ln(1.0237)} \approx 2017.96 \Rightarrow 2018$$

81. Using the formula from the example, let $T(x) = 140$.

$$60(1.066)^{x-1999} = 140 \Rightarrow 1.0661^{x-1999} = \frac{7}{3} \Rightarrow \ln 1.066^{x-1999} = \ln\frac{7}{3} \Rightarrow (x-1999)\ln 1.066 = \ln\frac{7}{3}$$

$$x - 1999 = \frac{\ln(7/3)}{\ln 1.066} \Rightarrow x = \frac{\ln(7/3)}{\ln 1.066} + 1999 \approx 2012.3$$

The number of individuals waiting for organ transplants may reach 140,000 in about 2012.

82. (a) Since $y = 131$ when $x = 1989$ we may solve for $C$ using the function $f(x) = Ca^{(x-1989)}$.

$$131 = Ca^{(1989-1989)} \Rightarrow 131 = Ca^0 \Rightarrow 131 = C(1) \Rightarrow C = 131$$

Since $y = 34$ when $x = 1995$ we may solve for $a$ using the function $f(x) = 131a^{(x-1989)}$.

$$34 = 134a^{(1995-1989)} \Rightarrow 34 = 131a^6 \Rightarrow \frac{34}{131} = a^6 \Rightarrow a = \left(\frac{34}{131}\right)^{1/6} \Rightarrow a \approx 0.799$$

Therefore, $C = 131$ and $a \approx 0.799$. ***Answers may vary slightly.***

(b) Graph $Y_1 = 131(0.799)$^(X − 1989) together with the data points as shown in Figure 82.

[1988, 1996, 1] by [0, 150, 25]

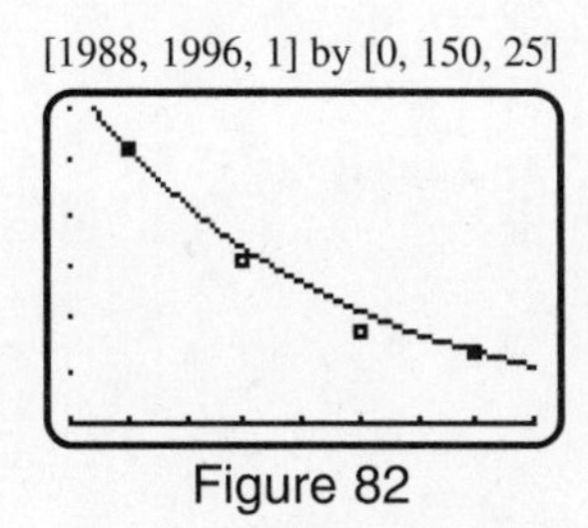

Figure 82

[0, 1.5, 0.5] by [0, 225, 25]

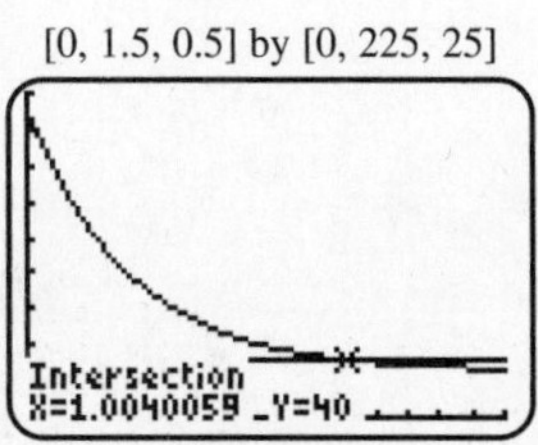


Figure 83

83. (a) $T_0 = 32$, $D = 212 - 32 \Rightarrow D = 180$. Solving for $a$ use $70 = 32 + 180a^{1/2} \Rightarrow 38 = 180a^{1/2} \Rightarrow$

$$\frac{38}{180} = a^{1/2} \Rightarrow a = 0.045$$

(b) $T(t) = 32 + 180(0.045)^t \Rightarrow T\left(\frac{1}{6}\right) = 32 + 180(0.045)^{1/6} \Rightarrow T\left(\frac{1}{6}\right) \approx 139°\text{F}$

(c) $40 = 32 + 180(0.045)^t \Rightarrow 8 = 180(0.045)^t \Rightarrow \frac{8}{180} = 0.045^t \Rightarrow \log\frac{8}{180} = \log 0.045^t \Rightarrow$

$$\log\frac{8}{180} = t\log 0.045 \Rightarrow t = \frac{\log\frac{8}{180}}{\log 0.045} \Rightarrow t \approx 1$$

Graph $Y_1 = 32 + 180(0.045)^t$ and $Y_2 = 40$. The lines intersect at $t \approx 1$. See Figure 83.

84. (a) $T_0 = 75, D = 35 - 75 \Rightarrow D = -40$. Solving for $a$ use $45 = 75 - 40a^1 \Rightarrow -30 = -40a^1 \Rightarrow$

$a = \frac{3}{4} \Rightarrow a = 0.75$

(b) $T(3) = 75 - 40(0.75)^3 \Rightarrow T(3) \approx 58°\text{F}$

(c) $60 = 75 - 40(0.75)^t \Rightarrow -15 = -40(0.75)^t \Rightarrow \frac{15}{40} = 0.75^t \Rightarrow \log \frac{15}{40} = \log 0.75^t \Rightarrow$

$\log \frac{15}{40} = t \log 0.75 \Rightarrow t = \frac{\log \frac{15}{40}}{\log 0.75} \Rightarrow t \approx 3.4$ hours.

85. (a) $f(1.5) = 20 - 15(0.365)^{1.5} \approx 16.7°\text{C}$

(b) $15 = 20 - 15(0.365)^t \Rightarrow 15(0.365)^t = 5 \Rightarrow 0.365^t = \frac{1}{3} \Rightarrow \ln 0.365^t = \ln \frac{1}{3} \Rightarrow t \ln 0.365 = \ln \frac{1}{3} \Rightarrow$

$t = \frac{\ln \frac{1}{3}}{\ln 0.365} \approx 1.09$; the soda can warmed to 15°C after about 1.09 minutes or 1 hour 5.4 minutes.

86. (a) $T(t) = 32 + 48(0.9)^t \Rightarrow T(30) = 32 + 48(0.9)^{30} \approx 34$; after 30 minutes the soda can cooled to about 34°F.

(b) $50 = 32 + 48(0.9)^t \Rightarrow 48(0.9)^t = 18 \Rightarrow 0.9^t = 0.375 \Rightarrow \ln 0.9^t = \ln 0.375 \Rightarrow t \ln 0.9 = \ln 0.375 \Rightarrow$

$t = \frac{\ln 0.375}{\ln 0.9} \approx 9.3$; the soda can cooled to 50°F after about 9.3 minutes.

87. $280 \ln (x + 1) + 1925 = 2300 \Rightarrow 280 \ln (x + 1) = 375 \Rightarrow \ln (x + 1) = \frac{375}{280} \Rightarrow e^{\ln (x+1)} = e^{375/280} \Rightarrow$

$x + 1 = e^{375/280} \Rightarrow x = e^{375/280} - 1 \approx 2.8$; a person who consumes 2300 calories daily owns about 2.8 acres.

88. (a) $s(500) = 31.5 + 1.1 \log (500 + 1) \approx 34.47$. At a depth of 500 meters, the salinity is about 34,47 g/kg.

(b) See Figure 88. The salinity changes most dramatically in the first 200 feet but then levels off. The deeper the seawater gets the less the salinity changes.

(c) $31.5 + 1.1 \log (x + 1) = 33 \Rightarrow 1.1 \log (x + 1) = 1.5 \Rightarrow \log (x + 1) = \frac{15}{11} \Rightarrow$

$x + 1 = 10^{15/11} \Rightarrow x = 10^{15/11} - 1 \approx 22.1$

[0, 1000, 100] by [30, 36, 1]

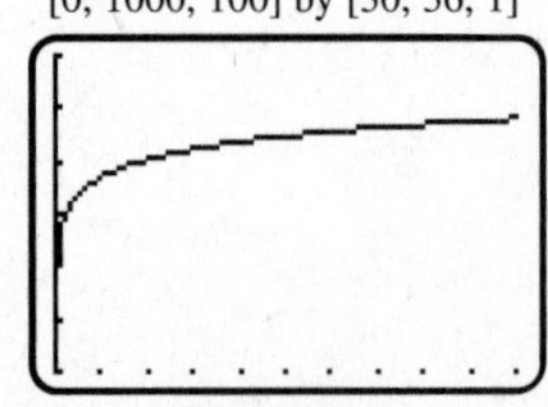

Figure 88

89. $\frac{2 - \log (100 - x)}{0.42} = 2 \Rightarrow 2 - \log (100 - x) = 0.84 \Rightarrow \log (100 - x) = 1.16 \Rightarrow$

$10^{\log (100-x)} = 10^{1.16} \Rightarrow 100 - x = 10^{1.16} \Rightarrow x = 100 - 10^{1.16} \approx 85.546$; after 2 years approximately 85.5% of the robins have died.

90. (a) $y = \frac{2 - \log (100 - 40)}{0.37} \approx 0.5996$. 40% of the sparrow population died in about 0.6 yrs.

(b) $1.5 = \frac{2 - \log (100 - x)}{0.37} \Rightarrow 0.555 = 2 - \log (100 - x) \Rightarrow \log (100 - x) = 1.445 \Rightarrow$

$10^{1.445} = 100 - x \Rightarrow x = 100 - 10^{1.445} \approx 72.14\%$. In 1.5 yrs about 72% of the sparrows died.

91. (a) A concentration increase of 15% implies $B(t) = 1.15$ when $B_0 = 1$.

$1.15 = e^{6k} \Rightarrow \ln(1.15) = 6k \Rightarrow k = \dfrac{\ln(1.15)}{6} \approx 0.0233.$

(b) $B(t) = 1.2e^{0.0233(8.2)} \approx 1.45$ billion per liter.

(c) $B(t) = 1e^{0.0233(1)} \approx 1.0236 \Rightarrow$ the concentration increases by about 2.36% per hour.

92. (a) The voltage decrease of 85% implies $V(t) = 0.15$ when $V_0 = 1$.

$0.15 = e^{5k} \Rightarrow \ln(0.15) = 5k \Rightarrow k = \dfrac{\ln(0.15)}{5} \approx -0.38.$

(b) $V(t) = 4.5e^{-0.38(2.3)} \approx 1.878$ volts.

(c) $V(t) = 1e^{-0.38(1)} \approx 0.684$ of the original remains. Therefore $1 - 0.684 = 0.316$. The voltage decreases by about 31.6% each millisecond.

93. $A = P\left(1 + \dfrac{r}{n}\right)^{nt} \Rightarrow 2000 = 1000\left(1 + \dfrac{0.085}{4}\right)^{0.4t} \Rightarrow 2 = (1.02125)^{4t} \Rightarrow \ln(2) = \ln(1.02125)^{4t} \Rightarrow$

$\dfrac{\ln(2)}{\ln(1.02125)} = 4t \Rightarrow t = \dfrac{\frac{\ln(2)}{\ln(1.02125)}}{4} \approx 8.25$ yrs.

94. $A = Pe^{rt} \Rightarrow 1500 = 750e^{0.12t} \Rightarrow 2 = e^{0.12t} \Rightarrow \ln(2) = 0.12t \Rightarrow t = \dfrac{\ln(2)}{0.12} \approx 5.78$ yrs.

95. (a) $P(t) = 750 \Rightarrow 500e^{0.09x} = 750 \Rightarrow e^{0.09x} = 1.5 \Rightarrow \ln e^{0.09x} = \ln 1.5 \Rightarrow 0.09x = \ln 1.5 \Rightarrow$

$t = \dfrac{\ln 1.5}{0.09} \approx 4.505$

(b) If \$500 is invested at 9% compounded continuously, it will grow to approximately \$750 after 4.5 years.

96. (a) $P(t) = 2000 \Rightarrow 1000e^{0.09x} = 2000 \Rightarrow e^{0.09x} = 2 \Rightarrow \ln e^{0.09x} = \ln 2 \Rightarrow 0.09x = \ln 2 \Rightarrow$

$t = \dfrac{\ln 2}{0.09} \approx 7.7$

(b) If \$1000 is invested at 9% compounded continuously, it will grow to approximately \$2000 after 7.7 years.

97. $P = 100\left(\dfrac{1}{2}\right)^{t/5700} \Rightarrow 35 = 100\left(\dfrac{1}{2}\right)^{t/5700} \Rightarrow \left(\dfrac{1}{2}\right)^{t/5700} = 0.35 \Rightarrow \ln\left(\dfrac{1}{2}\right)^{t/5700} = \ln 0.35 \Rightarrow$

$\dfrac{t}{5700}\ln\dfrac{1}{2} = \ln 0.35 \Rightarrow \dfrac{t}{5700} = \dfrac{\ln 0.35}{\ln\frac{1}{2}} \Rightarrow t = 5700\left(\dfrac{\ln 0.35}{\ln\frac{1}{2}}\right) \approx 8633.$ The fossil is about 8633 years old.

98. $A(t) = 0.02\left(\dfrac{1}{2}\right)^{t/1600} \Rightarrow 0.004 = 0.02\left(\dfrac{1}{2}\right)^{t/1600} \Rightarrow \left(\dfrac{1}{2}\right)^{t/1600} = 0.2 \Rightarrow \ln\left(\dfrac{1}{2}\right)^{t/1600} = \ln 0.2 \Rightarrow$

$\dfrac{t}{1600}\ln\dfrac{1}{2} = \ln 0.2 \Rightarrow \dfrac{t}{1600} = \dfrac{\ln 0.2}{\ln\frac{1}{2}} \Rightarrow t = 1600\left(\dfrac{\ln 0.2}{\ln\frac{1}{2}}\right) \approx 3715$

The sample will decay to 0.004 milligrams in about 3715 years.

99. $0.5 = 1 - e^{-0.5x} \Rightarrow -0.5 = -e^{-0.5x} \Rightarrow 0.5 = e^{-0.5x} \Rightarrow \ln(0.5) = -0.5x \Rightarrow x = \dfrac{\ln(0.5)}{-0.5} \Rightarrow$

$x = -2\ln(0.5) \approx 1.39$ min.

100. (a) $f(x) = 1 - e^{-x} \Rightarrow f(5) = 1 - e^{-5} \approx 0.993$, or 99.3%

(b) $0.40 = 1 - e^{-x} \Rightarrow e^{-x} = 0.6 \Rightarrow \ln e^{-x} = \ln 0.6 \Rightarrow -x = \ln 0.6 \Rightarrow x = -\ln 0.6 \approx 0.51$

During an interval of about 0.5 minute, there is a 40% chance that at least one car enters the intersection.

101. $N(t) = 100{,}000e^{rt} \Rightarrow 200{,}000 = 100{,}000e^{r(2)} \Rightarrow 2 = e^{2r} \Rightarrow \ln 2 = \ln e^{2r} \Rightarrow \ln 2 = 2r \Rightarrow$

$\dfrac{\ln 2}{2} = r \Rightarrow r = 0.3466$. Now $350{,}000 = 100{,}000e^{0.3466t} \Rightarrow 3.5 = e^{0.3466t} \Rightarrow \ln 3.5 = \ln e^{0.3466t} \Rightarrow$

$\ln 3.5 = 0.3466t \Rightarrow t = \dfrac{\ln 3.5}{0.3466} \Rightarrow t \approx 3.6$ hrs.

102. $N(t) = 50{,}000e^{rt} \Rightarrow 150{,}000 = 50{,}000e^{4r} \Rightarrow 3 = e^{4r} \Rightarrow \ln(3) = 4r \Rightarrow r = \dfrac{\ln(3)}{4} \approx 0.275$.

Now $85{,}000 = 50{,}000e^{0.275t} \Rightarrow 1.7 = e^{0.275t} \Rightarrow \ln(1.7) = 0.275t \Rightarrow t = \dfrac{\ln(1.7)}{0.275} \approx 1.93$ days.

103. $A_n = A_0e^{rn} \Rightarrow 2300 = 2000e^{r(4)} \Rightarrow 1.15 = e^{4r} \Rightarrow \ln 1.15 = \ln e^{4r} \Rightarrow \ln 1.15 = 4r \Rightarrow$

$r = \dfrac{\ln 1.15}{4} \Rightarrow r = 0.03494$. Now $3200 = 2000e^{0.03494t} \Rightarrow 1.6 = e^{0.03494t} \Rightarrow \ln 1.6 = \ln e^{0.03494t} \Rightarrow$

$\ln 1.6 = 0.03494t \Rightarrow t = \dfrac{\ln 1.6}{0.03494} \Rightarrow t \approx 13.5$ years.

104. $A(x) = C\left(\dfrac{1}{2}\right)^{x/k} \Rightarrow 0.04 = 0.05\left(\dfrac{1}{2}\right)^{20/k} \Rightarrow 0.8 = \left(\dfrac{1}{2}\right)^{20/k} \Rightarrow \ln 0.8 = \dfrac{20}{k}\ln\dfrac{1}{2} \Rightarrow \dfrac{\ln 0.8}{\ln\frac{1}{2}} = \dfrac{20}{k} \Rightarrow$

$0.3219 = \dfrac{20}{k} \Rightarrow 0.3219k = 20 \Rightarrow k = 62.13$. Now $0.025 = 0.05\left(\dfrac{1}{2}\right)^{t/62.13} \Rightarrow 0.5 = \left(\dfrac{1}{2}\right)^{t/62.13} \Rightarrow$

$\ln 0.5 = \dfrac{t}{62.13}\ln\dfrac{1}{2} \Rightarrow \dfrac{\ln 0.5}{\ln\frac{1}{2}} = \dfrac{t}{62.13} \Rightarrow 1 = \dfrac{t}{62.13} \Rightarrow t = 62.13$ or about 62 days.

105. (a) The initial concentration of the drug is 11 milligrams per liter since $C(0) = 11(0.72)^0 = 11$ milligrams per liter.

(b) 50% of 11 = 5.5 milligrams per liter.

$11(0.72)^t = 5.5 \Rightarrow 0.72^t = 0.5 \Rightarrow \ln 0.72^t = \ln 0.5 \Rightarrow t\ln 0.72 = \ln 0.5 \Rightarrow t = \dfrac{\ln 0.5}{\ln 0.72} \approx 2.11$

The drug concentration decreases to 50% of its initial level after about 2 hours.

106. When $x = 60$ the equation becomes $\ln(1 - P) = -0.0034 - 0.0053(60) \Rightarrow \ln(1 - P) = -0.3214$.

$\ln(1 - P) = -0.3214 \Rightarrow e^{\ln(1-P)} = e^{-0.3214} \Rightarrow 1 - P = e^{-0.3214} \Rightarrow P = 1 - e^{-0.3214} \approx 0.275$

According to this model, if a \$60 tax was placed on each ton of carbon that was burned into the atmosphere, carbon dioxide emissions would be reduced by 27.5%.

107. $P\left(1 + \dfrac{r}{n}\right)^{nt} = A \Rightarrow \left(1 + \dfrac{r}{n}\right)^{nt} = \dfrac{A}{P} \Rightarrow \log\left(1 + \dfrac{r}{n}\right)^{nt} = \log\left(\dfrac{A}{P}\right) \Rightarrow$

$nt\log\left(1 + \dfrac{r}{n}\right) = \log\left(\dfrac{A}{P}\right) \Rightarrow t = \dfrac{\log(A/P)}{n\log(1 + r/n)}$

108. $D = 160 + 10\log x \Rightarrow 10\log x = D - 160 \Rightarrow \log x = \dfrac{D - 160}{10} \Rightarrow 10^{\log x} = 10^{(D-160)/10} \Rightarrow$

$x = 10^{(D-160)/10}$ or $x = 10^{(D/10-16)}$

## Extended and Discovery Exercises for Section 5.6

1. $f(x) = Ca^x = Ce^{\ln(a^x)} = Ce^{x\ln(a)}$, that is $k = \ln a$; $g(x) = 2^x = e^{\ln(2^x)} = e^{x\ln(2)} \Rightarrow k = \ln(2)$

## Checking Basic Concepts for Sections 5.5 and 5.6

1. $\log \frac{x^2y^3}{\sqrt[3]{z}} = \log x^2 + \log y^3 - \log z^{1/3} = 2 \log x + 3 \log y - \frac{1}{3} \log z$

2. $\frac{1}{2} \ln x - 3 \ln y + \ln z = \ln \sqrt{x} - \ln y^3 + \ln z = \ln \frac{z\sqrt{x}}{y^3}$

3. (a) $5(1.4)^x - 4 = 25 \Rightarrow 5(1.4)^x = 29 \Rightarrow 1.4^x = \frac{29}{5} \Rightarrow \ln 1.4^x = \ln \frac{29}{5} \Rightarrow x \ln 1.4 = \ln \frac{29}{5} \Rightarrow$

   $x = \frac{\ln \frac{29}{5}}{\ln 1.4} \approx 5.224$

   (b) $4^{2-x} = 4^{2x+1} \Rightarrow \log_4 4^{2-x} = \log_4 4^{2x+1} \Rightarrow 2 - x = 2x + 1 \Rightarrow 3x = 1 \Rightarrow x = \frac{1}{3}$

4. (a) $5 \log_2 2x = 25 \Rightarrow \log_2 2x = 5 \Rightarrow 2^{\log_2 2x} = 2^5 \Rightarrow 2x = 32 \Rightarrow x = 16$

   (b) $\ln (x + 1) + \ln (x - 1) = \ln 3 \Rightarrow \ln [(x + 1)(x - 1)] = \ln 3 \Rightarrow \ln (x^2 - 1) = \ln 3 \Rightarrow$

   $e^{\ln (x^2-1)} = e^{\ln 3} \Rightarrow x^2 - 1 = 3 \Rightarrow x^2 = 4 \Rightarrow x = -2$ or $x = 2$

   When $x = -2$ both $\ln (x - 1)$ and $\ln (x + 1)$ are undefined. The only solution is $x = 2$.

5. (a) Looking at the graph of $y = 80 + 120(0.9)^x$ we see that eventually the values stay around 80. After a long time, the temperature of the object stays around 80°F

   (b) $80 + 120(0.9)^x = 100 \Rightarrow 120(0.9)^x = 20 \Rightarrow 0.9^x = \frac{1}{6} \Rightarrow \ln 0.9^x = \ln \frac{1}{6} \Rightarrow x \ln 0.9 = \ln \frac{1}{6} \Rightarrow$

   $x = \frac{\ln \frac{1}{6}}{\ln 0.9} \approx 17$; the object's temperature is 100°F after about 17 minutes.

## 5.7: Constructing Nonlinear Models

1. Growth slows down as $x$ increases; logarithmic.
2. Levels off as $x$ increases; logistic.
3. Growth rate increases as $x$ increases; exponential.
4. Decreases at a decreasing rate; exponential.
5. Exponential; least-squares regression gives $f(x) = 1.2(1.7)^x$.
6. Logarithmic; least-squares regression gives $f(x) = 1.987 + 0.5086 \ln x$.
7. Logarithmic; least-squares regression gives $f(x) = 1.088 + 2.937 \ln x$.
8. Logistic; least-squares regression gives $f(x) = \frac{10.789}{1 + 34.241e^{-1.025x}}$.
9. Logistic; least-squares regression gives $f(x) = \frac{9.96}{1 + 30.6e^{-1.51x}}$.
10. Exponential; least-squares regression gives $f(x) \approx 2.51(0.798)^x$.

11. (a) See Figure 11.

    (b) $f(x) = 1.568(1.109)^x$ deaths per 100,000.

    (c) $f(80) = 1.568(1.109)^{80} \approx 6164$; about 6164 deaths per 100,000.

[25, 75, 5] by [−100, 2100, 200]

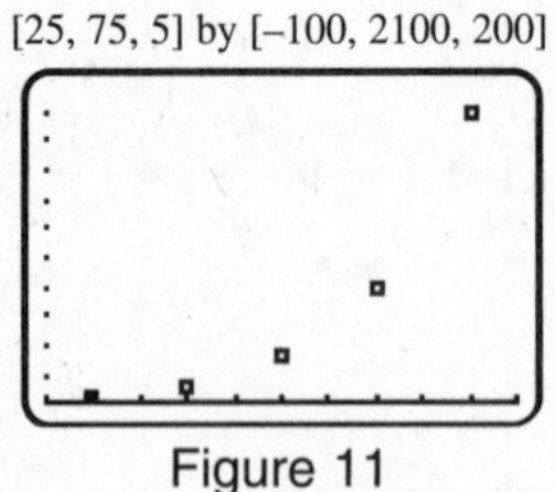

Figure 11

[0, 110, 70] by [27, 30, 1]

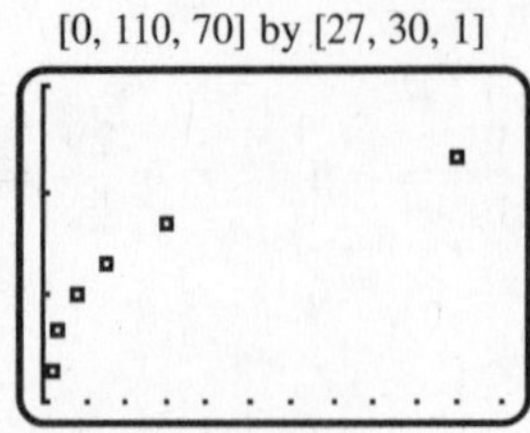

Figure 14

12. (a) Let $y$ be the number of female technicians and $x$ be the year, where $x = 0$ corresponds to 1988, $x = 1$ to 1989, and so on until $x = 7$ corresponds to 1995. The data is increasing rapidly and an exponential function might model these data.

    (b) Expontial: least-squares regession gives $f(x) = 507.1(1.166)^x$.

    (c) Since $x = 17$ corresponds to the year 2005, $f(17) = 507.1(1.166)^{17} \approx 6900$.

13. $a \approx 9.02$, $b \approx 1.03$, or $f(x) = 9.02 + 1.03 \ln x$.

14. (a) See Figure 14.

    (b) $f(x) = 26.97 + 0.506 \ln x$ inches of mercury.

    (c) $f(50) = 26.97 + 0.506 \ln 50 \approx 28.95$; about 28.95 inches of mercury.

15. (a) $a \approx 1.4734$, $b \approx 0.99986$, or $f(x) = 1.4734(0.99986)^x$.

    (b) $f(7000) = 1.4734(0.99986)^{7000} \approx 0.55$; approximately 0.55 kg/m$^3$.

16. (a) Using the power regression function on the calculator: $f(x) = 2.563x^{-0.31575}$. *Answers may vary.*

    (b) $2.563x^{-0.31575} = 1.8 \Rightarrow x^{-0.31575} = \dfrac{1.8}{2.563} \Rightarrow (x^{-0.31575})^{1/-0.31575} = \left(\dfrac{1.8}{2.563}\right)^{-0.31575} \Rightarrow x \approx 3.06$

17. (a) $f(x) = \dfrac{4.9955}{1 + 49.7081e^{-0.6998x}}$

    (b) For large $x$, $f(x) \approx \dfrac{4.9955}{1} \approx 5$; the density after a long time is about 5 thousand per acre.

18. (a) From the table we see that $P(25) = 7\%$. A 25 year old has a 7% chance of having signs of CHD.

    (b) Logistic: least-squares regressions gives $P(x) \approx \dfrac{89.5}{1 + 266.5e^{-0.122x}}$.

    (c) See Figure 18.

    (d) $50 = \dfrac{89.5}{1 + 266.5e^{-0.122x}} \Rightarrow \dfrac{89.5}{50} = 1 + 266.5e^{-0.122x} \Rightarrow 1.79 = 1 + 266.5e^{-0.122x} \Rightarrow$

    $0.79 = 266.5e^{-0.122x} \Rightarrow \dfrac{0.79}{266.5} = e^{-0.122x} \Rightarrow \ln\left(\dfrac{0.79}{266.5}\right) = -0.122x \Rightarrow x = \dfrac{\ln\left(\frac{0.79}{266.5}\right)}{-0.122} \approx 48$ years.

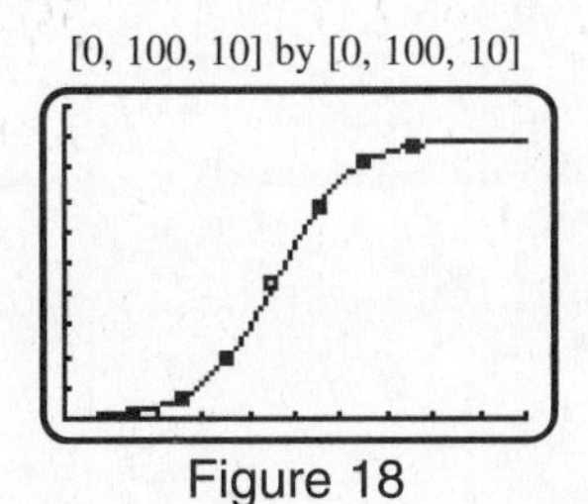


Figure 18

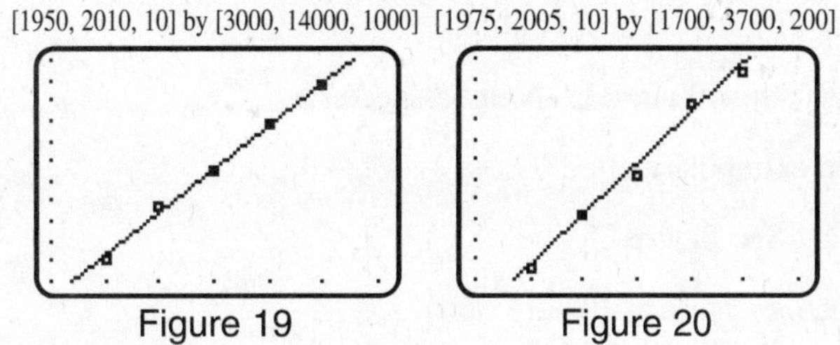


Figure 19

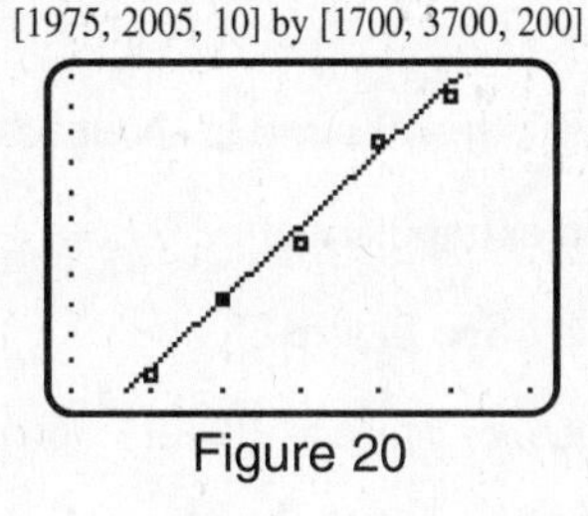


Figure 20

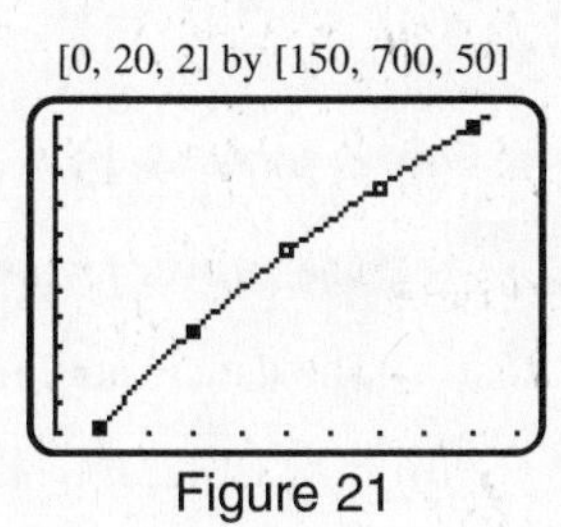


Figure 21

19. (a) Linear: least-squares regession gives $N(x) \approx 213.78x - 414{,}673$.

    (b) See Figure 19.

    (c) $9500 = 213.78x - 414{,}673 \Rightarrow 424{,}173 = 213.78x \Rightarrow x \approx 1984.2$. The number of radio stations reached 9500 during 1984.

20. (a) Linear: least-squares regession gives $T(x) = 100.6x - 197{,}442$.

    (b) See Figure 20.

    (c) $3000 = 100.6x - 197{,}442 \Rightarrow 200{,}442 = 100.6x \Rightarrow x \approx 1992.5$. Tuition and fees first reached \$3000 during 1992.

21. (a) Power: least-squares regession gives $A(w) \approx 101x^{0.662}$.

    (b) See Figure 21.

    (c) $500 = 101w^{0.662} \Rightarrow \dfrac{500}{101} = w^{0.662} \Rightarrow \left(\dfrac{500}{101}\right)^{1/0.662} = (w^{0.662})^{1/0.662} \Rightarrow w \approx 11.2$. lbs. A weight of about 11.2 lbs. corresponds to a bird with a wing area of 500 in$^2$.

22. (a) Power: least-squares regession gives $A(w) \approx 2.286x^{0.334}$.

    (b) See Figure 22.

    (c) $2 = 2.286w^{0.3334} \Rightarrow \dfrac{2}{2.286} = w^{0.3334} \Rightarrow \left(\dfrac{2}{2.286}\right)^{1/0.3334} = (w^{0.3334})^{1/0.3334} \Rightarrow w \approx 0.67$ lb. A weight of about 0.67 lb. corresponds to a bird with a wing span of 2 ft.

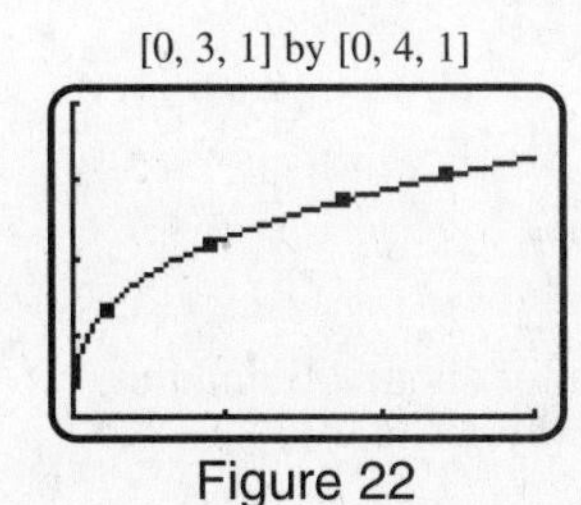


Figure 22

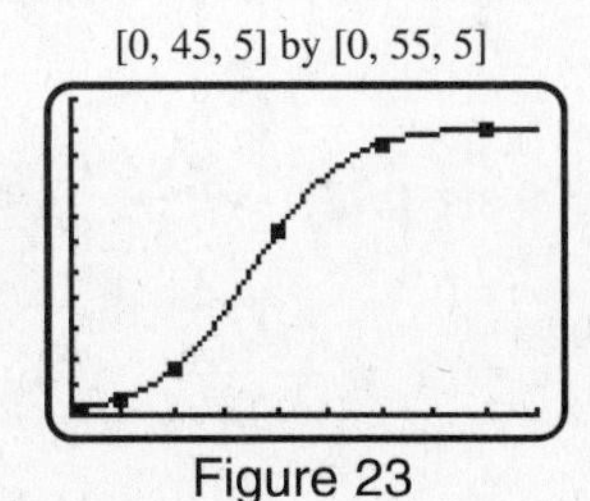


Figure 23

23. (a) From the table we see that $H(5) = 3$. After 5 years the tree is 3 feet tall.

    (b) Logistic: least-squares regressions gives $H(x) \approx \dfrac{50.1}{1 + 47.4e^{-0.221x}}$.

    (c) See Figure 23.

    (d) $25 = \dfrac{50.1}{1 + 47.4e^{-0.221x}} \Rightarrow \dfrac{50.1}{25} = 1 + 47.4e^{-0.221x} \Rightarrow \dfrac{50.1}{25} - 1 = 47.4e^{-0.221x} \Rightarrow$

    $\dfrac{\frac{50.1}{25} - 1}{47.4} = e^{-0.221x} \Rightarrow \ln\left(\dfrac{\frac{50.1}{25} - 1}{47.4}\right) = -0.221x \Rightarrow x = \dfrac{\ln\left(\dfrac{\frac{50.1}{25} - 1}{47.4}\right)}{-0.221} \approx 17.4$ years. After about 17.4 years the tree is 25 feet tall.

    (e) The answer involved interpolation.

24. (a) $a = 15, b \approx 2.17$, or $f(x) = 15 + 2.17 \ln x$.

    (b) $f(5000) = 15 + 2.17 \ln 5000 \approx 33$; about 33 species.

    (c) The answer involved extrapolation.

25. (a) The data is not linear. See Figure 25.

    (b) $a \approx 12.42, b \approx 1.066$, or $f(x) = 12.42(1.066)^x$.

    (c) $f(39) = 12.42(1.066)^{39} \approx 150$; 150 kilograms per hectare. Chemical fertilizer use increased, but at a slower rate than predicted by $f$.

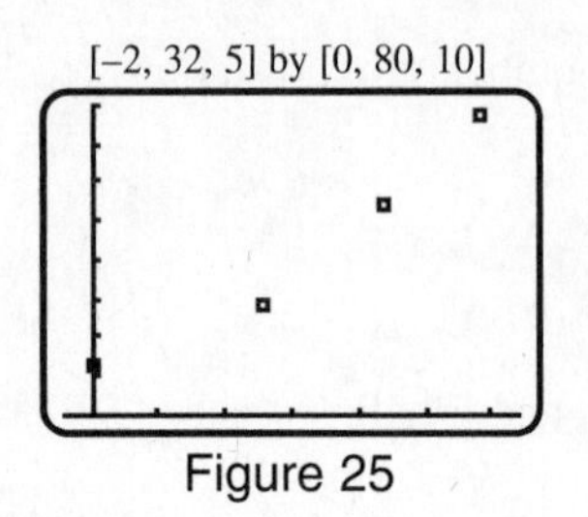

Figure 25

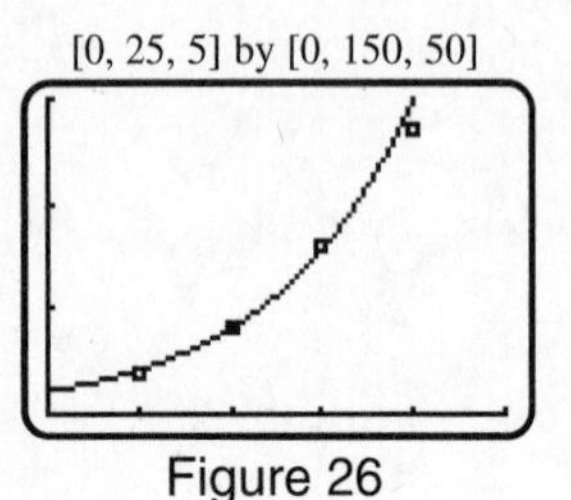

Figure 26

26. (a) $a \approx 10.98, b \approx 1.14$, or $f(x) = 10.98(1.14)^x$.

    (b) See Figure 14.

    (c) $f(13) = 10.98(1.14)^{13} \approx 60$; the fees in 2013 would be about \$60 billion.

    (d) The answer involoved interpolation.

## Extended and Discovery Exercises for Section 5.7

1. (a) Least-squares regression gives $f(x) \approx 0.09(0.844)^x$. A better fit by trial and error is $f(x) \approx 0.128(0.777)^x$.

   (b) 30% of 0.133 is 0.0399 $\Rightarrow 0.128(0.777)^x = 0.0399 \Rightarrow 0.777^x = \dfrac{0.0399}{0.128} \Rightarrow$

   $\ln 0.777^x = \ln \dfrac{0.0399}{0.128} \Rightarrow x \ln 0.777 = \ln \dfrac{0.0399}{0.128} \Rightarrow x = \dfrac{\ln \frac{0.0399}{0.128}}{\ln 0.777} \approx 4.6$; after about 4.6 minutes.

   (c) *Answers may vary.*

## Checking Basic Concepts for Section 5.7

1. Exponential; least-squares regression gives $f(x) \approx 0.5(1.2)^x$.
2. Logarithmic; least-squares regression gives $f(x) \approx -2 + 3 \ln x$.
3. Logistic; least-squares regression gives $f(x) = \dfrac{4.5}{1 + 277e^{-1.4x}}$.
4. Logistic; least-squares regression gives $f(x) \approx \dfrac{9.76}{1 + 2.085e^{-0.0329x}}$.

## Chapter 5 Review Exercises

1. (a) $(f + g)(1) = f(1) + g(1) = 7 + 1 = 8$

(b) $(f - g)(3) = f(3) - g(3) = 9 - 9 = 0$

(c) $(fg)(-1) = f(-1)g(-1) = 3(-2) = -6$

(d) $(f/g)(0) = \dfrac{f(0)}{g(0)} = \dfrac{5}{0}$; undefined.

2. (a) From the graph $f(2) = 4$ and $g(2) = 0$. Thus, $(f - g)(2) = f(2) - g(2) = 4 - 0 = 4$.

(b) Similarly, $f(0) = 0$ and $g(0) = -2$. Thus, $(fg)(0) = f(0)g(0) = (0)(-2) = 0$.

3. (a) $f(x) = x^2 \Rightarrow f(3) = 9$ and $g(x) = 1 - x \Rightarrow g(3) = 1 - 3 = -2$.

Thus, $(f + g)(3) = f(3) + g(3) = 9 + (-2) = 7$.

(b) $f(-2) = 4$ and $g(-2) = 1 - (-2) = 3$. Thus, $(f - g)(-2) = f(-2) - g(-2) = 4 - 3 = 1$.

(c) $f(1) = 1$ and $g(1) = 1 - 1 = 0$. Thus, $(fg)(1) = f(1)g(1) = (1)(0) = 0$.

(d) $f(3) = 9$ and $g(3) = 1 - 3 = -2$. Thus, $(f/g)(3) = \dfrac{f(3)}{g(3)} = \dfrac{9}{-2} = -\dfrac{9}{2}$.

4. (a) $(f + g)(x) = f(x) + g(x) = (x^2 + 3x) + (x^2 - 1) = 2x^2 + 3x - 1$; Domain is all real numbers.

(b) $(f - g)(x) = f(x) - g(x) = (x^2 + 3x) - (x^2 - 1) = 3x + 1$; Domain is all real numbers.

(c) $(fg)(x) = f(x)g(x) = (x^2 + 3x)(x^2 - 1)$; Domain is all real numbers.

(d) $(f/g)(x) = f(x)/g(x) = \dfrac{x^2 + 3x}{x^2 - 1}$; Domain is $\{x \mid x \neq \pm 1\}$.

5. (a) $(g \circ f)(-2) = g(f(-2)) = g(1) = 2$

(b) $(f \circ g)(3) = f(g(3)) = f(-2) = 1$

(c) $f^{-1}(3) = 2$ since $f(2) = 3$

6. (a) $(f \circ g)(2) = f(g(2)) = f(-2) = 0$

(b) $(g \circ f)(0) = g(f(0)) = g(2) = -2$

(c) $f^{-1}(1) = -1$ since $f(-1) = 1$

7. (a) $f(x) = \sqrt{x}$ and $g(x) = x^2 + x \Rightarrow (f \circ g)(2) = f(g(2)) = f(6) = \sqrt{6}$

(b) $(g \circ f)(9) = g(f(9)) = g(\sqrt{9}) = g(3) = 3^2 + 3 = 12$

8 (a) $(f \circ g)(x) = f(g(x)) = f(x^3 - x^2 + 2x + 1) = (x^3 - x^2 + 2x + 1)^2 + 1$

(b) $(g \circ f)(x) = g(f(x)) = g(x^2 + 1) = (x^2 + 1)^3 - (x^2 + 1)^2 + 2(x^2 + 1) + 1$

9. $(f \circ g) = f(g(x)) = f\left(\dfrac{1}{x}\right) = \left(\dfrac{1}{x}\right)^3 - \left(\dfrac{1}{x}\right)^2 + 3\left(\dfrac{1}{x}\right) - 2$; $D = \{x \mid x \neq 0\}$

10. $(f \circ g) = f(g(x)) = f(1 - x^2) = \sqrt{1 - x^2 + 3} = \sqrt{4 - x^2}$; $D = \{x \mid -2 \leq x \leq 2\}$

11. $(f \circ g) = f(g(x)) = f\left(\dfrac{1}{2}x^3 + \dfrac{1}{2}\right) = \sqrt[3]{2\left(\dfrac{1}{2}x^3 + \dfrac{1}{2}\right) - 1} = \sqrt[3]{x^3 + 1 - 1} = \sqrt[3]{x^3} = x$;

$D =$ all real numbers

12. $(f \circ g) = f(g(x)) = f\left(\dfrac{1}{x + 1}\right) = \dfrac{2}{\frac{1}{x + 1} - 5} = \dfrac{2}{\frac{1}{x + 1} - \frac{5x + 5}{x + 1}} = \dfrac{2}{\frac{-5x - 4}{x + 1}} = \dfrac{2}{1} \cdot \dfrac{x + 1}{-5x - 4} = \dfrac{2x + 2}{-5x - 4} =$

$-\dfrac{2(x + 1)}{5x + 4}$; $D = \left\{x \mid x \neq -\dfrac{4}{5}, x \neq -1\right\}$

13. $h(x) = (g \circ f)(x) \Rightarrow h(x) = \sqrt{x^2 + 3} \Rightarrow f(x) = x^2 + 3, g(x) = \sqrt{x}$. *Answers may vary.*

14. $h(x) = (g \circ f)(x) \Rightarrow h(x) = \dfrac{1}{(2x + 1)^2} \Rightarrow f(x) = 2x + 1, g(x) = \dfrac{1}{x^2}$. *Answers may vary.*

15. Subtract 6 from $x$ and then multiply the results by 10. $\dfrac{x}{10} + 6$ and $10(x - 6)$.

16. Cube $x$ and then add 5. $\sqrt[3]{x - 5}$ and $x^3 + 5$.

17. Since the graph of $f(x) = 3x - 1$ is a line sloping upward from left to right, a horizontal line can intersect it at most once. Therefore, $f$ is one-to-one.

18. Since the graph of $f(x) = 3x^2 - 2x + 1$ is a parabola, a horizontal line can intersect it more than once. Therefore, $f$ is not one-to-one.

19. $f$ is not one-to-one. It does not pass the Horizontal line test.

20. $f$ is one-to-one. It passes the Horizontal line test.

21. See Figure 21. The domain of $f$ is $D = \{-1, 0, 4, 6\}$ and its range is $R = \{1, 3, 4, 6\}$. The domain and range of $f^{-1}$ are $D = \{1, 3, 4, 6\}$ and $R = \{-1, 0, 4, 6\}$, repectively.

| $x$ | 6 | 4 | 3 | 1 |
|---|---|---|---|---|
| $f^{-1}(x)$ | −1 | 0 | 4 | 6 |

Figure 21

22. The graph of $f$ passes through the points $(-4, -1)$ and $(4, 3)$. Therefore the graph of $f^{-1}$ must pass through the points $(-1, -4)$ and $(3, 4)$. Both $f$ and $f^{-1}$ are linear. Draw the reflection of the graph of $f$ in the line $y = x$ to obtain the graph of $f^{-1}$. See Figure 22.

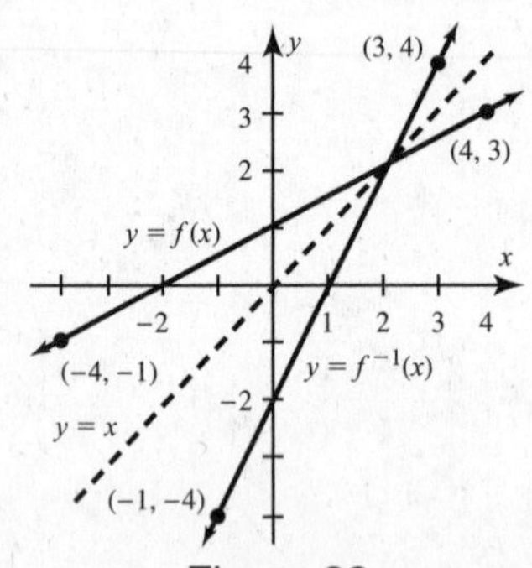

Figure 22

23. The inverse operations are add 5 to $x$ and divide by 3. Therefore, $f^{-1}(x) = \dfrac{x + 5}{3}$.

24. $y = \dfrac{3x}{x + 7} \Rightarrow y(x + 7) = 3x \Rightarrow xy + 7y = 3x \Rightarrow 7y = 3x - xy \Rightarrow 7y = x(3 - y) \Rightarrow$

$x = \dfrac{7y}{3 - y}; \Rightarrow f^{-1}(x) = \dfrac{7x}{3 - x}$

25. $(f \circ f^{-1})(x) = f(f^{-1}(x)) = f\left(\dfrac{x + 1}{2}\right) = 2\left(\dfrac{x + 1}{2}\right) - 1 = (x + 1) - 1 = x$

$(f^{-1} \circ f)(x) = f^{-1}(f(x)) = f^{-1}(2x - 1) = \dfrac{(2x - 1) + 1}{2} = \dfrac{2x}{2} = x$

26. $\{x \mid x \geq 4\}$, $y = 2(x-4)^2 + 3 \Rightarrow \dfrac{y-3}{2} = (x-4)^2 \Rightarrow \sqrt{\dfrac{y-3}{2}} = x - 4 \Rightarrow$

$x = \sqrt{\dfrac{y-3}{2}} + 4; \Rightarrow f^{-1}(x) = \sqrt{\dfrac{x-3}{2}} + 4;\ x \geq 3$

27. $(f \circ g^{-1})(4) = f(g^{-1}(4)) = f(3) = 1$

28. $(g^{-1} \circ f^{-1})(1) = g^{-1}(f^{-1}(1)) = g^{-1}(3) = 2$

29. $y = \sqrt{x+1} \Rightarrow y^2 = x + 1 \Rightarrow y^2 - 1 = x; \Rightarrow f^{-1}(x) = x^2 - 1, x \geq 0$

For $f$: $D = \{x \mid x \geq -1\}$ and $R = \{y \mid y \geq 0\}$; for $f^{-1}$: $D = \{x \mid x \geq 0\}$ and $R = \{y \mid y \geq -1\}$

30. $e^x e^{-2x} = e^{x-2x} = e^{-x}$

31. If $f(0) = 3 \Rightarrow Ca^x = 3 \Rightarrow Ca^0 = 3 \Rightarrow a^0 = 1;\ C(1) = 3 \Rightarrow C = 3$; then $f(3) = 24 \Rightarrow$

$Ca^x = 24 \Rightarrow 3a^3 = 24 \Rightarrow a^3 = 8 \Rightarrow a = 2$. Therefore $C = 3$ and $a = 2$.

32. If $Ca^{-1} = 8 \Rightarrow C\left(\dfrac{1}{a}\right) = 8 \Rightarrow \dfrac{C}{a} = 8 \Rightarrow C = 8a$ and if $Ca = 2$, using substitution we get:

$8a(a) = 2 \Rightarrow 8a^2 = 2 \Rightarrow a^2 = \dfrac{1}{4} \Rightarrow a = \dfrac{1}{2}$. Substituting $a = \dfrac{1}{2}$ into $C = 8a \Rightarrow$

$C = 8\left(\dfrac{1}{2}\right) \Rightarrow C = 4$.

33. See Figure 33. $D$ = all real numbers.

34. See Figure 34. $D$ = all real numbers.

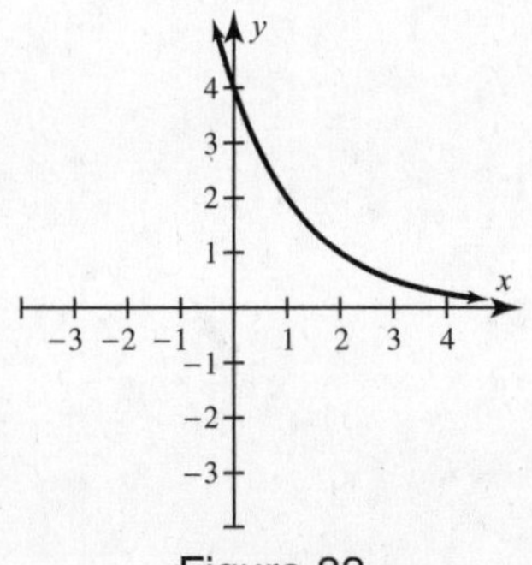
Figure 33

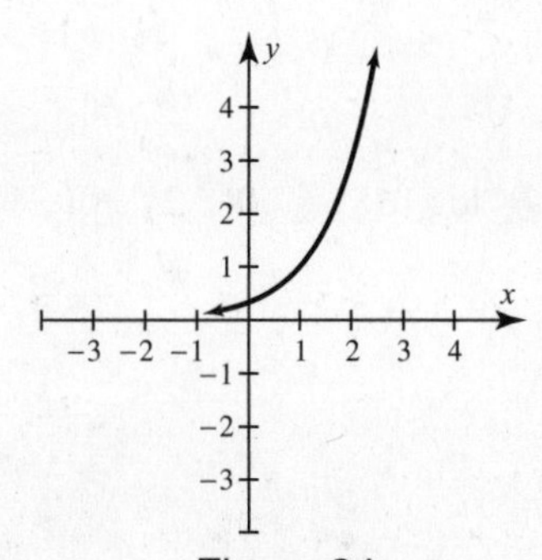
Figure 34

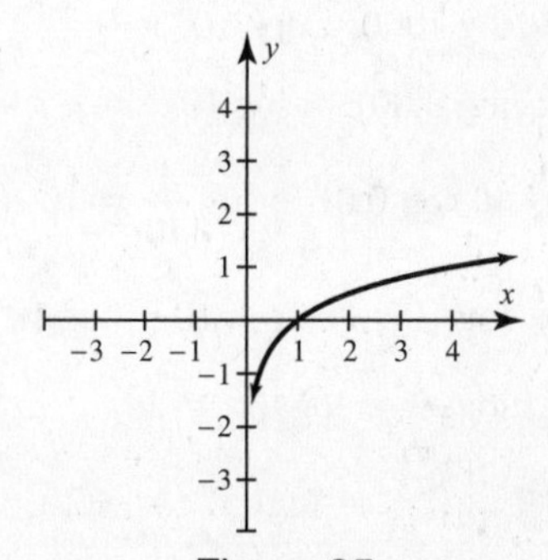
Figure 35

35. See Figure 35. $D = \{x \mid x > 0\}$.

36. See Figure 36. $D = \{x \mid x > -1\}$.

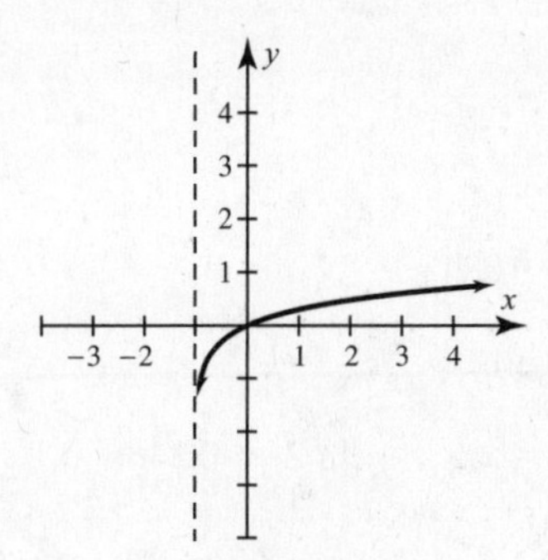
Figure 36

37. $y = Ca^x \Rightarrow y = 2(2)^x \Rightarrow C = 2;\ a = 2$

38. $y = Ca^x \Rightarrow y = 3\left(\frac{1}{3}\right)^x \Rightarrow C = 3;\ a = \frac{1}{3}$

39. $A = 1200\left(1 + \frac{0.09}{2}\right)^{2(3)} \approx \$1562.71$

40. $A = 500e^{0.065(8)} \approx \$841.01$

41. $e^x = 19 \Rightarrow \ln e^x = \ln 19 \Rightarrow x = \ln 19 \approx 2.9444$; the result can be supported graphically using the intersection method with the graphs $Y_1 = e$^X and $Y_2 = 19$. The intersection point is near (2.9444, 19). The result may also be supported numerically with a table of $Y_1 = e$^X starting at 2.9 and incrementing by 0.01. Here $Y_1 = 19$ when $x \approx 2.94$.

42. Graph $Y_1 =$ 2^X − X^2 − X in $[-10, 10, 1]$ by $[-10, 10, 1]$ and find the three $x$-intercepts. See Figure 42. The solutions are $x \approx -1.309$, $x = 1$, and $x \approx 4.798$.

[−10, 10, 1] by [−10, 10, 1]

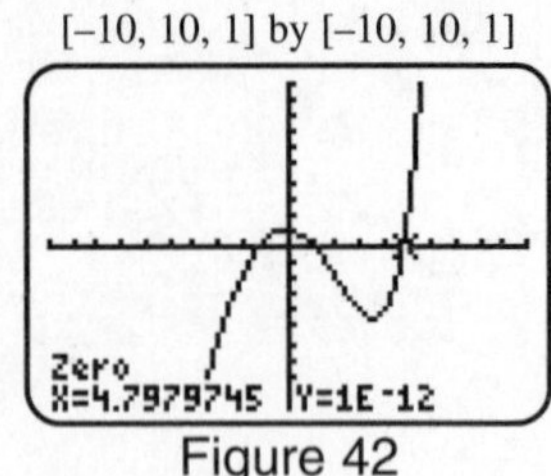

Figure 42

43. $\log 1000 = \log 10^3 = 3$

44. $\log 0.001 = \log 10^{-3} = -3$

45. $10 \log 0.01 + \log \frac{1}{10} = 10 \log 10^{-2} + \log 10^{-1} = 10(-2) + (-1) = -21$

46. $\log 100 + \log \sqrt[3]{10} = \log 10^2 + \log 10^{1/3} = 2 + \frac{1}{3} = \frac{7}{3}$

47. $\log_3 9 = \log_3 3^2 = 2$

48. $\log_5 \frac{1}{25} = \log_5 5^{-2} = -2$

49. $\ln e = \ln e^1 = 1$

50. $\log_2 32 = \log_2 2^5 = 5$

51. $\log_3 18 = \frac{\log 18}{\log 3} \approx 2.631$

52. $\log_2 173 = \frac{\log 173}{\log 2} \approx 7.435$

53. $10^x = 125 \Rightarrow \log 10^x = \log 125 \Rightarrow x = \log 125 \approx 2.097$

54. $1.5^x = 55 \Rightarrow \log 1.5^x = \log 55 \Rightarrow x \log 1.5 = \log 55 \Rightarrow x = \frac{\log 55}{\log 1.5} \approx 9.883$

55. $e^{0.1x} = 5.2 \Rightarrow \ln e^{0.1x} = \ln 5.2 \Rightarrow 0.1x = \ln 5.2 \Rightarrow x = 10 \ln 5.2 \approx 16.49$

56. $4e^{2x} - 5 = 3 \Rightarrow 4e^{2x} = 8 \Rightarrow e^{2x} = 2 \Rightarrow \ln e^{2x} = \ln 2 \Rightarrow 2x = \ln 2 \Rightarrow x = \frac{1}{2} \ln 2 \approx 0.3466$

57. $5^{-x} = 10 \Rightarrow \log 5^{-x} = \log 10 \Rightarrow -x \log 5 = 1 \Rightarrow -x = \frac{1}{\log 5} \Rightarrow x = -\frac{1}{\log 5} \approx -1.431$

58. $3(10^{-x}) = 6 \Rightarrow 10^{-x} = 2 \Rightarrow \log(10^{-x}) = \log 2 \Rightarrow -x = \log 2 \Rightarrow x = -\log 2 \approx -0.301$

59. $50 - 3(0.78)^{x-10} = 21 \Rightarrow -3(0.78)^{x-10} = -29 \Rightarrow (0.78)^{x-10} = \dfrac{29}{3} \Rightarrow$

$(x - 10)\log(0.78) = \log\left(\dfrac{29}{3}\right) \Rightarrow x - 10 = \dfrac{\log\left(\frac{29}{3}\right)}{\log(0.78)} \Rightarrow x = 10 + \dfrac{\log\left(\frac{29}{3}\right)}{\log(0.78)} \approx 0.869$

60. $5(1.3)^x + 4 = 104 \Rightarrow 5(1.3)^x = 100 \Rightarrow (1.3)^x = 20 \Rightarrow x\log(1.3) = \log(20) \Rightarrow$

$x = \dfrac{\log(20)}{\log(1.3)} \approx 11.418$

61. For each unit increase in $x$, the $y$-values are multiplied by 2, so the data are exponential. Since $y = 1.5$ when $x = 0$, the initial value is 1.5, so $f(x) = Ca^x \Rightarrow f(x) = 1.5a^x$. Since $y = 3$ when $x = 1$, $f(1) = 1.5a^1 \Rightarrow$ $3 = 1.5a \Rightarrow a = 2$. Thus the function $f(x) = 1.5(2^x)$ can model the data.

62. For each unit increase in $x$, the $y$-values increase by 1.5, so the data are linear. Since $y = 3$ when $x = 0$, the function $f(x) = 1.5x + 3$ can model the data.

63. $\log x = 1.5 \Rightarrow 10^{\log x} = 10^{1.5} \Rightarrow x = 10^{1.5} \approx 31.62$

64. $\log_3 x = 4 \Rightarrow 3^{\log_3 x} = 3^4 \Rightarrow x = 3^4 \Rightarrow x = 81$

65. $\ln x = 3.4 \Rightarrow e^{\ln x} = e^{3.4} \Rightarrow x = e^{3.4} \approx 29.96$

66. $4 - \ln(5 - x) = \dfrac{5}{2} \Rightarrow -\ln(5 - x) = -1.5 \Rightarrow \ln(5 - x) = 1.5 \Rightarrow e^{\ln(5-x)} = e^{1.5} \Rightarrow$

$5 - x = e^{1.5} \Rightarrow x = 5 - e^{1.5} \approx 0.5183$

67. $\log 6 + \log 5x = \log(6 \cdot 5x) = \log 30x$

68. $\log\sqrt{3} - \log\sqrt[3]{3} = \log(3^{1/2}) - \log(3^{1/3}) = \dfrac{1}{2}\log 3 - \dfrac{1}{3}\log 3 = \dfrac{1}{6}\log 3$

69. $\ln\dfrac{y}{x^2} = \ln(y) - \ln(x^2) = \ln(y) - 2\ln(x)$

70. $\log\dfrac{4x^3}{k} = \log 4x^3 - \log k = \log 4 + \log x^3 - \log k = \log 4 + 3\log x - \log k$

71. $8\log x = 2 \Rightarrow \log x = \dfrac{1}{4} \Rightarrow 10^{\log x} = 10^{1/4} \Rightarrow x = 10^{1/4} \Rightarrow x = \sqrt[4]{10} \approx 1.778$

72. $\ln 2x = 2 \Rightarrow e^{\ln 2x} = e^2 \Rightarrow 2x = e^2 \Rightarrow x = \dfrac{e^2}{2} \approx 3.695$

73. $2\log 3x + 5 = 15 \Rightarrow 2\log 3x = 10 \Rightarrow \log 3x = 5 \Rightarrow 10^{\log 3x} = 10^5 \Rightarrow 3x = 100{,}000 \Rightarrow$

$x = \dfrac{100{,}000}{3} \approx 33{,}333$

74. $5\log_2 x = 25 \Rightarrow \log_2 x = 5 \Rightarrow 2^{\log_2 x} = 2^5 \Rightarrow x = 2^5 \Rightarrow x = 32$

75. $2\log_5(x + 2) = \log_5(x + 8) \Rightarrow \log_5(x + 2)^2 = \log_5(x + 8) \Rightarrow 10^{\log_5(x+2)^2} = 10^{\log_5(x+8)} \Rightarrow$

$(x + 2)^2 = (x + 8) \Rightarrow x^2 + 4x + 4 = x + 8 \Rightarrow x^2 + 3x - 4 = 0 \Rightarrow (x + 4)(x - 1) = 0 \Rightarrow$

$x = -4$ or $x = 1$; since $x = -4$ is undefined in $\log(x + 2)$, the only solution is $x = 1$.

76. $\ln(5 - x) - \ln(5 + x) = -\ln 9 \Rightarrow \ln\left(\dfrac{5 - x}{5 + x}\right) = \ln 9^{-1} \Rightarrow e^{\ln(5-x/5+x)} = e^{\ln(1/9)} \Rightarrow \dfrac{5 - x}{5 + x} = \dfrac{1}{9} \Rightarrow$

$45 - 9x = 5 + x \Rightarrow 10x = 40 \Rightarrow x = 4$

77. If $b$ is the $y$-intercept, then the point $(0, b)$ is on the graph of $f$. Therefore, the point $(b, 0)$ is on the graph of $f^{-1}$. The point $(b, 0)$ lies on the $x$-axis and is the $x$-intercept of the graph of $f^{-1}$.

78. (a) $y = ax + b \Rightarrow y - b = ax \Rightarrow \dfrac{y-b}{a} = x$. Thus, $f^{-1}(x) = \dfrac{x-b}{a} = \dfrac{1}{a}x - \dfrac{b}{a}$.

(b) The slope of the graph of $f$ is $a$, and the slope of the graph $f^{-1}$ is $\dfrac{1}{a}$. Their slopes are reciprocals of each other.

79. (a) $N(t) = N_0 e^{rt} \Rightarrow 6000 = 4000e^{r(1)} \Rightarrow 1.5 = e^r \Rightarrow \ln 1.5 = \ln e^r \Rightarrow \ln 1.5 = r \Rightarrow r = 0.4055$

Now $N(2.5) = 4000e^{0.4055(2.5)} \Rightarrow N(2.5) \approx 11{,}022$

(b) $8500 = 4000e^{0.4055t} \Rightarrow 2.125 = e^{0.4055t} \Rightarrow \ln 2.125 = \ln e^{0.4055t} \Rightarrow \ln 2.125 = 0.4055t \Rightarrow$

$\dfrac{\ln 2.125}{0.4055} = t \Rightarrow t \approx 1.86$ hours.

80. (a) $T_0 = 20$, $D = 100 - 20 \Rightarrow D = 80$. Solving for $a$ use $50 = 20 + 80a^{2/3} \Rightarrow 30 = 80a^{2/3} \Rightarrow$

$\dfrac{3}{8} = a^{2/3} \Rightarrow a = \left(\dfrac{3}{8}\right)^{3/2} \Rightarrow a = 0.23$

(b) $T\left(\dfrac{3}{2}\right) = 20 + 80(0.23)^{3/2} \Rightarrow T\left(\dfrac{3}{2}\right) \approx 28.8°\text{C}$

(c) $30 = 20 + 80(0.23)^t \Rightarrow 10 = 80(0.23)^t \Rightarrow \dfrac{1}{8} = (0.23)^t \Rightarrow \ln\dfrac{1}{8} = t\ln 0.23 \Rightarrow t = \dfrac{\ln\frac{1}{8}}{\ln 0.23} \Rightarrow$

$t = 1.4$ hours.

81. $h(x) = f(x) + g(x) = 10x + 5x = 15x$

82. To solve the equation $f(x) = 30$, we must solve the following equation

$36e^{-(x-20)^2/49} = 30 \Rightarrow e^{-(x-20)^2/49} = \dfrac{5}{6} \Rightarrow \ln e^{-(x-20)^2/49} = \ln\dfrac{5}{6} \Rightarrow -\dfrac{(x-20)^2}{49} = \ln\dfrac{5}{6} \Rightarrow$

$-(x-20)^2 = 49\ln\dfrac{5}{6} \Rightarrow (x-20)^2 = -49\ln\dfrac{5}{6} \Rightarrow x - 20 = \pm\sqrt{-49\ln\dfrac{5}{6}} \Rightarrow$

$x = 20 \pm \sqrt{-49\ln\dfrac{5}{6}} \Rightarrow x \approx 17$ or $23$. This means that 30 thousand people had scores of 17 or 23.

83. Use the intersection method by graphing $Y_1 = 175.6(1 - 0.66e$^$(-0.24X))$^$3$ and $Y_2 = 50$ in the viewing rectangle [0, 14, 1] by [0, 175, 25]. The intersection is near the point (2.74, 50). See Figure 83. This means that at approximately 3 weeks the fish weighed 50 milligrams.

[0, 14, 1] by [0, 175, 25]

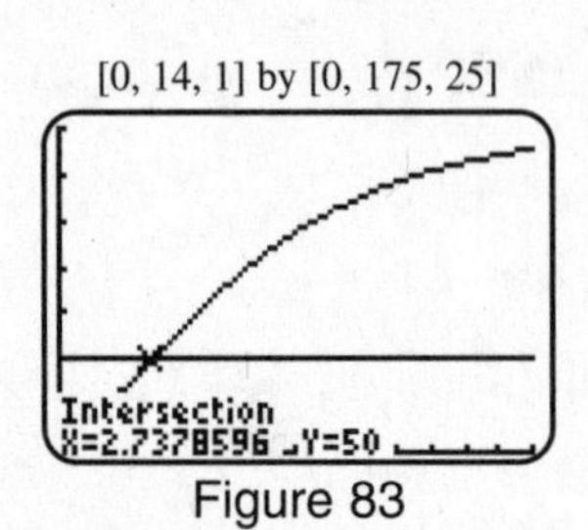


Figure 83

84. $1 = 10\left(\frac{1}{2}\right)^{t/23} \Rightarrow \frac{1}{10} = \left(\frac{1}{2}\right)^{t/23} \Rightarrow \log_2\left(\frac{1}{10}\right) = -\frac{t}{23} \Rightarrow t = (-23)\left(\log_2\left(\frac{1}{10}\right)\right) \Rightarrow$

$t = (-23)\frac{\log \frac{1}{10}}{\log 2} = \frac{23}{\log 2} \approx 76.4$; after about 76.4 days.

85. $15 = 32e^{-0.2t} \Rightarrow \frac{15}{32} = e^{-0.2t} \Rightarrow -0.2t = \ln\left(\frac{15}{32}\right) \Rightarrow t = \left(-\frac{1}{0.2}\right)\ln\left(\frac{15}{32}\right) \approx (-5)(-0.7577) \approx 3.8$;

after about 3.8 minutes.

86. (a) $(g \circ f)(32) = g(f(32)) = g(2) = 1$. $(g \circ f)(32)$ computes the number quarts in 32 fluid ounces, which is 1 quart.

(b) Since $f(16) = 1, f^{-1}(1) = 16$. $f^{-1}$ converts pints into fluid ounces. There are 16 fluid ounces in 1 pint.

(c) $(f^{-1} \circ g^{-1})(1) = f^{-1}(g^{-1}(1)) = f^{-1}(2) = 32$. $(f^{-1} \circ g^{-1})(1)$ computes the number of fluid ounces in 1 quart. There are 32 ounces in 1 quart.

87. Logistic: least-squares regression gives $f(x) \approx \frac{171.4}{1 + 18.4e^{-0.0744x}}$

88. (a) Use coordinates (1600, 700) and (2000, 1700) and exponential least-squares regression to find $C \approx 20.12$ and $a \approx 1.00222$. $f(x) = 20.12(1.00222)^x$.

(b) $1000 = 20.12(1.00222)^x \Rightarrow \frac{1000}{20.12} = (1.00222)^x \Rightarrow \ln\left(\frac{1000}{20.12}\right) = \ln(1.00222)^x \Rightarrow$

$\ln\left(\frac{1000}{20.12}\right) = x \ln(1.00222) \Rightarrow x = \frac{\ln\left(\frac{1000}{20.12}\right)}{\ln(1.00222)} \approx 1761$. In 1761 methane levels were 1000 ppb.

89. See Figure 89. $a \approx 3.50, b \approx 0.74$, or $f(x) = 3.50(0.74)^x$

90. See Figure 90. $a \approx 2.1, b \approx 1.2$, or $f(x) = 2.1 + 1.2 \ln x$

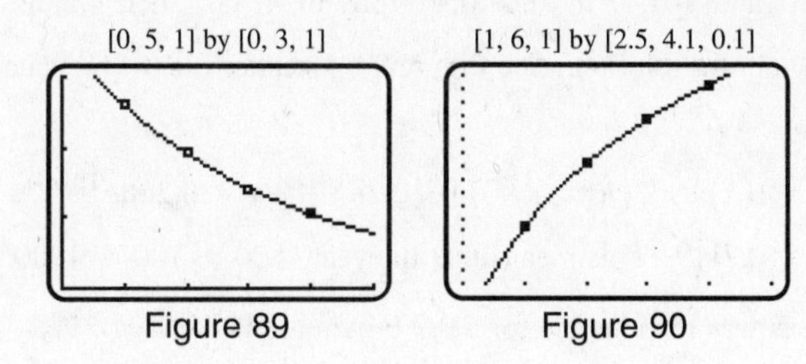


Figure 89 Figure 90

## Extended and Discovery Exercises for Chapter 5

1. STEP 1: Using $w = \ln x$ and $z = \ln y$, the data points $(w, z)$ are approximately (4.85, –1.24), (5.20, –0.69), (5.40, –0.40), (6.05, 0.57), (6.51, 1.27), (6.98, 1.97), and (7.54, 2.81). Plot these points as shown in Figure 1a.

STEP 2: Use the linear regression feature of the graphing calculator to find the values $b$ and $d$. See Figure 1b.

STEP 3: Here the slope of the line is approximately 1.505, so $b \approx 1.505$ in the equation $y = ax^b$. The $y$-intercept of the regression line is approximately –8.513, so $a \approx e^{-8.513} \approx 0.0002$ in the equation $y = ax^b$.

The equation $y = 0.0002x^{1.5}$ models the data. A graph of $y = 0.0002x^{1.5}$ along with the original data is shown in Figure 1c.

[4, 8, 1] by [–2, 4, 1]

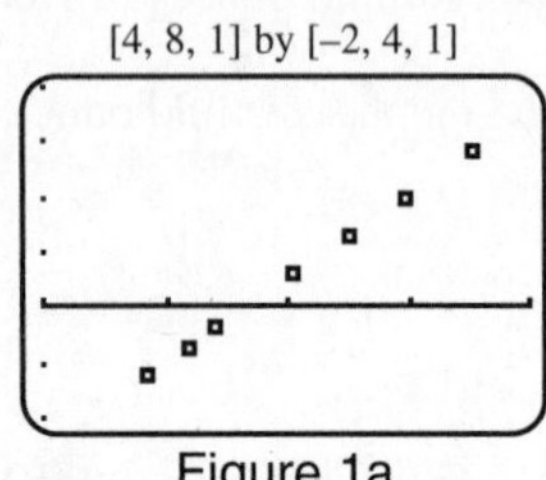

Figure 1a

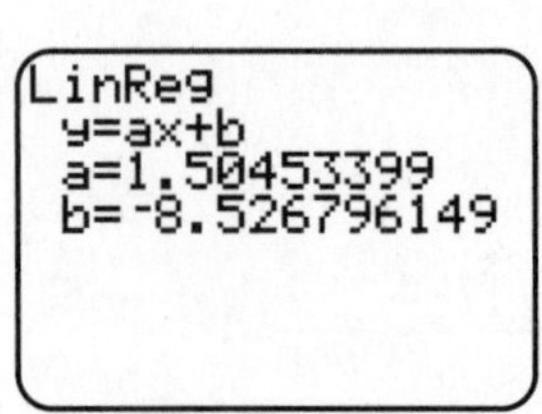


Figure 1b

[0, 2000, 500] by [0, 20, 2]

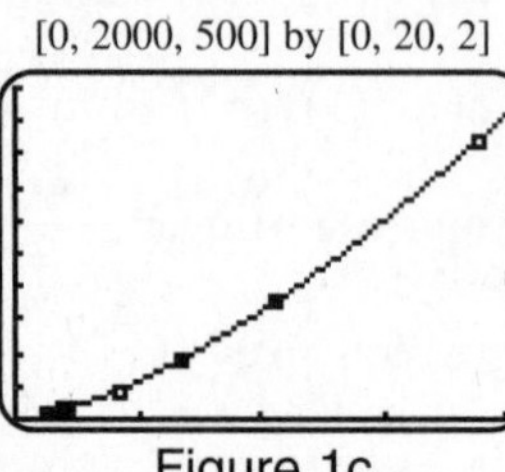

Figure 1c

[0, 300, 100] by [0, 4, 1]

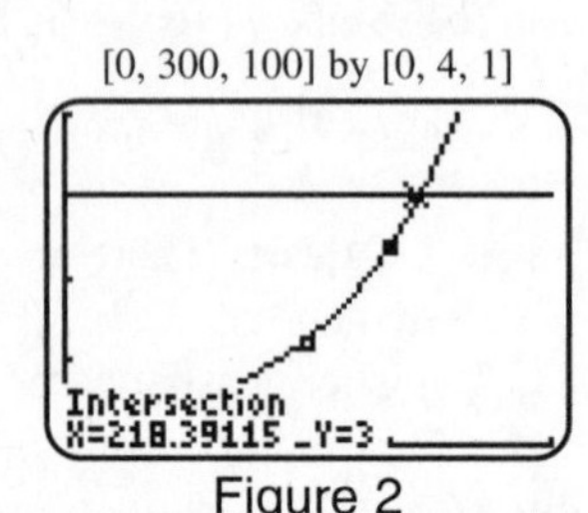


Figure 2

2. (a) $R(0) = Ce^0 = C(1) = 0.2$; therefore $C = 0.2$. The equation can be written $R(x) = 0.2e^{kx}$. Since $R(200) = 2.4$, we find $k$ by solving $0.2e^{200k} = 2.4 \Rightarrow e^{200k} = \frac{2.4}{0.2} \Rightarrow e^{200k} = 12 \Rightarrow$ $\ln e^{200k} = \ln 12 \Rightarrow 200k = \ln 12 \Rightarrow k = \frac{\ln 12}{200} \approx 0.0124$.

(b) We must solve the equation $R(x) = 3$ symbolically.

$0.2e^{0.0124x} = 3 \Rightarrow e^{0.0124x} = 15 \Rightarrow \ln e^{0.0124x} = \ln 15 \Rightarrow 0.0124x = \ln 15 \Rightarrow x = \frac{\ln 15}{0.0124} \approx 218.$

Thus, in the year 1800 + 218 = 2018, this model predicts $R$ will be 3 watts per square meter. To support this result graphically, graph $Y_1 = 0.2e$^(0.0124X) and $Y_2 = 3$ in [0, 300, 100] by [0, 4, 1]. Their graphs intersect when $x = 218$, which agrees with the symbolic solution. See Figure 2. A scatter plot of the data has also been included.

3. (a) $T(R) = 1.03R$ and $R(x) = 0.2e^{0.0124x} \Rightarrow (T \circ R)(x) = T(R(x)) = 1.03(0.2e^{0.0124x}) = 0.206e^{0.0124x}$.

(b) $(T \circ R)(100) = 0.206e^{0.0124(100)} = 0.206e^{1.24} \approx 0.7119$. This means that the year 1800 + 100 = 1900, radiative forcing due to increased greenhouse gases was responsible for a 0.7ºF increase in average global temperature.

4. $\left(\frac{1}{\pi}\ln(640{,}320^3 + 744)\right)^2 \approx 163.00000000000000000000000000000232$

That is, $\left(\frac{1}{\pi}\ln(640{,}320^3 + 744)\right)^2 - 163 \approx 2.32 \times 10^{-30}$. It is not an integer.

5. $e^{\pi\sqrt{163}} \approx 262{,}537{,}412{,}640{,}768{,}743.99999999999925$. It is not an integer.

# Chapter 6: Systems of Equations and Inequalities

## 6.1: Functions and Systems of Equations in Two Variables

1. $A(5,8) = \frac{1}{2}(5)(8) = 20$. The area of a triangle with a base of 5 and height of 8 is 20 square units.
2. $A(20,35) = (20)(35) = 700$. The area of a rectangle having a width of 20 and length of 35 is 700 square units.
3. $f(2,-3)$ if $f(x,y) = x^2 + y^2 \Rightarrow f(2,-3) = 2^2 + (-3)^2 = 4 + 9 = 13$
4. $f(-1,3)$ if $f(x,y) = 2x^2 - y^2 \Rightarrow f(-1,3) = 2(-1)^2 - 3^2 = 2(1) - 9 = -7$
5. $f(-2,3)$ if $f(x,y) = 3x - 4y \Rightarrow f(-2,3) = 3(-2) - 4(3) = -6 - 12 = -18$
6. $f(5,-2)$ if $f(x,y) = 6y - \frac{1}{2}x \Rightarrow f(5,-2) = 6(-2) - \frac{1}{2}(5) = -12 - \frac{5}{2} = -\frac{29}{2}$
7. $f\left(\frac{1}{2}, -\frac{7}{4}\right)$ if $f(x,y) = \frac{2x}{y+3} \Rightarrow f\left(\frac{1}{2}, -\frac{7}{4}\right) = \frac{2(\frac{1}{2})}{(-\frac{7}{4}) + 3} = \frac{1}{\frac{5}{4}} = \frac{4}{5}$
8. $f(0.2, 0.5)$ if $f(x,y) = \frac{5x}{2y+1} \Rightarrow f(0.2,0.5) = \frac{5(0.2)}{2(0.5)+1} = \frac{1}{2}$
9. The sum of $y$ and twice $x$ is computed by $f(x,y) = y + 2x$.
10. The product of $x^2$ and $y^2$ is computed by $f(x,y) = x^2y^2$.
11. The product of $x$ and $y$ divided by $1 + x$ is computed by $f(x,y) = \frac{xy}{1+x}$.
12. The square root of the sum of $x$ and $y$ is computed by $f(x,y) = \sqrt{x+y}$.
13. $3x - 4y = 7 \Rightarrow 3x = 4y + 7 \Rightarrow x = \frac{4y+7}{3}$; $3x - 4y = 7 \Rightarrow -4y = -3x + 7 \Rightarrow y = \frac{3x-7}{4}$
14. $-x - 5y = 4 \Rightarrow -x = 5y + 4 \Rightarrow x = -5y - 4$; $-x - 5y = 4 \Rightarrow -5y = x + 4 \Rightarrow y = \frac{-x-4}{5}$
15. $x - y^2 = 5 \Rightarrow x = y^2 + 5$; $x - y^2 = 5 \Rightarrow -y^2 = -x + 5 \Rightarrow y^2 = x - 5 \Rightarrow y = \pm\sqrt{x-5}$
16. $2x^2 + y = 4 \Rightarrow 2x^2 = -y + 4 \Rightarrow x^2 = \frac{-y+4}{2} \Rightarrow x = \pm\sqrt{\frac{-y+4}{2}}$; $2x^2 + y = 4 \Rightarrow y = -2x^2 + 4$
17. $\frac{2x-y}{3y} = 1 \Rightarrow 2x - y = 3y \Rightarrow 2x = 4y \Rightarrow x = 2y$; $\frac{2x-y}{3y} = 1 \Rightarrow 2x - y = 3y \Rightarrow 2x = 4y \Rightarrow$
    $y = \frac{x}{2}$
18. $\frac{x+y}{x-y} = 2 \Rightarrow x + y = 2(x-y) \Rightarrow x + y = 2x - 2y \Rightarrow -x = -3y \Rightarrow x = 3y$;
    $\frac{x+y}{x-y} = 2 \Rightarrow x + y = 2(x-y) \Rightarrow x + y = 2x - 2y \Rightarrow 3y = x \Rightarrow y = \frac{x}{3}$
19. The only ordered pair that satisfies both equations is (2, 1). The system is linear.

    $2(2) + 1 = 5$★ $\quad 2(-2) + 1 = -3 \quad 2(1) + 0 = 2$

    $2 + 1 = 3$★ $\quad -2 + 1 = -1 \quad 1 + 0 = 1$
20. The only ordered pair that satisfies both equations is (5, 0). The system is linear.

    $3 - 2 = 1 \quad 3 - (-4) = 7 \quad 5 - 0 = 5$★

    $2(3) + 2 = 8 \quad 2(3) + (-4) = 2 \quad 2(5) + 0 = 10$★

21. The only ordered pair that satisfies both equations is (4, –3). The system is non-linear.

$4^2 + (-3)^2 = 25$★ $0^2 + 5^2 = 25$★ $4^2 + 3^2 = 25$★

$2(4) + 3(-3) = -1$★ $2(0) + 3(5) = 15$ $2(4) + 3(3) = 17$

22. The ordered pairs that satisfies both equations are (4, 8) and (8, 4). The system is non-linear.

$4(8) = 32$★ $8(4) = 32$★ $-4(-8) = 32$★

$4 + 8 = 12$★ $8 + 4 = 12$★ $-4 + (-8) = -12$

23. From the graph the solution is (2, 2). The solution satisfies both $x - y = 0$ and $x + y = 4$.

24. From the graph the solution is (–2, 1). The solution satisfies both $x + y = -1$ and $-x + y = 3$.

25. From the graph the solution is $\left(\frac{1}{2}, -2\right)$. The solution satisfies both $6x + 4y = -5$ and $2x - 3y = 7$.

26. From the graph the solution is $\left(-1, -\frac{1}{2}\right)$. The solution satisfies both $5x - 2y = -4$ and $-x + 2y = 0$.

27. $x - y = 2$ and $2x + 2y = 38$. Multiply the second equation by $\frac{1}{2}$ and add to eliminate the $y$-variable.

$$\begin{array}{rl} x - y &= 2 \\ x + y &= 19 \\ \hline 2x \quad &= 21 \quad \Rightarrow x = 10.5 \end{array}$$

Since, $x - y = 2, y = 8.5$. The solution is $(10.5, 8.5)$.

28. $x + y = 300$ and $x - y = 8$. Add to eliminate the $y$-variable.

$$\begin{array}{rl} x + y &= 300 \\ x - y &= 8 \\ \hline 2x \quad &= 308 \quad \Rightarrow x = 154 \end{array}$$

Since, $x + y = 300, y = 146$. The solution is $(154, 146)$.

29. $x + y = 75$ and $4x + 7y = 456$. Multiply the first equation by 7 and subtract to eliminate the $y$-variable.

$$\begin{array}{rl} 7x + 7y &= 525 \\ 4x + 7y &= 456 \\ \hline 3x \quad &= 69 \quad \Rightarrow x = 23 \end{array}$$

Since, $x + y = 75, y = 52$. The solution is $(23, 52)$.

30. $x + y = 16$ and $10x + 25y = 265$. Multiply the first equation by 10 and subtract to eliminate the $x$-variable.

$$\begin{array}{rl} 10x + 10y &= 160 \\ 10x + 25y &= 265 \\ \hline -15y &= -105 \end{array} \Rightarrow y = 7$$

Since, $x + y = 16, x = 9$. The solution is $(9, 7)$.

31. Since the lines intersect, the system is consistent with a unique solution at (2, 2).

$x + y = 4 \Rightarrow y = 4 - x$; We substitute $4 - x$ for $y$ in the other equation.

$2x - (4 - x) = 2 \Rightarrow 3x = 6 \Rightarrow x = 2$, then $2 + y = 4 \Rightarrow y = 2$. The solution is $(2, 2)$.

32. Since the lines are parallel, the system is inconsistent with no solutions.

33. Since the lines are parallel, the system is inconsistent with no solutions.

34. Since the lines intersect, the system is consistent with a unique solution at (–2, 0).

$2x + y = -4 \Rightarrow y = -4 - 2x$; We substitute $-4 - 2x$ for $y$ in the other equation.

$-x + 2(-4 - 2x) = 2 \Rightarrow x = -2$, then $2(-2) + y = -4 \Rightarrow y = 0$. The solution is $(-2, 0)$.

35. Parallel lines $\Rightarrow$ inconsistent system. See Figure 35.

36. Parallel lines $\Rightarrow$ inconsistent system. See Figure 36.

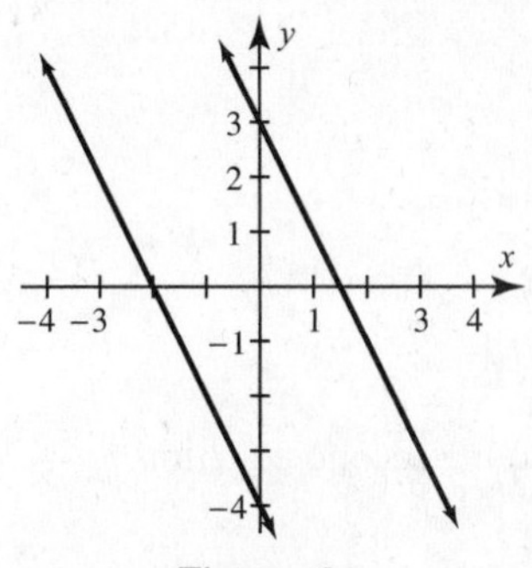
Figure 35

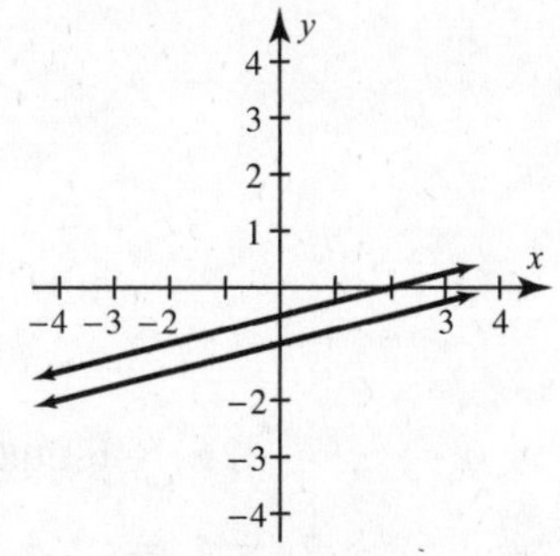
Figure 36

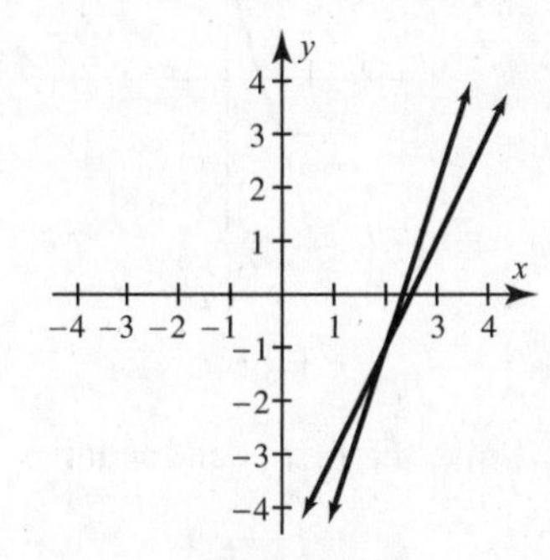
Figure 37

37. The lines intersect at $(2, -1)$. The system is consistent and independent. See Figure 37.

38. The lines intersect at $(1, 2)$. The system is consistent and independent. See Figure 38.

39. The lines intersect at $(-2, 2)$. The system is consistent and independent. See Figure 39.

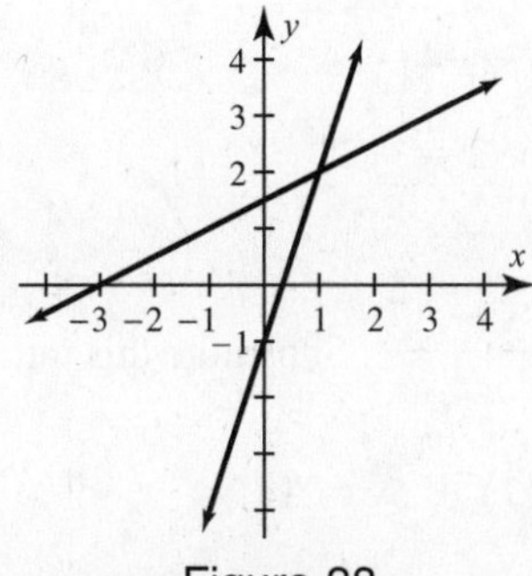
Figure 38

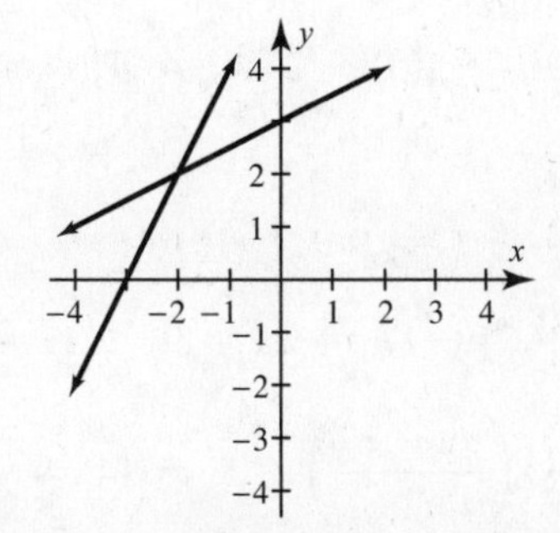
Figure 39

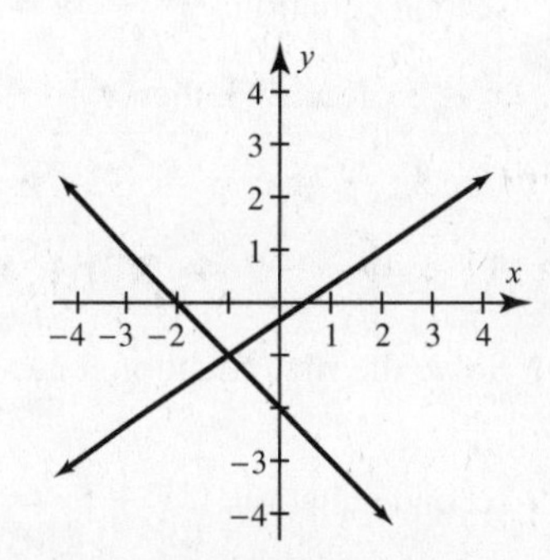
Figure 40

40. The lines intersect at $(-1, -1)$. The system is consistent and independent. See Figure 40.

41. The system has an infinite number of solutions. $\{(x, y) | 2x - y = -4\}$. The system is consistent and dependent. See Figure 41.

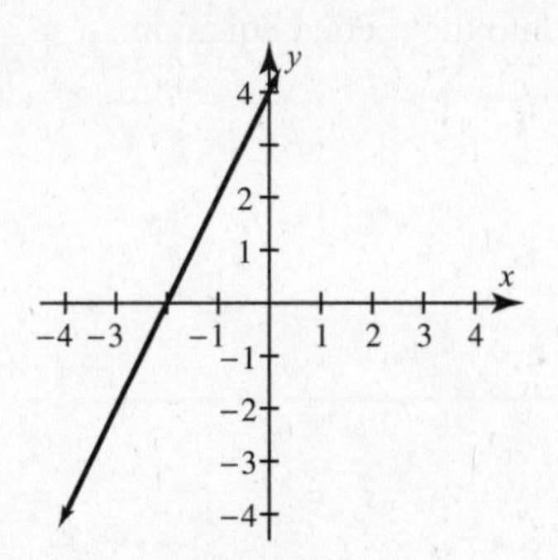
Figure 41

42. The system has an infinite number of solutions. $\{(x, y) \mid 3x - y = -2\}$. The system is consistent and dependent. See Figure 42.

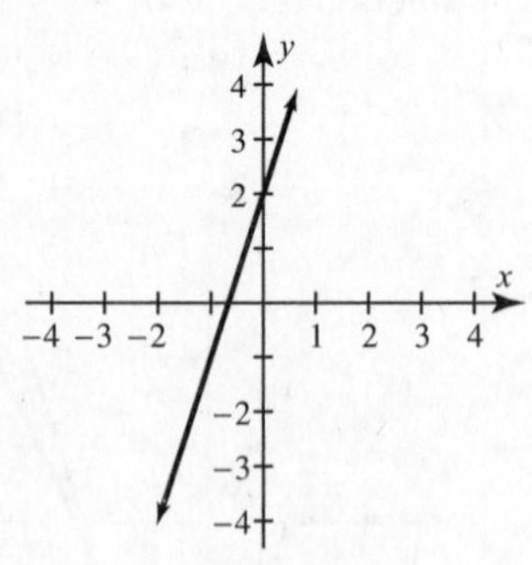


Figure 42

43. Solve the first equation for $x$: $x + 2y = 0 \Rightarrow x = -2y$. Substitute this into the second equation.

$3x + 7y = 1 \Rightarrow 3(-2y) + 7y = 1 \Rightarrow -6y + 7y = 1 \Rightarrow y = 1.$

If $y = 1$, then $x = -2(1) = -2$. The solution is $(-2, 1)$.

Check: $x + 2y = 0 \Rightarrow (-2) + 2(1) = 0 \Rightarrow 0 = 0$; $x = -2y \Rightarrow -2 = -2(1) \Rightarrow -2 = -2$

44. Solve the first equation for $y$: $-2x - y = -2 \Rightarrow -y = 2x - 2 \Rightarrow y = -2x + 2$. Substitute this into the second equation. $3x + 4y = -7 \Rightarrow 3x + 4(-2x + 2) = -7 \Rightarrow 3x - 8x + 8 = -7 \Rightarrow -5x = -15 \Rightarrow x = 3$. If $x = 3$, then $y = -2x + 2 = -2(3) + 2 = -4$. The solution is $(3, -4)$.

Check: $-2x - y = -2 \Rightarrow -2(3) - (-4) = -2 \Rightarrow -6 + 4 = -2 \Rightarrow -2 = -2;$

$3x + 4y = -7 \Rightarrow 3(3) + 4(-4) = -7 \Rightarrow 9 + (-16) = -7 \Rightarrow -7 = -7$

45. Solve the first equation for $x$: $2x - 9y = -17 \Rightarrow 2x = 9y - 17 \Rightarrow x = \frac{9y - 17}{2}$. Substitute this into the second equation. $8x + 5y = 14 \Rightarrow 8\left(\frac{9y - 17}{2}\right) + 5y = 14 \Rightarrow 4(9y - 17) + 5y = 14 \Rightarrow$

$36y - 68 + 5y = 14 \Rightarrow 41y = 82 \Rightarrow y = 2$. If $y = 2$, then $x = \frac{9(2) - 17}{2} = \frac{1}{2}$. The solution is $(0.5, 2)$.

Check: $2x - 9y = -17 \Rightarrow 2(0.5) - 9(2) = -17 \Rightarrow 1 - 18 = -17 \Rightarrow -17 = -17;$

$8x + 5y = 14 \Rightarrow 8(0.5) + 5(2) = 14 \Rightarrow 4 + 10 = 14 \Rightarrow 14 = 14$

46. Solve the first equation for $x$: $3x + 6y = 0 \Rightarrow x = -2y$. Substitute this into the second equation.

$4x - 2y = -5 \Rightarrow 4(-2y) - 2y = -5 \Rightarrow -10y = -5 \Rightarrow y = \frac{1}{2}.$

If $y = \frac{1}{2}$, then $x = -2\left(\frac{1}{2}\right) = -1$. The solution is $\left(-1, \frac{1}{2}\right)$.

Check: $3x + 6y = 0 \Rightarrow 3(-1) + 6\left(\frac{1}{2}\right) = 0 \Rightarrow -3 + 3 = 0 \Rightarrow 0 = 0$

$4x - 2y = -5 \Rightarrow 4(-1) - 2\left(\frac{1}{2}\right) = -5 \Rightarrow -4 - 1 = -5 \Rightarrow -5 = -5$

47. Solve the second equation for $x$: $x + \frac{1}{2}y = 10 \Rightarrow x = -\frac{1}{2}y + 10$. Substitute this into the first equation.

$\frac{1}{2}x - y = -5 \Rightarrow \frac{1}{2}\left(-\frac{1}{2}y + 10\right) - y = -5 \Rightarrow -\frac{1}{4}y + 5 - y = -5 \Rightarrow -\frac{5}{4}y = -10 \Rightarrow y = 8.$

If $y = 8$, then $x = -\frac{1}{2}(8) + 10 = 6$. The solution is $(6, 8)$.

Check: $x + \frac{1}{2}y = 10 \Rightarrow 6 + \frac{1}{2}(8) = 10 \Rightarrow 6 + 4 = 10 \Rightarrow 10 = 10$

$\frac{1}{2}x - y = -5 \Rightarrow \frac{1}{2}(6) - 8 = -5 \Rightarrow 3 - 8 = -5 \Rightarrow -5 = -5$

48. Solve the first equation for $x$: $-x - \frac{1}{3}y = -4 \Rightarrow x = 4 - \frac{1}{3}y$. Substitute this into the second equation.

$\frac{1}{3}x + 2y = 7 \Rightarrow \frac{1}{3}\left(4 - \frac{1}{3}y\right) + 2y = 7 \Rightarrow \frac{4}{3} - \frac{1}{9}y + 2y = 7 \Rightarrow \frac{17}{9}y = \frac{17}{3} \Rightarrow y = 3.$

If $y = 3$, then $x = 4 - \frac{1}{3}(3) = 3$. The solution is $(3, 3)$.

Check: $-x - \frac{1}{3}y = -4 \Rightarrow -(3) - \frac{1}{3}(3) = -4 \Rightarrow -3 - 1 = -4 \Rightarrow -4 = -4$

$\frac{1}{3}x + 2y = 7 \Rightarrow \frac{1}{3}(3) + 2(3) = 7 \Rightarrow 1 + 6 = 7 \Rightarrow 7 = 7$

49. Solve the first equation for $y$: $3x - 2y = 5 \Rightarrow -2y = -3x + 5 \Rightarrow y = \frac{3}{2}x - \frac{5}{2}$. Substitute this into the second equation. $-6x + 4\left(\frac{3}{2}x - \frac{5}{2}\right) = -10 \Rightarrow -6x + 6x - 10 = -10 \Rightarrow -10 = -10 \Rightarrow$ there are infinitely many solutions. $\{(x, y) \mid 3x - 2y = 5\}$.

50. Solve the first equation for $x$: $\frac{1}{2}x - \frac{3}{4}y = \frac{1}{2} \Rightarrow 2x - 3y = 2 \Rightarrow 2x = 3y + 2 \Rightarrow x = \frac{3}{2}y + 1$. Substitute this into the second equation. $\frac{1}{5}\left(\frac{3}{2}y + 1\right) - \frac{3}{10}y = \frac{1}{5} \Rightarrow \frac{3}{10}y + \frac{1}{5} - \frac{3}{10}y = \frac{1}{5} \Rightarrow \frac{1}{5} = \frac{1}{5} \Rightarrow$ there are infinitely many solutions. $\{(x, y) \mid 2x - 3y = 2\}$.

51. Solve the first equation for $x$: $2x - 7y = 8 \Rightarrow 2x = 7y + 8 \Rightarrow x = \frac{7}{2}y + 4$. Substitute this into the second equation. $-3\left(\frac{7}{2}y + 4\right) + \frac{21}{2}y = 5 \Rightarrow -\frac{21}{2}y - 12 + \frac{21}{2}y = 5 \Rightarrow -12 = 5 \Rightarrow$ there are no real solutions.

52. Solve the first equation for $y$: $0.6x - 0.2y = 2 \Rightarrow 6x - 2y = 20 \Rightarrow -2y = -6x + 20 \Rightarrow y = 3x - 10$. Substitute this into the second equation. $-1.2x + 0.4(3x - 10) = 3 \Rightarrow -1.2x + 1.2x - 4 = 3 \Rightarrow$ $-4 = 3 \Rightarrow$ there are no real solutions.

53. $0.2x - 0.1y = 0.5 \Rightarrow 2x - y = 5$ and $0.4x + 0.3y = 2.5 \Rightarrow 4x + 3y = 25$

Solve the first equation for $y$: $2x - y = 5 \Rightarrow y = 2x - 5$. Substitute this into the second equation.

$4x + 3y = 25 \Rightarrow 4x + 3(2x - 5) = 25 \Rightarrow 4x + 6x - 15 = 25 \Rightarrow 10x = 40 \Rightarrow x = 4.$

If $x = 4$, then $y = 2(4) - 5 \Rightarrow y = 3$. The solution is $(4, 3)$.

54. Solve the first equation for $x$: $100x + 200y = 300 \Rightarrow x = 3 - 2y$. Substitute this into the second equation.

$200x + 100y = 0 \Rightarrow 200(3 - 2y) + 100y = 0 \Rightarrow 600 - 400y + 100y = 0 \Rightarrow -300y = -600 \Rightarrow$

$y = 2$. If $y = 2$, then $x = 3 - 2(2) \Rightarrow x = -1$. The solution is $(-1, 2)$.

55. Solve the second equation for $y$: $2x + y = 0 \Rightarrow y = -2x$. Substitute this into the first equation.

$x^2 - y = 0 \Rightarrow x^2 - (-2x) = 0 \Rightarrow x^2 + 2x = 0 \Rightarrow x(x + 2) = 0 \Rightarrow x = 0$ or $x = -2$.

When $x = 0$, $y = -2(0) = 0$ and when $x = -2$, $y = -2(-2) = 4$. The solutions are $(0, 0)$ and $(-2, 4)$.

56. Solve the second equation for $y$: $x + y = 3 \Rightarrow y = 3 - x$. Substitute this into the first equation.

$x^2 - y = 3 \Rightarrow x^2 - (3 - x) = 3 \Rightarrow x^2 + x - 6 = 0 \Rightarrow (x + 3)(x - 2) = 0 \Rightarrow x = -3$ or $x = 2$.

When $x = -3$, $y = 3 - (-3) = 6$ and when $x = 2$, $y = 3 - (2) = 1$. The solutions are $(-3, 6)$ and $(2, 1)$.

57. Solve the second equation for $y$: $x + y = 6 \Rightarrow y = 6 - x$. Substitute this into the first equation.

$xy = 8 \Rightarrow x(6 - x) = 8 \Rightarrow 6x - x^2 = 8 \Rightarrow x^2 - 6x + 8 = 0 \Rightarrow (x - 4)(x - 2) = 0 \Rightarrow$

$x = 4$ or $x = 2$.

When $x = 4$, $y = 6 - 4 = 2$ and when $x = 2$, $y = 6 - 2 = 4$. The solutions are $(4, 2)$ and $(2, 4)$.

58. Solve the first equation for $y$: $2x - y = 0 \Rightarrow y = 2x$. Substitute this into the second equation.

$2xy = 4 \Rightarrow 2x(2x) = 4 \Rightarrow 4x^2 = 4 \Rightarrow x^2 = 1 \Rightarrow x = \pm 1$.

When $x = -1$, $y = 2(-1) = -2$ and when $x = 1$, $y = 2(1) = 2$. The solutions are $(-1, -2)$ and $(1, 2)$.

59. Substitute the second equation, $y = 2x$, into the first equation.

$x^2 + y^2 = 20 \Rightarrow x^2 + (2x)^2 = 20 \Rightarrow x^2 + 4x^2 = 20 \Rightarrow 5x^2 = 20 \Rightarrow x^2 = 4 \Rightarrow x = \pm 2$.

When $x = -2$, $y = 2(-2) = -4$ and when $x = 2$, $y = 2(2) = 4$. The solutions are $(-2, -4)$ and $(2, 4)$.

60. Solve the second equation for $y$: $x + y = 3 \Rightarrow y = 3 - x$. Substitute this into the first equation.

$x^2 + y^2 = 9 \Rightarrow x^2 + (3 - x)^2 = 9 \Rightarrow x^2 + 9 - 6x + x^2 = 9 \Rightarrow 2x^2 - 6x = 0 \Rightarrow$

$2x(x - 3) = 0 \Rightarrow x = 0$ or $x = 3$. When $x = 0$, $y = 3 - 0 = 3$ and when $x = 3$, $y = 3 - 3 = 0$.

The solutions are $(0, 3)$ and $(3, 0)$.

61. Solve the second equation for $x$: $x - y = -2 \Rightarrow x = y - 2$. Substitute this into the first equation.

$\sqrt{y - 2} - 2y = 0 \Rightarrow \sqrt{y - 2} = 2y \Rightarrow y - 2 = 4y^2 \Rightarrow 4y^2 - y + 2 = 0$. Using the quadratic formula

to solve we get: $\dfrac{1 \pm \sqrt{1 - 4(4)(2)}}{2(4)} = \dfrac{1 \pm \sqrt{-31}}{8} \Rightarrow$ no real solutions.

62. Before solving either equation for a variable, note that the graph of the first equation is a circle centered at the origin with radius 2 and the graph of the second equation is a parabola that opens downward with vertex $(0, -3)$. The graphs do not intersect and thus the system has no real solutions.

63. Solve the first equation for $y$: $2x^2 - y = 5 \Rightarrow -y = -2x^2 + 5 \Rightarrow y = 2x^2 - 5$. Substitute this into the second equation. $-4x^2 + 2(2x^2 - 5) = -10 \Rightarrow -4x^2 + 4x^2 - 10 = -10 \Rightarrow -10 = -10 \Rightarrow$ there are infinitely many solutions, $\{(x, y) \mid 2x^2 - y = 5\}$.

64. Solve the first equation for $x$: $-6\sqrt{x} + 2y = -3 \Rightarrow -6\sqrt{x} = -2y - 3 \Rightarrow \sqrt{x} = \frac{1}{3}y + \frac{1}{2} \Rightarrow$

$x = \left(\frac{1}{3}y + \frac{1}{2}\right)^2$. Substitute this into the second equation. $2\sqrt{\left(\frac{1}{3}y + \frac{1}{2}\right)^2} - \frac{2}{3}y = 1 \Rightarrow$

$2\left(\frac{1}{3}y + \frac{1}{2}\right) - \frac{2}{3}y = 1 \Rightarrow \frac{2}{3}y + 1 - \frac{2}{3}y = 1 \Rightarrow 1 = 1 \Rightarrow$ there are infinitely many solutions,

$\{(x, y) \mid -6\sqrt{x} + 2y = -3\}$.

65. Solve the second equation for $y$: $x^2 + y = 4 \Rightarrow y = 4 - x^2$. Substitute this into the first equation.

$x^2 - y = 4 \Rightarrow x^2 - (4 - x^2) = 4 \Rightarrow 2x^2 = 8 \Rightarrow x^2 = 4 \Rightarrow x = \pm 2$.

When $x = -2$, $y = 4 - (-2)^2 = 0$ and when $x = 2$, $y = 4 - (2)^2 = 0$.

The solutions are $(-2, 0)$ and $(2, 0)$.

66. Substitute the first equation, $y = x^2 + x$, into the second equation.

$2x^2 - y = 2 \Rightarrow 2x^2 - (x^2 + x) = 2 \Rightarrow x^2 - x - 2 = 0 \Rightarrow (x - 2)(x + 1) = 0 \Rightarrow$

$x = 2$ or $x = -1$. When $x = -1$, $y = (-1)^2 + (-1) = 0$ and when $x = 2$, $y = (2)^2 + 2 = 6$.

The solutions are $(-1, 0)$ and $(2, 6)$.

67. Solve the second equation for $y$: $x - y = 0 \Rightarrow y = x$. Substitute this into the first equation.

$x^3 - x = 3y \Rightarrow x^3 - x = 3x \Rightarrow x^3 - 4x = 0 \Rightarrow x(x + 2)(x - 2) = 0 \Rightarrow x = 0, x = -2$, or $x = 2$.

When $x = 0$, $y = 0$, when $x = -2$, $y = -2$, and when $x = 2$, $y = 2$.

The solutions are $(-2, -2)$, $(0, 0)$, and $(2, 2)$.

68. Solve the first equation for $y$: $x^4 + y = 4 \Rightarrow y = 4 - x^4$. Substitute this into the second equation.

$3x^2 - y = 0 \Rightarrow 3x^2 - (4 - x^4) = 0 \Rightarrow x^4 + 3x^2 - 4 = 0 \Rightarrow (x^2 + 4)(x^2 - 1) = 0 \Rightarrow x = \pm 1$.

When $x = -1$, $y = 4 - (-1)^4 = 3$ and when $x = 1$, $y = 4 - (1)^4 = 3$. The solutions are $(-1, 3)$ and $(1, 3)$.

69. The given equations result in the following nonlinear system of equations.

$A(l, w) = 35 \Rightarrow lw = 35$ and $P(l, w) = 24 \Rightarrow 2l + 2w = 24$

Begin solving the second equation for $l$. $2l + 2w = 24 \Rightarrow l + w = 12 \Rightarrow l = 12 - w$. Substitute this into the first equation. $lw = 35 \Rightarrow (12 - w)w = 35 \Rightarrow 12w - w^2 = 35 \Rightarrow w^2 - 12w + 35 = 0$. This is a quadratic equation that can be solved by factoring, graphing, or the quadratic formula. The solutions to this quadratic are found using factoring. $w^2 - 12w + 35 = 0 \Rightarrow (w - 5)(w - 7) = 0 \Rightarrow w = 5$ or $7$.

Since $l = 12 - w$, if $w = 5$, then $l = 7$, and if $w = 7$, then $l = 5$. If the length is greater than the width, the solution is $l = 7$ and $w = 5$. A rectangle with length 7 and width 5 has an area of 35 and a perimeter of 24.

70. The given equations result in the following nonlinear system of equations.

$A(l, w) = 300 \Rightarrow lw = 300$ and $P(l, w) = 70 \Rightarrow 2l + 2w = 70$

Begin solving the second equation for $l$. $2l + 2w = 70 \Rightarrow l + w = 35 \Rightarrow l = 35 - w$. Substitute this into the first equation. $lw = 300 \Rightarrow (35 - w)w = 300 \Rightarrow 35w - w^2 = 300 \Rightarrow w^2 - 35w + 300 = 0$. This is a quadratic equation that can be solved by factoring, graphing, or the quadratic formula. Using factoring, its solution is as follows. $w^2 - 35w + 300 = 0 \Rightarrow (w - 15)(w - 20) = 0 \Rightarrow w = 15$ or $20$.

Since $l = 35 - w$, if $w = 15$, then $l = 20$, and if $w = 20$, then $l = 15$. If the length is greater than the width, the solution is $l = 20$ and $w = 15$. A rectangle with length 20 and width 15 has an area of 300 and a perimeter of 70.

71. Add the two equations together to eliminate the $y$-variable.

$$\begin{array}{rcl} x + y &=& 20 \\ x - y &=& 8 \\ \hline 2x \qquad &=& 28 \Rightarrow x = 14 \end{array}$$

Since $x + y = 20$, it follows that $y = 6$. The unique solution is (14, 6). The system is consistent and independent. Graphical and numerical support are shown in Figure 71a & 71b, where $Y_1 = 20 - X$ and $Y_2 = X - 8$.

[0, 24, 4] by [0, 16, 4]

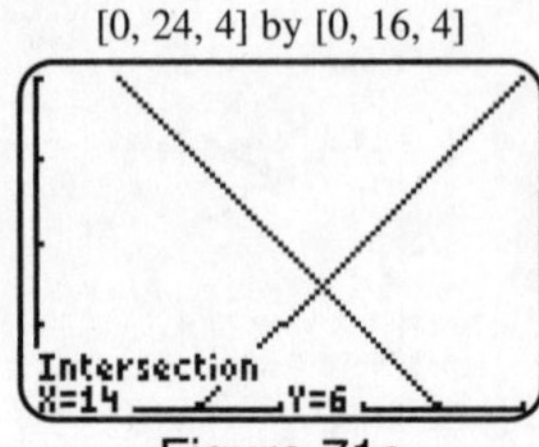

Figure 71a

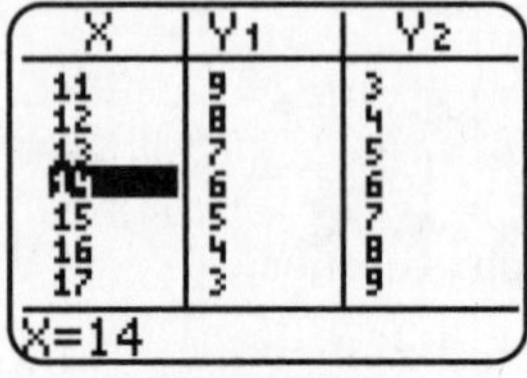

Figure 71b

72. Add the two equations together to eliminate the $y$-variable.

$$\begin{array}{rcl} 2x + y &=& 15 \\ x - y &=& 0 \\ \hline 3x \qquad &=& 15 \Rightarrow x = 5 \end{array}$$

Since $x - y = 0$, it follows that $y = 5$. The solution is (5, 5). The system is consistent and independent.

73. Subtract the two equations to eliminate the $x$-variable.

$$\begin{array}{rcl} x + 3y &=& 10 \\ x - 2y &=& -5 \\ \hline 5y &=& 15 \Rightarrow y = 3 \end{array}$$

Since $x + 3y = 10$, it follows that $x = 1$. The solution is (1, 3). The system is consistent and independent.

74. Multiply the second equation by 2 and add. This eliminates both variables.

$$\begin{array}{rcl} 4x + 2y &=& 10 \\ -4x - 2y &=& 20 \\ \hline 0 &=& 30 \Rightarrow \text{no solution} \end{array}$$

Since $0 \neq 30$, the system is inconsistent.

75. Multiply the second equation by $-1$ and subtract to eliminate both variables.

$$\begin{array}{rcl} x + y &=& 500 \\ x + y &=& 500 \\ \hline 0 &=& 0 \Rightarrow \text{infinite number of solutions} \end{array}$$

The solution is $\{(x, y) \mid x + y = 500\}$. The system is consistent but dependent.

76. Multiply the first equation by 2, the second equation by 3, and add to eliminate the $y$-variable.

$$\begin{array}{rcl} 4x + 6y &=& 10 \\ 15x - 6y &=& 9 \\ \hline 19x \qquad &=& 19 \Rightarrow x = 1 \end{array}$$

Since $2x + 3y = 5$, it follows that $y = 1$. The solution is (1, 1). The system is consistent and independent.

77. Multiply the second equation by 2 and add. This eliminates both variables.

$$\begin{array}{r} 2x + 4y = 7 \\ -2x - 4y = 10 \\ \hline 0 = 17 \end{array} \Rightarrow \text{no solution}$$

Since $0 \neq 17$, the system is inconsistent.

78. Multiply the first equation by 4, the second equation by 3, and add to eliminate the $y$-variable.

$$\begin{array}{r} 16x - 12y = 20 \\ 9x + 12y = 6 \\ \hline 25x \quad = 26 \end{array} \Rightarrow x = \frac{26}{25}$$

Since $4x - 3y = 5 \Rightarrow y = \dfrac{4x - 5}{3}$, it follows that $y = -\dfrac{7}{25}$. The solution is $\left(\dfrac{26}{25}, -\dfrac{7}{25}\right)$. The system is consistent and independent.

79. Multiply the second equation by 2 and subtract to eliminate the $x$-variable.

$$\begin{array}{r} 2x + 3y = 2 \\ 2x - 4y = -10 \\ \hline 7y = 12 \end{array} \Rightarrow y = \frac{12}{7}$$

Since $2x + 3y = 2$, it follows that $x = \dfrac{2 - 3y}{2} \Rightarrow x = -\dfrac{11}{7}$. The solution is $\left(-\dfrac{11}{7}, \dfrac{12}{7}\right)$. The system is consistent and independent.

80. Multiply the first equation by 2 and subtract. This eliminates both variables.

$$\begin{array}{r} 2x - 6y = 2 \\ 2x - 6y = 2 \\ \hline 0 = 0 \end{array} \Rightarrow \text{infinite number of solutions}$$

The solution is $\{(x, y) \mid x - 3y = 1\}$. The system is consistent but dependent.

81. Multiply the second equation by $-\dfrac{1}{2}$ and add to eliminate the $x$-variable.

$$\begin{array}{r} \frac{1}{2}x - y = 5 \\ -\frac{1}{2}x + \frac{1}{4}y = -2 \\ \hline -\frac{3}{4}y = 3 \end{array} \Rightarrow y = -4$$

Then, $x - \dfrac{1}{2}y = 4 \Rightarrow x = 4 + \dfrac{1}{2}y \Rightarrow x = 2$. The solution is $(2, -4)$.

82. Multiply the first equation by –3, and the second equation by 2. Then add to eliminate the $y$-variable.

$$\begin{array}{r} -\frac{3}{2}x + y = -3 \\ \frac{2}{3}x - y = 2 \\ \hline -\frac{5}{6}x \quad = -1 \end{array} \Rightarrow x = \frac{6}{5}$$

Then, $-\dfrac{1}{2}y = 1 - \dfrac{1}{3}x \Rightarrow y = -2 + \dfrac{2}{3}x \Rightarrow y = -2 + \dfrac{2}{3}\left(\dfrac{6}{5}\right) \Rightarrow y = -\dfrac{6}{5}$. The solution is $\left(\dfrac{6}{5}, -\dfrac{6}{5}\right)$.

83. Multiply the first equation by 3 and add to eliminate both variables.

$$\begin{array}{rcl} 21x - 9y &=& -51 \\ -21x + 9y &=& 51 \\ \hline 0 &=& 0 \end{array} \Rightarrow \text{infinite number of solutions}$$

There are infinitely many solutions of the form $\{(x, y) | 7x - 3y = -17\}$.

84. Multiply the second equation by $\frac{1}{6}$ and add to eliminate both variables.

$$\begin{array}{rcl} -\frac{1}{3}x + \frac{1}{6}y &=& -1 \\ \frac{1}{3}x - \frac{1}{6}y &=& 1 \\ \hline 0 &=& 0 \end{array} \Rightarrow \text{infinite number of solutions}$$

There are infinitely many solutions of the form $\{(x, y) | 2x - y = 6\}$.

85. Multiply the first equation by 3 and add to eliminate both variables.

$$\begin{array}{rcl} 2x + 4y &=& 1 \\ -2x - 4y &=& 5 \\ \hline 0 &=& 6 \end{array} \Rightarrow \text{no solutions}$$

86. Multiply the first equation by –2 and add to eliminate both variables.

$$\begin{array}{rcl} -10x + 4y &=& -14 \\ 10x - 4y &=& 6 \\ \hline 0 &=& -8 \end{array} \Rightarrow \text{no solutions}$$

87. Clear decimals: $0.2x + 0.3y = 8 \Rightarrow 2x + 3y = 80$ and $-0.4x + 0.2y = 0 \Rightarrow -4x + 2y = 0$.

Multiply the first equation by 2 and add to eliminate the $x$-variable.

$$\begin{array}{rcl} 4x + 6y &=& 160 \\ -4x + 2y &=& 0 \\ \hline 8y &=& 160 \end{array} \Rightarrow y = 20$$

Then, $-4x + 2y = 0 \Rightarrow 4x = 2y \Rightarrow x = \frac{1}{2}y \Rightarrow x = \frac{1}{2}(20) = 10$. The solution is $(10, 20)$.

88. Multiply the first equation by 2, and the second equation by –3. Then add to eliminate the $y$-variable.

$$\begin{array}{rcl} 4x - 6y &=& 2 \\ -9x + 6y &=& -6 \\ \hline -5x &=& -4 \end{array} \Rightarrow x = \frac{4}{5}$$

Then, $2x - 3y = 1 \Rightarrow 3y = 2x - 1 \Rightarrow y = \frac{2x - 1}{3} \Rightarrow y = \frac{2(\frac{4}{5}) - 1}{3} = \frac{\frac{3}{5}}{3} = \frac{1}{5}$. The solution is $\left(\frac{4}{5}, \frac{1}{5}\right)$.

89. Multiply the first equation by 3 and the second equation by 2. Add to eliminate the $x$-variable.

$$\begin{array}{rcl} 6x + 9y &=& 21 \\ -6x + 4y &=& -8 \\ \hline 13y &=& 13 \end{array} \Rightarrow y = 1$$

Then, $2x + 3y = 7 \Rightarrow 2x + 3 = 7 \Rightarrow 2x = 4 \Rightarrow x = 2$. The solution is $(2, 1)$.

90. Multiply the first equation by 3 and the second equation by 2. Add to eliminate the $y$-variable.

$$\begin{array}{rl} 15x + 12y = & -9 \\ 6x - 12y = & -12 \\ \hline 21x \quad\quad = & -21 \Rightarrow x = -1 \end{array}$$

Then, $6x - 12y = -12 \Rightarrow -6 - 12y = -12 \Rightarrow -12y = -6 \Rightarrow y = \frac{1}{2}$. The solution is $\left(-1, \frac{1}{2}\right)$.

91. Multiply the first equation by 3, and the second equation by 5. Add to elimate the $y$-variable.

$$\begin{array}{rl} 21x - 15y = & -45 \\ -10x + 15y = & -10 \\ \hline 11x \quad\quad = & -55 \Rightarrow x = -5 \end{array}$$

Then, $-10x + 15y = -10 \Rightarrow 50 + 15y = -10 \Rightarrow 15y = -60 \Rightarrow y = -4$. The solution is $(-5, -4)$.

92. Multiply the first equation by 5, and the second equation by 3. Add to elimate the $y$-variable.

$$\begin{array}{rl} -25x + 15y = & -180 \\ 12x - 15y = & 102 \\ \hline -13x \quad\quad = & -78 \Rightarrow x = 6 \end{array}$$

Then, $12x - 15y = 102 \Rightarrow 72 - 15y = 102 \Rightarrow -15y = 30 \Rightarrow y = -2$. The solution is $(6, -2)$.

93. Add the two equations:

$$\begin{array}{rl} x^2 + y = & 12 \\ x^2 - y = & 6 \\ \hline 2x^2 \quad = & 18 \Rightarrow x^2 = 9 \Rightarrow x = \pm 3. \end{array}$$

If $x = 3$, then $3^2 + y = 12 \Rightarrow y = 3$, and if $x = -3$ then $(-3)^2 + y = 12 \Rightarrow y = 3$. Therefore the solutions are: $(3, 3)$ and $(-3, 3)$.

94. Multiply the second equation by 2 and add:

$$\begin{array}{rl} x^2 + 2y = & 15 \\ 4x^2 - 2y = & 20 \\ \hline 5x^2 \quad = & 35 \Rightarrow x^2 = 7 \Rightarrow x = \pm\sqrt{7}. \end{array}$$

If $x = \sqrt{7}$, then $(\sqrt{7})^2 + 2y = 15 \Rightarrow 7 + 2y = 15 \Rightarrow 2y = 8 \Rightarrow y = 4$, and if $x = -\sqrt{7}$ then $(-\sqrt{7})^2 + 2y = 15 \Rightarrow 7 + 2y = 15 \Rightarrow 2y = 8 \Rightarrow y = 4$. Therefore the solutions are: $(\sqrt{7}, 4)$ and $(-\sqrt{7}, 4)$.

95. Subtract the two equations:

$$\begin{array}{rl} x^2 + y^2 = & 25 \\ x^2 + 7y = & 37 \\ \hline y^2 - 7y = & -12 \Rightarrow y^2 - 7y + 12 = 0 \Rightarrow (y-3)(y-4) = 0 \Rightarrow y = 3, 4. \end{array}$$

If $y = 3$, then $x^2 + 7(3) = 37x^2 = 16 \Rightarrow x = \pm 4$, and if $y = 4$ then $x^2 + 7(4) = 37 \Rightarrow x^2 = 9 \Rightarrow x = \pm 3$. Therefore the solutions are: $(4, 3), (-4, 3), (3, 4)$, and $(-3, 4)$.

96. Subtract the two equations:

$$\begin{array}{rl} x^2 + y^2 = & 36 \\ x^2 - 6y = & 36 \\ \hline y^2 + 6y = & 0 \Rightarrow y(y+6) = 0 \Rightarrow y = 0, -6.. \end{array}$$

If $y = 0$, then $x^2 - 6(0) = 36 \Rightarrow x^2 = 36 \Rightarrow x = \pm 6$, and if $y = -6$ then $x^2 - 6(-6) = 36 \Rightarrow x^2 = 0 \Rightarrow x = 0$. Therefore the solutions are: $(6, 0), (-6, 0)$, and $(0, -6)$.

97. Subtract the two equations:

$$\begin{array}{l} x^2 + y^2 = 4 \\ \underline{2x^2 + y^2 = 8} \\ -x^2 \quad = -4 \Rightarrow x^2 = 4 \Rightarrow x = \pm 2. \end{array}$$

If $x = -2$, then $(-2)^2 + y^2 = 4 \Rightarrow 4 + y^2 = 4 \Rightarrow y^2 = 0 \Rightarrow y = 0$,

and if $x = 2$ then $(2)^2 + y^2 = 4 \Rightarrow y^2 = 0 \Rightarrow y = 0$. Therefore the solutions are: $(-2, 0)$ and $(2, 0)$.

98. Add the two equations:

$$\begin{array}{l} x^2 + y^2 = 4 \\ \underline{x^2 - y^2 = 4} \\ 2x^2 \quad = 8 \Rightarrow x^2 = 4 \Rightarrow x = \pm 2. \end{array}$$

If $x = -2$, then $(-2)^2 + y^2 = 4 \Rightarrow 4 + y^2 = 4 \Rightarrow y^2 = 0 \Rightarrow y = 0$,

and if $x = 2$ then $(2)^2 + y^2 = 4 \Rightarrow y^2 = 0 \Rightarrow y = 0$. Therefore the solutions are: $(-2, 0)$ and $(2, 0)$.

99. $x^2 + y^2 = 16 \Rightarrow y = \pm\sqrt{16 - x^2}$ and $x - y = 0 \Rightarrow y = x$

Graph $Y_1 = \sqrt{}(16 - X^\wedge 2)$, $Y_2 = -\sqrt{}(16 - X^\wedge 2)$, and $Y_3 = X$. Their graphs intersect near the points (–2.828, –2.828) and (2.828, 2.828). See Figures 99a & 99b.

Substituting $y = x$ into the first equation gives $x^2 + x^2 = 16 \Rightarrow 2x^2 = 16 \Rightarrow x^2 = 8 \Rightarrow x = \pm\sqrt{8}$

Since $y = x$, the solutions are $(-\sqrt{8}, -\sqrt{8})$ and $(\sqrt{8}, \sqrt{8})$

[–9, 9, 1] by [–6, 6, 1]

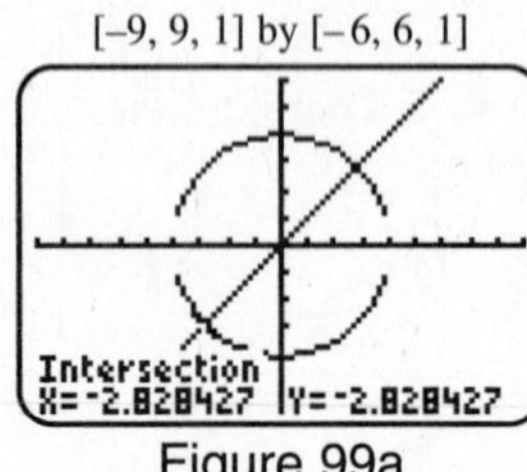


Figure 99a

[–9, 9, 1] by [–6, 6, 1]

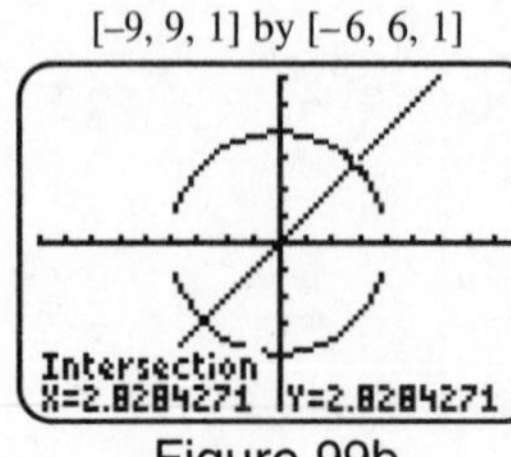


Figure 99b

[–10, 10, 1] by [–5, 15, 1]

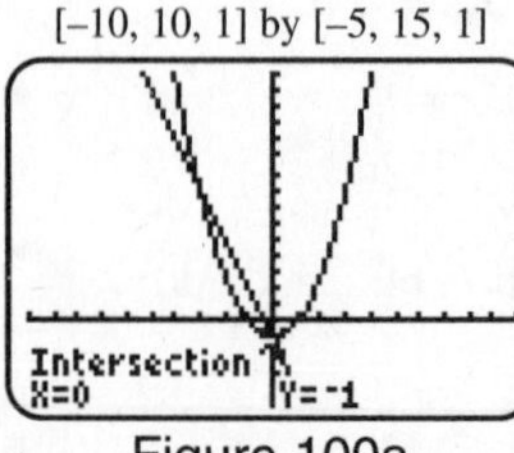


Figure 100a

[–10, 10, 1] by [–5, 15, 1]

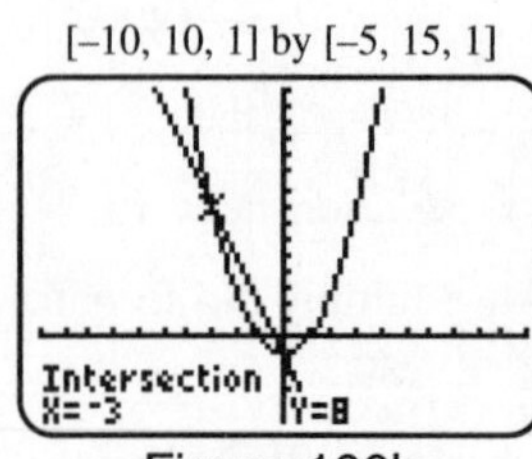


Figure 100b

100. $x^2 - y = 1 \Rightarrow y = x^2 - 1$ and $3x + y = -1 \Rightarrow y = -3x - 1$. Graph $Y_1 = X^\wedge 2 - 1$, $Y_2 = -3X - 1$.

Their graphs intersect near the points (–3, 8) and (0, –1). See Figures 100a & 100b.

Substituting $y = x^2 - 1$ into the second equation gives $3x + x^2 - 1 = -1 \Rightarrow x^2 + 3x = 0 \Rightarrow$

$x(x + 3) = 0 \Rightarrow x = -3$ or 0. Since $y = x^2 - 1$, the solutions are $(-3, 8)$ and $(0, -1)$.

101. $xy = 12 \Rightarrow y = \dfrac{12}{x}$ and $x - y = 4 \Rightarrow y = x - 4$. Graph $Y_1 = 12/X$, $Y_2 = X - 4$.

Their graphs intersect near the points $(6, 2)$ and $(-2, -6)$. See Figures 101a & 101b.

Substituting $y = x - 4$ into the first equation gives $x(x - 4) = 12 \Rightarrow x^2 - 4x - 12 = 0 \Rightarrow$

$(x + 2)(x - 6) = 0 \Rightarrow x = -2$ or 6. Since $y = x - 4$, the solutions are $(-2, -6)$ and $(6, 2)$.

[–10, 10, 2] by [–12, 8, 1]

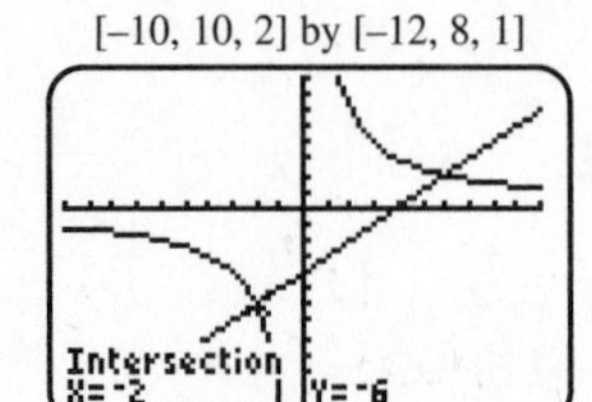


Figure 101a

[–10, 10, 2] by [–12, 8, 1]

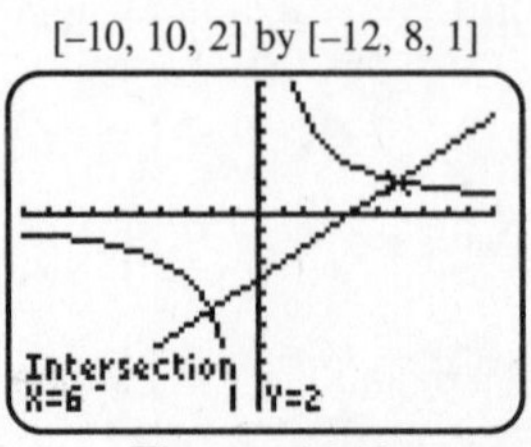


Figure 101b

102. $x^2 + y^2 = 2 \Rightarrow y = \pm\sqrt{2 - x^2}$ and $x^2 - y = 0 \Rightarrow y = x^2$

Graph $Y_1 = \sqrt{}(2 - X^\wedge 2)$, $Y_2 = -\sqrt{}(2 - X^\wedge 2)$, and $Y_3 = X^\wedge 2$. Their graphs intersect near the points (–1, 1) and (1, 1). See Figures 102a & 102b.

Substituting $y = x^2$ into the first equation gives $x^2 + x^4 = 2 \Rightarrow x^4 + x^2 - 2 = 0 \Rightarrow$ $(x^2 + 2)(x^2 - 1) = 0 \Rightarrow x = -1$ or 1. Since $y = x^2$, the solutions are $(-1, 1)$ and $(1, 1)$.

[–3, 3, 1] by [–2, 2, 1]

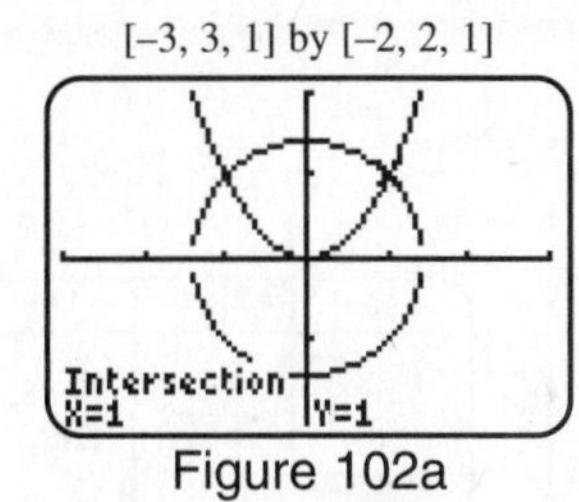

Figure 102a

[–3, 3, 1] by [–2, 2, 1]

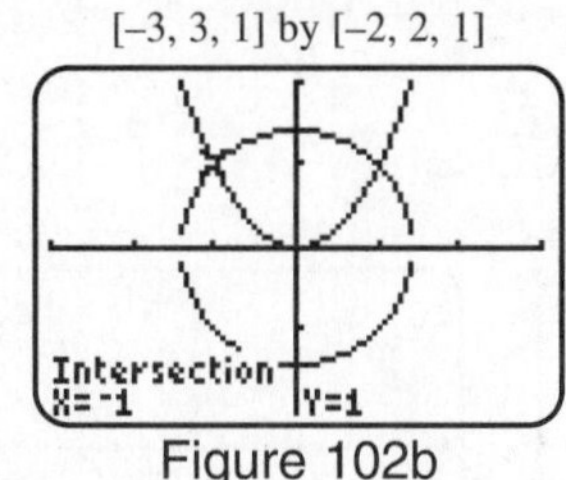

Figure 102b

[–10, 10, 1] by [–10, 10, 1]

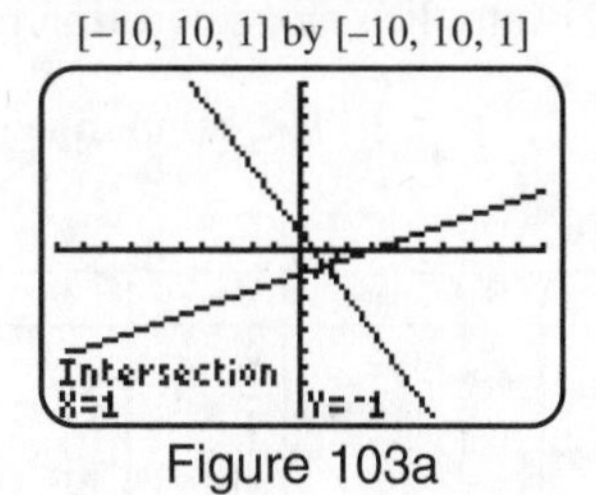

Figure 103a

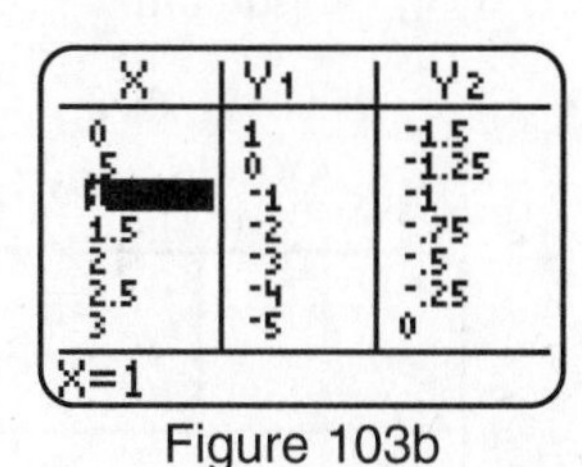

| X | Y1 | Y2 |
|---|---|---|
| 0 | 1 | -1.5 |
| .5 | 0 | -1.25 |
| 1 | -1 | -1 |
| 1.5 | -2 | -.75 |
| 2 | -3 | -.5 |
| 2.5 | -4 | -.25 |
| 3 | -5 | 0 |

X=1

Figure 103b

103. (a) $2x + y = 1 \Rightarrow y = 1 - 2x$ and $x - 2y = 3 \Rightarrow y = \frac{1}{2}(x - 3)$

Graph $Y_1 = 1 - 2X$ and $Y_2 = 0.5(X - 3)$. Their graphs intersect at the point (1, –1), which is the solution. See Figure 103a.

(b) Table $Y_1 = 1 - 2X$ and $Y_2 = 0.5(X - 3)$ starting at 0 and incrementing by 0.5. See Figure 103b.

Here $Y_1 = Y_2 = -1$ when $x = 1$. The solution is (1, –1).

(c) Substituting $y = 1 - 2x$ into the equation $x - 2y = 3$ gives $x - 2(1 - 2x) = 3 \Rightarrow$ $x - 2 + 4x = 3 \Rightarrow 5x = 5 \Rightarrow x = 1$. If $x = 1$, then $y = 1 - 2(1) = -1$. The solution is $(1, -1)$.

104. (a) $3x + 2y = -2 \Rightarrow y = \dfrac{-3x - 2}{2}$ and $2x - y = -6 \Rightarrow y = 2x + 6$

Graph $Y_1 = 0.5(-3X - 2)$ and $Y_2 = 2X + 6$. Their graphs intersect at the point (–2, 2), which is the solution. See Figure 104a.

(b) Table $Y_1 = 0.5(-3X - 2)$ and $Y_2 = 2X + 6$. starting at –3 and incrementing by 0.5. See Figure 104b.

Here $Y_1 = Y_2 = 2$ when $x = -2$. The solution is (–2, 2).

(c) Substituting $y = 2x + 6$ into the first equation gives $3x + 2(2x + 6) = -2 \Rightarrow 7x + 12 = -2 \Rightarrow$ $7x = -14 \Rightarrow x = -2$. If $x = -2$, then $y = 2(-2) + 6 = 2$. The solution is $(-2, 2)$.

[–10, 10, 1] by [–10, 10, 1]

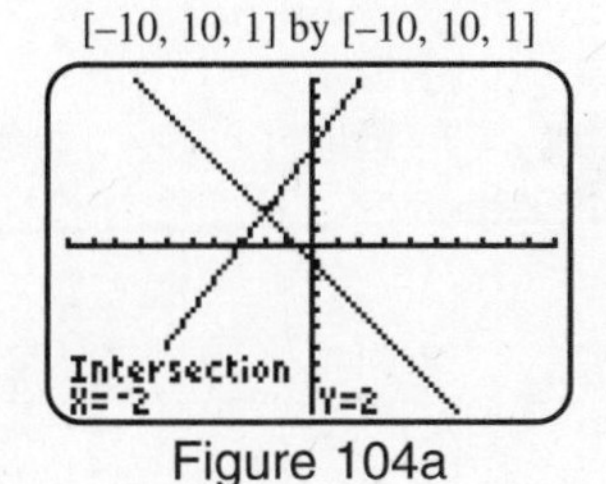

Figure 104a

| X | Y1 | Y2 |
|---|---|---|
| -3 | 3.5 | 0 |
| -2.5 | 2.75 | 1 |
| -2 | 2 | 2 |
| -1.5 | 1.25 | 3 |
| -1 | .5 | 4 |
| -.5 | -.25 | 5 |
| 0 | -1 | 6 |

X=-2

Figure 104b

105. (a) $-2x + y = 0 \Rightarrow y = 2x$ and $7x - 2y = 3 \Rightarrow 7x - 3 = 2y \Rightarrow y = \dfrac{7x - 3}{2}$

Graph $Y_1 = 2X$ and $Y_2 = (7X - 3)/2$. Their graphs intersect at the point (1, 2), which is the solution. See Figure 105a.

(b) Table $Y_1 = 2X$ and $Y_2 = (7X - 3)/2$ starting at 0 and incrementing by 0.5. See Figure 105b. Here $Y_1 = Y_2 = 2$ when $x = 1$. The solution is (1, 2).

(c) Substituting $y = 2x$ into the second equation gives $7x - 2(2x) = 3 \Rightarrow 3x = 3 \Rightarrow x = 1$. If $x = 1$, then $y = 2(1) = 2$. The solution is (1, 2).

[−10, 10, 1] by [−10, 10, 1]

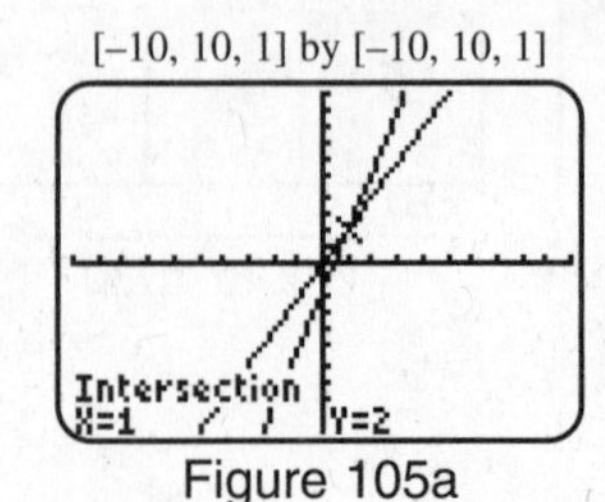

Figure 105a

| X | Y1 | Y2 |
|---|---|---|
| 0 | 0 | -1.5 |
| .5 | 1 | .25 |
| 1 | 2 | 2 |
| 1.5 | 3 | 3.75 |
| 2 | 4 | 5.5 |
| 2.5 | 5 | 7.25 |
| 3 | 6 | 9 |

X=1

Figure 105b

[−10, 10, 1] by [−10, 10, 1]

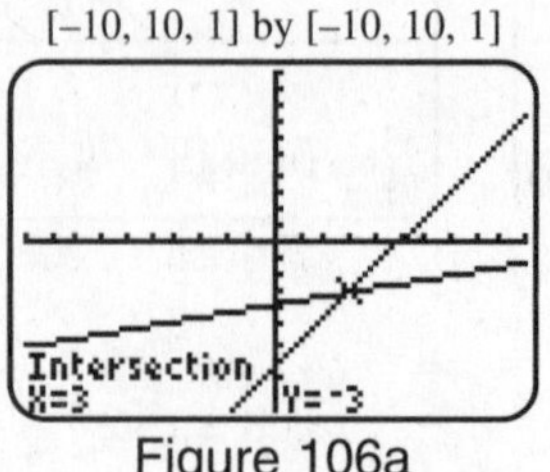

Figure 106a

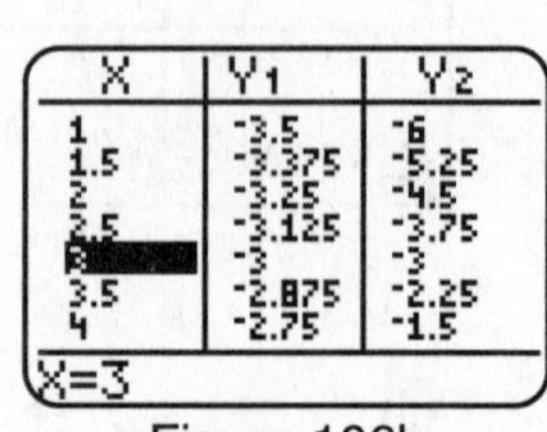

| X | Y1 | Y2 |
|---|---|---|
| 1 | -3.5 | -6 |
| 1.5 | -3.375 | -5.25 |
| 2 | -3.25 | -4.5 |
| 2.5 | -3.125 | -3.75 |
| 3 | -3 | -3 |
| 3.5 | -2.875 | -2.25 |
| 4 | -2.75 | -1.5 |

X=3

Figure 106b

106. (a) $x - 4y = 15 \Rightarrow y = \dfrac{x - 15}{4}$ and $3x - 2y = 15 \Rightarrow y = \dfrac{3x - 15}{2}$

Graph $Y_1 = (X - 15)/4$ and $Y_2 = (3X - 15)/2$. Their graphs intersect at the point (3, –3), which is the solution. See Figure 106a.

(b) Table $Y_1 = (X - 15)/4$ and $Y_2 = (3X - 15)/2$ starting at 1 and incrementing by 0.5. See Figure 106b. Here $Y_1 = Y_2 = -3$ when $x = 3$. The solution is (3, –3).

(c) Solve the first equation for $x$, $x = 4y + 15$. Substituting this into the second equation gives $3(4y + 15) - 2y = 15 \Rightarrow 10y = -30 \Rightarrow y = -3$.

If $y = -3$, then $x = 4(-3) + 15 = 3$. The solution is $(3, -3)$.

107. $x^3 - 3x + y = 1 \Rightarrow y = 1 + 3x - x^3$ and $x^2 + 2y = 3 \Rightarrow y = \dfrac{3 - x^2}{2}$. Graph $Y_1 = 1 + 3X - X$^3 and $Y_2 = (3 - X$^2$)/2$. See Figure 107. There are three points of intersection. The coordinates of these points are near (–1.588, 0.239), (0.164, 1.487), and (1.924, –0.351).

108. $x^2 + y = 5 \Rightarrow y = 5 - x^2$ and $x + y^2 = 6 \Rightarrow y^2 = 6 - x \Rightarrow y = \pm\sqrt{6 - x}$. Graph $Y_1 = 5 - X$^2, $Y_2 = \sqrt{}(6 - X)$, and $Y_3 = -\sqrt{}(6 - X)$. See Figure 108. Their graphs intersect at four points located near (–2.823, –2.970), (–1.504, 2.739), (1.711, 2.071), and (2.615, –1.840).

[−4, 4, 1] by [−4, 4, 1]

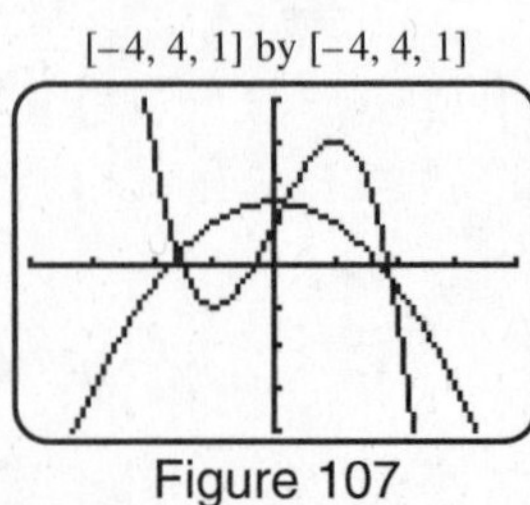
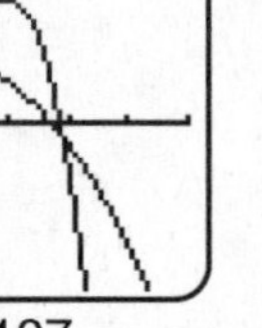
Figure 107

[−10, 10, 1] by [−10, 10, 1]

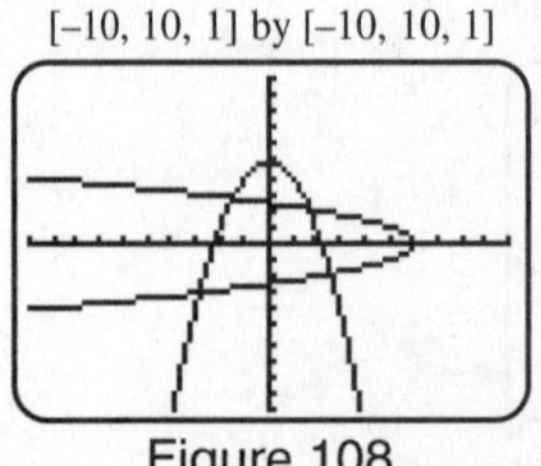
Figure 108

109. $2x^3 - x^2 = 5y \Rightarrow y = \dfrac{2x^3 - x^2}{5}$ and $2^{-x} - y = 0 \Rightarrow y = 2^{-x}$. Graph $Y_1 = (2X\verb|^|3 - X\verb|^|2)/5$ and $Y_2 = 2\verb|^|(-X)$. See Figure 109. There is one point of intersection. The coordinates of this point are near (1.220, 0.429).

110. $y = x^4 - 3x^3$ and $\log x^2 - y = 0 \Rightarrow y = \log x^2$. Graph $Y_1 = X\verb|^|4 - 3X\verb|^|3$ and $Y_2 = \log(X\verb|^|2)$. See Figure 110. There are two points of intersection. The coordinates of these points are near (0.580, −0.473) and (3.035, 0.964).

[−5, 5, 1] by [−3, 3, 1]

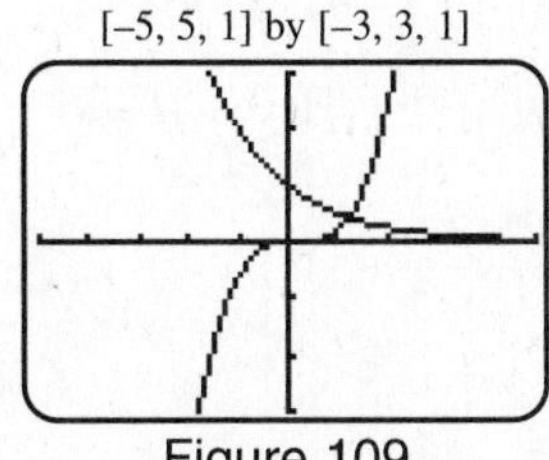

Figure 109

[−5, 5, 1] by [−10, 5, 1]

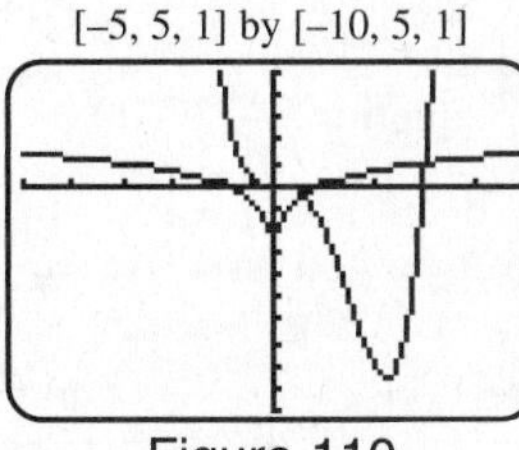

Figure 110

[−3, 3, 1] by [−5, 5, 1]

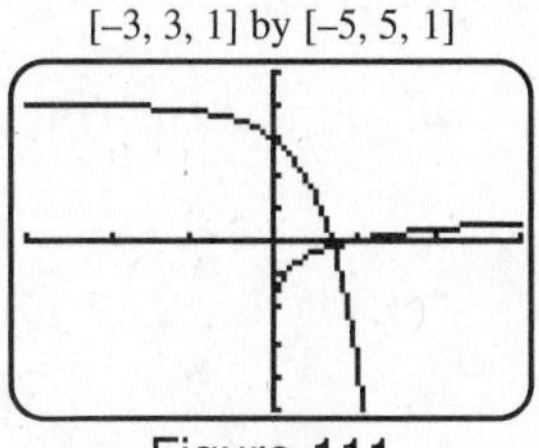

Figure 111

[−3, 3, 1] by [−4, 4, 1]

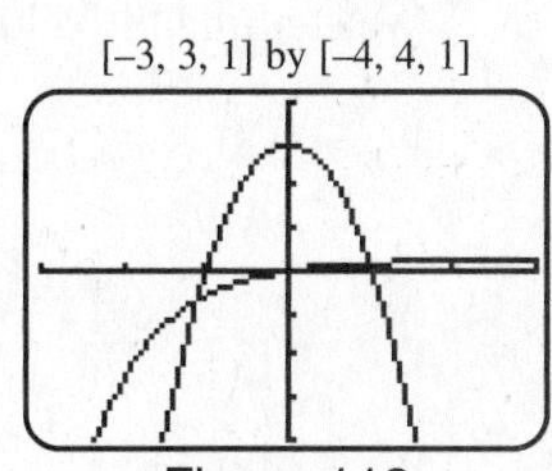

Figure 112

111. $e^{2x} + y = 4 \Rightarrow y = 4 - e^{2x}$ and $\ln x - 2y = 0 \Rightarrow y = \dfrac{\ln x}{2}$. Graph $Y_1 = 4 - e\verb|^|(2X)$ and $Y_2 = \ln(X)/2$. See Figure 111. There is one point of intersection. The coordinates of this point are near (0.714, −0.169).

112. $3x^2 + y = 3 \Rightarrow y = 3 - 3x^2$ and $(0.3)^x + 4y = 1 \Rightarrow y = \dfrac{1 - (0.3)^x}{4}$. Graph $Y_1 = 3 - 3X\verb|^|2$, $Y_2 = (1 - 0.3\verb|^|X)/4$. See Figure 112. There are two points of intersection. The coordinates of these points are near (−1.111, −0.702) and (0.971, 0.172).

113. (a) Let $x$ = population of Minneapolis and $y$ = population of St. Paul. Then $x + y = 670$ and $x - y = 96$.

(b)
$$\begin{array}{l} x + y = 670 \\ \underline{x - y = \ \ 96} \\ 2x \qquad = 766 \Rightarrow x = 383. \end{array}$$

Then, $x - y = 96 \Rightarrow 383 - y = 96 \Rightarrow y = 287$. The solution is (383, 287).

(c) The system is consistent and independent.

114. (a) Let $x$ = the amount of natural gas consumed and $y$ = the amount of petroleum consumed. Then $x + y = 3.74$ and $x - y = 3.02$.

(b)
$$\begin{array}{l} x + y = 3.74 \\ \underline{x - y = 3.02} \\ 2x \qquad = 6.76 \Rightarrow x = 3.38. \end{array}$$

Then, $x - y = 3.02 \Rightarrow 3.38 - y = 3.02 \Rightarrow y = 0.36$. The solution is (3.38, 0.36).

(c) The system is consistent and independent.

115. $W_1 + \sqrt{2}W_2 = 300 \Rightarrow W_2 = \dfrac{300 - W_1}{\sqrt{2}}$ and $\sqrt{3}W_1 - \sqrt{2}W_2 = 0 \Rightarrow W_2 = \dfrac{\sqrt{3}W_1}{\sqrt{2}}$

Graph $Y_1 = (300 - X)/\sqrt{(2)}$ and $Y_2 = \sqrt{(3)}X/\sqrt{(2)}$. Their graphs intersect near the point (109.81, 134.49) as shown in Figure 115a. The forces on the rafters are approximately 110 and 134 pounds.

To find the solution numerically, table $Y_1$ and $Y_2$ starting at 107 and incrementing by 1. We find that $Y_1 = Y_2 \approx 134$ when $x \approx 110$. See Figure 115b.

We can find the solution symbolically by using the substitution method. Since $W_1 + \sqrt{2}W_2 = 300 \Rightarrow W_1 = 300 - \sqrt{2}W_2$, we will substitute into the other equation. $\sqrt{3}(300 - \sqrt{2}W_2) - \sqrt{2}W_2 = 0 \Rightarrow$ $300\sqrt{3} - \sqrt{6}W_2 - \sqrt{2}W_2 = 0 \Rightarrow 300\sqrt{3} = (\sqrt{6} + \sqrt{2})W_2 \Rightarrow W_2 = \dfrac{300\sqrt{3}}{\sqrt{6} + \sqrt{2}}$ and

$$W_1 = 300 - \sqrt{2}\left[\frac{300\sqrt{3}}{\sqrt{6} + \sqrt{2}}\right] \Rightarrow W_1 = 300 - \frac{300\sqrt{3}}{1 + \sqrt{3}} \Rightarrow W_1 = \frac{300}{1 + \sqrt{3}}$$

$$W_1 = \frac{300}{1 + \sqrt{3}} \approx 109.8 \text{ lbs}, \quad W_2 = \frac{300\sqrt{3}}{\sqrt{6} + \sqrt{2}} \approx 134.5 \text{ lbs}$$

[0, 200, 50] by [0, 200, 50]

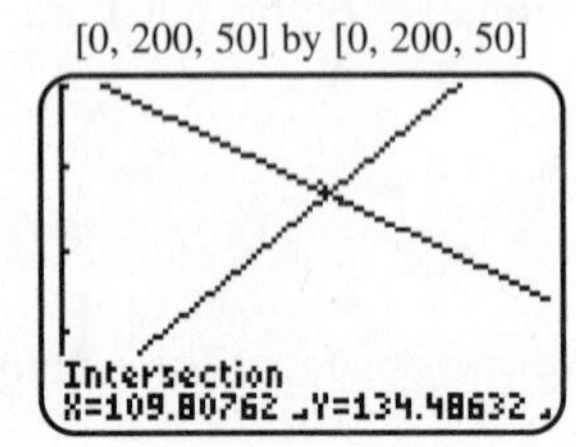

Figure 115a

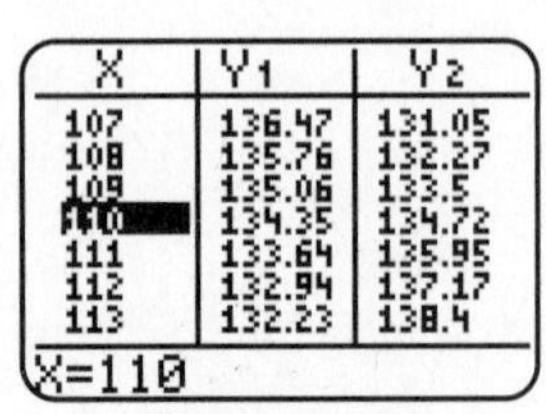

| X | Y1 | Y2 |
|---|---|---|
| 107 | 136.47 | 131.05 |
| 108 | 135.76 | 132.27 |
| 109 | 135.06 | 133.5 |
| 110 | 134.35 | 134.72 |
| 111 | 133.64 | 135.95 |
| 112 | 132.94 | 137.17 |
| 113 | 132.23 | 138.4 |

X=110

Figure 115b

[0, 4, 1] by [0, 20, 1]

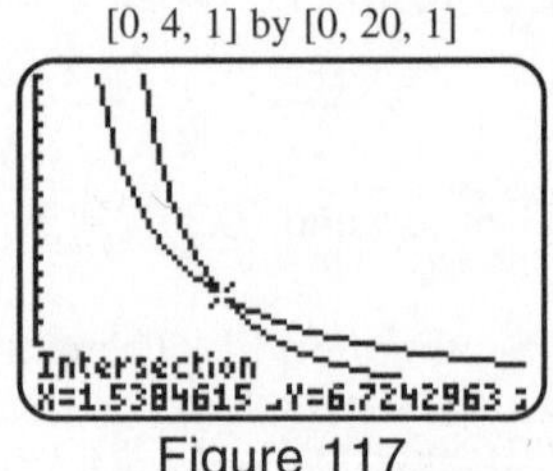

Figure 117

[−8, −8, 1] by [−8, 8, 1]

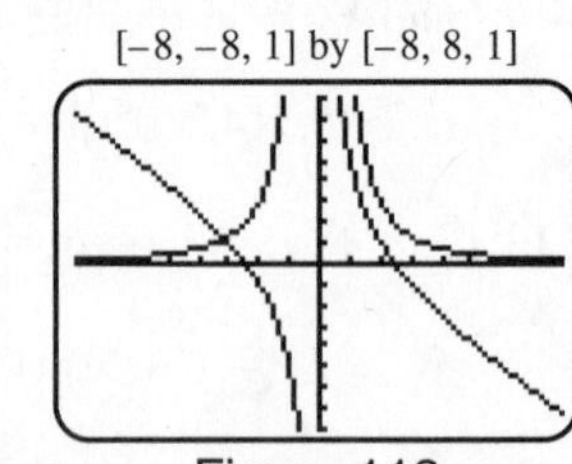
Figure 118

116. Let $x$ = hours spent on the internet in 2001. Then $1.1x = 11 \Rightarrow x = 10$. Therefore, 10 hours were spent on the internet in 2001 and 10 + 11 or 21 hours in 2005.

117. We must solve the system of nonlinear equations: $\pi r^2 h = 50$ and $2\pi rh = 65$.

Solving each equation for $h$ results in the following: $\pi r^2 h = 50 \Rightarrow h = \dfrac{50}{\pi r^2}$ and $2\pi rh = 65 \Rightarrow h = \dfrac{65}{2\pi r}$.

Graph $Y_1 = 50/(\pi X\text{^}2)$ and $Y_2 = 65/(2\pi X)$. Their graphs intersect near (1.538, 6.724). See Figure 117.

A cylinder with approximate measurements of $r \approx 1.538$ inches and $h \approx 6.724$ inches has a volume of 50 cubic inches and a lateral surface area of 65 square inches.

118. We must solve the system of nonlinear equations: $\pi r^2 h = 38$ and $2\pi rh + 2\pi r^2 = 38$

Solving each equation for $h$ results in the following:

$$\pi r^2 h = 38 \Rightarrow h = \frac{38}{\pi r^2} \text{ and } 2\pi rh + 2\pi r^2 = 38 \Rightarrow h = \frac{38 - 2\pi r^2}{2\pi r}.$$

Graph $Y_1 = 38/(\pi X\text{^}2)$ and $Y_2 = (38 - 2\pi X\text{^}2)/(2\pi X)$. Their graphs do not intersect for positive values of $r$ and $h$. Therefore, no such container exists. See Figure 118.

119. Let $x$ = the length of each side of the base and let $y$ = the height of the box. Since the volume $= 576 \text{ in}^3$, $x^2y = 576$, and so $y = \dfrac{576}{x^2}$. Since the surface are is $336 \text{ in}^2$, $x^2 + 4xy = 336$. Substituting for $y$ in this equation yields $x^2 + 4x \cdot \dfrac{576}{x^2} = 336$. Simplifying we get: $x^3 - 336x + 2304 = 0$. By graphing the left side of the equation, the $x$-intercepts are approximately 9.1 and 12. See Figure 119. When $x \approx 9.1$, the dimensions are: 9.1 by 9.1 by $\dfrac{576}{(9.1)^2} \approx 6.96$ inches. When $x = 12$, the dimensions are: 12 by 12 by $\dfrac{576}{(12)^2} = 4$ inches.

120. Let $x$ = the width of the base therefore the length $2x$, and let $y$ = the height of the box. Since the volume is $588 \text{ in}^3$, $2x^2y = 588$ and so $y = \dfrac{588}{2x^2} = \dfrac{294}{x^2}$. Since the surface area is $448 \text{ in}^2$, $2(2x)(x) + 2(x)(y) + 2(2x)(y) = 448 \Rightarrow 4x^2 + 6xy = 448$. Substituting for $y$ in this equation yields $4x^2 + 6x \cdot \dfrac{294}{x^2} = 448$. Simplifying we get: $4x^3 - 448x + 1764 = 0$. By graphing the left side of the equation, the $x$-intercepts are approximately 5.17 and 7. See Figure 120. When $x \approx 5.17$, the dimensions are: 5.17 by $2(5.17) \approx 10.34$ by $\dfrac{294}{(5.17)^2} \approx 11.00$ inches. When $x = 7$, the dimensions are: 7 by $2(7) = 14$ by $\dfrac{294}{(7)^2} = 6$ inches.

[0, 20, 2] by [–500, 1000, 100]

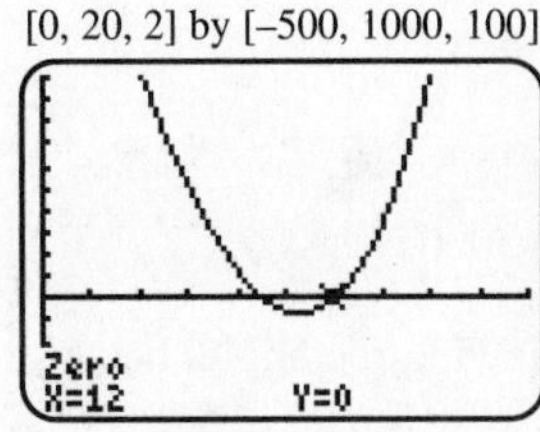


Figure 119

[0, 20, 2] by [0, 1000, 100]

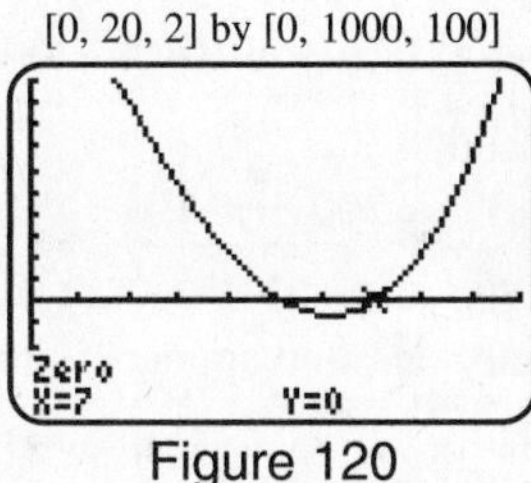


Figure 120

[0, 800,000, 100,000] by [0, 800,000, 100,000]

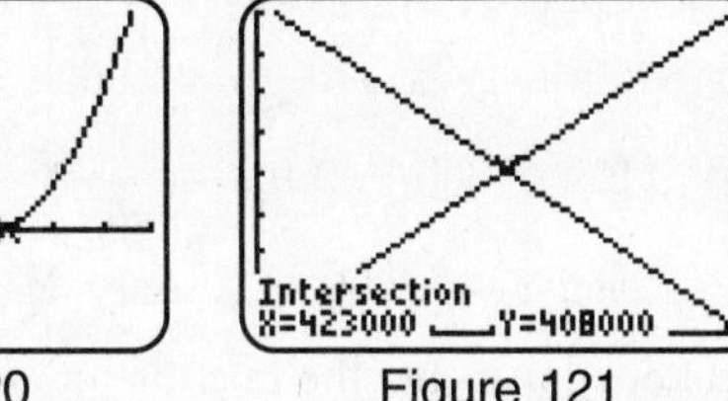


Figure 121

[0, 5000, 1000] by [0, 5000, 1000]

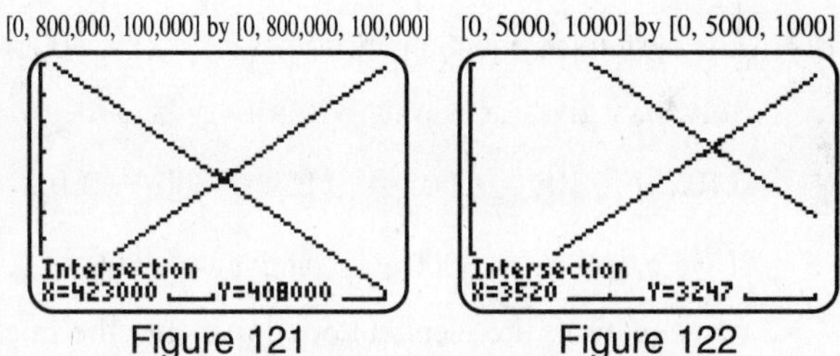


Figure 122

121. (a) Let $x$ represent the number of robberies in 2000 and let $y$ represent the number of robberies in 2001. The required system of equations is $x + y = 831{,}000$ and $x - y = 15{,}000$.

(b) Adding the two equations results in $2x = 846{,}000 \Rightarrow x = 423{,}000$. From the first equation, $423{,}000 + y = 831{,}000 \Rightarrow y = 408{,}000$. There were 423,000 robberies in 2000 and 408,000 in 2001.

(c) Solve each equation for $y$ and graph $Y_1 = 831{,}000 - X$ and $Y_2 = X - 15{,}000$ as shown in Figure 121. The solution is the intersection point (423,000, 408,000).

122. (a) Let $x$ = number vaccinated in Florida and let $y$ = number vaccinated in Texas. Then $x + y = 6767$ and $x - y = 273$.

(b) Substitute $x - y = 273$ or $x = y + 273$ into $x + y = 6767 \Rightarrow (y + 273) + y = 6767 \Rightarrow 2y + 273 = 6767 \Rightarrow 2y = 6494 \Rightarrow y = 3247$. Solving for $x$ we get: $x = 3247 + 273 \Rightarrow x = 3520$. Therefore there were 3520 vaccinated in Florida and 3247 vaccinated in Texas.

(c) Graph $x + y = 6767$ or $Y_1 = -X + 6767$, and $x = y + 273$ or $Y_2 = X - 273$. See Figure 122. The lines intersect at (3520, 3247), which is 3520 vaccinated in Florida and 3247 vaccinated in Texas.

123. (a) To solve this problem start by letting $x$ represent the amount of the 8% loan and $y$ the 10% loan. Since the total of both loans is \$3000, the equation $x + y = 3000$ must be satisfied. The annual interest rate for the 8% loan is given by $0.08x$, while the annual interest rate for the 10% loan is expressed by $0.10y$. the total interest for both loans is their sum $0.08x + 0.10y = 264$.

(b) Thus, to determine a solution, the following linear system of equations could be solved.

$x + y = 3000$ and $0.08x + 0.10y = 264$. Start by solving each for $y$.

$x + y = 3000 \Rightarrow y = 3000 - x$

and $0.08x + 0.10y = 264 \Rightarrow 0.10y = 264 - 0.08x \Rightarrow y = \dfrac{264 - 0.08x}{0.10} \Rightarrow y = 2640 - 0.8x$. The two equations can be solved using the intersection-of-graphs method. Let $Y_1 = 3000 - X$ and $Y_2 = 2640 - 0.8X$. Since the system of equations is linear, each graph is a line. The lines are not parallel and intersect at the point (1800, 1200), as shown in Figure 123. Thus, the 8% loan is for \$1800 and the 10% loan is for \$1200.

[0, 3000, 1000] by [0, 3000, 1000] [0, 3000, 1000] by [0, 3000, 1000] [0, 3000, 1000] by [0, 3000, 1000]

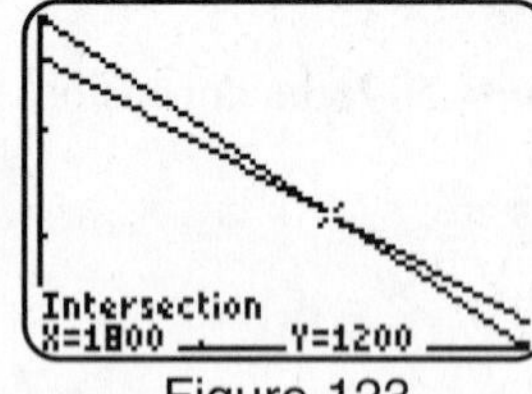

Figure 123

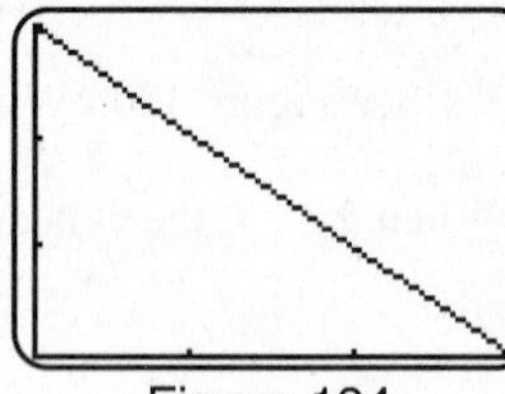
Figure 124

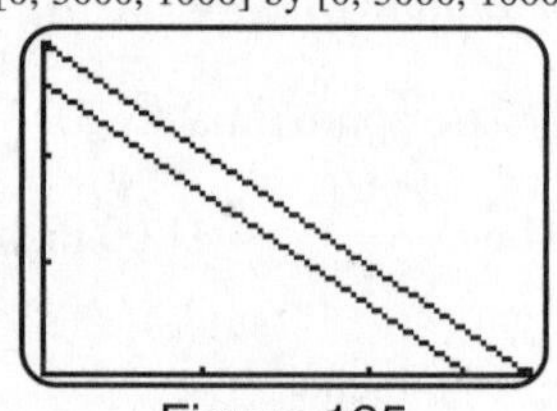
Figure 125

124. The system of equations becomes $x + y = 3000$ and $0.10x + 0.10y = 300$.
Solving $y$ gives, $x + y = 3000 \Rightarrow y = 3000 - x$ and

$0.10x + 0.10y = 300 \Rightarrow 0.10y = 300 - 0.10x \Rightarrow y = \dfrac{300 - 0.10x}{0.10} \Rightarrow y = 3000 - x$.

If we graph $Y_1 = 3000 - X$ and $Y_2 = 3000 - X$, only one line appears in the viewing rectangle, because the two equations are identical or equivalent. the lines are coincident, as shown in Figure 124.
The solution consists of positive values for $x$ and $y$ that satisfy the equation $y = 3000 - x$. The mathematics of the problem is telling us that both loans are at 10% interest, the individual loan amounts are unimportant. It does not matter whether the loans are for \$1000 and \$2000 or \$1500 and \$1500. The only critical factor is that their total is \$3000. Regardless of the mix, the total interest of these loans is 10% of \$3000 or \$300 annually. Assuming that loans can be made for any amount in the interval (0, 3000). there is an infinite number of solutions to this system of equations. In set building notation, the solution could be expressed as $\{(x, y) \mid x + y = 3000, x > 0, \text{and } y > 0\}$.

125. With these conditions the system of equations becomes $x + y = 3000$ and $0.10x + 0.10y = 264$.
Solving each equation for $y$ provides the following results, $y = 3000 - x$ and $y = 2640 - x$.
Graphs of $Y_1 = 3000 - X$ and $Y_2 = 2640 - X$ are shown in Figure 125. Notice that their graphs are parallel lines with slope –1 that do not intersect. There is no solution. This means that there is no way to have two loans totaling \$3000, both with an interest rate of 10%, and only pay \$264 in interest each year. The interest must be 10% of \$3000 or \$300. This system of equations is inconsistent - there is no solution. Graphs of inconsistent systems in two variables consist of parallel lines.

126. Let $x$ = amount invested at 5% and $y$ = amount invested at 7%, then $x + y = 5000$ and $0.05x + 0.07y = 325$.

Multiply $x + y = 5000$ by 0.05 and subtract from $0.05x + 0.07y = 325$.

$$\begin{array}{r} 0.05x + 0.07y = 325 \\ 0.05x + 0.05y = 250 \\ \hline 0.02y = \ \ 75 \Rightarrow y = 3750 \end{array}$$

Substitute $y = 3750$ into $x + y = 5000 \Rightarrow x + 3750 = 5000 \Rightarrow x = 1250$. Therefore \$1250 was invested at 5% and \$3750 was invested at 7%.

127. (a) The perimeter is 40, thus $2l + 2w = 40 \Rightarrow l + w = 20 \Rightarrow l = 20 - w$. Since the area is 91, we have that $lw = 91$. Use the substitution method to solve this system.

$(20 - w)w = 91 \Rightarrow 20w - w^2 = 91 \Rightarrow w^2 - 20w + 91 = 0 \Rightarrow (w - 13)(w - 7) = 0 \Rightarrow$ $w = 7$ or $w = 13$. When $w = 7, l = 13$ and when $w = 13, l = 7$. Since length is longer than width, the solution is $l = 13$ feet and $w = 7$ feet.

(b) $P = 2l + 2w = 40 \Rightarrow l + w = 20 \Rightarrow l = 20 - w$. Then, $A = lw = (20 - w)w = 20w - w^2$.

Graph $Y_1 = 20X - X^2$ in $[0, 25, 5]$ by $[0, 150, 25]$.

(c) The area can be any positive number less than or equal to 100 square feet. The maximum area of 100 square feet occurs when $w = 10$ and $l = 10$. See Figure 127. Since all sides are equal to 10, the shape of the rectangle is a square. That is, a square pen will provide the largest area.

[0, 25, 5] by [0, 150, 25]

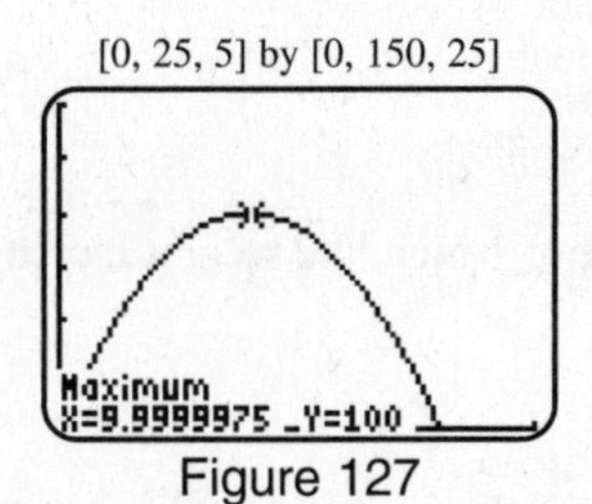


Figure 127

128. Let $x$ represent the speed of the tugboat pushing the barge and $y$ the speed of the current. Traveling against the current the speed of the barge is $\frac{60}{15} = 4$ mph, while with the current its speed is $\frac{60}{6} = 10$ mph. Thus,

$$\begin{array}{l} x + y = 10 \\ x - y = \ \ 4 \\ \hline 2x \qquad = 14 \ \Rightarrow x = 7 \end{array}$$

Thus, $y = 10 - x = 3$. The current is 3 mph.

129. Let $x$ represent the air speed of the plane and $y$ the wind speed. Traveling with the wind, the average ground speed of the plane is $\frac{1680}{3} = 560$ mph, while its ground speed against the wind was $\frac{1680}{3.5} = 480$ mph. Thus,

$$\begin{array}{l} x + y = \ \ 560 \\ x - y = \ \ 480 \\ \hline 2x \qquad = 1040 \ \Rightarrow x = 520 \end{array}$$

Thus, $y = 560 - x = 40$. The air speed of the plane is 520 mph and the wind speed is 40 mph.

130. Let $x$ = rate of the airplane and $y$ = rate of the wind, then $(x - y)3.75 = 1500$ and $(x + y)3 = 1500$.

Now, $3.75x - 3.75y = 1500$ and $3x + 3y = 1500$. Multiply $3x + 3y = 1500$ by 1.25 and add to

$$\begin{aligned} 3.75x - 3.75y &= 1500 \\ 3.75x - 3.75y &= 1500 \\ \underline{3.75x + 3.75y} &\underline{= 1875} \\ 7.50x \quad &= 3375 \Rightarrow x = 450 \end{aligned}$$

Substitute $x = 450$ into $(x + y)3 = 1500$ gives $(450 + y)3 = 1500 \Rightarrow 450 + y = 500 \Rightarrow y = 50$.

Therefore the airplane was traveling at 450 mph and the wind was at 50 mph.

131. Let $x$ represent the number of deaths in WWI and $y$ the number of deaths in WWII, then

$x + y = 345{,}000$ and $y = 5.5x$. Substituting the second equation into the first we get:

$x + 5.5x = 345{,}000 \Rightarrow 6.5x = 345{,}000 \Rightarrow x \approx 53{,}077$, then $y \approx 291{,}923$. Thus there were 53,077 deaths in WWI and 291,923 deaths in WWII.

132. Let $x$ represent the number of cigarettes sold in 1990 and $y$ the number of cigarettes sold in 2000, then

$x + y = 10.9$ and $y = x + 0.1$. Substituting the second equation into the first we get:

$x + (x + 0.1) = 10.9 \Rightarrow 2x + 0.1 = 10.9 \Rightarrow 2x = 10.8 \Rightarrow x = 5.4$, then $y = 5.5$. Thus there were 5.4 trillion cigarettes sold in 1990 and 5.5 trillion cigarettes sold in 2000.

133. (a) A 6' 11" person is 83 inches tall.

$w = 7.46(83) - 374 = 245.18 \approx 245$ lbs; $w = 7.93(83) - 405 = 253.19 \approx 253$ lbs

(b) Graph $Y_1 = 7.46X - 374$ and $Y_2 = 7.93X - 405$. Their graphs intersect near (65.96, 118.04).

See Figure 133. The models agree when $h \approx 65.96$ inches and $w \approx 118$ pounds.

(c) The first model's coefficient for $h$ is 7.46. Thus, for each increase in height of 1 inch, the weight increases by 7.46 lbs. Similarly, for the second equation the increase is 7.93 lbs.

[65, 70, 1] by [100, 150, 10]

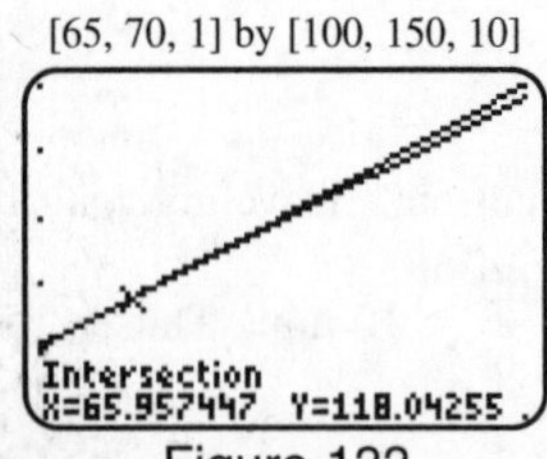


Figure 133

[0, 300, 50] by [0, 300, 50]

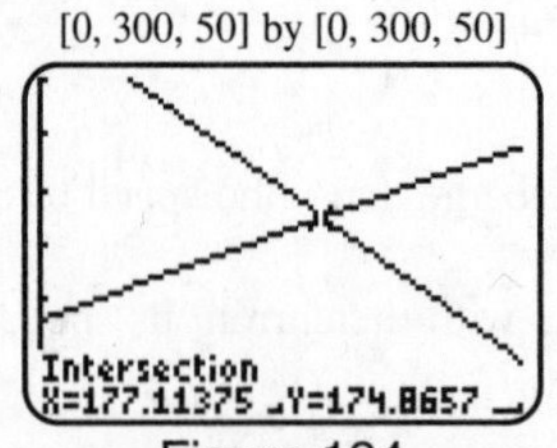


Figure 134

134. Let $H = 180$ in each equation and solve for $y$.

$$180 = 0.491x + 0.468y + 11.2 \Rightarrow y = \frac{1}{0.468}(180 - 0.491x - 11.2)$$

$$180 = -0.981x + 1.872y + 26.4 \Rightarrow y = \frac{1}{1.872}(180 + 0.981x - 26.4)$$

Since we are solving this system graphically, it is not necessary to simplify them. The graph of both equations and their point of intersection near (177.1, 174.9) is shown in Figure 134. This means that at exhaustion, if an athlete achieves a maximum heart rate of 180 beats per minute, then 5 seconds after stopping his or her heart rate would be approximately 177.1 and after 10 seconds it would be approximately 174.9.

135. Substitute 165.1 for $h$ and 70 for $w$: $S(70, 165.1) = 0.007184(70)^{0.425}(165.1)^{0.725} \approx 1.77\text{m}^2$

136. $S(w, h) = 0.007184(w^{0.425})(h^{0.725}) \Rightarrow S(86, 185) = 0.007184(86^{0.425})(185^{0.725}) \approx 2.1 \text{ m}^2$

137. $w = 132 \text{ lb} \approx \frac{132}{2.2} \text{ kg} = 60 \text{ kg};\ h = 62 \text{ inches} \approx 62 \cdot 2.54 \text{ cm} = 157.48 \text{ cm}$

$S(w, h) = 0.007184(w^{0.425})(h^{0.725}) \Rightarrow S(60, 157.48) = 0.007184(60^{0.425})(157.48^{0.725}) \approx 1.6 \text{ m}^2$

138. $w = 220 \text{ lb} \approx \frac{220}{2.2} \text{ kg} = 100 \text{ kg};\ h = 75 \text{ inches} \approx 75 \cdot 2.54 \text{ cm} = 190.5 \text{ cm}$

$S(w, h) = 0.007184(w^{0.425})(h^{0.725}) \Rightarrow S(100, 190.5) = 0.007184(100^{0.425})(190.5^{0.725}) \approx 2.3 \text{ m}^2$

139. Since $z = kx^2y^3$ and $z = 31.9$ when $x = 2$ and $y = 2.5$.

$31.9 = k(2)^2(2.5)^3 \Rightarrow 31.9 = 62.5k \Rightarrow k = \frac{31.9}{62.5} \approx 0.51$

140. Since $z = kx^{1.5}y^{2.1}$ and $z = 397$ when $x = 4$ and $y = 3.5$.

$397 = k(4)^{1.5}(3.5)^{2.1} \Rightarrow k = \frac{397}{(4)^{1.5}(3.5)^{2.1}} \approx 3.57$

141. $z = k\sqrt{x} \cdot \sqrt[3]{y} \Rightarrow 10.8 = k\sqrt{4} \cdot \sqrt[3]{8} \Rightarrow 10.8 = k \cdot 2 \cdot 2 \Rightarrow 10.8 = 4k \Rightarrow k = 2.7$

Therefore: $z = 2.7\sqrt{x} \cdot \sqrt[3]{y}$ and now $z = 2.7\sqrt{16} \cdot \sqrt[3]{27} \Rightarrow z = 2.7(4)(3) \Rightarrow z = 32.4$.

142. $z = kx^3 \cdot y^3 \Rightarrow 2160 = k(3)^3(4)^3 \Rightarrow 2160 = k(27)(64) \Rightarrow 2160 = 1728k \Rightarrow k = 1.25$

Therefore: $z = 1.25x^3 \cdot y^3$ and now $z = 1.25(2)^3(5)^3 \Rightarrow z = 1.25(8)(125) \Rightarrow z = 1250$.

143. Let $d$ represent the diameter of the blades, $v$ represent the wind velocity, and $w$ represent the watts of power generated by the windmill. Then $w = kd^2v^3$ and $w = 2405$ when $d = 8$ and $v = 10$.

$2405 = k(8)^2(10)^3 \Rightarrow 2405 = 64{,}000k \Rightarrow k = \frac{481}{12{,}800}$. The variation equation becomes

$w = \frac{481}{12{,}800}d^2v^3$. Thus, when $d = 6$ and $v = 20$; $w = \frac{481}{12{,}800}(6)^2(20)^3 = 10{,}822.5$.

With six-foot blades and a 20 mile-per-hour wind, the windmill will produce about 10,823 watts.

144. Let $x$ represent the beam width, $y$ represent the beam thickness, and $z$ represent beam strength.

Then, $z = kxy^2$ and $z = 600$ when $x = 5.5$ and $y = 2.5$.

$600 = k(5.5)(2.5)^2 \Rightarrow 600 = 34.375k \Rightarrow k = \frac{600}{34.375} \approx 17.455$. The variation equation becomes

$z = 17.455xy^2$. Thus, when $x = 4$ and $y = 1.5$; $z = 17.455(4)(1.5)^2 \approx 157$ lbs.

A four inch wide beam which is 1.5 inches thick can support about 157 pounds.

145. From the example $V = 0.00132h^{1.12}d^{1.98}$. When $h = 105$ and $d = 38$ we have

$V = 0.00132(105)^{1.12}(38)^{1.98} \approx 325.295$. A tree which is 105 feet tall with a diameter of 38 inches contains approximately 325.295 cubic feet of wood. To find the number of cords, divide this result by 128:

$\frac{325.295}{128} \approx 2.54$ cords.

146. Let $x$ represent the width of the room, $y$ represent the length of the room, and $z$ represent the cost of carpeting the room. Then, $z = kxy$ and $z = 1560$ when $x = 10$ and $y = 12$.

$1560 = k(10)(12) \Rightarrow 1560 = 120k \Rightarrow k = \frac{1560}{120} = 13$. The variation equation becomes $z = 13xy$. Thus, when $x = 11$ and $y = 23$; $z = 13(11)(23) = 3289$. The cost is \$3289. The constant of variation represents the cost per square foot of the carpet.

147. From exercise 135, $S(w, h) = 0.007184(w^{0.425})(h^{0.725})$ where $w$ is weight in kilograms and $h$ is height in centimeters. Let $S = 1.77$, $w = 154$, and $h = 65$. Then, $1.77 = k(154^{0.425})(65^{0.725})$, which results in $k \approx 0.0101$. Thus, $S(w, h) = 0.0101(w^{0.425})(h^{0.725})$, where $w$ is in pounds, $h$ is in inches, and $S$ is in square meters.

148. Exercise 137; $S(132, 62) = 0.0101(132^{0.425})(62^{0.725}) \approx 1.603$. A person who is 62 inches tall and weights 132 pounds has a surface area of approximately 1.60 $m^2$.

Exercise 138; $S(220, 75) = 0.0101(220^{0.425})(75^{0.725}) \approx 2.287$. A person who is 75 inches tall and weights 220 pounds has a surface area of approximately 2.29 $m^2$.

## 6.2: Systems of Inequalities in Two Variables

1. Graph the boundary line $y = x$. Choose (1, 0) as a test point. Since $1 \geq 0$, the region containing (1, 0) is part of the solution set. The inequality $x \geq y$ includes this region and the line $y = x$. See Figure 1.
2. Graph the boundary line $y = -3$. Choose (0, 2) as a test point. Since $2 > -3$, the region containing (0, 2) is the solution set. The boundary line $y = -3$ is not part of the solution set. See Figure 2.

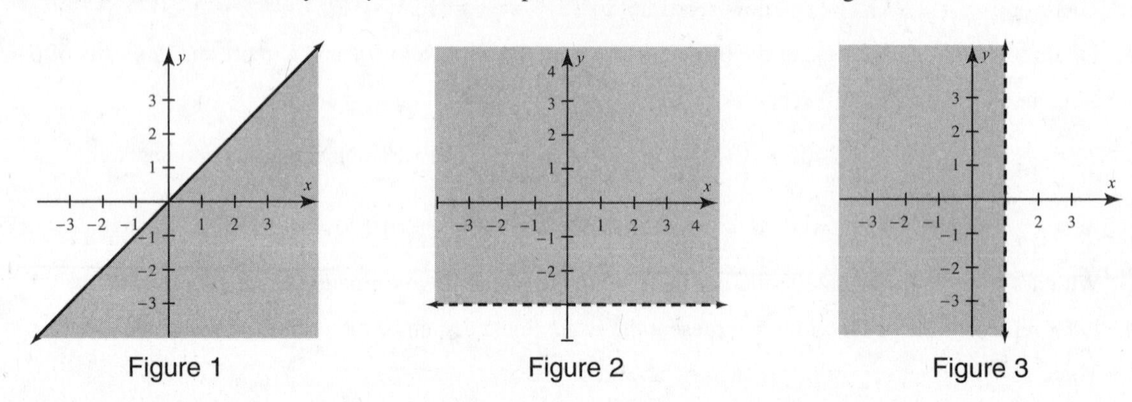

Figure 1 Figure 2 Figure 3

3. Graph the boundary line $x = 1$. Choose (0, 0) as a test point. Since $0 < 1$, the region containing (0, 0) is the solution set. The boundary line $x = 1$ is not part of the solution set. See Figure 3.
4. Graph the boundary line $y = 2x$. Choose (0, 1) as a test point. Since $1 > 2(0)$, the region containing (0, 1) is the solution set. The boundary line $y = 2x$ is not part of the solution set. See Figure 4.

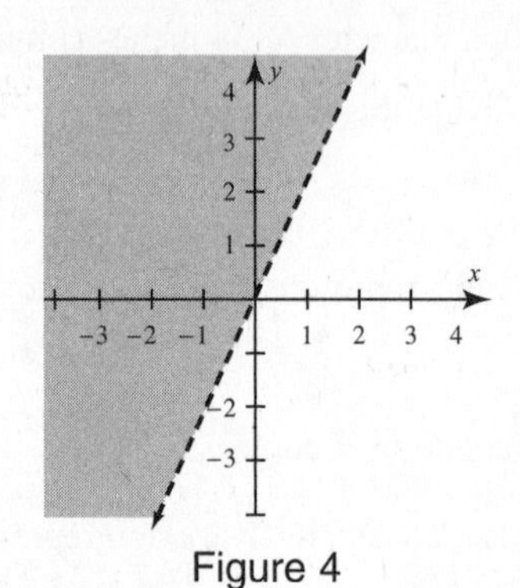

Figure 4

5. Graph the boundary line $x + y = 2 \Rightarrow y = 2 - x$. Choose (0, 0) as a test point. Since $0 + 0 \le 2$, the region containing (0, 0) is part of the solution set. The boundary line $y = 2 - x$ is also part of the solution set. See Figure 5.

6. Graph the boundary line $x + y = -3 \Rightarrow y = -3 - x$. Choose (0, 0) as a test point. Since $0 > -3 - 0$, the region containing (0, 0) is part of the solution set. The boundary line $y = -3 - x$ is not part of the solution set. See Figure 6.

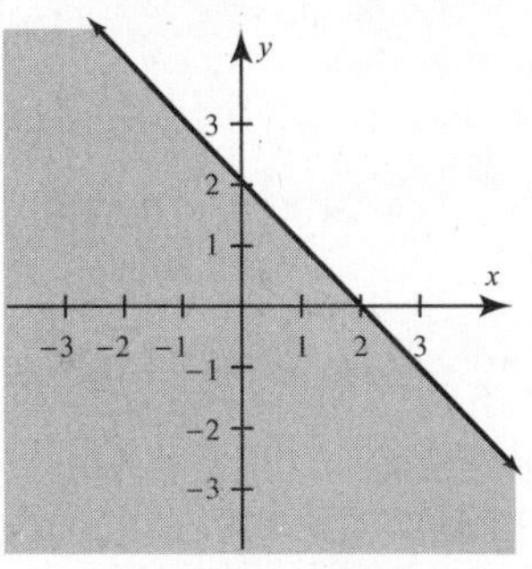

Figure 5

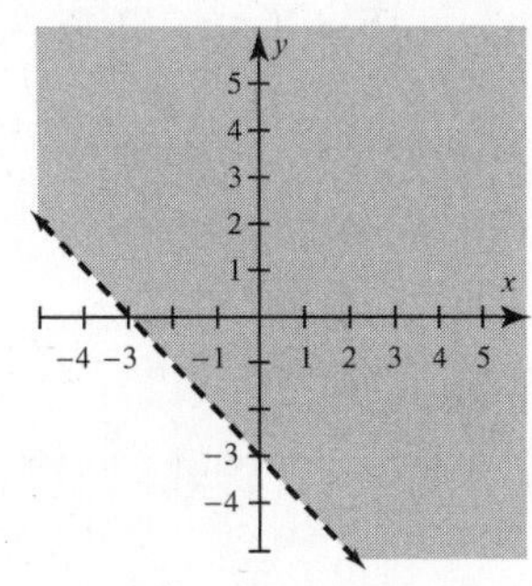

Figure 6

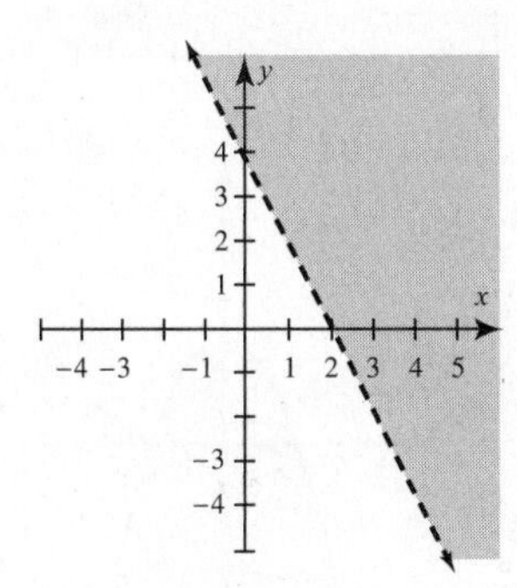

Figure 7

7. Graph the boundary line $2x + y = 4 \Rightarrow y = 4 - 2x$. Choose (3, 0) as a test point. Since $0 > 4 - 2(3)$, the region containing (3, 0) is the solution set. The boundary line $y = 4 - 2x$ is not part of the solution set. See Figure 7.

8. Graph the boundary line $2x + 3y = 6 \Rightarrow y = -\frac{2}{3}x + 2$. Choose (0, 0) as a test point. Since $0 \le -\frac{2}{3}(0) + 2$, the region containing (0, 0) is part of the solution set. The boundary line $y = -\frac{2}{3}x + 2$ is also part of the solution set. See Figure 8.

9. Graph the circle determined by $x^2 + y^2 = 4$. Choose (0, 0) as a test point. Since $0 > 4$, the region inside the circle is not part of the solution $\Rightarrow$ shade the region outside the circle. Note, the circle is not part of the solution. See Figure 9.

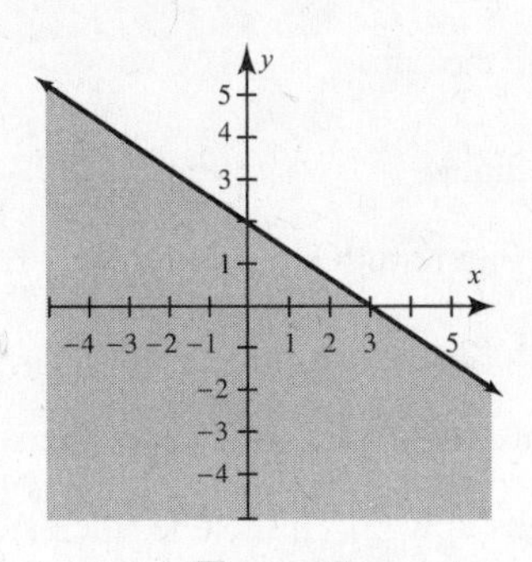

Figure 8

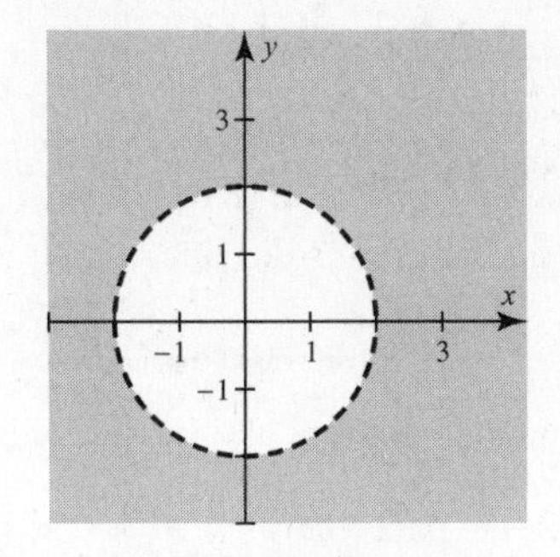

Figure 9

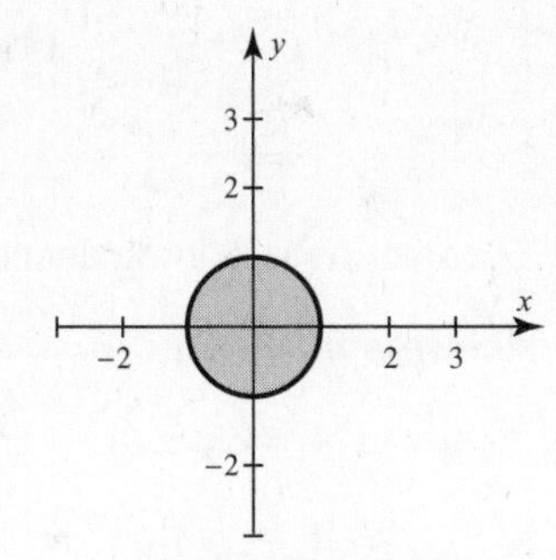

Figure 10

10. Graph the circle determined by $x^2 + y^2 = 1$. Choose (0, 0) as a test point. Since $0 \le 1$, the region inside the circle is part of the solution $\Rightarrow$ shade the inside of the circle. Note, the circle is part of the solution. See Figure 10.

11. Graph the boundary parabola determined by $x^2 + y = 2 \Rightarrow y = -x^2 + 2$. Choose (0, 0) as a test point.

Since $0 \leq 2$, the region inside the parabola is part of the solution $\Rightarrow$ shade the region inside of the parabola.

Note, the parabola is part of the solution. See Figure 11.

12. Graph the boundary parabola determined by $2x^2 - y = 1 \Rightarrow y = 2x^2 - 1$. Choose (0, 0) as a test point.

Since $0 < 1$, the region inside the parabola is part of the solution $\Rightarrow$ shade the region inside of the parabola.

Note, the parabola is not part of the solution. See Figure 12.

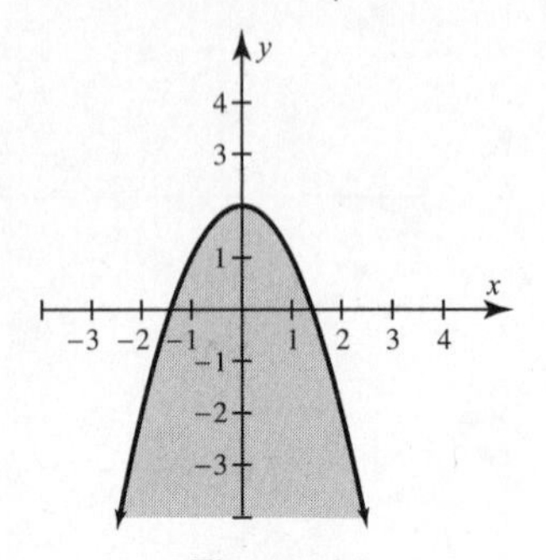

Figure 11

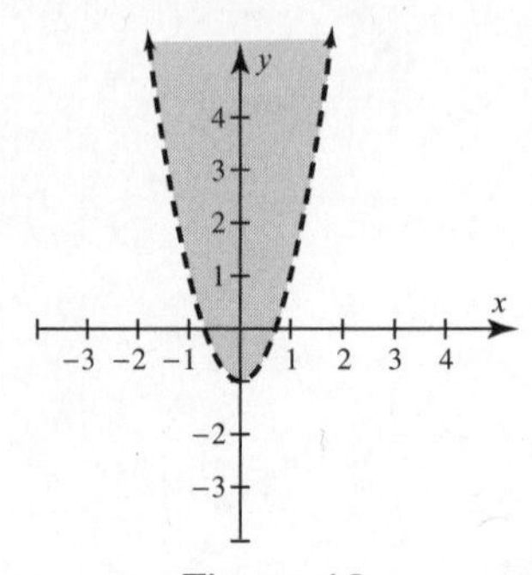

Figure 12

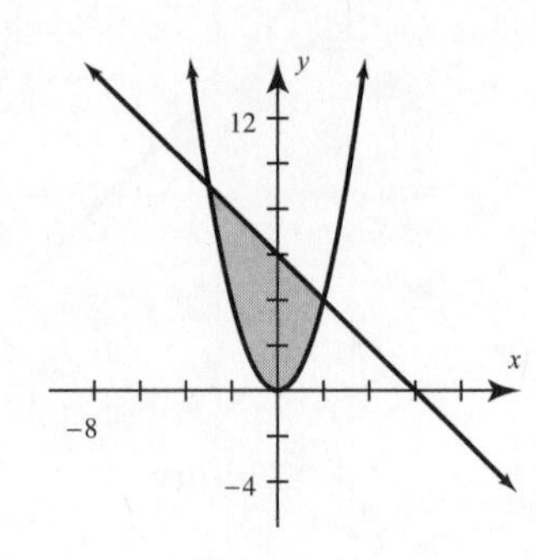

Figure 17

13. $x + y \geq 2 \Rightarrow y \geq 2 - x$ is above the line $y = 2 - x$. It includes the line.

$x - y \leq 1 \Rightarrow y \geq x - 1$ is above the line $y = x - 1$. It includes the line.

The solution is above two lines, which matches Figure c. One solution is (2, 3). *Answers may vary.*

14. $2x - y > 0 \Rightarrow y < 2x$ is below the line $y = 2x$. It does not include the line.

$x - 2y \leq 1 \Rightarrow y \geq \frac{1}{2}x - \frac{1}{2}$ is above the line $y = \frac{1}{2}x - \frac{1}{2}$. It includes the line.

The solution is below a dotted line with slope 2 above a solid line with slope $\frac{1}{2}$. This matches Figure b. One solution is (3, 3). *Answers may vary.*

15. $\frac{1}{2}x^3 - y > 0 \Rightarrow y < \frac{1}{2}x^3$ is below the curve $y = \frac{1}{2}x^3$. It does not include the curve.

$2x - y \leq 1 \Rightarrow y \geq 2x - 1$ is above the line $y = 2x - 1$. It includes the line.

The solution is below a dotted curve and above a solid line, which matches Figure d. One solution is (–1, –1).

*Answers may vary.*

16. $x^2 + y \leq 4 \Rightarrow y \leq 4 - x^2$ is below the parabola $y = 4 - x^2$ which opens downward. It includes the parabola.

$x^2 - y \leq 2 \Rightarrow y \geq x^2 - 2$ is above the parabola $y = x^2 - 2$, which opens upward. It includes the parabola.

The solution is trapped between two parabolas, which matches Figure a. One solution is (0, 0).

*Answers may vary.*

17. The solution region is above the parabola $y = x^2$ and below the line $y = 6 - x$. It includes the boundary. See Figure 17. One solution is (0, 2). *Answers may vary.*

18. The solution region lies below the graph of $y = \sqrt{x}$ and above the horizontal line $y = 1$. It includes the boundary. See Figure 18. One solution is (4, 1.5). *Answers may vary.*

19. The solution region lies between the parallel lines $y = -\frac{1}{2}x - 1$ and $y = -\frac{1}{2}x + \frac{5}{2}$. It does not include the boundary. See Figure 19. One solution is (0, 0). *Answers may vary.*

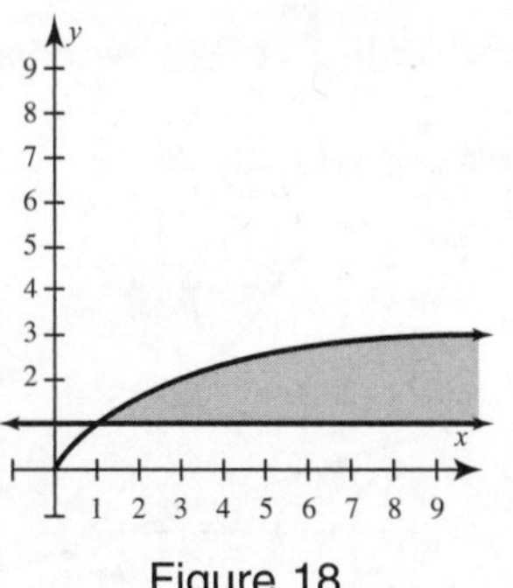

Figure 18

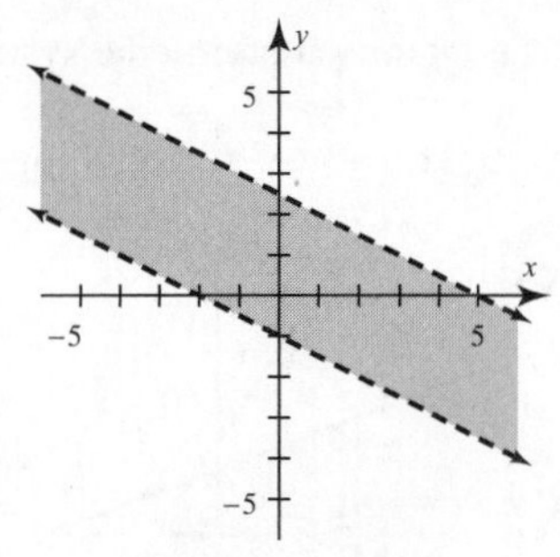

Figure 19

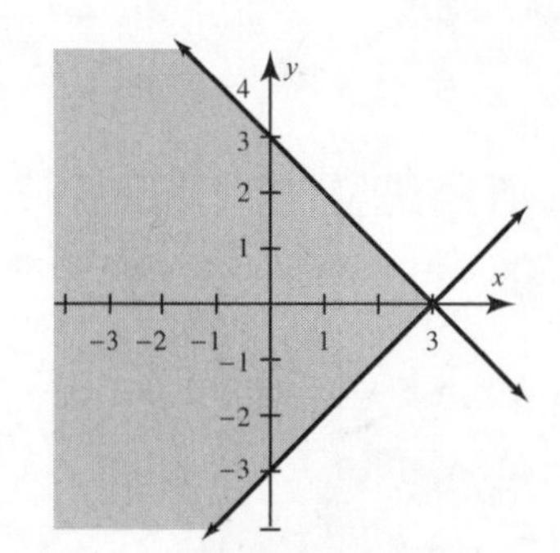

Figure 20

20. The solution region is above the line $y = x + 3$ and below the line $y = -x + 3$. It includes the boundary. See Figure 20. One solution is (0, 0). *Answers may vary.*

21. The solution region lies inside the circle centered at the origin with radius 4 and below the line $y = -x + 2$. It does not include the boundary determined by the line. See Figure 21. One solution is (–1, 1). *Answers may vary.*

22. The solution region lies below the parabola $y = 4 - x^2$ and above the parabola $y = x^2 - 3$. It includes the boundary determined by these equations. See Figure 22. One solution is (0, 0). *Answers may vary.*

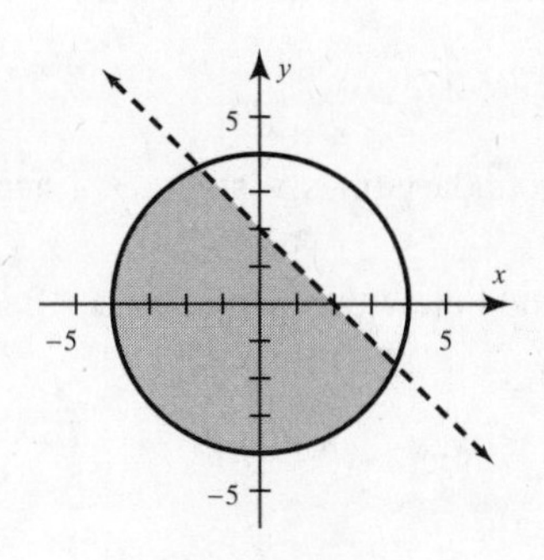

Figure 21

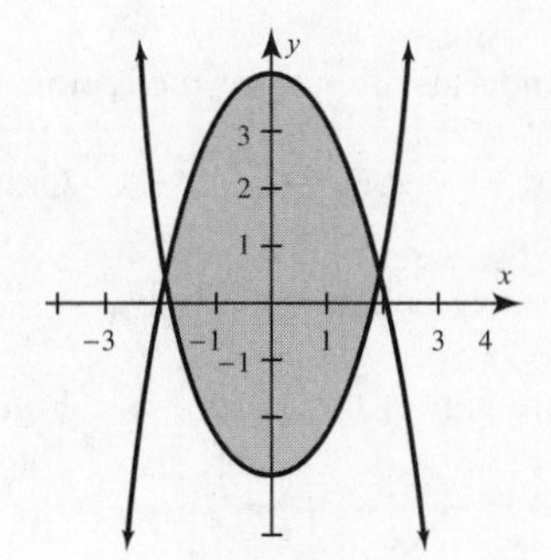

Figure 22

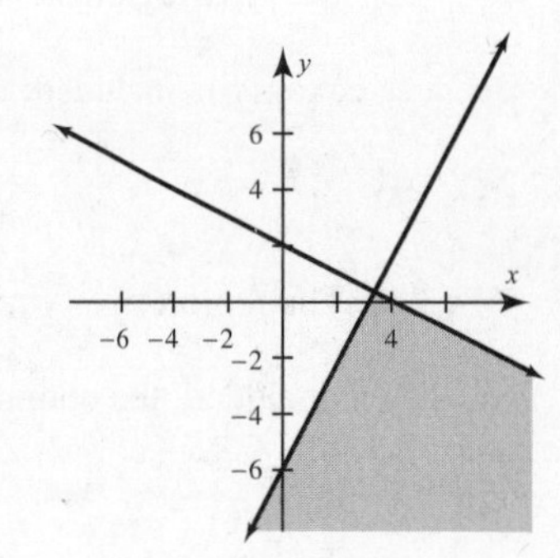

Figure 23

23. $x + 2y \le 4 \Rightarrow y \le -\frac{1}{2}x + 2$ and $2x - y \ge 6 \Rightarrow y \le 2x - 6$. Graph the boundary lines $y = -\frac{1}{2}x + 2$ and $y = 2x - 6$. The region satisfying the system is below the line $x + 2y = 4$ and below the line $2x - y = 6$. Because equality is included, the boundaries are part of the region. See Figure 23.

24. $3x - y \le 3 \Rightarrow y \ge 3x - 3$ and $x + 2y \le 2 \Rightarrow y \le -\frac{1}{2}x + 1$. Graph the boundary lines $y = 3x - 3$ and $y = -\frac{1}{2}x + 1$. The region satisfying the system is below the line $x + 2y = 2$ and above the line $3x - y = 3$. Because equality is included, the boundaries are part of the region. See Figure 24.

25. $3x + 2y < 6 \Rightarrow y < -\frac{3}{2}x + 3$ and $x + 3y \le 6 \Rightarrow y \le -\frac{1}{3}x + 2$. Graph the boundary lines $y = -\frac{3}{2}x + 3$ and $y = -\frac{1}{3}x + 2$. The region satisfying the system is below the line $3x + 2y = 6$, not including the boundary and below the line $x + 3y = 6$, including the boundary. See Figure 25.

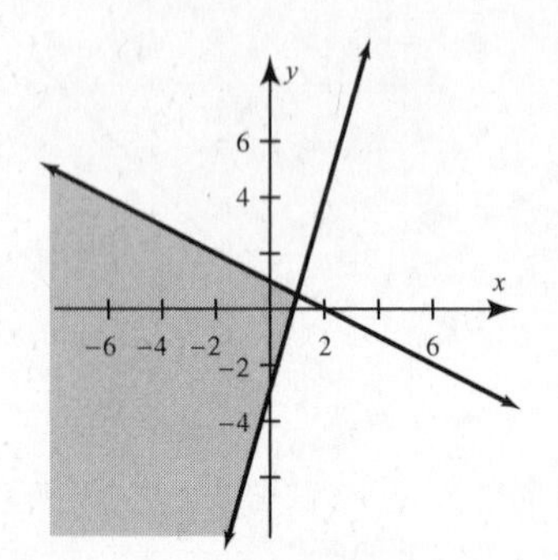

Figure 24

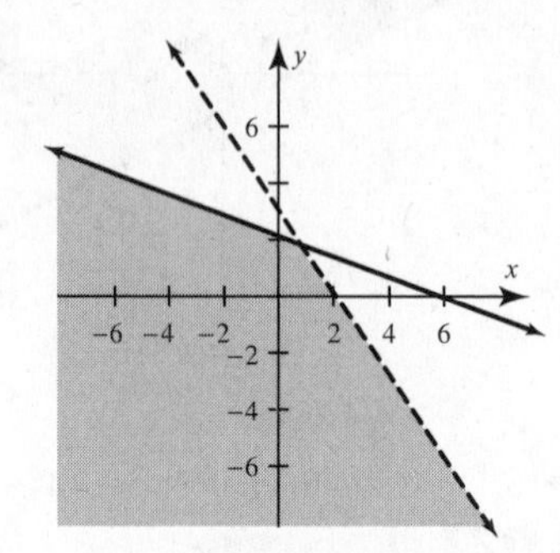

Figure 25

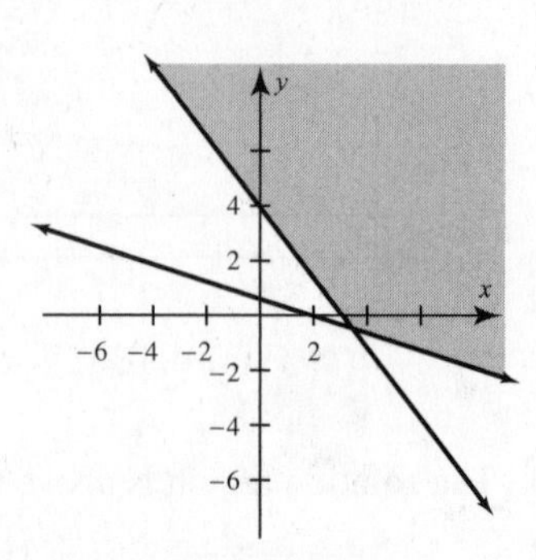

Figure 26

26. $4x + 3y \ge 12 \Rightarrow y \ge -\frac{4}{3}x + 4$ and $2x + 6y \ge 4 \Rightarrow y \ge -\frac{1}{3}x + \frac{2}{3}$. Graph the boundary lines $y = -\frac{4}{3}x + 4$ and $y = -\frac{1}{3}x + \frac{2}{3}$. The region satisfying the system is above the line $4x + 3y = 12$ and above the line $2x + 6y = 4$. Because equality is included, the boundaries are part of the region. See Figure 26.

27. $x - 2y \ge 0 \Rightarrow y \le \frac{1}{2}x$ and $x - 3y \le 3 \Rightarrow y \ge \frac{1}{3}x - 1$. Graph the boundary lines $y = \frac{1}{2}x$ and $y = \frac{1}{3}x - 1$. The region satisfying the system is below the line $y = \frac{1}{2}x$ and above the line $y = \frac{1}{3}x - 1$. Because equality is included, the boundaries are part of the region. See Figure 27.

28. $2x - 4y \ge 4 \Rightarrow y \le \frac{1}{2}x - 1$ and $x + y \le 0 \Rightarrow y \le -x$. Graph the boundary lines $y = \frac{1}{2}x - 1$ and $y = -x$. The region satisfying the system is below the line $y = \frac{1}{2}x - 1$ and below the line $y = -x$. Because equality is included, the boundaries are part of the region. See Figure 28.

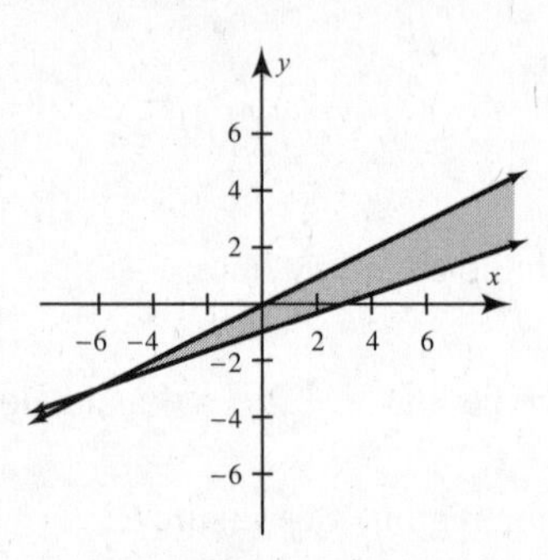

Figure 27

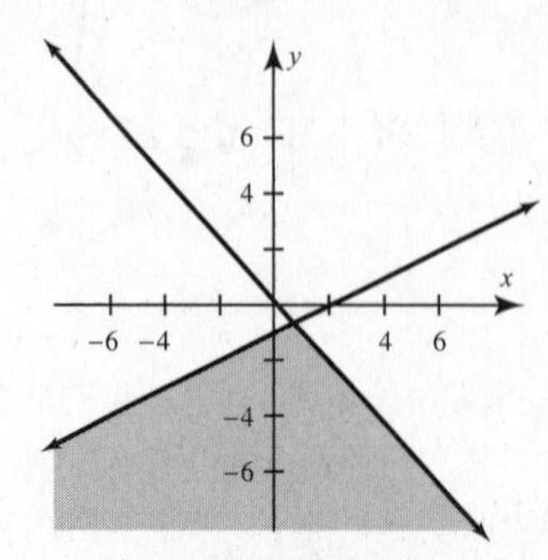

Figure 28

29. $x^2 + y^2 \le 4$ and $y \ge 1$. Graph the boundary circle $x^2 + y^2 = 4$ and the boundary line $y = 1$. The region satisfying the system is inside the circle $x^2 + y^2 = 4$ and above the line $y = 1$. Because equality is included, the boundaries are part of the region. See Figure 29.

30. $x^2 - y \le 0 \Rightarrow y \ge x^2$ and $x^2 + y^2 \le 6$. Graph the boundary parabola $y = x^2$ and the boundary circle $x^2 + y^2 = 6$. The region satisfying the system is above (inside) the parabola $y = x^2$ and inside the circle $x^2 + y^2 = 6$. Because equality is included, the boundaries are part of the region. See Figure 30.

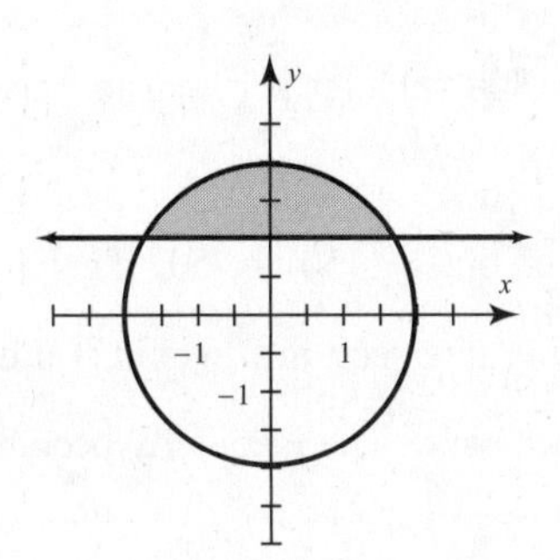

Figure 29

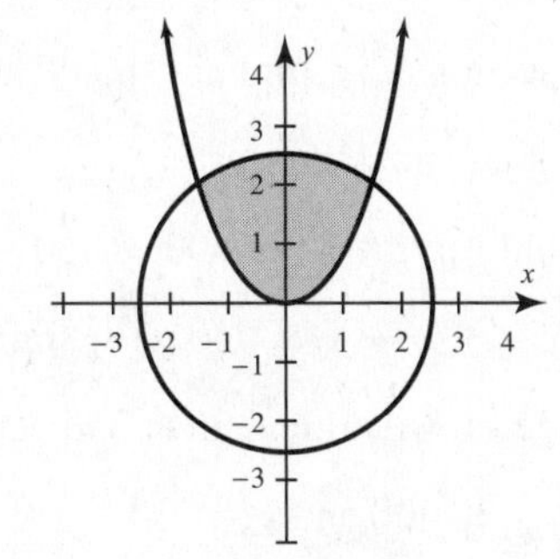

Figure 30

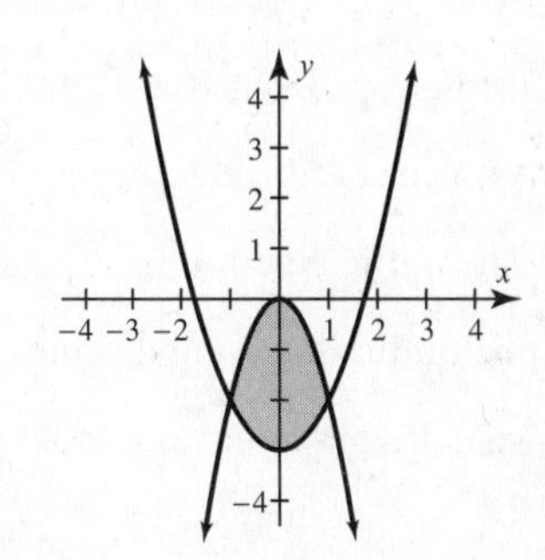

Figure 31

31. $2x^2 + y \le 0 \Rightarrow y \le -2x^2$ and $x^2 - y \le 3 \Rightarrow y \ge x^2 - 3$. Graph the boundary parabolas $y = -2x^2$ and $y = x^2 - 3$. Because equality is included, the boundaries are part of the region. See Figure 31.

32. $x^2 + 2y \le 4 \Rightarrow y \le 2 - \dfrac{x^2}{2}$ and $x^2 - y \le 0 \Rightarrow y \ge x^2$. Graph the boundary parabolas $y = 2 - \dfrac{x^2}{2}$ and $y = x^2$. Because equality is included, the boundaries are part of the region. See Figure 32.

33. $x^2 + 2y \le 2 \Rightarrow y \le 1 - \dfrac{x^2}{2}$ and $x^2 + y^2 \le 4$. Graph the boundary parabola $y = 1 - \dfrac{x^2}{2}$ and the boundary circle $x^2 + y^2 = 4$. Because equality is included, the boundaries are part of the region. See Figure 33.

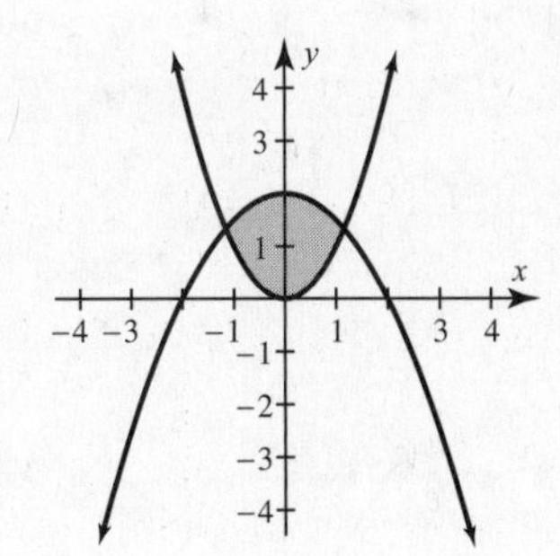

Figure 32

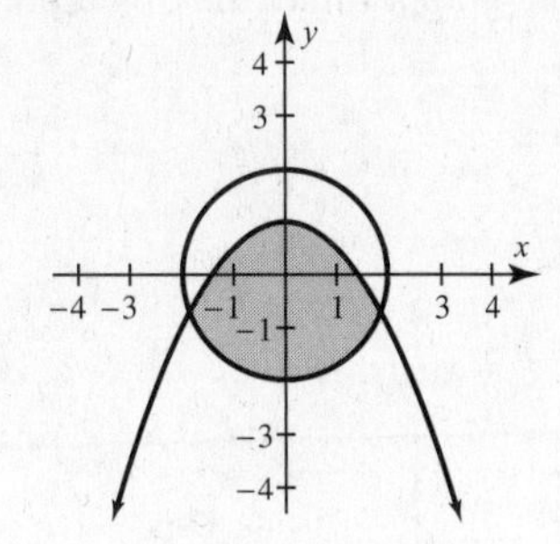

Figure 33

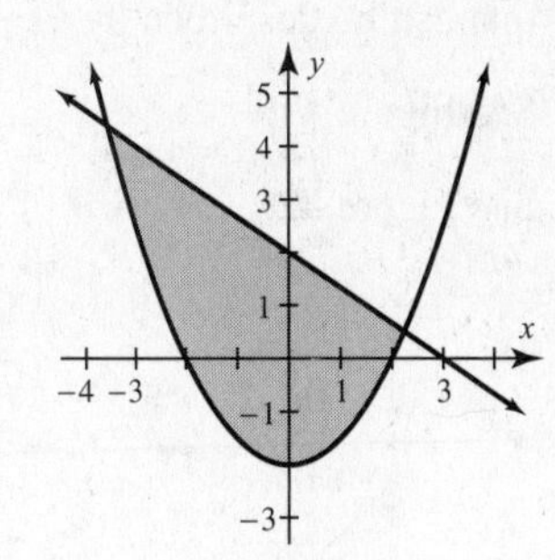

Figure 34

34. $2x + 3y \le 6 \Rightarrow y \le 2 - \dfrac{2}{3}x$ and $\dfrac{1}{2}x^2 - y \le 2 \Rightarrow y \ge \dfrac{1}{2}x^2 - 2$. Graph the boundary line $y = 2 - \dfrac{2}{3}x$ and the boundary parabola $y = \dfrac{1}{2}x^2 - 2$. Because equality is included, the boundaries are part of the region. See Figure 34.

35. The total number of vehicles entering intersection A is $500 + 150 = 650$ vehicles per hour. The expression $x + y$ represents the number of vehicles leaving intersection A each hour. Therefore, we have $x + y = 650$. The total number of vehicles leaving intersection B is $50 + 400 = 450$. There are 100 vehicles entering intersection B from the south and $y$ vehicles entering intersection B from the west. Thus, $y + 100 = 450$. We must solve the system;

$$\begin{array}{l} x + y \qquad = 650 \\ \qquad y + 100 = 450 \\ \hline x \qquad - 100 = 200 \quad \Rightarrow x = 300 \end{array}$$

Thus, $y = 350$ and $x = 300$. At intersection A, a stoplight should allow for 300 vehicles per hour to travel south and 350 vehicles per hour to continue traveling east.

36. The traffic entering intersection A would vary between $400 + 150 = 550$ and $600 + 150 = 750$. Therefore, the traffic flows $x$ and $y$ must satisfy $550 \le x + y \le 750$. The traffic leaving intersection B would still be 450 vehicles per hour, so $y$ could not change - it would remain at 350 vehicles per hour. The inequality becomes $550 \le x + 350 \le 750$. Thus, $200 \le x \le 400$ and $y = 350$.

37. This region corresponds to weights that are less and heights that are greater than recommended. This individual has weight that is less than recommended for his or her height.

38. A person 74 inches tall has an approximate recommended weight range of 150 to 200 pounds.

39. The upper left boundary is given by $25h - 7w = 800$ or $h = \dfrac{7w + 800}{25}$. The region is below and includes this line, which is described by $h \le \dfrac{7w + 800}{25}$ or $25h - 7w \le 800$. The lower right boundary of this region is given by $5h - w = 170$. The region is above and includes this line, which is described by $5h - w \ge 170$. Thus, the region can be described by the system of inequalities: $25h - 7w \le 800$, $5h - w \ge 170$.

40. There is no single ideal weight or height. There is only a general recommended ranges of weights and heights that can be described by a region on the graph, rather than by a point or line.

41. See Figure 41.

42. See Figure 42.

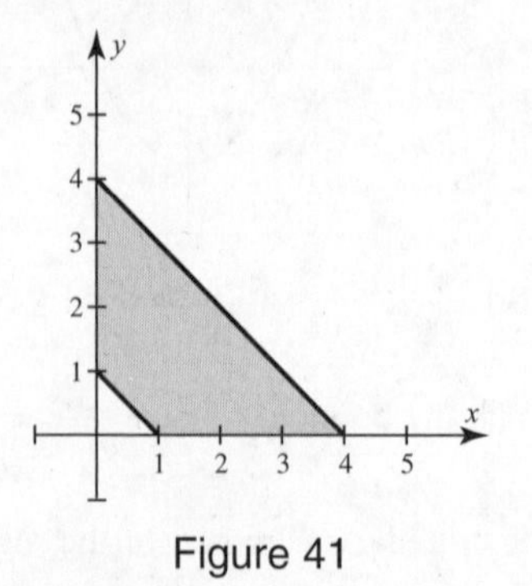


Figure 41

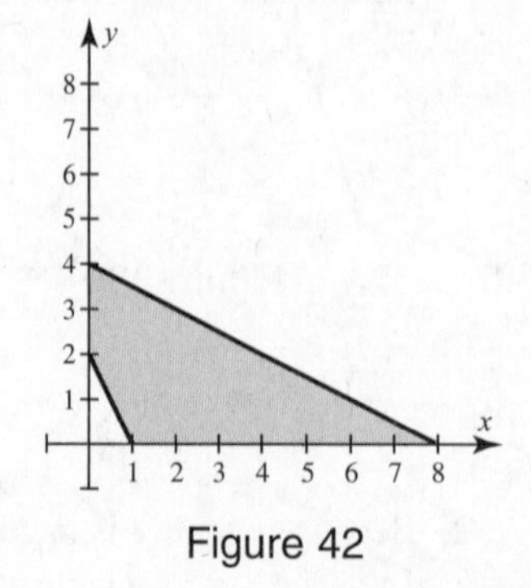


Figure 42

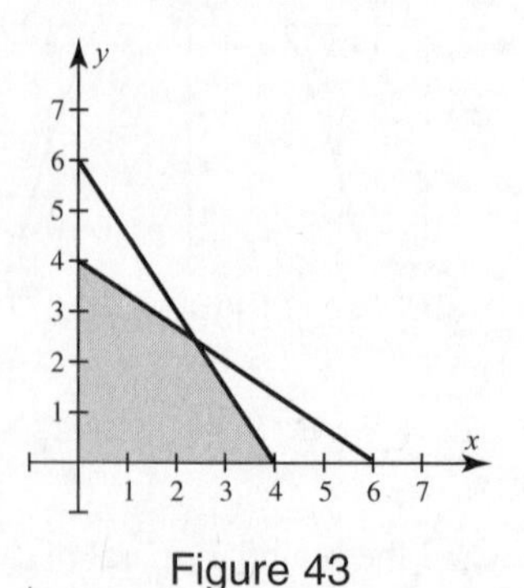


Figure 43

43. See Figure 43.

44. See Figure 44.

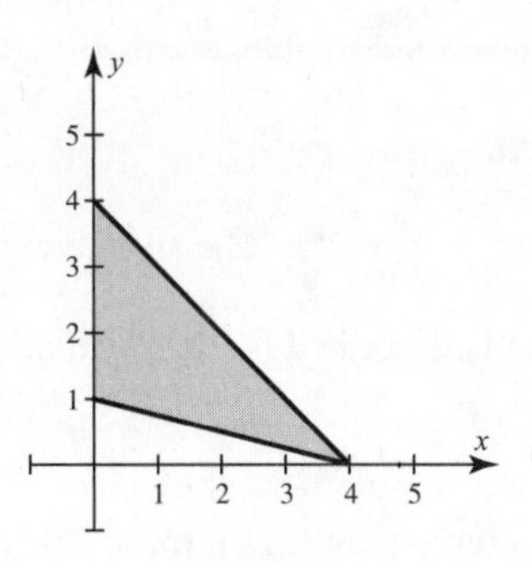

Figure 44

45. To find the maximum and minimum values of $P$ in the region, we must evaluate $P$ at each of the vertices. These values are shown in the table. See Figure 45. From the table the maximum is 65 and the minimum is 8.

46. To find the maximum and minimum values of $P$ in the region, we must evaluate $P$ at each of the vertices. These values are shown in the table. See Figure 46. From the table the maximum is 55 and the minimum is 8.

| Vertex | $P = 3x + 5y$ |
|---|---|
| (1, 1) | $3(1) + 5(1) = 8$ |
| (6, 3) | $3(6) + 5(3) = 33$ |
| (5, 10) | $3(5) + 5(10) = 65$ |
| (2, 7) | $3(2) + 5(7) = 41$ |

Figure 45

| Vertex | $P = 6x + y$ |
|---|---|
| (1, 2) | $6(1) + (2) = 8$ |
| (9, 1) | $6(9) + (1) = 55$ |
| (6, 8) | $6(6) + (8) = 44$ |
| (1, 5) | $6(1) + (5) = 11$ |

Figure 46

| Vertex | $C = 3x + 5y$ |
|---|---|
| (1, 0) | $3(1) + 5(0) = 3$ |
| (7, 6) | $3(7) + 5(6) = 51$ |
| (7, 9) | $3(7) + 5(9) = 66$ |
| (1, 10) | $3(1) + 5(10) = 53$ |

Figure 47

47. To find the maximum and minimum values of $C$ in the region, we must evaluate $C$ at each of the vertices. These values are shown in the table. See Figure 47. From the table the maximum is 66 and the minimum is 3.

48. To find the maximum and minimum values of $C$ in the region, we must evaluate $C$ at each of the vertices. These values are shown in the table. See Figure 48. From the table the maximum is 80 and the minimum is 5.

49. To find the maximum and minimum values of $C$ in the region, we must evaluate $C$ at each of the vertices. These values are shown in the table. See Figure 49. From the table the maximum is 100 and the minimum is 0.

| Vertex | $C = 5x + 5y$ |
|---|---|
| (1, 0) | $5(1) + 5(0) = 5$ |
| (7, 6) | $5(7) + 5(6) = 65$ |
| (7, 9) | $5(7) + 5(9) = 80$ |
| (1, 10) | $5(1) + 5(10) = 55$ |

Figure 48

| Vertex | $C = 10y$ |
|---|---|
| (1, 0) | $10(0) = 0$ |
| (7, 6) | $10(6) = 60$ |
| (7, 9) | $10(9) = 90$ |
| (1, 10) | $10(10) = 100$ |

Figure 49

| Vertex | $C = 3x - y$ |
|---|---|
| (1, 0) | $3(1) - (0) = 3$ |
| (7, 6) | $3(7) - (6) = 15$ |
| (7, 9) | $3(7) - (9) = 12$ |
| (1, 10) | $3(1) - (10) = -7$ |

Figure 50

50. To find the maximum and minimum values of $C$ in the region, we must evaluate $C$ at each of the vertices. These values are shown in the table. See Figure 50. From the table the maximum is 15 and the minimum is –7.

51. The line that goes through the points (0, 4) and (4, 0) has the equation $x + y = 4$. The shaded region is also bounded by the line $x = 0$ and the line $y = 0$. Thus, the shaded region is described by the system: $x + y \leq 4$, $x \geq 0$, and $y \geq 0$.

52. The line that goes through the points (0, 2.5) and (3, 1) has the equation $0.5x + y = 2.5$. The shaded region is also bounded by the lines $x = 0$, $y = 0$ and $x = 3$. Thus, the shaded region is described by the system: $0.5x + y \leq 2.5$, $x \leq 3$, $x \geq 0$, and $y \geq 0$.

53. The region of feasible solutions is shown in Figure 53a. The vertices of this region are (3, 0), (6, 0), (0, 4), and (0, 3). To find the minimum value of $C$ in the region, we must evaluate $C$ at each of the vertices. These values are shown in Figure 53b. From the table the minimum is 6 at the point (0, 3).

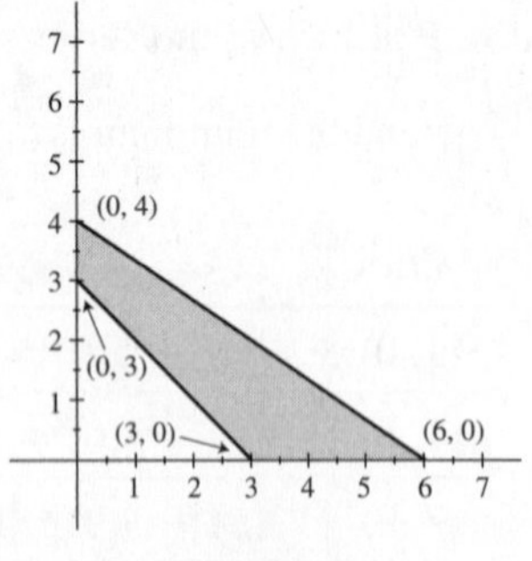


Figure 53a

| Vertex | $C = 4x + 2y$ |
|---|---|
| (3, 0) | $4(3) + 2(0) = 12$ |
| (6, 0) | $4(6) + 2(0) = 24$ |
| (0, 4) | $4(0) + 2(4) = 8$ |
| (0, 3) | $4(0) + 2(3) = 6$ |

Figure 53b

54. The region of feasible solutions is shown in Figure 54a. The vertices of this region are (0, 0), $\left(\frac{8}{3}, 0\right)$, (2, 2), and $\left(0, \frac{8}{3}\right)$. To find the maximum value of $P$ in the region, we must evaluate $P$ at each of the vertices. These values are shown in Figure 54b. From the table the maximum is 16 at the point (2, 2).

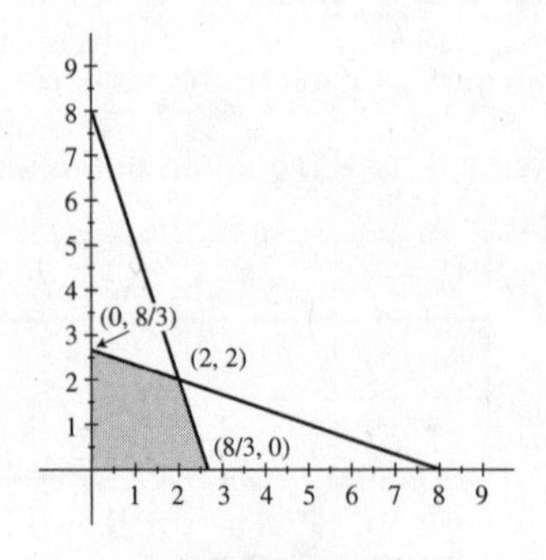


Figure 54a

| Vertex | $P = 3x + 5y$ |
|---|---|
| (0, 0) | $3(0) + 5(0) = 0$ |
| $(\frac{8}{3}, 0)$ | $3(\frac{8}{3}) + 5(0) = 8$ |
| (2, 2) | $3(2) + 5(2) = 16$ |
| $(0, \frac{8}{3})$ | $3(0) + 5(\frac{8}{3}) = 13\frac{1}{3}$ |

Figure 54b

55. The region of feasible solutions is shown in Figure 55a. The vertices of this region are (0, 4), (0, 8), (4, 0), and (8, 0). To find the maximum and minimum values of $z = 7x + 6y$ in the region, we must evaluate $z$ at each of the vertices. These values are shown in Figure 55b. From the table the maximum is 56 and the minimum is 24.

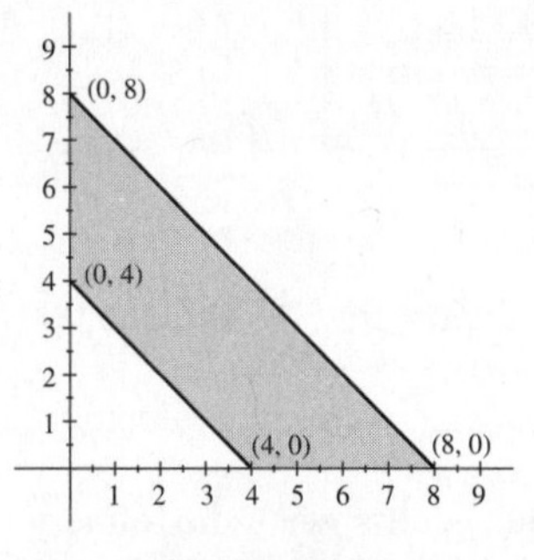


Figure 55a

| Vertex | $z = 7x + 6y$ |
|---|---|
| (0, 4) | $7(0) + 6(4) = 24$ |
| (0, 8) | $7(0) + 6(8) = 48$ |
| (4, 0) | $7(4) + 6(0) = 28$ |
| (8, 0) | $7(8) + 6(0) = 56$ |

Figure 55b

56. The region of feasible solutions is shown in Figure 56a. The vertices of the region are (0, 12), $\left(\frac{18}{7}, \frac{12}{7}\right)$, and (6, 0). Since the region is not bounded from above, there can not be a maximum value. To find the minimum value, we must evaluate $z = 8x + 3y$ at each of the vertices. These values are shown in Figure 56b. From the table the minimum value is about 25.7.

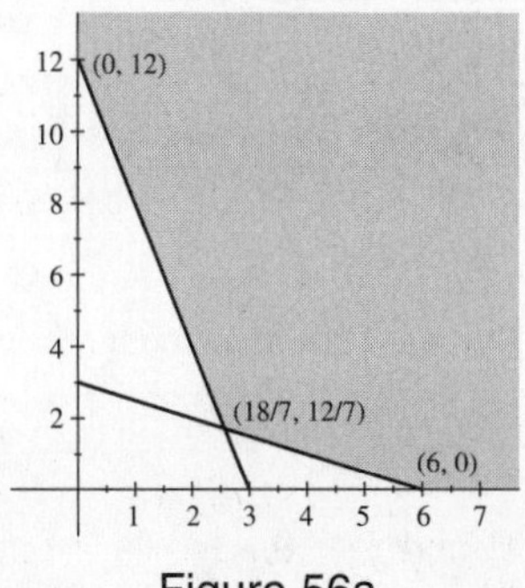


Figure 56a

| Vertex | $z = 8x + 3y$ |
|---|---|
| (0, 12) | $8(0) + 3(12) = 36$ |
| $(\frac{18}{7}, \frac{12}{7})$ | $8(\frac{18}{7}) + 3(\frac{12}{7}) \approx 25.7$ |
| (6, 0) | $8(6) + 3(0) = 48$ |

Figure 56b

57. The new objective equation is $P = 20x + 15y$. To find the maximum profit we must evaluate $P$ at each of the vertices. These values are shown in Figure 57. From the table the maximum is 950 at the vertex (25, 30). The maximum profit will be \$950 when 25 radios and 30 CD players are manufactured.

| Vertex | $P = 20x + 15y$ |
|---|---|
| (5, 5) | $20(5) + 15(5) = 175$ |
| (25, 25) | $20(25) + 15(25) = 875$ |
| (25, 30) | $20(25) + 15(30) = 950$ |
| (5, 30) | $20(5) + 15(30) = 550$ |

Figure 57

58. Make a table to list the information given. See Figure 58a.

Revenue: $R = 1.00x + 0.90y$, $x + y \leq 600{,}000$, $x \leq \frac{1}{2}y$, $y \geq 150{,}000$, $x \geq 0$, and $y \geq 0$.

| Product | Gallons | Minimum | Revenue |
|---|---|---|---|
| Gasoline | $x$ | $0.5y$ | \$4.00 |
| Fuel Oil | $y$ | 150,000 | \$3.60 |
| Maximum | 600,000 | | |

Figure 58a

The region of feasible solutions is shown in Figure 58b. The vertices of this region are (75,000, 150,000), (0, 150,000), (0, 600,000), and (200,000, 400,000). To find the maximum revenue, we must evaluate $R$ at each of the vertices. These values are shown in Figure 58c. The maximum revenue occurs when the refinery produces 200,000 gallons of gasoline and 400,000 gallons of fuel oil.

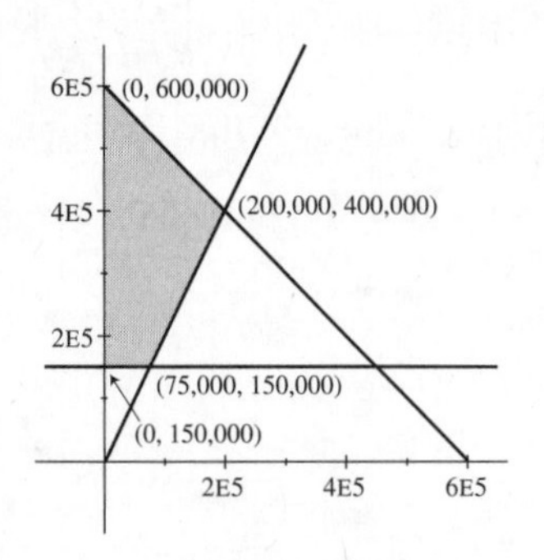


Figure 58b

| Vertex | $R = 1.00x + 0.90y$ |
|---|---|
| (0, 600,000) | $4.00(0) + 3.60(600{,}000) = 2{,}160{,}000$ |
| (0, 150,000) | $4.00(0) + 3.60(150{,}000) = 540{,}000$ |
| (75,000, 150,000) | $4.00(75{,}000) + 3.60(150{,}000) = 840{,}000$ |
| (200,000, 400,000) | $4.00\ (200{,}000) + 3.60\ (400{,}000) = 2{,}240{,}000$ |

Figure 58c

59. Make a table to list the information given. See Figure 59a. Using the table, we can write the linear programming problem as follows;

Cost: $C = 80x + 50y$, Protein: $15x + 20y \geq 60$, Fat: $10x + 5y \geq 30$, $x \geq 0$, and $y \geq 0$.

| Brand | Units | Protein | Fat | Cost |
|---|---|---|---|---|
| A | $x$ | 15 | 10 | 80¢ |
| B | $y$ | 20 | 5 | 50¢ |
| Minimum | | 60 | 30 | |

Figure 59a

The region of feasible solutions is shown in Figure 59b. The vertices of this region are (0, 6), (2.4, 1.2), and (4, 0). To find the minimum value of $C$ in the region, we must evaluate $C$ at each of the vertices. These values are shown in Figure 59c. The minimum cost occurs when 2.4 units of Brand A and 1.2 units of Brand B are mixed, to give a cost of \$2.52 per serving.

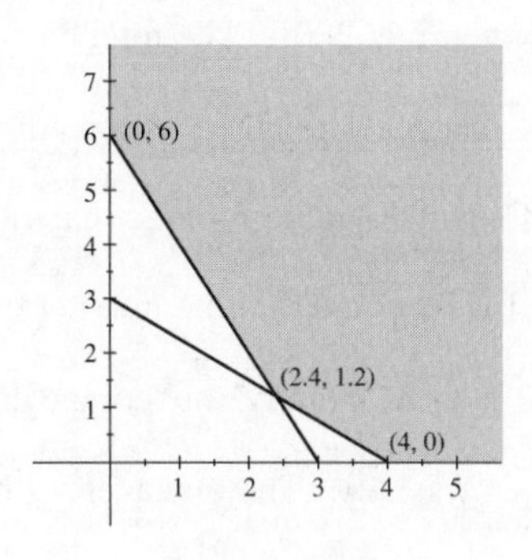


Figure 59b

| Vertex | $C = 80x + 50y$ |
|---|---|
| (0, 6) | $80(0) + 50(6) = 300$ |
| (2.4, 1.2) | $80(2.4) + 50(1.2) = 252$ |
| (4, 0) | $80(4) + 50(0) = 320$ |

Figure 59c

60. Let $x$ and $y$ represent the amount of Brand X and Brand Y respectively. Since each unit of Brand X contains 20 grams of protein, each unit of Brand Y contains 10 grams of protein and the total amount of protein must be at least 60 grams, $20x + 10y \geq 60$. Since each unit of Brand X contains 10 grams of fat, each unit of Brand Y contains 10 grams of fat and the total amount of fat must be at least 40 grams, $10x + 10y \geq 40$. Finally the quantities cannot be negative so $x \geq 0$ and $y \geq 0$. Here the cost function is $C = 0.75x + 0.50y$. From the graph of the region of feasible solutions (not shown), the vertices are (0, 6), (2, 2), and (4, 0). Note that this region is unbounded. To find the point (2, 2) solve the equations $20x + 10y = 60$ and $10x + 10y = 40$. The minimum value of $C$ occurs at one of the vertices. For $(0, 6), C = 0.75(0) + 0.50(6) = 3.00$. For $(2, 2), C = 0.75(2) + 0.50(2) = 2.50$. For $(4, 0), C = 0.75(4) + 0.50(0) = 3.00$.

    To minimize cost, 2 units of Brand X and 2 units of Brand Y should be mixed.

61. Let $x$ and $y$ represent the number of hamsters and mice respectively. Since the total number of animals cannot exceed 50, $x + y \leq 50$. Because no more than 20 hamsters can be raised, $x \leq 20$. Here the revenue function is $R = 15x + 10y$. From the graph of the region of feasible solutions (not shown), the vertices are (0, 0), (0, 50), (20, 30), and (20, 0). To find (20, 30) solve the equations $x + y = 50$ and $x = 20$. The maximum value of $R$ occurs at one of the vertices. For $(0, 50), R = 15(0) + 10(50) = 500$. For $(20, 30), R = 15(20) + 10(30) = 600$. For $(20, 0), R = 15(20) + 10(0) = 300$.

    The maximum revenue is \$600.

62. The cost of $x$ units of cabinet X is $100x$. Similarly, the cost of $y$ units of cabinet Y is $200y$. The total cost must not exceed \$1400, thus, $100x + 200y \leq 1400$ is one constraint. The square footage needed for $x$ units of cabinet X is $6x$ while the square footage needed for $y$ units of cabinet Y is $8y$. The total square footage may not exceed 72 square feet, thus $6x + 8y \leq 72$ is another constraint. It should also be noted that the number of cabinets of each type can not be negative. This gives the constraints $x \geq 0$ and $y \geq 0$. Finally, the storage capacity of $x$ units of cabinet X is $8x$ while the storage capacity of $y$ units of cabinet Y is $12y$. The manager wishes to maximize the storage space which gives the objective function $S = 8x + 12y$. Graph the constraints and shade the region. The region of feasible solutions is shown in Figure 62a. The vertices of this region are (0, 0), (12, 0), (8, 3), and (0, 7). To find the maximum value of $S$ in the region, we must evaluate $S$ at each of the vertices. These values are shown in Figure 62b. From the table the maximum is 100 at point (8, 3). The maximum storage space is 100 cubic feet when there are 8 cabinets of type X and 3 cabinets of type Y.

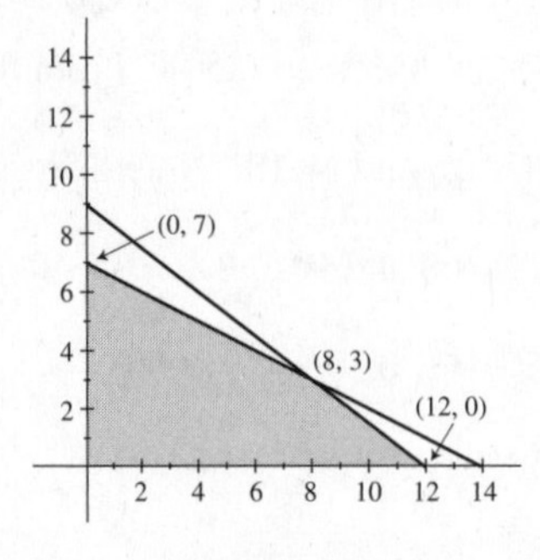

Figure 62a

| Vertex | $S = 8x + 12y$ |
|---|---|
| (0, 0) | $8(0) + 12(0) = 0$ |
| (12, 0) | $8(12) + 12(0) = 96$ |
| (8, 3) | $8(8) + 12(3) = 100$ |
| (0, 7) | $8(0) + 12(7) = 84$ |

Figure 62b

63. The number of hours on machine A needed to manufacture $x$ units of part X is $4x$ while the number of hours on machine A needed to manufacture $y$ units of part Y is $1y$. Since machine A is only available for 40 hours each week we have the constraint $4x + y \leq 40$. Similarly, the number of hours on machine B needed to manufacture $x$ units of part X is $2x$ while the number of hours on machine B to make $y$ units of part Y is $3y$. Since machine B is only available for 30 hours each week we have the constraint $2x + 3y \leq 30$. It should be noted that the number of parts of each type cannot be negative. This gives the constraint $x \geq 0$ and $y \geq 0$. The profit earned on $x$ units of part X is $500x$ while the profit earned on $y$ units of part Y is $600y$. Thus, the total weekly profit is $P = 500x + 600y$. This is our objective function. Graph the constraints and shade the region. The region of feasible solutions is shown in Figure 63a. The vertices of this region are (0, 0), (10, 0), (9, 4), and (0, 10). To find the maximum value of $P$ in the region, we must evaluate $P$ at each of the vertices. These values are shown in Figure 63b. From the table the maximum is 6900 at the point (9, 4). The maximum profit is \$6900 when there are 9 parts of type X and 4 parts of type Y manufactured.

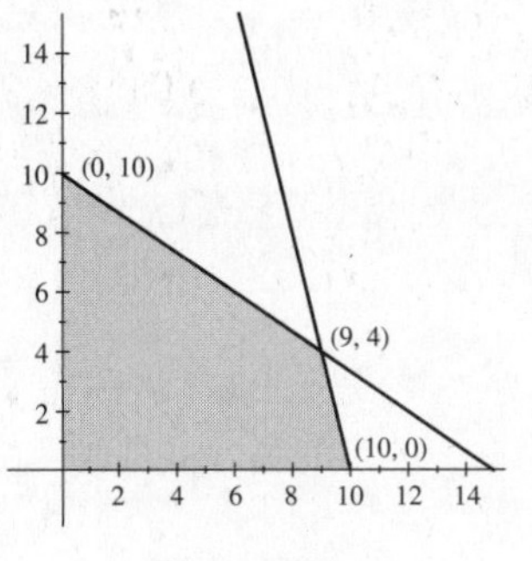


Figure 63a

| Vertex | $P = 500x + 600y$ |
|---|---|
| (0, 0) | $500(0) + 600(0) = 0$ |
| (10, 0) | $500(10) + 600(0) = 5000$ |
| (9, 4) | $500(9) + 600(4) = 6900$ |
| (0, 10) | $500(0) + 600(10) = 6000$ |

Figure 63b

64. The number of pounds of ingredient A found in $x$ pounds of substance X is $0.2x$ while the number of pounds of ingredient A found in $y$ pounds of substance Y is $0.5y$. Since the pet store needs at least 251 pounds of ingredient A, we have the constraint $0.2x + 0.5y \geq 251$. Similarly, the number of pounds of ingredient B found in $x$ pounds of substance X is $0.5x$ while the number of pounds of ingredient B found in $y$ pounds of substance Y is $0.3y$. Since the pet store needs at least 200 pounds of ingredient B, we have the constraint $0.5x + 0.3y \geq 200$. It should be noted that the number of pounds of each substance cannot be negative. This gives the constraints $x \geq 0$ and $y \geq 0$. The cost of $x$ pounds of substance X is $2x$ while the cost of $y$ pounds of substance Y is $3y$. Thus, the total cost is $C = 2x + 3y$. This is our objective function. Graph the constraints and shade the region. The region of feasible solutions is shown in Figure 64a. The vertices of this region are (1255, 0), (130, 450), and $\left(0, \frac{2000}{3}\right)$. To find the minimum value of $C$ in the region we must evaluate $C$ at each of the vertices. These values are shown in Figure 64b. From the table the minimum 1610 at the point (130, 450). The minimum cost is \$1610 when there are 130 pounds of substance X and 450 pounds of substance Y purchased.

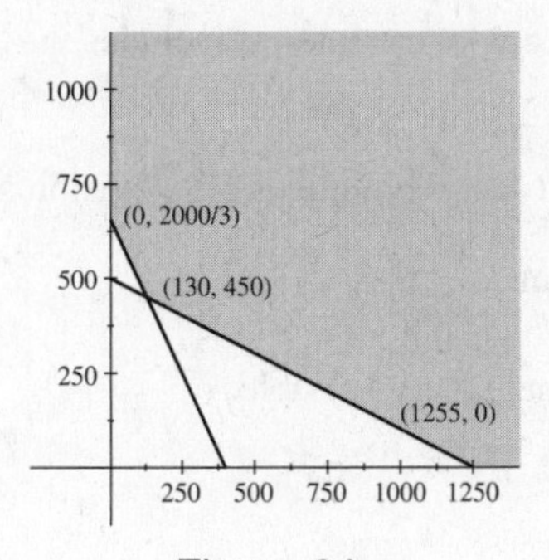


Figure 64a

| Vertex | $C = 2x + 3y$ |
|---|---|
| (1255, 0) | $2(1255) + 3(0) = 2510$ |
| (130, 450) | $2(130) + 3(450) = 1610$ |
| $(0, \frac{2000}{3})$ | $2(0) + 3(\frac{2000}{3}) = 2000$ |

Figure 64b

## Checking Basic Concepts for Sections 6.1 and 6.2

1. $d(13, 18) = \sqrt{(13 - 1)^2 + (18 - 2)^2} = \sqrt{12^2 + 16^2} = \sqrt{400} = 20$

2. Solve the first equation for $y$ and substitute it into the second equation. $2x^2 - y = 0 \Rightarrow y = 2x^2$. Substituting $y = 2x^2$ into the second equation gives the following. $3x + 2y = 7 \Rightarrow 3x + 2(2x^2) = 7 \Rightarrow$ $4x^2 + 3x - 7 = 0 \Rightarrow (4x + 7)(x - 1) = 0 \Rightarrow x = -\frac{7}{4}$ or 1. The solutions are $\left(-\frac{7}{4}, \frac{49}{8}\right)$ and $(1, 2)$.
3. $z = x^2 + y^2 \Rightarrow y^2 = z - x^2 \Rightarrow y = \pm\sqrt{z - x^2}$
4. Multiply the first equation by 3 and add the two equations:

$$\begin{array}{rl} 9x - 6y &= 12 \\ -x + 6y &= 8 \\ \hline 8x \quad\quad &= 20 \Rightarrow x = \frac{5}{2}. \end{array}$$

If $x = \frac{5}{2}$, then $-\frac{5}{2} + 6y = 8 \Rightarrow 6y = \frac{21}{2} \Rightarrow y = \frac{21}{12} \Rightarrow y = \frac{7}{4}$. Therefore the solution is: $\left(\frac{5}{2}, \frac{7}{4}\right)$.
5. Graph the boundary line $3x - 2y = 6 \Rightarrow y = \frac{3}{2}x - 3$. Choose $(0, 0)$ as a test point. Since $0 \le 6$, the region containing $(0, 0)$ is the solution set. The boundary line $y = \frac{3}{2}x - 3$ is part of the solution set. See Figure 5.

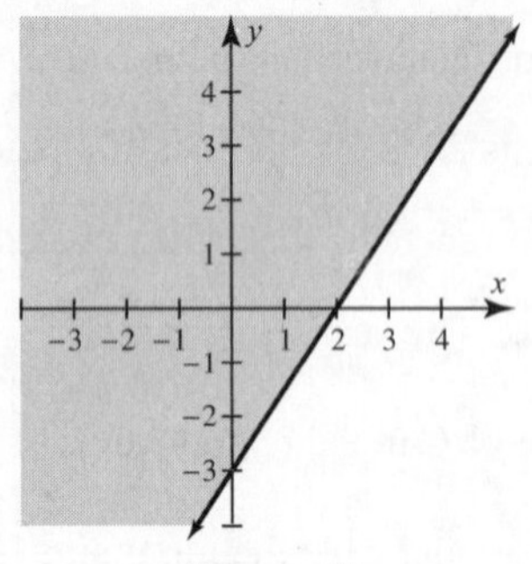

Figure 5

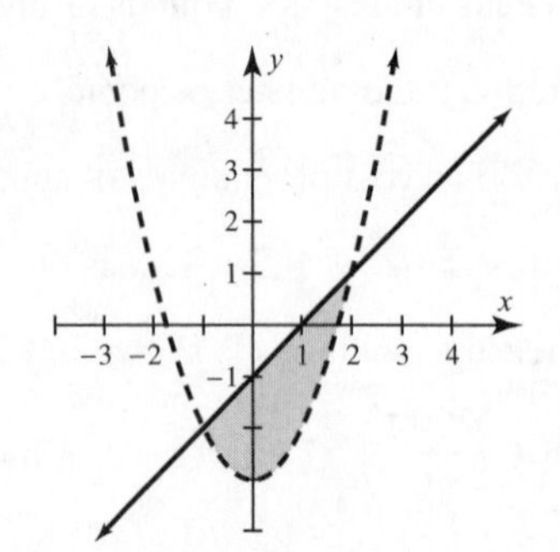

Figure 6

6. $x^2 - y < 3 \Rightarrow x^2 - 3 < y$ or $y > x^2 - 3$. This region is above the parabola $y = x^2 - 3$ and does not include the boundary of the parabola. $x - y \ge 1 \Rightarrow x - 1 \ge y$ or $y \le x - 1$. This region is below the line $y = x - 1$ and includes the line. The solution lies above the parabola and below the line. It includes the boundary determined by the line but not the parabola. One solution is $(0, -2)$. See Figure 6.
7. (a) Let $x$ represent the number of television sets sold with stereo and $y$ represent the number of television sets sold without stereo. Thus, the system we want to solve is $x + y = 32$ and $\frac{19}{10}x = y$.

(b) Since, $\frac{19}{10}x = y \Rightarrow \frac{19}{10}x - y = 0$, we add the two equations to eliminate the $y$-variable.

$$\begin{array}{rl} x + y &= 32 \\ \frac{19}{10}x - y &= 0 \\ \hline \frac{29}{10}x \quad\quad &= 32 \quad \Rightarrow x = \frac{320}{29} \approx 11.03 \end{array}$$

$$x + y = 32 \Rightarrow \frac{320}{29} + y = 32 \Rightarrow y = \frac{608}{29} \approx 20.97$$

In 1999, about 11 million television sets were sold with stereo sound and about 21 million sets were sold without stereo sound.

## 6.3 Systems of Linear Equations in Three Variables

1. No, systems of linear equations can have zero, one, or infinitely many solutions.

2. Yes, $3(1) + 2(2) + 3 = 10 \Rightarrow 3 + 4 + 3 = 10 \Rightarrow 10 = 10$

3. 2, the same as the number of variables.

4. 3, the same as the number of variables.

5. Testing $(0, 2, -2)$: $0 + 2 - (-2) = 4$, true; $-0 + 2 + (-2) = 2$, false; $0 + 2 + (-2) = 0$, true; since the second equation is false, $(0, 2, -2)$ is not a solution for the system.

   Testing $(-1, 3, -2)$: $-1 + 3 - (-2) = 4$, true; $-(-1) + 3 + (-2) = 2$, true; $-1 + 3 + (-2) = 0$, true; since all equation are true, $(-1, 3, -2)$ is a solution for the system.

6. Testing $(5, 2, 2)$: $2(5) - 3(2) + 3(2) = 10 \Rightarrow 10 - 6 + 6 = 10$, true;

   $5 - 2(2) - 3(2) = 1 \Rightarrow 5 - 4 - 6 = 1$, false; $4(5) - 2 + 2 = 10 \Rightarrow 20 - 2 + 2 = 10$, false; since two of the equations are false, $(5, 2, 2)$ is not a solution for the system.

   Testing $(2, -1, 1)$: $2(2) - 3(-1) + 3(1) = 10 \Rightarrow 4 + 3 + 3 = 10$, true;

   $2 - 2(-1) - 3(1) = 1 \Rightarrow 2 + 2 - 3 = 1$, true; $4(2) - (-1) + 1 = 10 \Rightarrow 8 + 1 + 1 = 10$, true; since all equations are true, $(2, -1, 1)$ is a solution for the system.

7. Testing $\left(-\frac{5}{11}, \frac{20}{11}, -2\right)$: $-\frac{5}{11} + 3\left(\frac{20}{11}\right) - 2(-2) = 9 \Rightarrow -\frac{5}{11} + \frac{60}{11} + \frac{44}{11} = 9 \Rightarrow \frac{99}{11} = 9$, true;

   $-3\left(-\frac{5}{11}\right) + 2\left(\frac{20}{11}\right) + 4(-2) = -3 \Rightarrow \frac{15}{11} + \frac{40}{11} - \frac{88}{11} = -3 \Rightarrow -\frac{33}{11} = -3$, true;

   $-2\left(-\frac{5}{11}\right) + 5\left(\frac{20}{11}\right) + 2(-2) = 6 \Rightarrow \frac{10}{11} + \frac{100}{11} - \frac{44}{11} = 6 \Rightarrow \frac{66}{11} = 6$, true; since all of the equations are true, $\left(-\frac{5}{11}, \frac{20}{11}, -2\right)$ is a solution for the system.

   Testing $(1, 2, -1)$: $1 + 3(2) - 2(-1) = 9 \Rightarrow 1 + 6 + 2 = 9 \Rightarrow 9 = 9$, true;

   $-3(1) + 2(2) + 4(-1) = -3 \Rightarrow -3 + 4 + (-4) = -3 \Rightarrow -3 = -3$, true;

   $-2(1) + 5(2) + 2(-1) = 6 \Rightarrow (-2) + 10 + (-2) = 6 \Rightarrow 6 = 6$, true; since all equations are true, $(1, 2, -1)$ is a solution for the system. Therefore they are both solutions.

8. Testing $(1, 2, 3)$: $4(1) - 2(2) + 2(3) = 6 \Rightarrow 4 - 4 + 6 = 6$, true;

   $2(1) - 4(2) - 6(3) = -24 \Rightarrow 2 - 8 - 18 = -24$, true;

   $-3(1) + 3(2) + 2(3) = 9 \Rightarrow -3 + 6 + 6 = 9$, true; since all equations are true, $(1, 2, 3)$ is a solution for the system. Testing $(11, 16, -3)$: $4(11) - 2(16) + 2(-3) = 6 \Rightarrow 44 - 32 + (-6) = 6 \Rightarrow 6 = 6$, true;

   $2(11) - 4(16) - 6(-3) = -24 \Rightarrow 22 - 64 + 18 = -24 \Rightarrow -24 = -24$, true;

   $-3(11) + 3(16) + 2(-3) = 9 \Rightarrow -33 + 48 + (-6) = 9 \Rightarrow 9 = 9$, true; since all equations are true, $(11, 16, -3)$ is a solution for the system.

9. Add The first two equations:

$$\begin{array}{r} x + y + z = 6 \\ -x + 2y + z = 6 \\ \hline 3y + 2z = 12. \end{array}$$

Subtract 2 times the third equation from this equation:

$$\begin{array}{l} 3y + 2z = 12 \\ 2y + 2z = 10 \\ \hline y \quad\quad = 2. \end{array}$$

Substitute $y = 2$ into the equation: $3y + 2z = 12 \Rightarrow 3(2) + 2z = 12 \Rightarrow 6 + 2z = 12 \Rightarrow 2z = 6 \Rightarrow$ $z = 3$. Finally, substitute $y = 2$ and $z = 3$ into one of the original equations: $x + 2 + 3 = 6 \Rightarrow x = 1$. The solution is $(1, 2, 3)$.

10. Subtract the first two equations:

$$\begin{array}{l} x - y + z = -2 \\ x - 2y + z = 0 \\ \hline y \quad\quad = -2. \end{array}$$

Substitute this into the third equation: $(-2) - z = 1 \Rightarrow -z = 3 \Rightarrow z = -3$.

Substitute $y = -2$ and $z = -3$ into the first equation: $x - (-2) + (-3) = -2 \Rightarrow x - 1 = -2 \Rightarrow$. $x = -1$. The solution is: $(-1, -2, -3)$.

11. Multiply the first equation by 2 and subtract the second equation:

$$\begin{array}{r} 2x + 4y + 6z = 8 \\ 2x + y + 3z = 5 \\ \hline 3y + 3z = 3. \end{array}$$

Subtract the third equation from the first:

$$\begin{array}{r} x + 2y + 3z = 4 \\ x - y + z = 2 \\ \hline 3y + 2z = 2. \end{array}$$

Now subtract these two equations:

$$\begin{array}{r} 3y + 3z = 3 \\ 3y + 2z = 2 \\ \hline z = 1. \end{array}$$

Substitute $z = 1$ into $3y + 2z = 2$: $3y + 2(1) = 2 \Rightarrow 3y = 0 \Rightarrow y = 0$.

Finally substitute $y = 0$ and $z = 1$ into the original equation $x - y + z = 2$: $x - 0 + 1 = 2 \Rightarrow x = 1$.

The solution is: $(1, 0, 1)$.

12. Subtract the first two equations:

$$\begin{array}{r} x - y + z = 2 \\ \underline{3x - 2y + z = -1} \\ -2x + y \quad = 3. \end{array}$$

Subtract this equation from the third:

$$\begin{array}{r} x + y = -3 \\ \underline{-2x + y = 3} \\ 3x \quad = -6 \Rightarrow x = -2. \end{array}$$

Substitute $x = -2$ into $x + y = -3$: $(-2) + y = -3 \Rightarrow y = -1$.

Substitute $x = -2$ and $y = -1$ into $x - y + z = 2$: $(-2) - (-1) + z = 2 \Rightarrow -1 + z = 2 \Rightarrow z = 3$.

The solution is: $(-2, -1, 3)$.

13. Add the second and third equations:

$$\begin{array}{l} 4x + 2y + z = 1 \\ \underline{2x - 2y - z = 2} \\ 6x \qquad = 3 \Rightarrow x = \frac{1}{2}. \end{array}$$

Subtract the first two equations:

$$\begin{array}{r} 3x + y + z = 0 \\ \underline{4x + 2y + z = 1} \\ -x - y \quad = -1. \end{array}$$

Substitute $x = \frac{1}{2}$ into $-x - y = -1$: $-\frac{1}{2} - y = -1 \Rightarrow -y = -\frac{1}{2} \Rightarrow y = \frac{1}{2}$.

Substitute $x = \frac{1}{2}$ and $y = \frac{1}{2}$ into $3x + y + z = 0$: $3\left(\frac{1}{2}\right) + \frac{1}{2} + z = 0 \Rightarrow \frac{3}{2} + \frac{1}{2} + z = 0 \Rightarrow$
$2 + z = 0 \Rightarrow z = -2$.

The solution is: $\left(\frac{1}{2}, \frac{1}{2}, -2\right)$.

14. Add the first two equations:

$$\begin{array}{r} -x - 5y + 2z = 2 \\ \underline{x + y + 2z = 2} \\ -4y + 4z = 4. \end{array}$$

Multiply the second equation by 3 and subtract the third equation:

$$\begin{array}{r} 3x + 3y + 6z = 6 \\ \underline{3x + y - 4z = -10} \\ 2y + 10z = 16. \end{array}$$

Now multiply the new equation by $2y + 10z = 16$ by 2 and add $-4y + 4z = 4$:

$$\begin{array}{r} 4y + 20z = 32 \\ \underline{-4y + 4z = 4} \\ 24z = 36 \Rightarrow z = \frac{36}{24} = \frac{3}{2}. \end{array}$$

Substitute $z = \frac{3}{2}$ into $2y + 10z = 16$: $2y + 10\left(\frac{3}{2}\right) = 16 \Rightarrow 2y + 15 = 16 \Rightarrow 2y = 1 \Rightarrow y = \frac{1}{2}$.

Substitute $y = \frac{1}{2}$ and $z = \frac{3}{2}$ into $x + y + 2z = 2$: $x + \frac{1}{2} + 2\left(\frac{3}{2}\right) = 2 \Rightarrow x + \frac{7}{2} = 2 \Rightarrow x = -\frac{3}{2}$.

The solution is: $\left(-\frac{3}{2}, \frac{1}{2}, \frac{3}{2}\right)$.

15. Subtract the third equation from the first:

$$\begin{array}{l} x + 3y + z = 6 \\ \underline{x - y - z = 0} \\ \quad 4y + 2z = 6. \end{array}$$

Multiply the third equation by 3 and subtract it from the second equation:

$$\begin{array}{l} 3x + y - z = 6 \\ \underline{3x - 3y - 3z = 0} \\ \quad 4y + 2z = 6. \end{array}$$

Subtracting these two equations we get:

$$\begin{array}{l} 4y + 2z = 6 \\ \underline{4y + 2z = 6} \\ \quad 0 = 0. \end{array}$$

Therefore infinitely many solutions and $4y + 2z = 6 \Rightarrow 4y = -2z + 6 \Rightarrow y = \dfrac{-z + 3}{2}$.

Adding the last two original equations we get:

$$\begin{array}{l} 3x + y - z = 6 \\ \underline{x - y - z = 0} \\ 4x \quad - 2z = 6 \Rightarrow 4x = 2z + 6 \Rightarrow x = \dfrac{z + 3}{2}. \end{array}$$

We have infinitely many solutions: $\left(\dfrac{z + 3}{2}, \dfrac{-z + 3}{2}, z\right)$.

16. Add the first two equations:

$$\begin{array}{l} 2x - y + 2z = 6 \\ \underline{-x + y + z = 0} \\ x \quad + 3z = 6. \end{array}$$

Add this equation to the third equation:

$$\begin{array}{l} x + 3z = 6 \\ \underline{-x - 3z = -6} \\ \quad 0 = 0. \end{array}$$

Therefore infinitely many solutions.

$x + 3z = 6 \Rightarrow x = -3z + 6$

Multiply the second equation by 2 and add to the first equation:

$$\begin{array}{l} 2x - y + 2z = 6 \\ \underline{-2x + 2y + 2z = 0} \\ \quad y + 4z = 6 \Rightarrow y = -4z + 6. \end{array}$$

We have infinitely many solutions: $(-3z + 6, -4z + 6, z)$

17. Add the first two equations:

$$\begin{array}{l} x - 4y + 2z = -2 \\ \underline{x + 2y - 2z = -3} \\ 2x - 2y \quad = -5. \end{array}$$

Multiply the third equation by 2 and subtract from $2x - 2y = -5$:

$$\begin{array}{r} 2x - 2y = -5 \\ \underline{2x - 2y = \phantom{-}8} \\ 0 = -13. \end{array}$$

Therefore we have no solutions.

18. Add the first two equations:

$$\begin{array}{l} 2x + y + 3z = 4 \\ \underline{-3x - y - 4z = 5} \\ -x \quad - z = 9. \end{array}$$

Add the last two equations:

$$\begin{array}{l} -3x - y - 4z = 5 \\ \underline{x + y + 2z = 0} \\ -2x \quad - 2z = 5. \end{array}$$

Multiply $-x - z = 9$ by 2 and subtract $-2x - 2z = 5$:

$$\begin{array}{r} -2x - 2z = 18 \\ \underline{-2x - 2z = \phantom{1}5} \\ 0 = 13. \end{array}$$

Therefore we have no solutions.

19. Add the last two equations:

$$\begin{array}{l} 2a + b - c = -11 \\ \underline{2a - 2b + c = \phantom{-1}3} \\ 4a - b \quad = -8. \end{array}$$

Multiply the second equation by 2 and add to the first equation:

$$\begin{array}{l} 4a - b + 2c = 0 \\ \underline{4a + 2b - 2c = -22} \\ 8a + b \quad = -22. \end{array}$$

Now add the equation $4a - b = -8$ to $8a + b = -8$:

$$\begin{array}{l} 4a - b = -8 \\ \underline{8a + b = -22} \\ 12a \quad = -30 \Rightarrow a = \dfrac{-30}{12} \Rightarrow a = \dfrac{-5}{2}. \end{array}$$

Substitute $a = \dfrac{-5}{2}$: $8\left(\dfrac{-5}{2}\right) + b = -22 \Rightarrow -20 + b = -22 \Rightarrow b = -2.$

Substitute $a = \dfrac{-5}{2}$ and $b = -2$ into $4\left(\dfrac{-5}{2}\right) - (-2) + 2c = 0 \Rightarrow -10 + 2 + 2c = 0 \Rightarrow 2c = 8 \Rightarrow$

$c = 4$. The solution is: $\left(\dfrac{-5}{2}, -2, 4\right)$.

20. Add the last two equations:

$$\begin{array}{r} -a - 2b + 5c = 9 \\ a + 2b + c = 6 \\ \hline 6c = 15 \Rightarrow c = \frac{5}{2}. \end{array}$$

Add the first two equations:

$$\begin{array}{r} a - 4b + 3c = 2 \\ -a - 2b + 5c = 9 \\ \hline -6b + 8c = 11. \end{array}$$

Substitute $c = \frac{5}{2}$ into $-6b + 8c = 11$: $-6b + 8\left(\frac{5}{2}\right) = 11 \Rightarrow -6b + 20 = 11 \Rightarrow -6b = -9 \Rightarrow b = \frac{3}{2}$.

Substitute $b = \frac{3}{2}$ and $c = \frac{5}{2}$ into $a - 4b + 3c = 2 \Rightarrow a - 4\left(\frac{3}{2}\right) + 3\left(\frac{5}{2}\right) = 2 \Rightarrow a - 6 + \frac{15}{2} = 2 \Rightarrow$

$a + \frac{3}{2} = 2 \Rightarrow a = \frac{1}{2}$.

The solution is: $\left(\frac{1}{2}, \frac{3}{2}, \frac{5}{2}\right)$.

21. Subtract the first and third equations:

$$\begin{array}{r} a + b + c = 0 \\ a + 3b + 3c = 5 \\ \hline -2b - 2c = -5. \end{array}$$

Subtract the second and third equations:

$$\begin{array}{r} a - b - c = 3 \\ a + 3b + 3c = 5 \\ \hline -4b - 4c = -2. \end{array}$$

Multiply $-2b - 2c = -5$ by 2 and subtract $-4b - 4c = -2$:

$$\begin{array}{r} -4b - 4c = -10 \\ -4b - 4c = -2 \\ \hline 0 = -8. \end{array}$$

Therefore, we have no solution.

22. Subtract the first and third equations:

$$\begin{array}{r} a - 2b + c = -1 \\ 2a + 3b + c = -2 \\ \hline -a - 5b = 1. \end{array}$$

Add this to the second equation:

$$\begin{array}{r} a + 5b = -3 \\ -a - 5b = 1 \\ \hline 0 = -2. \end{array}$$

Therefore, we have no solution.

23. Add the first two equations:

$$\begin{aligned} 3x + 2y + z &= -1 \\ 3x + 4y - z &= 1 \\ \hline 6x + 6y \quad &= 0. \end{aligned}$$

Add the last two equations:

$$\begin{aligned} 3x + 4y - z &= 1 \\ x + 2y + z &= 0 \\ \hline 4x + 6y \quad &= 1. \end{aligned}$$

Now, subtract $6x + 6y = 0$ and $4x + 6y = 1$:

$$\begin{aligned} 6x + 6y &= 0 \\ 4x + 6y &= 1 \\ \hline 2x \quad &= -1 \Rightarrow x = -\frac{1}{2}. \end{aligned}$$

Substitute $x = -\frac{1}{2}$ into $6x + 6y = 0$: $6\left(-\frac{1}{2}\right) + 6y = 0 \Rightarrow 6y = 3 \Rightarrow y = \frac{1}{2}$.

Substitute $x = -\frac{1}{2}$ and $y = \frac{1}{2}$ into $x + 2y + x = 0 \Rightarrow -\frac{1}{2} + 2\left(\frac{1}{2}\right) + z = 0 \Rightarrow z = -\frac{1}{2}$.

The solution is: $\left(-\frac{1}{2}, \frac{1}{2}, -\frac{1}{2}\right)$.

24. Subtract the first two equations:

$$\begin{aligned} x - 2y + z &= 1 \\ x + y + 2z &= 2 \\ \hline -3y - z &= -1. \end{aligned}$$

Multiply the second equation by 2 and subtract the third equation:

$$\begin{aligned} 2x + 2y + 4z &= 4 \\ 2x + 3y + z &= 6 \\ \hline -y + 3z &= -2. \end{aligned}$$

Multiply $-3y - z = -1$ by 3 and add $-y + 3z = -2$:

$$\begin{aligned} -9y - 3z &= -3 \\ -y + 3z &= -2 \\ \hline -10y \quad &= -5 \Rightarrow y = \frac{1}{2}. \end{aligned}$$

Substitute $y = \frac{1}{2}$ into $-y + 3z = -2 \Rightarrow -\frac{1}{2} + 3z = -2 \Rightarrow 3z = -\frac{3}{2} \Rightarrow z = -\frac{1}{2}$.

Substitute $y = \frac{1}{2}$ and $z = -\frac{1}{2}$ into $x - 2y + z = 1$: $x - 2\left(\frac{1}{2}\right) + \left(-\frac{1}{2}\right) = 1 \Rightarrow x = \frac{5}{2}$.

The solution is: $\left(\frac{5}{2}, \frac{1}{2}, -\frac{1}{2}\right)$.

25. Multiply the first equation by 2 and add the second equation:

$$\begin{array}{r} -2x + 6y + 2z = 6 \\ 2x + 7y + 4z = 13 \\ \hline 13y + 6z = 19. \end{array}$$

Multiply the second equation by 2 and subtract the third equation:

$$\begin{array}{r} 4x + 14y + 8z = 26 \\ 4x + y + 2z = 7 \\ \hline 13y + 6z = 19. \end{array}$$

Subtracting the two new equations we get:

$$\begin{array}{r} 13y + 6z = 19 \\ 13y + 6z = 19 \\ \hline 0 = 0. \end{array}$$

Therefore, we have infinitely many solutions.

$13y + 6z = 19 \Rightarrow 13y = -6z + 19 \Rightarrow y = \dfrac{-6z + 19}{13}.$

Multiply the third equation by 3 and subtract from the first equation:

$$\begin{array}{r} -x + 3y + z = 3 \\ 12x + 3y + 6z = 21 \\ \hline -13x - 5z = -18 \Rightarrow x = \dfrac{-5z + 18}{13}. \end{array}$$

We have infinitely many solutions: $\left(\dfrac{-5z + 18}{13}, \dfrac{-6z + 19}{13}, z\right)$.

26. Multiply the first equation by 3 and subtract the second equation:

$$\begin{array}{r} 3x + 6y + 3z = 0 \\ 3x + 2y - z = 4 \\ \hline 4y + 4z = -4. \end{array}$$

Add the first and third equations:

$$\begin{array}{r} x + 2y + z = 0 \\ -x + 2y + 3z = -4 \\ \hline 4y + 4z = -4. \end{array}$$

Subtracting the two new equations we get:

$$\begin{array}{r} 4y + 4z = -4 \\ 4y + 4z = -4 \\ \hline 0 = 0. \end{array}$$

Therefore, we have infinitely many solutions.

Then, $4y + 4z = -4 \Rightarrow 4y = -4z - 4 \Rightarrow y = -z - 1.$

Subtracting the first two equations we get:

$$\begin{array}{r} x + 2y + z = 0 \\ 3x + 2y - z = 4 \\ \hline -2x + 2z = -4. \end{array}$$

Then, $-2x + 2z = -4 \Rightarrow -2x = -2z - 4 \Rightarrow x = z + 2.$

We have infinitely many solutions: $(z + 2, -z - 1, z)$.

27. Subtract the second and third equations:

$$\begin{array}{rl} y + 4z &= -13 \\ 3x + y \phantom{+ 4z} &= 13 \\ \hline -3x \phantom{+ y} + 4z &= -26. \end{array}$$

Multiply the first equation by 3 and subtract $-3x + 4z = -26$ from it:

$$\begin{array}{rl} -3x + 6z &= -27 \\ -3x + 4z &= -26 \\ \hline 2z &= -1 \Rightarrow z = -\frac{1}{2}. \end{array}$$

Substitute $z = -\frac{1}{2}$ into $y + 4z = -13$: $y + 4\left(-\frac{1}{2}\right) = -13 \Rightarrow y = -11$.

Substitute $z = -\frac{1}{2}$ into $-x + 2z = -9 \Rightarrow -x + 2\left(-\frac{1}{2}\right) = -9 \Rightarrow -x = -8 \Rightarrow x = 8$.

The solution is: $\left(8, -11, -\frac{1}{2}\right)$.

28. Multiply the first equation by 2 and subtract the second equation:

$$\begin{array}{rl} 2x + 2y + 2z &= -2 \\ 2x \phantom{+ 2y} + z &= -6 \\ \hline 2y + z &= 4. \end{array}$$

Subtract this from the third equation:

$$\begin{array}{rl} 2y + 3z &= 0 \\ 2y + z &= 4 \\ \hline 2z &= -4 \Rightarrow z = -2. \end{array}$$

Substitute $z = -2$ into $2x + (-2) = -6 \Rightarrow 2x = -4 \Rightarrow x = -2$.

Substitute $x = -2$ and $z = -2$ into $x + y + z = -1$: $(-2) + y + (-2) = -1 \Rightarrow y = 3$.

The solution is: $(-2, 3, -2)$.

29. Multiply the first equation by 2 and subtract the second equation:

$$\begin{array}{rl} x - 2y + z &= -8 \\ x + 2y - 3z &= 20 \\ \hline -4y + 4z &= -28. \end{array}$$

Add the first and third equations:

$$\begin{array}{rl} \frac{1}{2}x - y + \frac{1}{2}z &= -4 \\ -\frac{1}{2}x + 3y + 2z &= 0 \\ \hline 2y + \frac{5}{2}z &= -4. \end{array}$$

Multiply $2y + \frac{5}{2}z = -4$ by 2 and add $-4y + 4z = -28$:

$$\begin{array}{rl} 4y + 5z &= -8 \\ -4y + 4z &= -28 \\ \hline 9z &= -36 \Rightarrow z = -4. \end{array}$$

Substitute $z = -4$ into $-4y + 4z = -28$: $-4y + 4(-4) = -28 \Rightarrow -4y - 16 = -28 \Rightarrow$

$-4y = -12 \Rightarrow y = 3$.

Substitute $y = 3$ and $z = -4$ into $x + 2y - 3z = 20$: $x + 2(3) - 3(-4) = 20 \Rightarrow x + 18 = 20 \Rightarrow x = 2$

The solution is: $(2, 3, -4)$.

30. Subtract the first two equations:

$$\begin{array}{rl} \frac{3}{4}x + y + \frac{1}{2}z = & -3 \\ x + y - z = & -8 \\ \hline -\frac{1}{4}x + \frac{3}{2}z = & 5. \end{array}$$

Multiply the second equation by 2 and the third equation:

$$\begin{array}{rl} 2x + 2y - 2z = & -16 \\ \frac{1}{4}x - 2y + z = & -4 \\ \hline \frac{9}{4}x - z = & -20 \end{array}$$

Multiply $-\dfrac{1}{4}x + \dfrac{3}{2}z = 5$ by 9 and add the third equation $\dfrac{9}{4}x - z = -20$:

$$\begin{array}{rl} -\frac{9}{4}x + \frac{27}{2}z = & 45 \\ \frac{9}{4}x - z = & -20 \\ \hline \frac{25}{2}z = & 25 \Rightarrow z = 2. \end{array}$$

Substitute $z = 2$ into $\dfrac{9}{4}x - z = -20$: $\dfrac{9}{4}x - 2 = -20 \Rightarrow \dfrac{9}{4}x = -18 \Rightarrow x = -8.$

Substitute $x = -8$ and $z = 2$ into $x + y - z = -8$: $(-8) + y - 2 = -8 \Rightarrow y = 2.$

The solution is: $(-8, 2, 2)$.

31. Let $x$ = children tickets sold, $y$ = student tickets sold, and $z$ = adult tickets sold. Then: $x + y + z = 500$,

$5x + 7y + 10z = 3560$, and $y = z + 180$ or $y - z = 180$.

Multiply the first equation by 5 and subtract the second equation:

$$\begin{array}{rl} 5x + 5y + 5z = & 2500 \\ 5x + 7y + 10z = & 3560 \\ \hline -2y - 5z = & -1060. \end{array}$$

Now, multiply $y - z = 180$ by 2 and add $-2y - 5z = -1060$:

$$\begin{array}{rl} 2y - 2z = & 360 \\ -2y - 5z = & -1060 \\ \hline -7z = & -700 \Rightarrow z = 100. \end{array}$$

Substitute $z = 100$ into $y - z = 180$: $y - 100 = 180 \Rightarrow y = 280.$

Substitute $y = 280$ and $z = 100$ into $x + y + z = 500$: $x + 280 + 100 = 500 \Rightarrow x = 120.$

There were 120 children tickets, 280 student tickets, and 100 adult tickets sold.

32. Let $x$ = children tickets sold, $y$ = student tickets sold, and $z$ = adult tickets sold. Then $x + y + z = 1000$; $z = y + 100 \Rightarrow z - y = 100$ or $-y + z = 100$; and $4x = y \Rightarrow 4x - y = 0$.

    Subtract the equations $x + y + z = 1000$ and $-y + z = 100$:

$$\begin{array}{l} x + y + z = 1000 \\ \underline{\quad -y + z = 100} \\ x + 2y \quad\quad = 900. \end{array}$$

    Now, multiply $4x - y = 0$ by 2 and add $x + 2y = 900$:

$$\begin{array}{l} 8x - 2y = 0 \\ \underline{x + 2y = 900} \\ 9x \quad\quad = 900 \Rightarrow x = 100. \end{array}$$

    Substitute $x = 100$ into $x + 2y = 900$: $100 + 2y = 900 \Rightarrow 2y = 800 \Rightarrow y = 400$.

    Substitute $x = 100$ and $y = 400$ into $x + y + z = 1000$: $100 + 400 + z = 1000 \Rightarrow z = 500$.

    There were 100 children tickets, 400 student tickets, and 500 adult tickets sold.

33. Let $x$ = cost of a hamburger, $y$ = cost of fries, and $z$ = cost of a soda. Then $2x + 2y + z = 9$; $x + y + z = 5$; and $x + y = 5$.

    Multiply the equation $x + y + z = 5$ by 2 and subtract from the equation $2x + 2y + z = 9$:

$$\begin{array}{l} 2x + 2y + z = 9 \\ \underline{2x + 2y + 2z = 10} \\ \quad\quad\quad -z = -1 \Rightarrow z = 1. \end{array}$$

    Subtract $x + y + z = 5$ and $x + y = 5$:

$$\begin{array}{l} x + y + z = 5 \\ \underline{x + y \quad\quad = 5} \\ \quad\quad\quad z = 0. \end{array}$$

    $z$ cannot equal both 0 and 1 therefore there is no solution, at least one student was charged incorrectly.

34. (a) $2a + b + c = 48$; $3a + 2b + c = 71$; and $a + b + 2c = 53$.

    (b) Subtract the first two equations:

$$\begin{array}{l} 2a + b + c = 48 \\ \underline{3a + 2b + c = 71} \\ -a - b \quad\quad = -23. \end{array}$$

    Multiply the second equation by 2 and subtract the third equation:

$$\begin{array}{l} 6a + 4b + 2c = 142 \\ \underline{a + b + 2c = 53} \\ 5a + 3b \quad\quad = 89. \end{array}$$

    Multiply $-a - b = -23$ by 3 and add $5a + 3b = 89$:

$$\begin{array}{l} -3a - 3b = -69 \\ \underline{5a + 3b = 89} \\ 2a \quad\quad = 20 \Rightarrow a = 10. \end{array}$$

    Substitute $a = 10$ into $-a - b = -23$: $-10 - b = -23 \Rightarrow -b = -13 \Rightarrow b = 13$.

    Substitute $a = 10$ and $b = 13$ into $a + b + 2c = 53$: $10 + 13 + 2c = 53 \Rightarrow 2c = 30 \Rightarrow c = 15$.

    So CD $a$ cost \$10, CD $b$ cost \$13, and CD $c$ cost \$15.

    Check: $2(10) + 13 + 15 = 48 \Rightarrow 48 = 48$; $3(10) + 2(13) + 15 = 71 \Rightarrow 71 = 71$; $10 + 13 + 2(15) = 53 \Rightarrow 53 = 53$.

35. (a) $x + y + z = 180$; $x = z + 25 \Rightarrow x - z = 25$; and $y + z = x + 30 \Rightarrow -x + y + z = 30$.

(b) Add $x - z = 25$ to $-x + y + z = 30$:

$$\begin{array}{rl} x \qquad - z &= 25 \\ -x + y + z &= 30 \\ \hline y \qquad &= 55. \end{array}$$

Add $x + y + z = 180$ to $x - z = 25$:

$$\begin{array}{rl} x + y + z &= 180 \\ x \qquad - z &= 25 \\ \hline 2x + y \qquad &= 205. \end{array}$$

Substitute $y = 55$ into $2x + y = 205$: $2x + 55 = 205 \Rightarrow 2x = 150 \Rightarrow x = 75$.

Substitute $x = 75$ and $y = 55$ into $x + y + z = 180$: $75 + 55 + z = 180 \Rightarrow z = 50$.

The angles are: $75°$, $55°$, and $50°$.

Check: $75 + 55 + 50 = 180 \Rightarrow 180 = 180$; $75 - 50 = 25 \Rightarrow 25 = 25$; $-75 + 55 + 50 = 30 \Rightarrow 30 = 30$.

36. Let $a$, $b$, and $c$ be the lengths of the sides of a triangle from longest to shortest.

Then $a + b + c = 105$; $a = c + 22 \Rightarrow a - c = 22$; and $b + c = a + 15 \Rightarrow -a + b + c = 15$.

Add $a - c = 22$ and $-a + b + c = 15$:

$$\begin{array}{rl} a \qquad - c &= 22 \\ -a + b + c &= 15 \\ \hline b \qquad &= 37. \end{array}$$

Add $a + b + c = 105$ and $a - c = 22$:

$$\begin{array}{rl} a + b + c &= 105 \\ a \qquad - c &= 22 \\ \hline 2a + b \qquad &= 127. \end{array}$$

Substitute $b = 37$ into $2a + b = 127$: $2a + 37 = 127 \Rightarrow 2a = 90 \Rightarrow a = 45$.

Substitute $a = 45$ and $b = 37$ into $a + b + c = 105$: $45 + 37 + c = 105 \Rightarrow c = 23$.

The sides of the triangle are: 45, 37, and 23 inches.

37. Let $x$, $y$, and $z$ equal the amounts invested in the three mutual funds.

Then $x + y + z = 20{,}000$; $0.05x + 0.07y + 0.10z = 1650$; and $4x = z \Rightarrow 4x - z = 0$.

Multiply $x + y + z = 20{,}000$ by 0.07 and subtract $0.05x + 0.07y + 0.10z = 1650$:

$$\begin{array}{rl} 0.07x + 0.07y + 0.07z &= 1400 \\ 0.05x + 0.07y + 0.10z &= 1650 \\ \hline 0.02x \qquad - 0.03z &= -250. \end{array}$$

Now multiply $0.02x - 0.03z = -250$ by 200 and subtract $4x - z = 0$:

$$\begin{array}{rl} 4x - 6z &= -50{,}000 \\ 4x - z &= 0 \\ \hline -5z &= -50{,}000 \Rightarrow z = 10{,}000. \end{array}$$

Substitute $z = 10{,}000$ into $4x - z = 0$: $4x - 10{,}000 = 0 \Rightarrow 4x = 10{,}000 \Rightarrow x = 2500$.

Substitute $x = 2500$ and $z = 10{,}000$ into $x + y + z = 20{,}000$: $2500 + y + 10{,}000 = 20{,}000 \Rightarrow y = 7500$.

The fund amounts are: \$2500 at 5%, \$7500 at 7%, and \$10,000 at 10%.

38. (a) $a + 20b + 2c = 190$
$a + 5b + 3c = 320$
$a + 40b + c = 50$

(b) Using technology to solve the system, the solution is (30, –2, 100).

That is, $a = 30$, $b = -2$, and $c = 100$ and so the equation is $P = 30 - 2A + 100S$.

(c) When $A = 10$ and $S = 2500$, $P = 30 - 2(1) + 100(2.5) = 260$ or $260,000.

39. (a) $N + P + K = 80$
$N + P - K = 8$
$9P - K = 0$

(b) Using technology to solve the system, the solution is (40, 4, 36).

The sample contains 40 pounds of nitrogen, 4 pounds of phosphorus and 36 pounds of potassium.

40. (a) $x + y + z = 100$
$x + y = 80$
$x - z = 34$

(b) Using technology to solve the system, the solution is (54, 26, 20).

The machines make 54, 26 and 20 containers, respectively, per day.

## 6.4 Solutions to Linear Systems Using Matrices

1. (a) Since there are three rows and one column, its dimension is $3 \times 1$.

(b) Since there are two rows and three columns, its dimension is $2 \times 3$.

(c) Since there are two rows and two columns, its dimension is $2 \times 2$.

2. (a) $1 \times 2$

(b) $3 \times 2$

(c) $3 \times 4$

3. This system can be written using a $2 \times 3$ matrix:

$$\left[\begin{array}{cc|c} 5 & -2 & 3 \\ -1 & 3 & -1 \end{array}\right]$$

4. This system can be written using a $2 \times 3$ matrix:

$$\left[\begin{array}{cc|c} 3 & 1 & 4 \\ -1 & 4 & 5 \end{array}\right]$$

5. This system can be written using a $3 \times 4$ matrix:

$$\left[\begin{array}{ccc|c} -3 & 2 & 1 & -4 \\ 5 & 0 & -1 & 9 \\ 1 & -3 & -6 & -9 \end{array}\right]$$

6. This system can be written using a $3 \times 4$ matrix:

$$\left[\begin{array}{ccc|c} 1 & 2 & -1 & 2 \\ -2 & 1 & -2 & -3 \\ 7 & 1 & -1 & 7 \end{array}\right]$$

7. $3x + 2y = 4$ and $y = 5$

8. $-2x + y = 5$ and $7x + 9y = 2$

9. $3x + y + 4z = 0$, $5y + 8z = -1$, and $-7z = 1$

10. $x - y + 3z = 2$, $-2x + y + z = -2$, and $-x - 2z = 1$

11. (a) Yes

    (b) No, since $a_{22} = -1$ and $a_{32} \neq 0$. The diagonal is not all 1's and there are not all 0's below the diagonal.

    (c) Yes

12. (a) No, since $a_{22} = -1$. The diagonal is not all 1's.

    (b) Yes

    (c) No. Rows 1 & 3 should be interchanged.

13. The system can be written as $x + 2y = 3$ and $y = -1$. Substituting $y = -1$ into the first equation gives $x + 2(-1) = 3 \Rightarrow x = 5$. The solution is (5, –1).

14. The system can be written as $x - 5y = 6$ and $0 = 1$. Since $0 \neq 1$, there is no solution.

15. The system can be written as $x - y = 2$ and $y = 0$. Substituting $y = 0$ into the first equation gives $x - 0 = 2 \Rightarrow x = 2$. The solution is (2, 0).

16. The system can be written as $x + 4y = -2$ and $y = 3$. Substituting $y = 3$ into the first equation gives $x + 4(3) = -2 \Rightarrow x = -14$. The solution is (–14, 3).

17. The system can be written as $x + y - z = 4$, $y - z = 2$, and $z = 1$. Substituting $z = 1$ into the second equation gives $y - (1) = 2 \Rightarrow y = 3$. Substituting $y = 3$ and $z = 1$ into the first equation gives $x + (3) - (1) = 4 \Rightarrow x = 2$. The solution is (2, 3, 1).

18. The system can be written as $x - 2y - z = 0$, $y - 3z = 1$, and $z = 2$. Substituting $z = 2$ into the second equation gives $y - 3(2) = 1 \Rightarrow y = 7$. Substituting $y = 7$ and $z = 2$ into the first equation gives $x - 2(7) - (2) = 0 \Rightarrow x = 16$. The solution is (16, 7, 2).

19. The system can be written as $x + 2y - z = 5$, $y - 2z = 1$, and $0 = 0$. Since $0 = 0$, there are an infinite number of solutions. The second equation gives $y = 1 + 2z$. Substituting this into the first equation gives $x + 2(1 + 2z) - z = 5 \Rightarrow x = 3 - 3z$. The solution can be written as $\{(3 - 3z, 1 + 2z, z) \mid z \text{ is a real number}\}$.

20. The system can be written as $x - y + 2z = 8$ and $y - 4z = 2$. The second equation gives $y = 4z + 2$. Substituting into the first equation gives $x - (4z + 2) + 2z = 8 \Rightarrow x = 2z + 10$. The solution can be written as $(2z + 10, 4z + 2, z)$.

21. The system can be written as $x + 2y + z = -3$, $y - 3z = \frac{1}{2}$, and $0 = 4$. Since $0 = 4$ is false, there are no solutions.

22. The system can be written as $x - 4z = \frac{3}{4}$, $y + 2z = 1$, and $0 = -3$. Since $0 = -3$ is false, there are no solutions.

23. $$\begin{array}{r} (1/2)R_1 \rightarrow \\ \\ (1/4)R_3 \rightarrow \end{array} \left[\begin{array}{rrr|r} 1 & -2 & 3 & 5 \\ -3 & 5 & 3 & 2 \\ 1 & 2 & 1 & -2 \end{array}\right]$$

24. $$\begin{array}{r} \\ R_2 - R_1 \rightarrow \\ R_3 - 2R_1 \rightarrow \end{array} \left[\begin{array}{rrr|r} 1 & -2 & 1 & 3 \\ 0 & 6 & -1 & -4 \\ 0 & 4 & -1 & -1 \end{array}\right]$$

25. $$\begin{array}{r} \\ R_2 + R_1 \rightarrow \\ R_3 - R_1 \rightarrow \end{array} \left[\begin{array}{rrr|r} 1 & -1 & 1 & 2 \\ 0 & 1 & -1 & 2 \\ 0 & 8 & -1 & 3 \end{array}\right]$$

26. $$\begin{array}{r} \\ R_2 - 2R_1 \rightarrow \\ R_3 + 3R_1 \rightarrow \end{array} \left[\begin{array}{rrr|r} 1 & -2 & 3 & 6 \\ 0 & 5 & -2 & -7 \\ 0 & -1 & 12 & 20 \end{array}\right]$$

27. The system can be written as follows:

$$\left[\begin{array}{rr|r} 1 & 2 & 3 \\ -1 & -1 & 7 \end{array}\right] \begin{array}{r} \\ R_2 + R_1 \rightarrow \end{array} \left[\begin{array}{rr|r} 1 & 2 & 3 \\ 0 & 1 & 10 \end{array}\right]$$

The solution is $y = 10$ and $x + 2y = 3 \Rightarrow x + 2(10) = 3 \Rightarrow x = -17$. The solution is $(-17, 10)$.

28. The system can be written as follows:

$$\left[\begin{array}{rr|r} 2 & 4 & 10 \\ 1 & -2 & -3 \end{array}\right] \begin{array}{r} (1/2)R_1 \rightarrow \\ \\ \end{array} \left[\begin{array}{rr|r} 1 & 2 & 5 \\ 1 & -2 & -3 \end{array}\right] \begin{array}{r} \\ R_2 - R_1 \rightarrow \end{array} \left[\begin{array}{rr|r} 1 & 2 & 5 \\ 0 & -4 & -8 \end{array}\right] \begin{array}{r} \\ (-1/4)R_2 \rightarrow \end{array} \left[\begin{array}{rr|r} 1 & 2 & 5 \\ 0 & 1 & 2 \end{array}\right]$$

The solution is $y = 2$ and $x + 2y = 5 \Rightarrow x + 2(2) = 5 \Rightarrow x = 1$. The solution is $(1, 2)$.

29. The system can be written as follows:

$$\left[\begin{array}{rrr|r} 1 & 2 & 1 & 3 \\ 1 & 1 & -1 & 3 \\ -1 & -2 & 1 & -5 \end{array}\right] \begin{array}{r} \\ R_2 - R_1 \rightarrow \\ R_3 + R_1 \rightarrow \end{array} \left[\begin{array}{rrr|r} 1 & 2 & 1 & 3 \\ 0 & -1 & -2 & 0 \\ 0 & 0 & 2 & -2 \end{array}\right] \begin{array}{r} \\ (-1)R_2 \rightarrow \\ (1/2)R_3 \rightarrow \end{array} \left[\begin{array}{rrr|r} 1 & 2 & 1 & 3 \\ 0 & 1 & 2 & 0 \\ 0 & 0 & 1 & -1 \end{array}\right]$$

Back substitution produces $z = -1$; $y + 2z = 0 \Rightarrow y = 2$; $x + 2y + z = 3 \Rightarrow x = 0$.

The solution is (0, 2, –1).

30. The system can be written as follows:

$$\left[\begin{array}{rrr|r} 1 & 1 & 1 & 6 \\ 2 & 3 & -1 & 3 \\ 1 & 1 & 2 & 10 \end{array}\right] \begin{array}{r} \\ R_2 - 2R_1 \rightarrow \\ R_3 - R_1 \rightarrow \end{array} \left[\begin{array}{rrr|r} 1 & 1 & 1 & 6 \\ 0 & 1 & -3 & -9 \\ 0 & 0 & 1 & 4 \end{array}\right]$$

Back substitution produces $z = 4$; $y - 3z = -9 \Rightarrow y = 3$; $x + y + z = 6 \Rightarrow x = -1$.

The solution is (–1, 3, 4).

31. The system can be written as follows:

$$\left[\begin{array}{rrr|r} 1 & 2 & -1 & -1 \\ 2 & -1 & 1 & 0 \\ -1 & -1 & 2 & 7 \end{array}\right] \begin{array}{r} \\ -2R_1 + R_2 \rightarrow \\ R_1 + R_3 \rightarrow \end{array} \left[\begin{array}{rrr|r} 1 & 2 & -1 & -1 \\ 0 & -5 & 3 & 2 \\ 0 & 1 & 1 & 6 \end{array}\right] \begin{array}{r} \\ R_3 \Leftrightarrow R_2 \rightarrow \\ \\ \end{array} \left[\begin{array}{rrr|r} 1 & 2 & -1 & -1 \\ 0 & 1 & 1 & 6 \\ 0 & -5 & 3 & 2 \end{array}\right]$$

$$\begin{array}{r} \\ 5R_2 + R_3 \rightarrow \\ \\ \end{array} \left[\begin{array}{rrr|r} 1 & 2 & -1 & -1 \\ 0 & 1 & 1 & 6 \\ 0 & 0 & 8 & 32 \end{array}\right] \begin{array}{r} \\ \frac{1}{8}R_3 \rightarrow \\ \\ \end{array} \left[\begin{array}{rrr|r} 1 & 2 & -1 & -1 \\ 0 & 1 & 1 & 6 \\ 0 & 0 & 1 & 4 \end{array}\right]$$

Back substitution produces $z = 4$; $y + z = 6 \Rightarrow y = 2$; $x + 2y - z = -1 \Rightarrow x = -1$.

The solution is (–1, 2, 4).

32. The system can be written as follows:

$$\left[\begin{array}{ccc|c} 1 & 3 & -2 & -4 \\ 2 & 6 & 1 & -3 \\ 1 & 1 & -4 & -2 \end{array}\right] \begin{array}{r} \\ -2R_1 + R_2 \rightarrow \\ R_1 + R_3 \rightarrow \end{array} \left[\begin{array}{ccc|c} 1 & 3 & -2 & 3 \\ 0 & 0 & 5 & 5 \\ 0 & -2 & -2 & 2 \end{array}\right] \begin{array}{r} \\ 1/5R_2 \rightarrow \\ (-1/2)R_3 \rightarrow \end{array} \left[\begin{array}{ccc|c} 1 & 3 & -2 & 3 \\ 0 & 0 & 1 & 1 \\ 0 & 1 & 1 & -1 \end{array}\right]$$

Back substitution produces $z = 1$; $y + z = -1 \Rightarrow y = -2$; $x + 3y - 2z = 3 \Rightarrow x = 4$.

The solution is $(4, -2, 1)$.

33. The system can be written as follows:

$$\left[\begin{array}{ccc|c} 3 & 1 & 3 & 14 \\ 1 & 1 & 1 & 6 \\ -2 & -2 & 3 & -7 \end{array}\right] \begin{array}{r} R_2 \rightarrow \\ R_1 \rightarrow \\ \end{array} \left[\begin{array}{ccc|c} 1 & 1 & 1 & 6 \\ 3 & 1 & 3 & 14 \\ -2 & -2 & 3 & -7 \end{array}\right] \begin{array}{r} \\ R_2 - 3R_1 \rightarrow \\ R_3 + 2R_1 \rightarrow \end{array} \left[\begin{array}{ccc|c} 1 & 1 & 1 & 6 \\ 0 & -2 & 0 & -4 \\ 0 & 0 & 5 & 5 \end{array}\right]$$

$$\begin{array}{r} \\ (-1/2)R_2 \rightarrow \\ (1/5)R_3 \rightarrow \end{array} \left[\begin{array}{ccc|c} 1 & 1 & 1 & 6 \\ 0 & 1 & 0 & 2 \\ 0 & 0 & 1 & 1 \end{array}\right]$$

Back substitution produces $z = 1$; $y = 2$; $x + y + z = 6 \Rightarrow x = 3$. The solution is (3, 2, 1).

34. The system can be written as follows:

$$\left[\begin{array}{ccc|c} 1 & 3 & -2 & 3 \\ -1 & -2 & 1 & -2 \\ 2 & -7 & 1 & 1 \end{array}\right] \begin{array}{r} \\ R_2 + R_1 \rightarrow \\ R_3 - 2R_1 \rightarrow \end{array} \left[\begin{array}{ccc|c} 1 & 3 & -2 & 3 \\ 0 & 1 & -1 & 1 \\ 0 & -13 & 5 & -5 \end{array}\right] \begin{array}{r} \\ \\ R_3 + 13R_2 \rightarrow \end{array} \left[\begin{array}{ccc|c} 1 & 3 & -2 & 3 \\ 0 & 1 & -1 & 1 \\ 0 & 0 & -8 & 8 \end{array}\right]$$

$$\begin{array}{r} \\ \\ (-1/8)R_3 \rightarrow \end{array} \left[\begin{array}{ccc|c} 1 & 3 & -2 & 3 \\ 0 & 1 & -1 & 1 \\ 0 & 0 & 1 & -1 \end{array}\right]$$

Back substitution produces $z = -1$; $y - z = 1 \Rightarrow y = 0$; $x + 3y - 2z = 3 \Rightarrow x = 1$.

The solution is (1, 0, –1).

35. The system can be written as follows:

$$\left[\begin{array}{ccc|c} 1 & 2 & -1 & 2 \\ 2 & 5 & 1 & 8 \\ 3 & 7 & 0 & 5 \end{array}\right] \begin{array}{r} \\ R_2 - 2R_1 \rightarrow \\ R_3 - 3R_1 \rightarrow \end{array} \left[\begin{array}{ccc|c} 1 & 2 & -1 & 2 \\ 0 & 1 & 3 & 4 \\ 0 & 1 & 3 & -1 \end{array}\right] \begin{array}{r} \\ \\ R_3 - R_2 \rightarrow \end{array} \left[\begin{array}{ccc|c} 1 & 2 & -1 & 2 \\ 0 & 1 & 3 & 4 \\ 0 & 0 & 0 & -5 \end{array}\right]$$

The last equation indicates that $0 = -5$, which is false. Therefore, there are no solutions.

36. The system can be written as follows:

$$\left[\begin{array}{ccc|c} 1 & 1 & 1 & 3 \\ 1 & 1 & 2 & 4 \\ 2 & 2 & 3 & 7 \end{array}\right] \begin{array}{r} \\ R_2 - R_1 \rightarrow \\ R_3 - 2R_1 \rightarrow \end{array} \left[\begin{array}{ccc|c} 1 & 1 & 1 & 3 \\ 0 & 0 & 1 & 1 \\ 0 & 0 & 1 & 1 \end{array}\right] \begin{array}{r} \\ \\ R_3 - R_2 \rightarrow \end{array} \left[\begin{array}{ccc|c} 1 & 1 & 1 & 3 \\ 0 & 0 & 1 & 1 \\ 0 & 0 & 0 & 0 \end{array}\right]$$

The last equation indicates that $0 = 0$, which is true. Therefore, there is an infinite number of solutions. The second equation gives $z = 1$. From the first equation $x + y + z = 3 \Rightarrow x + y = 2$. The solution can be written as $\{(2 - y, y, 1) \mid y \text{ is a real number}\}$.

37. The system can be written as follows:

$$\begin{bmatrix} -1 & 2 & 4 & | & 10 \\ 3 & -2 & -2 & | & -12 \\ 1 & 2 & 6 & | & 8 \end{bmatrix} \begin{matrix} (-1)R_1 \rightarrow \\ R_2 + 3R_1 \rightarrow \\ R_1 + R_3 \rightarrow \end{matrix} \begin{bmatrix} 1 & -2 & -4 & | & -10 \\ 0 & 4 & 10 & | & 18 \\ 0 & 4 & 10 & | & 18 \end{bmatrix} \begin{matrix} R_1 + (1/2)R_2 \rightarrow \\ (1/4)R_2 \rightarrow \\ R_2 - R_3 \rightarrow \end{matrix} \begin{bmatrix} 1 & 0 & 1 & | & -1 \\ 0 & 1 & \frac{5}{2} & | & \frac{9}{2} \\ 0 & 0 & 0 & | & 0 \end{bmatrix}$$

The last equation indicates that $0 = 0$, which is true. Therefore, there is an infinite number of solutions.

The second equation gives: $y + \frac{5}{2}z = \frac{9}{2} \Rightarrow y = \frac{-5z + 9}{2}$. The first equation gives: $x + z = -1 \Rightarrow$ $x = -1 - z$. Therefore there are infinitely many solutions which can be written as $\left(-1 - z, \frac{-5z + 9}{2}, z\right)$.

38. The system can be written as follows:

$$\begin{bmatrix} 4 & -2 & 4 & | & 8 \\ 3 & -7 & 6 & | & 4 \\ -1 & -5 & 2 & | & 7 \end{bmatrix} \begin{matrix} (1/4)R_1 \rightarrow \\ R_2 + 3R_3 \rightarrow \\ 4R_3 + R_1 \rightarrow \end{matrix} \begin{bmatrix} 1 & -\frac{1}{2} & 1 & | & 2 \\ 0 & -22 & 12 & | & 25 \\ 0 & -22 & 12 & | & 36 \end{bmatrix} \begin{matrix} \\ \\ R_2 - R_3 \rightarrow \end{matrix} \begin{bmatrix} 1 & -\frac{1}{2} & 1 & | & 2 \\ 0 & -22 & 12 & | & 25 \\ 0 & 0 & 0 & | & -11 \end{bmatrix}$$

The last equation indicates that $0 = -11$, which is false. Therefore there are no solutions.

39. $$\begin{bmatrix} 1 & -1 & 1 & | & 1 \\ 1 & 2 & -1 & | & 2 \\ 0 & 1 & -1 & | & 0 \end{bmatrix} R_2 - R_1 \rightarrow \begin{bmatrix} 1 & -1 & 1 & | & 1 \\ 0 & 3 & -2 & | & 1 \\ 0 & 1 & -1 & | & 0 \end{bmatrix} (1/3)R_2 \rightarrow \begin{bmatrix} 1 & -1 & 1 & | & 1 \\ 0 & 1 & -\frac{2}{3} & | & \frac{1}{3} \\ 0 & 1 & -1 & | & 0 \end{bmatrix}$$

$$\begin{matrix} \\ \\ R_3 - R_2 \rightarrow \end{matrix} \begin{bmatrix} 1 & -1 & 1 & | & 1 \\ 0 & 1 & -\frac{2}{3} & | & \frac{1}{3} \\ 0 & 0 & -\frac{1}{3} & | & -\frac{1}{3} \end{bmatrix} \begin{matrix} \\ \\ -3R_3 \rightarrow \end{matrix} \begin{bmatrix} 1 & -1 & 1 & | & 1 \\ 0 & 1 & -\frac{2}{3} & | & \frac{1}{3} \\ 0 & 0 & 1 & | & 1 \end{bmatrix}$$

The matrix is now in row-echelon form. We see that $z = 1$. Thus, $y - \frac{2}{3}z = \frac{1}{3} \Rightarrow$

$y - \frac{2}{3}(1) = \frac{1}{3} \Rightarrow y = 1$ and $x - y + z = 1 \Rightarrow x - 1 + 1 = 1 \Rightarrow x = 1$. The solution is (1, 1, 1).

40. $$\begin{bmatrix} 1 & -1 & -2 & | & -11 \\ 1 & -2 & -1 & | & -11 \\ -1 & 1 & 3 & | & 14 \end{bmatrix} \begin{matrix} \\ R_2 - R_1 \rightarrow \\ R_3 + R_1 \rightarrow \end{matrix} \begin{bmatrix} 1 & -1 & -2 & | & -11 \\ 0 & -1 & 1 & | & 0 \\ 0 & 0 & 1 & | & 3 \end{bmatrix}$$

The matrix is now in row-echelon form. We see that $z = 3$. Thus, $-y + z = 0 \Rightarrow -y + 3 = 0 \Rightarrow y = 3$ and $x - 2y - z = -11 \Rightarrow x - 2(3) - 3 = -11 \Rightarrow x = -2$. The solution is (–2, 3, 3).

41. $$\begin{bmatrix} 2 & -4 & 2 & | & 11 \\ 1 & 3 & -2 & | & -9 \\ 4 & -2 & 1 & | & 7 \end{bmatrix} (1/2)R_1 \rightarrow \begin{bmatrix} 1 & -2 & 1 & | & \frac{11}{2} \\ 1 & 3 & -2 & | & -9 \\ 4 & -2 & 1 & | & 7 \end{bmatrix} \begin{matrix} \\ R_2 - R_1 \rightarrow \\ R_3 - 4R_1 \rightarrow \end{matrix} \begin{bmatrix} 1 & -2 & 1 & | & \frac{11}{2} \\ 0 & 5 & -3 & | & -\frac{29}{2} \\ 0 & 6 & -3 & | & -15 \end{bmatrix}$$

$$(1/5)R_2 \rightarrow \begin{bmatrix} 1 & -2 & 1 & | & \frac{11}{2} \\ 0 & 1 & -\frac{3}{5} & | & -\frac{29}{10} \\ 0 & 6 & -3 & | & -15 \end{bmatrix} \begin{matrix} \\ \\ R_3 - 6R_2 \rightarrow \end{matrix} \begin{bmatrix} 1 & -2 & 1 & | & \frac{11}{2} \\ 0 & 1 & -\frac{3}{5} & | & -\frac{29}{10} \\ 0 & 0 & \frac{3}{5} & | & \frac{24}{10} \end{bmatrix} \begin{matrix} \\ \\ (5/3)R_3 \rightarrow \end{matrix} \begin{bmatrix} 1 & -2 & 1 & | & \frac{11}{2} \\ 0 & 1 & -\frac{3}{5} & | & -\frac{29}{10} \\ 0 & 0 & 1 & | & 4 \end{bmatrix}$$

The matrix is now in row-echelon form. We see that $z = 4$. Thus, $y - \frac{3}{5}z = -\frac{29}{10} \Rightarrow$

$y - \frac{3}{5}(4) = -\frac{29}{10} \Rightarrow y = -\frac{1}{2}$ and $x - 2y + z = \frac{11}{2} \Rightarrow x - 2\left(-\frac{1}{2}\right) + 4 = \frac{11}{2} \Rightarrow x = \frac{1}{2}$.

The solution is $\left(\frac{1}{2}, -\frac{1}{2}, 4\right)$.

42. $\left[\begin{array}{ccc|c} 1 & -4 & 1 & 9 \\ 0 & 3 & -2 & -7 \\ -1 & 0 & 1 & 0 \end{array}\right] \begin{array}{r} \\ \\ R_3 + R_1 \rightarrow \end{array} \left[\begin{array}{ccc|c} 1 & -4 & 1 & 9 \\ 0 & 3 & -2 & -7 \\ 0 & -4 & 2 & 9 \end{array}\right] \begin{array}{r} \\ (1/3)R_2 \rightarrow \\ \\ \end{array} \left[\begin{array}{ccc|c} 1 & -4 & 1 & 9 \\ 0 & 1 & -\frac{2}{3} & -\frac{7}{3} \\ 0 & -4 & 2 & 9 \end{array}\right]$

$\begin{array}{r} \\ \\ R_3 + 4R_2 \rightarrow \end{array} \left[\begin{array}{ccc|c} 1 & -4 & 1 & 9 \\ 0 & 1 & -\frac{2}{3} & -\frac{7}{3} \\ 0 & 0 & -\frac{2}{3} & -\frac{1}{3} \end{array}\right] \begin{array}{r} \\ \\ (-3/2)R_3 \rightarrow \end{array} \left[\begin{array}{ccc|c} 1 & -4 & 1 & 9 \\ 0 & 1 & -\frac{2}{3} & -\frac{7}{3} \\ 0 & 0 & 1 & \frac{1}{2} \end{array}\right]$

The matrix is now in row-echelon form. We see that $z = \frac{1}{2}$. Thus, $y - \frac{2}{3}z = -\frac{7}{3} \Rightarrow$

$y - \frac{2}{3}\left(\frac{1}{2}\right) = -\frac{7}{3} \Rightarrow y = -2$ and $x - 4y + z = 9 \Rightarrow x - 4(-2) + \frac{1}{2} = 9 \Rightarrow x = \frac{1}{2}$.

The solution is $\left(\frac{1}{2}, -2, \frac{1}{2}\right)$.

43. $\left[\begin{array}{ccc|c} 3 & -2 & 2 & -18 \\ -1 & 2 & -4 & 16 \\ 4 & -3 & -2 & -21 \end{array}\right] \begin{array}{r} (1/3)R_1 \rightarrow \\ \\ \\ \end{array} \left[\begin{array}{ccc|c} 1 & -\frac{2}{3} & \frac{2}{3} & -6 \\ -1 & 2 & -4 & 16 \\ 4 & -3 & -2 & -21 \end{array}\right] \begin{array}{r} \\ R_2 + R_1 \rightarrow \\ R_3 - 4R_1 \rightarrow \end{array} \left[\begin{array}{ccc|c} 1 & -\frac{2}{3} & \frac{2}{3} & -6 \\ 0 & \frac{4}{3} & -\frac{10}{3} & 10 \\ 0 & -\frac{1}{3} & -\frac{14}{3} & 3 \end{array}\right]$

$\begin{array}{r} \\ (3/4)R_2 \rightarrow \\ 4R_3 + R_2 \rightarrow \end{array} \left[\begin{array}{ccc|c} 1 & -\frac{2}{3} & \frac{2}{3} & -6 \\ 0 & 1 & -\frac{5}{2} & \frac{15}{2} \\ 0 & 0 & -22 & 22 \end{array}\right] \begin{array}{r} \\ \\ (-1/22)R_3 \rightarrow \end{array} \left[\begin{array}{ccc|c} 1 & -\frac{2}{3} & \frac{2}{3} & -6 \\ 0 & 1 & -\frac{5}{2} & \frac{15}{2} \\ 0 & 0 & 1 & -1 \end{array}\right]$

The matrix is now in row-echelon form. We see that $z = -1$. Thus, $y - \frac{5}{2}z = \frac{15}{2} \Rightarrow$

$y - \frac{5}{2}(-1) = \frac{15}{2} \Rightarrow y = 5$ and $x - \frac{2}{3}y + \frac{2}{3}z = -6 \Rightarrow x - \frac{2}{3}(5) + \frac{2}{3}(-1) = -6 \Rightarrow x = -2$.

The solution is $(-2, 5, -1)$.

44. $\left[\begin{array}{ccc|c} 2 & -1 & -1 & 0 \\ 1 & -1 & -1 & -2 \\ 3 & -2 & -2 & -2 \end{array}\right] \begin{array}{r} (1/2)R_1 \rightarrow \\ \\ \\ \end{array} \left[\begin{array}{ccc|c} 1 & -\frac{1}{2} & -\frac{1}{2} & 0 \\ 1 & -1 & -1 & -2 \\ 3 & -2 & -2 & -2 \end{array}\right] \begin{array}{r} \\ R_2 - R_1 \rightarrow \\ R_3 - 3R_1 \rightarrow \end{array} \left[\begin{array}{ccc|c} 1 & -\frac{1}{2} & -\frac{1}{2} & 0 \\ 0 & -\frac{1}{2} & -\frac{1}{2} & -2 \\ 0 & -\frac{1}{2} & -\frac{1}{2} & -2 \end{array}\right]$

$\begin{array}{r} \\ -2R_2 \rightarrow \\ R_3 - R_2 \rightarrow \end{array} \left[\begin{array}{ccc|c} 1 & -\frac{1}{2} & -\frac{1}{2} & 0 \\ 0 & 1 & 1 & 4 \\ 0 & 0 & 0 & 0 \end{array}\right]$

The last equation indicates that $0 = 0$, which is always true. Therefore, there is an infinite number of solutions.

The second equation gives $y + z = 4 \Rightarrow y = 4 - z$ and the first equation

gives $x - \frac{1}{2}y - \frac{1}{2}z = 0 \Rightarrow x - \frac{1}{2}(4 - z) - \frac{1}{2}z = 0 \Rightarrow x - 2 + \frac{1}{2}z - \frac{1}{2}z = 0 \Rightarrow x = 2$. The

solution can be written as $\{(2, 4 - z, z) \mid z \text{ is a real number}\}$.

45. $\left[\begin{array}{ccc|c} 1 & -4 & 3 & 26 \\ -1 & 3 & -2 & -19 \\ 0 & -1 & 1 & 10 \end{array}\right] \begin{array}{r} \\ R_2 + R_1 \rightarrow \\ \\ \end{array} \left[\begin{array}{ccc|c} 1 & -4 & 3 & 26 \\ 0 & -1 & 1 & 7 \\ 0 & -1 & 1 & 10 \end{array}\right] \begin{array}{r} \\ -R_2 \rightarrow \\ R_3 - R_2 \rightarrow \end{array} \left[\begin{array}{ccc|c} 1 & -4 & 3 & 26 \\ 0 & 1 & -1 & -7 \\ 0 & 0 & 0 & 3 \end{array}\right]$

The last equation indicates that $0 = 3$, which is always false. Therefore, the system has no solutions.

46. $\begin{bmatrix} 4 & -1 & -1 & | & 0 \\ 4 & -2 & 0 & | & 0 \\ 2 & 0 & 1 & | & 1 \end{bmatrix} \begin{matrix} (1/4)R_1 \rightarrow \\ \\ \\ \end{matrix} \begin{bmatrix} 1 & -\frac{1}{4} & -\frac{1}{4} & | & 0 \\ 4 & -2 & 0 & | & 0 \\ 2 & 0 & 1 & | & 1 \end{bmatrix} \begin{matrix} \\ R_2 - 4R_1 \rightarrow \\ R_3 - 2R_1 \rightarrow \end{matrix} \begin{bmatrix} 1 & -\frac{1}{4} & -\frac{1}{4} & | & 0 \\ 0 & -1 & 1 & | & 0 \\ 0 & \frac{1}{2} & \frac{3}{2} & | & 1 \end{bmatrix}$

$\begin{matrix} \\ -R_2 \rightarrow \\ R_3 + (1/2)R_2 \rightarrow \end{matrix} \begin{bmatrix} 1 & -\frac{1}{4} & -\frac{1}{4} & | & 0 \\ 0 & 1 & -1 & | & 0 \\ 0 & 0 & 2 & | & 1 \end{bmatrix} \begin{matrix} \\ \\ (1/2)R_3 \rightarrow \end{matrix} \begin{bmatrix} 1 & -\frac{1}{4} & -\frac{1}{4} & | & 0 \\ 0 & 1 & -1 & | & 0 \\ 0 & 0 & 1 & | & \frac{1}{2} \end{bmatrix}$

The matrix is now in row-echelon form. We see that $z = \frac{1}{2}$. Thus, $y - z = 0 \Rightarrow$

$y - \frac{1}{2} = 0 \Rightarrow y = \frac{1}{2}$ and $x - \frac{1}{4}y - \frac{1}{4}z = 0 \Rightarrow x - \frac{1}{4}\left(\frac{1}{2}\right) - \frac{1}{4}\left(\frac{1}{2}\right) = 0 \Rightarrow x = \frac{1}{4}$.

The solution is $\left(\frac{1}{4}, \frac{1}{2}, \frac{1}{2}\right)$.

47. $\begin{bmatrix} 5 & 0 & 4 & | & 7 \\ 2 & -4 & 0 & | & 6 \\ 0 & 3 & 3 & | & 3 \end{bmatrix} \begin{matrix} (1/5)R_1 \rightarrow \\ 2R_1 - 5R_2 \rightarrow \\ (1/3)R_3 \rightarrow \end{matrix} \begin{bmatrix} 1 & 0 & \frac{4}{5} & | & \frac{7}{5} \\ 0 & 20 & 8 & | & -16 \\ 0 & 1 & 1 & | & 1 \end{bmatrix} \begin{matrix} \\ (1/20)R_2 \rightarrow \\ R_2 - 20R_3 \rightarrow \end{matrix} \begin{bmatrix} 1 & 0 & \frac{4}{5} & | & \frac{7}{5} \\ 0 & 1 & \frac{2}{5} & | & -\frac{4}{5} \\ 0 & 0 & -12 & | & -36 \end{bmatrix}$

$\begin{matrix} \\ \\ (-1/12)R_3 \rightarrow \end{matrix} \begin{bmatrix} 1 & 0 & \frac{4}{5} & | & \frac{7}{5} \\ 0 & 1 & \frac{2}{5} & | & -\frac{4}{5} \\ 0 & 0 & 1 & | & 3 \end{bmatrix} \begin{matrix} (-4/5)R_3 + R_1 \rightarrow \\ (-2/5)R_3 + R_2 \rightarrow \\ \\ \end{matrix} \begin{bmatrix} 1 & 0 & 0 & | & -1 \\ 0 & 1 & 0 & | & -2 \\ 0 & 0 & 1 & | & 3 \end{bmatrix}$ The solution is $(-1, -2, 3)$.

48. $\begin{bmatrix} 0 & 1 & 2 & | & -5 \\ 3 & 0 & -2 & | & -6 \\ -1 & -4 & 0 & | & 11 \end{bmatrix} \begin{matrix} (-1)R_3 \rightarrow \\ R_1 \rightarrow \\ R_2 + 3R_3 \rightarrow \end{matrix} \begin{bmatrix} 1 & 4 & 0 & | & -11 \\ 0 & 1 & 2 & | & -5 \\ 0 & -12 & -2 & | & 27 \end{bmatrix} \begin{matrix} \\ \\ 12R_2 + R_3 \rightarrow \end{matrix} \begin{bmatrix} 1 & 4 & 0 & | & -11 \\ 0 & 1 & 2 & | & -5 \\ 0 & 0 & 22 & | & -33 \end{bmatrix}$

$\begin{matrix} \\ \\ (-1/22)R_3 \rightarrow \end{matrix} \begin{bmatrix} 1 & 4 & 0 & | & -11 \\ 0 & 1 & 2 & | & -5 \\ 0 & 0 & 1 & | & -\frac{3}{2} \end{bmatrix} \begin{matrix} \\ (-2)R_3 + R_2 \rightarrow \\ \\ \end{matrix} \begin{bmatrix} 1 & 4 & 0 & | & -11 \\ 0 & 1 & 0 & | & -2 \\ 0 & 0 & 1 & | & -\frac{3}{2} \end{bmatrix} \begin{matrix} (-4)R_2 + R_1 \rightarrow \\ \\ \\ \end{matrix} \begin{bmatrix} 1 & 0 & 0 & | & -3 \\ 0 & 1 & 0 & | & -2 \\ 0 & 0 & 1 & | & -\frac{3}{2} \end{bmatrix}$

The solution is $\left(-3, -2, -\frac{3}{2}\right)$.

49. $\begin{bmatrix} 5 & -2 & 1 & | & 5 \\ 1 & 1 & -2 & | & -2 \\ 4 & -3 & 3 & | & 7 \end{bmatrix} \begin{matrix} R_2 \rightarrow \\ 5R_2 - R_1 \rightarrow \\ 4R_2 - R_3 \rightarrow \end{matrix} \begin{bmatrix} 1 & 1 & -2 & | & -2 \\ 0 & 7 & -11 & | & -15 \\ 0 & 7 & -11 & | & -15 \end{bmatrix} \begin{matrix} \\ (1/7)R_2 \rightarrow \\ R_2 - R_3 \rightarrow \end{matrix} \begin{bmatrix} 1 & 1 & -2 & | & -2 \\ 0 & 1 & -\frac{11}{7} & | & -\frac{15}{7} \\ 0 & 0 & 0 & | & 0 \end{bmatrix}$

$\begin{matrix} (-1)R_2 + R_1 \rightarrow \\ \\ \\ \end{matrix} \begin{bmatrix} 1 & 0 & -\frac{3}{7} & | & \frac{1}{7} \\ 0 & 1 & -\frac{11}{7} & | & -\frac{15}{7} \\ 0 & 0 & 0 & | & 0 \end{bmatrix}$

The last equation indicates that $0 = 0$, which is true. Therefore, there is an infinite number of solutions.

The second equation gives: $y - \frac{11}{7}z = -\frac{15}{7} \Rightarrow y = \frac{11z - 15}{7}$. The first equation gives: $x - \frac{3}{7}z = \frac{1}{7} \Rightarrow$

$x = \frac{3z + 1}{7}$. Therefore, there are infinitely many solutions which can be written as: $\left(\frac{3z + 1}{7}, \frac{11z - 15}{7}, z\right)$.

50. $\begin{bmatrix} 2 & -4 & -1 & | & 2 \\ 1 & 1 & -3 & | & 10 \\ -1 & -7 & 8 & | & 2 \end{bmatrix} \begin{matrix} R_2 \rightarrow \\ 2R_2 - R_1 \rightarrow \\ R_2 + R_3 \rightarrow \end{matrix} \begin{bmatrix} 1 & 1 & -3 & | & 10 \\ 0 & 6 & -5 & | & 18 \\ 0 & -6 & 5 & | & 12 \end{bmatrix} \begin{matrix} \\ \\ R_2 + R_3 \rightarrow \end{matrix} \begin{bmatrix} 1 & 1 & -3 & | & 10 \\ 0 & 6 & -5 & | & 18 \\ 0 & 0 & 0 & | & 30 \end{bmatrix}$

The last equation indicates that $0 = 30$, which is always false. Therefore, there are no solutions.

51. The equations are: $x = 12$ and $y = 3 \Rightarrow (12, 3)$.

52. The last equation indicates that $0 = 0$, which is true. Therefore, there is an infinite number of solutions. The first equation gives: $x - y = 1 \Rightarrow x = y + 1$. We have infinitely many solutions which can be written as: $(y + 1, y)$.

53. The equations are: $x = -2, y = 4$, and $z = \frac{1}{2} \Rightarrow \left(-2, 4, \frac{1}{2}\right)$.

54. The equations are: $x = 7, y = -9$, and $z = 3 \Rightarrow (7, -9, 3)$.

55. The last equation indicates that $0 = 0$, which is true. Therefore, there is an infinite number of solutions. The first equation gives: $x + 2z = 4 \Rightarrow x = -2z + 4$. The second equation gives: $y - z = -3 \Rightarrow y = z - 3$. The system has infinitely many solutions which can be written as: $(-2z + 4, z - 3, z)$.

56. The last equation indicates that $0 = 0$, which is true. Therefore, there is an infinite number of solutions. The first equation gives: $x + z = -2 \Rightarrow x = -z - 2$. The second equation gives: $y + 3z = 5 \Rightarrow y = 5 - 3z$. The system has infinitely many solutions which can be written as: $(-z - 2, 5 - 3z, z)$.

57. The last equation indicates that $0 = \frac{2}{3}$, which is always false. Therefore, there are no solutions.

58. The last equation indicates that $0 = -2$, which is always false. Therefore, there are no solutions.

59. $$\left[\begin{array}{cc|c} 1 & -1 & 1 \\ 1 & 1 & 5 \end{array}\right] \begin{array}{l} \\ R_2 - R_1 \rightarrow \end{array} \left[\begin{array}{cc|c} 1 & -1 & 1 \\ 0 & 2 & 4 \end{array}\right] \begin{array}{l} \\ (1/2)R_2 \rightarrow \end{array} \left[\begin{array}{cc|c} 1 & -1 & 1 \\ 0 & 1 & 2 \end{array}\right] \begin{array}{l} R_1 + R_2 \rightarrow \\ \end{array} \left[\begin{array}{cc|c} 1 & 0 & 3 \\ 0 & 1 & 2 \end{array}\right]$$

The solution is (3, 2)

60. $$\left[\begin{array}{cc|c} 2 & 3 & 1 \\ 1 & -2 & -3 \end{array}\right] R_2 \leftrightarrow R_1 \left[\begin{array}{cc|c} 1 & -2 & -3 \\ 2 & 3 & 1 \end{array}\right] \begin{array}{l} \\ R_2 - 2R_1 \rightarrow \end{array} \left[\begin{array}{cc|c} 1 & -2 & -3 \\ 0 & 7 & 7 \end{array}\right] \begin{array}{l} \\ (1/7)R_2 \rightarrow \end{array} \left[\begin{array}{cc|c} 1 & -2 & -3 \\ 0 & 1 & 1 \end{array}\right]$$

$$\begin{array}{l} R_1 + 2R_2 \rightarrow \\ \end{array} \left[\begin{array}{cc|c} 1 & 0 & -1 \\ 0 & 1 & 1 \end{array}\right]$$ The solution is (–1, 1)

61. $$\left[\begin{array}{ccc|c} 1 & 2 & 1 & 3 \\ 0 & 1 & -1 & -2 \\ -1 & -2 & 2 & 6 \end{array}\right] \begin{array}{l} \\ \\ R_1 + R_3 \rightarrow \end{array} \left[\begin{array}{ccc|c} 1 & 2 & 1 & 3 \\ 0 & 1 & -1 & -2 \\ 0 & 0 & 3 & 9 \end{array}\right] \begin{array}{l} R_1 - 2R_2 \rightarrow \\ \\ (1/3)R_3 \rightarrow \end{array} \left[\begin{array}{ccc|c} 1 & 0 & 3 & 7 \\ 0 & 1 & -1 & -2 \\ 0 & 0 & 1 & 3 \end{array}\right]$$

$$\begin{array}{l} R_1 - 3R_3 \rightarrow \\ R_2 + R_3 \rightarrow \\ \end{array} \left[\begin{array}{ccc|c} 1 & 0 & 0 & -2 \\ 0 & 1 & 0 & 1 \\ 0 & 0 & 1 & 3 \end{array}\right]$$ The solution is (–2, 1, 3).

62. $$\left[\begin{array}{ccc|c} 1 & 0 & 1 & 2 \\ 1 & -1 & -1 & 0 \\ -2 & 1 & 0 & -2 \end{array}\right] \begin{array}{l} \\ R_2 - R_1 \rightarrow \\ R_3 + 2R_1 \rightarrow \end{array} \left[\begin{array}{ccc|c} 1 & 0 & 1 & 2 \\ 0 & -1 & -2 & -2 \\ 0 & 1 & 2 & 2 \end{array}\right] \begin{array}{l} \\ -1R_2 \rightarrow \\ \end{array} \left[\begin{array}{ccc|c} 1 & 0 & 1 & 2 \\ 0 & 1 & 2 & 2 \\ 0 & 1 & 2 & 2 \end{array}\right]$$

$$\begin{array}{l} \\ \\ R_3 - R_2 \rightarrow \end{array} \left[\begin{array}{ccc|c} 1 & 0 & 1 & 2 \\ 0 & 1 & 2 & 2 \\ 0 & 0 & 0 & 0 \end{array}\right]$$ The last equation indicates that $0 = 0$, which is always true. Therefore, there is an infinite number of solutions. The second equation gives $y + 2z = 2 \Rightarrow y = 2 - 2z$. The first equation gives $x + z = 2 \Rightarrow x = 2 - z$.

The solution can be written as $\{(2 - z, 2 - 2z, z) \mid z \text{ is a real number}\}$.

63. $\left[\begin{array}{ccc|c} 1 & -1 & 2 & 7 \\ 2 & 1 & -4 & -27 \\ -1 & 1 & -1 & 0 \end{array}\right] \begin{array}{l} \\ R_2 - 2R_1 \rightarrow \\ R_1 + R_3 \rightarrow \end{array} \left[\begin{array}{ccc|c} 1 & -1 & 2 & 7 \\ 0 & 3 & -8 & -41 \\ 0 & 0 & 1 & 7 \end{array}\right] \begin{array}{l} \\ (1/3)R_2 \rightarrow \\ \\ \end{array} \left[\begin{array}{ccc|c} 1 & -1 & 2 & 7 \\ 0 & 1 & -\frac{8}{3} & -\frac{41}{3} \\ 0 & 0 & 1 & 7 \end{array}\right]$

$\begin{array}{l} R_2 + R_1 \rightarrow \\ \\ \\ \end{array} \left[\begin{array}{ccc|c} 1 & 0 & -\frac{2}{3} & -\frac{20}{3} \\ 0 & 1 & -\frac{8}{3} & -\frac{41}{3} \\ 0 & 0 & 1 & 7 \end{array}\right] \begin{array}{l} (2/3)R_3 + R_1 \rightarrow \\ (8/3)R_3 + R_2 \rightarrow \\ \\ \end{array} \left[\begin{array}{ccc|c} 1 & 0 & 0 & -2 \\ 0 & 1 & 0 & 5 \\ 0 & 0 & 1 & 7 \end{array}\right]$ The solution is (–2, 5, 7).

64. $\left[\begin{array}{ccc|c} 2 & -4 & -6 & 2 \\ 1 & -3 & 1 & 12 \\ 2 & 1 & 3 & 5 \end{array}\right] \begin{array}{l} (1/2)R_1 \rightarrow \\ \\ \\ \end{array} \left[\begin{array}{ccc|c} 1 & -2 & -3 & 1 \\ 1 & -3 & 1 & 12 \\ 2 & 1 & 3 & 5 \end{array}\right] \begin{array}{l} \\ R_1 - R_2 \rightarrow \\ 2R_1 - R_3 \rightarrow \end{array} \left[\begin{array}{ccc|c} 1 & -2 & -3 & 1 \\ 0 & 1 & -4 & -11 \\ 0 & -5 & -9 & -3 \end{array}\right]$

$\begin{array}{l} 2R_2 + R_1 \rightarrow \\ \\ 5R_2 + R_3 \rightarrow \end{array} \left[\begin{array}{ccc|c} 1 & 0 & -11 & -21 \\ 0 & 1 & -4 & -11 \\ 0 & 0 & -29 & -58 \end{array}\right] \begin{array}{l} \\ \\ (-1/29)R_3 \rightarrow \end{array} \left[\begin{array}{ccc|c} 1 & 0 & -11 & -21 \\ 0 & 1 & -4 & -11 \\ 0 & 0 & 1 & 2 \end{array}\right]$

$\begin{array}{l} 11R_3 + R_1 \rightarrow \\ 4R_3 + R_2 \rightarrow \\ \\ \end{array} \left[\begin{array}{ccc|c} 1 & 0 & 0 & 1 \\ 0 & 1 & 0 & -3 \\ 0 & 0 & 1 & 2 \end{array}\right]$

The solution is (1, –3, 2).

65. $\left[\begin{array}{ccc|c} 2 & 1 & -1 & 2 \\ 1 & -2 & 1 & 0 \\ 1 & 3 & -2 & 4 \end{array}\right] \begin{array}{l} R_2 \rightarrow \\ 2R_2 - R_1 \rightarrow \\ R_2 - R_3 \rightarrow \end{array} \left[\begin{array}{ccc|c} 1 & -2 & 1 & 0 \\ 0 & -5 & 3 & -2 \\ 0 & -5 & 3 & -4 \end{array}\right] \begin{array}{l} \\ (-1/5)R_2 \rightarrow \\ R_2 - R_3 \rightarrow \end{array} \left[\begin{array}{ccc|c} 1 & -2 & 1 & 0 \\ 0 & 1 & -\frac{3}{5} & \frac{2}{5} \\ 0 & 0 & 0 & 2 \end{array}\right]$

The last equation indicates that $0 = 2$, which is always false. Therefore, there are no solutions.

66. $\left[\begin{array}{ccc|c} -2 & -1 & 1 & 3 \\ 1 & 1 & -3 & 1 \\ 1 & -2 & -4 & 2 \end{array}\right] \begin{array}{l} R_2 \rightarrow \\ 2R_2 + R_1 \rightarrow \\ R_2 - R_3 \rightarrow \end{array} \left[\begin{array}{ccc|c} 1 & 1 & -3 & 1 \\ 0 & 1 & -5 & 5 \\ 0 & 3 & 1 & -1 \end{array}\right] \begin{array}{l} \\ \\ 3R_2 - R_3 \rightarrow \end{array} \left[\begin{array}{ccc|c} 1 & 1 & -3 & 1 \\ 0 & 1 & -5 & 5 \\ 0 & 0 & -16 & 16 \end{array}\right]$

$\begin{array}{l} \\ \\ (-1/16)R_3 \rightarrow \end{array} \left[\begin{array}{ccc|c} 1 & 1 & -3 & 1 \\ 0 & 1 & -5 & 5 \\ 0 & 0 & 1 & -1 \end{array}\right] \begin{array}{l} 3R_3 + R_1 \rightarrow \\ 5R_3 + R_2 \rightarrow \\ \\ \end{array} \left[\begin{array}{ccc|c} 1 & 1 & 0 & -2 \\ 0 & 1 & 0 & 0 \\ 0 & 0 & 1 & -1 \end{array}\right] \begin{array}{l} (-1)R_2 + R_1 \rightarrow \\ \\ \\ \end{array} \left[\begin{array}{ccc|c} 1 & 0 & 0 & -2 \\ 0 & 1 & 0 & 0 \\ 0 & 0 & 1 & -1 \end{array}\right]$

The solution is $(-2, 0, -1)$.

67. Enter the coefficients of the linear system into a $3 \times 4$ matrix, as shown in Figure 67a. Reduce the matrix to reduced row-echelon form, as shown in Figure 67b. The solution is the ordered triple (–9.266, –9.167, 2.440).

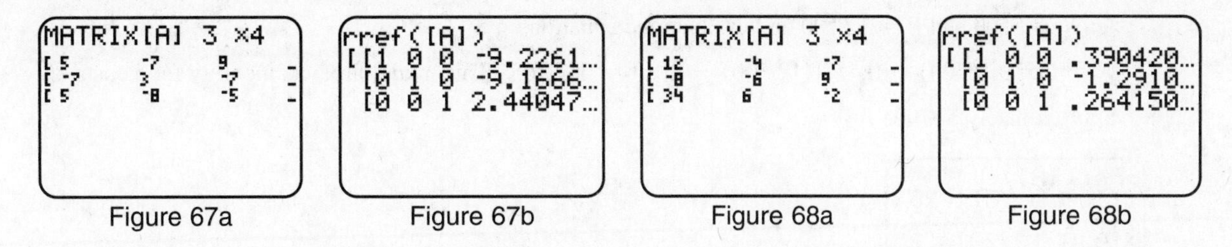


Figure 67a Figure 67b Figure 68a Figure 68b

68. Enter the coefficients of the linear system into a $3 \times 4$ matrix, as shown in Figure 68a. Reduce the matrix to reduced row-echelon form, as shown in Figure 68b. The solution is the ordered triple (0.390, –1.291, 0.264).

69. Enter the coefficients of the linear system into a $3 \times 4$ matrix, as shown in Figure 69a. Reduce the matrix to reduced row-echelon form, as shown in Figure 69b. The solution is the ordered triple (5.211, 3.739, –4.655).

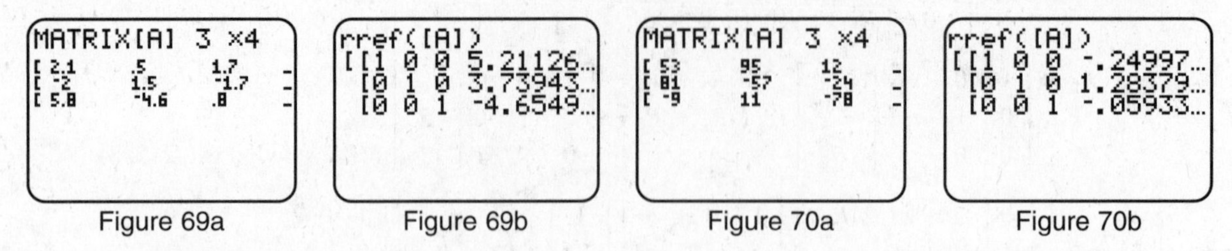


Figure 69a Figure 69b Figure 70a Figure 70b

70. Enter the coefficients of the linear system into a $3 \times 4$ matrix, as shown in Figure 70a. Reduce the matrix to reduced row-echelon form, as shown in Figure 70b. The solution is the ordered triple (–0.250, 1.284, –0.059).

71. Enter the coefficients of the linear system into a $3 \times 4$ matrix, as shown in Figure 71a. Reduce the matrix to reduced row-echelon form, as shown in Figure 71b. The solution is the ordered triple (7.993, 1.609, –0.401).

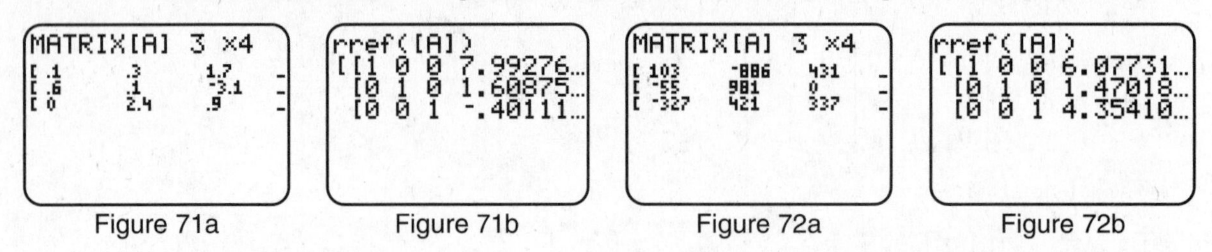


Figure 71a Figure 71b Figure 72a Figure 72b

72 Enter the coefficients of the linear system into a $3 \times 4$ matrix, as shown in Figure 72a. Reduce the matrix to reduced row-echelon form, as shown in Figure 72b. The solution is the ordered triple (6.077, 1.470, 4.354).

73. (a) The constants $a$, $b$, and $c$ should satisfy the following three equations:

$1300 = a(1800) + b(5000) + c, 5300 = a(3200) + b(12{,}000) + c,$

and $6500 = a(4500) + b(13{,}000) + c$

This can be written:

$1800a + 5000b + c = 1300, 3200a + 12{,}000b + c = 5300,$ and $4500a + 13{,}000b + c = 6500$

The associated augmented matrix is: $\left[\begin{array}{ccc|c} 1800 & 5000 & 1 & 1300 \\ 3200 & 12{,}000 & 1 & 5300 \\ 4500 & 13{,}000 & 1 & 6500 \end{array}\right]$

Using technology, the solution is $a \approx 0.5714$, $b \approx 0.4571$, and $c \approx -2014$. See Figure 73. Thus, the equation modeling the data can be expressed (approximately) as $F = 0.5714N + 0.4571R - 2014$.

(b) To predict the food costs for a shelter that serves 3500 people and receives charitable receipts of \$12,500, let $N = 3500$ and $R = 12{,}500$ and evaluate the equation.

$F = 0.5714(3500) + 0.4571(12{,}500) - 2014 = 5699.65$. This model predicts monthly food costs of approximately \$5700.

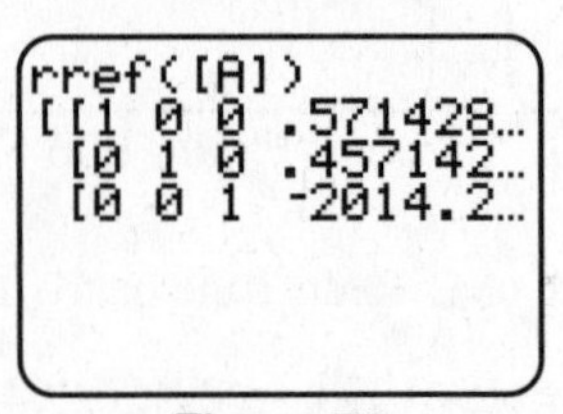


Figure 73

74. (a) The constants $a$, $b$, and $c$ should satisfy the following three equations:

$100 = a + 17b + 27c$, $272 = a + 25b + 36c$, and $381 = a + 30b + 43c$

The associated augmented matrix is: $\left[\begin{array}{ccc|c} 1 & 17 & 27 & 100 \\ 1 & 25 & 36 & 272 \\ 1 & 30 & 43 & 381 \end{array}\right]$

Using technology, the solution is $a \approx -274.1$, $b \approx 20.27$, and $c \approx 1.091$. See Figure 74.

(b) To estimate the weight of the bear let $N = 20$ and $C = 30$ and evaluate the equation.

$W = -274.1 + (20.27)(20) + (1.091)(30) \approx 165$ pounds.

(c) If the neck or chest size increases, then the weight of the bear should increase.

75. Let $x$ represent the fraction of the pool that the first pump can empty each hour, and $y$ the fraction of the pool that the second pump can empty each hour, and $z$ the fraction for the third pump. Since the first pump is twice as fast we have $x = 2y$ or $x - 2y = 0$. Since the first two pumps can empty the pool in 8 hours, it follows that they can empty $\frac{1}{8}$ of the pool in an hour. Thus, $x + y = \frac{1}{8}$. Similarly, all three pumps can empty the pool in 6 hours, so $x + y + z = \frac{1}{6}$. Putting these equations in an augmented matrix results in the following:

$$\left[\begin{array}{ccc|c} 1 & -2 & 0 & 0 \\ 1 & 1 & 0 & \frac{1}{8} \\ 1 & 1 & 1 & \frac{1}{6} \end{array}\right] \left[\begin{array}{ccc|c} 1 & -2 & 0 & 0 \\ 0 & 3 & 0 & \frac{1}{8} \\ 0 & 3 & 1 & \frac{1}{6} \end{array}\right] \left[\begin{array}{ccc|c} 1 & -2 & 0 & 0 \\ 0 & 1 & 0 & \frac{1}{24} \\ 0 & 0 & 1 & \frac{1}{24} \end{array}\right] \left[\begin{array}{ccc|c} 1 & 0 & 0 & \frac{1}{12} \\ 0 & 1 & 0 & \frac{1}{24} \\ 0 & 0 & 1 & \frac{1}{24} \end{array}\right]$$

Thus, $x = \frac{1}{12}$, $y = z = \frac{1}{24}$. The first pump could empty $\frac{1}{12}$ of the pool in one hour or the entire pool in 12 hours, while the second and third pumps individually could empty the pool in 24 hours. Using technology, this solution can be obtained as shown in Figure 75.

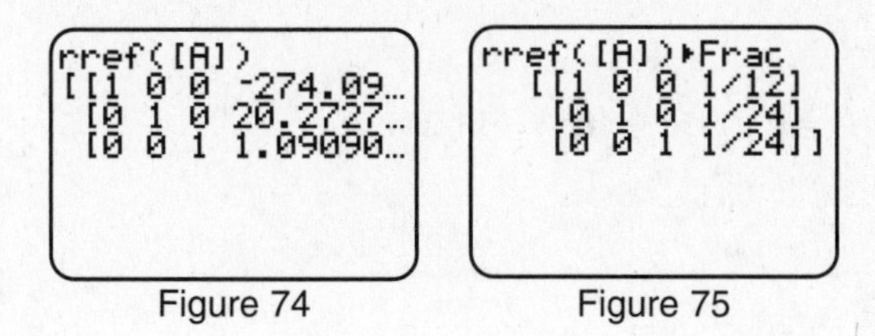


Figure 74 Figure 75

76. (a) The data is not realistic because three pumps are slower than two. This could happen only if one or two of the pumps were adding water to the pool rather than removing water from the pool. Typically, one would not pump water into and out of a pool at the same time.

(b) One possibility is that there is no solution to the problem. Another is that there is a solution but involves a negative value indicating that a pump is filling the pool.

(c) Let $x$ represent the fraction of the pool that the first pump can empty each hour, and $y$ the fraction of the pool that the second pump can empty each hour, and $z$ the fraction for the third pump. Since the first pump is three times as fast as the third pump, we have $x = 3z$ or $x - 3z = 0$. Since the first two pumps can empty the pool in 6 hours, $x + y = \frac{1}{6}$. Since all three pumps can empty the pool in 8 hours, $x + y + z = \frac{1}{8}$. Putting these equations in an augmented matrix results in the following:

$$\left[\begin{array}{ccc|c} 1 & 0 & -3 & 0 \\ 1 & 1 & 0 & \frac{1}{6} \\ 1 & 1 & 1 & \frac{1}{8} \end{array}\right]\left[\begin{array}{ccc|c} 1 & 0 & -3 & 0 \\ 0 & 1 & 3 & \frac{1}{6} \\ 0 & 1 & 4 & \frac{1}{8} \end{array}\right]\left[\begin{array}{ccc|c} 1 & 0 & -3 & 0 \\ 0 & 1 & 3 & \frac{1}{6} \\ 0 & 0 & 1 & -\frac{1}{24} \end{array}\right]\left[\begin{array}{ccc|c} 1 & 0 & 0 & -\frac{1}{8} \\ 0 & 1 & 0 & \frac{7}{24} \\ 0 & 0 & 1 & -\frac{1}{24} \end{array}\right]$$

Thus, $x = -\frac{1}{8}$, $y = \frac{7}{24}$, and $z = -\frac{1}{24}$. If all three pumps are removing water there is no solution, since the rates for the first and third pumps are negative. If the first and third pumps are filling the pool and the second pump is emptying the pool, then there is a solution: the first pump can fill the pool in 8 hours, the second pump can empty the pool in $\frac{24}{7}$ hours, the third pump can fill the pool in 24 hours. Using technology, this solution can be obtained as shown in Figure 76.

```
rref([A])▸Frac
 [[1 0 0 -1/8 ]
  [0 1 0 7/24 ]
  [0 0 1 -1/24]]
```

Figure 76

77. $I_1 = I_2 + I_3 \Rightarrow I_1 - I_2 - I_3 = 0$, $15 + 4I_3 = 14I_2 \Rightarrow -14I_2 + 4I_3 = -15$, and $10 + 4I_3 = 5I_1 \Rightarrow -5I_1 + 4I_3 = -10$

Therefore the matrix is:

$$\left[\begin{array}{ccc|c} 1 & -1 & -1 & 0 \\ 0 & -14 & 4 & -15 \\ -5 & 0 & 4 & -10 \end{array}\right] \begin{array}{l} \\ (-1/14)R_2 \rightarrow \\ 5R_1 + R_3 \rightarrow \end{array} \left[\begin{array}{ccc|c} 1 & -1 & -1 & 0 \\ 0 & 1 & -\frac{2}{7} & \frac{15}{14} \\ 0 & -5 & -1 & -10 \end{array}\right] 5R_2 + R_3 \rightarrow \left[\begin{array}{ccc|c} 1 & -1 & -1 & 0 \\ 0 & 1 & -\frac{2}{7} & \frac{15}{14} \\ 0 & 0 & -\frac{17}{7} & -\frac{65}{14} \end{array}\right]$$

$$(-7/17)R_3 \rightarrow \left[\begin{array}{ccc|c} 1 & -1 & -1 & 0 \\ 0 & 1 & -\frac{2}{7} & \frac{15}{14} \\ 0 & 0 & 1 & \frac{65}{34} \end{array}\right] \begin{array}{l} R_1 + R_3 \rightarrow \\ (2/7)R_3 + R_2 \rightarrow \\ \end{array} \left[\begin{array}{ccc|c} 1 & -1 & 0 & \frac{65}{34} \\ 0 & 1 & 0 & \frac{385}{238} \\ 0 & 0 & 1 & \frac{65}{34} \end{array}\right] R_2 + R_1 \rightarrow \left[\begin{array}{ccc|c} 1 & 0 & 0 & \frac{840}{238} \\ 0 & 1 & 0 & \frac{385}{238} \\ 0 & 0 & 1 & \frac{65}{34} \end{array}\right]$$

The solution is: (3.53, 1.62, 1.91).

78. $I_1 = I_2 + I_3 \Rightarrow I_1 - I_2 - I_3 = 0$, $20 = 4I_1 + 7I_3 \Rightarrow 4I_1 + 7I_3 = 20$, and

$10 + 7I_3 = 6I_2 \Rightarrow 6I_2 - 7I_3 = 10$

Therefore the matrix is:

$$\left[\begin{array}{ccc|c} 1 & -1 & -1 & 0 \\ 4 & 0 & 7 & 20 \\ 0 & 6 & -7 & 10 \end{array}\right] \; -4R_1 + R_2 \rightarrow \left[\begin{array}{ccc|c} 1 & -1 & -1 & 0 \\ 0 & 4 & 11 & 20 \\ 0 & 6 & -7 & 10 \end{array}\right] \; (1/4)R_2 \rightarrow \left[\begin{array}{ccc|c} 1 & -1 & -1 & 0 \\ 0 & 1 & \frac{11}{4} & 5 \\ 0 & 0 & -7 & 10 \end{array}\right]$$

$$-6R_2 + R_3 \rightarrow \left[\begin{array}{ccc|c} 1 & -1 & -1 & 0 \\ 0 & 1 & \frac{11}{4} & 5 \\ 0 & 0 & -\frac{94}{4} & -20 \end{array}\right] \; \begin{array}{l} R_2 + R_1 \rightarrow \\ \\ (-4/94)R_3 \rightarrow \end{array} \left[\begin{array}{ccc|c} 1 & 0 & \frac{7}{4} & 5 \\ 0 & 1 & \frac{11}{4} & 5 \\ 0 & 0 & 1 & \frac{80}{94} \end{array}\right]$$

$$\begin{array}{l} (-7/4)R_3 + R_1 \rightarrow \\ (-11/4)R_3 + R_2 \rightarrow \\ \end{array} \left[\begin{array}{ccc|c} 1 & 0 & 0 & \frac{330}{94} \\ 0 & 1 & 0 & \frac{250}{94} \\ 0 & 0 & 1 & \frac{80}{94} \end{array}\right]$$

The solution is: $(3.51, 2.66, 0.85)$.

79. Let $x$ equal the amount invested at 8%, $y$ equal the amount invested at 11% and $z$ equal the amount invested at 14%.

(a) $x + y + z = 5000$, $x + y - z = 0$, and $0.08x + 0.11y + 0.14z = 595$

(b) Enter the coefficients of the following $3 \times 4$ augmented matrix into a calculator.

$$\left[\begin{array}{ccc|c} 1 & 1 & 1 & 5000 \\ 1 & 1 & -1 & 0 \\ 0.08 & 0.11 & 0.14 & 595 \end{array}\right]$$

Using technology, the solution is $x = 1000$, $y = 1500$, and $z = 2500$. See Figure 79. Thus, \$1000 needs to be invested at 8%, \$1500 at 11%, and \$2500 at 14% in order to earn the total amount interest of \$595.

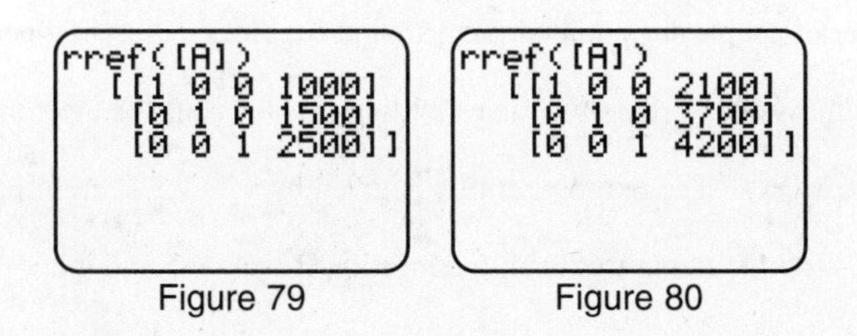

Figure 79 Figure 80

80. Let $x$ equal the amount invested at 6%, $y$ equal the amount invested at 8% and $z$ equal the amount invested at 10%.

(a) $x + y + z = 10{,}000$, $2x - z = 0$, and $0.06x + 0.08y + 0.10z = 842$

(b) Enter the coefficients of the following $3 \times 4$ augmented matrix into a calculator.

$$\left[\begin{array}{ccc|c} 1 & 1 & 1 & 10{,}000 \\ 2 & 0 & -1 & 0 \\ 0.06 & 0.08 & 0.10 & 842 \end{array}\right]$$

Using technology, the solution is $x = 2100$, $y = 3700$, and $z = 4200$. See Figure 80. Thus, \$2100 needs to be invested at 6%, \$3700 at 8%, and \$4200 at 10% in order to earn the total amount interest of \$842.

81. (a) At intersection A incoming traffic is equal to $x + 5$. The outgoing traffic is given by $y + 7$. Therefore, $x + 5 = y + 7$, which is the first equation. The incoming traffic at intersection B is $z + 6$ and the outgoing traffic is $x + 3$, so $z + 6 = x + 3$. Finally at intersection C, the incoming flow is $y + 3$ and the outgoing flow is $z + 4$, so $y + 3 = z + 4$.

(b) These three equations can be written as: $x - y = 2$, $x - z = 3$, and $y - z = 1$.

The system of linear equations can be represented by the following augmented matrix:

$$\left[\begin{array}{ccc|c} 1 & -1 & 0 & 2 \\ 1 & 0 & -1 & 3 \\ 0 & 1 & -1 & 1 \end{array}\right]$$

Begin by subtracting the first row from the second, followed by subtracting the second row from the third.

Gaussian elimination results in the following augmented matrix:

$$\left[\begin{array}{ccc|c} 1 & -1 & 0 & 2 \\ 0 & 1 & -1 & 1 \\ 0 & 0 & 0 & 0 \end{array}\right]$$

The last row of zeros indicates that the linear system is dependent and has an infinite number of solutions.

Back solving produces $y - z = 1 \Rightarrow y = z + 1$. Substituting into the first equation gives $x - (z + 1) = 2 \Rightarrow x = z + 3$. Thus, the solution can be written

$\{(z + 3, z + 1, z) \mid z \text{ is any nonnegative real number}\}$.

(c) There are an infinite number of solutions to the system. However, solutions such as $z = 1000$, $x = 1003$, and $y = 1001$ are likely, unless a large number of people are simply driving around the block. In reality there is an average traffic flow rate for $z$ that could be measured. From this, values for both $x$ and $y$ could be determined.

82. (a) At intersection A incoming traffic is equal to $x + 7$. The outgoing traffic is given by $y + 4$. Therefore, $x + 7 = y + 4$, which is the first equation. The incoming traffic at intersection B is $4 + 5$ and the outgoing traffic is $x + z$, so $4 + 5 = x + z$. Finally at intersection C, the incoming flow is $y + 8$ and the outgoing flow is $9 + 4$, so $y + 8 = 9 + 4$.

(b) These three equations can be written as: $x - y = -3$, $x + z = 9$, and $y = 5$. This system of linear equation could be solved without Gaussian elimination. However, since $y = 5$, the first equation implies that $x - 5 = -3 \Rightarrow x = 2$. Then, $x = 2$ in the second equation implies that $z = 7$. the solution is (2, 5, 7).

(c) There is only one solution, which is 2 vehicles per minute from B to A, 5 from A to C, and 7 out away from B. Notice that the number of vehicles entering the system per minute is always $7 + 8 + 5 = 20$ and the number leaving the system per minute is $4 + 9 + 7 = 20$. They are equal.

83. (a) The three equations can be written as: $3 = 0^2 + 0 + c$, $55 = 2^2a + 2b + c$, and $150 = 4^2a + 4b + c \Rightarrow 16a + 4b + c = 150$, $4a + 2b + c = 55$, and $c = 3$.

Therefore, the matrix is:

$$\left[\begin{array}{ccc|c} 16 & 4 & 1 & 150 \\ 4 & 2 & 1 & 55 \\ 0 & 0 & 1 & 3 \end{array}\right]$$

(b) Using technology, $a = 5.375$, $b = 15.25$, and $c = 3$. $f(x) = 5.375x^2 + 15.25x + 3$.

(c) See Figure 83.

(d) For example, in 2012 the predicted sales is $f(8) = 5.375(8)^2 + 15.25(8) + 3 = 469$. *Answers may vary.*

84. (a) The three equations can be written as: $376 = 0^2 + 0 + c$, $541 = 10^2a + 10b + c$, and $909 = 26^2a + 26b + c \Rightarrow 676a + 26b + c = 909$, $100a + 10b + c = 541$ and $c = 376$.

Therefore, the matrix is:

$$\left[\begin{array}{ccc|c} 676 & 26 & 1 & 909 \\ 100 & 10 & 1 & 541 \\ 0 & 0 & 1 & 376 \end{array}\right]$$

(b) Using technology, $a = 0.25$, $b = 14$, and $c = 376$. $f(x) = 0.25x^2 + 14x + 376$.

(c) See Figure 84.

(d) For example, in 2015 the predicted enrollment is $f(35) = 0.25(35)^2 + 14(35) + 376 = 1172.25$.

*Answers may vary.*

[−0.5, 5, 1] by [−10, 175, 25]

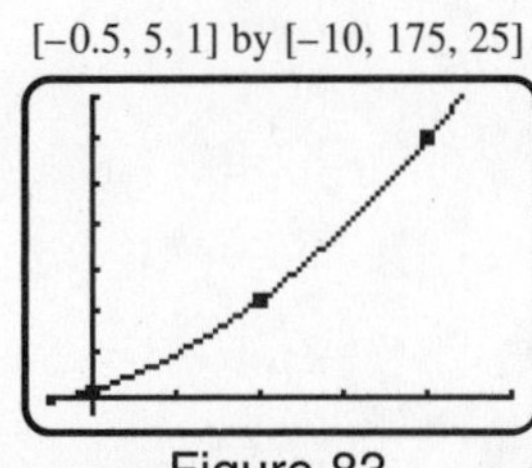

Figure 83

[−1, 30, 5] by [−50, 1000, 100]

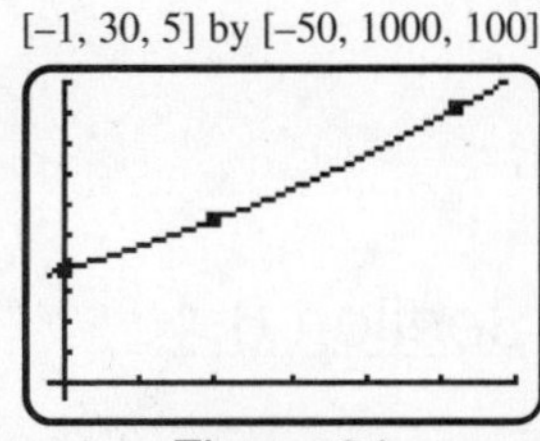

Figure 84

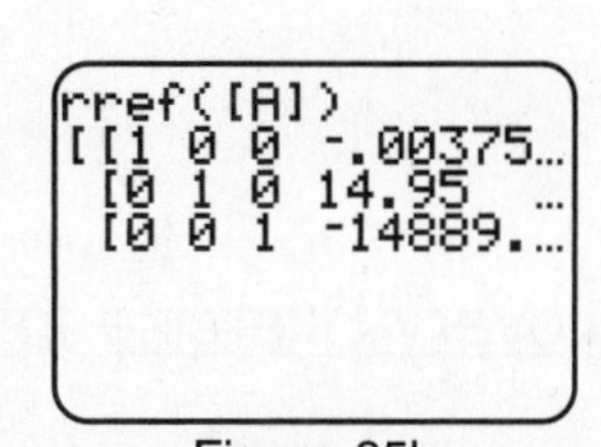


Figure 85b

[1985, 2035, 5] by [5, 12, 1]

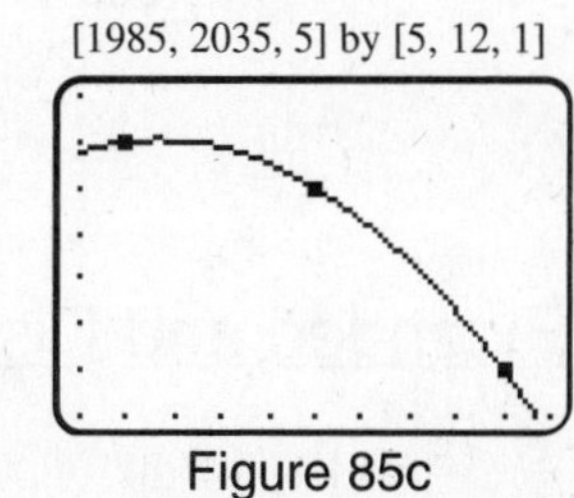

Figure 85c

85. (a) Let $f(x) = ax^2 + bx + c$. The constants $a$, $b$, and $c$ must satisfy the following equations: $f(1990) = a(1990)^2 + b(1990) + c = 11$, $f(2010) = a(2010)^2 + b(2010) + c = 10$, and $f(2030) = a(2030)^2 + b(2030) + c = 6$. This system of equations can be represented by the following augmented matrix:

$$\left[\begin{array}{ccc|c} 1990^2 & 1990 & 1 & 11 \\ 2010^2 & 2010 & 1 & 10 \\ 2030^2 & 2030 & 1 & 6 \end{array}\right]$$

(b) Using technology to solve the system results in the reduced row-echelon form shown in Figure 85b. The solution is $a = -0.00375$, $b = 14.95$, and $c = -14{,}889.125$. Therefore, the symbolic representation of $f$ is $f(x) = -0.00375x^2 + 14.95x - 14{,}889.125$.

(c) The data and $f$ are graphed in Figure 85c. Notice that the graph of $f$ passes through each data point.

(d) *Answers may vary.* For example, in 2015 the ratio could be $f(2015) \approx 9.3$.

86. (a) For 1958: $f(1958) = a(1958)^2 + b(1958) + c = 315$

For 1973: $f(1973) = a(1973)^2 + b(1973) + c = 325$

For 2003: $f(2003) = a(2003)^2 + b(2003) + c = 376$

This results in the following linear system of equations:

$$\left[\begin{array}{ccc|c} 1958^2 & 1958 & 1 & 315 \\ 1973^2 & 1973 & 1 & 325 \\ 2003^2 & 2003 & 1 & 376 \end{array}\right]$$

(b) Using technology, this system has the following approximate reduced row-echelon form. The solution to this system is $a \approx 0.022962$, $b \approx -89.600$, and $c \approx 87{,}718.6$. See Figure 86b. Thus, $f(x) = 0.022962x^2 - 89.600x + 87{,}718.6$.

(c) The data and $f$ are graphed in Figure 86c.

(d) *Answers may vary.* For example, in 2001 this level could be $f(2001) \approx 369$ ppm.

[1950, 2010, 5] by [300, 400, 10]

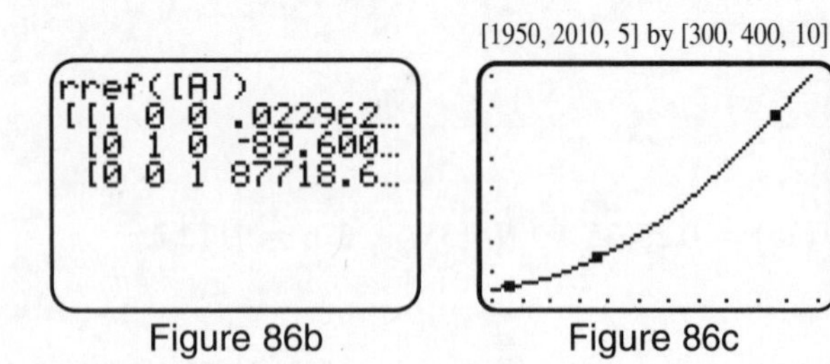


Figure 86b Figure 86c

## Extended and Discovery Exercise for Section 6.4

1. Using technology: $w = 1, x = -1, y = 2, z = 0$. The solution is $(1, -1, 2, 0)$.

2. Using technology: $w = -1, x = 1, y = 0, z = 3$. The solution is $(-1, 1, 0, 3)$.

## Checking Basic Concepts for Sections 6.3 and 6.4

1. (a) $\left[\begin{array}{ccc|c} 1 & -2 & 1 & -2 \\ 1 & 1 & 2 & 3 \\ 2 & -1 & -1 & 5 \end{array}\right] \begin{array}{l} \\ R_1 - R_2 \rightarrow \\ 2R_2 - R_3 \rightarrow \end{array} \left[\begin{array}{ccc|c} 1 & -2 & 1 & -2 \\ 0 & -3 & -1 & -5 \\ 0 & 3 & 5 & 1 \end{array}\right] \begin{array}{l} \\ (-1/3)R_2 \rightarrow \\ R_2 + R_3 \rightarrow \end{array} \left[\begin{array}{ccc|c} 1 & -2 & 1 & -2 \\ 0 & 1 & \frac{1}{3} & \frac{5}{3} \\ 0 & 0 & 4 & -4 \end{array}\right]$

$\begin{array}{l} \\ \\ (1/4)R_3 \rightarrow \end{array} \left[\begin{array}{ccc|c} 1 & -2 & 1 & -2 \\ 0 & 1 & \frac{1}{3} & \frac{5}{3} \\ 0 & 0 & 1 & -1 \end{array}\right] \begin{array}{l} (-1)R_3 + R_1 \rightarrow \\ (-1/3)R_3 + R_2 \rightarrow \\ \end{array} \left[\begin{array}{ccc|c} 1 & -2 & 0 & -1 \\ 0 & 1 & 0 & 2 \\ 0 & 0 & 1 & -1 \end{array}\right]$

$\begin{array}{l} 2R_2 + R_1 \rightarrow \\ \\ \end{array} \left[\begin{array}{ccc|c} 1 & 0 & 0 & 3 \\ 0 & 1 & 0 & 2 \\ 0 & 0 & 1 & -1 \end{array}\right]$

The solution is: $(3, 2, -1)$.

(b) $\left[\begin{array}{ccc|c} 1 & -2 & 1 & -2 \\ 1 & 1 & 2 & 3 \\ 2 & -1 & 3 & 1 \end{array}\right] \begin{array}{l} \\ R_1 - R_2 \rightarrow \\ 2R_2 - R_3 \rightarrow \end{array} \left[\begin{array}{ccc|c} 1 & -2 & 1 & -2 \\ 0 & -3 & -1 & -5 \\ 0 & 3 & 1 & 5 \end{array}\right] \begin{array}{l} \\ (-1/3)R_2 \rightarrow \\ R_2 + R_3 \rightarrow \end{array} \left[\begin{array}{ccc|c} 1 & -2 & 1 & -2 \\ 0 & 1 & \frac{1}{3} & \frac{5}{3} \\ 0 & 0 & 0 & 0 \end{array}\right]$

$\begin{array}{l} 2R_2 + R_1 \rightarrow \\ \\ \end{array} \left[\begin{array}{ccc|c} 1 & 0 & \frac{5}{3} & \frac{4}{3} \\ 0 & 1 & \frac{1}{3} & \frac{5}{3} \\ 0 & 0 & 0 & 0 \end{array}\right]$

The last equation indicates that $0 = 0$, which is true. Therefore, there is an infinite number of solutions. The second equation gives: $y + \frac{1}{3}z = \frac{5}{3} \Rightarrow y = \frac{5 - z}{3}$. The first equation gives: $x + \frac{5}{3}z = \frac{4}{3} \Rightarrow$ $x = \frac{4 - 5z}{3}$. Therefore, there are infinitely many solutions which can be written as: $\left(\frac{4 - 5z}{3}, \frac{-z + 5}{3}, z\right)$.

(c) $\left[\begin{array}{ccc|c} 1 & -2 & 1 & -2 \\ 1 & 1 & 2 & 3 \\ 2 & -1 & 3 & 5 \end{array}\right] \begin{array}{l} \\ R_1 - R_2 \rightarrow \\ 2R_2 - R_3 \rightarrow \end{array} \left[\begin{array}{ccc|c} 1 & -2 & 1 & -2 \\ 0 & -3 & -1 & -5 \\ 0 & 3 & 1 & 1 \end{array}\right] \begin{array}{l} \\ (-1/3)R_2 \rightarrow \\ R_2 + R_3 \rightarrow \end{array} \left[\begin{array}{ccc|c} 1 & -2 & 1 & -2 \\ 0 & 1 & \frac{1}{3} & \frac{5}{3} \\ 0 & 0 & 0 & -4 \end{array}\right]$

The last equation gives: $0 = -4$, which is false. Therefore there is no solution.

2. Let $x$ = child tickets sold, $y$ = student tickets sold, and $z$ = adult tickets sold. Then $x + y + z = 2000$, $5x + 10y + 12z = 19{,}700$, and $y + 100 = z \Rightarrow -y + z = 100$. The matrix is:

$\left[\begin{array}{ccc|c} 1 & 1 & 1 & 2000 \\ 5 & 10 & 12 & 19{,}700 \\ 0 & -1 & 1 & 100 \end{array}\right] \begin{array}{l} \\ 5R_1 - R_2 \rightarrow \\ \\ \end{array} \left[\begin{array}{ccc|c} 1 & 1 & 1 & 2000 \\ 0 & -5 & -7 & -9700 \\ 0 & -1 & 1 & 100 \end{array}\right] \begin{array}{l} \\ (-1/5)R_2 \rightarrow \\ -5R_3 + R_2 \rightarrow \end{array} \left[\begin{array}{ccc|c} 1 & 1 & 1 & 2000 \\ 0 & 1 & \frac{7}{5} & 1940 \\ 0 & 0 & -12 & -10{,}200 \end{array}\right]$

$\begin{array}{l} \\ \\ (-1/12)R_3 \rightarrow \end{array} \left[\begin{array}{ccc|c} 1 & 1 & 1 & 2000 \\ 0 & 1 & \frac{7}{5} & 1940 \\ 0 & 0 & 1 & 850 \end{array}\right] \begin{array}{l} \\ (-7/5)R_3 + R_2 \rightarrow \\ \\ \end{array} \left[\begin{array}{ccc|c} 1 & 1 & 1 & 2000 \\ 0 & 1 & 0 & 750 \\ 0 & 0 & 1 & 850 \end{array}\right] \begin{array}{l} R_1 - R_2 \rightarrow \\ \\ \\ \end{array} \left[\begin{array}{ccc|c} 1 & 0 & 1 & 1250 \\ 0 & 1 & 0 & 750 \\ 0 & 0 & 1 & 850 \end{array}\right]$

$\begin{array}{l} R_1 - R_3 \rightarrow \\ \\ \end{array} \left[\begin{array}{ccc|c} 1 & 0 & 0 & 400 \\ 0 & 1 & 0 & 750 \\ 0 & 0 & 1 & 850 \end{array}\right]$

The solution is: 400 children tickets sold, 750 student tickets sold, and 850 adult tickets sold.

3. $\left[\begin{array}{rrr|r} 1 & 0 & 1 & 2 \\ 1 & 1 & -1 & 1 \\ -1 & -2 & -1 & 0 \end{array}\right] \begin{array}{l} \\ R_2 - R_1 \rightarrow \\ R_3 + R_1 \rightarrow \end{array} \left[\begin{array}{rrr|r} 1 & 0 & 1 & 2 \\ 0 & 1 & -2 & -1 \\ 0 & -2 & 0 & 2 \end{array}\right] \begin{array}{l} \\ \\ (-1/2)R_3 \rightarrow \end{array} \left[\begin{array}{rrr|r} 1 & 0 & 1 & 2 \\ 0 & 1 & -2 & -1 \\ 0 & 1 & 0 & -1 \end{array}\right]$

$\begin{array}{l} \\ \\ R_3 - R_2 \rightarrow \end{array} \left[\begin{array}{rrr|r} 1 & 0 & 0 & -2 \\ 0 & 1 & -2 & -1 \\ 0 & 0 & 2 & 0 \end{array}\right]$

Backward substitution produces $z = 0, y - 2z = -1 \Rightarrow y - 0 = -1 \Rightarrow y = -1$. Substituting $z = 0$ and $y = -1$ into the first equation results in $x + 0(-1) + (0) = 2 \Rightarrow x = 2$. The solution is (2, –1, 0).

4. The solution of the system is given in Figure 4 using reduced row-echelon form.

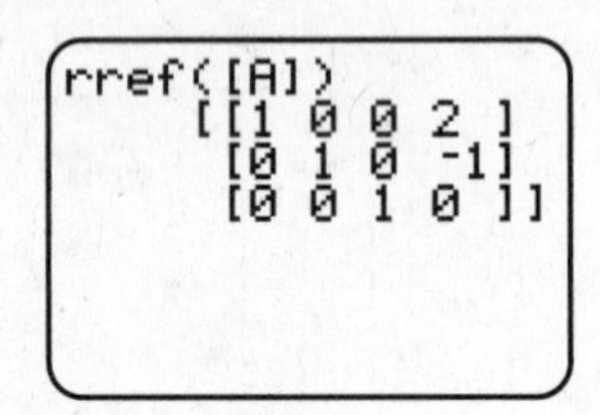


Figure 4

## 6.5 Properties and Applications of Matrices

1. (a) $a_{12} = 2$ and $a_{21} = 4$. The element $a_{32}$ is undefined since there is no row three.

   (b) $a_{11}a_{22} + 3a_{23} = (1)(5) + 3(6) = 23$

2. (a) $a_{12} = 2, a_{21} = 5$ and $a_{32} = 10$

   (b) $a_{11}a_{22} + 3a_{23} = (1)(6) + 3(7) = 27$

3. (a) $a_{12} = -1, a_{21} = 3$ and $a_{32} = 0$

   (b) $a_{11}a_{22} + 3a_{23} = (1)(-2) + 3(5) = 13$

4. (a) $a_{12} = -2$ and $a_{21} = -4$. The element $a_{32}$ is undefined since there is no row three.

   (b) $a_{11}a_{22} + 3a_{23}$ is undefined since the element $a_{23}$ is undefined (there is no column three).

5. $x = 1$ and $y = 1$

6. $x + y = 2$ and $y = 7$. Substituting $y = 7$ into $x + y = 2$: $x + 7 = 2 \Rightarrow x = -5$.

   Therefore $x = -5$ and $y = 7$.

7. The matrices are not the same size, therefore not possible.

8. The matrices are not the same size, therefore not possible.

9. (a) $a_{12} = 3, b_{32} = 1, b_{22} = 0$

   (b) $a_{11} = 1, b_{11} = 1 \Rightarrow a_{11}b_{11} = 1;\ a_{12} = 3, b_{21} = 3 \Rightarrow a_{12}b_{21} = 9;$

   $a_{13} = -4, b_{31} = 3 \Rightarrow a_{13}b_{31} = -12 \Rightarrow a_{11}b_{11} + a_{12}b_{21} + a_{13}b_{31} = -2$

   (c) If $A = B$, then all elements of $A$ must be equal to all elements of $B$. Then $x = 3$.

10. (a) $a_{12} = -1, b_{32} = -2, b_{22} = 6$

(b) $a_{11} = 0, b_{11} = 0 \Rightarrow a_{11}b_{11} = 0;\ a_{12} = -1, b_{21} = 2 \Rightarrow a_{12}b_{21} = -2;$

$a_{13} = 6, b_{31} = 7 \Rightarrow a_{13}b_{31} = 42 \Rightarrow a_{11}b_{11} + a_{12}b_{21} + a_{13}b_{31} = 40$

(c) If $A = B$, then all elements of $A$ must be equal to all elements of $B$. Thus, there is no one value of $x$ that will make $A = B$.

11. (a) $\begin{bmatrix} 4 & -1 \\ -1 & 4 \end{bmatrix} + \begin{bmatrix} -1 & 4 \\ 4 & -1 \end{bmatrix} = \begin{bmatrix} 3 & 3 \\ 3 & 3 \end{bmatrix}$

(b) $\begin{bmatrix} -1 & 4 \\ 4 & -1 \end{bmatrix} + \begin{bmatrix} 4 & -1 \\ -1 & 4 \end{bmatrix} = \begin{bmatrix} 3 & 3 \\ 3 & 3 \end{bmatrix}$

(c) $\begin{bmatrix} 4 & -1 \\ -1 & 4 \end{bmatrix} - \begin{bmatrix} -1 & 4 \\ 4 & -1 \end{bmatrix} = \begin{bmatrix} 5 & -5 \\ -5 & 5 \end{bmatrix}$

12. (a) $\begin{bmatrix} 2 & -4 \\ -1 & \frac{1}{2} \\ 3 & -2 \end{bmatrix} + \begin{bmatrix} 5 & 0 \\ 3 & \frac{1}{2} \\ -1 & 1 \end{bmatrix} = \begin{bmatrix} 7 & -4 \\ 2 & 1 \\ 2 & -1 \end{bmatrix}$

(b) $\begin{bmatrix} 5 & 0 \\ 3 & \frac{1}{2} \\ -1 & 1 \end{bmatrix} + \begin{bmatrix} 2 & -4 \\ -1 & \frac{1}{2} \\ 3 & -2 \end{bmatrix} = \begin{bmatrix} 7 & -4 \\ 2 & 1 \\ 2 & -1 \end{bmatrix}$

(c) $\begin{bmatrix} 2 & -4 \\ -1 & \frac{1}{2} \\ 3 & -2 \end{bmatrix} - \begin{bmatrix} 5 & 0 \\ 3 & \frac{1}{2} \\ -1 & 1 \end{bmatrix} = \begin{bmatrix} -3 & -4 \\ -4 & 0 \\ 4 & -3 \end{bmatrix}$

13. (a) $\begin{bmatrix} 3 & 4 & -1 \\ 0 & -3 & 2 \\ -2 & 5 & 10 \end{bmatrix} + \begin{bmatrix} 11 & 5 & -2 \\ 4 & -7 & 12 \\ 6 & 6 & 6 \end{bmatrix} = \begin{bmatrix} 14 & 9 & -3 \\ 4 & -10 & 14 \\ 4 & 11 & 16 \end{bmatrix}$

(b) $\begin{bmatrix} 11 & 5 & -2 \\ 4 & -7 & 12 \\ 6 & 6 & 6 \end{bmatrix} + \begin{bmatrix} 3 & 4 & -1 \\ 0 & -3 & 2 \\ -2 & 5 & 10 \end{bmatrix} = \begin{bmatrix} 14 & 9 & -3 \\ 4 & -10 & 14 \\ 4 & 11 & 16 \end{bmatrix}$

(c) $\begin{bmatrix} 3 & 4 & -1 \\ 0 & -3 & 2 \\ -2 & 5 & 10 \end{bmatrix} - \begin{bmatrix} 11 & 5 & -2 \\ 4 & -7 & 12 \\ 6 & 6 & 6 \end{bmatrix} = \begin{bmatrix} -8 & -1 & 1 \\ -4 & 4 & -10 \\ -8 & -1 & 4 \end{bmatrix}$

14. (a) $\begin{bmatrix} 1 & 6 & 1 & -2 \\ 0 & 1 & 3 & 5 \\ 0 & 0 & 1 & -2 \end{bmatrix} + \begin{bmatrix} 1 & 0 & 0 & 9 \\ 3 & 1 & 0 & 3 \\ -1 & 4 & 1 & -2 \end{bmatrix} = \begin{bmatrix} 2 & 6 & 1 & 7 \\ 3 & 2 & 3 & 8 \\ -1 & 4 & 2 & -4 \end{bmatrix}$

(b) $\begin{bmatrix} 1 & 0 & 0 & 9 \\ 3 & 1 & 0 & 3 \\ -1 & 4 & 1 & -2 \end{bmatrix} + \begin{bmatrix} 1 & 6 & 1 & -2 \\ 0 & 1 & 3 & 5 \\ 0 & 0 & 1 & -2 \end{bmatrix} = \begin{bmatrix} 2 & 6 & 1 & 7 \\ 3 & 2 & 3 & 8 \\ -1 & 4 & 2 & -4 \end{bmatrix}$

(c) $\begin{bmatrix} 1 & 6 & 1 & -2 \\ 0 & 1 & 3 & 5 \\ 0 & 0 & 1 & -2 \end{bmatrix} - \begin{bmatrix} 1 & 0 & 0 & 9 \\ 3 & 1 & 0 & 3 \\ -1 & 4 & 1 & -2 \end{bmatrix} = \begin{bmatrix} 0 & 6 & 1 & -11 \\ -3 & 0 & 3 & 2 \\ 1 & -4 & 0 & 0 \end{bmatrix}$

15. (a) $A + B = \begin{bmatrix} 2 & -6 \\ 3 & 1 \end{bmatrix} + \begin{bmatrix} -1 & 0 \\ -2 & 3 \end{bmatrix} = \begin{bmatrix} 1 & -6 \\ 1 & 4 \end{bmatrix}$

(b) $3A = 3\begin{bmatrix} 2 & -6 \\ 3 & 1 \end{bmatrix} = \begin{bmatrix} 6 & -18 \\ 9 & 3 \end{bmatrix}$

(c) $2A - 3B = 2\begin{bmatrix} 2 & -6 \\ 3 & 1 \end{bmatrix} - 3\begin{bmatrix} -1 & 0 \\ -2 & 3 \end{bmatrix} = \begin{bmatrix} 7 & -12 \\ 12 & -7 \end{bmatrix}$

16. (a) $A + B = \begin{bmatrix} 1 & -2 & 5 \\ 3 & -4 & -1 \end{bmatrix} + \begin{bmatrix} 0 & -1 & -5 \\ -3 & 1 & 2 \end{bmatrix} = \begin{bmatrix} 1 & -3 & 0 \\ 0 & -3 & 1 \end{bmatrix}$

(b) $3A = 3\begin{bmatrix} 1 & -2 & 5 \\ 3 & -4 & -1 \end{bmatrix} = \begin{bmatrix} 3 & -6 & 15 \\ 9 & -12 & -3 \end{bmatrix}$

(c) $2A - 3B = 2\begin{bmatrix} 1 & -2 & 5 \\ 3 & -4 & -1 \end{bmatrix} - 3\begin{bmatrix} 0 & -1 & -5 \\ -3 & 1 & 2 \end{bmatrix} = \begin{bmatrix} 2 & -1 & 25 \\ 15 & -11 & -8 \end{bmatrix}$

17. (a) $A + B$ is undefined since $A$ is $3 \times 3$ and $B$ is $2 \times 3$. They do not have the same dimension.

(b) $3A = 3\begin{bmatrix} 1 & -1 & 0 \\ 1 & 5 & 9 \\ -4 & 8 & -5 \end{bmatrix} = \begin{bmatrix} 3 & -3 & 0 \\ 3 & 15 & 27 \\ -12 & 24 & -15 \end{bmatrix}$

(c) $2A - 3B$ is undefined since $A$ is $3 \times 3$ and $B$ is $2 \times 3$. They do not have the same dimension.

18. (a) $A + B = \begin{bmatrix} 6 & 2 & 9 \\ 3 & -2 & 0 \\ -1 & 4 & 8 \end{bmatrix} + \begin{bmatrix} 1 & 0 & -1 \\ 3 & 0 & 7 \\ 0 & -2 & -5 \end{bmatrix} = \begin{bmatrix} 7 & 2 & 8 \\ 6 & -2 & 7 \\ -1 & 2 & 3 \end{bmatrix}$

(b) $3A = 3\begin{bmatrix} 6 & 2 & 9 \\ 3 & -2 & 0 \\ -1 & 4 & 8 \end{bmatrix} = \begin{bmatrix} 18 & 6 & 27 \\ 9 & -6 & 0 \\ -3 & 12 & 24 \end{bmatrix}$

(c) $2A - 3B = 2\begin{bmatrix} 6 & 2 & 9 \\ 3 & -2 & 0 \\ -1 & 4 & 8 \end{bmatrix} - 3\begin{bmatrix} 1 & 0 & -1 \\ 3 & 0 & 7 \\ 0 & -2 & -5 \end{bmatrix} = \begin{bmatrix} 9 & 4 & 21 \\ -3 & -4 & -21 \\ -2 & 14 & 31 \end{bmatrix}$

19. (a) $A + B = \begin{bmatrix} -2 & -1 \\ -5 & 1 \\ 2 & -3 \end{bmatrix} + \begin{bmatrix} 2 & -1 \\ 3 & 1 \\ 7 & -5 \end{bmatrix} = \begin{bmatrix} 0 & -2 \\ -2 & 2 \\ 9 & -8 \end{bmatrix}$

(b) $3A = 3\begin{bmatrix} -2 & -1 \\ -5 & 1 \\ 2 & -3 \end{bmatrix} = \begin{bmatrix} -6 & -3 \\ -15 & 3 \\ 6 & -9 \end{bmatrix}$

(c) $2A - 3B = 2\begin{bmatrix} -2 & -1 \\ -5 & 1 \\ 2 & -3 \end{bmatrix} - 3\begin{bmatrix} 2 & -1 \\ 3 & 1 \\ 7 & -5 \end{bmatrix} = \begin{bmatrix} -10 & 1 \\ -19 & -1 \\ -17 & 9 \end{bmatrix}$

20. (a) $A + B$ is undefined since $A$ is $3 \times 2$ and $B$ is $2 \times 3$. They do not have the same dimension.

(b) $3A = 3\begin{bmatrix} 0 & 1 \\ 3 & 2 \\ 4 & -9 \end{bmatrix} = \begin{bmatrix} 0 & 3 \\ 9 & 6 \\ 12 & -27 \end{bmatrix}$

(c) $2A - 3B$ is undefined since $A$ is $3 \times 2$ and $B$ is $2 \times 3$. They do not have the same dimension.

21. $2\begin{bmatrix} 2 & -1 \\ 5 & 1 \\ 0 & 3 \end{bmatrix} + \begin{bmatrix} 5 & 0 \\ 7 & -3 \\ 1 & 1 \end{bmatrix} - \begin{bmatrix} 9 & -4 \\ 4 & 4 \\ 1 & 6 \end{bmatrix} = \begin{bmatrix} 0 & 2 \\ 13 & -5 \\ 0 & 1 \end{bmatrix}$

22. $-3\begin{bmatrix} 3 & 8 \\ -1 & -9 \end{bmatrix} + 5\begin{bmatrix} 4 & -8 \\ 1 & 6 \end{bmatrix} = \begin{bmatrix} 11 & -64 \\ 8 & 57 \end{bmatrix}$

23. $\begin{bmatrix} 4 & 6 \\ 3 & -7 \end{bmatrix} - 2\begin{bmatrix} 1 & 0 \\ -4 & 1 \end{bmatrix} = \begin{bmatrix} 2 & 6 \\ 11 & -9 \end{bmatrix}$

24. $\begin{bmatrix} 5 & -1 & 6 \\ -2 & 10 & 12 \\ 5 & 2 & 9 \end{bmatrix} - \begin{bmatrix} -1 & 2 & 2 \\ 2 & -1 & 2 \\ 2 & 2 & -1 \end{bmatrix} = \begin{bmatrix} 6 & -3 & 4 \\ -4 & 11 & 10 \\ 3 & 0 & 10 \end{bmatrix}$

25. $2\begin{bmatrix} 2 & -1 & -1 \\ -1 & 2 & -1 \\ -1 & -1 & 2 \end{bmatrix} + 3\begin{bmatrix} 1 & 2 & 3 \\ 2 & 1 & 3 \\ 2 & 3 & 1 \end{bmatrix} = \begin{bmatrix} 7 & 4 & 7 \\ 4 & 7 & 7 \\ 4 & 7 & 7 \end{bmatrix}$

26. $3\begin{bmatrix} 1 & 0 & 3 & -1 \\ 0 & 1 & 2 & -1 \\ 1 & 0 & -3 & 1 \end{bmatrix} - 4\begin{bmatrix} -1 & 0 & 0 & 4 \\ 0 & -1 & 3 & 2 \\ 2 & 0 & 1 & -1 \end{bmatrix} = \begin{bmatrix} 7 & 0 & 9 & -19 \\ 0 & 7 & -6 & -11 \\ -5 & 0 & -13 & 7 \end{bmatrix}$

27. The "1" is dark gray and the background is light gray.

$$A = \begin{bmatrix} 1 & 2 & 1 \\ 1 & 2 & 1 \\ 1 & 2 & 1 \end{bmatrix}$$

28. The picture can be made darker by adding 1 to each element in matrix $A$. This could be accomplished by the $3 \times 3$ matrix $B$ consisting of only 1's.

$$B = \begin{bmatrix} 1 & 1 & 1 \\ 1 & 1 & 1 \\ 1 & 1 & 1 \end{bmatrix}; \; A + B = \begin{bmatrix} 1 & 2 & 1 \\ 1 & 2 & 1 \\ 1 & 2 & 1 \end{bmatrix} + \begin{bmatrix} 1 & 1 & 1 \\ 1 & 1 & 1 \\ 1 & 1 & 1 \end{bmatrix} = \begin{bmatrix} 2 & 3 & 2 \\ 2 & 3 & 2 \\ 2 & 3 & 2 \end{bmatrix}$$

29. To enhance the contrast, change light gray to white and change dark gray to black. This could be accomplished by adding the $3 \times 3$ matrix $B$ to $A$.

$$B = \begin{bmatrix} -1 & 1 & -1 \\ -1 & 1 & -1 \\ -1 & 1 & -1 \end{bmatrix}; \; A + B = \begin{bmatrix} 1 & 2 & 1 \\ 1 & 2 & 1 \\ 1 & 2 & 1 \end{bmatrix} + \begin{bmatrix} -1 & 1 & -1 \\ -1 & 1 & -1 \\ -1 & 1 & -1 \end{bmatrix} = \begin{bmatrix} 0 & 3 & 0 \\ 0 & 3 & 0 \\ 0 & 3 & 0 \end{bmatrix}$$

30. The picture can be made lighter by subtracting 1 from each element in matrix $A$. This could be accomplished by the $3 \times 3$ matrix $B$ consisting of only 1's.

$$B = \begin{bmatrix} 1 & 1 & 1 \\ 1 & 1 & 1 \\ 1 & 1 & 1 \end{bmatrix}; \; A - B = \begin{bmatrix} 1 & 2 & 1 \\ 1 & 2 & 1 \\ 1 & 2 & 1 \end{bmatrix} - \begin{bmatrix} 1 & 1 & 1 \\ 1 & 1 & 1 \\ 1 & 1 & 1 \end{bmatrix} = \begin{bmatrix} 0 & 1 & 0 \\ 0 & 1 & 0 \\ 0 & 1 & 0 \end{bmatrix}$$

31. $A$ and $B$ are both $2 \times 2$ so $AB$ and $BA$ are also both $2 \times 2$.

$$AB = \begin{bmatrix} 1 & -1 \\ 2 & 0 \end{bmatrix}\begin{bmatrix} -2 & 3 \\ 1 & 2 \end{bmatrix} = \begin{bmatrix} -3 & 1 \\ -4 & 6 \end{bmatrix}; \; BA = \begin{bmatrix} -2 & 3 \\ 1 & 2 \end{bmatrix}\begin{bmatrix} 1 & -1 \\ 2 & 0 \end{bmatrix} = \begin{bmatrix} 4 & 2 \\ 5 & -1 \end{bmatrix}$$

32. $A$ and $B$ are both $2 \times 2$ so $AB$ and $BA$ are also both $2 \times 2$.

$$AB = \begin{bmatrix} -3 & 5 \\ 2 & 7 \end{bmatrix}\begin{bmatrix} -1 & 2 \\ 0 & 7 \end{bmatrix} = \begin{bmatrix} 3 & 29 \\ -2 & 53 \end{bmatrix};\ BA = \begin{bmatrix} -1 & 2 \\ 0 & 7 \end{bmatrix}\begin{bmatrix} -3 & 5 \\ 2 & 7 \end{bmatrix} = \begin{bmatrix} 7 & 9 \\ 14 & 49 \end{bmatrix}$$

33. Since both $A$ and $B$ are $2 \times 3$, the number of rows in $B$ is not equal to the number of columns in $A$, so $AB$ is undefined. Also, the number of rows in $A$ is not equal to the number of columns in $B$ so $BA$ is undefined.

34. $A$ is $3 \times 3$ and $B$ is $3 \times 2$ so $AB$ is $3 \times 2$. However $BA$ is undefined since the number of rows in $A$ is not equal to the number of columns in $B$.

$$AB = \begin{bmatrix} 2 & 1 & -1 \\ 0 & 2 & 1 \\ 3 & 2 & -1 \end{bmatrix}\begin{bmatrix} 1 & 0 \\ 2 & -1 \\ 3 & 1 \end{bmatrix} = \begin{bmatrix} 1 & -2 \\ 7 & -1 \\ 4 & -3 \end{bmatrix}$$

35. $$AB = \begin{bmatrix} 3 & -1 \\ 1 & 0 \\ -2 & -4 \end{bmatrix}\begin{bmatrix} -2 & 5 & -3 \\ 9 & -7 & 0 \end{bmatrix} =$$

$$\begin{bmatrix} 3(-2) + (-1)(9) & 3(5) + (-1)(-7) & 3(-3) + (-1)(0) \\ 1(-2) + 0(9) & 1(5) + 0(-7) & 1(-3) + 0(0) \\ -2(-2) + (-4)(9) & -2(5) + (-4)(-7) & -2(-3) + (-4)(0) \end{bmatrix} \Rightarrow AB = \begin{bmatrix} -15 & 22 & -9 \\ -2 & 5 & -3 \\ -32 & 18 & 6 \end{bmatrix}$$

$$BA = \begin{bmatrix} -2 & 5 & -3 \\ 9 & -7 & 0 \end{bmatrix}\begin{bmatrix} 3 & -1 \\ 1 & 0 \\ -2 & -4 \end{bmatrix} =$$

$$\begin{bmatrix} -2(3) + 5(1) + (-3)(-2) & -2(-1) + (5)(0) + (-3)(-4) \\ 9(3) + (-7)(1) + 0(-2) & 9(-1) + (-7)(0) + 0(-4) \end{bmatrix} \Rightarrow BA = \begin{bmatrix} 5 & 14 \\ 20 & -9 \end{bmatrix}$$

36. $$AB = \begin{bmatrix} -1 & 0 & -2 \\ 4 & -2 & 1 \end{bmatrix}\begin{bmatrix} 2 & -2 \\ 5 & -1 \\ 0 & 1 \end{bmatrix} = \begin{bmatrix} -1(2) + 0(5) + (-2)(0) & -1(-2) + 0(-1) + (-2)(1) \\ 4(2) + (-2)(5) + 1(0) & 4(-2) + (-2)(-1) + 1(1) \end{bmatrix} \Rightarrow$$

$$AB = \begin{bmatrix} -2 & 0 \\ -2 & -5 \end{bmatrix}$$

$$BA = \begin{bmatrix} 2 & -2 \\ 5 & -1 \\ 0 & 1 \end{bmatrix}\begin{bmatrix} -1 & 0 & -2 \\ 4 & -2 & 1 \end{bmatrix} = \begin{bmatrix} 2(-1) + (-2)(4) & 2(0) + (-2)(-2) & 2(-2) + (-2)(1) \\ 5(-1) + (-1)(4) & 5(0) + (-1)(-2) & 5(-2) + (-1)(1) \\ 0(-1) + 1(4) & 0(0) + 1(-2) & 0(-2) + 1(1) \end{bmatrix} \Rightarrow$$

$$BA = \begin{bmatrix} -10 & 4 & -6 \\ -9 & 2 & -11 \\ 4 & -2 & 1 \end{bmatrix}$$

37. $AB$ is undefined, we cannot multiply a $3 \times 3$ by a $2 \times 3$.

$$BA = \begin{bmatrix} -1 & 3 & -1 \\ 7 & -7 & 1 \end{bmatrix}\begin{bmatrix} 1 & -1 & 0 \\ 2 & -1 & 5 \\ 6 & 1 & -4 \end{bmatrix} =$$

$$\begin{bmatrix} -1(1) + 3(2) + (-1)(6) & -1(-1) + 3(-1) + (-1)(1) & -1(0) + 3(5) + (-1)(-4) \\ 7(1) + (-7)(2) + 1(6) & 7(-1) + (-7)(-1) + 1(1) & 7(0) + (-7)(5) + 1(-4) \end{bmatrix} \Rightarrow$$

$$BA = \begin{bmatrix} -1 & -3 & 19 \\ -1 & 1 & -39 \end{bmatrix}$$

38. $AB = \begin{bmatrix} 2 & -1 & -5 \\ 4 & -1 & 6 \\ -2 & 0 & 9 \end{bmatrix}\begin{bmatrix} 1 & 2 \\ -1 & -1 \\ 2 & 0 \end{bmatrix} =$

$$\begin{bmatrix} 2(1)+(-1)(-1)+(-5)(2) & 2(2)+(-1)(-1)+(-5)(0) \\ 4(1)+(-1)(-1)+6(2) & 4(2)+(-1)(-1)+6(0) \\ -2(1)+0(-1)+9(2) & -2(2)+0(-1)+9(0) \end{bmatrix} \Rightarrow AB = \begin{bmatrix} -7 & 5 \\ 17 & 9 \\ 16 & -4 \end{bmatrix}$$

BA is undefined, we cannot multiply a $3 \times 2$ by a $3 \times 3$.

39. Since $A$ is $2 \times 2$ and $B$ is $3 \times 1$, the number of rows in $B$ is not equal to the number of columns in $A$, so $AB$ is undefined. Also, the number of rows in $A$ is not equal to the number of columns in $B$ so $BA$ is undefined.

40. $A$ is $3 \times 2$ and $B$ is $2 \times 3$ so $AB$ is $3 \times 3$ and $BA$ is $2 \times 2$.

$$AB = \begin{bmatrix} 3 & -1 \\ 2 & -2 \\ 0 & 4 \end{bmatrix}\begin{bmatrix} 1 & -4 & 0 \\ -1 & 3 & 2 \end{bmatrix} = \begin{bmatrix} 4 & -15 & -2 \\ 4 & -14 & -4 \\ -4 & 12 & 8 \end{bmatrix}; BA = \begin{bmatrix} 1 & -4 & 0 \\ -1 & 3 & 2 \end{bmatrix}\begin{bmatrix} 3 & -1 \\ 2 & -2 \\ 0 & 4 \end{bmatrix} = \begin{bmatrix} -5 & 7 \\ 3 & 3 \end{bmatrix}$$

41. $A$ and $B$ are both $3 \times 3$ so $AB$ and $BA$ are also both $3 \times 3$.

$$AB = \begin{bmatrix} 2 & -1 & 3 \\ 0 & 1 & 0 \\ 2 & -2 & 3 \end{bmatrix}\begin{bmatrix} 1 & 5 & -1 \\ 0 & 1 & 3 \\ -1 & 2 & 1 \end{bmatrix} = \begin{bmatrix} -1 & 15 & -2 \\ 0 & 1 & 3 \\ -1 & 14 & -5 \end{bmatrix};$$

$$BA = \begin{bmatrix} 1 & 5 & -1 \\ 0 & 1 & 3 \\ -1 & 2 & 1 \end{bmatrix}\begin{bmatrix} 2 & -1 & 3 \\ 0 & 1 & 0 \\ 2 & -2 & 3 \end{bmatrix} = \begin{bmatrix} 0 & 6 & 0 \\ 6 & -5 & 9 \\ 0 & 1 & 0 \end{bmatrix}$$

42. $A$ and $B$ are both $3 \times 3$ so $AB$ and $BA$ are also both $3 \times 3$.

$$AB = \begin{bmatrix} 1 & -2 & 5 \\ 1 & 0 & -2 \\ 1 & 3 & 2 \end{bmatrix}\begin{bmatrix} -1 & 4 & 2 \\ -3 & 0 & 1 \\ 5 & 1 & 0 \end{bmatrix} = \begin{bmatrix} 30 & 9 & 0 \\ -11 & 2 & 2 \\ 0 & 6 & 5 \end{bmatrix};$$

$$BA = \begin{bmatrix} -1 & 4 & 2 \\ -3 & 0 & 1 \\ 5 & 1 & 0 \end{bmatrix}\begin{bmatrix} 1 & -2 & 5 \\ 1 & 0 & -2 \\ 1 & 3 & 2 \end{bmatrix} = \begin{bmatrix} 5 & 8 & -9 \\ -2 & 9 & -13 \\ 6 & -10 & 23 \end{bmatrix}$$

43. $A$ is $2 \times 2$ and $B$ is $2 \times 1$ so $AB$ is $2 \times 1$. However $BA$ is undefined since the number of rows in $A$ is not equal to the number of columns in $B$.

$$AB = \begin{bmatrix} 2 & -1 \\ 3 & 1 \end{bmatrix}\begin{bmatrix} 1 \\ 3 \end{bmatrix} = \begin{bmatrix} -1 \\ 6 \end{bmatrix}$$

44. $A$ is $1 \times 2$ and $B$ is $2 \times 1$ so $AB$ is $1 \times 1$ and $BA$ is $2 \times 2$.

$$AB = \begin{bmatrix} 5 & -3 \end{bmatrix}\begin{bmatrix} 1 \\ 3 \end{bmatrix} = [-4]; BA = \begin{bmatrix} 1 \\ 3 \end{bmatrix}\begin{bmatrix} 5 & -3 \end{bmatrix} = \begin{bmatrix} 5 & -3 \\ 15 & -9 \end{bmatrix}$$

45. $A$ is $2 \times 2$ and $B$ is $2 \times 3$ so $AB$ is $2 \times 3$. However $BA$ is undefined since the number of rows in $A$ is not equal to the number of columns in $B$.

$$AB = \begin{bmatrix} -3 & 1 \\ 2 & -4 \end{bmatrix}\begin{bmatrix} 1 & 0 & -2 \\ -4 & 8 & 1 \end{bmatrix} = \begin{bmatrix} -7 & 8 & 7 \\ 18 & -32 & -8 \end{bmatrix}$$

46. $A$ is $3 \times 3$ and $B$ is $3 \times 1$ so $AB$ is $3 \times 1$. However $BA$ is undefined since the number of rows in $A$ is not equal to the number of columns in $B$.

$$AB = \begin{bmatrix} 6 & 1 & 0 \\ -2 & 5 & 1 \\ 4 & -7 & 10 \end{bmatrix}\begin{bmatrix} 10 \\ 20 \\ 30 \end{bmatrix} = \begin{bmatrix} 80 \\ 110 \\ 200 \end{bmatrix}$$

47. $A$ is $3 \times 3$ and $B$ is $3 \times 1$ so $AB$ is $3 \times 1$. However $BA$ is undefined since the number of rows in $A$ is not equal to the number of columns in $B$.

$$AB = \begin{bmatrix} 1 & 0 & -2 \\ 3 & -4 & 1 \\ 2 & 0 & 5 \end{bmatrix}\begin{bmatrix} 1 \\ -1 \\ 3 \end{bmatrix} = \begin{bmatrix} -5 \\ 10 \\ 17 \end{bmatrix}$$

48. $A$ is $3 \times 4$ and $B$ is $4 \times 2$ so $AB$ is $3 \times 2$. However $BA$ is undefined since the number of rows in $A$ is not equal to the number of columns in $B$.

$$AB = \begin{bmatrix} 1 & -1 & 3 & -2 \\ 1 & 0 & 3 & 4 \\ 2 & -2 & 0 & 8 \end{bmatrix}\begin{bmatrix} 1 & -1 \\ 0 & 5 \\ 2 & 3 \\ -5 & 4 \end{bmatrix} = \begin{bmatrix} 17 & -5 \\ -13 & 24 \\ -38 & 20 \end{bmatrix}$$

49. Using technology; $BA = \begin{bmatrix} 3 & -2 & 4 \\ 5 & 2 & 3 \\ 7 & 5 & 4 \end{bmatrix}\begin{bmatrix} 1 & 1 & -5 \\ -1 & 0 & -7 \\ -6 & 4 & 3 \end{bmatrix} = \begin{bmatrix} -19 & 19 & 11 \\ 21 & -7 & -48 \\ -22 & 23 & -58 \end{bmatrix}$

50. Using technology; $BA = \begin{bmatrix} 1 & 1 & -5 \\ -1 & 0 & -7 \\ -6 & 4 & 3 \end{bmatrix}\begin{bmatrix} 3 & -2 & 4 \\ 5 & 2 & 3 \\ 7 & 5 & 4 \end{bmatrix} = \begin{bmatrix} -27 & -25 & -19 \\ -52 & -33 & -32 \\ 23 & 35 & -24 \end{bmatrix}$

51. Using technology; $3A^2 + 2B = 3\begin{bmatrix} 3 & -2 & 4 \\ 5 & 2 & 3 \\ 7 & 5 & 4 \end{bmatrix}^2 + 2\begin{bmatrix} 1 & 1 & -5 \\ -1 & 0 & -7 \\ -6 & 4 & 3 \end{bmatrix} = \begin{bmatrix} 83 & 32 & 92 \\ 10 & -63 & -8 \\ 210 & 56 & 93 \end{bmatrix}$

52. Using technology; $B^2 - 3A = \begin{bmatrix} 1 & 1 & -5 \\ -1 & 0 & -7 \\ -6 & 4 & 3 \end{bmatrix}^2 - 3\begin{bmatrix} 3 & -2 & 4 \\ 5 & 2 & -3 \\ 7 & 5 & 4 \end{bmatrix} = \begin{bmatrix} 21 & -13 & -39 \\ 26 & -35 & -7 \\ -49 & -9 & -1 \end{bmatrix}$

53. (a) $B + C = \begin{bmatrix} 6 & 2 & 7 \\ 3 & -4 & -5 \\ 7 & 1 & 0 \end{bmatrix} + \begin{bmatrix} 1 & 4 & -3 \\ 8 & 1 & -1 \\ 4 & 6 & -2 \end{bmatrix} = \begin{bmatrix} 7 & 6 & 4 \\ 11 & -3 & -6 \\ 11 & 7 & -2 \end{bmatrix}$

$$A(B + C) = \begin{bmatrix} 2 & -1 & 3 \\ 1 & 3 & -5 \\ 0 & -2 & 1 \end{bmatrix}\begin{bmatrix} 7 & 6 & 4 \\ 11 & -3 & -6 \\ 11 & 7 & -2 \end{bmatrix} = \begin{bmatrix} 36 & 36 & 8 \\ -15 & -38 & -4 \\ -11 & 13 & 10 \end{bmatrix}$$

(b) $AB = \begin{bmatrix} 2 & -1 & 3 \\ 1 & 3 & -5 \\ 0 & -2 & 1 \end{bmatrix}\begin{bmatrix} 6 & 2 & 7 \\ 3 & -4 & -5 \\ 7 & 1 & 0 \end{bmatrix} = \begin{bmatrix} 30 & 11 & 19 \\ -20 & -15 & -8 \\ 1 & 9 & 10 \end{bmatrix}$

$$AC = \begin{bmatrix} 2 & -1 & 3 \\ 1 & 3 & -5 \\ 0 & -2 & 1 \end{bmatrix}\begin{bmatrix} 1 & 4 & -3 \\ 8 & 1 & -1 \\ 4 & 6 & -2 \end{bmatrix} = \begin{bmatrix} 6 & 25 & -11 \\ 5 & -23 & 4 \\ -12 & 4 & 0 \end{bmatrix}; \ AB + AC = \begin{bmatrix} 36 & 36 & 8 \\ -15 & -38 & -4 \\ -11 & 13 & 10 \end{bmatrix}$$

$A(B + C) = AB + AC$, which indicates that the distributive property holds for matrices.

54. (a) $A - B = \begin{bmatrix} -4 & -3 & -4 \\ -2 & 7 & 0 \\ -7 & -3 & 1 \end{bmatrix}$ and $(A - B)C = \begin{bmatrix} -44 & -43 & 23 \\ 54 & -1 & -1 \\ -27 & -25 & 22 \end{bmatrix}$

(b) $AC = \begin{bmatrix} 6 & 25 & -11 \\ 5 & -23 & 4 \\ -12 & 4 & 0 \end{bmatrix}$ and $BC = \begin{bmatrix} 50 & 68 & -34 \\ -49 & -22 & 5 \\ 15 & 29 & -22 \end{bmatrix}$; $AC - BC = \begin{bmatrix} -44 & -43 & 23 \\ 54 & -1 & -1 \\ -27 & -25 & 22 \end{bmatrix}$

$(A - B)C = AC - BC$, which indicates that the distributive property holds for matrices.

55. (a) $(A - B)^2 = \begin{bmatrix} -4 & -3 & -4 \\ -2 & 7 & 0 \\ -7 & -3 & 1 \end{bmatrix}\begin{bmatrix} -4 & -3 & -4 \\ -2 & 7 & 0 \\ -7 & -3 & 1 \end{bmatrix} = \begin{bmatrix} 50 & 3 & 12 \\ -6 & 55 & 8 \\ 27 & -3 & 29 \end{bmatrix}$

(b) $A^2 - AB - BA + B^2 =$

$$\begin{bmatrix} 3 & -11 & 14 \\ 5 & 18 & -17 \\ -2 & -8 & 11 \end{bmatrix} - \begin{bmatrix} 30 & 11 & 19 \\ -20 & -15 & -8 \\ 1 & 9 & 10 \end{bmatrix} - \begin{bmatrix} 14 & -14 & 15 \\ 2 & -5 & 24 \\ 15 & -4 & 16 \end{bmatrix} + \begin{bmatrix} 91 & 11 & 32 \\ -29 & 17 & 41 \\ 45 & 10 & 44 \end{bmatrix} =$$

$$\begin{bmatrix} 50 & 3 & 12 \\ -6 & 55 & 8 \\ 27 & -3 & 29 \end{bmatrix}$$

$(A - B)^2 = A^2 - AB - BA + B^2$, which indicates that matrices seem to conform to common rules of algebra except for the commutative property since $AB \neq BA$, in general.

56. (a) $(AB)C = \begin{bmatrix} 30 & 11 & 19 \\ -20 & -15 & -8 \\ 1 & 9 & 10 \end{bmatrix}\begin{bmatrix} 1 & 4 & -3 \\ 8 & 1 & -1 \\ 4 & 6 & -2 \end{bmatrix} = \begin{bmatrix} 194 & 245 & -13 \\ -172 & -143 & 91 \\ 113 & 73 & -32 \end{bmatrix}$

(b) $A(BC) = \begin{bmatrix} 2 & -1 & 3 \\ 1 & 3 & -5 \\ 0 & -2 & 1 \end{bmatrix}\begin{bmatrix} 50 & 68 & -34 \\ -49 & -22 & 5 \\ 15 & 29 & -22 \end{bmatrix} = \begin{bmatrix} 194 & 245 & -13 \\ -172 & -143 & 91 \\ 113 & 73 & -32 \end{bmatrix}$

$(AB)C = A(BC)$, which indicates that the associative property holds for matrices.

57. To make a negative image, subtract the matrix $A$ from a completely black image matrix $B$.

$$B = \begin{bmatrix} 3 & 3 & 3 \\ 3 & 3 & 3 \\ 3 & 3 & 3 \end{bmatrix};\ B - A = \begin{bmatrix} 3 & 3 & 3 \\ 3 & 3 & 3 \\ 3 & 3 & 3 \end{bmatrix} - \begin{bmatrix} 0 & 3 & 0 \\ 0 & 3 & 0 \\ 0 & 3 & 0 \end{bmatrix} = \begin{bmatrix} 3 & 0 & 3 \\ 3 & 0 & 3 \\ 3 & 0 & 3 \end{bmatrix}$$

58. Black can be changed to white by subtracting 3 and white can be changed to black by adding 3. In the negative, light gray would change to dark gray by adding 1, and dark gray would change to light gray by subtracting 1.

$$B = \begin{bmatrix} 3 & 0 & 3 \\ 2 & 0 & 2 \\ 1 & 0 & 1 \end{bmatrix}$$

59. $A = \begin{bmatrix} 3 & 3 & 3 & 3 \\ 3 & 0 & 0 & 0 \\ 3 & 3 & 3 & 0 \\ 3 & 0 & 0 & 0 \\ 3 & 0 & 0 & 0 \end{bmatrix}$

60. (a) $B = \begin{bmatrix} 3 & 3 & 3 & 3 \\ 3 & 3 & 3 & 3 \\ 3 & 3 & 3 & 3 \\ 3 & 3 & 3 & 3 \\ 3 & 3 & 3 & 3 \end{bmatrix}$ and $B - A = \begin{bmatrix} 3 & 3 & 3 & 3 \\ 3 & 3 & 3 & 3 \\ 3 & 3 & 3 & 3 \\ 3 & 3 & 3 & 3 \\ 3 & 3 & 3 & 3 \end{bmatrix} - \begin{bmatrix} 3 & 3 & 3 & 3 \\ 3 & 0 & 0 & 0 \\ 3 & 3 & 3 & 0 \\ 3 & 0 & 0 & 0 \\ 3 & 0 & 0 & 0 \end{bmatrix} = \begin{bmatrix} 0 & 0 & 0 & 0 \\ 0 & 3 & 3 & 3 \\ 0 & 0 & 0 & 3 \\ 0 & 3 & 3 & 3 \\ 0 & 3 & 3 & 3 \end{bmatrix}$

(b) $C = \begin{bmatrix} -1 & -1 & -1 & -1 \\ -1 & 1 & 1 & 1 \\ -1 & -1 & -1 & 1 \\ -1 & 1 & 1 & 1 \\ -1 & 1 & 1 & 1 \end{bmatrix}$ and $A + C = \begin{bmatrix} 3 & 3 & 3 & 3 \\ 3 & 0 & 0 & 0 \\ 3 & 3 & 3 & 0 \\ 3 & 0 & 0 & 0 \\ 3 & 0 & 0 & 0 \end{bmatrix} + \begin{bmatrix} -1 & -1 & -1 & -1 \\ -1 & 1 & 1 & 1 \\ -1 & -1 & -1 & 1 \\ -1 & 1 & 1 & 1 \\ -1 & 1 & 1 & 1 \end{bmatrix} =$

$\begin{bmatrix} 2 & 2 & 2 & 2 \\ 2 & 1 & 1 & 1 \\ 2 & 2 & 2 & 1 \\ 2 & 1 & 1 & 1 \\ 2 & 1 & 1 & 1 \end{bmatrix}$

61. (a) One possible solution for a "Z" is $A = \begin{bmatrix} 3 & 3 & 3 & 3 \\ 0 & 0 & 3 & 0 \\ 0 & 3 & 0 & 0 \\ 3 & 3 & 3 & 3 \end{bmatrix}$

(b) If $A$ is the matrix in part (a) then

$B = \begin{bmatrix} 3 & 3 & 3 & 3 \\ 3 & 3 & 3 & 3 \\ 3 & 3 & 3 & 3 \\ 3 & 3 & 3 & 3 \end{bmatrix}$ and $B - A = \begin{bmatrix} 3 & 3 & 3 & 3 \\ 3 & 3 & 3 & 3 \\ 3 & 3 & 3 & 3 \\ 3 & 3 & 3 & 3 \end{bmatrix} - \begin{bmatrix} 3 & 3 & 3 & 3 \\ 0 & 0 & 3 & 0 \\ 0 & 3 & 0 & 0 \\ 3 & 3 & 3 & 3 \end{bmatrix} = \begin{bmatrix} 0 & 0 & 0 & 0 \\ 3 & 3 & 0 & 3 \\ 3 & 0 & 3 & 3 \\ 0 & 0 & 0 & 0 \end{bmatrix}$

62. (a) One possible solution for a "N" is $A = \begin{bmatrix} 3 & 0 & 0 & 3 \\ 3 & 3 & 0 & 3 \\ 3 & 0 & 3 & 3 \\ 3 & 0 & 0 & 3 \end{bmatrix}$

(b) If $A$ is the matrix in part (a) then

$B = \begin{bmatrix} 3 & 3 & 3 & 3 \\ 3 & 3 & 3 & 3 \\ 3 & 3 & 3 & 3 \\ 3 & 3 & 3 & 3 \end{bmatrix}$ and $B - A = \begin{bmatrix} 3 & 3 & 3 & 3 \\ 3 & 3 & 3 & 3 \\ 3 & 3 & 3 & 3 \\ 3 & 3 & 3 & 3 \end{bmatrix} - \begin{bmatrix} 3 & 0 & 0 & 3 \\ 3 & 3 & 0 & 3 \\ 3 & 0 & 3 & 3 \\ 3 & 0 & 0 & 3 \end{bmatrix} = \begin{bmatrix} 0 & 3 & 3 & 0 \\ 0 & 0 & 3 & 0 \\ 0 & 3 & 0 & 0 \\ 0 & 3 & 3 & 0 \end{bmatrix}$

63. (a) One possible solution for a "L" is $A = \begin{bmatrix} 3 & 0 & 0 & 0 \\ 3 & 0 & 0 & 0 \\ 3 & 0 & 0 & 0 \\ 3 & 3 & 3 & 3 \end{bmatrix}$

(b) If $A$ is the matrix in part (a) then

$B = \begin{bmatrix} 3 & 3 & 3 & 3 \\ 3 & 3 & 3 & 3 \\ 3 & 3 & 3 & 3 \\ 3 & 3 & 3 & 3 \end{bmatrix}$ and $B - A = \begin{bmatrix} 3 & 3 & 3 & 3 \\ 3 & 3 & 3 & 3 \\ 3 & 3 & 3 & 3 \\ 3 & 3 & 3 & 3 \end{bmatrix} - \begin{bmatrix} 3 & 0 & 0 & 0 \\ 3 & 0 & 0 & 0 \\ 3 & 0 & 0 & 0 \\ 3 & 3 & 3 & 3 \end{bmatrix} = \begin{bmatrix} 0 & 3 & 3 & 3 \\ 0 & 3 & 3 & 3 \\ 0 & 3 & 3 & 3 \\ 0 & 0 & 0 & 0 \end{bmatrix}$

64. (a) One possible solution for a "O" is $A = \begin{bmatrix} 0 & 3 & 3 & 0 \\ 3 & 0 & 0 & 3 \\ 3 & 0 & 0 & 3 \\ 0 & 3 & 3 & 0 \end{bmatrix}$

(b) If $A$ is the matrix in part (a) then

$$B = \begin{bmatrix} 3 & 3 & 3 & 3 \\ 3 & 3 & 3 & 3 \\ 3 & 3 & 3 & 3 \\ 3 & 3 & 3 & 3 \end{bmatrix} \text{ and } B - A = \begin{bmatrix} 3 & 3 & 3 & 3 \\ 3 & 3 & 3 & 3 \\ 3 & 3 & 3 & 3 \\ 3 & 3 & 3 & 3 \end{bmatrix} - \begin{bmatrix} 0 & 3 & 3 & 0 \\ 3 & 0 & 0 & 3 \\ 3 & 0 & 0 & 3 \\ 0 & 3 & 3 & 0 \end{bmatrix} = \begin{bmatrix} 3 & 0 & 0 & 3 \\ 0 & 3 & 3 & 0 \\ 0 & 3 & 3 & 0 \\ 3 & 0 & 0 & 3 \end{bmatrix}$$

65. (a) These tables can be represented by the matrices $A$ and $B$ where $A = \begin{bmatrix} 12 & 4 \\ 8 & 7 \end{bmatrix}$ and $B = \begin{bmatrix} 55 \\ 70 \end{bmatrix}$.

(b) The product $AB$ of these matrices calculates tuition cost for each student.

$$AB = \begin{bmatrix} 12 & 4 \\ 8 & 7 \end{bmatrix}\begin{bmatrix} 55 \\ 70 \end{bmatrix} = \begin{bmatrix} 12(55) + 4(70) \\ 8(55) + 7(70) \end{bmatrix} = \begin{bmatrix} 940 \\ 930 \end{bmatrix}$$

Student 1 is taking 12 credits at \$55 each and 4 credits at \$70 each. The total tuition for student 1 is $12(\$55) + 4(\$70) = \$940$. Similarly, the tuition for student 2 is \$930.

66. (a) These tables can be represented by the matrices $A$ and $B$ where $A = \begin{bmatrix} 15 & 2 \\ 12 & 4 \end{bmatrix}$ and $B = \begin{bmatrix} 90 \\ 75 \end{bmatrix}$.

(b) The product $AB$ of these matrices calculates tuition cost for each student.

$$AB = \begin{bmatrix} 15 & 2 \\ 12 & 4 \end{bmatrix}\begin{bmatrix} 90 \\ 75 \end{bmatrix} = \begin{bmatrix} 15(90) + 2(75) \\ 12(90) + 4(75) \end{bmatrix} = \begin{bmatrix} 1500 \\ 1380 \end{bmatrix}$$

Student 1 is taking 15 credits at \$90 each and 2 credits at \$75 each. The total tuition for student 1 is $15(\$90) + 2(\$75) = \$1500$. Similarly, the tuition for student 2 is \$1380.

67. (a) These tables can be represented by the matrices $A$ and $B$ where $A = \begin{bmatrix} 10 & 5 \\ 9 & 8 \\ 11 & 3 \end{bmatrix}$ and $B = \begin{bmatrix} 60 \\ 70 \end{bmatrix}$.

(b) The product $AB$ of these matrices calculates tuition cost for each student.

$$AB = \begin{bmatrix} 10 & 5 \\ 9 & 8 \\ 11 & 3 \end{bmatrix}\begin{bmatrix} 60 \\ 70 \end{bmatrix} = \begin{bmatrix} 10(60) + 5(70) \\ 9(60) + 8(70) \\ 11(60) + 3(70) \end{bmatrix} = \begin{bmatrix} 950 \\ 1100 \\ 870 \end{bmatrix}$$

The total tuition for student 1 is $10(\$60) + 5(\$70) = \$950$. Similarly, the tuition for student 2 is \$1100 and the tuition for student 3 is \$870.

68. (a) These tables can be represented by the matrices $A$ and $B$ where $A = \begin{bmatrix} 6 & 0 & 3 \\ 11 & 3 & 0 \\ 0 & 12 & 3 \end{bmatrix}$ and $B = \begin{bmatrix} 50 \\ 65 \\ 60 \end{bmatrix}$.

(b) The product $AB$ of these matrices calculates tuition cost for each student.

$$AB = \begin{bmatrix} 6 & 0 & 3 \\ 11 & 3 & 0 \\ 0 & 12 & 3 \end{bmatrix}\begin{bmatrix} 50 \\ 65 \\ 60 \end{bmatrix} = \begin{bmatrix} 6(50) + 0(65) + 3(60) \\ 11(50) + 3(65) + 0(60) \\ 0(50) + 12(65) + 3(60) \end{bmatrix} = \begin{bmatrix} 480 \\ 745 \\ 960 \end{bmatrix}$$

The total tuition for student 1 is $6(\$50) + 0(\$65) + 3(\$60) = \$480$.

Similarly, the tuition for student 2 is \$745 and the tuition for student 3 is \$960.

69. $AB = \begin{bmatrix} 3 & 4 & 8 \\ 5 & 6 & 2 \end{bmatrix} \begin{bmatrix} 10 \\ 20 \\ 30 \end{bmatrix} = \begin{bmatrix} 350 \\ 230 \end{bmatrix}$; The total cost of Order 1 is $350, and the total cost of Order 2 is $230.

70. $AB = \begin{bmatrix} 1 & 3 & 8 & 4 \\ 3 & 5 & 7 & 0 \end{bmatrix} \begin{bmatrix} 15 \\ 21 \\ 28 \\ 38 \end{bmatrix} = \begin{bmatrix} 454 \\ 346 \end{bmatrix}$

Dealer 1 spent a total of $454,000 on the cars sold, and Dealer 2 spent a total of $346,000 on the cars sold.

## Extended and Discovery Exercises for Section 6.5

1. $\begin{bmatrix} C \\ M \\ Y \end{bmatrix} = \begin{bmatrix} 1 \\ 1 \\ 1 \end{bmatrix} - \begin{bmatrix} 0.631 \\ 1 \\ 0.933 \end{bmatrix} = \begin{bmatrix} 0.369 \\ 0 \\ 0.067 \end{bmatrix}$

   Aquamarine is represented by (0.369, 0, 0.067) in *CMY*.

2. $\begin{bmatrix} C \\ M \\ Y \end{bmatrix} = \begin{bmatrix} 1 \\ 1 \\ 1 \end{bmatrix} - \begin{bmatrix} 0.552 \\ 0.168 \\ 0.066 \end{bmatrix} = \begin{bmatrix} 0.448 \\ 0.832 \\ 0.934 \end{bmatrix}$

   Rust is represented by (0.448, 0.832, 0.934) in *CMY*. The color rust is created by 0.448 of cyan, 0.832 of magenta, and 0.934 of yellow.

3. $\begin{bmatrix} R \\ G \\ B \end{bmatrix} = \begin{bmatrix} 1 \\ 1 \\ 1 \end{bmatrix} - \begin{bmatrix} C \\ M \\ Y \end{bmatrix}$

4. $\begin{bmatrix} R \\ G \\ B \end{bmatrix} = \begin{bmatrix} 1 \\ 1 \\ 1 \end{bmatrix} - \begin{bmatrix} 0.012 \\ 0 \\ 0.597 \end{bmatrix} = \begin{bmatrix} 0.988 \\ 1 \\ 0.403 \end{bmatrix}$

   Cream is represented by (0.988, 1, 0.403) in *RGB*.

## 6.6 Inverses of Matrices

1. *B* is the inverse of *A*.

   $AB = \begin{bmatrix} 4 & 3 \\ 5 & 4 \end{bmatrix} \begin{bmatrix} 4 & -3 \\ -5 & 4 \end{bmatrix} = \begin{bmatrix} 1 & 0 \\ 0 & 1 \end{bmatrix}$ and $BA = \begin{bmatrix} 4 & -3 \\ -5 & 4 \end{bmatrix} \begin{bmatrix} 4 & 3 \\ 5 & 4 \end{bmatrix} = \begin{bmatrix} 1 & 0 \\ 0 & 1 \end{bmatrix}$

2. *B* is not the inverse of *A*.

   $AB = \begin{bmatrix} -1 & 2 \\ -3 & 8 \end{bmatrix} \begin{bmatrix} -4 & 1 \\ -2 & 0.5 \end{bmatrix} = \begin{bmatrix} 0 & 0 \\ -4 & 1 \end{bmatrix}$ and $BA = \begin{bmatrix} -4 & 1 \\ -2 & 0.5 \end{bmatrix} \begin{bmatrix} -1 & 2 \\ -3 & 8 \end{bmatrix} = \begin{bmatrix} 1 & 0 \\ 0.5 & 0 \end{bmatrix}$

3. $B$ is the inverse of $A$.

$$AB = \begin{bmatrix} 1 & -1 & 2 \\ 0 & 1 & -1 \\ 1 & 0 & 2 \end{bmatrix}\begin{bmatrix} 2 & 2 & -1 \\ -1 & 0 & 1 \\ -1 & -1 & 1 \end{bmatrix} = \begin{bmatrix} 1 & 0 & 0 \\ 0 & 1 & 0 \\ 0 & 0 & 1 \end{bmatrix};$$

$$BA = \begin{bmatrix} 2 & 2 & -1 \\ -1 & 0 & 1 \\ -1 & -1 & 1 \end{bmatrix}\begin{bmatrix} 1 & -1 & 2 \\ 0 & 1 & -1 \\ 1 & 0 & 2 \end{bmatrix} = \begin{bmatrix} 1 & 0 & 0 \\ 0 & 1 & 0 \\ 0 & 0 & 1 \end{bmatrix}$$

4. $B$ is the inverse of $A$.

$$AB = \begin{bmatrix} 2 & 1 & 1 \\ -1 & 0 & -1 \\ 0 & 2 & -1 \end{bmatrix}\begin{bmatrix} 2 & 3 & -1 \\ -1 & -2 & 1 \\ -2 & -4 & 1 \end{bmatrix} = \begin{bmatrix} 1 & 0 & 0 \\ 0 & 1 & 0 \\ 0 & 0 & 1 \end{bmatrix};$$

$$BA = \begin{bmatrix} 2 & 3 & -1 \\ -1 & -2 & 1 \\ -2 & -4 & 1 \end{bmatrix}\begin{bmatrix} 2 & 1 & 1 \\ -1 & 0 & -1 \\ 0 & 2 & -1 \end{bmatrix} = \begin{bmatrix} 1 & 0 & 0 \\ 0 & 1 & 0 \\ 0 & 0 & 1 \end{bmatrix}$$

5. $B$ is not the inverse of $A$.

$$AB = \begin{bmatrix} 2 & 1 & -1 \\ 3 & 0 & 2 \\ -1 & 0 & 1 \end{bmatrix}\begin{bmatrix} 0 & 1 & -2 \\ 1 & -3 & 7 \\ 0 & -1 & 3 \end{bmatrix} = \begin{bmatrix} 1 & 0 & 0 \\ 0 & 1 & 0 \\ 0 & -2 & 5 \end{bmatrix};$$

$$BA = \begin{bmatrix} 0 & 1 & -2 \\ 1 & -3 & 7 \\ 0 & -1 & 3 \end{bmatrix}\begin{bmatrix} 2 & 1 & -1 \\ 3 & 0 & 2 \\ -1 & 0 & 1 \end{bmatrix} = \begin{bmatrix} 5 & 0 & 0 \\ -14 & 1 & 0 \\ -6 & 0 & 1 \end{bmatrix}$$

6. $B$ is the inverse of $A$.

$$AB = \begin{bmatrix} 1 & -1 & 1 \\ 0 & 1 & 0 \\ 1 & 1 & 2 \end{bmatrix}\begin{bmatrix} 2 & 3 & -1 \\ 0 & 1 & 0 \\ -1 & -2 & 1 \end{bmatrix} = \begin{bmatrix} 1 & 0 & 0 \\ 0 & 1 & 0 \\ 0 & 0 & 1 \end{bmatrix};$$

$$BA = \begin{bmatrix} 2 & 3 & -1 \\ 0 & 1 & 0 \\ -1 & -2 & 1 \end{bmatrix}\begin{bmatrix} 1 & -1 & 1 \\ 0 & 1 & 0 \\ 1 & 1 & 2 \end{bmatrix} = \begin{bmatrix} 1 & 0 & 0 \\ 0 & 1 & 0 \\ 0 & 0 & 1 \end{bmatrix}$$

7. $AA^{-1} = \begin{bmatrix} 1 & 1 \\ 1 & 2 \end{bmatrix}\begin{bmatrix} 2 & -1 \\ -1 & k \end{bmatrix} = \begin{bmatrix} 1 & -1 + k \\ 0 & 2k - 1 \end{bmatrix}$

We must have $-1 + k = 0$ and $2k - 1 = 1$. The solution to both equations is $k = 1$.

8. $AA^{-1} = \begin{bmatrix} -2 & 2 \\ 1 & -2 \end{bmatrix}\begin{bmatrix} -1 & k \\ -0.5 & -1 \end{bmatrix} = \begin{bmatrix} 1 & -2k - 2 \\ 0 & k + 2 \end{bmatrix}$

We must have $-2k - 2 = 0$ and $k + 2 = 1$. The solution to both equations is $k = -1$.

9. $AA^{-1} = \begin{bmatrix} 1 & 3 \\ -1 & -5 \end{bmatrix}\begin{bmatrix} k & 1.5 \\ -0.5 & -0.5 \end{bmatrix} = \begin{bmatrix} k - 1.5 & 0 \\ -k + 2.5 & 1 \end{bmatrix}$

We must have $k - 1.5 = 1$ and $-k + 2.5 = 0$. The solution to both equations is $k = 2.5$.

10. $AA^{-1} = \begin{bmatrix} -2 & 5 \\ -3 & 4 \end{bmatrix}\begin{bmatrix} \frac{4}{7} & -\frac{5}{7} \\ k & -\frac{2}{7} \end{bmatrix} = \begin{bmatrix} -\frac{8}{7} + 5k & 0 \\ -\frac{12}{7} + 4k & 1 \end{bmatrix}$

We must have $-\dfrac{8}{7} + 5k = 1$ and $-\dfrac{12}{7} + 4k = 0$. The solution to both equations is $k = \dfrac{3}{7}$.

11. $I_2$ multiplied by any $2 \times 2$ matrix $A$ is equal to $A$, that is, $I_2A = AI_2 = A$.

12. $I_3$ multiplied by any $3 \times 3$ matrix $A$ is equal to $A$, that is, $I_3A = AI_3 = A$.

13. $I_3$ multiplied by any $3 \times 3$ matrix $A$ is equal to $A$, that is, $I_3A = AI_3 = A$.

14. $I_4$ multiplied by any $4 \times 4$ matrix $A$ is equal to $A$, that is, $I_4A = AI_4 = A$.

15. $A\,|\,I_2 = \left[\begin{array}{cc|cc} 1 & 2 & 1 & 0 \\ 1 & 3 & 0 & 1 \end{array}\right] \begin{array}{l} \\ R_2 - R_1 \to \end{array} \left[\begin{array}{cc|cc} 1 & 2 & 1 & 0 \\ 0 & 1 & -1 & 1 \end{array}\right] \begin{array}{l} R_1 - 2R_2 \to \\ \end{array} \left[\begin{array}{cc|cc} 1 & 0 & 3 & -2 \\ 0 & 1 & -1 & 1 \end{array}\right];\ A^{-1} = \begin{bmatrix} 3 & -2 \\ -1 & 1 \end{bmatrix}$

16. $A\,|\,I_2 = \left[\begin{array}{cc|cc} 1 & 0 & 1 & 0 \\ 1 & -1 & 0 & 1 \end{array}\right] \begin{array}{l} \\ R_2 - R_1 \to \end{array} \left[\begin{array}{cc|cc} 1 & 0 & 1 & 0 \\ 0 & -1 & -1 & 1 \end{array}\right] \begin{array}{l} \\ -1R_2 \to \end{array} \left[\begin{array}{cc|cc} 1 & 0 & 1 & 0 \\ 0 & 1 & 1 & -1 \end{array}\right];\ A^{-1} = \begin{bmatrix} 1 & 0 \\ 1 & -1 \end{bmatrix}$

17. $A\,|\,I_2 = \left[\begin{array}{cc|cc} -1 & 2 & 1 & 0 \\ 3 & -5 & 0 & 1 \end{array}\right] \begin{array}{l} -1R_1 \to \\ \end{array} \left[\begin{array}{cc|cc} 1 & -2 & -1 & 0 \\ 3 & -5 & 0 & 1 \end{array}\right] \begin{array}{l} \\ R_2 - 3R_1 \to \end{array} \left[\begin{array}{cc|cc} 1 & -2 & -1 & 0 \\ 0 & 1 & 3 & 1 \end{array}\right]$

$R_1 + 2R_2 \to \left[\begin{array}{cc|cc} 1 & 0 & 5 & 2 \\ 0 & 1 & 3 & 1 \end{array}\right];\ A^{-1} = \begin{bmatrix} 5 & 2 \\ 3 & 1 \end{bmatrix}$

18. $A\,|\,I_2 = \left[\begin{array}{cc|cc} 1 & 3 & 1 & 0 \\ 2 & 5 & 0 & 1 \end{array}\right] \begin{array}{l} \\ R_2 - 2R_1 \to \end{array} \left[\begin{array}{cc|cc} 1 & 3 & 1 & 0 \\ 0 & -1 & -2 & 1 \end{array}\right] \begin{array}{l} \\ -1R_2 \to \end{array} \left[\begin{array}{cc|cc} 1 & 3 & 1 & 0 \\ 0 & 1 & 2 & -1 \end{array}\right]$

$R_1 - 3R_2 \to \left[\begin{array}{cc|cc} 1 & 0 & -5 & 3 \\ 0 & 1 & 2 & -1 \end{array}\right];\ A^{-1} = \begin{bmatrix} -5 & 3 \\ 2 & -1 \end{bmatrix}$

19. $A\,|\,I_2 = \left[\begin{array}{cc|cc} 8 & 5 & 1 & 0 \\ 2 & 1 & 0 & 1 \end{array}\right] \begin{array}{l} (1/8)R_1 \to \\ R_1 - 4R_2 \to \end{array} \left[\begin{array}{cc|cc} 1 & \frac{5}{8} & \frac{1}{8} & 0 \\ 0 & 1 & 1 & -4 \end{array}\right] \begin{array}{l} (-5/8)R_2 + R_1 \to \\ \end{array} \left[\begin{array}{cc|cc} 1 & 0 & -\frac{1}{2} & \frac{5}{2} \\ 0 & 1 & 1 & -4 \end{array}\right];$

$A^{-1} = \begin{bmatrix} -\frac{1}{2} & \frac{5}{2} \\ 1 & -4 \end{bmatrix}$

20. $A\,|\,I_2 = \left[\begin{array}{cc|cc} -2 & 4 & 1 & 0 \\ -5 & 9 & 0 & 1 \end{array}\right] \begin{array}{l} (-1/2)R_1 \to \\ 5R_1 - 2R_2 \to \end{array} \left[\begin{array}{cc|cc} 1 & -2 & -\frac{1}{2} & 0 \\ 0 & 2 & 5 & -2 \end{array}\right] \begin{array}{l} \\ (1/2)R_2 \to \end{array} \left[\begin{array}{cc|cc} 1 & -2 & -\frac{1}{2} & 0 \\ 0 & 1 & \frac{5}{2} & -1 \end{array}\right]$

$2R_2 + R_1 \to \left[\begin{array}{cc|cc} 1 & 0 & \frac{9}{2} & -2 \\ 0 & 1 & \frac{5}{2} & -1 \end{array}\right];\ A^{-1} = \begin{bmatrix} \frac{9}{2} & -2 \\ \frac{5}{2} & -1 \end{bmatrix}$

21. $A\,|\,I_3 = \left[\begin{array}{ccc|ccc} 0 & 0 & 1 & 1 & 0 & 0 \\ 1 & 0 & 0 & 0 & 1 & 0 \\ 0 & 1 & 0 & 0 & 0 & 1 \end{array}\right] \begin{array}{l} R_2 \to \\ R_3 \to \\ R_1 \to \end{array} \left[\begin{array}{ccc|ccc} 1 & 0 & 0 & 0 & 1 & 0 \\ 0 & 1 & 0 & 0 & 0 & 1 \\ 0 & 0 & 1 & 1 & 0 & 0 \end{array}\right];\ A^{-1} = \begin{bmatrix} 0 & 1 & 0 \\ 0 & 0 & 1 \\ 1 & 0 & 0 \end{bmatrix}$

22. $A\,|\,I_3 = \left[\begin{array}{ccc|ccc} 1 & 0 & 0 & 1 & 0 & 0 \\ 1 & 1 & 0 & 0 & 1 & 0 \\ 0 & 1 & 1 & 0 & 0 & 1 \end{array}\right] \begin{array}{l} \\ R_2 - R_1 \to \\ \end{array} \left[\begin{array}{ccc|ccc} 1 & 0 & 0 & 1 & 0 & 0 \\ 0 & 1 & 0 & -1 & 1 & 0 \\ 0 & 1 & 1 & 0 & 0 & 1 \end{array}\right]$

$\begin{array}{l} \\ \\ R_3 - R_2 \to \end{array} \left[\begin{array}{ccc|ccc} 1 & 0 & 0 & 1 & 0 & 0 \\ 0 & 1 & 0 & -1 & 1 & 0 \\ 0 & 0 & 1 & 1 & -1 & 1 \end{array}\right];\ A^{-1} = \begin{bmatrix} 1 & 0 & 0 \\ -1 & 1 & 0 \\ 1 & -1 & 1 \end{bmatrix}$

23. $A\,|\,I_3 = \left[\begin{array}{ccc|ccc} 1 & 0 & 1 & 1 & 0 & 0 \\ 2 & 1 & 3 & 0 & 1 & 0 \\ -1 & 1 & 1 & 0 & 0 & 1 \end{array}\right] \begin{array}{l} \\ R_2 - 2R_1 \to \\ R_3 + R_1 \to \end{array} \left[\begin{array}{ccc|ccc} 1 & 0 & 1 & 1 & 0 & 0 \\ 0 & 1 & 1 & -2 & 1 & 0 \\ 0 & 1 & 2 & 1 & 0 & 1 \end{array}\right] \begin{array}{l} \\ \\ R_3 - R_2 \to \end{array}$

$\left[\begin{array}{ccc|ccc} 1 & 0 & 1 & 1 & 0 & 0 \\ 0 & 1 & 1 & -2 & 1 & 0 \\ 0 & 0 & 1 & 3 & -1 & 1 \end{array}\right] \begin{array}{l} R_1 - R_3 \to \\ R_2 - R_3 \to \\ \end{array} \left[\begin{array}{ccc|ccc} 1 & 0 & 0 & -2 & 1 & -1 \\ 0 & 1 & 0 & -5 & 2 & -1 \\ 0 & 0 & 1 & 3 & -1 & 1 \end{array}\right];\ A^{-1} = \begin{bmatrix} -2 & 1 & -1 \\ -5 & 2 & -1 \\ 3 & -1 & 1 \end{bmatrix}$

24. $$A|I_3 = \left[\begin{array}{ccc|ccc} -2 & 1 & 0 & 1 & 0 & 0 \\ 1 & 0 & 1 & 0 & 1 & 0 \\ -1 & 1 & 0 & 0 & 0 & 1 \end{array}\right] \begin{array}{r} R_2 \rightarrow \\ R_1 \rightarrow \\ \phantom{x} \end{array} \left[\begin{array}{ccc|ccc} 1 & 0 & 1 & 0 & 1 & 0 \\ -2 & 1 & 0 & 1 & 0 & 0 \\ -1 & 1 & 0 & 0 & 0 & 1 \end{array}\right] \begin{array}{r} \phantom{x} \\ R_2 + 2R_1 \rightarrow \\ R_3 + R_1 \rightarrow \end{array} \left[\begin{array}{ccc|ccc} 1 & 0 & 1 & 0 & 1 & 0 \\ 0 & 1 & 2 & 1 & 2 & 0 \\ 0 & 1 & 1 & 0 & 1 & 1 \end{array}\right]$$

$$\begin{array}{r} \phantom{x} \\ \phantom{x} \\ R_3 - R_2 \rightarrow \end{array} \left[\begin{array}{ccc|ccc} 1 & 0 & 1 & 0 & 1 & 0 \\ 0 & 1 & 2 & 1 & 2 & 0 \\ 0 & 0 & -1 & -1 & -1 & 1 \end{array}\right] \begin{array}{r} \phantom{x} \\ \phantom{x} \\ -1R_3 \rightarrow \end{array} \left[\begin{array}{ccc|ccc} 1 & 0 & 1 & 0 & 1 & 0 \\ 0 & 1 & 2 & 1 & 2 & 0 \\ 0 & 0 & 1 & 1 & 1 & -1 \end{array}\right]$$

$$\begin{array}{r} R_1 - R_3 \rightarrow \\ R_2 - 2R_3 \rightarrow \\ \phantom{x} \end{array} \left[\begin{array}{ccc|ccc} 1 & 0 & 0 & -1 & 0 & 1 \\ 0 & 1 & 0 & -1 & 0 & 2 \\ 0 & 0 & 1 & 1 & 1 & -1 \end{array}\right]; \quad A^{-1} = \begin{bmatrix} -1 & 0 & 1 \\ -1 & 0 & 2 \\ 1 & 1 & -1 \end{bmatrix}$$

25. $$\left[\begin{array}{ccc|ccc} 1 & 2 & -1 & 1 & 0 & 0 \\ 2 & 5 & 0 & 0 & 1 & 0 \\ -1 & -1 & 2 & 0 & 0 & 1 \end{array}\right] \begin{array}{r} \phantom{x} \\ 2R_1 - R_2 \rightarrow \\ R_3 + R_1 \rightarrow \end{array} \left[\begin{array}{ccc|ccc} 1 & 2 & -1 & 1 & 0 & 0 \\ 0 & -1 & -2 & 2 & -1 & 0 \\ 0 & 1 & 1 & 1 & 0 & 1 \end{array}\right]$$

$$\begin{array}{r} \phantom{x} \\ (-1)R_2 \rightarrow \\ R_2 + R_3 \rightarrow \end{array} \left[\begin{array}{ccc|ccc} 1 & 2 & -1 & 1 & 0 & 0 \\ 0 & 1 & 2 & -2 & 1 & 0 \\ 0 & 0 & -1 & 3 & -1 & 1 \end{array}\right] \begin{array}{r} R_1 - R_3 \rightarrow \\ 2R_3 + R_2 \rightarrow \\ (-1)R_3 \rightarrow \end{array} \left[\begin{array}{ccc|ccc} 1 & 2 & 0 & -2 & 1 & -1 \\ 0 & 1 & 0 & 4 & -1 & 2 \\ 0 & 0 & 1 & -3 & 1 & -1 \end{array}\right]$$

$$\begin{array}{r} R_1 - 2R_2 \rightarrow \\ \phantom{x} \\ \phantom{x} \end{array} \left[\begin{array}{ccc|ccc} 1 & 0 & 0 & -10 & 3 & -5 \\ 0 & 1 & 0 & 4 & -1 & 2 \\ 0 & 0 & 1 & -3 & 1 & -1 \end{array}\right]; \quad A^{-1} = \begin{bmatrix} -10 & 3 & -5 \\ 4 & -1 & 2 \\ -3 & 1 & -1 \end{bmatrix}$$

26. $$\left[\begin{array}{ccc|ccc} 2 & -2 & 1 & 1 & 0 & 0 \\ 1 & 3 & 2 & 0 & 1 & 0 \\ 4 & -2 & 4 & 0 & 0 & 1 \end{array}\right] \begin{array}{r} (1/2)R_1 \rightarrow \\ R_1 - 2R_2 \rightarrow \\ 2R_1 - R_3 \rightarrow \end{array} \left[\begin{array}{ccc|ccc} 1 & -1 & \frac{1}{2} & \frac{1}{2} & 0 & 0 \\ 0 & -8 & -3 & 1 & -2 & 0 \\ 0 & -2 & -2 & 2 & 0 & -1 \end{array}\right]$$

$$\begin{array}{r} \phantom{x} \\ (-1/8)R_2 \rightarrow \\ R_2 - 4R_3 \rightarrow \end{array} \left[\begin{array}{ccc|ccc} 1 & -1 & \frac{1}{2} & \frac{1}{2} & 0 & 0 \\ 0 & 1 & \frac{3}{8} & -\frac{1}{8} & \frac{1}{4} & 0 \\ 0 & 0 & 5 & -7 & -2 & 4 \end{array}\right]$$

$$\begin{array}{r} \phantom{x} \\ \phantom{x} \\ (1/5)R_3 \rightarrow \end{array} \left[\begin{array}{ccc|ccc} 1 & -1 & \frac{1}{2} & \frac{1}{2} & 0 & 0 \\ 0 & 1 & \frac{3}{8} & -\frac{1}{8} & \frac{1}{4} & 0 \\ 0 & 0 & 1 & -\frac{7}{5} & -\frac{2}{5} & \frac{4}{5} \end{array}\right] \begin{array}{r} (-1/2)R_3 + R_1 \rightarrow \\ (-3/8)R_3 + R_2 \rightarrow \\ \phantom{x} \end{array} \left[\begin{array}{ccc|ccc} 1 & -1 & 0 & \frac{6}{5} & \frac{1}{5} & -\frac{2}{5} \\ 0 & 1 & 0 & \frac{2}{5} & \frac{2}{5} & -\frac{3}{10} \\ 0 & 0 & 1 & -\frac{7}{5} & -\frac{2}{5} & \frac{4}{5} \end{array}\right]$$

$$\begin{array}{r} R_1 + R_2 \rightarrow \\ \phantom{x} \\ \phantom{x} \end{array} \left[\begin{array}{ccc|ccc} 1 & 0 & 0 & \frac{8}{5} & \frac{3}{5} & -\frac{7}{10} \\ 0 & 1 & 0 & \frac{2}{5} & \frac{2}{5} & -\frac{3}{10} \\ 0 & 0 & 1 & -\frac{7}{5} & -\frac{2}{5} & \frac{4}{5} \end{array}\right]; \quad A^{-1} = \begin{bmatrix} \frac{8}{5} & \frac{3}{5} & -\frac{7}{10} \\ \frac{2}{5} & \frac{2}{5} & -\frac{3}{10} \\ -\frac{7}{5} & -\frac{2}{5} & \frac{4}{5} \end{bmatrix}$$

27. $\left[\begin{array}{ccc|ccc} -2 & 1 & -3 & 1 & 0 & 0 \\ 0 & 1 & 2 & 0 & 1 & 0 \\ 1 & -2 & 1 & 0 & 0 & 1 \end{array}\right] \begin{array}{l} (-1/2)R_1 \to \\ \\ 2R_3 + R_1 \to \end{array} \left[\begin{array}{ccc|ccc} 1 & -\frac{1}{2} & \frac{3}{2} & -\frac{1}{2} & 0 & 0 \\ 0 & 1 & 2 & 0 & 1 & 0 \\ 0 & -3 & -1 & 1 & 0 & 2 \end{array}\right]$

$3R_2 + R_3 \to \left[\begin{array}{ccc|ccc} 1 & -\frac{1}{2} & \frac{3}{2} & -\frac{1}{2} & 0 & 0 \\ 0 & 1 & 2 & 0 & 1 & 0 \\ 0 & 0 & 5 & 1 & 3 & 2 \end{array}\right] (1/5)R_3 \to \left[\begin{array}{ccc|ccc} 1 & -\frac{1}{2} & \frac{3}{2} & -\frac{1}{2} & 0 & 0 \\ 0 & 1 & 2 & 0 & 1 & 0 \\ 0 & 0 & 1 & \frac{1}{5} & \frac{3}{5} & \frac{2}{5} \end{array}\right]$

$\begin{array}{r} R_1 - (3/2)R_3 \to \\ (-2)R_3 + R_2 \to \\ \\ \end{array} \left[\begin{array}{ccc|ccc} 1 & -\frac{1}{2} & 0 & -\frac{4}{5} & -\frac{9}{10} & -\frac{3}{5} \\ 0 & 1 & 0 & -\frac{2}{5} & -\frac{1}{5} & -\frac{4}{5} \\ 0 & 0 & 1 & \frac{1}{5} & \frac{3}{5} & \frac{2}{5} \end{array}\right] R_1 + (1/2)R_2 \to \left[\begin{array}{ccc|ccc} 1 & 0 & 0 & -1 & -1 & -1 \\ 0 & 1 & 0 & -\frac{2}{5} & -\frac{1}{5} & -\frac{4}{5} \\ 0 & 0 & 1 & \frac{1}{5} & \frac{3}{5} & \frac{2}{5} \end{array}\right];$

$A^{-1} = \begin{bmatrix} -1 & -1 & -1 \\ -\frac{2}{5} & -\frac{1}{5} & -\frac{4}{5} \\ \frac{1}{5} & \frac{3}{5} & \frac{2}{5} \end{bmatrix}$

28. $\left[\begin{array}{ccc|ccc} 1 & -1 & 1 & 1 & 0 & 0 \\ -1 & 2 & 1 & 0 & 1 & 0 \\ 0 & 2 & 1 & 0 & 0 & 1 \end{array}\right] R_1 + R_2 \to \left[\begin{array}{ccc|ccc} 1 & -1 & 1 & 1 & 0 & 0 \\ 0 & 1 & 2 & 1 & 1 & 0 \\ 0 & 2 & 1 & 0 & 0 & 1 \end{array}\right]$

$R_3 - 2R_2 \to \left[\begin{array}{ccc|ccc} 1 & -1 & 1 & 1 & 0 & 0 \\ 0 & 1 & 2 & 1 & 1 & 0 \\ 0 & 0 & -3 & -2 & -2 & 1 \end{array}\right] (-1/3)R_3 \to \left[\begin{array}{ccc|ccc} 1 & -1 & 1 & 1 & 0 & 0 \\ 0 & 1 & 2 & 1 & 1 & 0 \\ 0 & 0 & 1 & \frac{2}{3} & \frac{2}{3} & -\frac{1}{3} \end{array}\right]$

$\begin{array}{r} R_1 - R_3 \to \\ (-2)R_3 + R_2 \to \\ \\ \end{array} \left[\begin{array}{ccc|ccc} 1 & -1 & 0 & \frac{1}{3} & -\frac{2}{3} & \frac{1}{3} \\ 0 & 1 & 0 & -\frac{1}{3} & -\frac{1}{3} & \frac{2}{3} \\ 0 & 0 & 1 & \frac{2}{3} & \frac{2}{3} & -\frac{1}{3} \end{array}\right] R_1 + R_2 \to \left[\begin{array}{ccc|ccc} 1 & 0 & 0 & 0 & -1 & 1 \\ 0 & 1 & 0 & -\frac{1}{3} & -\frac{1}{3} & \frac{2}{3} \\ 0 & 0 & 1 & \frac{2}{3} & \frac{2}{3} & -\frac{1}{3} \end{array}\right];$

$A^{-1} = \begin{bmatrix} 0 & -1 & 1 \\ -\frac{1}{3} & -\frac{1}{3} & \frac{2}{3} \\ \frac{2}{3} & \frac{2}{3} & -\frac{1}{3} \end{bmatrix}$

29. $A = \begin{bmatrix} 0.5 & -1.5 \\ 0.2 & -0.5 \end{bmatrix} \Rightarrow A^{-1} = \begin{bmatrix} -10 & 30 \\ -4 & 10 \end{bmatrix}$ as shown in Figure 29.

30. $A = \begin{bmatrix} -0.5 & 0.5 \\ 3 & 2 \end{bmatrix} \Rightarrow A^{-1} = \begin{bmatrix} -0.8 & 0.2 \\ 1.2 & 0.2 \end{bmatrix}$ as shown in Figure 30.

```
[A]-1
      [[-10 30]
       [-4  10]]
```

Figure 29

```
[A]-1
      [[-.8 .2]
       [1.2 .2]]
```

Figure 30

```
[A]-1
 [[.2  0  .4  ]
  [.4  0  -.2 ]
  [1.4 -1 -1.2]]
```

Figure 31

```
[A]-1
 [[-.2 .2 -.4]
  [-.1 .1 -.7]
  [.6  .4 -.8]]
```

Figure 32

31. $A = \begin{bmatrix} 1 & 2 & 0 \\ -1 & 4 & -1 \\ 2 & -1 & 0 \end{bmatrix} \Rightarrow A^{-1} = \begin{bmatrix} 0.2 & 0 & 0.4 \\ 0.4 & 0 & -0.2 \\ 1.4 & -1 & -1.2 \end{bmatrix}$ as shown in Figure 31.

32. $A = \begin{bmatrix} -2 & 0 & 1 \\ 5 & -4 & 1 \\ 1 & -2 & 0 \end{bmatrix} \Rightarrow A^{-1} = \begin{bmatrix} -0.2 & 0.2 & -0.4 \\ -0.1 & 0.1 & -0.7 \\ 0.6 & 0.4 & -0.8 \end{bmatrix}$ as shown in Figure 32.

33. $A = \begin{bmatrix} 2 & -2 & 1 \\ 0 & 5 & 8 \\ 0 & 0 & -1 \end{bmatrix} \Rightarrow A^{-1} = \begin{bmatrix} 0.5 & 0.2 & 2.1 \\ 0 & 0.2 & 1.6 \\ 0 & 0 & -1 \end{bmatrix}$ as shown in Figure 33.

34. $A = \begin{bmatrix} 2 & 0 & 2 \\ 1 & 5 & 0 \\ -1 & 0 & 2 \end{bmatrix} \Rightarrow A^{-1} = \begin{bmatrix} \frac{1}{3} & 0 & -\frac{1}{3} \\ -\frac{1}{15} & \frac{1}{5} & \frac{1}{15} \\ \frac{1}{6} & 0 & \frac{1}{3} \end{bmatrix}$ as shown in Figure 34.

```
[A]-1
  [[.5 .2 2.1]
   [0  .2 1.6]
   [0  0   -1 ]]
```

Figure 33

```
[A]-1▸Frac
[[1/3   0      -1/…
 [-1/15 1/5  1/1…
 [1/6   0      1/3…
```

Figure 34

```
[A]-1
 [[.5  .25 .25]
  [.25 .5  .25]
  [.25 .25 .5 ]]
```

Figure 35

```
[A]-1▸Frac
[[6/11    -2/11 …
 [-9/11   3/11  …
 [-28/11 13/11  …
```

Figure 36

35. $A = \begin{bmatrix} 3 & -1 & -1 \\ -1 & 3 & -1 \\ -1 & -1 & 3 \end{bmatrix} \Rightarrow A^{-1} = \begin{bmatrix} 0.5 & 0.25 & 0.25 \\ 0.25 & 0.5 & 0.25 \\ 0.25 & 0.25 & 0.5 \end{bmatrix}$ as shown in Figure 35.

36. $A = \begin{bmatrix} 2 & -3 & 1 \\ 5 & -6 & 3 \\ 3 & 2 & 0 \end{bmatrix} \Rightarrow A^{-1} = \begin{bmatrix} \frac{6}{11} & -\frac{2}{11} & \frac{3}{11} \\ -\frac{9}{11} & \frac{3}{11} & \frac{1}{11} \\ -\frac{28}{11} & \frac{13}{11} & -\frac{3}{11} \end{bmatrix}$ as shown in Figure 36.

37. $A = \begin{bmatrix} 1 & -1 & 0 & 0 \\ -1 & 5 & -1 & 0 \\ 0 & -1 & 5 & -1 \\ 0 & 0 & -1 & 1 \end{bmatrix} \Rightarrow A^{-1} = \begin{bmatrix} 1.2\overline{6} & 0.2\overline{6} & 0.0\overline{6} & 0.0\overline{6} \\ 0.2\overline{6} & 0.2\overline{6} & 0.0\overline{6} & 0.0\overline{6} \\ 0.0\overline{6} & 0.0\overline{6} & 0.2\overline{6} & 0.2\overline{6} \\ 0.0\overline{6} & 0.0\overline{6} & 0.2\overline{6} & 1.2\overline{6} \end{bmatrix}$ as shown in Figure 37.

```
[A]-1
[[1.266666667 .…
 [.2666666667 .…
 [.0666666667 .…
 [.0666666667 .…
```

Figure 37

```
[A]-1
[[.3818181818  …
 [-.1454545455 …
 [.0545454545  …
 [-.0181818182 …
```

Figure 38

38. $A = \begin{bmatrix} 3 & 1 & 0 & 0 \\ 1 & 3 & 1 & 0 \\ 0 & 1 & 3 & 1 \\ 0 & 0 & 1 & 3 \end{bmatrix} \Rightarrow A^{-1} = \begin{bmatrix} 0.3\overline{81} & -0.1\overline{45} & 0.0\overline{54} & -0.0\overline{18} \\ -0.1\overline{45} & 0.4\overline{36} & -0.1\overline{63} & 0.0\overline{54} \\ 0.0\overline{54} & -0.1\overline{63} & 0.4\overline{36} & -0.1\overline{45} \\ -0.0\overline{18} & 0.0\overline{54} & -0.1\overline{45} & 0.3\overline{81} \end{bmatrix}$ as shown in Figure 38.

39. $\begin{aligned} 2x - 3y &= 7 \\ -3x - 4y &= 9 \end{aligned} \Rightarrow AX = \begin{bmatrix} 2 & -3 \\ -3 & -4 \end{bmatrix}\begin{bmatrix} x \\ y \end{bmatrix} = \begin{bmatrix} 7 \\ 9 \end{bmatrix} = B$

40. $\begin{aligned} -x + 3y &= 10 \\ 2x - 6y &= -1 \end{aligned} \Rightarrow AX = \begin{bmatrix} -1 & 3 \\ 2 & -6 \end{bmatrix}\begin{bmatrix} x \\ y \end{bmatrix} = \begin{bmatrix} 10 \\ -1 \end{bmatrix} = B$

41. $\begin{aligned} \tfrac{1}{2}x - \tfrac{3}{2}y &= \tfrac{1}{4} \\ -x + 2y &= 5 \end{aligned} \Rightarrow AX = \begin{bmatrix} \frac{1}{2} & -\frac{3}{2} \\ -1 & 2 \end{bmatrix}\begin{bmatrix} x \\ y \end{bmatrix} = \begin{bmatrix} \frac{1}{4} \\ 5 \end{bmatrix} = B$

42. $\begin{aligned} -1.1x + 3.2y &= -2.7 \\ 5.6x - 3.8y &= -3.0 \end{aligned} \Rightarrow AX = \begin{bmatrix} -1.1 & 3.2 \\ 5.6 & -3.8 \end{bmatrix} \begin{bmatrix} x \\ y \end{bmatrix} = \begin{bmatrix} -2.7 \\ -3.0 \end{bmatrix} = B$

43. $\begin{aligned} x - 2y + z &= 5 \\ 3y - z &= 6 \\ 5x - 4y - 7z &= 0 \end{aligned} \Rightarrow AX = \begin{bmatrix} 1 & -2 & 1 \\ 0 & 3 & -1 \\ 5 & -4 & -7 \end{bmatrix} \begin{bmatrix} x \\ y \\ z \end{bmatrix} = \begin{bmatrix} 5 \\ 6 \\ 0 \end{bmatrix} = B$

44. $\begin{aligned} 4x - 3y + 2z &= 8 \\ -x + 4y + 3z &= 2 \\ -2x - 5z &= 2 \end{aligned} \Rightarrow AX = \begin{bmatrix} 4 & -3 & 2 \\ -1 & 4 & 3 \\ -2 & 0 & -5 \end{bmatrix} \begin{bmatrix} x \\ y \\ z \end{bmatrix} = \begin{bmatrix} 8 \\ 2 \\ 2 \end{bmatrix} = B$

45. $\begin{aligned} 4x - y + 3z &= -2 \\ x + 2y + 5z &= 11 \\ 2x - 3y &= -1 \end{aligned} \Rightarrow AX = \begin{bmatrix} 4 & -1 & 3 \\ 1 & 2 & 5 \\ 2 & -3 & 0 \end{bmatrix} \begin{bmatrix} x \\ y \\ z \end{bmatrix} = \begin{bmatrix} -2 \\ 11 \\ -1 \end{bmatrix} = B$

46. $\begin{aligned} x - 2y + z &= 12 \\ 4y + 3z &= 13 \\ -2x + 7y &= -2 \end{aligned} \Rightarrow AX = \begin{bmatrix} 1 & -2 & 1 \\ 0 & 4 & 3 \\ -2 & 7 & 0 \end{bmatrix} \begin{bmatrix} x \\ y \\ z \end{bmatrix} = \begin{bmatrix} 12 \\ 13 \\ -2 \end{bmatrix} = B$

47. (a) $\begin{aligned} x + 2y &= 3 \\ x + 3y &= 6 \end{aligned} \Rightarrow AX = \begin{bmatrix} 1 & 2 \\ 1 & 3 \end{bmatrix} \begin{bmatrix} x \\ y \end{bmatrix} = \begin{bmatrix} 3 \\ 6 \end{bmatrix} = B$

(b) If $AX = B \Rightarrow \begin{bmatrix} 1 & 2 \\ 1 & 3 \end{bmatrix} \begin{bmatrix} x \\ y \end{bmatrix} = \begin{bmatrix} 3 \\ 6 \end{bmatrix} \Rightarrow X = A^{-1}B \Rightarrow \begin{bmatrix} x \\ y \end{bmatrix} = \begin{bmatrix} 3 & -2 \\ -1 & 1 \end{bmatrix} \begin{bmatrix} 3 \\ 6 \end{bmatrix} = \begin{bmatrix} -3 \\ 3 \end{bmatrix}$

The solution to the system is $(-3, 3)$.

48. (a) $\begin{aligned} 2x + y &= 4 \\ -x + 2y &= -1 \end{aligned} \Rightarrow AX = \begin{bmatrix} 2 & 1 \\ -1 & 2 \end{bmatrix} \begin{bmatrix} x \\ y \end{bmatrix} = \begin{bmatrix} 4 \\ -1 \end{bmatrix} = B$

(b) If $AX = B \Rightarrow \begin{bmatrix} 2 & 1 \\ -1 & 2 \end{bmatrix} \begin{bmatrix} x \\ y \end{bmatrix} = \begin{bmatrix} 4 \\ -1 \end{bmatrix} \Rightarrow X = A^{-1}B \Rightarrow \begin{bmatrix} x \\ y \end{bmatrix} = \begin{bmatrix} \frac{2}{5} & -\frac{1}{5} \\ \frac{1}{5} & \frac{2}{5} \end{bmatrix} \begin{bmatrix} 4 \\ -1 \end{bmatrix} = \begin{bmatrix} 1.8 \\ 0.4 \end{bmatrix}$

The solution to the system is $(1.8, 0.4)$.

49. (a) $\begin{aligned} -x + 2y &= 5 \\ 3x - 5y &= -2 \end{aligned} \Rightarrow AX = \begin{bmatrix} -1 & 2 \\ 3 & -5 \end{bmatrix} \begin{bmatrix} x \\ y \end{bmatrix} = \begin{bmatrix} 5 \\ -2 \end{bmatrix} = B$

(b) If $AX = B \Rightarrow \begin{bmatrix} -1 & 2 \\ 3 & -5 \end{bmatrix} \begin{bmatrix} x \\ y \end{bmatrix} = \begin{bmatrix} 5 \\ -2 \end{bmatrix} \Rightarrow X = A^{-1}B \Rightarrow \begin{bmatrix} x \\ y \end{bmatrix} = \begin{bmatrix} 5 & 2 \\ 3 & 1 \end{bmatrix} \begin{bmatrix} 5 \\ -2 \end{bmatrix} = \begin{bmatrix} 21 \\ 13 \end{bmatrix}$

The solution to the system is $(21, 13)$.

50. (a) $\begin{aligned} x + 3y &= -3 \\ 2x + 5y &= -2 \end{aligned} \Rightarrow AX = \begin{bmatrix} 1 & 3 \\ 2 & 5 \end{bmatrix} \begin{bmatrix} x \\ y \end{bmatrix} = \begin{bmatrix} -3 \\ -2 \end{bmatrix} = B$

(b) If $AX = B \Rightarrow \begin{bmatrix} 1 & 3 \\ 2 & 5 \end{bmatrix} \begin{bmatrix} x \\ y \end{bmatrix} = \begin{bmatrix} -3 \\ -2 \end{bmatrix} \Rightarrow X = A^{-1}B \Rightarrow \begin{bmatrix} x \\ y \end{bmatrix} = \begin{bmatrix} -5 & 3 \\ 2 & -1 \end{bmatrix} \begin{bmatrix} -3 \\ -2 \end{bmatrix} = \begin{bmatrix} 9 \\ -4 \end{bmatrix}$

The solution to the system is $(9, -4)$.

51. (a) $\begin{aligned} x \quad + z &= -7 \\ 2x + y + 3z &= -13 \\ -x + y + z &= -4 \end{aligned} \Rightarrow AX = \begin{bmatrix} 1 & 0 & 1 \\ 2 & 1 & 3 \\ -1 & 1 & 1 \end{bmatrix}\begin{bmatrix} x \\ y \\ z \end{bmatrix} = \begin{bmatrix} -7 \\ -13 \\ -4 \end{bmatrix} = B$

(b) If $AX = B \Rightarrow \begin{bmatrix} 1 & 0 & 1 \\ 2 & 1 & 3 \\ -1 & 1 & 1 \end{bmatrix}\begin{bmatrix} x \\ y \\ z \end{bmatrix} = \begin{bmatrix} -7 \\ -13 \\ -4 \end{bmatrix} \Rightarrow X = A^{-1}B = \begin{bmatrix} x \\ y \\ z \end{bmatrix} = \begin{bmatrix} -2 & 1 & -1 \\ -5 & 2 & -1 \\ 3 & -1 & 1 \end{bmatrix}\begin{bmatrix} -7 \\ -13 \\ -4 \end{bmatrix} =$

$\begin{bmatrix} 5 \\ 13 \\ -12 \end{bmatrix}$ The solution to the system is $(5, 13, -12)$.

52. (a) $\begin{aligned} -2x + y &= -5 \\ x + z &= -5 \\ -x + y &= -4 \end{aligned} \Rightarrow AX = \begin{bmatrix} -2 & 1 & 0 \\ 1 & 0 & 1 \\ -1 & 1 & 0 \end{bmatrix}\begin{bmatrix} x \\ y \\ z \end{bmatrix} = \begin{bmatrix} -5 \\ -5 \\ -4 \end{bmatrix} = B$

(b) If $AX = B \Rightarrow \begin{bmatrix} -2 & 1 & 0 \\ 1 & 0 & 1 \\ -1 & 1 & 0 \end{bmatrix}\begin{bmatrix} x \\ y \\ z \end{bmatrix} = \begin{bmatrix} -5 \\ -5 \\ -4 \end{bmatrix} \Rightarrow X = A^{-1}B = \begin{bmatrix} x \\ y \\ z \end{bmatrix} = \begin{bmatrix} -1 & 0 & 1 \\ -1 & 0 & 2 \\ 1 & 1 & -1 \end{bmatrix}\begin{bmatrix} -5 \\ -5 \\ -4 \end{bmatrix} =$

$\begin{bmatrix} 1 \\ -3 \\ -6 \end{bmatrix}$ The solution to the system is $(1, -3, -6)$.

53. (a) $\begin{aligned} x + 2y - z &= 2 \\ 2x + 5y \quad &= -1 \\ -x - y + 2z &= 0 \end{aligned} \Rightarrow AX = \begin{bmatrix} 1 & 2 & -1 \\ 2 & 5 & 0 \\ -1 & -1 & 2 \end{bmatrix}\begin{bmatrix} x \\ y \\ z \end{bmatrix} = \begin{bmatrix} 2 \\ -1 \\ 0 \end{bmatrix} = B$

(b) If $AX = B \Rightarrow \begin{bmatrix} 1 & 2 & -1 \\ 2 & 5 & 0 \\ -1 & -1 & 2 \end{bmatrix}\begin{bmatrix} x \\ y \\ z \end{bmatrix} = \begin{bmatrix} 2 \\ -1 \\ 0 \end{bmatrix} \Rightarrow X = A^{-1}B = \begin{bmatrix} x \\ y \\ z \end{bmatrix} = \begin{bmatrix} -10 & 3 & -5 \\ 4 & -1 & 2 \\ -3 & 1 & -1 \end{bmatrix}\begin{bmatrix} 2 \\ -1 \\ 0 \end{bmatrix} =$

$\begin{bmatrix} -23 \\ 9 \\ -7 \end{bmatrix}$ The solution to the system is $(-23, 9, -7)$.

54. (a) $\begin{aligned} 2x - 2y + z &= 1 \\ x + 3y + 2z &= 3 \\ 4x - 2y + 4z &= 4 \end{aligned} \Rightarrow AX = \begin{bmatrix} 2 & -2 & 1 \\ 1 & 3 & 2 \\ 4 & -2 & 4 \end{bmatrix}\begin{bmatrix} x \\ y \\ z \end{bmatrix} = \begin{bmatrix} 1 \\ 3 \\ 4 \end{bmatrix} = B$

(b) If $AX = B \Rightarrow \begin{bmatrix} 2 & -2 & 1 \\ 1 & 3 & 2 \\ 4 & -2 & 4 \end{bmatrix}\begin{bmatrix} x \\ y \\ z \end{bmatrix} = \begin{bmatrix} 1 \\ 3 \\ 4 \end{bmatrix} \Rightarrow X = A^{-1}B = \begin{bmatrix} x \\ y \\ z \end{bmatrix} = \begin{bmatrix} \frac{8}{5} & \frac{3}{5} & -\frac{7}{10} \\ \frac{2}{5} & \frac{2}{5} & -\frac{3}{10} \\ -\frac{7}{5} & -\frac{2}{5} & \frac{4}{5} \end{bmatrix}\begin{bmatrix} 1 \\ 3 \\ 4 \end{bmatrix} =$

$\begin{bmatrix} 0.6 \\ 0.4 \\ 0.6 \end{bmatrix}$ The solution to the system is $(0.6, 0.4, 0.6)$.

55. (a) $AX = B \Rightarrow \begin{bmatrix} 1.5 & 3.7 \\ -0.4 & -2.1 \end{bmatrix}\begin{bmatrix} x \\ y \end{bmatrix} = \begin{bmatrix} 0.32 \\ 0.36 \end{bmatrix}$

(b) See Figure 55. $X = A^{-1}B \Rightarrow X = \begin{bmatrix} 1.2 \\ -0.4 \end{bmatrix}$

56. (a) $AX = B \Rightarrow \begin{bmatrix} 31 & 18 \\ 5 & -23 \end{bmatrix}\begin{bmatrix} x \\ y \end{bmatrix} = \begin{bmatrix} 64.1 \\ -59.6 \end{bmatrix}$

(b) See Figure 56. $X = A^{-1}B \Rightarrow X = \begin{bmatrix} 0.5 \\ 2.7 \end{bmatrix}$

```
[A]-1*[B]
        [[1.2]
         [-.4]]
```

Figure 55

```
[A]-1*[B]
        [[.5 ]
         [2.7]]
```

Figure 56

```
[A]-1*[B]
        [[.7]
         [.8]]
```

Figure 57

```
[A]-1*[B]
        [[15]
         [17]]
```

Figure 58

57. (a) $AX = B \Rightarrow \begin{bmatrix} 0.08 & -0.7 \\ 1.1 & -0.05 \end{bmatrix}\begin{bmatrix} x \\ y \end{bmatrix} = \begin{bmatrix} -0.504 \\ 0.73 \end{bmatrix}$

(b) See Figure 57. $X = A^{-1}B \Rightarrow X = \begin{bmatrix} 0.7 \\ 0.8 \end{bmatrix}$

58. (a) $AX = B \Rightarrow \begin{bmatrix} -231 & 178 \\ 525 & -329 \end{bmatrix}\begin{bmatrix} x \\ y \end{bmatrix} = \begin{bmatrix} -439 \\ 2282 \end{bmatrix}$

(b) See Figure 58. $X = A^{-1}B \Rightarrow X = \begin{bmatrix} 15 \\ 17 \end{bmatrix}$

59. (a) $AX = B \Rightarrow \begin{bmatrix} 3.1 & 1.9 & -1 \\ 6.3 & 0 & -9.9 \\ -1 & 1.5 & 7 \end{bmatrix}\begin{bmatrix} x \\ y \\ z \end{bmatrix} = \begin{bmatrix} 1.99 \\ -3.78 \\ 5.3 \end{bmatrix}$

(b) See Figure 59. $X = A^{-1}B \Rightarrow X = \begin{bmatrix} 0.5 \\ 0.6 \\ 0.7 \end{bmatrix}$

60. (a) $AX = B \Rightarrow \begin{bmatrix} 17 & -22 & -19 \\ 3 & 13 & -9 \\ 1 & -2 & 6.1 \end{bmatrix}\begin{bmatrix} x \\ y \\ z \end{bmatrix} = \begin{bmatrix} -25.2 \\ 105.9 \\ -23.55 \end{bmatrix}$

(b) See Figure 60. $X = A^{-1}B \Rightarrow X = \begin{bmatrix} 3.1 \\ 5.7 \\ -2.5 \end{bmatrix}$

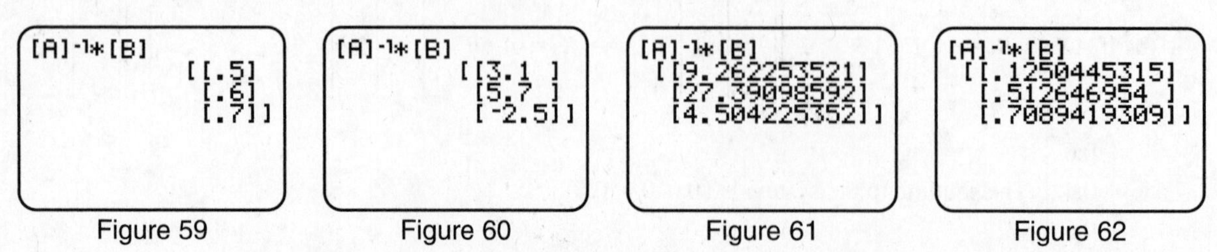


Figure 59 Figure 60 Figure 61 Figure 62

61. (a) $AX = B \Rightarrow \begin{bmatrix} 3 & -1 & 1 \\ 5.8 & -2.1 & 0 \\ -1 & 0 & 2.9 \end{bmatrix} \begin{bmatrix} x \\ y \\ z \end{bmatrix} = \begin{bmatrix} 4.9 \\ -3.8 \\ 3.8 \end{bmatrix}$

(b) See Figure 61. $X = A^{-1}B \Rightarrow X \approx \begin{bmatrix} 9.26 \\ 27.39 \\ 4.50 \end{bmatrix}$

62. (a) $AX = B \Rightarrow \begin{bmatrix} 1.2 & -0.3 & -0.7 \\ -0.4 & 1.3 & 0.4 \\ 1.7 & 0.6 & 1.1 \end{bmatrix} \begin{bmatrix} x \\ y \\ z \end{bmatrix} = \begin{bmatrix} -0.5 \\ 0.9 \\ 1.3 \end{bmatrix}$

(b) See Figure 62. $X = A^{-1}B \Rightarrow X \approx \begin{bmatrix} 0.13 \\ 0.51 \\ 0.71 \end{bmatrix}$

63. (a) Since $h = 2$ and $k = 3$, the matrix $A$ will translate the point (0, 1) to the right 2 units and up 3 units. Its new location will be $(0 + 2, 1 + 3) = (2, 4)$. This is verified by the following computation:

$$AX = \begin{bmatrix} 1 & 0 & 2 \\ 0 & 1 & 3 \\ 0 & 0 & 1 \end{bmatrix} \begin{bmatrix} 0 \\ 1 \\ 1 \end{bmatrix} = \begin{bmatrix} 2 \\ 4 \\ 1 \end{bmatrix}$$

(b) $A^{-1}Y = X$. That is, $A^{-1}$ will translate (2, 4) back to (0, 1) by moving it left 2 units and down 3 units. Thus $h = -2$ and $k = -3$ in $A^{-1}$.

$$A^{-1}Y = \begin{bmatrix} 1 & 0 & -2 \\ 0 & 1 & -3 \\ 0 & 0 & 1 \end{bmatrix} \begin{bmatrix} 2 \\ 4 \\ 1 \end{bmatrix} = \begin{bmatrix} 0 \\ 1 \\ 1 \end{bmatrix}$$

(c) The product $AA^{-1} = I_3 = A^{-1}A$, since they are $3 \times 3$ inverse matrices.

64. (a) Since $h = -4$ and $k = 5$, the matrix $A$ will translate the point (4, 2) to the left 4 units and up 5 units. Its new location will be $(4 - 4, 2 + 5) = (0, 7)$. This is verified by the following computation:

$$AX = \begin{bmatrix} 1 & 0 & -4 \\ 0 & 1 & 5 \\ 0 & 0 & 1 \end{bmatrix} \begin{bmatrix} 4 \\ 2 \\ 1 \end{bmatrix} = \begin{bmatrix} 0 \\ 7 \\ 1 \end{bmatrix}$$

(b) $A^{-1}Y = X$. That is, $A^{-1}$ will translate (0, 7) back to (4, 2) by moving it right 4 units and down 5 units. Thus $h = 4$ and $k = -5$ in $A^{-1}$.

$$A^{-1}Y = \begin{bmatrix} 1 & 0 & 4 \\ 0 & 1 & -5 \\ 0 & 0 & 1 \end{bmatrix} \begin{bmatrix} 0 \\ 7 \\ 1 \end{bmatrix} = \begin{bmatrix} 4 \\ 2 \\ 1 \end{bmatrix}$$

(c) The product $AA^{-1} = I_3 = A^{-1}A$, since they are $3 \times 3$ inverse matrices.

65. Three units left implies that $h = -3$ and five units down implies that $k = -5$.

$$A = \begin{bmatrix} 1 & 0 & -3 \\ 0 & 1 & -5 \\ 0 & 0 & 1 \end{bmatrix} \text{ and } A^{-1} = \begin{bmatrix} 1 & 0 & 3 \\ 0 & 1 & 5 \\ 0 & 0 & 1 \end{bmatrix}$$

$A^{-1}$ will translate a point 3 units to the right and 5 units up.

66. Six units right implies that $h = 6$ and one unit up implies that $k = 1$.

$$A = \begin{bmatrix} 1 & 0 & 6 \\ 0 & 1 & 1 \\ 0 & 0 & 1 \end{bmatrix} \text{ and } A^{-1} = \begin{bmatrix} 1 & 0 & -6 \\ 0 & 1 & -1 \\ 0 & 0 & 1 \end{bmatrix}$$

$A^{-1}$ will translate a point 6 units to the left and 1 unit down.

67. (a) $BX = \begin{bmatrix} \frac{1}{\sqrt{2}} & \frac{1}{\sqrt{2}} & 0 \\ -\frac{1}{\sqrt{2}} & \frac{1}{\sqrt{2}} & 0 \\ 0 & 0 & 1 \end{bmatrix} \begin{bmatrix} -\sqrt{2} \\ -\sqrt{2} \\ 1 \end{bmatrix} = \begin{bmatrix} -2 \\ 0 \\ 1 \end{bmatrix} = Y$

(b) $B^{-1}Y = \begin{bmatrix} \frac{1}{\sqrt{2}} & -\frac{1}{\sqrt{2}} & 0 \\ \frac{1}{\sqrt{2}} & \frac{1}{\sqrt{2}} & 0 \\ 0 & 0 & 1 \end{bmatrix} \begin{bmatrix} -2 \\ 0 \\ 1 \end{bmatrix} = \begin{bmatrix} -\sqrt{2} \\ -\sqrt{2} \\ 1 \end{bmatrix} = X$

$B^{-1}$ rotates the point represented by $Y$ counterclockwise 45° about the origin.

68. Since $B$ and $B^{-1}$ are inverses, $BB^{-1}X = X = B^{-1}BX$ for any point $(x, y)$. In addition, $BB^{-1} = I_3 = B^{-1}B$. Geometrically, $B$ will rotate a point clockwise 45° about the origin, while $B^{-1}$ will rotate a point counterclockwise 45° about the origin. The net result is no change in the location of the original point.

69. (a) In the computation $ABX$, $B$ translates (1, 1) left 3 units and up 3 units to (–2, 4). Then, $A$ translates (–2, 4) right 4 units and down 2 units to (2, 2).

$ABX = \begin{bmatrix} 1 & 0 & 4 \\ 0 & 1 & -2 \\ 0 & 0 & 1 \end{bmatrix} \begin{bmatrix} 1 & 0 & -3 \\ 0 & 1 & 3 \\ 0 & 0 & 1 \end{bmatrix} \begin{bmatrix} 1 \\ 1 \\ 1 \end{bmatrix} = \begin{bmatrix} 2 \\ 2 \\ 1 \end{bmatrix} = Y$; This represents the point (2, 2) as expected.

(b) The net result of $A$ and $B$ is to translate a point 1 unit right and 1 unit up. Therefore, it is reasonable to expect that $h = 1$ and $k = 1$ in the matrix of the form $AB$.

$$AB = \begin{bmatrix} 1 & 0 & 4 \\ 0 & 1 & -2 \\ 0 & 0 & 1 \end{bmatrix} \begin{bmatrix} 1 & 0 & -3 \\ 0 & 1 & 3 \\ 0 & 0 & 1 \end{bmatrix} = \begin{bmatrix} 1 & 0 & 1 \\ 0 & 1 & 1 \\ 0 & 0 & 1 \end{bmatrix}$$

(c) Yes. If a point is translated left 3 units and up 3 units followed by right 4 units and down 2 units, the final result will be the same as the translation obtained when the point is first translated right 4 units and down 2 units followed by left 3 units and up 3. Therefore, we might expect that $AB = BA$.

$$BA = \begin{bmatrix} 1 & 0 & -3 \\ 0 & 1 & 3 \\ 0 & 0 & 1 \end{bmatrix} \begin{bmatrix} 1 & 0 & 4 \\ 0 & 1 & -2 \\ 0 & 0 & 1 \end{bmatrix} = \begin{bmatrix} 1 & 0 & 1 \\ 0 & 1 & 1 \\ 0 & 0 & 1 \end{bmatrix} = AB$$

(d) Since $AB$ translates a point 1 unit right and 1 unit up, the inverse of $AB$ would translate a point 1 unit left and 1 unit down. So $h = -1$ and $k = -1$ in $(AB)^{-1}$.

$(AB)^{-1} = \begin{bmatrix} 1 & 0 & -1 \\ 0 & 1 & -1 \\ 0 & 0 & 1 \end{bmatrix}$; Notice that $(AB)(AB)^{-1} = I_3$ as expected.

70. (a) If $(0, \sqrt{2})$ is rotated clockwise 45° about the origin, its new coordinates are (1, 1). Then (1, 1) is translated right 2 units and up 3 units. Its new coordinates are $(1 + 2, 1 + 3) = (3, 4)$.

(b) $$ABX = \begin{bmatrix} 1 & 0 & 2 \\ 0 & 1 & 3 \\ 0 & 0 & 1 \end{bmatrix} \begin{bmatrix} \frac{1}{\sqrt{2}} & \frac{1}{\sqrt{2}} & 0 \\ -\frac{1}{\sqrt{2}} & \frac{1}{\sqrt{2}} & 0 \\ 0 & 0 & 1 \end{bmatrix} \begin{bmatrix} 0 \\ \sqrt{2} \\ 1 \end{bmatrix} = \begin{bmatrix} 3 \\ 4 \\ 1 \end{bmatrix};$$

This agrees with the geometric location of (3, 4).

(c) $$BAX = \begin{bmatrix} \frac{1}{\sqrt{2}} & \frac{1}{\sqrt{2}} & 0 \\ -\frac{1}{\sqrt{2}} & \frac{1}{\sqrt{2}} & 0 \\ 0 & 0 & 1 \end{bmatrix} \begin{bmatrix} 1 & 0 & 2 \\ 0 & 1 & 3 \\ 0 & 0 & 1 \end{bmatrix} \begin{bmatrix} 0 \\ \sqrt{2} \\ 1 \end{bmatrix} \approx \begin{bmatrix} 4.536 \\ 1.707 \\ 1 \end{bmatrix} \neq \begin{bmatrix} 3 \\ 4 \\ 1 \end{bmatrix}$$

No. Rotating the point 45° and then translating it is not equivalent to translating the point and then rotating it. The matrices $A$ and $B$ do not commute.

(d) We must compute the inverse operations of rotating and translating. We must translate back to (1, 1) and then rotate to $(0, \sqrt{2})$. This is done by computing $B^{-1}A^{-1}X$.

$$B^{-1}A^{-1} = \begin{bmatrix} \frac{1}{\sqrt{2}} & -\frac{1}{\sqrt{2}} & 0 \\ \frac{1}{\sqrt{2}} & \frac{1}{\sqrt{2}} & 0 \\ 0 & 0 & 1 \end{bmatrix} \begin{bmatrix} 1 & 0 & -2 \\ 0 & 1 & -3 \\ 0 & 0 & 1 \end{bmatrix} = \begin{bmatrix} \frac{1}{\sqrt{2}} & -\frac{1}{\sqrt{2}} & \frac{1}{\sqrt{2}} \\ \frac{1}{\sqrt{2}} & \frac{1}{\sqrt{2}} & -\frac{5}{\sqrt{2}} \\ 0 & 0 & 1 \end{bmatrix}$$

$$B^{-1}A^{-1}X = \begin{bmatrix} \frac{1}{\sqrt{2}} & -\frac{1}{\sqrt{2}} & \frac{1}{\sqrt{2}} \\ \frac{1}{\sqrt{2}} & \frac{1}{\sqrt{2}} & -\frac{5}{\sqrt{2}} \\ 0 & 0 & 1 \end{bmatrix} \begin{bmatrix} 3 \\ 4 \\ 1 \end{bmatrix} = \begin{bmatrix} 0 \\ \sqrt{2} \\ 1 \end{bmatrix}$$ It works as expected.

71. Let $x$ be the number of CDs of type A purchased, let $y$ be the CDs of type B and let $z$ be the CDs of type C. The first row in the table implies that $2x + 3y + 4z = 120.91$. The other rows can be interpreted similarly. The system in matrix form is shown below.

$$AX = B \Rightarrow \begin{bmatrix} 2 & 3 & 4 \\ 1 & 4 & 0 \\ 2 & 1 & 3 \end{bmatrix} \begin{bmatrix} x \\ y \\ z \end{bmatrix} = \begin{bmatrix} 120.91 \\ 62.95 \\ 79.94 \end{bmatrix}$$

Use a graphing calculator to find the solution as shown in Figure 71. Type A CDs cost \$10.99, type B cost \$12.99, and type C cost \$14.99.

72. (a) At intersection A, incoming traffic is $x_1 + 5$ and outgoing traffic is $4 + 6$. Thus, $x_1 + 5 = 4 + 6$. At intersection B, incoming traffic is $x_2 + 6$ and outgoing traffic is $x_1 + 3$. Thus, $x_2 + 6 = x_1 + 3$. At intersection C, incoming traffic is $x_3 + 4$ and outgoing traffic is $x_2 + 7$. Thus, $x_3 + 4 = x_2 + 7$. At intersection D, incoming traffic is $6 + 5$ and outgoing traffic is $x_3 + x_4$. Thus, $6 + 5 = x_3 + x_4$.

(b) $$AX = B \Rightarrow \begin{bmatrix} 1 & 0 & 0 & 0 \\ -1 & 1 & 0 & 0 \\ 0 & -1 & 1 & 0 \\ 0 & 0 & 1 & 1 \end{bmatrix} \begin{bmatrix} x_1 \\ x_2 \\ x_3 \\ x_4 \end{bmatrix} = \begin{bmatrix} 5 \\ -3 \\ 3 \\ 11 \end{bmatrix}$$

The solution is given by $X = A^{-1}B$ and can be computed using a graphing calculator. See Figure 72.

Since $X = A^{-1}B = \begin{bmatrix} 5 \\ 2 \\ 5 \\ 6 \end{bmatrix}$, the solution is $x_1 = 5$, $x_2 = 2$, $x_3 = 5$, and $x_4 = 6$.

(c) The traffic traveling west from intersection $B$ to intersection $A$ has a rate of $x_1 = 5$ cars per minute. The values for $x_2$, $x_3$, and $x_4$ can be interpreted in a similar manner.

```
[A]-1*[B]
   [[10.99]
    [12.99]
    [14.99]]
```

Figure 71

```
[A]-1*[B]
        [[5]
         [2]
         [5]
         [6]]
```

Figure 72

```
[A]-1*[B]
       [[30 ]
        [.04]
        [4  ]]
```

Figure 73

73. (a) The following three equations must be solved, using the equation $P = a + bS + cC$.

$a + b(1500) + c(8) = 122$
$a + b(2000) + c(5) = 130$
$a + b(2200) + c(10) = 158$

These equations can be written in matrix form as follows:

$$AX = B \Rightarrow \begin{bmatrix} 1 & 1500 & 8 \\ 1 & 2000 & 5 \\ 1 & 2200 & 10 \end{bmatrix} \begin{bmatrix} a \\ b \\ c \end{bmatrix} = \begin{bmatrix} 122 \\ 130 \\ 158 \end{bmatrix}$$

The solution is given by $X = A^{-1}B$ as shown in Figure 73. It is $a = 30$, $b = 0.04$, and $c = 4$. That is, $P$ is given by $P = 30 + 0.04S + 4C$

(b) $P = 30 + 0.04(1800) + 4(7) = 130$, or \$130,000

74. (a) The following three equations must be solved.

$$a(113) + b(308) + c = 10{,}170$$
$$a(133) + b(622) + c = 15{,}305$$
$$a(155) + b(1937) + c = 21{,}289$$

These equations can be written in matrix form as follows:

$$AX = B \Rightarrow \begin{bmatrix} 113 & 308 & 1 \\ 133 & 622 & 1 \\ 155 & 1937 & 1 \end{bmatrix}\begin{bmatrix} a \\ b \\ c \end{bmatrix} = \begin{bmatrix} 10{,}170 \\ 15{,}305 \\ 21{,}289 \end{bmatrix}$$

(b) The solution is given by $X = A^{-1}B$ as shown in Figure 74. It is $a \approx 251$, $b \approx 0.346$, and $c \approx -18{,}300$. That is, $T$ is given by $T \approx 251A + 0.346I - 18{,}300$.

(c) $T \approx 251(118) + 0.346(311) - 18{,}300 \approx 11{,}426$ (this is quite close to the actual value of 11,314).

Figure 74

Figure 76

75. (a) Although this system of equations can be solved using matrices, we will use elimination to avoid performing row operations on variables. Subtracting the second equation from the third equations gives

$$\begin{array}{rl} 0.4S + 0.4E + 0.1T &= T \\ -\ 0.4S + 0.2E + 0.1T &= E \\ \hline 0.2E \qquad\qquad &= T - E \Rightarrow E = \frac{5}{6}T. \end{array}$$

Substituting $E = \frac{5}{6}T$ in the first equation gives $0.2S + 0.4\left(\frac{5}{6}T\right) + 0.8T = S \Rightarrow$

$\frac{17}{15}T = \frac{4}{5}S \Rightarrow S = \frac{17}{12}T$. The solution is $\left(\frac{17}{12}T, \frac{5}{6}T, T\right)$.

(b) When $T = 60$ units, $S = \frac{17}{12}(60) = 85$ units and $E = \frac{5}{6}(60) = 50$ units. That is, service should produce 85 units and electrical should produce 50 units.

76. (a) The following three equations must be solved, using the equation $G = aA + bB + c$.

$$a(5.54) + b(37.1) + c = 603$$
$$a(6.93) + b(41.3) + c = 657$$
$$a(7.64) + b(45.6) + c = 779$$

These equations can be written in matrix form as follows:

$$AX = B \Rightarrow \begin{bmatrix} 5.54 & 37.1 & 1 \\ 6.93 & 41.3 & 1 \\ 7.64 & 45.6 & 1 \end{bmatrix}\begin{bmatrix} a \\ b \\ c \end{bmatrix} = \begin{bmatrix} 603 \\ 657 \\ 779 \end{bmatrix}$$

(b) The solution is given by $X = A^{-1}B$ as shown in Figure 76. It is $a \approx -93.6$, $b \approx 43.8$, and $c \approx -504$. That is, $G$ is given by $G \approx -93.6A + 43.8B - 504$

(c) $G = -93.6(7.75) + 43.8(47.4) - 504 \approx 847$, or \$847 million (this compares favorably with the actual value of \$878 million).

## Checking Basic Concepts for Sections 6.5 and 6.6

1. (a) $A + B = \begin{bmatrix} 1 & 0 & 1 \\ -1 & 1 & 2 \\ 1 & 3 & 0 \end{bmatrix} + \begin{bmatrix} -1 & 1 & 2 \\ 0 & 4 & 1 \\ 1 & -2 & 0 \end{bmatrix} = \begin{bmatrix} 0 & 1 & 3 \\ -1 & 5 & 3 \\ 2 & 1 & 0 \end{bmatrix}$

(b) $2A - B = 2\begin{bmatrix} 1 & 0 & 1 \\ -1 & 1 & 2 \\ 1 & 3 & 0 \end{bmatrix} - \begin{bmatrix} -1 & 1 & 2 \\ 0 & 4 & 1 \\ 1 & -2 & 0 \end{bmatrix} = \begin{bmatrix} 3 & -1 & 0 \\ -2 & -2 & 3 \\ 1 & 8 & 0 \end{bmatrix}$

(c) $AB = \begin{bmatrix} 1 & 0 & 1 \\ -1 & 1 & 2 \\ 1 & 3 & 0 \end{bmatrix}\begin{bmatrix} -1 & 1 & 2 \\ 0 & 4 & 1 \\ 1 & -2 & 0 \end{bmatrix} = \begin{bmatrix} 0 & -1 & 2 \\ 3 & -1 & -1 \\ -1 & 13 & 5 \end{bmatrix}$

2. $A \mid I_3 = \left[\begin{array}{ccc|ccc} 0 & 0 & 1 & 1 & 0 & 0 \\ 1 & 1 & 0 & 0 & 1 & 0 \\ 1 & 0 & 1 & 0 & 0 & 1 \end{array}\right] \begin{array}{l} R_3 \rightarrow \\ \\ R_1 \rightarrow \end{array} \left[\begin{array}{ccc|ccc} 1 & 0 & 1 & 0 & 0 & 1 \\ 1 & 1 & 0 & 0 & 1 & 0 \\ 0 & 0 & 1 & 1 & 0 & 0 \end{array}\right] \begin{array}{l} \\ R_2 - R_1 \rightarrow \\ \\ \end{array} \left[\begin{array}{ccc|ccc} 1 & 0 & 1 & 0 & 0 & 1 \\ 0 & 1 & -1 & 0 & 1 & -1 \\ 0 & 0 & 1 & 1 & 0 & 0 \end{array}\right]$

$\begin{array}{l} R_1 - R_3 \rightarrow \\ R_2 + R_3 \rightarrow \\ \\ \end{array} \left[\begin{array}{ccc|ccc} 1 & 0 & 0 & -1 & 0 & 1 \\ 0 & 1 & 0 & 1 & 1 & -1 \\ 0 & 0 & 1 & 1 & 0 & 0 \end{array}\right]; \; A^{-1} = \begin{bmatrix} -1 & 0 & 1 \\ 1 & 1 & -1 \\ 1 & 0 & 0 \end{bmatrix}$

3. (a) If $\begin{array}{r} x - 2y = 13 \\ 2x + 3y = 5 \end{array} \Rightarrow AX = \begin{bmatrix} 1 & -2 \\ 2 & 3 \end{bmatrix}\begin{bmatrix} x \\ y \end{bmatrix} = \begin{bmatrix} 13 \\ 5 \end{bmatrix}$

$A^{-1} = \left[\begin{array}{cc|cc} 1 & -2 & 1 & 0 \\ 2 & 3 & 0 & 1 \end{array}\right] \; 2R_1 - R_2 \rightarrow \left[\begin{array}{cc|cc} 1 & -2 & 1 & 0 \\ 0 & -7 & 2 & -1 \end{array}\right] \; (-1/7)R_2 \rightarrow \left[\begin{array}{cc|cc} 1 & -2 & 1 & 0 \\ 0 & 1 & -\frac{2}{7} & \frac{1}{7} \end{array}\right]$

$2R_2 + R_1 \rightarrow \left[\begin{array}{cc|cc} 1 & 0 & \frac{3}{7} & \frac{2}{7} \\ 0 & 1 & -\frac{2}{7} & \frac{1}{7} \end{array}\right] \Rightarrow A^{-1} = \begin{bmatrix} \frac{3}{7} & \frac{2}{7} \\ -\frac{2}{7} & \frac{1}{7} \end{bmatrix} \Rightarrow X = A^{-1}B \Rightarrow \begin{bmatrix} x \\ y \end{bmatrix} = \begin{bmatrix} \frac{3}{7} & \frac{2}{7} \\ -\frac{2}{7} & \frac{1}{7} \end{bmatrix}\begin{bmatrix} 13 \\ 5 \end{bmatrix} = \begin{bmatrix} 7 \\ -3 \end{bmatrix}$

The solution to the system is $(7, -3)$. See Figure 3a.

(b) If $\begin{array}{r} x - y + z = 2 \\ -x + y + z = 4 \\ y - z = -1 \end{array} \Rightarrow AX = \begin{bmatrix} 1 & -1 & 1 \\ -1 & 1 & 1 \\ 0 & 1 & -1 \end{bmatrix}\begin{bmatrix} x \\ y \\ z \end{bmatrix} = \begin{bmatrix} 2 \\ 4 \\ -1 \end{bmatrix} \Rightarrow$

$A^{-1} = \left[\begin{array}{ccc|ccc} 1 & -1 & 1 & 1 & 0 & 0 \\ -1 & 1 & 1 & 0 & 1 & 0 \\ 0 & 1 & -1 & 0 & 0 & 1 \end{array}\right]$

$\begin{array}{l} \\ R_1 + R_2 \rightarrow \\ \\ \end{array} \left[\begin{array}{ccc|ccc} 1 & -1 & 1 & 1 & 0 & 0 \\ 0 & 0 & 2 & 1 & 1 & 0 \\ 0 & 1 & -1 & 0 & 0 & 1 \end{array}\right] \begin{array}{l} \\ R_3 \rightarrow \\ R_2 \rightarrow \end{array} \left[\begin{array}{ccc|ccc} 1 & -1 & 1 & 1 & 0 & 0 \\ 0 & 1 & -1 & 0 & 0 & 1 \\ 0 & 0 & 2 & 1 & 1 & 0 \end{array}\right]$

$\begin{array}{l} \\ R_2 + R_3 \rightarrow \\ (1/2)R_3 \rightarrow \end{array} \left[\begin{array}{ccc|ccc} 1 & -1 & 1 & 1 & 0 & 0 \\ 0 & 1 & 1 & 1 & 1 & 1 \\ 0 & 0 & 1 & \frac{1}{2} & \frac{1}{2} & 0 \end{array}\right] \begin{array}{l} R_1 - R_3 \rightarrow \\ \\ \\ \end{array} \left[\begin{array}{ccc|ccc} 1 & -1 & 0 & \frac{1}{2} & -\frac{1}{2} & 0 \\ 0 & 1 & 1 & 1 & 1 & 1 \\ 0 & 0 & 1 & \frac{1}{2} & \frac{1}{2} & 0 \end{array}\right]$

$\begin{array}{l} \\ R_2 - R_3 \rightarrow \\ \\ \end{array} \left[\begin{array}{ccc|ccc} 1 & -1 & 0 & \frac{1}{2} & -\frac{1}{2} & 0 \\ 0 & 1 & 0 & \frac{1}{2} & \frac{1}{2} & 1 \\ 0 & 0 & 1 & \frac{1}{2} & \frac{1}{2} & 0 \end{array}\right] \begin{array}{l} R_1 + R_2 \rightarrow \\ \\ \\ \end{array} \left[\begin{array}{ccc|ccc} 1 & 0 & 0 & 1 & 0 & 1 \\ 0 & 1 & 0 & \frac{1}{2} & \frac{1}{2} & 1 \\ 0 & 0 & 1 & \frac{1}{2} & \frac{1}{2} & 0 \end{array}\right] \Rightarrow$

$A^{-1} = \begin{bmatrix} 1 & 0 & 1 \\ \frac{1}{2} & \frac{1}{2} & 1 \\ \frac{1}{2} & \frac{1}{2} & 0 \end{bmatrix} \Rightarrow X = A^{-1}B \Rightarrow \begin{bmatrix} x \\ y \\ z \end{bmatrix} = \begin{bmatrix} 1 & 0 & 1 \\ \frac{1}{2} & \frac{1}{2} & 1 \\ \frac{1}{2} & \frac{1}{2} & 0 \end{bmatrix}\begin{bmatrix} 2 \\ 4 \\ -1 \end{bmatrix} = \begin{bmatrix} 1 \\ 2 \\ 3 \end{bmatrix}$

The solution to the system is $(1, 2, 3)$. See Figure 3b.

(c) $AX = B \Rightarrow \begin{bmatrix} 3.1 & -5.3 \\ -0.1 & 1.8 \end{bmatrix}\begin{bmatrix} x \\ y \end{bmatrix} = \begin{bmatrix} -2.682 \\ 0.787 \end{bmatrix}$. Then $X = A^{-1}B \Rightarrow X = \begin{bmatrix} -0.13 \\ 0.43 \end{bmatrix}$ as shown in Figure 3c.

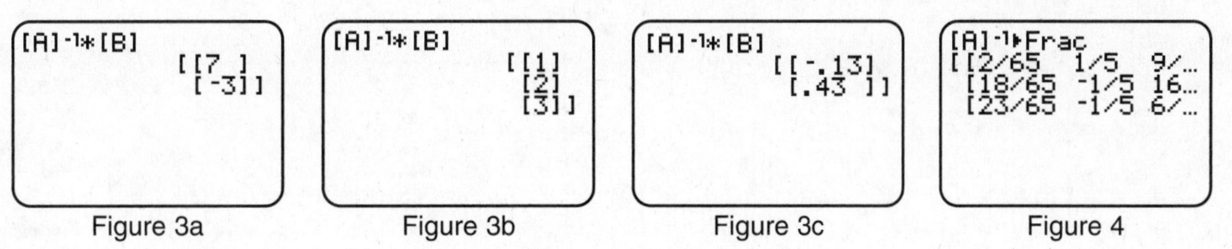

Figure 3a Figure 3b Figure 3c Figure 4

4. If $A = \begin{bmatrix} 2 & -3 & 5 \\ 4 & -3 & 2 \\ 1 & 5 & -4 \end{bmatrix}$ then $A^{-1} = \begin{bmatrix} \frac{2}{65} & \frac{1}{5} & \frac{9}{65} \\ \frac{18}{65} & -\frac{1}{5} & \frac{16}{65} \\ \frac{23}{65} & -\frac{1}{5} & \frac{6}{65} \end{bmatrix}$ See Figure 4.

## 6.7 Determinants

1. $\det A = \det\begin{bmatrix} 4 & 3 \\ 5 & 4 \end{bmatrix} = (4)(4) - (5)(3) = 1 \neq 0$; $A$ is invertible.

2. $\det A = \det\begin{bmatrix} 1 & -3 \\ 2 & 6 \end{bmatrix} = (1)(6) - (2)(-3) = 12 \neq 0$; $A$ is invertible.

3. $\det A = \det\begin{bmatrix} -4 & 6 \\ -8 & 12 \end{bmatrix} = (-4)(12) - (-8)(6) = 0$; $A$ is not invertible.

4. $\det A = \det\begin{bmatrix} 10 & -20 \\ -5 & 10 \end{bmatrix} = (10)(10) - (-5)(-20) = 0$; $A$ is not invertible.

5. Deleting the first row and second column gives $M_{12} = \det A = \det\begin{bmatrix} 2 & -2 \\ 0 & 5 \end{bmatrix} = (2)(5) - (0)(-2) = 10$.

   The cofactor is $A_{12} = (-1)^{1+2}M_{12} = -1(10) = -10$.

6. Deleting the second row and third column gives $M_{23} = \det A = \det\begin{bmatrix} 1 & 2 \\ 2 & 3 \end{bmatrix} = (1)(3) - (2)(2) = -1$.

   The cofactor is $A_{23} = (-1)^{2+3}M_{23} = -1(-1) = 1$.

7. Deleting the second row and second column gives $M_{22} = \det A = \det\begin{bmatrix} 7 & 1 \\ 1 & -2 \end{bmatrix} = (7)(-2) - (1)(1) = -15$.

   The cofactor is $A_{22} = (-1)^{2+2}M_{22} = 1(-15) = -15$.

8. Deleting the third row and first column gives $M_{31} = \det A = \det\begin{bmatrix} 0 & -1 \\ -7 & 1 \end{bmatrix} = (0)(1) - (-7)(-1) = -7$.

   The cofactor is $A_{31} = (-1)^{3+1}M_{31} = 1(-7) = -7$.

9. $\det A = a_{11}A_{11} + a_{21}A_{21} + a_{31}A_{31} = a_{11}M_{11} - a_{21}M_{21} + a_{31}M_{31} \Rightarrow$

   $\det A = (1)\det\begin{bmatrix} 2 & -3 \\ -1 & 3 \end{bmatrix} - (0)\det\begin{bmatrix} 4 & -7 \\ -1 & 3 \end{bmatrix} + (0)\det\begin{bmatrix} 4 & -7 \\ 2 & -3 \end{bmatrix} = (1)(6 - 3) = 3$

   Since $\det A = 3 \neq 0$, $A^{-1}$ exists.

10. $\det A = a_{11}A_{11} + a_{21}A_{21} + a_{31}A_{31} = a_{11}M_{11} - a_{21}M_{21} + a_{31}M_{31} \Rightarrow$

$$\det A = (0)\det\begin{bmatrix} 3 & 5 \\ 4 & 1 \end{bmatrix} - (-1)\det\begin{bmatrix} 2 & 8 \\ 4 & 1 \end{bmatrix} + (0)\det\begin{bmatrix} 2 & 8 \\ 3 & 5 \end{bmatrix} = (1)(2 - 32) = -30$$

Since $\det A = -30 \neq 0$, $A^{-1}$ exists.

11. $\det A = a_{11}A_{11} + a_{21}A_{21} + a_{31}A_{31} = a_{11}M_{11} - a_{21}M_{21} + a_{31}M_{31} \Rightarrow$

$$\det A = (5)\det\begin{bmatrix} -2 & 0 \\ 4 & 0 \end{bmatrix} - (0)\det\begin{bmatrix} 1 & 6 \\ 4 & 0 \end{bmatrix} + (0)\det\begin{bmatrix} 1 & 6 \\ -2 & 0 \end{bmatrix} = (5)(0 - 0) = 0$$

Since $\det A = 0$, $A^{-1}$ does not exist.

12. $\det A = a_{11}A_{11} + a_{21}A_{21} + a_{31}A_{31} = a_{11}M_{11} - a_{21}M_{21} + a_{31}M_{31} \Rightarrow$

$$\det A = (3)\det\begin{bmatrix} 2 & 2 \\ 3 & 1 \end{bmatrix} - (2)\det\begin{bmatrix} 2 & 3 \\ 3 & 1 \end{bmatrix} + (1)\det\begin{bmatrix} 2 & 3 \\ 2 & 2 \end{bmatrix} = (3)(2 - 6) - (2)(2 - 9) + (1)(4 - 6) = 0$$

Since $\det A = 0$, $A^{-1}$ does not exist.

13. Expanding about the first column results in $\det A = 2\det\begin{bmatrix} 3 & 0 \\ 0 & 5 \end{bmatrix} - 0 + 0 = (2)(15 - 0) = 30.$

14. Expanding about the first column results in $\det A = 0 - 0 + 5\det\begin{bmatrix} 0 & 2 \\ 3 & 0 \end{bmatrix} = (5)(0 - 6) = -30.$

15. Expanding about the first row results in $\det A = 0$.

16. Expanding about the last column results in $\det A = 5\det\begin{bmatrix} -3 & -3 \\ 7 & 0 \end{bmatrix} - 0 + 0 = (5)(0 - (-21)) = 105.$

17. Expanding about the first column results in

$$\det A = 3\det\begin{bmatrix} 5 & 7 \\ 0 & -1 \end{bmatrix} - 0 + 1\det\begin{bmatrix} -1 & 2 \\ 5 & 7 \end{bmatrix} = (3)(-5 - 0) + (1)(-7 - 10) = -32.$$

18. Expanding about the first row results in

$$\det A = 3\det\begin{bmatrix} 3 & -4 \\ -5 & 1 \end{bmatrix} - 0 + (-1)\det\begin{bmatrix} 2 & 3 \\ 6 & -5 \end{bmatrix} = (3)(3 - 20) + (-1)(-10 - 18) = -23.$$

19. Expanding about the first column results in

$$\det A = 1\det\begin{bmatrix} 1 & 3 \\ 4 & -2 \end{bmatrix} - (-7)\det\begin{bmatrix} -5 & 2 \\ 4 & -2 \end{bmatrix} + 0 = (1)(-2 - 12) - (-7)(10 - 8) = 0.$$

20. Expanding about the second row results in

$$\det A = -(-2)\det\begin{bmatrix} -1 & 2 \\ 1 & -1 \end{bmatrix} + 0 - 1\det\begin{bmatrix} 1 & -1 \\ 1 & 1 \end{bmatrix} = (2)(1 - 2) - (1)(1 - (-1)) = -4.$$

21. $\det A = \det\begin{bmatrix} 11 & -32 \\ 1.2 & 55 \end{bmatrix} = 643.4$

22. $\det A = \det\begin{bmatrix} 17 & -4 & 3 \\ 11 & 5 & -15 \\ 7 & -9 & 23 \end{bmatrix} = 690$

23. $\det A = \det\begin{bmatrix} 2.3 & 5.1 & 2.8 \\ 1.2 & 4.5 & 8.8 \\ -0.4 & -0.8 & -1.2 \end{bmatrix} = -4.484$

24. $\det A = \det\begin{bmatrix} 1 & -1 & 3 & 7 \\ 9 & 2 & -7 & -4 \\ 5 & -7 & 1 & -9 \\ 7 & 1 & 3 & 6 \end{bmatrix} = 2886$

25. By Cramer's rule, the solution can be found as follows:

$E = \det\begin{bmatrix} 5 & 2 \\ 1 & 3 \end{bmatrix} = 13$; $F = \det\begin{bmatrix} -1 & 5 \\ 3 & 1 \end{bmatrix} = -16$; $D = \det\begin{bmatrix} -1 & 2 \\ 3 & 3 \end{bmatrix} = -9$

Thus $x = \dfrac{E}{D} = \dfrac{13}{-9}$ and $y = \dfrac{F}{D} = \dfrac{-16}{-9} = \dfrac{16}{9}$. The solution is $\left(-\dfrac{13}{9}, \dfrac{16}{9}\right)$.

26. By Cramer's rule, the solution can be found as follows:

$E = \det\begin{bmatrix} -3 & 1 \\ -7 & -6 \end{bmatrix} = 25$; $F = \det\begin{bmatrix} 2 & -3 \\ -4 & -7 \end{bmatrix} = -26$; $D = \det\begin{bmatrix} 2 & 1 \\ -4 & -6 \end{bmatrix} = -8$

Thus $x = \dfrac{E}{D} = \dfrac{25}{-8}$ and $y = \dfrac{F}{D} = \dfrac{-26}{-8} = \dfrac{26}{8} = \dfrac{13}{4}$. The solution is $\left(-\dfrac{25}{8}, \dfrac{13}{4}\right)$.

27. By Cramer's rule, the solution can be found as follows:

$E = \det\begin{bmatrix} 8 & 3 \\ 3 & -5 \end{bmatrix} = -49$; $F = \det\begin{bmatrix} -2 & 8 \\ 4 & 3 \end{bmatrix} = -38$; $D = \det\begin{bmatrix} -2 & 3 \\ 4 & -5 \end{bmatrix} = -2$

Thus $x = \dfrac{E}{D} = \dfrac{-49}{-2} = \dfrac{49}{2}$ and $y = \dfrac{F}{D} = \dfrac{-38}{-2} = 19$. The solution is $\left(\dfrac{49}{2}, 19\right)$.

28. By Cramer's rule, the solution can be found as follows:

$E = \det\begin{bmatrix} 4 & -3 \\ 5 & -7 \end{bmatrix} = -13$; $F = \det\begin{bmatrix} 5 & 4 \\ -3 & 5 \end{bmatrix} = 37$; $D = \det\begin{bmatrix} 5 & -3 \\ -3 & -7 \end{bmatrix} = -44$

Thus $x = \dfrac{E}{D} = \dfrac{-13}{-44} = \dfrac{13}{44}$ and $y = \dfrac{F}{D} = \dfrac{37}{-44} = -\dfrac{37}{44}$. The solution is $\left(\dfrac{13}{44}, -\dfrac{37}{44}\right)$.

29. By Cramer's rule, the solution can be found as follows:

$E = \det\begin{bmatrix} 23 & 4 \\ 70 & -5 \end{bmatrix} = -395$; $F = \det\begin{bmatrix} 7 & 23 \\ 11 & 70 \end{bmatrix} = 237$; $D = \det\begin{bmatrix} 7 & 4 \\ 11 & -5 \end{bmatrix} = -79$

Thus $x = \dfrac{E}{D} = \dfrac{-395}{-79} = 5$ and $y = \dfrac{F}{D} = \dfrac{237}{-79} = -3$. The solution is (5, –3).

30. By Cramer's rule, the solution can be found as follows:

$E = \det\begin{bmatrix} 8.2 & 5 \\ -0.4 & 4 \end{bmatrix} = 34.8$; $F = \det\begin{bmatrix} -7 & 8.2 \\ 6 & -0.4 \end{bmatrix} = -46.4$; $D = \det\begin{bmatrix} -7 & 5 \\ 6 & 4 \end{bmatrix} = -58$

Thus $x = \dfrac{E}{D} = \dfrac{34.8}{-58} = -0.6$ and $y = \dfrac{F}{D} = \dfrac{-46.4}{-58} = 0.8$. The solution is (–0.6, 0.8).

31. By Cramer's rule, the solution can be found as follows:

$E = \det\begin{bmatrix} -0.91 & -2.5 \\ 0.423 & 0.9 \end{bmatrix} = 0.2385$; $F = \det\begin{bmatrix} 1.7 & -0.91 \\ -0.4 & 0.423 \end{bmatrix} = 0.3551$; $D = \det\begin{bmatrix} 1.7 & -2.5 \\ -0.4 & 0.9 \end{bmatrix} = 0.53$

Thus $x = \dfrac{E}{D} = \dfrac{0.2385}{0.53} = 0.45$ and $y = \dfrac{F}{D} = \dfrac{0.3551}{0.53} = 0.67$. The solution is (0.45, 0.67).

32. By Cramer's rule, the solution can be found as follows:

$$E = \det\begin{bmatrix} -1.53 & 1.5 \\ -1.68 & -5.5 \end{bmatrix} = 10.935;\ F = \det\begin{bmatrix} -2.7 & -1.53 \\ 1.8 & -1.68 \end{bmatrix} = 7.29;\ D = \det\begin{bmatrix} -2.7 & 1.5 \\ 1.8 & -5.5 \end{bmatrix} = 12.15$$

Thus $x = \dfrac{E}{D} = \dfrac{10.935}{12.15} = 0.9$ and $y = \dfrac{F}{D} = \dfrac{7.29}{12.15} = 0.6$. The solution is (0.9, 0.6).

33. Enter the vertices as columns in a counterclockwise direction.

$$D = \frac{1}{2}\det\begin{bmatrix} 0 & 4 & 1 \\ 0 & 2 & 4 \\ 1 & 1 & 1 \end{bmatrix} = 7;$$ The area of the triangle is 7 square units.

34. Enter the vertices as columns in a counterclockwise direction.

$$D = \frac{1}{2}\det\begin{bmatrix} -3 & -1 & 2 \\ 3 & -3 & 3 \\ 1 & 1 & 1 \end{bmatrix} = 15;$$ The area of the triangle is 15 square units.

35. A line segment between (1, 3) and (3, 2) divides the quadrangle into two triangles whose areas can be found using determinants. Enter the vertices of each triangle as columns in a counterclockwise direction.

$$D = \frac{1}{2}\det\begin{bmatrix} 0 & 3 & 1 \\ 0 & 2 & 3 \\ 1 & 1 & 1 \end{bmatrix} + \frac{1}{2}\det\begin{bmatrix} 1 & 3 & 5 \\ 3 & 2 & 4 \\ 1 & 1 & 1 \end{bmatrix} = 6.5;$$ The area of the quadrangle is 6.5 square units.

36. A line segment between (–1, –3) and (–1, 3) and a second line segment between (–1, –3) and (2, 2) divides the pentagon into three triangles whose areas can be found using determinants. Enter the vertices of each triangle as columns in a counterclockwise direction.

$$D = \frac{1}{2}\det\begin{bmatrix} -1 & -1 & -4 \\ -3 & 3 & 1 \\ 1 & 1 & 1 \end{bmatrix} + \frac{1}{2}\det\begin{bmatrix} -1 & 2 & -1 \\ -3 & 2 & 3 \\ 1 & 1 & 1 \end{bmatrix} + \frac{1}{2}\det\begin{bmatrix} -1 & 4 & 2 \\ -3 & 0 & 2 \\ 1 & 1 & 1 \end{bmatrix} = 26$$

The area of the pentagon is 26 square units.

37. If the three points form a triangle with no area ($D = 0$ using determinants), then the points must be collinear.

$$D = \frac{1}{2}\det\begin{bmatrix} 1 & -3 & 2 \\ 3 & 11 & 1 \\ 1 & 1 & 1 \end{bmatrix} = 0;$$ The points are collinear.

38. If the three points form a triangle with no area ($D = 0$ using determinants), then the points must be collinear.

$$D = \frac{1}{2}\det\begin{bmatrix} 3 & -1 & 5 \\ 6 & -6 & 11 \\ 1 & 1 & 1 \end{bmatrix} = 2 \neq 0;$$ The points are not collinear.

39. If the three points form a triangle with no area ($D = 0$ using determinants), then the points must be collinear.

$$D = \frac{1}{2}\det\begin{bmatrix} -2 & 4 & 2 \\ -5 & 4 & 3 \\ 1 & 1 & 1 \end{bmatrix} = 6 \neq 0;$$ The points are not collinear.

40. If the three points form a triangle with no area ($D = 0$ using determinants), then the points must be collinear.

$$D = \frac{1}{2}\det\begin{bmatrix} 4 & -2 & 6 \\ -5 & 10 & -10 \\ 1 & 1 & 1 \end{bmatrix} = 0;$$ The points are collinear.

41. Use cofactors to expand about row 1 of $\begin{bmatrix} x & y & 1 \\ 2 & 1 & 1 \\ -1 & 4 & 1 \end{bmatrix} = 0 \Rightarrow x(-3) - y(3) + 9 = 0 \Rightarrow$

$-3x - 3y = -9 \Rightarrow x + y = 3.$

42. Use cofactors to expand about row 1 of $\begin{bmatrix} x & y & 1 \\ -1 & 3 & 1 \\ 4 & 2 & 1 \end{bmatrix} = 0 \Rightarrow x(1) - y(-5) + (-14) = 0 \Rightarrow$

$x + 5y = 14.$

43. Use cofactors to expand about row 1 of $\begin{bmatrix} x & y & 1 \\ 6 & -7 & 1 \\ 4 & -3 & 1 \end{bmatrix} = 0 \Rightarrow x(-4) - y(2) + (10) = 0 \Rightarrow 2x + y = 5.$

44. Use cofactors to expand about row 1 of $\begin{bmatrix} x & y & 1 \\ 5 & 1 & 1 \\ 2 & -2 & 1 \end{bmatrix} = 0 \Rightarrow x(3) - y(3) + (-12) = 0 \Rightarrow x - y = 4.$

## Extended and Discovery Exercises for Section 6.7

1. $D = 1[(1)(3) - (1)(2)] - 2[(1)(3) - (1)(1)] + 0[(1)(2) - (1)(1)] = 1 - 4 + 0 = -3$

   $E = 6[(1)(3) - (1)(2)] - 9[(1)(3) - (1)(1)] + 9[(1)(2) - (1)(1)] = 6 - 18 + 9 = -3$

   $F = 1[(9)(3) - (9)(2)] - 2[(6)(3) - (9)(1)] + 0[(6)(2) - (9)(1)] = 9 - 18 + 0 = -9$

   $G = 1[(1)(9) - (1)(9)] - 2[(1)(9) - (1)(6)] + 0[(1)(9) - (1)(6)] = 0 - 6 + 0 = -6$

   $x = \frac{E}{D} = \frac{-3}{-3} = 1, y = \frac{F}{D} = \frac{-9}{-3} = 3, z = \frac{G}{D} = \frac{-6}{-3} = 2.$ The solution is $(1, 3, 2)$.

2. $D = 0[(-1)(-1) - (1)(-1)] - 2[(1)(-1) - (1)(1)] + 1[(1)(-1) - (-1)(1)] = 0 + 4 + 0 = 4$

   $E = 1[(-1)(-1) - (1)(-1)] - (-1)[(1)(-1) - (1)(1)] + 3[(1)(-1) - (-1)(1)] = 2 - 2 + 0 = 0$

   $F = 0[(-1)(-1) - (3)(-1)] - 2[(1)(-1) - (3)(1)] + 1[(1)(-1) - (-1)(1)] = 0 + 8 + 0 = 8$

   $G = 0[(-1)(3) - (1)(-1)] - 2[(1)(3) - (1)(1)] + 1[(1)(-1) - (-1)(1)] = 0 - 4 + 0 = -4$

   $x = \frac{E}{D} = \frac{0}{4} = 0, y = \frac{F}{D} = \frac{8}{4} = 2, z = \frac{G}{D} = \frac{-4}{4} = -1.$ The solution is $(0, 2, -1)$.

3. $D = 1[(1)(2) - (1)(0)] - 1[(0)(2) - (1)(1)] + 0[(0)(0) - (1)(1)] = 2 + 1 + 0 = 3$

   $E = 2[(1)(2) - (1)(0)] - 0[(0)(2) - (1)(1)] + 1[(0)(0) - (1)(1)] = 4 + 0 - 1 = 3$

   $F = 1[(0)(2) - (1)(0)] - 1[(2)(2) - (1)(1)] + 0[(0)(2) - (1)(0)] = 0 - 3 + 0 = -3$

   $G = 1[(1)(1) - (1)(0)] - 1[(0)(1) - (1)(2)] + 0[(0)(0) - (1)(2)] = 1 + 2 + 0 = 3$

   $x = \frac{E}{D} = \frac{3}{3} = 1, y = \frac{F}{D} = \frac{-3}{3} = -1, z = \frac{G}{D} = \frac{3}{3} = 1.$ The solution is $(1, -1, 1)$.

4. $D = 1[(-2)(-3) - (1)(-3)] - (-1)[(1)(-3) - (1)(2)] + 0[(1)(-3) - (-2)(2)] = 9 - 5 + 0 = 4$

$E = 1[(-2)(-3) - (1)(-3)] - (-2)[(1)(-3) - (1)(2)] + 5[(1)(-3) - (-2)(2)] = 9 - 10 + 5 = 4$

$F = 1[(-2)(-3) - (5)(-3)] - (-1)[(1)(-3) - (5)(2)] + 0[(1)(-3) - (-2)(2)] = 21 - 13 + 0 = 8$

$G = 1[(-2)(5) - (1)(-2)] - (-1)[(1)(5) - (1)(1)] + 0[(1)(-2) - (-2)(1)] = -8 + 4 + 0 = -4$

$x = \frac{E}{D} = \frac{4}{4} = 1, y = \frac{F}{D} = \frac{8}{4} = 2, z = \frac{G}{D} = \frac{-4}{4} = -1$. The solution is $(1, 2, -1)$.

5. $D = 1[(1)(2) - (-1)(1)] - (-1)[(0)(2) - (-1)(2)] + 2[(0)(1) - (1)(2)] = 3 + 2 - 4 = 1$

$E = 7[(1)(2) - (-1)(1)] - 5[(0)(2) - (-1)(2)] + 6[(0)(1) - (1)(2)] = 21 - 10 - 12 = -1$

$F = 1[(5)(2) - (6)(1)] - (-1)[(7)(2) - (6)(2)] + 2[(7)(1) - (5)(2)] = 4 + 2 - 6 = 0$

$G = 1[(1)(6) - (-1)(5)] - (-1)[(0)(6) - (-1)(7)] + 2[(0)(5) - (1)(7)] = 11 + 7 - 14 = 4$

$x = \frac{E}{D} = \frac{-1}{1} = -1, y = \frac{F}{D} = \frac{0}{1} = 0, z = \frac{G}{D} = \frac{4}{1} = 4$. The solution is $(-1, 0, 4)$.

6. $D = 1[(-3)(-2) - (4)(-1)] - 2[(2)(-2) - (4)(3)] + 1[(2)(-1) - (-3)(3)] = 10 + 32 + 7 = 49$

$E = -1[(-3)(-2) - (4)(-1)] - 12[(2)(-2) - (4)(3)] + (-12)[(2)(-1) - (-3)(3)] =$

$-10 + 192 - 84 = 98$

$F = 1[(12)(-2) - (-12)(-1)] - 2[(-1)(-2) - (-12)(3)] + 1[(-1)(-1) - (12)(3)] =$

$-36 - 76 - 35 = -147$

$G = 1[(-3)(-12) - (4)(12)] - 2[(2)(-12) - (4)(-1)] + 1[(2)(12) - (-3)(-1)] =$

$-12 + 40 + 21 = 49$

$x = \frac{E}{D} = \frac{98}{49} = 2, y = \frac{F}{D} = \frac{-147}{49} = -3, z = \frac{G}{D} = \frac{49}{49} = 1$. The solution is $(2, -3, 1)$.

7. Use cofactors to expand about row 1 of $\begin{bmatrix} x^2 + y^2 & x & y & 1 \\ 4 & 0 & 2 & 1 \\ 4 & 2 & 0 & 1 \\ 4 & -2 & 0 & 1 \end{bmatrix} = 0 \Rightarrow$

$(x^2 + y^2)[-8] - x(0) + y(0) - (-32) = 0 \Rightarrow x^2 + y^2 - 4 = 0.$

8. Use cofactors to expand about row 1 of $\begin{bmatrix} x^2 + y^2 & x & y & 1 \\ 0 & 0 & 0 & 1 \\ 16 & 4 & 0 & 1 \\ 8 & 2 & -2 & 1 \end{bmatrix} = 0 \Rightarrow$

$(x^2 + y^2)[-8] - x(-32) + y(0) - (0) = 0 \Rightarrow x^2 - 4x + y^2 = 0.$

9. Use cofactors to expand about row 1 of $\begin{bmatrix} x^2 + y^2 & x & y & 1 \\ 1 & 0 & 1 & 1 \\ 2 & 1 & -1 & 1 \\ 8 & 2 & 2 & 1 \end{bmatrix} = 0 \Rightarrow$

$(x^2 + y^2)(5) - x(15) + y(-5) - 0 = 0 \Rightarrow 5x^2 + 5y^2 - 15x - 5y = 0.$

10. Use cofactors to expand about row 1 of $\begin{bmatrix} x^2+y^2 & x & y & 1 \\ 1 & 1 & 0 & 1 \\ 5 & -1 & 2 & 1 \\ 13 & 3 & 2 & 1 \end{bmatrix} = 0 \Rightarrow$

$(x^2 + y^2)(-8) - x(-16) + y(32) - 8 = 0 \Rightarrow 8x^2 + 8y^2 - 16x - 32y + 8 = 0.$

## Checking Basic Concepts for Section 6.7

1. $\det A = a_{11}A_{11} + a_{21}A_{21} + a_{31}A_{31} = a_{11}M_{11} - a_{21}M_{21} + a_{31}M_{31} \Rightarrow$

   $\det A = (1)\det\begin{bmatrix} 3 & 1 \\ -2 & 5 \end{bmatrix} - (2)\det\begin{bmatrix} -1 & 2 \\ -2 & 5 \end{bmatrix} + (0)\det\begin{bmatrix} -1 & 2 \\ 3 & 1 \end{bmatrix} =$

   $(1)(15 - (-2)) - (2)(-5 - (-4)) + 0 = 19$. Since $\det A = 19 \neq 0$ $A$ is invertible.

2. By Cramer's rule, the solution can be found as follows:

   $E = \det\begin{bmatrix} 7 & -4 \\ 5 & 3 \end{bmatrix} = 41;\ F = \det\begin{bmatrix} 3 & 7 \\ -4 & 5 \end{bmatrix} = 43;\ D = \det\begin{bmatrix} 3 & -4 \\ -4 & 3 \end{bmatrix} = -7$

   Thus $x = \frac{E}{D} = \frac{41}{-7}$ and $y = \frac{F}{D} = \frac{43}{-7}$. The solution is $\left(-\frac{41}{7}, -\frac{43}{7}\right)$.

## Chapter 6 Review Exercises

1. $A(b, h) = \frac{1}{2}bh \Rightarrow A(3, 6) = \frac{1}{2}(3)(6) = 9$
2. $V(r, h) = \pi r^2 h \Rightarrow V(2, 5) = \pi(2^2)(5) = 20\pi$
3. (a) $3x + y = 1 \Rightarrow y = 1 - 3x$ and $2x - 3y = 8 \Rightarrow y = \frac{2x - 8}{3}$

   Graph $Y_1 = 1 - 3X$ and $Y_2 = (2X - 8)/3$. The graphs intersect at the point (1, –2). See Figure 3.

   (b) Substituting $y = 1 - 3x$ into the second equation gives $2x - 3(1 - 3x) = 8 \Rightarrow 2x - 3 + 9x = 8 \Rightarrow$

   $11x = 11 \Rightarrow x = 1$. If $x = 1$, then $y = 1 - 3(1) = -2$. The solution is (1, –2).
4. (a) $x^2 - y = 1 \Rightarrow y = x^2 - 1$ and $x + y = 1 \Rightarrow y = 1 - x$

   Graph $Y_1 = X\text{^}2 - 1$ and $Y_2 = 1 - X$. The graphs intersect at the points (1, 0) and (–2, 3). See Figure 4.

   (b) Substituting $y = 1 - x$ into the first equation gives $x^2 - (1 - x) = 1 \Rightarrow x^2 + x - 2 = 0 \Rightarrow$

   $(x - 1)(x + 2) = 0 \Rightarrow x = 1$ or $-2$. If $x = 1$, then $y = 1 - 1 = 0$, and if $x = -2$

   then $y = 1 - (-2) = 3$. The solutions are (1, 0) and (–2, 3).

[–10, 10, 1] by [–10, 10, 1]

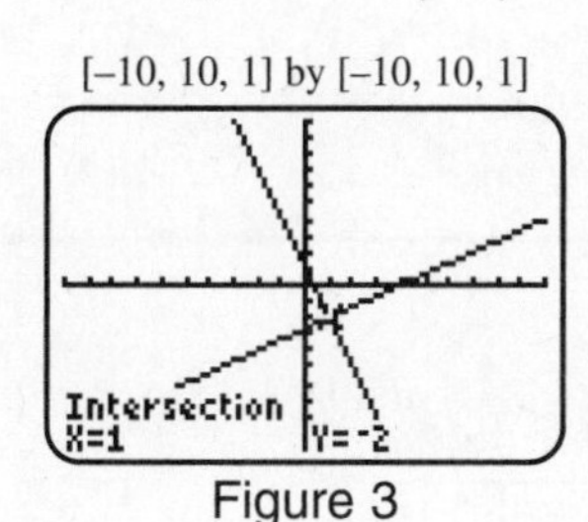


Figure 3

[–5, 5, 1] by [–5, 5, 1]

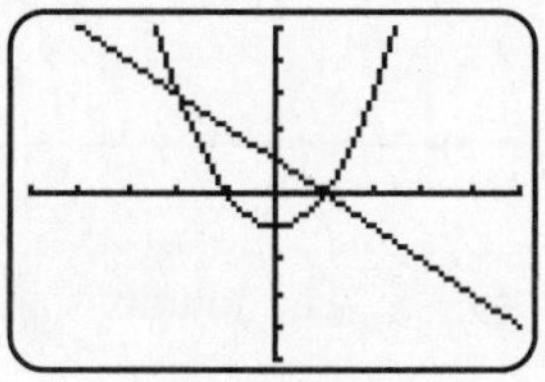

Figure 4

5. Multiply the first equation by 2 and add to eliminate the $y$-variable.

$$\begin{array}{rcl} 4x + 2y &=& 14 \\ x - 2y &=& -4 \\ \hline 5x \quad &=& 10 \Rightarrow x = 2 \end{array}$$

Since $2x + y = 7$, it follows that $y = 3$. The solution is $(2, 3)$. The system is consistent.

6. Multiply the second equation by 3 and add to eliminate both variables.

$$\begin{array}{rcl} 3x + 3y &=& 15 \\ -3x - 3y &=& -12 \\ \hline 0 &=& 3 \Rightarrow \text{no solutions} \end{array}$$

Since $0 \neq 3$, the system is inconsistent and there are no solutions.

7. Multiply the first equation by 2, the second equation by 3, and add to eliminate the $y$-variable.

$$\begin{array}{rcl} 12x - 30y &=& 24 \\ -12x + 30y &=& -24 \\ \hline 0 &=& 0 \Rightarrow \text{infinitely many solutions of the form } \{(x, y) \mid 2x - 5y = 4\} \end{array}$$

Since $0 = 0$, the system is consistent and there are infinitely many solutions.

8. Multiply the first equation by 3, the second equation by 4, and add to eliminate the $y$-variable.

$$\begin{array}{rcl} 9x - 12y &=& -30 \\ 16x + 12y &=& -120 \\ \hline 25x \quad &=& -150 \Rightarrow x = -6 \end{array}$$

Since $3x - 4y = -10$, then it follows that $3(-6) - 4y = -10 \Rightarrow -4y = 8 \Rightarrow y = -2$.

The solution is $(-6, -2)$. The system is consistent.

9. Subtract the equations to eliminate the $x$-variable.

$$\begin{array}{rcl} x^2 - 3y &=& 3 \\ x^2 + 2y^2 &=& 5 \\ \hline \end{array}$$

$$-3y - 2y^2 = -2 \Rightarrow 0 = 2y^2 + 3y - 2 \Rightarrow (2y - 1)(y + 2) = 0 \Rightarrow y = -2, \frac{1}{2}.$$

If $y = -2$ then $x^2 - 3(-2) = 3 \Rightarrow x^2 + 6 = 3 \Rightarrow x^2 = -3$. There is no real solution to this $\Rightarrow y \neq -2$.

If $y = \frac{1}{2}$ then $x^2 - 3\left(\frac{1}{2}\right) = 3 \Rightarrow x^2 = \frac{9}{2} \Rightarrow x = \pm\frac{3}{\sqrt{2}} \Rightarrow x = \pm\frac{3\sqrt{2}}{2}$.

The solutions are $\left(\frac{3\sqrt{2}}{2}, \frac{1}{2}\right)$ and $\left(\frac{-3\sqrt{2}}{2}, \frac{1}{2}\right)$.

10. Multiply the second equation by 3 and add the equations to eliminate the $y$-variable.

$$\begin{array}{rcl} 2x - 3y &=& 1 \\ 6x^2 + 3y &=& 3 \\ \hline \end{array}$$

$$2x + 6x^2 = 4 \Rightarrow 6x^2 + 2x - 4 = 0 \Rightarrow 2(3x^2 + x - 2) = 0 \Rightarrow 2(3x - 2)(x + 1) = 0 \Rightarrow x = \frac{2}{3}, -1.$$

If $x = \frac{2}{3}$ then $2\left(\frac{2}{3}\right) - 3y = 1 \Rightarrow \frac{4}{3} - 3y = 1 \Rightarrow -3y = -\frac{1}{3} \Rightarrow y = \frac{1}{9}$.

If $x = -1$ then $2(-1) - 3y = 1 \Rightarrow -3y = 3 \Rightarrow y = -1$. The solutions are $\left(\frac{2}{3}, \frac{1}{9}\right)$ and $(-1, -1)$.

11. See Figure 11.

12. $2x - y < 4 \Rightarrow -y < -2x + 4 \Rightarrow y > 2x - 4$. See Figure 12.

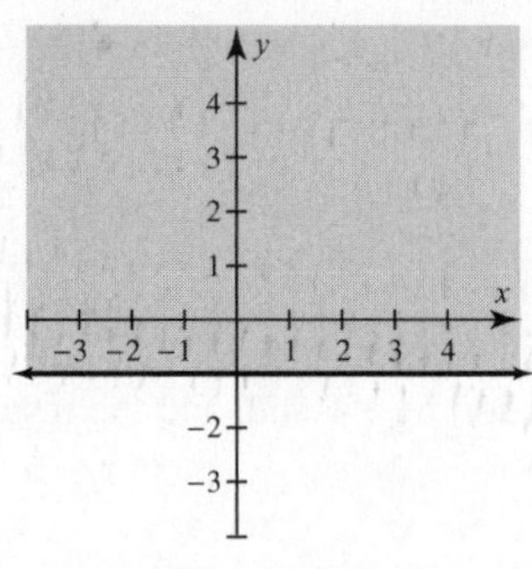

Figure 11

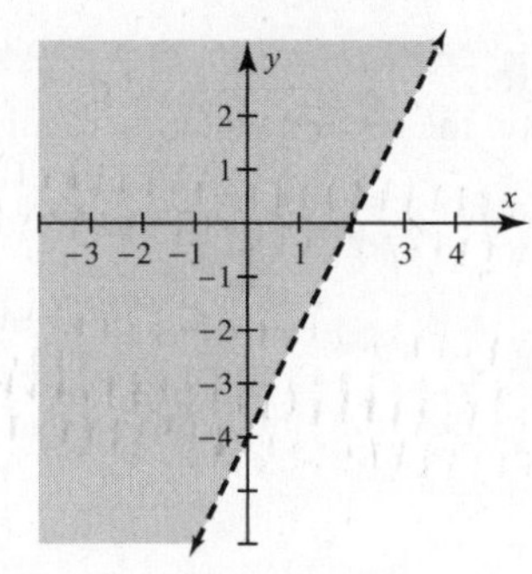

Figure 12

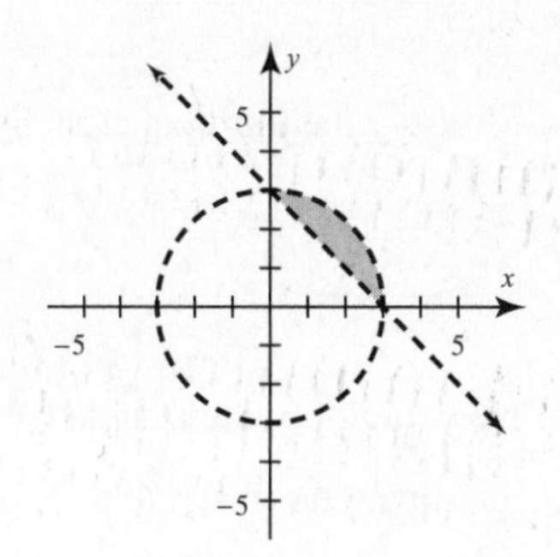

Figure 13

13. The solution region is inside the circle or radius 3 and above the line $y = 3 - x$. Their graphs intersect at the points (0, 3) and (3, 0). It does not include the boundary. See Figure 13. One solution to the system is (2, 2).

14. The solution region lies below the line $x + y = 4$ and above the line $x + 3y = 3$. Their graphs intersect at $\left(\frac{9}{2}, \frac{-1}{2}\right)$. The region includes the boundary. See Figure 14. One solution to the system is (0, 2).

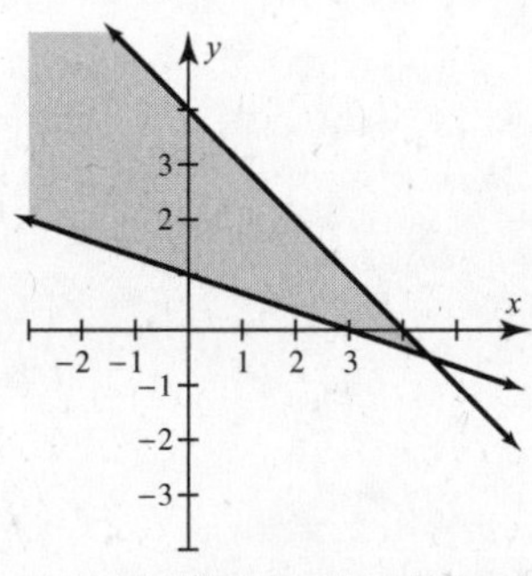

Figure 14

15. First, subtract the first two equations to eliminate the $x$-variable.

$$\begin{aligned} x - \phantom{2}y + \phantom{2}z &= -2 \\ x + 2y - \phantom{2}z &= \phantom{-}2 \\ \hline -3y + 2z &= -4 \end{aligned}$$

Multiply this equation by 2 and multiply the last equation by 3 to eliminate the $y$-variable.

$$\begin{aligned} -6y + 4z &= -8 \\ 6y + 9z &= 21 \\ \hline 13z &= 13 \Rightarrow z = 1 \end{aligned}$$

Substituting $z = 1$ into $2y + 3z = 7$ gives $2y + 3 = 7 \Rightarrow 2y = 4 \Rightarrow y = 2$. Substituting $y = 2$ and $z = 1$ into the original first equation gives $x - 2 + 1 = -2 \Rightarrow x - 1 = -2 \Rightarrow x = -1$.

The solution to the system is $(-1, 2, 1)$.

16. Add the first and third equations to eliminate the $x$-variable.

$$\begin{array}{r} x - 3y + 2z = -10 \\ -x - y + z = -1 \\ \hline -4y + 3z = -11 \end{array}$$

Multiply the third equation by 2 and add the second equation to eliminate the $x$-variable.

$$\begin{array}{r} -2x - 2y + 2z = -2 \\ 2x - y + 3z = -9 \\ \hline -3y + 5z = -11 \end{array}$$

Now, multiply the first new equation by 3, and multiply the second new equation by $-4$ and, add the results to eliminate the $y$-variable.

$$\begin{array}{r} -12y + 9z = -33 \\ 12y - 20z = 44 \\ \hline -11z = 11 \Rightarrow z = -1 \end{array}$$

Substituting $z = -1$ into $-3y + 5z = -11$ gives $-3y - 5 = -11 \Rightarrow -3y = -6 \Rightarrow y = 2$. Substituting $y = 2$ and $z = -1$ into the original third equation gives $-x - 2 + (-1) = -1 \Rightarrow -x = 2 \Rightarrow x = -2$. The solution is $(-2, 2, -1)$.

17. Add the first two equations to eliminate the $x$-variable.

$$\begin{array}{r} -x + 2y + 2z = 9 \\ x + y - 3z = 6 \\ \hline 3y - z = 15 \end{array}$$

Subtract this new equation from the third equation.

$$\begin{array}{r} 3y - z = 8 \\ 3y - z = 15 \\ \hline 0 = -7 \end{array}$$

Since $0 \neq -7$, there is no solution.

18. Multiply the first equation by 2 and add the third equation to eliminate the $y$-variable.

$$\begin{array}{r} 4x - 2y - 6z = -18 \\ -3x + 2y - 2z = -5 \\ \hline x \quad\quad - 8z = -23 \end{array}$$

Subtract this from the second equation.

$$\begin{array}{r} x - 8z = -23 \\ x - 8z = -23 \\ \hline 0 = 0 \end{array}$$

Since this is true that $0 = 0$, we have infinitely many solutions. These solutions can be found:

$x - 8z = -23 \Rightarrow x = 8z - 23$.

Multiply the second equation by 3, and add the third equation to eliminate the $x$-variable.

$$\begin{array}{r} 3x \quad\quad - 24z = -69 \\ -3x + 2y - 2z = -5 \\ \hline 2y - 26z = -74 \Rightarrow 2y = 26z - 74 \Rightarrow y = 13z - 37 \end{array}$$

We have infinitely many solution in the form: $(8z - 23, 13z - 37, z)$.

19. The system is $x + 5y = 6$ and $y = 3$.

Substituting $y = 3$ into the first equation gives $x + 5(3) = 6 \Rightarrow x = -9$. The solution is (–9, 3).

20. The system is $x + 2y - 2z = 8$, $y + z = 5$ and $0 = 0$. The second equation gives $y + z = 5 \Rightarrow y = 5 - z$.

Substituting $y = 5 - z$ into the first equation gives $x + 2(5 - z) - 2z = 8 \Rightarrow x = 4z - 2$.

The solution is $\{(4z - 2, 5 - z, z) \mid z \text{ is a real number}\}$.

21. The augmented matrix is in Row-Echelon Form $\Rightarrow x = -2, y = 3, z = 0 \Rightarrow (-2, 3, 0)$.

22. In this augmented matrix the third equation gives 0 = 5, which is false therefore there are no solutions.

23. $$\left[\begin{array}{ccc|c} 2 & -1 & 2 & 10 \\ 1 & -2 & 1 & 8 \\ 3 & -1 & 2 & 11 \end{array}\right] \begin{array}{l} (1/2)R_1 \rightarrow \\ R_1 - 2R_2 \rightarrow \\ 3R_2 - R_3 \rightarrow \end{array} \left[\begin{array}{ccc|c} 1 & -\frac{1}{2} & 1 & 5 \\ 0 & 3 & 0 & -6 \\ 0 & -5 & 1 & 13 \end{array}\right] (1/3)R_2 \rightarrow \left[\begin{array}{ccc|c} 1 & -\frac{1}{2} & 1 & 5 \\ 0 & 1 & 0 & -2 \\ 0 & -5 & 1 & 13 \end{array}\right]$$

$$5R_2 + R_3 \rightarrow \left[\begin{array}{ccc|c} 1 & -\frac{1}{2} & 1 & 5 \\ 0 & 1 & 0 & -2 \\ 0 & 0 & 1 & 3 \end{array}\right]$$

Backward substitution produces $z = 3$; $y = -2$; $x - \frac{1}{2}(-2) + 3 = 5 \Rightarrow x + 1 + 3 = 5 \Rightarrow x = 1$.

The solution is $(1, -2, 3)$.

24. $$\left[\begin{array}{ccc|c} 1 & -2 & 1 & 1 \\ 2 & -5 & 3 & 4 \\ 2 & -3 & 1 & 0 \end{array}\right] \begin{array}{l} \\ 2R_1 - R_2 \rightarrow \\ R_2 - R_3 \rightarrow \end{array} \left[\begin{array}{ccc|c} 1 & -2 & 1 & 1 \\ 0 & 1 & -1 & -2 \\ 0 & -2 & 2 & 4 \end{array}\right] 2R_2 + R_3 \rightarrow \left[\begin{array}{ccc|c} 1 & -2 & 1 & 1 \\ 0 & 1 & -1 & -2 \\ 0 & 0 & 0 & 0 \end{array}\right]$$

From the third equation $0 = 0 \Rightarrow$ there are infinitely many solutions. Use $y - z = -2 \Rightarrow y = z - 2$.

Now use the first equation and substitute $y = z - 2$: $x - 2(z - 2) + z = 1 \Rightarrow x - 2z + 4 + z = 1 \Rightarrow$

$x = z - 3$.

Therefore, there are infinitely solutions in the form $\{(z - 3, z - 2, z) \mid z \text{ is a real number}\}$.

25. (a) $a_{12} = 3$ and $a_{22} = 2 \Rightarrow a_{12} + a_{22} = 3 + 2 \Rightarrow a_{12} + a_{22} = 5$

(b) $a_{11} = -2$ and $a_{23} = 4 \Rightarrow a_{11} - 2a_{23} = -2 - 2(4) \Rightarrow a_{11} - 2a_{23} = -10$

26. (a) $a_{12} = 2$ and $a_{22} = -3 \Rightarrow a_{12} + a_{22} = 2 + (-3) \Rightarrow a_{12} + a_{22} = -1$

(b) $a_{11} = -1$ and $a_{23} = 7 \Rightarrow a_{11} - 2a_{23} = -1 - 2(7) \Rightarrow a_{11} - 2a_{23} = -15$

27. (a) $A + 2B = \begin{bmatrix} 1 & -3 \\ 2 & -1 \end{bmatrix} + 2\begin{bmatrix} 3 & 2 \\ -5 & 1 \end{bmatrix} = \begin{bmatrix} 7 & 1 \\ -8 & 1 \end{bmatrix}$

(b) $A - B = \begin{bmatrix} 1 & -3 \\ 2 & -1 \end{bmatrix} - \begin{bmatrix} 3 & 2 \\ -5 & 1 \end{bmatrix} = \begin{bmatrix} -2 & -5 \\ 7 & -2 \end{bmatrix}$

(c) $-4A = -4\begin{bmatrix} 1 & -3 \\ 2 & -1 \end{bmatrix} = \begin{bmatrix} -4 & 12 \\ -8 & 4 \end{bmatrix}$

28. (a) $A + 2B = \begin{bmatrix} 4 & 0 & 1 \\ -2 & 8 & 9 \end{bmatrix} + 2\begin{bmatrix} -5 & 3 & 2 \\ -4 & 0 & 7 \end{bmatrix} = \begin{bmatrix} -6 & 6 & 5 \\ -10 & 8 & 23 \end{bmatrix}$

(b) $A - B = \begin{bmatrix} 4 & 0 & 1 \\ -2 & 8 & 9 \end{bmatrix} - \begin{bmatrix} -5 & 3 & 2 \\ -4 & 0 & 7 \end{bmatrix} = \begin{bmatrix} 9 & -3 & -1 \\ 2 & 8 & 2 \end{bmatrix}$

(c) $-4A = -4\begin{bmatrix} 4 & 0 & 1 \\ -2 & 8 & 9 \end{bmatrix} = \begin{bmatrix} -16 & 0 & -4 \\ 8 & -32 & -36 \end{bmatrix}$

29. $A$ and $B$ are both $2 \times 2$ so $AB$ and $BA$ are also both $2 \times 2$.

$$AB = \begin{bmatrix} 2 & 0 \\ -5 & 3 \end{bmatrix}\begin{bmatrix} -1 & -2 \\ 4 & 7 \end{bmatrix} = \begin{bmatrix} -2 & -4 \\ 17 & 31 \end{bmatrix}; BA = \begin{bmatrix} -1 & -2 \\ 4 & 7 \end{bmatrix}\begin{bmatrix} 2 & 0 \\ -5 & 3 \end{bmatrix} = \begin{bmatrix} 8 & -6 \\ -27 & 21 \end{bmatrix}$$

30. $A$ is $2 \times 2$ and $B$ is $2 \times 3$ so $AB$ is $2 \times 3$. However $BA$ is undefined since the number of rows in $A$ is not equal to the number of columns in $B$.

$$AB = \begin{bmatrix} 1 & -2 \\ 2 & 3 \end{bmatrix}\begin{bmatrix} 1 & 0 & 2 \\ -1 & 3 & 4 \end{bmatrix} = \begin{bmatrix} 3 & -6 & -6 \\ -1 & 9 & 16 \end{bmatrix}$$

31. $A$ is $2 \times 3$ and $B$ is $3 \times 2$ so $AB$ is $2 \times 2$ and $BA$ is $3 \times 3$.

$$AB = \begin{bmatrix} 2 & -1 & 3 \\ 2 & 4 & 0 \end{bmatrix}\begin{bmatrix} 1 & 0 \\ -1 & 2 \\ 0 & 3 \end{bmatrix} = \begin{bmatrix} 3 & 7 \\ -2 & 8 \end{bmatrix}; BA = \begin{bmatrix} 1 & 0 \\ -1 & 2 \\ 0 & 3 \end{bmatrix}\begin{bmatrix} 2 & -1 & 3 \\ 2 & 4 & 0 \end{bmatrix} = \begin{bmatrix} 2 & -1 & 3 \\ 2 & 9 & -3 \\ 6 & 12 & 0 \end{bmatrix}$$

32. $A$ and $B$ are both $3 \times 3$ so $AB$ and $BA$ are also both $3 \times 3$.

$$AB = \begin{bmatrix} 1 & -1 & 2 \\ 0 & 3 & 4 \\ 1 & 0 & 2 \end{bmatrix}\begin{bmatrix} -1 & 0 & 0 \\ 2 & 0 & -1 \\ 1 & 4 & 2 \end{bmatrix} = \begin{bmatrix} -1 & 8 & 5 \\ 10 & 16 & 5 \\ 1 & 8 & 4 \end{bmatrix};$$

$$BA = \begin{bmatrix} -1 & 0 & 0 \\ 2 & 0 & -1 \\ 1 & 4 & 2 \end{bmatrix}\begin{bmatrix} 1 & -1 & 2 \\ 0 & 3 & 4 \\ 1 & 0 & 2 \end{bmatrix} = \begin{bmatrix} -1 & 1 & -2 \\ 1 & -2 & 2 \\ 3 & 11 & 22 \end{bmatrix}$$

33. $B$ is the inverse of $A$.

$$AB = \begin{bmatrix} 8 & 5 \\ 6 & 4 \end{bmatrix}\begin{bmatrix} 2 & -2.5 \\ -3 & 4 \end{bmatrix} = \begin{bmatrix} 1 & 0 \\ 0 & 1 \end{bmatrix} \text{ and } BA = \begin{bmatrix} 2 & -2.5 \\ -3 & 4 \end{bmatrix}\begin{bmatrix} 8 & 5 \\ 6 & 4 \end{bmatrix} = \begin{bmatrix} 1 & 0 \\ 0 & 1 \end{bmatrix}$$

34. $B$ is not the inverse of $A$.

$$AB = \begin{bmatrix} -1 & 1 & 2 \\ 1 & 0 & -1 \\ 0 & 1 & 2 \end{bmatrix}\begin{bmatrix} -1 & 0 & 1 \\ 2 & 2 & -1 \\ -1 & -1 & -1 \end{bmatrix} = \begin{bmatrix} 1 & 0 & -4 \\ 0 & 1 & 2 \\ 0 & 0 & -3 \end{bmatrix} \neq \begin{bmatrix} 1 & 0 & 0 \\ 0 & 1 & 0 \\ 0 & 0 & 1 \end{bmatrix}$$

35. (a) $\begin{aligned} x - 3y &= 4 \\ 2x - y &= 3 \end{aligned} \Rightarrow AX = \begin{bmatrix} 1 & -3 \\ 2 & -1 \end{bmatrix}\begin{bmatrix} x \\ y \end{bmatrix} = \begin{bmatrix} 4 \\ 3 \end{bmatrix} = B$

(b) $X = A^{-1}B \Rightarrow \begin{bmatrix} x \\ y \end{bmatrix} = \begin{bmatrix} -\frac{1}{5} & \frac{3}{5} \\ -\frac{2}{5} & \frac{1}{5} \end{bmatrix}\begin{bmatrix} 4 \\ 3 \end{bmatrix} = \begin{bmatrix} 1 \\ -1 \end{bmatrix}$

36. (a) $\begin{aligned} x - 2y + z &= 0 \\ 2x + y + 2z &= 10 \\ y + z &= 3 \end{aligned} \Rightarrow AX = \begin{bmatrix} 1 & -2 & 1 \\ 2 & 1 & 2 \\ 0 & 1 & 1 \end{bmatrix}\begin{bmatrix} x \\ y \\ z \end{bmatrix} = \begin{bmatrix} 0 \\ 10 \\ 3 \end{bmatrix} = B$

(b) $X = A^{-1}B = \begin{bmatrix} x \\ y \\ z \end{bmatrix} = \begin{bmatrix} -\frac{1}{5} & \frac{3}{5} & -1 \\ -\frac{2}{5} & \frac{1}{5} & 0 \\ \frac{2}{5} & -\frac{1}{5} & 1 \end{bmatrix}\begin{bmatrix} 0 \\ 10 \\ 3 \end{bmatrix} = \begin{bmatrix} 3 \\ 2 \\ 1 \end{bmatrix}$

37. (a) $AX = B \Rightarrow \begin{bmatrix} 12 & 7 & -3 \\ 8 & -11 & 13 \\ -23 & 0 & 9 \end{bmatrix} \begin{bmatrix} x \\ y \\ z \end{bmatrix} = \begin{bmatrix} 14.6 \\ -60.4 \\ -14.6 \end{bmatrix}$

(b) See Figure 37. $X = A^{-1}B \Rightarrow X = \begin{bmatrix} -0.5 \\ 1.7 \\ -2.9 \end{bmatrix}$

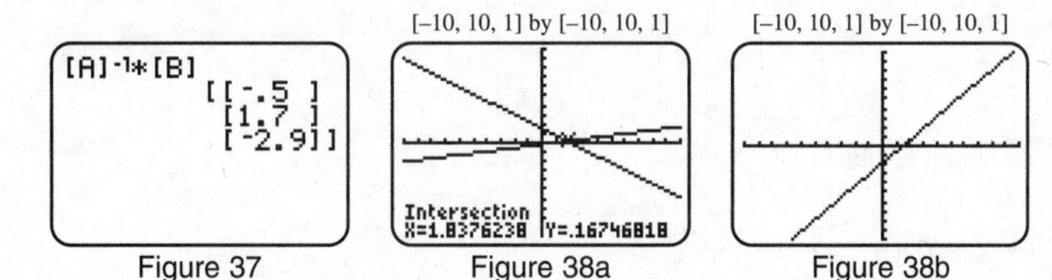

Figure 37 Figure 38a Figure 38b

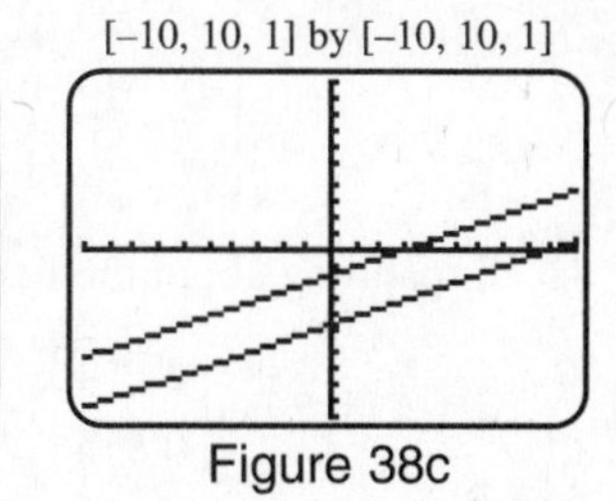

Figure 38c

38. (a) Start by solving each equation for $y$.

$3.1x + 4.2y = 6.4 \Rightarrow 4.2y = 6.4 - 3.1x \Rightarrow y = \dfrac{6.4 - 3.1x}{4.2}$

$1.7x - 9.1y = 1.6 \Rightarrow -9.1y = 1.6 - 1.7x \Rightarrow y = \dfrac{1.6 - 1.7x}{-9.1}$

Graph $Y_1 = (6.4 - 3.1X)/4.2$ and $Y_2 = (1.6 - 1.7X)/-9.1$. The graphs intersect near $(1.838, 0.1675)$ as shown in Figure 38a. The solution is $x \approx 1.838$ and $y \approx 0.1675$. The system is consistent and independent.

(b) Start by solving each equation for $y$.

$6.3x - 5.1y = 9.3 \Rightarrow -5.1y = 9.3 - 6.3x \Rightarrow y = \dfrac{9.3 - 6.3x}{-5.1}$

$4.2x - 3.4y = 6.2 \Rightarrow -3.4y = 6.2 - 4.2x \Rightarrow y = \dfrac{6.2 - 4.2x}{-3.4}$

Graph $Y_1 = (9.3 - 6.3X)/-5.1$ and $Y_2 = (6.2 - 4.2X)/-3.4$. The graphs are identical so the system is consistent and dependent. See Figure 38b. There are an infinite number of solutions. Any solution would have to be of the form $y = \dfrac{4.2x - 6.2}{3.4}$ where $x$ is any real number.

(c) Start by solving each equation for $y$.

$0.32x - 0.64y = 0.96 \Rightarrow -0.64y = 0.96 - 0.32x \Rightarrow y = \dfrac{0.96 - 0.32x}{-0.64}$

$-0.08x + 0.16y = -0.72 \Rightarrow 0.16y = -0.72 + 0.08x \Rightarrow y = \dfrac{-0.72 + 0.08x}{0.16}$

Graph $Y_1 = (0.96 - 0.32X)/-0.64$ and $Y_2 = (-0.72 + 0.08X)/0.16$. The graphs are parallel and do not intersect as shown in Figure 38c. The system is inconsistent and no solution exists.

39. $A|I_2 = \left[\begin{array}{cc|cc} 1 & -2 & 1 & 0 \\ -1 & 1 & 0 & 1 \end{array}\right] R_2 + R_1 \rightarrow \left[\begin{array}{cc|cc} 1 & -2 & 1 & 0 \\ 0 & -1 & 1 & 1 \end{array}\right] (-1)R_2 \rightarrow \left[\begin{array}{cc|cc} 1 & -2 & 1 & 0 \\ 0 & 1 & -1 & -1 \end{array}\right]$

$R_1 + 2R_2 \rightarrow \left[\begin{array}{cc|cc} 1 & 0 & -1 & -2 \\ 0 & 1 & -1 & -1 \end{array}\right]$; $A^{-1} = \begin{bmatrix} -1 & -2 \\ -1 & -1 \end{bmatrix}$

40. $A|I_3 = \left[\begin{array}{ccc|ccc} 1 & 0 & 1 & 1 & 0 & 0 \\ 1 & 1 & 1 & 0 & 1 & 0 \\ 0 & 1 & -1 & 0 & 0 & 1 \end{array}\right] R_2 - R_1 \rightarrow \left[\begin{array}{ccc|ccc} 1 & 0 & 1 & 1 & 0 & 0 \\ 0 & 1 & 0 & -1 & 1 & 0 \\ 0 & 1 & -1 & 0 & 0 & 1 \end{array}\right]$

$R_3 - R_2 \rightarrow \left[\begin{array}{ccc|ccc} 1 & 0 & 1 & 1 & 0 & 0 \\ 0 & 1 & 0 & -1 & 1 & 0 \\ 0 & 0 & -1 & 1 & -1 & 1 \end{array}\right] (-1)R_3 \rightarrow \left[\begin{array}{ccc|ccc} 1 & 0 & 1 & 1 & 0 & 0 \\ 0 & 1 & 0 & -1 & 1 & 0 \\ 0 & 0 & 1 & -1 & 1 & -1 \end{array}\right]$

$R_1 - R_3 \rightarrow \left[\begin{array}{ccc|ccc} 1 & 0 & 0 & 2 & -1 & 1 \\ 0 & 1 & 0 & -1 & 1 & 0 \\ 0 & 0 & 1 & -1 & 1 & -1 \end{array}\right]; A^{-1} = \begin{bmatrix} 2 & -1 & 1 \\ -1 & 1 & 0 \\ -1 & 1 & -1 \end{bmatrix}$

41. Expanding about the first column results in

$\det A = 2 \det\begin{bmatrix} 3 & 4 \\ 0 & 5 \end{bmatrix} - 0 + 1 \det\begin{bmatrix} 1 & 3 \\ 3 & 4 \end{bmatrix} = (2)(15 - 0) + (1)(4 - 9) = 25.$

42. Expanding about the first row results in

$\det A = 3 \det\begin{bmatrix} 3 & 5 \\ 2 & 0 \end{bmatrix} - 0 + 2 \det\begin{bmatrix} 1 & 3 \\ -5 & 2 \end{bmatrix} = (3)(0 - 10) + (2)(2 - (-15)) = 4.$

43. $\det A = \det\begin{bmatrix} 13 & 22 \\ 55 & -57 \end{bmatrix} = (13)(-57) - (55)(22) = -1951 \neq 0$; $A$ is invertible.

44. Using a graphing calculator, $\det A = \det\begin{bmatrix} 6 & -7 & -1 \\ -7 & 3 & -4 \\ 23 & 54 & 77 \end{bmatrix} = 0$; $A$ is not invertible.

45. The given equations result in the following nonlinear system of equations: $A(l, w) = 77 \Rightarrow lw = 77$ and $P(l, w) = 36 \Rightarrow 2l + 2w = 36$. Begin by solving the second equation for $l$.

$2l + 2w = 36 \Rightarrow 2l = 36 - 2w \Rightarrow l = 18 - w$. Substitute this into the first equation.

$lw = 77 \Rightarrow (18 - w)w = 77 \Rightarrow 18w - w^2 = 77 \Rightarrow w^2 - 18w + 77 = 0$. This is a quadratic equation that can be solved by factoring. $w^2 - 18w + 77 = 0 \Rightarrow (w - 7)(w - 11) = 0 \Rightarrow w = 7$ or 11.

Since $l = 18 - w$, if $w = 7$, then $l = 11$ and if $w = 11$ then $l = 7$. For this rectangle $l = 11$ and $w = 7$.

46. We must solve the system of nonlinear equations, $\pi r^2 h = 30$ and $2\pi rh = 45$.

Solving each equation for $h$ gives $\pi r^2 h = 30 \Rightarrow h = \dfrac{30}{\pi r^2}$ and $2\pi rh = 45 \Rightarrow h = \dfrac{45}{2\pi r}$.

Graph $Y_1 = 30/(\pi X\hat{}2)$ and $Y_2 = 45/(2\pi X)$. The graphs intersect near (1.333, 5.371). See Figure 46.

The cylinder has approximate measurements of $r \approx 1.333$ and $h \approx 5.371$.

[0, 4, 1] by [0, 20, 2]

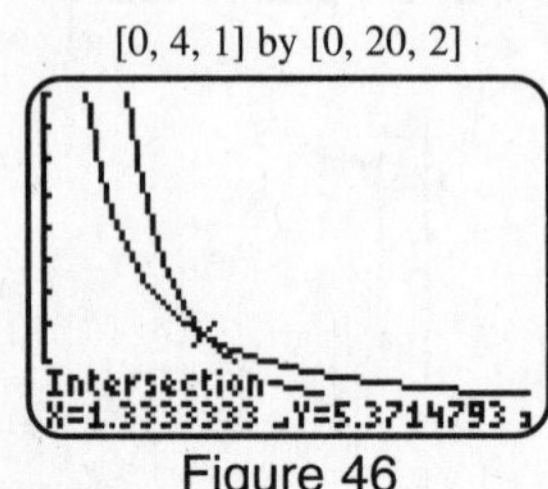


Figure 46

[0, 2000, 100] by [0, 2000, 100]

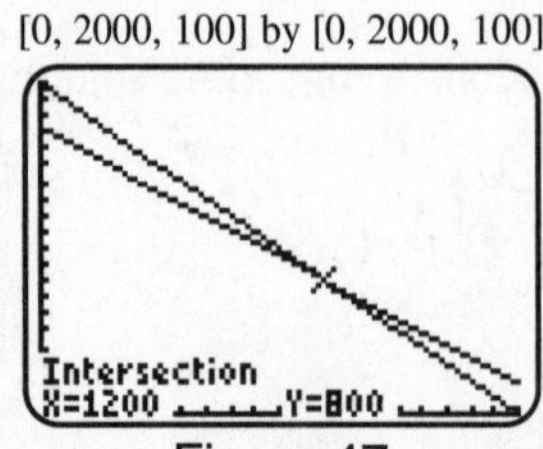


Figure 47

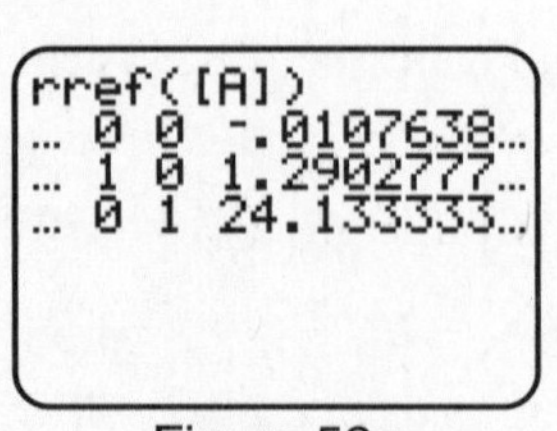


Figure 52a

[20, 100, 20] by [45, 65, 5]

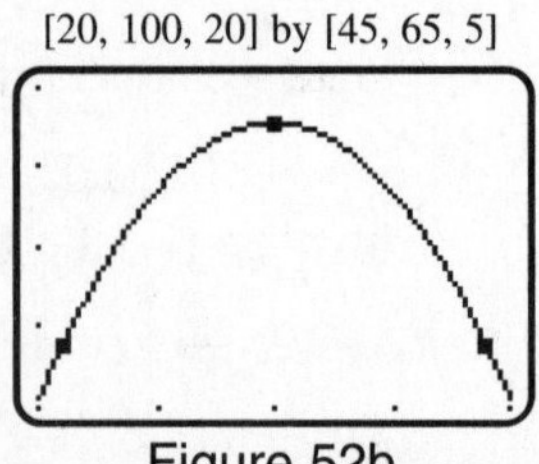

Figure 52b

47. (a) Let $x$ represent the amount of the 7% loan and let $y$ represent the amount of the 9% loan. Then the system of equations is $x + y = 2000$ and $0.07x + 0.09y = 156$. Multiply the first equation by 0.09 and subtract.

$$\begin{array}{rl} 0.09x + 0.09y &= 180 \\ 0.07x + 0.09y &= 156 \\ \hline 0.02x \qquad\quad &= 24 \Rightarrow x = 1200 \text{ and } y = 2000 - 1200 = 800 \end{array}$$

The loan amounts are \$1200 at 7% and \$800 at 9%.

(b) Graph $Y_1 = 2000 - X$ and $Y_2 = (156 - 0.07X)/0.09$. The graph intersect at (1200, 800). See Figure 47.

The loan amounts are \$1200 at 7% and \$800 at 9%.

48. Let $x$ represent the width and let $y$ represent the height. Then the system of equations is given by $x - y = 3$ and $2x + 2y = 42$. Multiply the second equation by $\frac{1}{2}$ and add to eliminate the $y$-variable.

$$\begin{array}{rl} x - y &= 3 \\ x + y &= 21 \\ \hline 2x \qquad &= 24 \Rightarrow x = 12 \end{array}$$

Since $x - y = 3$, it follows that $y = 9$. The screen is 12 inches wide and 9 inches high.

49. Let $x$ be the number of CDs of type A purchased and let $y$ be the number of CDs of type B. Then from the table we see that $1x + 2y = 37.47$ and $2x + 3y = 61.95$.

$$AX = B \Rightarrow \begin{bmatrix} 1 & 2 \\ 2 & 3 \end{bmatrix}\begin{bmatrix} x \\ y \end{bmatrix} = \begin{bmatrix} 37.47 \\ 61.95 \end{bmatrix}$$

Using a graphing calculator to solve the system yeilds that type A CDs cost \$11.49 and type B CD's cost \$12.99.

50. Let $A = \begin{bmatrix} 3 & 3 & 3 \\ 0 & 3 & 0 \\ 0 & 3 & 0 \end{bmatrix}$ and let $B = \begin{bmatrix} 0 & 0 & 0 \\ 1 & 0 & 1 \\ 1 & 0 & 1 \end{bmatrix}$. Then, $A + B = \begin{bmatrix} 3 & 3 & 3 \\ 1 & 3 & 1 \\ 1 & 3 & 1 \end{bmatrix}$.

51. Enter the vertices as columns in a counterclockwise direction.

$D = \frac{1}{2} \det \begin{bmatrix} 0 & 5 & 2 \\ 0 & 2 & 5 \\ 1 & 1 & 1 \end{bmatrix} = 10.5$; The area of the triangle is 10.5 square units.

52. The constants $a$, $b$, and $c$ must satisfy the following equations:

$a(24)^2 + b(24) + c = 48.9$, $a(60)^2 + b(60) + c = 62.8$, and $a(96)^2 + b(96) + c = 48.8$

This system of equations can be represented by the following augmented matrix:

$$\left[\begin{array}{ccc|c} 24^2 & 24 & 1 & 48.9 \\ 60^2 & 60 & 1 & 62.8 \\ 96^2 & 96 & 1 & 48.8 \end{array}\right]$$

Using technology to solve the system results in the reduced row-echelon form shown in Figure 52a. An approximate solution is $a \approx -0.010764$, $b \approx 1.2903$, and $c \approx 24.133$.

Therefore, an approximate representation of $f$ is $f(x) = -0.010764x^2 + 1.2903x + 24.133$.

The data and $f$ are graphed in Figure 52b.

53. Since $P$ varies jointly as the square of $x$ and the cube of $y$, the variation equation $P = kx^2y^3$ must hold.

If $P = 432$ when $x = 2$ and $y = 3$, then $432 = k(2)^2(3)^3 \Rightarrow 432 = 108k \Rightarrow k = 4$.

Our variation equation becomes $P = 4x^2y^3$. Thus, when $x = 3$ and $y = 5$, $P = 4(3)^2(5)^3 = 4500$.

54. The region of feasible solutions is shown in Figure 54a. The vertices of this region are (0, 0), (4, 0), (3, 3), and (0, 4). To find the maximum value of $P = 3x + 4y$ in the region, we must evaluate $P$ at each of the vertices. These values are shown in Figure 54b. From the table the maximum is 21 at the point (3, 3).

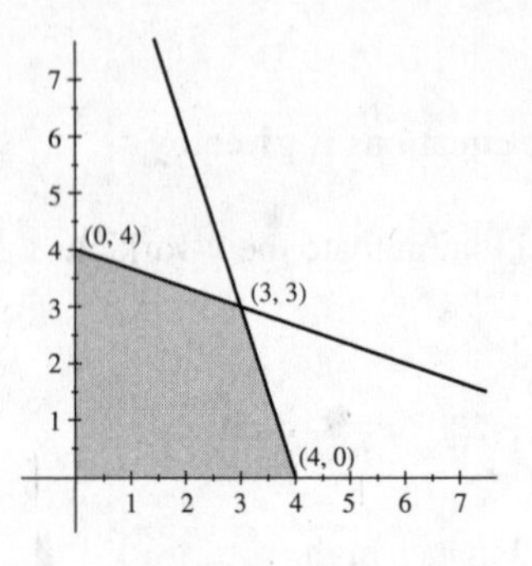


Figure 54a

| Vertex | $P = 3x + 4y$ |
|---|---|
| (0, 0) | $3(0) + 4(0) = 0$ |
| (4, 0) | $3(4) + 4(0) = 12$ |
| (3, 3) | $3(3) + 4(3) = 21$ |
| (0, 4) | $3(0) + 4(4) = 16$ |

Figure 54b

## Extended and Discovery Exercises for Chapter 6

1. (a) $A^T = \begin{bmatrix} 3 & 2 & 4 \\ -3 & 6 & 2 \end{bmatrix}$ (b) $A^T = \begin{bmatrix} 0 & 2 & -4 \\ 1 & 5 & 3 \\ -2 & 4 & 9 \end{bmatrix}$ (c) $A^T = \begin{bmatrix} 5 & 1 & 6 & -9 \\ 7 & -7 & 3 & 2 \end{bmatrix}$

2. Start by forming the following matrix equation:

$$AX = B \Rightarrow \begin{bmatrix} 0 & 1 \\ 5 & 1 \\ 10 & 1 \\ 15 & 1 \\ 20 & 1 \end{bmatrix} \begin{bmatrix} a \\ b \end{bmatrix} = \begin{bmatrix} 3617 \\ 6121 \\ 9340 \\ 12{,}216 \\ 16{,}233 \end{bmatrix}$$

To find the least-squares solution to this system of linear equations, solve the matrix equation $A^TAX = A^TB$ for $X$. The solution is given by $X = (A^TA)^{-1}A^TB$. Enter the matrices $A$ and $B$ and compute the solution as shown in Figure 2a. Thus, $f(x) = 626.54x + 3240$. The data and $f$ are graphed in Figure 2b.

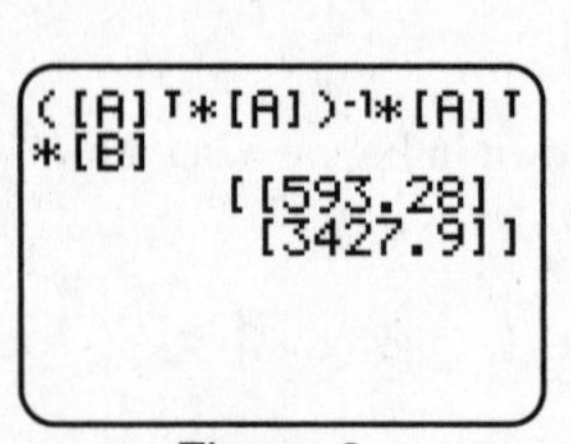


Figure 2a

[-1, 17, 1] by [2000, 13,000, 1000]

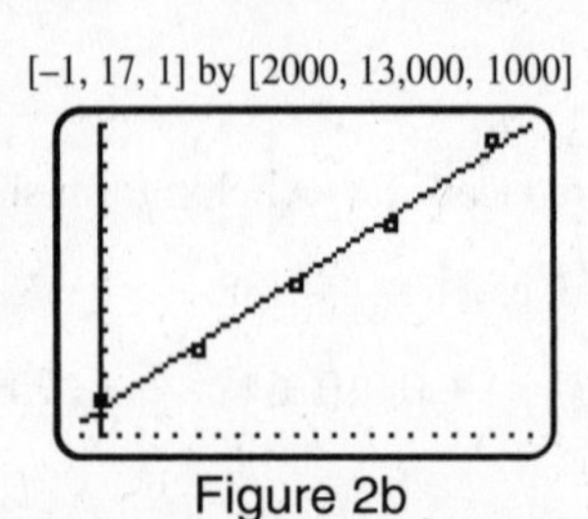

Figure 2b

3. Start by forming the following matrix equation:

$$AX = B \Rightarrow \begin{bmatrix} 0 & 1 \\ 1 & 1 \\ 2 & 1 \\ 3 & 1 \\ 4 & 1 \\ 5 & 1 \end{bmatrix} \begin{bmatrix} a \\ b \end{bmatrix} = \begin{bmatrix} 2.2 \\ 4.5 \\ 7.9 \\ 10.5 \\ 13 \\ 15 \end{bmatrix}$$

To find the least-squares solution to this system of linear equations, solve the matrix equation $A^{T}AX = A^{T}B$ for $X$. The solution is given by $X = (A^{T}A)^{-1}A^{T}B$. Enter the matrices $A$ and $B$ and compute the solution as shown in Figure 3a. Thus, $f(x) = 2.6314x + 2.2714$. The data and $f$ are graphed in Figure 3b.

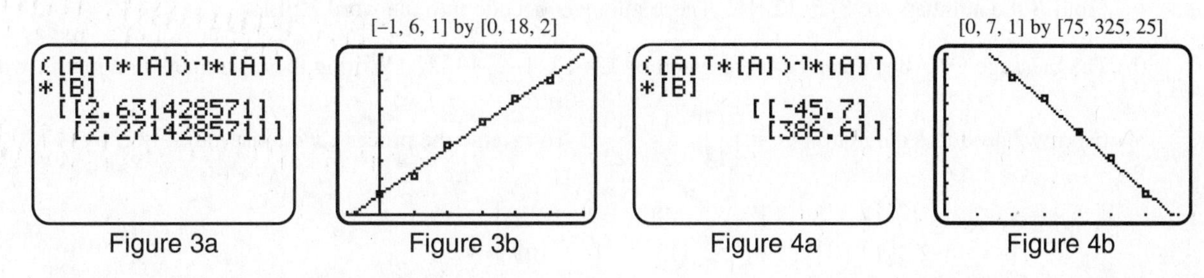


Figure 3a Figure 3b Figure 4a Figure 4b

4. Start by forming the following matrix equation:

$$AX = B \Rightarrow \begin{bmatrix} 2 & 1 \\ 3 & 1 \\ 4 & 1 \\ 5 & 1 \\ 6 & 1 \end{bmatrix} \begin{bmatrix} a \\ b \end{bmatrix} = \begin{bmatrix} 290 \\ 255 \\ 203 \\ 164 \\ 107 \end{bmatrix}$$

To find the least-squares solution to this system of linear equations, solve the matrix equation $A^{T}AX = A^{T}B$ for $X$. The solution is given by $X = (A^{T}A)^{-1}A^{T}B$. Enter the matrices $A$ and $B$ and compute the solution as shown in Figure 4a. Thus, $f(x) = -45.7x + 386.6$. The data and $f$ are graphed in Figure 4b.

5. (a) The word HELP would be written using the numbers 8 5 12 16. Then $B = \begin{bmatrix} 8 & 12 \\ 5 & 16 \end{bmatrix}$ and the word HELP could be coded by taking the product $AB = \begin{bmatrix} 2 & 1 \\ -5 & -2 \end{bmatrix}\begin{bmatrix} 8 & 12 \\ 5 & 16 \end{bmatrix} = \begin{bmatrix} 21 & 40 \\ -50 & -92 \end{bmatrix}$. Scaling the numbers results in $21 - 0(26) = 21$, $40 - 1(26) = 14$, $-50 + 2(26) = 2$, and $-92 + 4(26) = 12$. The new code matrix is written as $C = \begin{bmatrix} 21 & 14 \\ 2 & 12 \end{bmatrix}$. The entries of $C$ are written as 21 2 14 12 which become UBNL. Thus, HELP is coded as the word UBNL.

(b) The word LETTER would be written using the numbers 12 5 20 20 5 18. Then $B = \begin{bmatrix} 12 & 20 & 5 \\ 5 & 20 & 18 \end{bmatrix}$ and LETTER could be coded by the product $AB = \begin{bmatrix} 2 & 1 \\ -5 & -2 \end{bmatrix}\begin{bmatrix} 12 & 20 & 5 \\ 5 & 20 & 18 \end{bmatrix} = \begin{bmatrix} 29 & 60 & 28 \\ -70 & -140 & -61 \end{bmatrix}$. Scaling the numbers results in $29 - (1)26 = 3$, $60 - 2(26) = 8$, $28 - 1(26) = 2$, $-70 + 3(26) = 8$, $-140 - 6(26) = 16$, and $-61 + 3(26) = 17$. The new code matrix is written as $C = \begin{bmatrix} 3 & 8 & 2 \\ 8 & 16 & 17 \end{bmatrix}$. The entries of $C$ are written as 3 8 8 16 2 17 which become CHHPBQ.

6. (a) The message UBNL can be represented by 21 2 14 12. Writing these numbers in a matrix with two rows produces the matrix $C = \begin{bmatrix} 21 & 14 \\ 2 & 12 \end{bmatrix}$. To reverse the process, we must multiply $C$ by $A^{-1}$.

$A^{-1}C = \begin{bmatrix} -2 & -1 \\ 5 & 2 \end{bmatrix}\begin{bmatrix} 21 & 14 \\ 2 & 12 \end{bmatrix} = \begin{bmatrix} -44 & -40 \\ 109 & 94 \end{bmatrix}$. Next, scale the matrix elements between 1 and 26.

$-44 + 2(26) = 8,\ -40 + 2(26) = 12,\ 109 - 4(26) = 5$, and $94 + 3(26) = 16$.

This results in the matrix $B = \begin{bmatrix} 8 & 12 \\ 5 & 16 \end{bmatrix}$.

From $B$ the numbers are 8 5 12 16. These numbers decode into the word HELP.

(b) The message QNABMV can be represented by 17 14 1 2 13 22. Writing these numbers in a matrix with two rows produces the matrix $C = \begin{bmatrix} 17 & 1 & 13 \\ 14 & 2 & 22 \end{bmatrix}$. To reverse the process, we must multiply $C$ by $A^{-1}$.

$A^{-1}C = \begin{bmatrix} -2 & -1 \\ 5 & 2 \end{bmatrix}\begin{bmatrix} 17 & 1 & 13 \\ 14 & 2 & 22 \end{bmatrix} = \begin{bmatrix} -48 & -4 & -48 \\ 113 & 9 & 109 \end{bmatrix}$.

Next, scale the matrix elements between 1 and 26. $-48 + 2(26) = 4,\ -4 + 1(26) = 22,$

$-48 + 2(26) = 4,\ 113 - 4(26) = 9,\ 9 - 0(26) = 9$, and $109 - 4(26) = 5$.

This results in the matrix $B = \begin{bmatrix} 4 & 22 & 4 \\ 9 & 9 & 5 \end{bmatrix}$.

From $B$ the numbers are 4 9 22 9 4 5. These numbers decode into the word DIVIDE.

## Chapters 1-6 Cumulative Review Exercises

1. Move the decimal point 5 place to the left, $125{,}000 = 1.25 \times 10^5$.

   Move the decimal point 3 places to the left, $4.67 \times 10^{-3} = 0.00467$

2. Use the midpoint formula: $\left(\frac{-3 + (-1)}{2}, \frac{2 + 6}{2}\right) = (-2, 4)$.

3. $D$: $[-3, 2]$; $R = [-2, 2]$; $f(-0.5) = -2$

4. (a) See Figure 4a.

   (b) See Figure 4b.

   (c) See Figure 4c.

   (d) See Figure 4d.

   (e) See Figure 4e.

   (f) See Figure 4f.

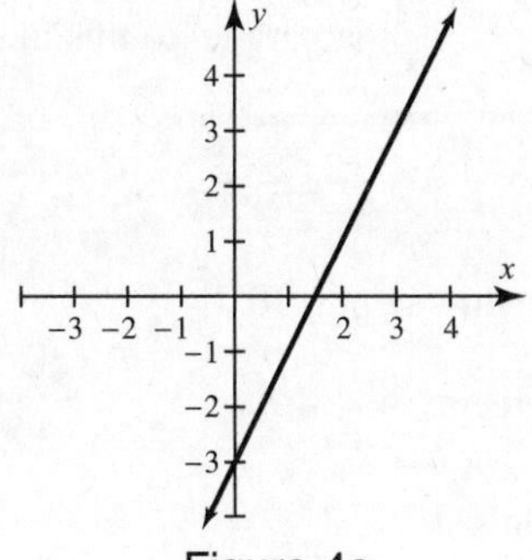

Figure 4a

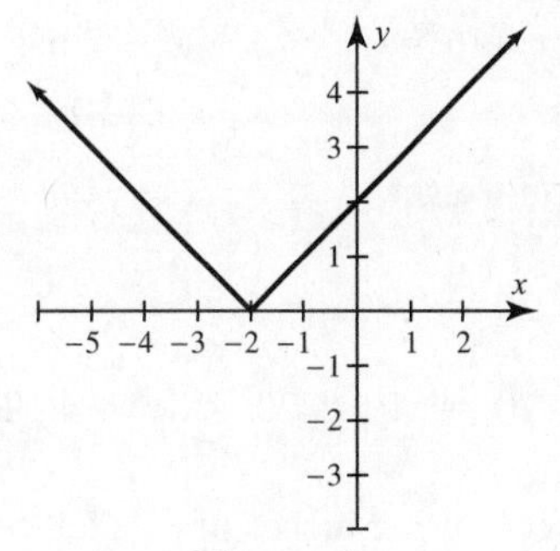

Figure 4b

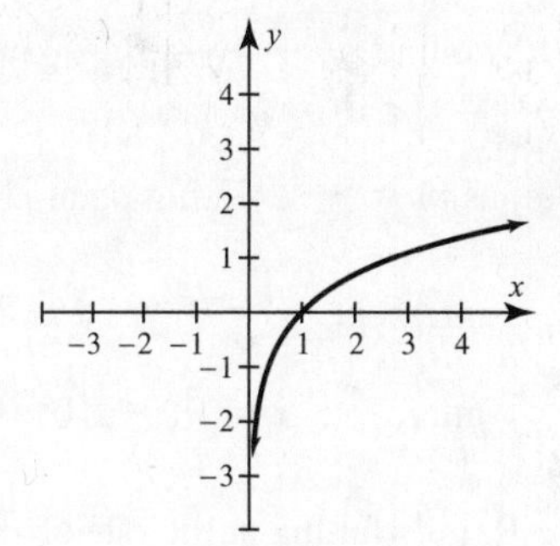

Figure 4c

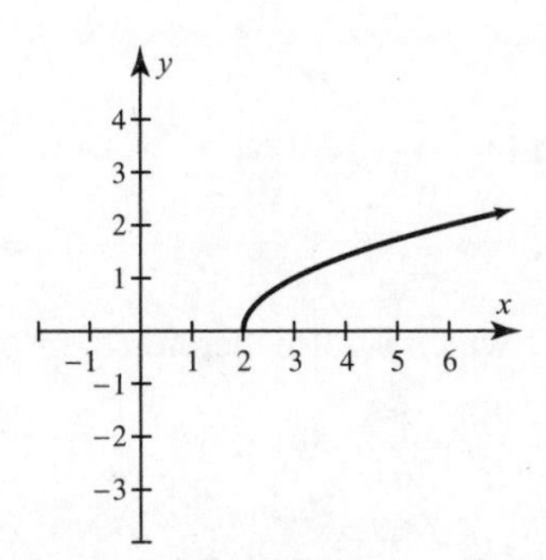

Figure 4d

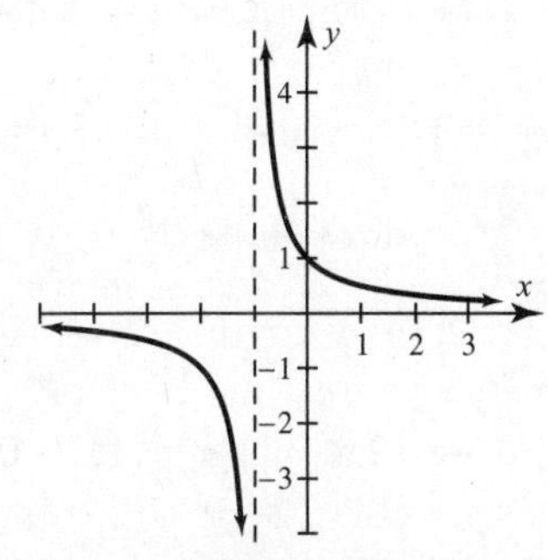

Figure 4e

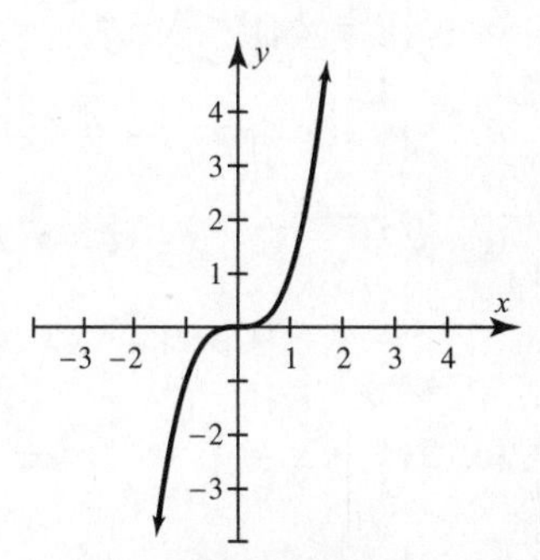

Figure 4f

5. (a) Because $4 - x \nless 0$: $4 - x \geq 0 \Rightarrow -x \geq -4 \Rightarrow x \leq 4$ or $D$: $\{x | x \leq 4\}$

   (b) $f(-1) = \sqrt{4 - (-1)} = \sqrt{5}$; $f(2a) = \sqrt{4 - (2a)}$

6. (a) Since $4x^2 - 16 \neq 0 \Rightarrow 4x^2 \neq 16 \Rightarrow x^2 \neq 4 \Rightarrow x \neq -2, 2 \Rightarrow D = \{x \,|\, x \neq -2, x \neq 2\}$.

   (b) $f(-1) = \dfrac{-1 - 2}{4(-1)^2 - 16} = \dfrac{-3}{-12} = \dfrac{1}{4}$

   $$f(2a) = \frac{2a - 2}{4(2a)^2 - 16} = \frac{2a - 2}{16a^2 - 16} = \frac{2(a - 1)}{16(a^2 - 1)} = \frac{2(a - 1)}{16(a - 1)(a + 1)} = \frac{1}{8(a + 1)}$$

7. $$\frac{f(x + h) - f(x)}{h} = \frac{3(x + h)^2 - 3x^2}{h} = \frac{3(x^2 + 2xh + h^2) - 3x^2}{h} = \frac{3x^2 + 6xh + 3h^2 - 3x^2}{h} =$$

   $$\frac{6xh + 3h^2}{h} = 6x + 3h$$

8. $f(1) = 10^1 = 10 \Rightarrow (1, 10)$, $f(2) = 10^2 = 100 \Rightarrow (2, 100)$, the average rate of change is $\dfrac{100 - 10}{2 - 1} =$

   $\dfrac{90}{1} = 90.$

9. (a) Using $(0, -1)$ and $(2, 0)$, $m = \dfrac{0 - (-1)}{2 - 0} = \dfrac{1}{2}$: $m = \dfrac{1}{2}$; $y$-intercept $(0, -1)$: $-1$; and $x$-intercept $(2, 0)$: $2$.

   (b) Using slope-intercept form: $f(x) = \dfrac{1}{2}x - 1.$

   (c) Graphical: Since the point $(-2, -2)$ is on the graph of $y = f(x)$ it follows that $f(-2) = -2$.

   (d) $f(x) = 0$ at $x = 2$.

10. The line $2x + 3y = 6 \Rightarrow 3y = -2x + 6 \Rightarrow y = \frac{-2}{3}x + 2$ has a slope $\frac{-2}{3}$. A line parallel to this line also has $m = \frac{-2}{3}$. Using point-slope form we get: $y = \frac{-2}{3}(x - 2) + (-3) \Rightarrow y = \frac{-2}{3}x - \frac{5}{3}$.

11. $x$-intercept: $y = 0$: $-2x + 5(0) = 20 \Rightarrow -2x = 20 \Rightarrow x = -10$. The $x$-intercept $-10$.

$y$-intercept: $x = 0$: $-2(0) + 5y = 20 \Rightarrow 5y = 20 \Rightarrow y = 4$. The $y$-intercept: 4.

12. Rain is falling at the rate of $\frac{1}{2}$ inch per hour; 2 inches of rain fell before midnight.

13. (a) $2(1 - 2x) = 5 - (4 - x) \Rightarrow 2 - 4x = 1 + x \Rightarrow 1 = 5x \Rightarrow x = \frac{1}{5}$

(b) $2e^x - 1 = 27 \Rightarrow 2e^x = 28 \Rightarrow e^x = 14 \Rightarrow \ln e^x = \ln 14 \Rightarrow x = \ln 14 \Rightarrow x \approx 2.64$

(c) $\sqrt{2x - 1} = x - 2 \Rightarrow 2x - 1 = x^2 - 4x + 4 \Rightarrow x^2 - 6x + 5 = 0 \Rightarrow (x - 5)(x - 1) = 0 \Rightarrow$

$x = 1, 5$; Checking: $x = 1$ we get $\sqrt{2(1) - 1} = 1 - 2 \Rightarrow \sqrt{1} = -1$ which is false therefore $x = 5$.

(d) $2x^2 + x = 1 \Rightarrow 2x^2 + x - 1 = 0 \Rightarrow (2x - 1)(x + 1) = 0 \Rightarrow x = -1, \frac{1}{2}$

(e) $x^3 - 3x^2 + 2x = 0 \Rightarrow x(x^2 - 3x + 2) = 0 \Rightarrow x(x - 2)(x - 1) = 0 \Rightarrow x = 0, 1, 2$

(f) $x^4 + 8 = 6x^2 \Rightarrow x^4 - 6x^2 + 8 = 0 \Rightarrow (x^2 - 4)(x^2 - 2) = 0 \Rightarrow$

$(x + 2)(x - 2)(x^2 - 2) = 0 \Rightarrow x = -2, 2, \pm\sqrt{2}$

(g) $\frac{x}{x - 2} = \frac{2x - 1}{x + 1} \Rightarrow x(x + 1) = (2x - 1)(x - 2) \Rightarrow x^2 + x = 2x^2 - 5x + 2 \Rightarrow x^2 - 6x + 2 = 0$

Using the quadratic formula: $\frac{6 \pm \sqrt{36 - 4(1)(2)}}{2(1)} = \frac{6 \pm \sqrt{28}}{2} = 3 \pm \sqrt{7}$

(h) $|4 - 5x| = 8 \Rightarrow 4 - 5x = -8$ or $4 - 5x = 8$; $4 - 5x = -8 \Rightarrow -5x = -12 \Rightarrow x = \frac{12}{5}$ or

$4 - 5x = 8 \Rightarrow -5x = 4 \Rightarrow x = -\frac{4}{5}$. Therefore $x = -\frac{4}{5}, \frac{12}{5}$.

14. See Figure 14. Because of the jump at $x = 2$, $f$ is not continuous on its domain; $f(1) = -2(1) = -2$

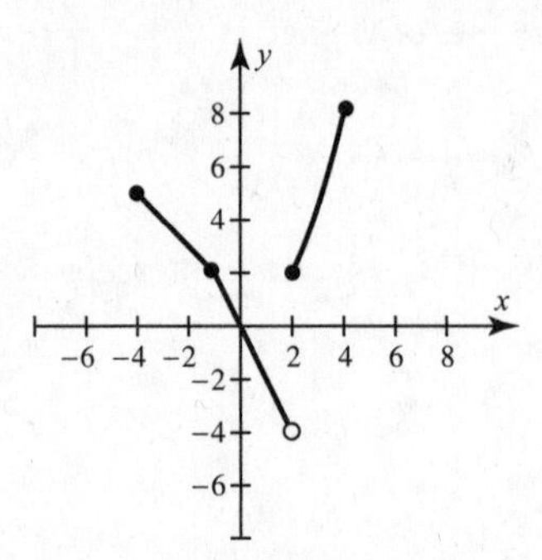

Figure 14

15. (a) $-3(2 - x) < 4 - (2x + 1) \Rightarrow -6 + 3x < 3 - 2x \Rightarrow 5x < 9 \Rightarrow x < \frac{9}{5} \Rightarrow \left(-\infty, \frac{9}{5}\right)$ or $\left\{x \mid x < \frac{9}{5}\right\}$

(b) $-3 \le 4 - 3x < 6 \Rightarrow -7 \le -3x < 2 \Rightarrow \frac{7}{3} \ge x > -\frac{2}{3} \Rightarrow \left(-\frac{2}{3}, \frac{7}{3}\right]$ or $\left\{x \mid -\frac{2}{3} < x \le \frac{7}{3}\right\}$

(c) The solutions to $|4x - 3| \ge 9$ satisfy $x \le s_1$ or $x \ge s_2$ where $s_1$ and $s_2$ are the solutions to $|4x - 3| = 9$.

$|4x - 3| = 9$ is equivalent to $4x - 3 = -9 \Rightarrow x = -\frac{3}{2}$ and $4x - 3 = 9 \Rightarrow x = 3$.

The interval is $\left(-\infty, -\frac{3}{2}\right] \cup [3, \infty)$ or $\left\{x \mid x \le -\frac{3}{2} \text{ or } x \ge 3\right\}$.

(d) For $x^2 - 5x + 4 \le 0$ first we solve $x^2 - 5x + 4 = 0 \Rightarrow (x - 4)(x - 1) = 0 \Rightarrow x = 1, 4$. These are the boundary numbers and divide the numberline into three sections: $(-\infty, 1]$, $[1, 4]$, and $[4, \infty)$.

Testing a value in each section we get: $x = 0 \Rightarrow 0^2 - 5(0) + 4 \le 0 \Rightarrow 4 \le 0$, which is false;

$x = 2 \Rightarrow 2^2 - 5(2) + 4 \le 0 \Rightarrow 4 - 10 + 4 \le 0 \Rightarrow -2 \le 0$, which is true;

$x = 5 \Rightarrow 5^2 - 5(5) + 4 \le 0 \Rightarrow 25 - 25 + 4 \le 0 \Rightarrow 4 \le 0$, which is false.

Therefore the solution is; $[1, 4]$ or $\{x \mid 1 \le x \le 4\}$.

(e) For $t^3 - t > 0$ first solve $t^3 - t = 0 \Rightarrow t(t^2 - 1) = 0 \Rightarrow t(t + 1)(t - 1) = 0 \Rightarrow t = -1, 0, 1$. These are the boundary numbers and divide the numberline into four sections:

$(-\infty, -1)$, $(-1, 0)$, $(0, 1)$, and $(1, \infty)$.

Testing a value in each section we get: $x = -2 \Rightarrow -2^3 - (-2) > 0 \Rightarrow -6 > 0$, which is false;

$x = -\frac{1}{2} \Rightarrow \left(-\frac{1}{2}\right)^3 - \left(-\frac{1}{2}\right) > 0 \Rightarrow -\frac{1}{8} + \frac{1}{2} > 0 \Rightarrow \frac{3}{8} > 0$, which is true;

$x = \frac{1}{2} \Rightarrow \left(\frac{1}{2}\right)^3 - \frac{1}{2} > 0 \Rightarrow \frac{1}{8} - \frac{1}{2} > 0 \Rightarrow -\frac{3}{8} > 0$, which is false;

$x = 2 \Rightarrow 2^3 - 2 > 0 \Rightarrow 8 - 2 > 0 \Rightarrow 6 > 0$, which is true.

Therefore the solution is: $(-1, 0) \cup (1, \infty)$ or $\{x \mid -1 < x < 0 \text{ or } x > 1\}$.

(f) One boundary number is: $t + 2 = 0 \Rightarrow t = -2$. For the other we solve: $\frac{1}{t + 2} - 3 = 0 \Rightarrow$

$1 - 3(t + 2) = 0 \Rightarrow 1 - 3t - 6 = 0 \Rightarrow -3t = 5 \Rightarrow t = -\frac{5}{3}$. The two boundary numbers are:

$-2$ and $-\frac{5}{3} \Rightarrow$ the possible intervals are: $(-\infty, -2)$, $\left(-2, -\frac{5}{3}\right]$, and $\left[-\frac{5}{3}, \infty\right)$.

Testing a value in each gives us: $x = -3 \Rightarrow \frac{1}{-3 + 2} - 3 \ge 0 \Rightarrow -4 \ge 0$, which is false;

$x = -\frac{11}{6} \Rightarrow \frac{1}{-\frac{11}{6} + 2} - 3 \ge 0 \Rightarrow 3 \ge 0$, which is true;

$x = 0 \Rightarrow \frac{1}{0 + 2} - 3 \ge 0 \Rightarrow -\frac{5}{2} \ge 0$, which is false. Therefore the solution is $\left(-2, -\frac{5}{3}\right]$ or $\left\{x \mid -2 < x \le -\frac{5}{3}\right\}$.

16. (a) $f(x) = 0$ or $y = 0$, $\Rightarrow x = -2, -1, 1$

 (b) $f(x) > 0$ or when the graph of the equation is above the $x$-axis $\Rightarrow (-2, -1) \cup (1, \infty)$ or $\{x \mid -2 < x < -1 \text{ or } x > 1\}$.

 (c) $f(x) \le 0$ or when the graph of the equation is below or on the $x$-axis $\Rightarrow (-\infty, -2] \cup [-1, 1]$ or $\{x \mid x \le -2 \text{ or } -1 \le x \le 1\}$.

17. $-2x^2 + 6x - 1 = 0 \Rightarrow -2x^2 + 6x = 1 \Rightarrow -2(x^2 - 3x) = 1 \Rightarrow$

$$-2\left(x^2 - 3x + \frac{9}{4}\right) = 1 + \left(-2\left(\frac{9}{4}\right)\right) \Rightarrow -2\left(x - \frac{3}{2}\right)^2 + \frac{7}{2} = 0 \Rightarrow f(x) = -2\left(x - \frac{3}{2}\right)^2 + \frac{7}{2}$$

18. $2x^2 + 4x = 1 \Rightarrow 2(x^2 + 2x) = 1 \Rightarrow 2(x^2 + 2x + 1) = 1 + 2 \Rightarrow 2(x + 1)^2 = 3 \Rightarrow$

$$(x + 1)^2 = \frac{3}{2} \Rightarrow x + 1 = \pm\sqrt{\frac{3}{2}} \Rightarrow x = -1 \pm \sqrt{\frac{3}{2}} \Rightarrow x = -1 \pm \frac{\sqrt{6}}{2} \Rightarrow \frac{-2 \pm \sqrt{6}}{2}$$

19. (a) Shift $f$ one unit right and 2 units up. See Figure 19a.

 (b) Make graph shorter by taking $\frac{1}{2}$ of all $y$-coordinates of $f$. See Figure 19b.

 (c) Reflect $f$ across both the $x$-axis and $y$-axis. Since the graph is symetric to the $y$-axis only the reflection across the $x$-axis will show a result. See Figure 19c.

 (d) Make the graph narrower by taking $\frac{1}{2}$ of all $x$-coordinates of $f$. See Figure 19d.

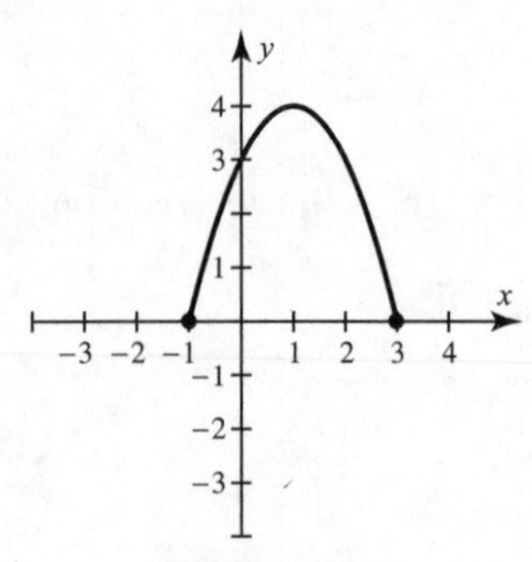

Figure 19a

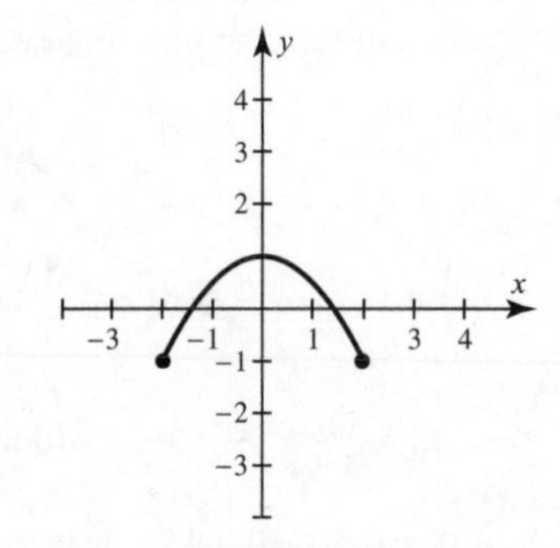

Figure 19b

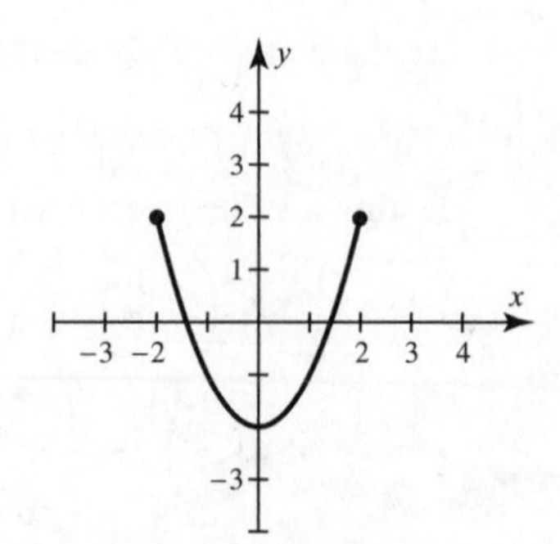

Figure 19c

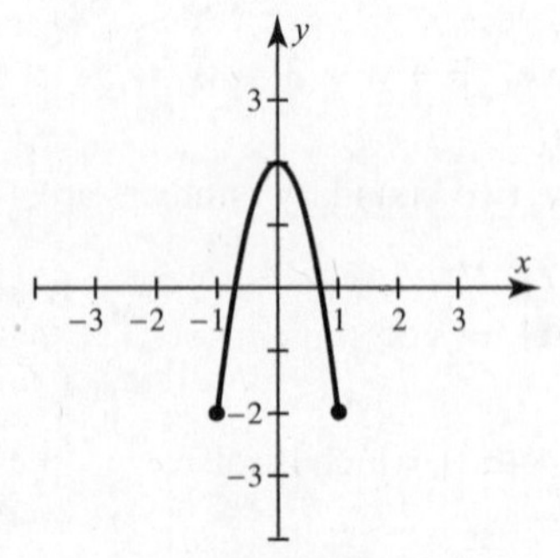

Figure 19d

20. (a) Increasing: $[-2, 0]$ and $[2, \infty]$; decreasing: $(-\infty, -2]$ and $[0, 2]$.

 (b) The graph crosses or touches the $x$-axis at $x \approx -2.8, 0, 2.8$.

 (c) The turning point coordinates: $(-2, -4)$, $(0, 0)$, and $(2, -4)$.

 (d) Local minimum: $-4$; local maximum: $0$.

21. See Figure 21. *Answers may vary*

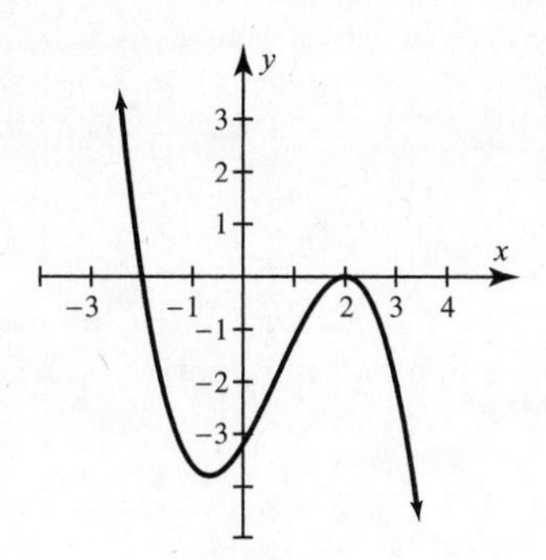


Figure 21

22. (a) $\frac{5a^4 - 2a^2 + 4}{2a^2} = \frac{5a^4}{2a^2} - \frac{2a^2}{2a^2} + \frac{4}{2a^2} = \frac{5a^2}{2} - 1 + \frac{2}{a^2}$

(b)
$$\begin{array}{r} x^3 + 3x^2 + 3x + 1 + \frac{1}{x-1} \\ x - 1\overline{)x^4 + 2x^3 \qquad\quad - 2x} \\ \underline{x^4 - x^3 \qquad\qquad\quad} \\ 3x^3 \qquad - 2x \\ \underline{3x^3 - 3x^2 \qquad\quad} \\ 3x^2 - 2x \\ \underline{3x^2 - 3x} \\ x \\ \underline{x - 1} \\ 1 \end{array}$$

The quotient is: $x^3 + 3x^2 + 3x + 1 + \frac{1}{x-1}$.

23. $2x^3 + x^2 - 8x - 4 = (2x^3 - 8x) + (x^2 - 4) = 2x(x^2 - 4) + (x^2 - 4) = (2x + 1)(x^2 - 4) =$
$(2x + 1)(x + 2)(x - 2) \Rightarrow f(x) = (2x + 1)(x + 2)(x - 2)$

24. If $2i$ is a solution then $-2i$ is a solution $\Rightarrow (x - 2i)(x + 2i) = x^2 - 4i^2 = x^2 + 4$ divides into
$x^3 - x^2 + 4x - 4$.

$$\begin{array}{r} x - 1 \\ x^2 + 4\overline{)x^3 - x^2 + 4x - 4} \\ \underline{x^3 \qquad\quad + 4x \qquad} \\ -x^2 \qquad\quad - 4 \\ \underline{-x^2 \qquad\quad - 4} \\ 0 \end{array}$$

$x - 1 = 0 \Rightarrow x = 1$. The solutions are $\pm 2i, 1$.

25. $(2 + i)^2 + (2 - 3i) = (4 + 4i - 1) + (2 - 3i) = 5 + i$

26. $3x - 7 \neq 0 \Rightarrow 3x \neq 7 \Rightarrow x \neq \frac{7}{3}$. Then $D = \left\{x \mid x \neq \frac{7}{3}\right\}$; the vertical asymptote is the denominator =
$0 \Rightarrow x = \frac{7}{3}$; and the horizontal asymptote is the ratio of the lead coefficients $\Rightarrow y = \frac{2}{3}$.

27. (a) $(f + g)(2) = f(2) + g(2) = 2 + 3 = 5$

(b) $(g/f)(4) = g(4)/f(4) = 1/0 \Rightarrow$ undefined

(c) $(f \circ g)(3) = f(g(3)) = f(2) = 2$

(d) $(f^{-1} \circ g)(1) = f^{-1}(g(1)) = f^{-1}(4) = 0$

28. (a) $f(-1) = 0$ and $g(-1) = 2 \Rightarrow (f - g)(-1) = 0 - 2 = -2$

(b) $f(2) = 3$ and $g(2) = -1 \Rightarrow (fg)(2) = 3 \cdot (-1) = -3$

(c) $(g \circ f)(0) = g(f(0))$. $f(0) = -1 \Rightarrow g(-1) = 2$

(d) $(g^{-1} \circ f)(2) = g^{-1}(f(2))$. $f(2) = 3 \Rightarrow g^{-1}(3) \Rightarrow 3 = g(x) \Rightarrow x = -2$

29. (a) $f(2) = 2^2 + 3(2) - 2 = 4 + 6 - 2 = 8$; $g(2) = 2 - 2 = 0$; $(f + g)(2) = 8 + 0 = 8$

(b) $(g \circ f)(1) = g(f(1)) \Rightarrow f(1) = 1^2 + 3(1) - 2 = 1 + 3 - 2 = 2$. Then $g(2) = 2 - 2 = 0 \Rightarrow$

$(g \circ f)(1) = 0$

(c) $f(x) = x^2 + 3x - 2$ and $g(x) = x - 2 \Rightarrow (f - g)(x) = x^2 + 3x - 2 - (x - 2) \Rightarrow$

$(f - g)(x) = x^2 + 2x$

(d) $(f \circ g)(x) = f(g(x)) \Rightarrow (f \circ g)(x) = (x - 2)^2 + 3(x - 2) - 2 \Rightarrow$

$(f \circ g)(x) = x^2 - 4x + 4 + 3x - 6 - 2 \Rightarrow (f \circ g)(x) = x^2 - x - 4$

30. If $f(x) = 2\sqrt[3]{x + 1}$ then $y = 2\sqrt[3]{x + 1} \Rightarrow \dfrac{y}{2} = \sqrt[3]{x + 1} \Rightarrow \left(\dfrac{y}{2}\right)^3 = x + 1 \Rightarrow \dfrac{y^3}{8} - 1 = x \Rightarrow$

$f^{-1}(x) = \dfrac{x^3}{8} - 1$

31. For each unit increase in $x$, the $y$-value is multiplied by $\dfrac{2}{3}$. This is an exponential function with $c = 9$ and

$a = \dfrac{2}{3}$, so $f(x) = 9\left(\dfrac{2}{3}\right)^x$.

32. If the initial bacteria count is 2000 then $C = 2000$ and it doubles every 3 hours. Then $4000 = 2000a^3 \Rightarrow$

$2 = a^3 \Rightarrow a = \sqrt[3]{2}$. Therefore $f(x) = 2000(\sqrt[3]{2})^x$ so $C = 2000$ and $a = \sqrt[3]{2}$.

33. From the graph when $x = 0$, $y = \dfrac{1}{2}$, $\Rightarrow C = \dfrac{1}{2}$ and when $x = 1$, $y = 1 \Rightarrow$ using $y = Ca^x \Rightarrow 1 = \dfrac{1}{2}a^1 \Rightarrow$

$a = 2$. So $C = \dfrac{1}{2}$ and $a = 2$.

34. Using the compound interest formula: $A_n = A_o\left(1 + \dfrac{r}{m}\right)^{mn} \Rightarrow A_n = 500\left(1 + \dfrac{0.05}{12}\right)^{12(10)} \Rightarrow$

$A_n = 500(1.00416667)^{120} \Rightarrow A_n = 500(1.647009498) \Rightarrow A_n \approx 823.50$

35. (a) $\log 100 \Rightarrow 10^x = 100 \Rightarrow x = 2 \Rightarrow \log 100 = 2$

(b) $\log_2 16 \Rightarrow 2^x = 16 \Rightarrow x = 4 \Rightarrow \log_2 16 = 4$

(c) $\ln \frac{1}{e^2} \Rightarrow e^x = \frac{1}{e^2} \Rightarrow x = -2 \Rightarrow \ln \frac{1}{e^2} = -2$

(d) $\log_6 24 - \log_6 4 = \log_6 \frac{24}{4} = \log_6 6 \Rightarrow 6^x = 6 \Rightarrow x = 1 \Rightarrow \log_6 24 - \log_6 4 = 1$

36. (a) Domain all real numbers $\Rightarrow D{:}(-\infty, \infty)$; Range: as $x$ increases towards $\infty$, $e^x$ increases towards $\infty$ and as $x$ goes towards $-\infty$, $e^x$ approaches 0 $\Rightarrow R{:}\ (0, \infty)$.

(b) Since, as the solution to $\log_2 x$ approaches $\infty$, $x$ approaches $\infty$, and as the solution approaches $-\infty$, $x$ approaches 0, $\Rightarrow D{:}\ (0, \infty)$; since all real powers of $x$ are possible, all real number solutions of $\log_2 x$ are possible $\Rightarrow R{:}\ (-\infty, \infty)$.

37. $\log_2 \frac{\sqrt[3]{x^2 - 4}}{\sqrt[3]{x^2 + 4}} = \log_2 \frac{(x^2 - 4)^{1/3}}{(x^2 + 4)^{1/2}} = \log_2 (x^2 - 4)^{1/3} - \log_2 (x^2 + 4)^{1/2} =$

$\frac{1}{3} \log_2 (x^2 - 4) - \frac{1}{2} \log_2 (x^2 + 4) = \frac{1}{3} \log_2 [(x + 2)(x - 2)] - \frac{1}{2} \log_2 (x^2 + 4) =$

$\frac{1}{3} [\log_2 (x + 2) + \log_2 (x - 2)] - \frac{1}{2} \log_2 (x^2 + 4) = \frac{1}{3} \log_2 (x + 2) + \frac{1}{3} \log_2 (x - 2) - \frac{1}{2} \log_2 (x^2 + 4)$

38. $3 \log x - 4 \log y + \frac{1}{2} \log z = \log x^3 - \log y^4 + \log z^{1/2} = \log \frac{x^3 \sqrt{z}}{y^4}$

39. $\log_3 125 = 4.395$

40. (a) $3(2)^{-2x} + 4 = 100 \Rightarrow 3(2)^{-2x} = 96 \Rightarrow 2^{-2x} = 32 \Rightarrow \log_2 2^{-2x} = \log_2 32 \Rightarrow -2x = 5 \Rightarrow x = -\frac{5}{2}$

(b) $2 \log_3 (3x) = 4 \Rightarrow \log_3 (3x) = 2 \Rightarrow 3^{\log_3 (3x)} = 3^2 \Rightarrow 3x = 9 \Rightarrow x = 3$

41. $f(3, 4) = 3^2 + 4^2 = 9 + 16 = 25$

42. (a) Multiply the first equation by 2, the second equation by 3 and subtract the results to eliminate the $x$ variable.

$$\begin{array}{r} 6x - 4y = 10 \\ \underline{6x - 9y = \ \ 0} \\ 5y = 10 \Rightarrow y = 2 \end{array}$$

Substitute $y = 2$ into the first equation and solve for $x$. $3x - 2(2) = 5 \Rightarrow 3x = 9 \Rightarrow x = 3$.

The solution to the system is: $(3, 2)$.

(b) Multiply the first equation by 4 and add.

$$\begin{array}{r} -4x + 3y = 4 \\ \underline{4x - 3y = 4} \\ 0 = 8 \end{array}$$

Since this is false, there is no solution to the system.

(c) Solve $2x - 3y = 0$ for $x$. $2x = 3y \Rightarrow x = \frac{3}{2}y$. Substitute $x = \frac{3}{2}y$ into $x^2 + y^2 = 13 \Rightarrow$

$\left(\frac{3}{2}y\right)^2 + y^2 = 13 \Rightarrow \frac{9}{4}y^2 + y^2 = 13 \Rightarrow \frac{13}{4}y^2 = 13 \Rightarrow y^2 = 4 \Rightarrow y = \pm 2$.

Substitute $y = -2$ into $2x - 3y = 0 \Rightarrow 2x - 3(-2) = 0 \Rightarrow 2x = -6 \Rightarrow x = -3 \Rightarrow (-3, -2)$.

Substitute $y = 2$ into $2x - 3y = 0 \Rightarrow 2x - 3(2) = 0 \Rightarrow 2x = 6 \Rightarrow x = 3 \Rightarrow (3, 2)$.

The solution to the system is: $(-3, -2)$ and $(3, 2)$.

(d) Multiply the first equation by 4 and add the two equations.

$$\begin{array}{r} -4x + 3y = \ \ 4 \\ \underline{4x - 3y = -4} \\ 0 = \ \ 0 \end{array}$$

Since this is true, there are infinitely many solutions. They will be in the form:

$4x - 3y = -4 \Rightarrow 4x = 3y - 4 \Rightarrow x = \frac{3y - 4}{4} = \left(\frac{3y - 4}{4}, y\right)$

(e) Add the first two equation to eliminate the $z$ variable.

$$\begin{array}{l} x - 4y + z = 2 \\ \underline{x + 5y - z = 0} \\ 2x + y \qquad = 2 \end{array}$$

Multiply the second equation by 3 and add the last equation to eliminate the $z$ variable.

$$\begin{array}{l} 3x + 15y - 3z = 0 \\ \underline{2x - \ \ 7y + 3z = 5} \\ 5x + \ \ 8y \qquad = 5 \end{array}$$

Now multiply the first new equation by $-8$ and add the second new equation to eliminate the $y$ variable.

$$\begin{array}{l} -16x - 8y = -16 \\ \underline{\ \ 5x + 8y = \ \ \ 5} \\ -11x \qquad = -11 \Rightarrow x = 1 \end{array}$$

Substitute this into $2x + y = 2 \Rightarrow 2(1) + y = 2 \Rightarrow 2 + y = 2 \Rightarrow y = 0$. Now substitute

$x = 1$ and $y = 0$ into the original first equation $1 - 4(0) + z = 2 \Rightarrow 1 + z = 2 \Rightarrow z = 1$.

The solution to the system is $(1, 0, 1)$.

(f) Multiply the second equation by 2 and add the first equation to eliminate the $x$ variable.

$$\begin{array}{r} 2x + y - 3z = 3 \\ -2x + 4y + 2z = 6 \\ \hline 5y - z = 9 \end{array}$$

Multiply the original second equation by 3 and add to the third equation to eliminate the $x$ variable.

$$\begin{array}{r} -3x + 6y + 3z = 9 \\ 3x - y - 4z = 0 \\ \hline 5y - z = 9 \end{array}$$

Now subtract the two new equations.

$$\begin{array}{r} 5y - z = 9 \\ 5y - z = 9 \\ \hline 0 = 0 \end{array}$$

Since this is true there are infinitely many solutions. To find the form first solve for $y$.

$5y - z = 9 \Rightarrow 5y = z + 9 \Rightarrow y = \dfrac{z + 9}{5}$. To find $x$, multiply the original third equation by 2 and add to the second equation to eliminate the $y$ variable.

$$\begin{array}{r} -x + 2y + z = 3 \\ 6x - 2y - 8z = 0 \\ \hline 5x - 7z = 3 \end{array}$$

Now solve for $x$. $5x - 7z = 3 \Rightarrow 5x = 7z + 3 \Rightarrow x = \dfrac{7z + 3}{5}$.

There are infinitely many solutions in the form: $\left(\dfrac{7z + 3}{5}, \dfrac{z + 9}{5}, z\right)$.

43. If $z = kx^2y^{1/2}$, then $7.2 = k(3)^2(16)^{1/2} \Rightarrow 7.2 = k(9)(4) \Rightarrow 7.2 = 36k \Rightarrow k = 0.2$.

Now $z = 0.2(5)^2(4)^{1/2} \Rightarrow z = 0.2(25)(2) \Rightarrow z = 10$.

44. (a) See Figure 44a.

(b) See Figure 44b.

(c) See Figure 44c.

(d) See Figure 44d.

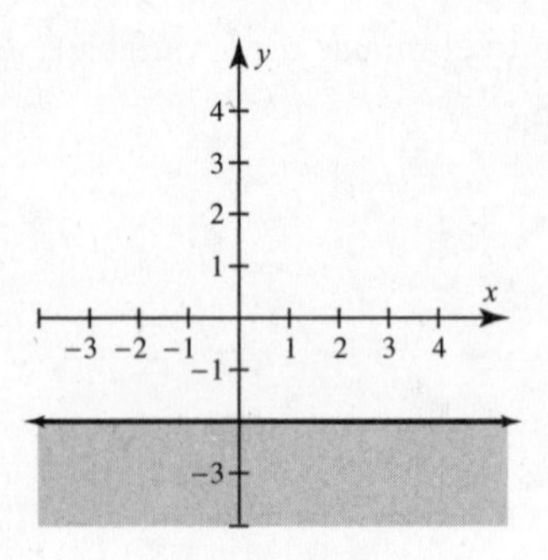
Figure 44a

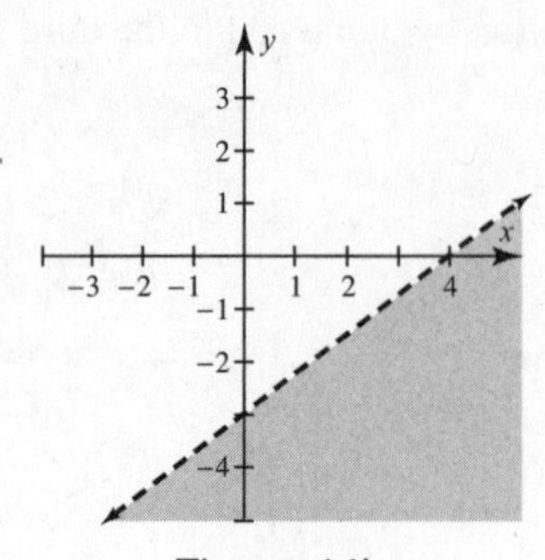
Figure 44b

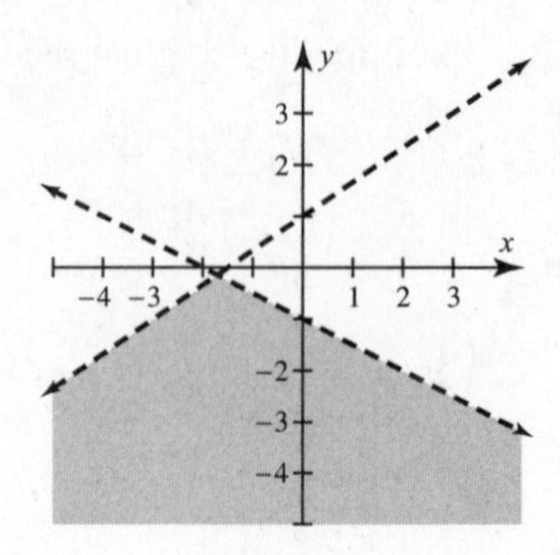
Figure 44c

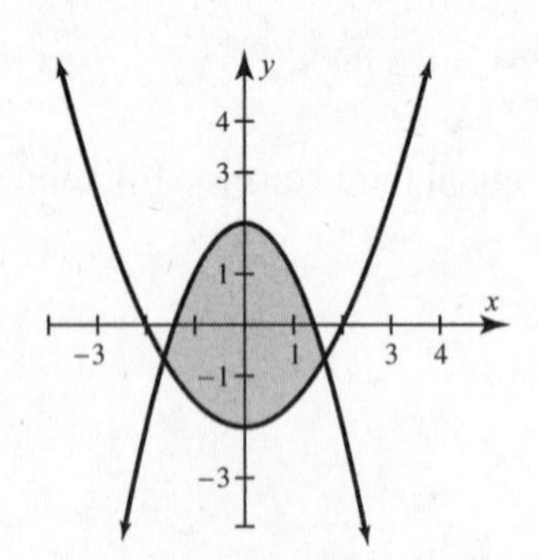
Figure 44d

45. $\left[\begin{array}{ccc|c} 1 & -1 & -1 & -2 \\ -1 & 1 & -1 & 0 \\ 0 & 1 & -2 & -6 \end{array}\right] R_1 + R_2 \rightarrow \left[\begin{array}{ccc|c} 1 & -1 & -1 & -2 \\ 0 & 0 & -2 & -2 \\ 0 & 1 & -2 & -6 \end{array}\right] \begin{array}{c} \\ R_3 \rightarrow \\ R_2 \rightarrow \end{array} \left[\begin{array}{ccc|c} 1 & -1 & -1 & -2 \\ 0 & 1 & -2 & -6 \\ 0 & 0 & -2 & -2 \end{array}\right]$

$(-1/2)R_3 \rightarrow \left[\begin{array}{ccc|c} 1 & -1 & -1 & -2 \\ 0 & 1 & -2 & -6 \\ 0 & 0 & 1 & 1 \end{array}\right]$

Therefore $z = 1$, substitute this into the second equation $y - 2z = -6 \Rightarrow y - 2(1) = -6 \Rightarrow$ $y - 2 = -6 \Rightarrow y = -4$. Now substitute $z = 1$ and $y = -4$ into $x - y - z = -2 \Rightarrow$ $x - 1 - (-4) = -2 \Rightarrow x + 3 = -2 \Rightarrow x = -5$. The solution is: $(-5, -4, 1)$.

46. $A - 3B = \begin{bmatrix} -2 & 3 & 4 \\ -5 & 1 & 5 \\ 7 & -1 & 0 \end{bmatrix} - 3\begin{bmatrix} 3 & 0 & -2 \\ 5 & -1 & 4 \\ -2 & 6 & -5 \end{bmatrix} = \begin{bmatrix} -2 & 3 & 4 \\ -5 & 1 & 5 \\ 7 & -1 & 0 \end{bmatrix} - \begin{bmatrix} 9 & 0 & -6 \\ 15 & -3 & 12 \\ -6 & 18 & -15 \end{bmatrix} =$

$\begin{bmatrix} -11 & 3 & 10 \\ -20 & 4 & -7 \\ 13 & -19 & 15 \end{bmatrix}$; $AB = \begin{bmatrix} -2 & 3 & 4 \\ -5 & 1 & 5 \\ 7 & -1 & 0 \end{bmatrix}\begin{bmatrix} 3 & 0 & -2 \\ 5 & -1 & 4 \\ -2 & 6 & -5 \end{bmatrix} =$

$\begin{bmatrix} -6 + 15 + (-8) & 0 + (-3) + 24 & 4 + 12 + (-20) \\ -15 + 5 + (-10) & 0 + (-1) + 30 & 10 + 4 + (-25) \\ 21 + (-5) + 0 & 0 + 1 + 0 & -14 + (-4) + 0 \end{bmatrix} = \begin{bmatrix} 1 & 21 & -4 \\ -20 & 29 & -11 \\ 16 & 1 & -18 \end{bmatrix}$

47. $\left[\begin{array}{cc|cc} 4 & -5 & 1 & 0 \\ 1 & -3 & 0 & 1 \end{array}\right] \begin{array}{l} (1/4)R_1 \to \\ R_1 - 4R_2 \to \end{array} \left[\begin{array}{cc|cc} 1 & -\frac{5}{4} & \frac{1}{4} & 0 \\ 0 & 7 & 1 & -4 \end{array}\right] \begin{array}{l} \\ (1/7)R_2 \to \end{array} \left[\begin{array}{cc|cc} 1 & -\frac{5}{4} & \frac{1}{4} & 0 \\ 0 & 1 & \frac{1}{7} & -\frac{4}{7} \end{array}\right]$

$R_1 + (5/4)R_2 \to \left[\begin{array}{cc|cc} 1 & 0 & \frac{3}{7} & -\frac{5}{7} \\ 0 & 1 & \frac{1}{7} & -\frac{4}{7} \end{array}\right] \Rightarrow A^{-1} = \begin{bmatrix} \frac{3}{7} & -\frac{5}{7} \\ \frac{1}{7} & -\frac{4}{7} \end{bmatrix}$

48. (a) $\det A = \det\begin{bmatrix} -2 & 3 \\ 3 & 5 \end{bmatrix} = -2(5) - 3(3) = -10 - 9 = -19$

(b) $\det A = a_{11}A_{11} + a_{21}A_{21} + a_{31}A_{31} = a_{11}m_{11} - a_{21}m_{21} + a_{31}m_{31} \Rightarrow$

$\det A = (1)\det\begin{bmatrix} -5 & 0 \\ 3 & 6 \end{bmatrix} - (4)\det\begin{bmatrix} -1 & 3 \\ 3 & 6 \end{bmatrix} + (0)\det\begin{bmatrix} -1 & 3 \\ -5 & 0 \end{bmatrix} = (1)(-30 - 0) - (4)(-6 - 9) =$

$-30 - (-60) = 30$. The $\det A = 30$.

49. If $V = \pi r^2 h$, then $12 = \pi(1)^2 h \Rightarrow 12 = \pi h \Rightarrow h = \dfrac{12}{\pi} \Rightarrow h = 3.82$ in.

50. From $(0, 0)$ to $(1, 40)$, $m_1 = \dfrac{40 - 0}{1 - 0} \Rightarrow m_1 = 40$ indicates that the car is moving away from home at 40 mph;

from $(1, 40)$ to $(2, 40)$, $m_2 = \dfrac{40 - 40}{2 - 1} \Rightarrow m_2 = 0$ indicates that the car is not moving;

from $(2, 40)$ to $(3, 20)$, $m_3 = \dfrac{20 - 40}{3 - 2} \Rightarrow m_3 = -20$ indicates that the car is moving toward home at 20 mph;

from $(3, 20)$ to $(5, 50)$, $m_4 = \dfrac{50 - 20}{5 - 3} \Rightarrow m_4 = 15$ indicates that the car is moving away from home at 15 mph.

51. (a) $t = 0 \Rightarrow D(t) = 16(0)^2 \Rightarrow (0, 0)$; $t = 1 \Rightarrow D(t) = 16(1)^2 \Rightarrow (1, 16)$

The average rate of change from 0 to 1 is: $\dfrac{16 - 0}{1 - 0} = 16$ ft/sec.

$t = 1 \Rightarrow D(t) = 16(1)^2 \Rightarrow (1, 16)$; $t = 2 \Rightarrow D(t) = 16(2)^2 \Rightarrow (2, 64)$

The average rate of change from 1 to 2 is: $\dfrac{64 - 16}{2 - 1} = 48$ ft/sec.

(b) During the first second, the average speed is 16 ft/sec. During the next second, the average speed is 48 ft/sec. The object is speeding up.

(c) The difference quotient is: $\dfrac{16(t + h)^2 - 16t^2}{h} = \dfrac{16(t^2 + 2th + h^2) - 16t^2}{h} =$

$\dfrac{16t^2 + 32th + 16h^2 - 16t^2}{h} = 32t + 16h$

52. Person one: $1 - r(4) \Rightarrow r = \dfrac{1}{4}$; person two: $1 = r(6) \Rightarrow r = \dfrac{1}{6}$. Therefore $\dfrac{1}{4}t + \dfrac{1}{6}t = 1 \Rightarrow$

$6t + 4t = 24 \Rightarrow 10t = 24 \Rightarrow t = \dfrac{12}{5} \Rightarrow t = 2.4$ hours or 2 hours and 24 minutes.

53. $F = \dfrac{k}{d^2} \Rightarrow 150 = \dfrac{k}{(4000)^2} \Rightarrow k = 2{,}400{,}000{,}000$. Now, $F = \dfrac{2{,}400{,}000{,}000}{(10{,}000)^2} \Rightarrow F = \dfrac{2{,}400{,}000{,}000}{100{,}000{,}000} \Rightarrow$

$F = 24$ lbs.

54. Graph the constraint equations. See Figure 54.

Now evaluate the objective function: $C = 3x + y$ at each vertex. $(0, 1), C = 3(0) + 1 \Rightarrow C = 1$;

$(0, 2), C = 3(0) + 2 \Rightarrow C = 2$; $(1, 0), C = 3(1) + 0 \Rightarrow C = 3$; $(3, 0), C = 3(3) + 0 \Rightarrow C = 9$.

The minimum value for $C$ is $C = 1$ and it occurs at vertex $(0, 1)$ or when $x = 0$ and $y = 1$.

[0, 4, 1] by [0, 4, 1]

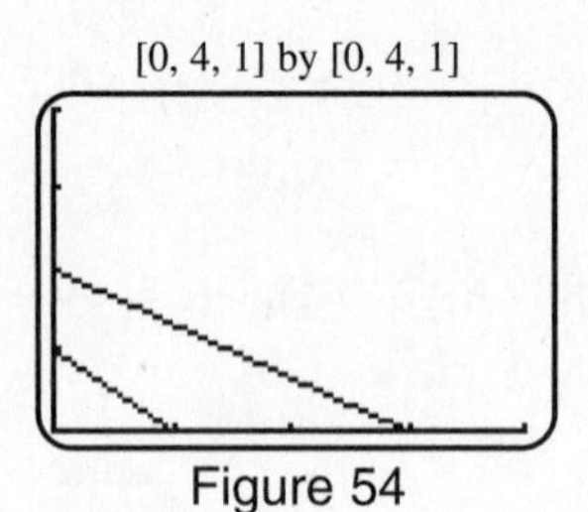

Figure 54

55. (a) $C(x) = x(112 - 2x) \Rightarrow C(x) = 112x - 2x^2$

(b) $1470 = 112x - 2x^2 \Rightarrow 2x^2 - 112x + 1470 = 0 \Rightarrow x^2 - 56x + 735 = 0 \Rightarrow$

$(x - 21)(x - 35) = 0 \Rightarrow x = 21, 35$; the cost is \$1470 when either 21 or 35 rooms are rented.

(c) Graph $C(x) = -2x^2 + 112x$. See Figure 55. The maximum occurs at the vertex $(28, 1568) \Rightarrow$ \$1568 when 28 rooms rented.

[0, 70, 10] by [0, 2000, 500]

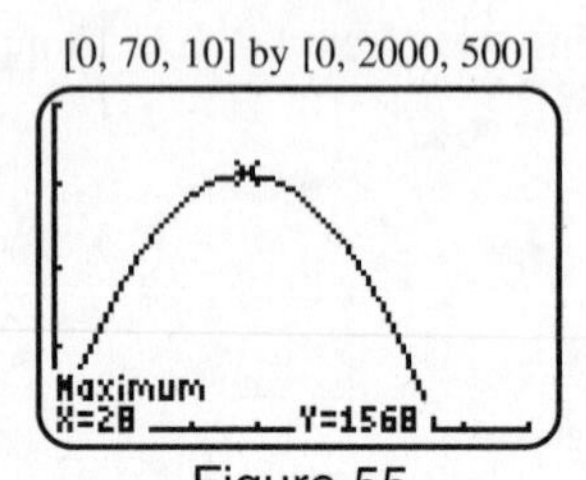


Figure 55

56. (a) As $t$ increases, $r$ also increases.

(b) $V = \frac{4}{3}\pi r^3 \Rightarrow V(t) = \frac{4}{3}\pi(\sqrt{t})^3$

(c) $V(4) = \frac{4}{3}\pi(\sqrt{4})^3 \Rightarrow V(4) = \frac{4}{3}\pi(2)^3 \Rightarrow V(4) = \frac{4}{3}\pi(8) \Rightarrow V(4) = \frac{32}{3}\pi \approx 33.5$; after 4 seconds the volume of the balloon is about 33.5 $\text{in}^3$.

57. (a) If $f(x) = \frac{5}{9}(x - 32)$, this is subtract 32 and multiply by $\frac{5}{9} \Rightarrow$ we divide by $\frac{5}{9}$, which is multiply by $\frac{9}{5}$, and add 32 $\Rightarrow f^{-1}(x) = \frac{9}{5}x + 32$.

(b) Since $f(x)$ converted Fahrenheit to Celsius, $f^{-1}(x)$ converts Celsius to Fahrenheit.

58. (a) $300{,}000 = 200{,}000e^{k(3)} \Rightarrow \dfrac{3}{2} = e^{3k} \Rightarrow \ln\dfrac{3}{2} = \ln e^{3k} \Rightarrow \ln\dfrac{3}{2} = 3k \Rightarrow \dfrac{\ln\frac{3}{2}}{3} = k \Rightarrow k \approx 0.135$

The formula that models this is: $N(t) = 200{,}000e^{0.135t}$

(b) $N(5) = 200{,}000e^{0.135(5)} \Rightarrow N(5) = 200{,}000e^{0.675} \Rightarrow N(5) \approx 392{,}807$; after 5 hours there are about 392,807 bacteria per ml. in the sample.

(c) $500{,}000 = 200{,}000e^{0.135t} \Rightarrow \dfrac{5}{2} = e^{0.135t} \Rightarrow \ln\dfrac{5}{2} = \ln e^{0.135t} \Rightarrow \ln\dfrac{5}{2} = 0.135t \Rightarrow \dfrac{\ln\frac{5}{2}}{0.135} = t \Rightarrow$

$t \approx 6.8$ hrs.

59. $A = P\left(1 + \dfrac{r}{n}\right)^{nt} \Rightarrow \dfrac{A}{P} = \left(1 + \dfrac{r}{n}\right)^{nt} \Rightarrow \dfrac{A}{P} = \left[\left(1 + \dfrac{r}{n}\right)^{n}\right]^{t} \Rightarrow \ln\left(\dfrac{A}{P}\right) = \ln\left[\left(1 + \dfrac{r}{n}\right)^{n}\right]^{t} \Rightarrow$

$\ln\left(\dfrac{A}{P}\right) = t\ln\left(1 + \dfrac{r}{n}\right)^{n} \Rightarrow \dfrac{\ln\left(\frac{A}{P}\right)}{\ln\left(a + \frac{r}{n}\right)^{n}} = t \Rightarrow t = \dfrac{\ln\left(\frac{A}{P}\right)}{n\ln\left(1 + \frac{r}{n}\right)}$

60. Let $x$ = length and $y$ = width, then $2x + 2y = 60$ and $xy = 209$. If $2x + 2y = 60$ then $2y = -2x + 60 \Rightarrow$ $y = -x + 30$. Now substitute this into $xy = 209$ and solve: $x(-x + 30) = 209 \Rightarrow -x^2 + 30x = 209 \Rightarrow$ $x^2 - 30x + 209 = 0 \Rightarrow (x - 19)(x - 11) = 0 \Rightarrow x = 19{,}11$. Therefore the dimensions are 19 in. by 11 in.

61. Let $x$ = amount borrowed at 4% and $y$ = amount borrowed at 3%, then $x + y = 5000$ and $0.04x + 0.03y = 173$.

Using elimination, multiply the second equation by 25 and subtract from the first equation:

$$\begin{array}{rl} x + \quad y &= 5000 \\ \underline{x + 0.75y} &\underline{= 4325} \\ 0.25y &= \ 675 \Rightarrow y = 2700. \end{array}$$

Therefore \$2300 was invested at 4% and \$2700 was invested at 3%.

62. Let $x$ = children tickets sold, $y$ = student tickets sold, and $z$ = adult tickets sold. Then $x + y + z = 900$; $6x + 7y + 10z = 7500$; and $z = y + 150$.

Multiply the first equation by 6 and subtract from the second equation:

$$\begin{array}{rl} 6x + 7y + 10z &= 7500 \\ \underline{6x + 6y + \ 6z} &\underline{= 5400} \\ y + \ 4z &= 2100. \end{array}$$

Now substitute $z = y + 150$ into this new equation $\Rightarrow y + 4(y + 150) = 2100 \Rightarrow$

$y + 4y + 600 = 2100 \Rightarrow 5y = 1500 \Rightarrow y = 300$. Substitute this into

$z = y + 150 \Rightarrow z = 300 + 150 \Rightarrow z = 450$.

Now substitute $y = 300$ and $z = 450$ into $x + y + z = 900 \Rightarrow x + 300 + 450 = 900 \Rightarrow x = 150$.

There were 150 children tickets, 300 student tickets, and 450 adult tickets sold.

63. $-8 = a(-1)^2 + b(-1) + c \Rightarrow -8 = a - b + c$; $6 = a(1)^2 + b(1) + c \Rightarrow 6 = a + b + c$;

$-4 = a(3)^2 + b(3) + c \Rightarrow -4 = 9a + 3b + c$

Add the first two equations to eliminate the $b$:

$$\begin{array}{rl} -8 = & a - b + c \\ 6 = & a + b + c \\ \hline -2 = & 2a \qquad + 2c. \end{array}$$

Multiply the first equation by 3 and add the third equation to eliminate the $b$:

$$\begin{array}{rl} -24 = & 3a - 3b + 3c \\ -4 = & 9a + 3b + c \\ \hline -28 = & 12a \qquad + 4c. \end{array}$$

Now multiply the first new equation by 2 and subtract the new second equation to eliminate the $c$:

$$\begin{array}{rl} -4 = & 4a + 4c \\ -28 = & 12a + 4c \\ \hline 24 = & -8a \qquad \Rightarrow a = -3. \end{array}$$

Substitute this into $-2 = 2a + 2c \Rightarrow -2 = 2(-3) + 2c \Rightarrow 4 = 2c \Rightarrow c = 2$. Substitute $a = -3$ and $c = 2$ into $6 = a + b + c \Rightarrow 6 = -3 + b + 2 \Rightarrow b = 7$. Therefore $a = -3$, $b = 7$, and $c = 2$.

64. $A = \frac{1}{2}\det\begin{bmatrix} -1 & 3 & 2 \\ 2 & -3 & 4 \\ 1 & 1 & 1 \end{bmatrix} \Rightarrow A = \frac{1}{2}(23) \Rightarrow A = 11.5$ square units.

# Chapter 7: Conic Sections

## 7.1: Parabolas

1. See Figure 1.
2. See Figure 2.

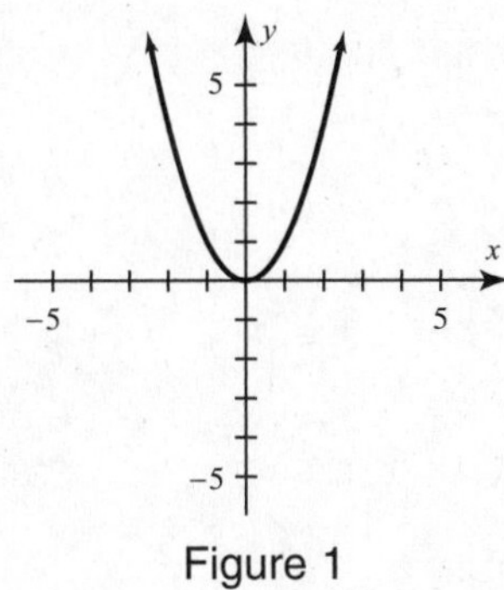

Figure 1

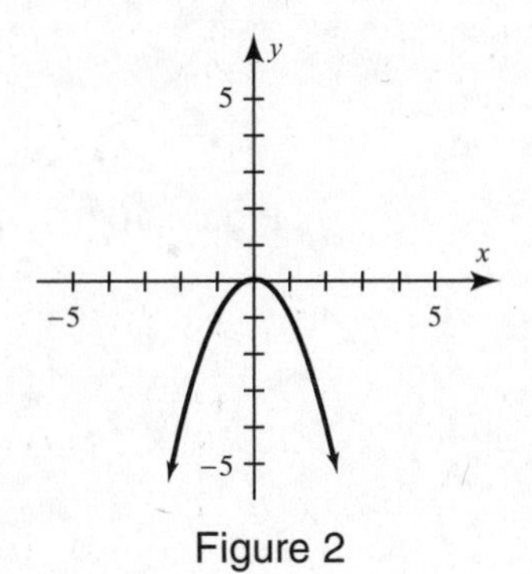

Figure 2

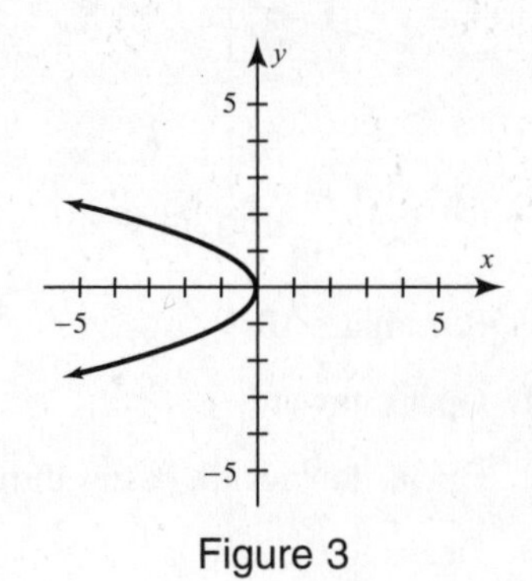

Figure 3

3. See Figure 3.
4. See Figure 4.
5. See Figure 5.

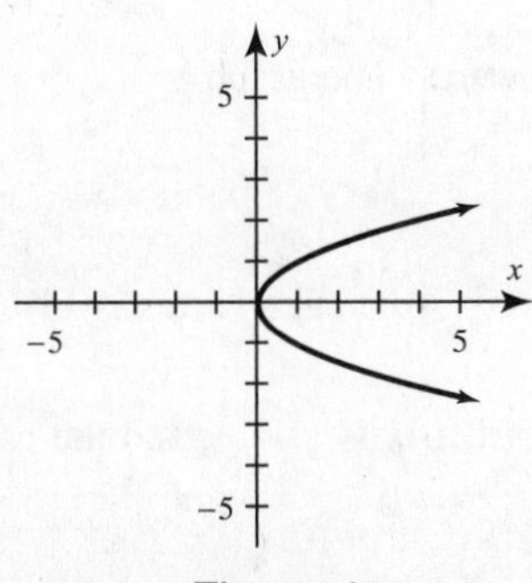

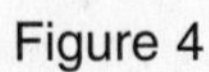
Figure 4

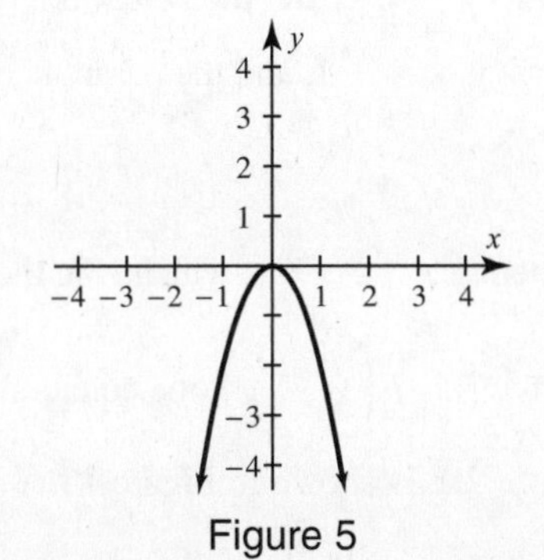

Figure 5

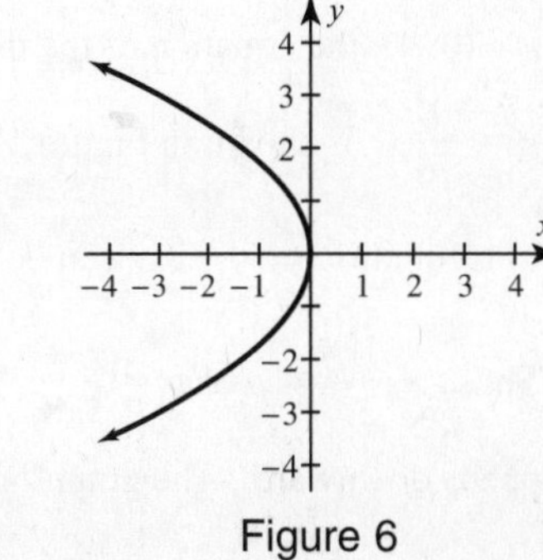

Figure 6

6. See Figure 6.
7. See Figure 7.

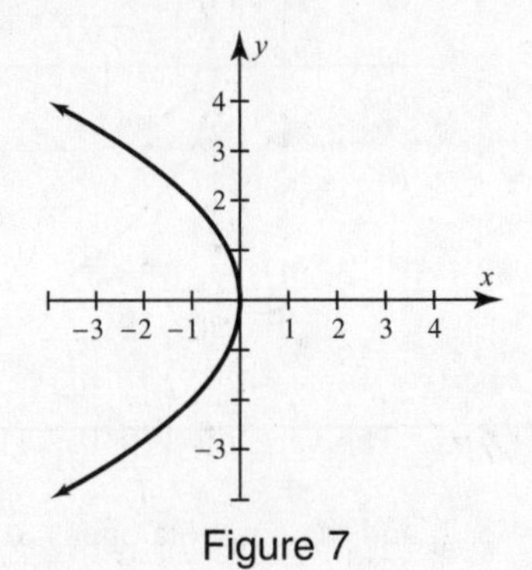

Figure 7

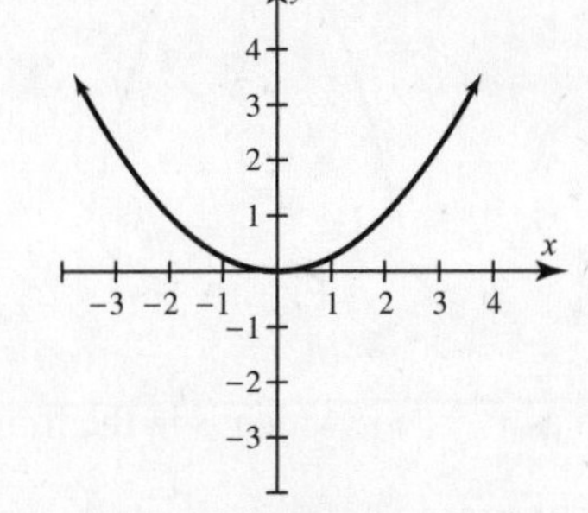

Figure 8

8. See Figure 8.

9. See Figure 9.

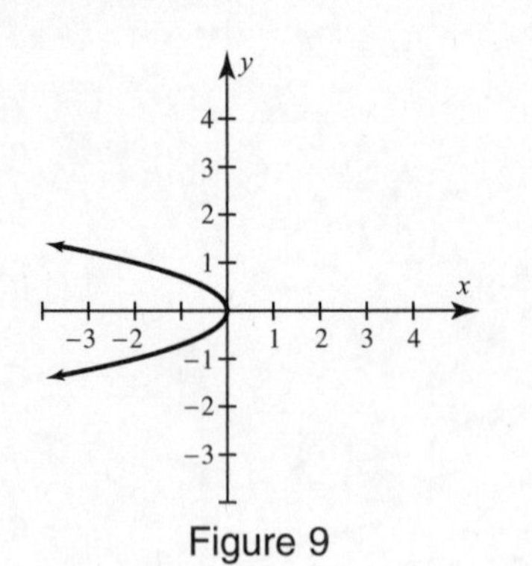


Figure 9

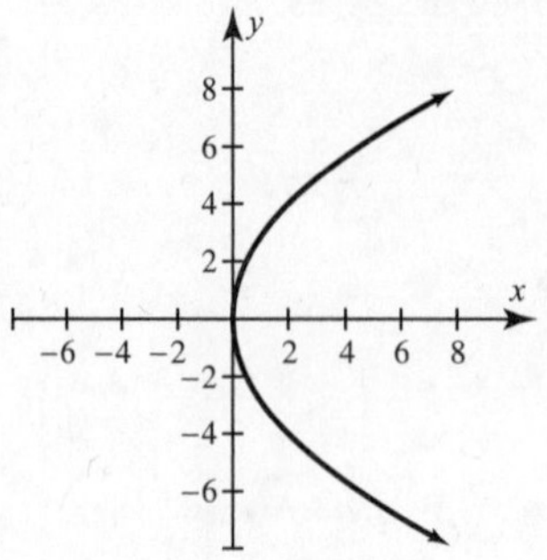

Figure 10

10. See Figure 10.
11. Opens upward; e
12. Opens downward, passes through (2, –2); c
13. Opens to the left; a
14. Opens to the right, passes through (4, 4); f
15. Opens to the right, passes through (2, 2); d
16. Opens downward, passes through (1, –2); b
17. The equation $16y = x^2$ is in the form $x^2 = 4py$, and the vertex is $V(0, 0)$. Thus, $16 = 4p$ or $p = 4$. The focus is $F(0, 4)$, the equation of the directrix is $y = -4$, and the parabola opens upward. The graph of $y = \frac{1}{16}x^2$ is shown in Figure 17.
18. The equation $y = -2x^2$ can be written as $x^2 = -\frac{1}{2}y$, which is in the form $x^2 = 4py$. The vertex is $V(0, 0)$. Thus, $-\frac{1}{2} = 4p$ or $p = -\frac{1}{8}$. The focus is $F\left(0, -\frac{1}{8}\right)$, the equation of the directrix is $y = \frac{1}{8}$, and the parabola opens downward. The graph of $y = -2x^2$ is shown in Figure 18.

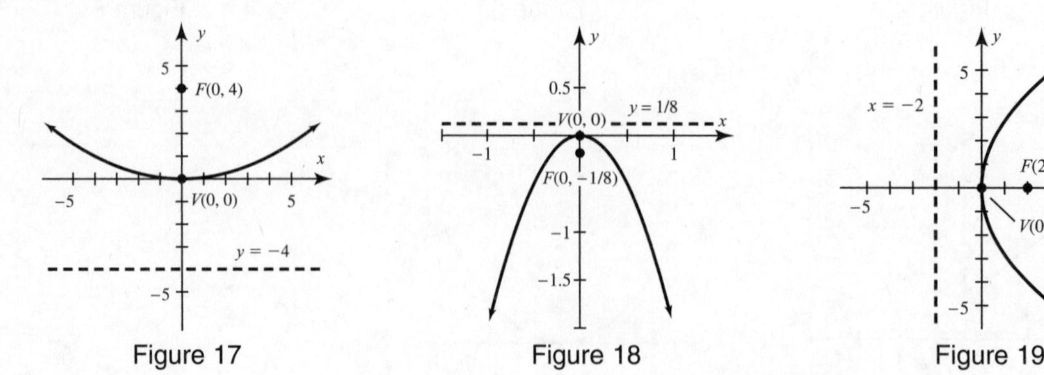


Figure 17 Figure 18 Figure 19

19. The equation $x = \frac{1}{8}y^2$ can be written as $y^2 = 8x$, which is in the form $y^2 = 4px$. The vertex is $V(0, 0)$. Thus, $8 = 4p$ or $p = 2$. The focus is $F(2, 0)$, the equation of the directrix is $x = -2$, and the parabola opens to the right. The graph of $x = \frac{1}{8}y^2$ is shown in Figure 19.

20. The equation $-y^2 = 6x$ can be written as $y^2 = -6x$, which is in the form $y^2 = 4px$. The vertex is $V(0, 0)$. Thus, $-6 = 4p$ or $p = -\frac{3}{2}$. The focus is $F\left(-\frac{3}{2}, 0\right)$, the equation of the directrix is $x = \frac{3}{2}$, and the parabola opens to the left. The graph of $x = -\frac{1}{6}y^2$ is shown in Figure 20.

21. The equation $-4x = y^2$ can be written as $y^2 = -4x$, which is in the form $y^2 = 4px$. The vertex is $V(0, 0)$. Thus, $-4 = 4p$ or $p = -1$. The focus is $F(-1, 0)$, the equation of the directrix is $x = 1$, and the parabola opens to the left. The graph of $x = -\frac{1}{4}y^2$ is shown in Figure 21.

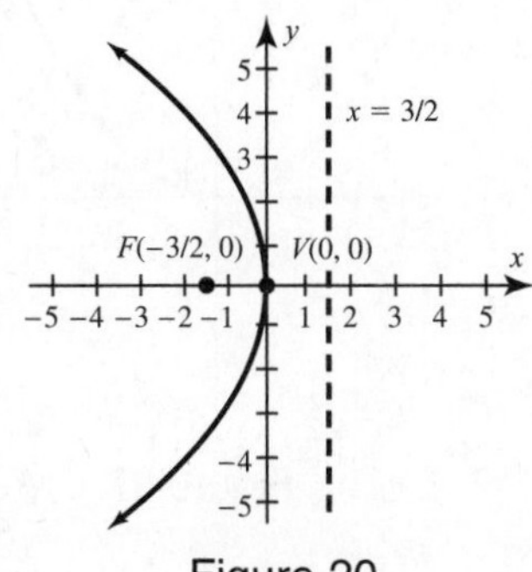

Figure 20

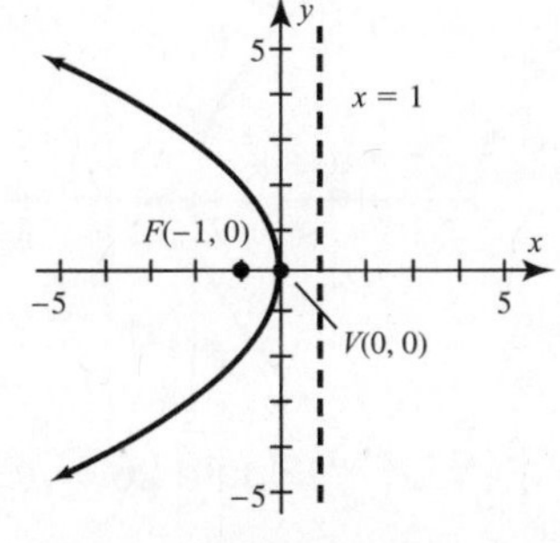

Figure 21

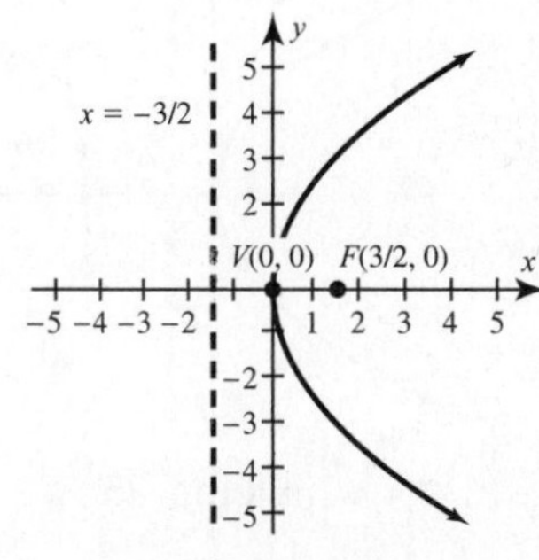

Figure 22

22. The equation $\frac{1}{2}y^2 = 3x$ can be written as $y^2 = 6x$, which is in the form $y^2 = 4px$. The vertex is $V(0, 0)$. Thus, $6 = 4p$ or $p = \frac{3}{2}$. The focus is $F\left(\frac{3}{2}, 0\right)$, the equation of the directrix is $x = -\frac{3}{2}$, and the parabola opens to the right. The graph of $x = \frac{1}{6}y^2$ is shown in Figure 22.

23. The equation $x^2 = -8y$ is in the form $x^2 = 4py$, and the vertex is $V(0, 0)$. Thus, $-8 = 4p$ or $p = -2$. The focus is $F(0, -2)$, the equation of the directrix is $y = 2$, and the parabola opens downward. The graph of $y = -\frac{1}{8}x^2$ is shown in Figure 23.

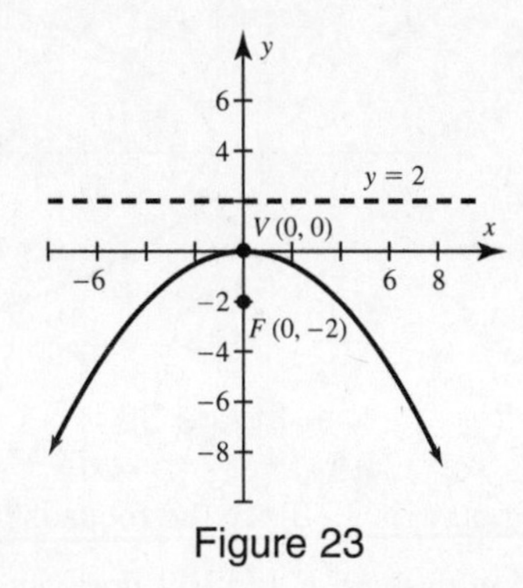

Figure 23

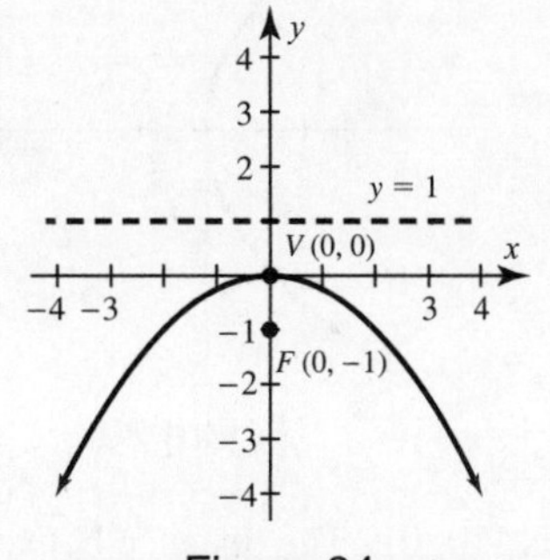

Figure 24

24. The equation $x^2 = -4y$ is in the form $x^2 = 4py$. The vertex is $V(0, 0)$. Thus, $-4 = 4p \Rightarrow p = -1$. The focus is $F(0, -1)$, the equation of the directrix is $y = 1$, and the parabola opens down. See Figure 24.

25. The equation $2y^2 = -8x$ can be written as $y^2 = -4x$, which is in the form $y^2 = 4px$. The vertex is $V(0, 0)$. Thus, $-4 = 4p$ or $p = -1$. The focus is $F(-1, 0)$, the equation of the directrix is $x = 1$, and the parabola opens to the left. The graph of $x = -\frac{1}{4}y^2$ is shown in Figure 25.

26. The equation $-3x = \frac{1}{4}y^2$ can be written as $y^2 = -12x$, which is in the form $y^2 = 4px$. The vertex is $V(0, 0)$. Thus, $-12 = 4p$ or $p = -3$. The focus is $F(-3, 0)$, the equation of the directrix is $x = 3$, and the parabola opens to the left. The graph of $x = -\frac{1}{12}y^2$ is shown in Figure 26.

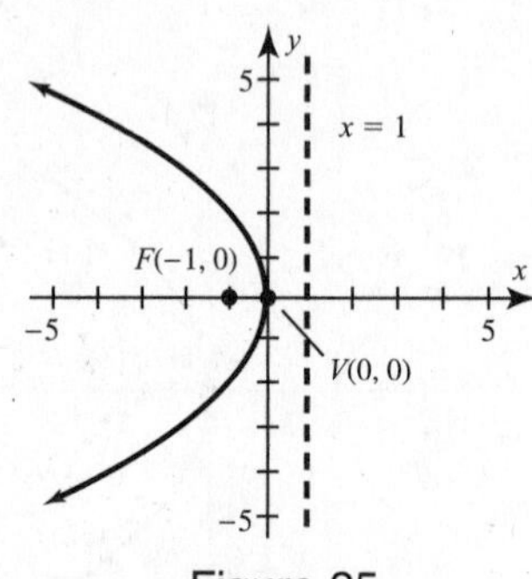

Figure 25

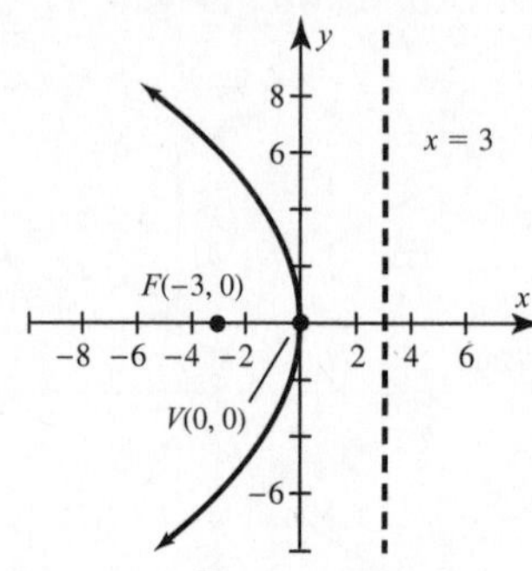

Figure 26

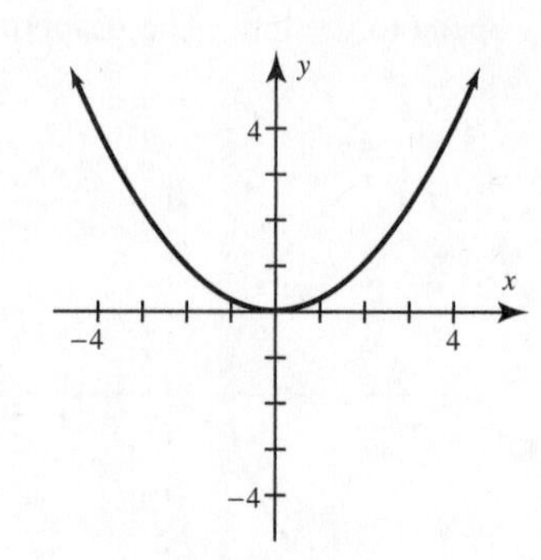

Figure 27

27. The focus is $F(0, 1)$ and the vertex is $V(0, 0)$. The distance between these points is 1. Since the focus is above the directrix, the parabola opens upward, so $p = 1$. Since the line passing through $F$ and $V$ is vertical, the parabola has a vertical axis. Its equation is given by $x^2 = 4py$ or $x^2 = 4y$. The graph of $y = \frac{1}{4}x^2$ is shown in Figure 27.

28. The focus is $F(0, -2)$ and the vertex is $V(0, 0)$. The distance between these points is 2. Since the focus is below the directrix, the parabola opens downward, so $p = -2$. Since the line passing through $F$ and $V$ is vertical, the parabola has a vertical axis. Its equation is given by $x^2 = 4py$ or $x^2 = -8y$. The graph of $y = -\frac{1}{8}x^2$ is shown in Figure 28.

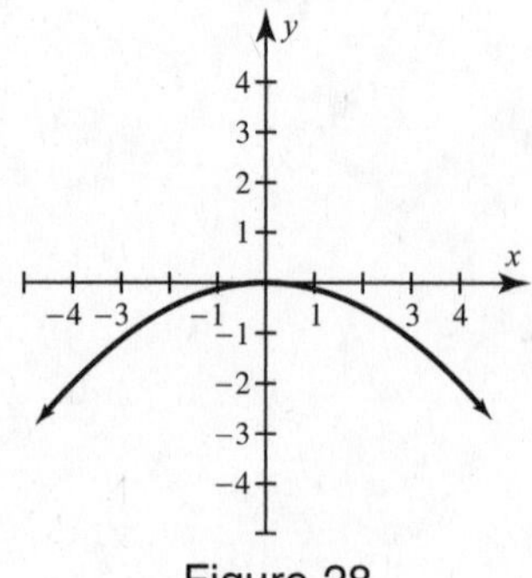

Figure 28

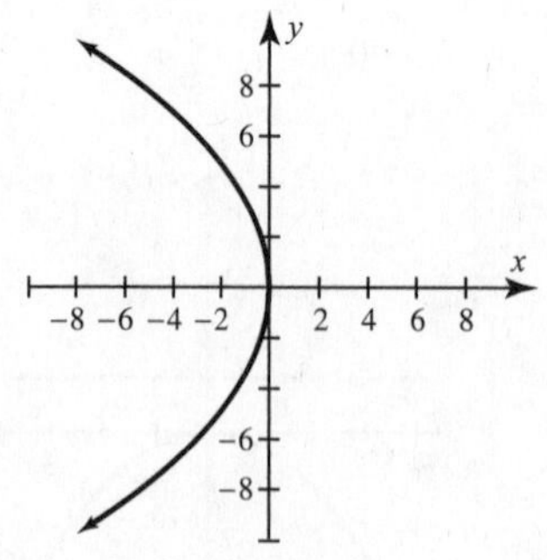

Figure 29

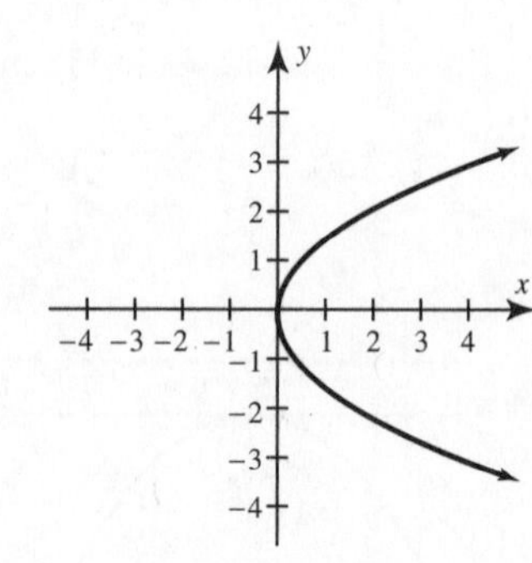

Figure 30

29. The focus is $F(-3, 0)$ and the vertex is $V(0, 0)$. The distance between these points is 3. Since the focus is left of the directrix, the parabola opens to the left, so $p = -3$. Since the line passing through $F$ and $V$ is horizontal, the parabola has a horizontal axis. Its equation is given by $y^2 = 4px$ or $y^2 = -12x$. The graph of $x = -\frac{1}{12}y^2$ is shown in Figure 29.

30. The focus is $F\left(\frac{1}{2}, 0\right)$ and the vertex is $V(0, 0)$. The distance between these points is $\frac{1}{2}$. Since the focus is right of the directrix, the parabola opens to the right, so $p = \frac{1}{2}$. Since the line passing through $F$ and $V$ is horizontal, the parabola has a horizontal axis. Its equation is given by $y^2 = 4px$ or $y^2 = 2x$. The graph of $x = \frac{1}{2}y^2$ is shown in Figure 30.

31. If the vertex is $V(0, 0)$ and the focus is $F\left(0, \frac{3}{4}\right)$, then the parabola opens upward and $p = \frac{3}{4}$. Thus, $x^2 = 4py \Rightarrow x^2 = 3y$. Its graph is shown in Figure 31.

32. If the vertex is $V(0, 0)$ and the directrix is $y = 2$, then the parabola opens downward and $p = -2$. Thus, $x^2 = 4py \Rightarrow x^2 = -8y$. Its graph is shown in Figure 32.

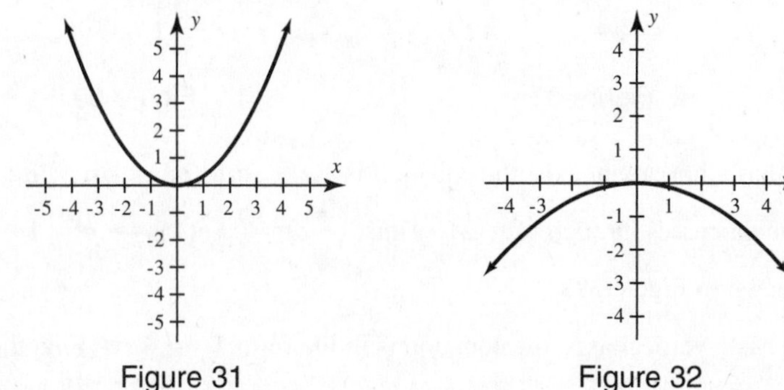


Figure 31

Figure 32

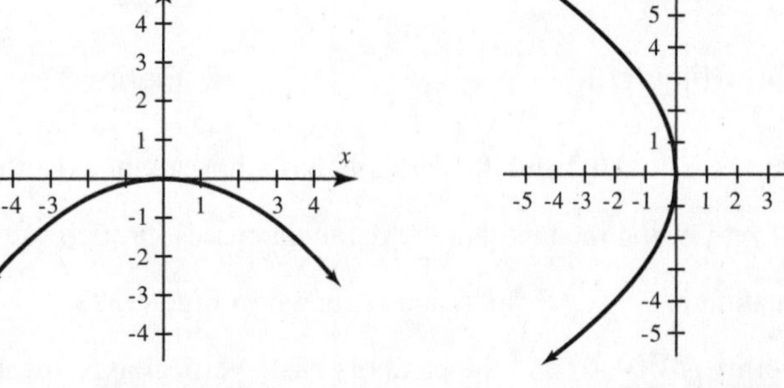


Figure 33

33. If the vertex is $V(0, 0)$ and the directrix is $x = 2$, then the parabola opens to the left and $p = -2$. Thus, $y^2 = 4px \Rightarrow y^2 = -8x$. Its graph is shown in Figure 33.

34. If the vertex is $V(0, 0)$ and the focus is $F(-1, 0)$, then the parabola opens to the left and $p = -1$. Thus, $y^2 = 4px \Rightarrow y^2 = -4x$. Its graph is shown in Figure 34.

35. If the vertex is $V(0, 0)$ and the focus is $F(1, 0)$, then the parabola opens to the right and $p = 1$. Thus, $y^2 = 4px \Rightarrow y^2 = 4x$. Its graph is shown in Figure 35.

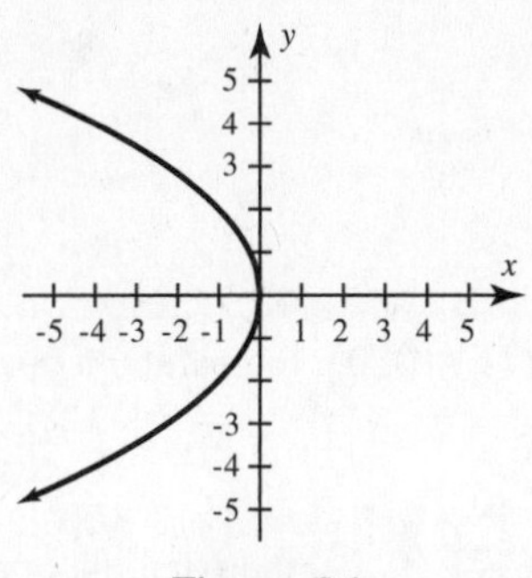


Figure 34

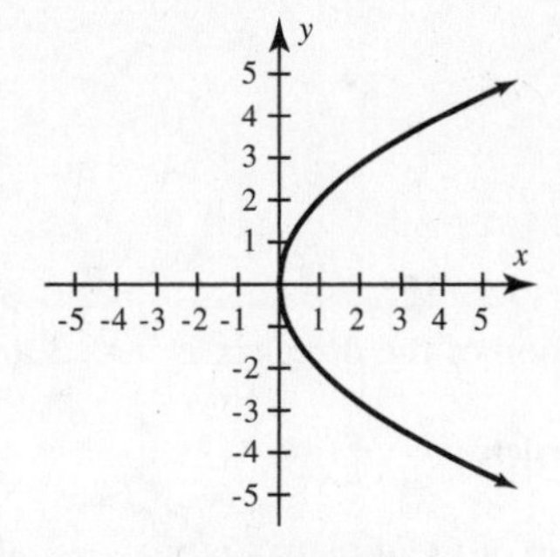


Figure 35

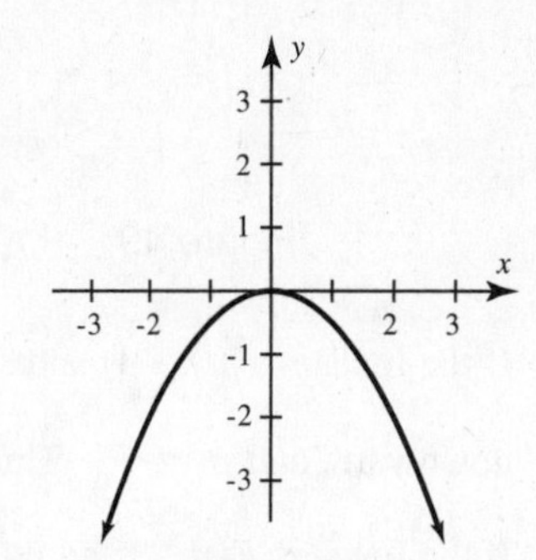


Figure 36

36. If the vertex is $V(0, 0)$ and the focus is $F\left(0, -\frac{1}{2}\right)$, then the parabola opens downward and $p = -\frac{1}{2}$. Thus, $x^2 = 4py \Rightarrow x^2 = -2y$. Its graph is shown in Figure 36.

37. If the vertex is $V(0, 0)$ and the directrix is $x = \frac{1}{4}$, then the parabola opens to the left and $p = -\frac{1}{4}$. Thus, $y^2 = 4px \Rightarrow y^2 = -x$. Its graph is shown in Figure 37.

38. If the vertex is $V(0, 0)$ and the directrix is $y = -1$, then the parabola opens upward and $p = 1$. Thus, $x^2 = 4py \Rightarrow x^2 = 4y$. Its graph is shown in Figure 38.

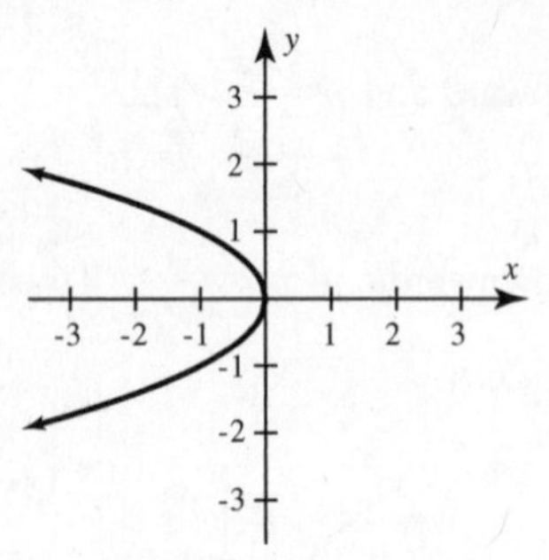

Figure 37

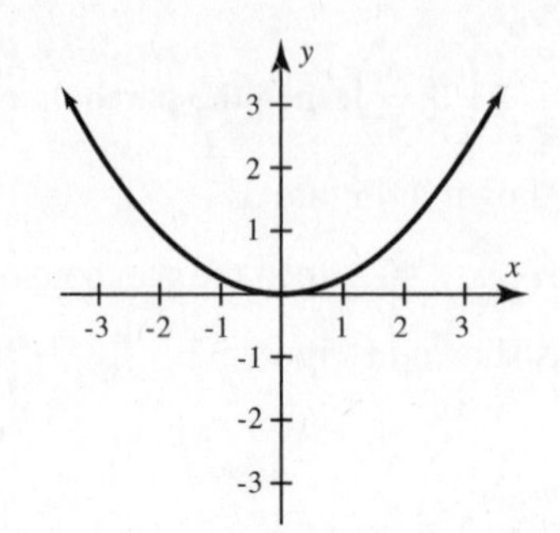

Figure 38

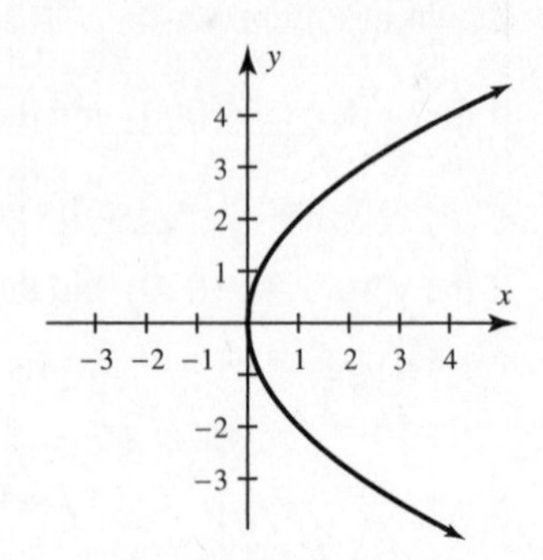

Figure 39

39. If the vertex is $V(0, 0)$ and the parabola has a horizontal axis, the equation is in the form $y^2 = 4px$. Find the value of $p$ by using the fact that the parabola passes through $(1, -2)$. Thus, $(-2)^2 = 4p(1) \Rightarrow p = 1$. The equation is $y^2 = 4x$. Its graph is shown in Figure 39.

40. If the vertex is $V(0, 0)$ and the parabola has a vertical axis, the equation is in the form $x^2 = 4py$. Find the value of $p$ by using the fact that the parabola passes through $(-2, 3)$. Thus, $(-2)^2 = 4p(3) \Rightarrow p = \frac{1}{3}$. The equation is $x^2 = \frac{4}{3}y$. Its graph is shown in Figure 40.

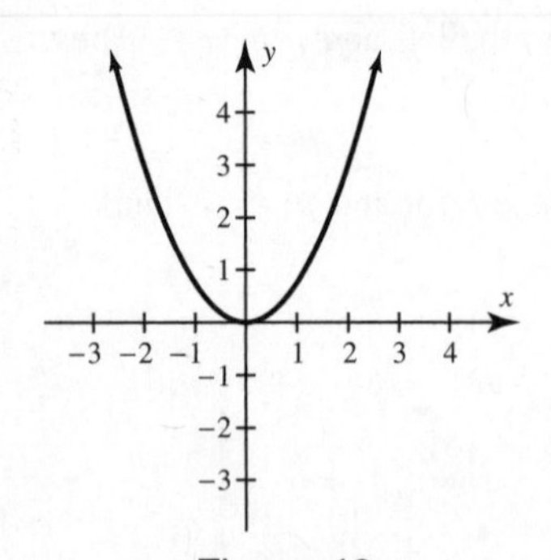

Figure 40

41. If the focus is $F(0, -3)$ and the equation of the directrix is $y = 3$, the vertex is $V(0, 0)$, the parabola opens downward, and $p = -3$. Thus, $x^2 = 4py \Rightarrow x^2 = -12y$.

42. If the focus is $F(0, 2)$ and the equation of the directrix is $y = -2$, the vertex is $V(0, 0)$, the parabola opens upward, and $p = 2$. Thus, $x^2 = 4py \Rightarrow x^2 = 8y$.

43. If the focus is $F(-1, 0)$ and the equation of the directrix is $x = 1$, the vertex is $V(0, 0)$, the parabola opens to the left, and $p = -1$. Thus, $y^2 = 4px \Rightarrow y^2 = -4x$.

44. If the focus is $F(3, 0)$ and the equation of the directrix is $x = -3$, the vertex is $V(0, 0)$, the parabola opens to the right, and $p = 3$. Thus, $y^2 = 4px \Rightarrow y^2 = 12x$.

45. See Figure 45.

46. See Figure 46.

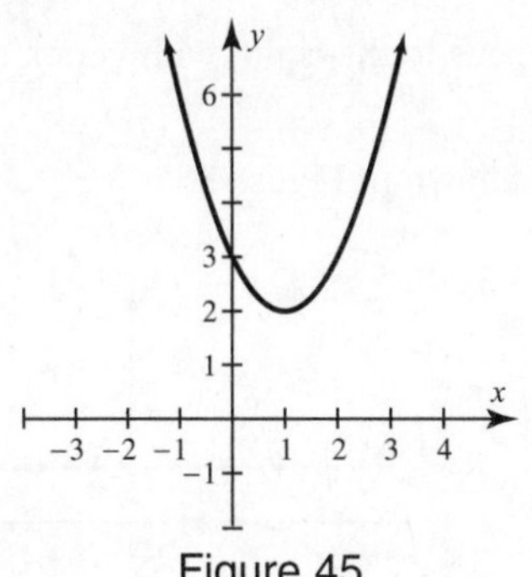

Figure 45

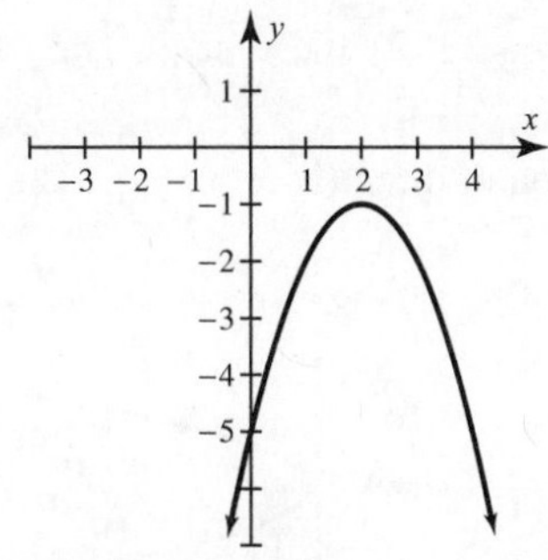

Figure 46

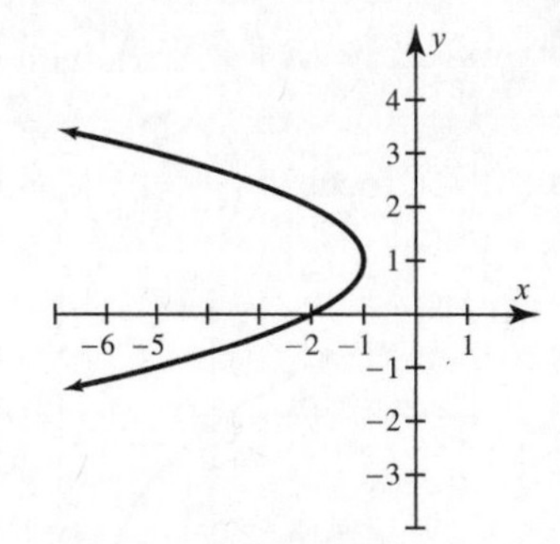

Figure 47

47. See Figure 47.

48. See Figure 48.

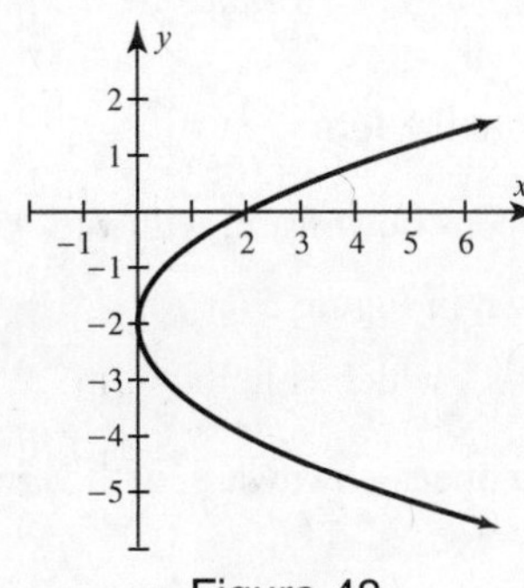

Figure 48

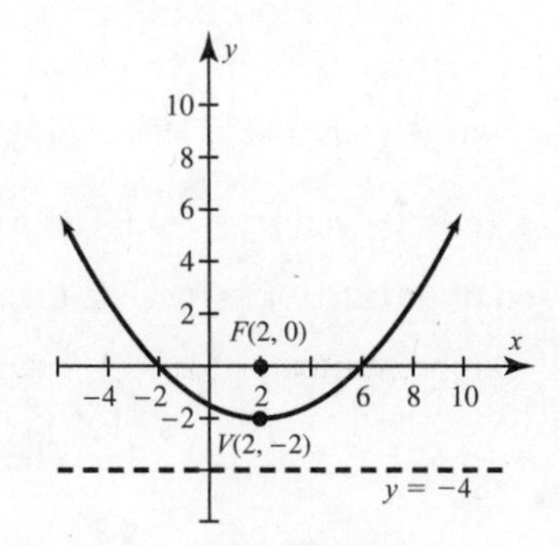

Figure 53

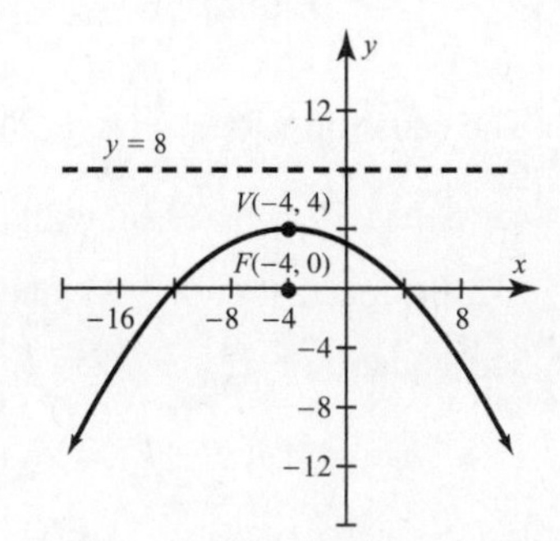

Figure 54

49. Vertex at (1, 1); c

50. Vertex at (–1, 2); d

51. Vertex at (0, 2); a

52. Vertex at (–3, –1); b

53. The equation $(x - 2)^2 = 8(y + 2)$ is in the form $(x - h)^2 = 4p(y - k)$, with $(h, k) = (2, -2)$ and $p = 2$. The parabola opens upward, with vertex at (2, –2), focus at (2, 0), and equation of directrix $y = -4$. The graph is shown in Figure 53.

54. The equation $\frac{1}{16}(x + 4)^2 = -(y - 4)$ can be written as $(x + 4)^2 = -16(y - 4)$, which is in the form $(x - h)^2 = 4p(y - k)$, with $(h, k) = (-4, 4)$ and $p = -4$. The parabola opens downward, with vertex at (–4, 4), focus at (–4, 0), and equation of directrix $y = 8$. The graph is shown in Figure 54.

55. The equation $x = -\frac{1}{4}(y+3)^2 + 2$ can be written as $(y+3)^2 = -4(x-2)$, which is in the form $(y-k)^2 = 4p(x-h)$, with $(h, k) = (2, -3)$ and $p = -1$. The parabola opens to the left, with vertex at (2, –3), focus at (1, –3), and equation of directrix $x = 3$. The graph is shown in Figure 55.

56. The equation $x = 2(y-2)^2 - 1$ can be written as $(y-2)^2 = \frac{1}{2}(x+1)$, which is in the form $(y-k)^2 = 4p(x-h)$, with $(h, k) = (-1, 2)$ and $p = \frac{1}{8}$. The parabola opens to the right, with vertex at (–1, 2), focus at $\left(-\frac{7}{8}, 2\right)$, and equation of directrix $x = -\frac{9}{8}$. The graph is shown in Figure 56.

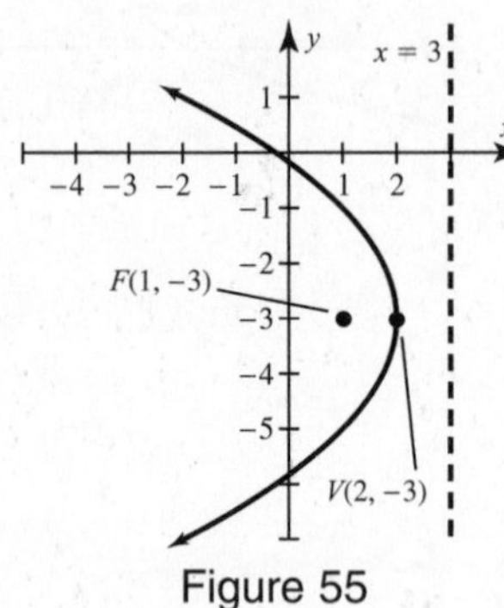

Figure 55

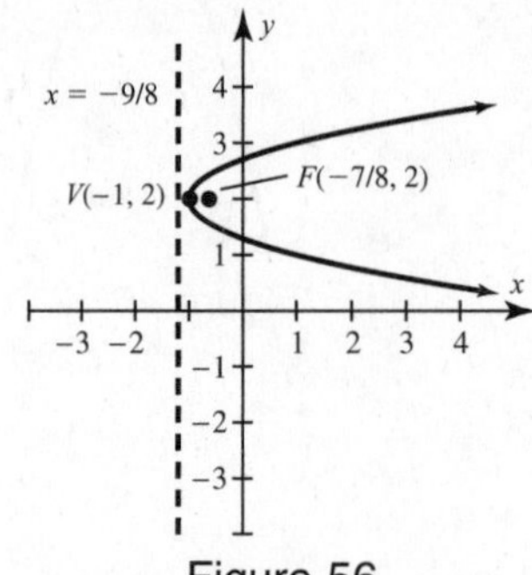

Figure 56

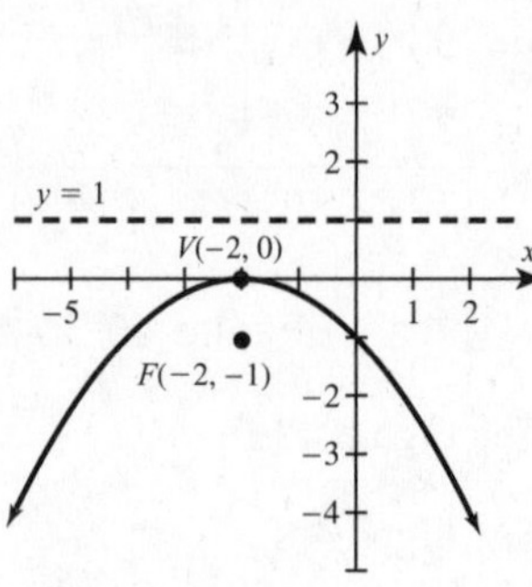

Figure 57

57. The equation $y = -\frac{1}{4}(x+2)^2$ can be written as $(x+2)^2 = -4y$, which is in the form $(x-h)^2 = 4p(y-k)$, with $(h, k) = (-2, 0)$ and $p = -1$. The parabola opens downward, with vertex at (–2, 0), focus at $(-2, -1)$, and equation of directrix $y = 1$. The graph is shown in Figure 57.

58 The equation $-2(y+1) = (x+3)^2$ can be written as $(x+3)^2 = -2(y+1)$, which is in the form $(x-h)^2 = 4p(y-k)$, with $(h, k) = (-3, -1)$ and $p = -\frac{1}{2}$. The parabola opens downward, with vertex at (–3, –1), focus at $\left(-3, -\frac{3}{2}\right)$, and equation of directrix $y = -\frac{1}{2}$. The graph is shown in Figure 58.

59. If the focus is at $(0, 2)$ and the vertex at $(0, 1)$, the parabola opens upward and $p = 1$. Substituting in $(x-h)^2 = 4p(y-k)$, we get $(x-0)^2 = 4(1)(y-1)$ or $x^2 = 4(y-1)$. See Figure 59.

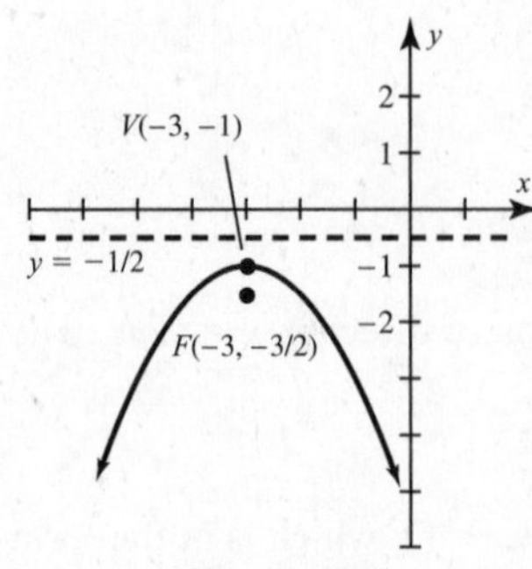

Figure 58

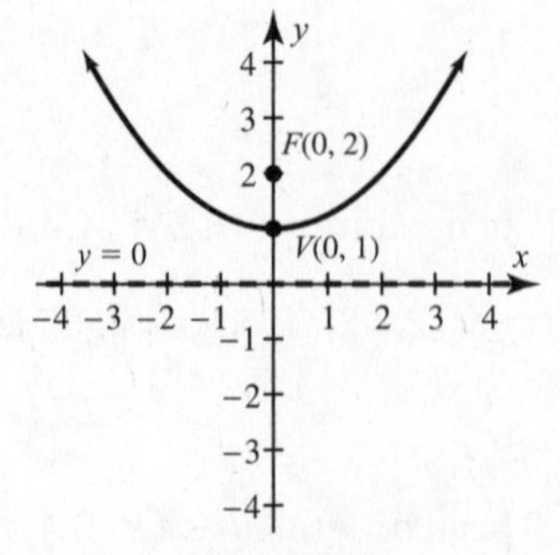

Figure 59

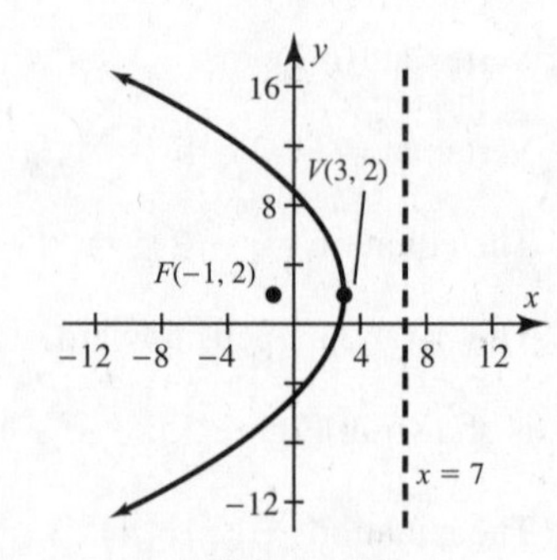

Figure 60

60. If the focus is at $(-1, 2)$ and the vertex at (3, 2), the parabola opens to the left and $p = -4$. Substituting in $(y-k)^2 = 4p(x-h)$, we get $(y-2)^2 = -16(x-3)$. See Figure 60.

61. If the focus is at $(0, 0)$ and the directrix has equation $x = -2$, the vertex is at $(-1, 0)$, $p = 1$, and the parabola opens to the right. Substituting in $(y - k)^2 = 4p(x - h)$, we get $(y - 0)^2 = 4(1)(x - (-1))$ or $y^2 = 4(x + 1)$. See Figure 61.

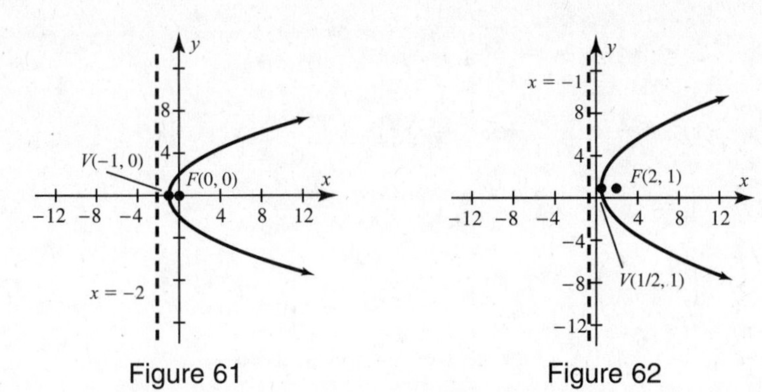


Figure 61 Figure 62

62. If the focus is at $(2, 1)$ and the directrix has equation $x = -1$, the vertex is at $\left(\frac{1}{2}, 1\right)$, $p = \frac{3}{2}$, and the parabola opens to the right. Substituting in $(y - k)^2 = 4p(x - h)$, we get $(y - 1)^2 = 4\left(\frac{3}{2}\right)\left(x - \frac{1}{2}\right)$ or $(y - 1)^2 = 6\left(x - \frac{1}{2}\right)$. See Figure 62.

63. If the focus is at $(-1, 3)$ and the directrix has equation $y = 7$, the vertex is at $(-1, 5)$, $p = -2$, and the parabola opens downward. Substituting in $(x - h)^2 = 4p(y - k)$, we get $(x + 1)^2 = 4(-2)(y - 5)$ or $(x + 1)^2 = -8(y - 5)$.

64. If the focus is at $(1, 2)$ and the directrix has equation $y = 4$, the vertex is at $(1, 3)$, $p = -1$, and the parabola opens downward. Substituting in $(x - h)^2 = 4p(y - k)$, we get $(x - 1)^2 = 4(-1)(y - 3)$ or $(x - 1)^2 = -4(y - 3)$.

65. Since the parabola has a horizontal axis, the equation is in the form $(y - k)^2 = a(x - h)$. Find the value of $a$ by using the fact that the parabola passes through $(-4, 0)$ and the vertex is $V(-2, 3)$.
Substituting $x = -4$, $y = 0$, $h = -2$ and $k = 3$ yields $(0 - 3)^2 = a(-4 - (-2)) \Rightarrow a = -\frac{9}{2}$.
The equation is $(y - 3)^2 = -\frac{9}{2}(x + 2)$.

66. Since the parabola has a horizontal axis, the equation is in the form $(y - k)^2 = a(x - h)$. Find the value of $a$ by using the fact that the parabola passes through $(2, 3)$ and the vertex is $V(-1, 2)$.
Substituting $x = 2$, $y = 3$, $h = -1$ and $k = 2$ yields $(3 - 2)^2 = a(2 - (-1)) \Rightarrow a = \frac{1}{3}$.
The equation is $(y - 2)^2 = \frac{1}{3}(x + 1)$.

67. $-2x = y^2 + 6x + 10 \Rightarrow y^2 = -8x - 10 \Rightarrow (y - 0)^2 = -8\left(x + \frac{5}{4}\right)$

68. $y^2 + 8x - 8 = 4x \Rightarrow y^2 = -4x + 8 \Rightarrow (y - 0)^2 = -4(x - 2)$

69. $x = 2y^2 + 4y - 1 \Rightarrow 2y^2 + 4y = x + 1 \Rightarrow y^2 + 2y = \frac{1}{2}(x + 1) \Rightarrow$

$y^2 + 2y + 1 = \frac{1}{2}(x + 1) + 1 \Rightarrow (y + 1)^2 = \frac{1}{2}(x + 1 + 2) \Rightarrow (y + 1)^2 = \frac{1}{2}(x + 3)$

70. $x = 3y^2 - 6y - 2 \Rightarrow 3y^2 - 6y = x + 2 \Rightarrow y^2 - 2y = \frac{1}{3}(x + 2) \Rightarrow$

$y^2 - 2y + 1 = \frac{1}{3}(x + 2) + 1 \Rightarrow (y - 1)^2 = \frac{1}{3}(x + 2 + 3) \Rightarrow (y - 1)^2 = \frac{1}{3}(x + 5)$

71. $x^2 - 3x + 4 = 2y \Rightarrow x^2 - 3x = 2y - 4 \Rightarrow x^2 - 3x + \frac{9}{4} = 2y - 4 + \frac{9}{4} \Rightarrow$

$\left(x - \frac{3}{2}\right)^2 = 2y - \frac{7}{4} \Rightarrow \left(x - \frac{3}{2}\right)^2 = 2\left(y - \frac{7}{8}\right)$

72. $-3y = -x^2 + 4x - 6 \Rightarrow x^2 - 4x = 3y - 6 \Rightarrow x^2 - 4x + 4 = 3y - 6 + 4 \Rightarrow$

$(x - 2)^2 = 3y - 2 \Rightarrow (x - 2)^2 = 3\left(y - \frac{2}{3}\right)$

73. $4y^2 + 4y - 5 = 5x \Rightarrow 4y^2 + 4y = 5x + 5 \Rightarrow y^2 + y = \frac{5}{4}(x + 1) \Rightarrow$

$y^2 + y + \frac{1}{4} = \frac{5}{4}(x + 1) + \frac{1}{4} \Rightarrow \left(y + \frac{1}{2}\right)^2 = \frac{5}{4}\left(x + 1 + \frac{1}{5}\right) \Rightarrow \left(y + \frac{1}{2}\right)^2 = \frac{5}{4}\left(x + \frac{6}{5}\right)$

74. $-2y^2 + 5y + 1 = -x \Rightarrow 2y^2 - 5y = x + 1 \Rightarrow y^2 - \frac{5}{2}y = \frac{1}{2}(x + 1) \Rightarrow$

$y^2 - \frac{5}{2}y + \frac{25}{16} = \frac{1}{2}(x + 1) + \frac{25}{16} \Rightarrow \left(y - \frac{5}{4}\right)^2 = \frac{1}{2}\left(x + 1 + \frac{25}{8}\right) \Rightarrow \left(y - \frac{5}{4}\right)^2 = \frac{1}{2}\left(x + \frac{33}{8}\right)$

75. $y = -0.75 \pm \sqrt{-3x}$; See Figure 75.

76. $y = \pm\sqrt{\frac{1}{7}x} + 3$ or $y = 3 \pm \sqrt{\frac{1}{7}x}$; See Figure 76.

[−6, 6, 1] by [−4, 4, 1]

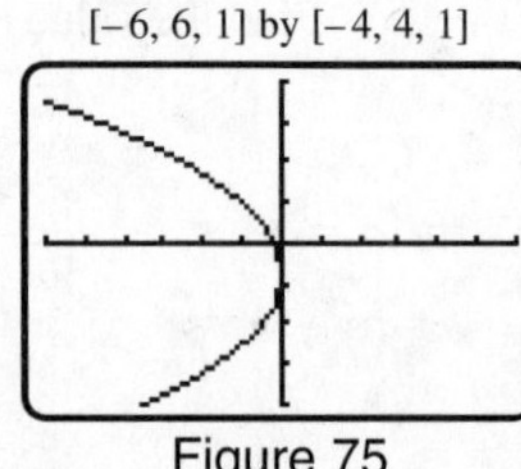

Figure 75

[−6, 6, 1] by [−4, 4, 1]

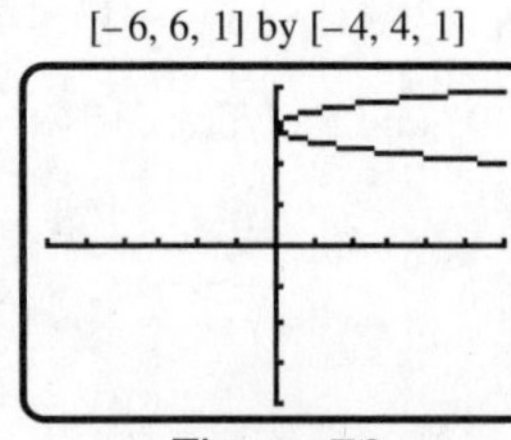

Figure 76

[−9, 9, 1] by [−6, 6, 1]

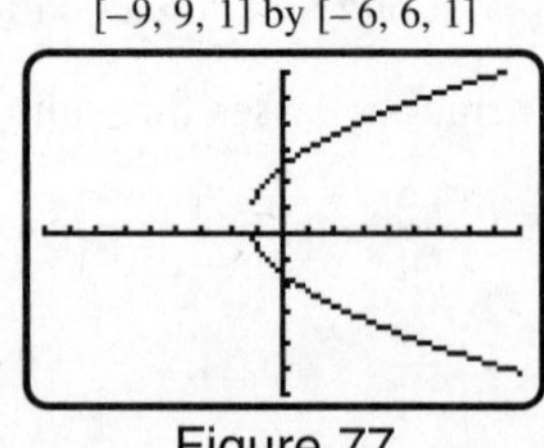

Figure 77

[−6, 6, 1] by [−4, 4, 1]

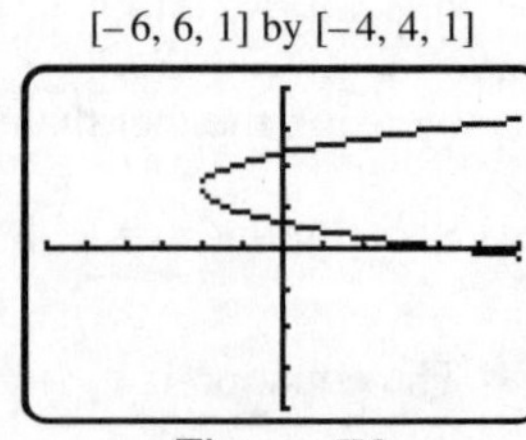

Figure 78

77. $y = 0.5 \pm \sqrt{3.1(x + 1.3)}$; See Figure 77. Note: If a break in the graph appears near the vertex, it should not be there. It is a result of the low resolution of the graphing calculator screen.

78. $y = 1.5 \pm \sqrt{\frac{0.5}{1.4}(x + 2.1)}$; See Figure 78.

79. $y = -1 \pm \sqrt{\frac{x}{2.3}}$; See Figure 79.

80. $y = 2.5 \pm \sqrt{1.4(x + 1)}$; See Figure 80.

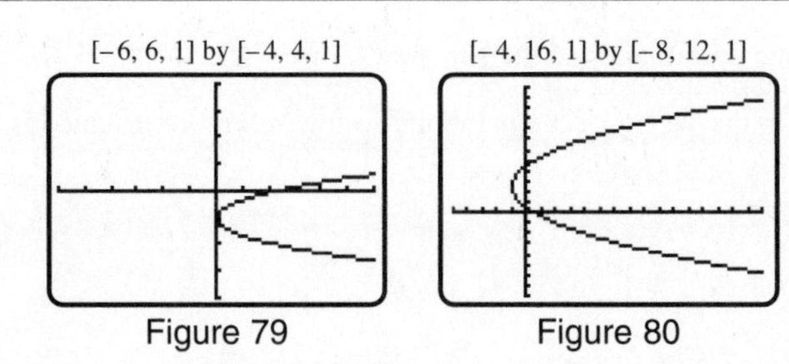


Figure 79 Figure 80

81. $x^2 = 2y$ and $x^2 = y + 1 \Rightarrow 2y = y + 1 \Rightarrow y = 1$; $x^2 = 2y$ when $y = 1 \Rightarrow x^2 = 2 \Rightarrow x = \pm\sqrt{2}$; the solution is $(\pm\sqrt{2}, 1)$.

82. $x^2 = -3y$ and $-x^2 = 2y - 2 \Rightarrow -3y = -2y + 2 \Rightarrow y = -2$; $x^2 = -3y$ when $y = -2 \Rightarrow$ $x^2 = -3(-2) \Rightarrow x = \pm\sqrt{6}$; the solution is $(\pm\sqrt{6}, -2)$.

83. $\frac{1}{3}y^2 = -3x$ and $y^2 = x + 1 \Rightarrow -9x = x + 1 \Rightarrow x = -\frac{1}{10}$; $y^2 = x + 1$ when $x = -\frac{1}{10} \Rightarrow$ $y^2 = -\frac{1}{10} + 1 \Rightarrow y = \pm\sqrt{0.9}$; the solution is $\left(-\frac{1}{10}, \pm\sqrt{0.9}\right)$.

84. $-2y^2 = x - 5$ and $y^2 = 2x \Rightarrow 2x = \frac{x - 5}{-2} \Rightarrow -4x = x - 5 \Rightarrow x = 1$; $y^2 = 2x$ when $x = 1 \Rightarrow$ $y = \pm\sqrt{2}$; the solution is $(1, \pm\sqrt{2})$.

85. $(y - 1)^2 = x + 1$ and $(y + 2)^2 = -x + 4 \Rightarrow (y - 1)^2 + (y + 2)^2 = 5 \Rightarrow$ $y^2 - 2y + 1 + y^2 + 4y + 4 = 5 \Rightarrow 2y^2 + 2y = 0 \Rightarrow 2y(y + 1) = 0 \Rightarrow y = 0$ or $y = -1$; $(y - 1)^2 = x + 1$ when $y = 0 \Rightarrow 1 = x + 1 \Rightarrow x = 0$, when $y = -1 \Rightarrow 4 = x + 1 \Rightarrow$ $x = 3$, the solution is $(0, 0), (3, -1)$.

86. $(y + 1)^2 = -x$ and $-(y - 1)^2 = x + 4 \Rightarrow (y + 1)^2 - (y - 1)^2 = 4 \Rightarrow$ $y^2 + 2y + 1 - (y^2 - 2y + 1) = 4 \Rightarrow 4y = 4 \Rightarrow y = 1$; $(y + 1)^2 = -x$ when $y = 1, 4 = -x \Rightarrow$ $x = -4$, the solution is $(-4, 1)$.

87. Substitute the point $(3, 0.75)$ into $x^2 = 4py$ and solve for $p$; $9 = 4p(0.75) \Rightarrow 9 = 3p \Rightarrow p = 3$. The receiver should be 3 feet from the vertex.

88. Substitute the point $(9, 2)$ into $x^2 = 4py$ and solve for $p$; $81 = 4p(2) \Rightarrow p = \frac{81}{8} \Rightarrow p = 10\frac{1}{8} = 10.125$. The receiver should be 10.125 inches from the vertex.

89. (a) Substitute the point $(105, 32)$ into $y = ax^2$ and solve for $a$; $32 = a(105)^2 \Rightarrow a = \frac{32}{11{,}025}$.
The equation is $y = \frac{32}{11{,}025}x^2$.
(b) Rewriting the answer in (a) we have $x^2 = \frac{11{,}025}{32}y$, so $4p = \frac{11{,}025}{32}$ and $p = \frac{11{,}025}{128} \approx 86.1$.
The receiver should be located about 86.1 feet from the vertex.

90. (a) Locate a parabola that passes through $(-25, -90)$ and $(25, 90)$. Substitute either point into $x = ay^2$.
$25 = a(90)^2 \Rightarrow a = \frac{25}{90^2} = \frac{25}{8100}$. The equation of the parabola is $x = \frac{1}{324}y^2$.
(b) The value of $p$ represents the distance from the vertex to the focus. To determine $p$, write the equation in the form $y^2 = 4px$. Then $y^2 = 324x \Rightarrow 4p = 324 \Rightarrow p = 81$ ft.

91. (a) Since $y^2 = 100x$, $4p = 100$ and $p = 25$. Thus, the coordinates of the sun are $(25, 0)$.

(b) The minimum distance occurs when the comet is at the vertex of the parabola, so the minimum distance is 25 million miles.

92. Substitute the point $\left(4, \frac{5}{2}\right)$ into $y^2 = 4px$ and solve for $p$; $\left(\frac{5}{2}\right)^2 = 4p(4) \Rightarrow p = \frac{25}{64}$.

The bulb should be $\frac{25}{64}$ inches from the vertex.

93. The pipe should be at the focus, so $p = 18$, $k = 4p = 72$ inches or 6 ft.

94. The pipe should be at the focus, so $p = 2$, $k = 4p = 8$ft.

## 7.2: Ellipses

1. $\frac{x^2}{4} + \frac{y^2}{9} = 1 \Rightarrow a = 3$ and $b = 2$. $a^2 - b^2 = 3^2 - 2^2 = 5 = c^2 \Rightarrow c = \sqrt{5}$. The foci are $(0, \pm\sqrt{5})$, the endpoints of the major axis (vertices) are $(0, \pm 3)$, while the endpoints of the minor axis are $(\pm 2, 0)$. The ellipse is graphed in Figure 1.

2. $\frac{x^2}{9} + \frac{y^2}{4} = 1 \Rightarrow a = 3$ and $b = 2$. $a^2 - b^2 = 3^2 - 2^2 = 5 = c^2 \Rightarrow c = \sqrt{5}$. The foci are $(\pm\sqrt{5}, 0)$, the endpoints of the major axis (vertices) are $(\pm 3, 0)$, while the endpoints of the minor axis are $(0, \pm 2)$. The ellipse is graphed in Figure 2.

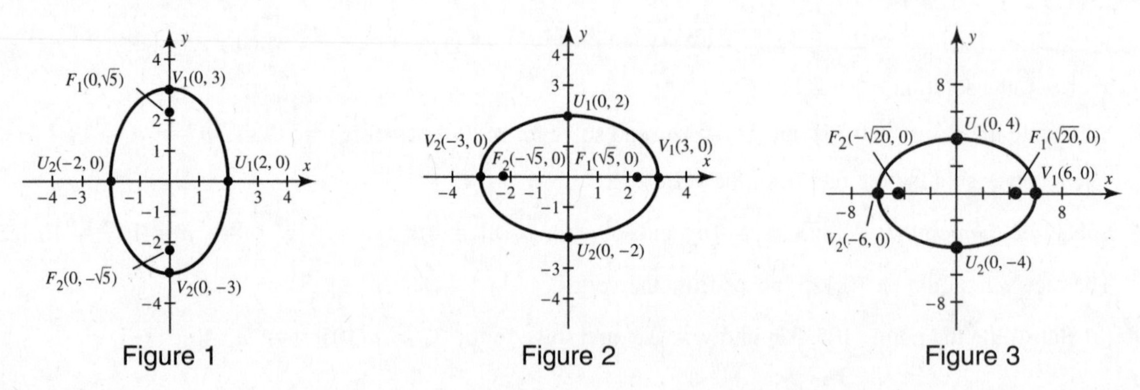

Figure 1 Figure 2 Figure 3

3. $\frac{x^2}{36} + \frac{y^2}{16} = 1 \Rightarrow a = 6$ and $b = 4$. $a^2 - b^2 = 6^2 - 4^2 = 20 = c^2 \Rightarrow c = \sqrt{20}$. The foci are $(\pm\sqrt{20}, 0)$, the endpoints of the major axis (vertices) are $(\pm 6, 0)$, while the endpoints of the minor axis are $(0, \pm 4)$. The ellipse is graphed in Figure 3.

4. $x^2 + \frac{y^2}{4} = 1 \Rightarrow a = 2$ and $b = 1$. $a^2 - b^2 = 2^2 - 1^2 = 3 = c^2 \Rightarrow c = \sqrt{3}$. The foci are $(0, \pm\sqrt{3})$, the endpoints of the major axis (vertices) are $(0, \pm 2)$, while the endpoints of the minor axis are $(\pm 1, 0)$. The ellipse is graphed in Figure 4.

5. $x^2 + 4y^2 = 400 \Rightarrow \dfrac{x^2}{400} + \dfrac{y^2}{100} = 1 \Rightarrow a = 20$ and $b = 10$.

$a^2 - b^2 = 400 - 100 = 300 = c^2 \Rightarrow c = \sqrt{300}$. The foci are $(\pm\sqrt{300}, 0)$, the endpoints of the major axis (vertices) are $(\pm 20, 0)$, while the endpoints of the minor axis are $(0, \pm 10)$. The ellipse is graphed in Figure 5.

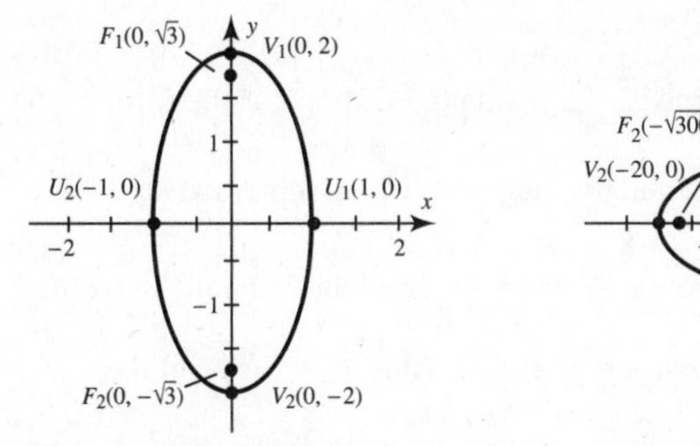

Figure 4

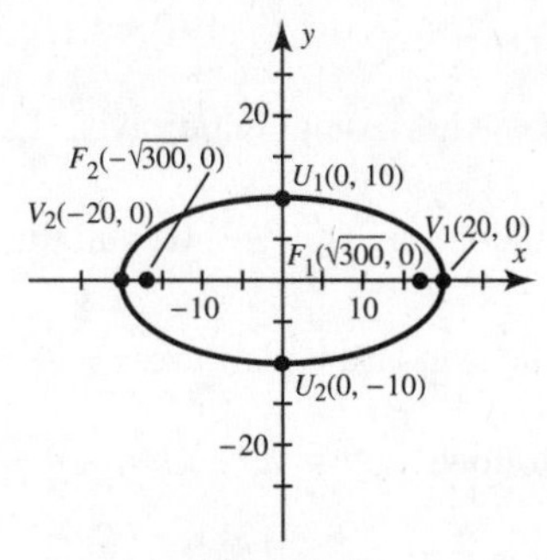

Figure 5

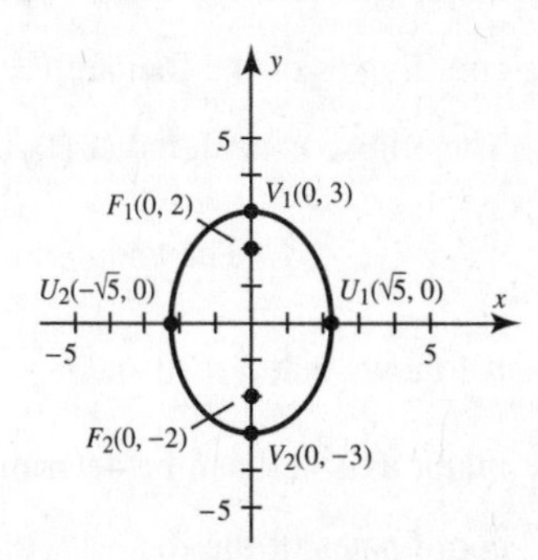

Figure 6

6. $9x^2 + 5y^2 = 45 \Rightarrow \dfrac{x^2}{5} + \dfrac{y^2}{9} = 1 \Rightarrow a = 3$ and $b = \sqrt{5}$. $a^2 - b^2 = 9 - 5 = 4 = c^2 \Rightarrow c = 2$. The foci are $(0, \pm 2)$, the endpoints of the major axis (vertices) are $(0, \pm 3)$, while the endpoints of the minor axis are $(\pm\sqrt{5}, 0)$. The ellipse is graphed in Figure 6.

7. $25x^2 + 9y^2 = 225 \Rightarrow \dfrac{x^2}{9} + \dfrac{y^2}{25} = 1 \Rightarrow a = 5$ and $b = 3$. $a^2 - b^2 = 25 - 9 = 16 = c^2 \Rightarrow c = 4$. The foci are $(0, \pm 4)$, the endpoints of the major axis (vertices) are $(0, \pm 5)$, while the endpoints of the minor axis are $(\pm 3, 0)$. The ellipse is graphed in Figure 7.

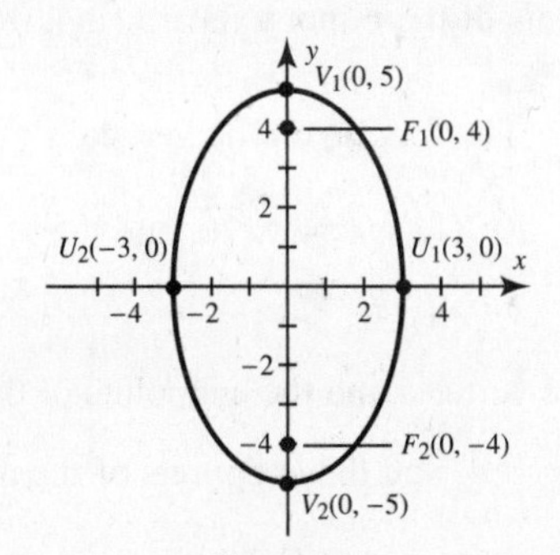

Figure 7

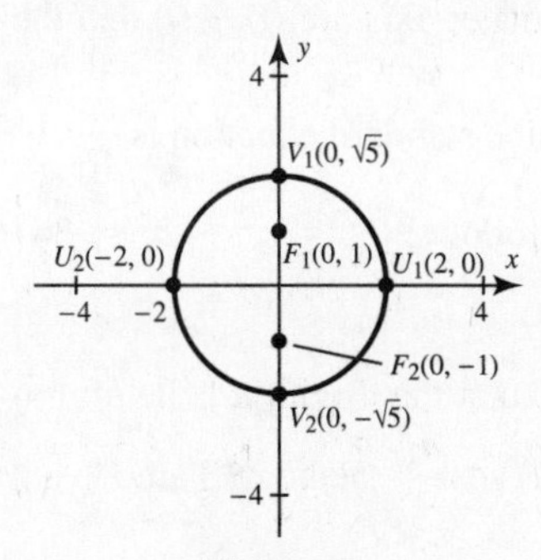

Figure 8

8. $5x^2 + 4y^2 = 20 \Rightarrow \dfrac{x^2}{4} + \dfrac{y^2}{5} = 1 \Rightarrow a = \sqrt{5}$ and $b = 2$. $a^2 - b^2 = 5 - 4 = 1 = c^2 \Rightarrow c = 1$. The foci are $(0, \pm 1)$, the endpoints of the major axis (vertices) are $(0, \pm\sqrt{5})$, while the endpoints of the minor axis are $(\pm 2, 0)$. The ellipse is graphed in Figure 8.

9. Vertices $(0, \pm 6)$; b

10. Vertices $(\pm 2, 0)$; d

11. Vertices $(\pm 4, 0)$; c

12. A circle; a

13. The ellipse is centered at $(0, 0)$ and has a horizontal major axis. Its standard equation has the form $\frac{x^2}{a^2} + \frac{y^2}{b^2} = 1$. The endpoints of the major axis are $(\pm 6, 0)$ and the endpoints of the minor axis are $(0, \pm 4)$. It follows that $a = 6$ and $b = 4$, and the standard equation is $\frac{x^2}{36} + \frac{y^2}{16} = 1$. The foci lie on the horizontal major axis and can be determined as follows. $c^2 = a^2 - b^2 = 36 - 16 = 20$. Thus, $c = \sqrt{20}$, and the coordinates of the foci are $(\pm\sqrt{20}, 0)$.

14. The ellipse is centered at $(0, 0)$ and has a horizontal major axis. Its standard equation has the form $\frac{x^2}{a^2} + \frac{y^2}{b^2} = 1$. The endpoints of the major axis are $(\pm 3, 0)$ and the endpoints of the minor axis are $(0, \pm 1)$. It follows that $a = 3$ and $b = 1$, and the standard equation is $\frac{x^2}{9} + \frac{y^2}{1} = 1$. The foci lie on the horizontal major axis and can be determined as follows. $c^2 = a^2 - b^2 = 9 - 1 = 8$ Thus, $c = \sqrt{8}$, and the coordinates of the foci are $(\pm\sqrt{8}, 0)$.

15. The ellipse is centered at $(0, 0)$ and has a vertical major axis. Its standard equation has the form $\frac{x^2}{b^2} + \frac{y^2}{a^2} = 1$. The endpoints of the major axis are $(0, \pm 4)$ and the endpoints of the minor axis are $(\pm 2, 0)$. It follows that $a = 4$ and $b = 2$, and the standard equation is $\frac{x^2}{4} + \frac{y^2}{16} = 1$. The foci lie on the vertical major axis and can be determined as follows. $c^2 = a^2 - b^2 = 16 - 4 = 12$. Thus, $c = \sqrt{12}$, and the coordinates of the foci are $(0, \pm\sqrt{12})$.

16. The ellipse is centered at $(0, 0)$ and has a vertical major axis. Its standard equation has the form $\frac{x^2}{b^2} + \frac{y^2}{a^2} = 1$. The endpoints of the major axis are $(0, \pm 6)$ and the endpoints of the minor axis are $(\pm 4, 0)$. It follows that $a = 6$ and $b = 4$, and the standard equation is $\frac{x^2}{16} + \frac{y^2}{36} = 1$. The foci lie on the vertical major axis and can be determined as follows. $c^2 = a^2 - b^2 = 36 - 16 = 20$ Thus, $c = \sqrt{20}$, and the coordinates of the foci are $(0, \pm\sqrt{20})$.

17. To sketch a graph of an ellipse centered at the origin, it is helpful to plot the vertices and the endpoints of the minor axis. The vertices are $V(\pm 5, 0)$ so $a = 5$, the foci are $F(\pm 4, 0)$ so $c = 4$, and the endpoints of the minor axis are $U(0, \pm 3)$ so $b = 3$. A graph of the ellipse is shown in Figure 17. Its equation is $\frac{x^2}{25} + \frac{y^2}{9} = 1$.

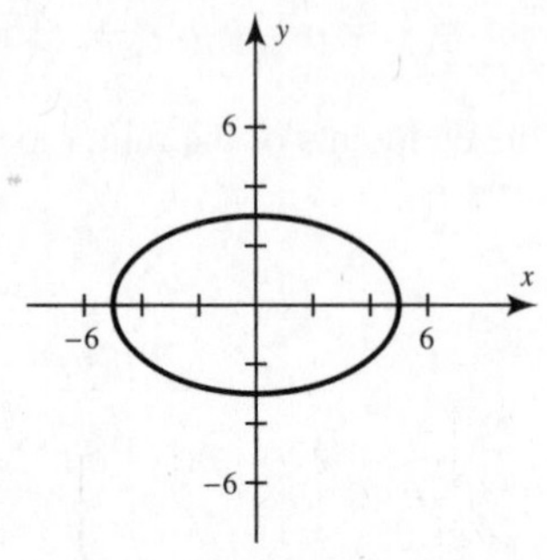

Figure 17

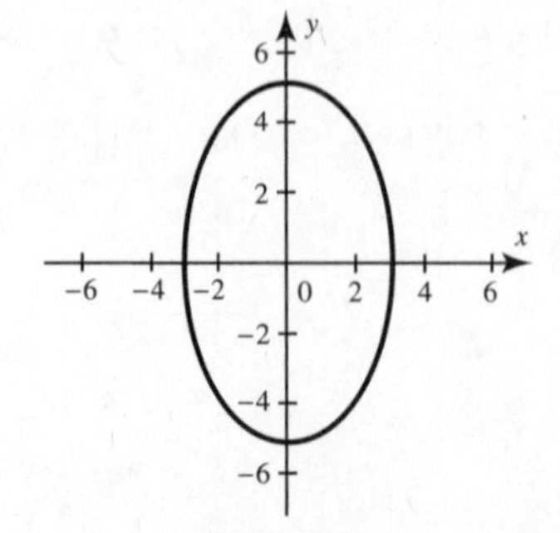

Figure 18

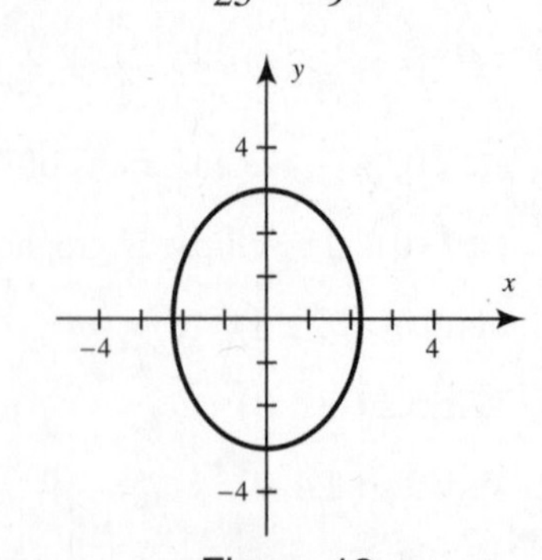

Figure 19

18. The vertices are $V(0, \pm 5)$ so $a = 5$, the foci are $F(0, \pm 4)$ so $c = 4$, and the endpoints of the minor axis are $U(\pm 3, 0)$ so $b = 3$. A graph of the ellipse is shown in Figure 18. Its equation is $\frac{x^2}{9} + \frac{y^2}{25} = 1$.

19. The vertices are $V(0, \pm 3)$ so $a = 3$, the foci are $F(0, \pm 2)$ so $c = 2$, and the endpoints of the minor axis are $U(\pm\sqrt{5}, 0)$ so $b = \sqrt{5}$. A graph of the ellipse is shown in Figure 19. Its equation is $\frac{x^2}{5} + \frac{y^2}{9} = 1$.

20. The vertices are $V(\pm 2, 0)$ so $a = 2$, the foci are $F(\pm 1, 0)$ so $c = 1$, and the endpoints of the minor axis are $U(0, \pm\sqrt{3})$ so $b = \sqrt{3}$. A graph of the ellipse is shown in Figure 20. Its equation is $\frac{x^2}{4} + \frac{y^2}{3} = 1$.

21. Foci of $F(0, \pm 2) \Rightarrow c = 2$ and $V(0, \pm 4) \Rightarrow a = 4$. The major axis lies on the $y$-axis. The value of $b$ is as follows: $a^2 - b^2 = c^2 \Rightarrow a^2 - c^2 = b^2 \Rightarrow 4^2 - 2^2 = b^2 \Rightarrow b^2 = 12 \Rightarrow b = \sqrt{12}$. The equation of the ellipse is $\frac{x^2}{12} + \frac{y^2}{16} = 1$. Its graph is shown in Figure 21.

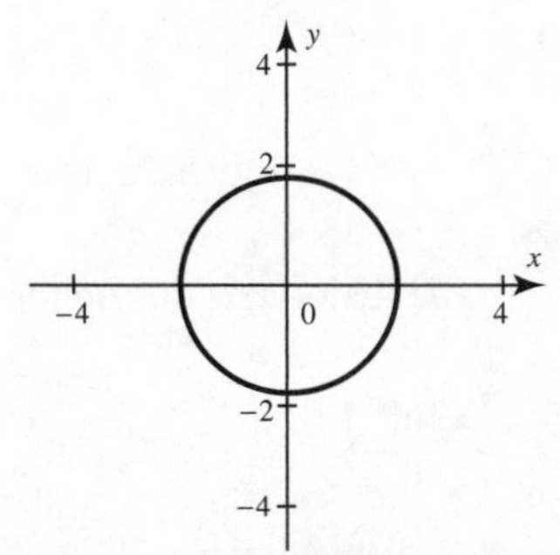

Figure 20

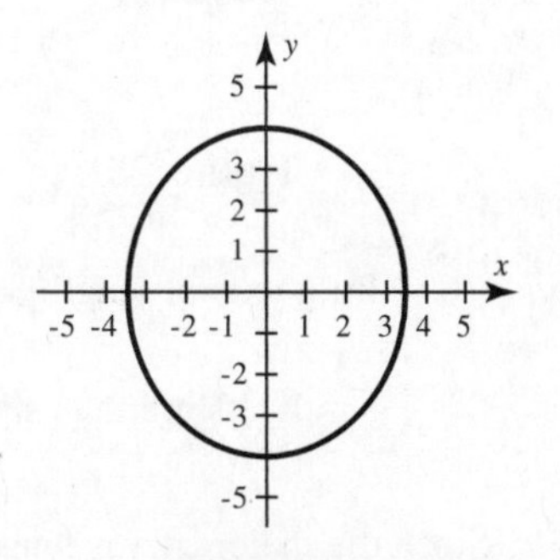

Figure 21

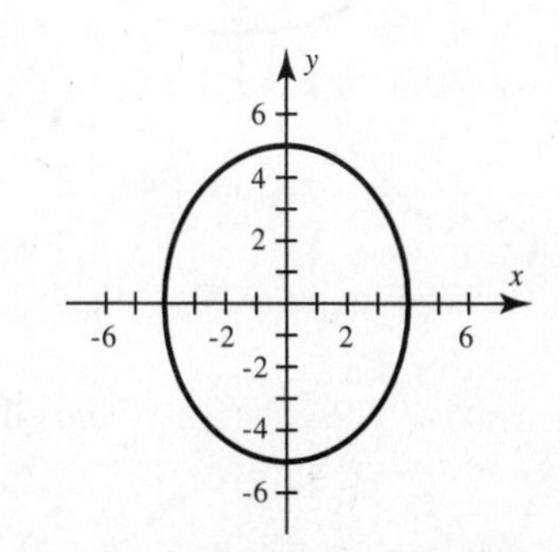

Figure 22

22. Foci of $F(0, \pm 3) \Rightarrow c = 3$ and $V(0, \pm 5) \Rightarrow a = 5$. The major axis lies on the $y$-axis. The value of $b$ is as follows: $a^2 - b^2 = c^2 \Rightarrow a^2 - c^2 = b^2 \Rightarrow 5^2 - 3^2 = b^2 \Rightarrow b^2 = 16 \Rightarrow b = 4$. The equation of the ellipse is $\frac{x^2}{16} + \frac{y^2}{25} = 1$. Its graph is shown in Figure 22.

23. Foci of $F(\pm 5, 0) \Rightarrow c = 5$ and $V(\pm 6, 0) \Rightarrow a = 6$. The major axis lies on the $x$-axis. The value of $b$ is as follows: $a^2 - b^2 = c^2 \Rightarrow a^2 - c^2 = b^2 \Rightarrow 6^2 - 5^2 = b^2 \Rightarrow b^2 = 11 \Rightarrow b = \sqrt{11}$. The equation of the ellipse is $\frac{x^2}{36} + \frac{y^2}{11} = 1$. Its graph is shown in Figure 23.

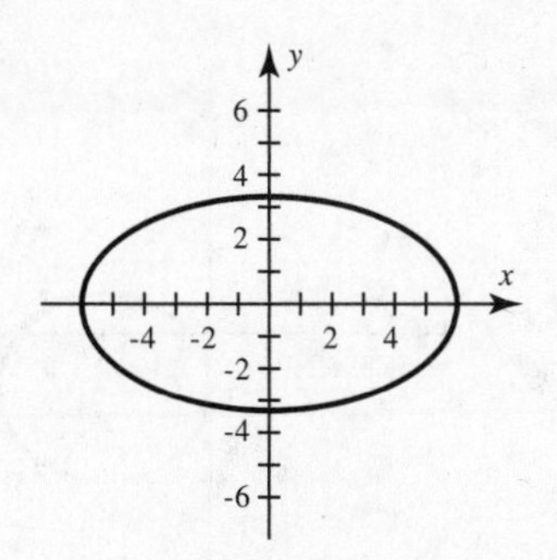

Figure 23

24. Foci of $F(\pm 4, 0) \Rightarrow c = 4$ and $V(\pm 6, 0) \Rightarrow a = 6$. The major axis lies on the $x$-axis. The value of $b$ is as follows: $a^2 - b^2 = c^2 \Rightarrow a^2 - c^2 = b^2 \Rightarrow 36 - 16 = b^2 \Rightarrow b^2 = 20 \Rightarrow b = 2\sqrt{5}$. The equation of the ellipse is $\frac{x^2}{36} + \frac{y^2}{20} = 1$. Its graph is shown in Figure 24.

25. Horizontal major axis of length $8 \Rightarrow a = 4$. Minor axis of length $6 \Rightarrow b = 3$. The major axis lies on the $x$-axis. The equation of the ellipse is $\frac{x^2}{16} + \frac{y^2}{9} = 1$. Its graph is shown in Figure 25.

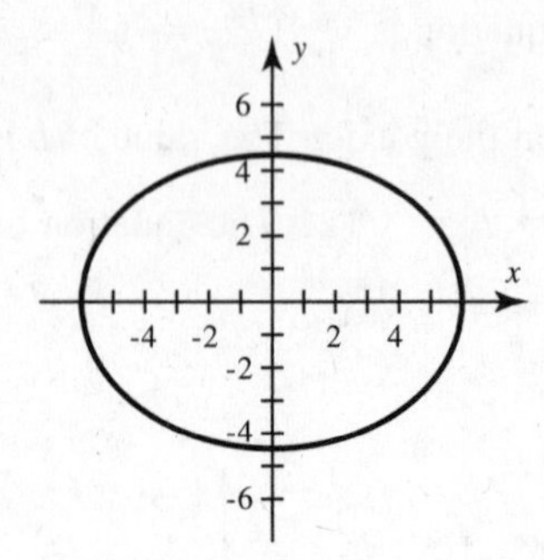

Figure 24

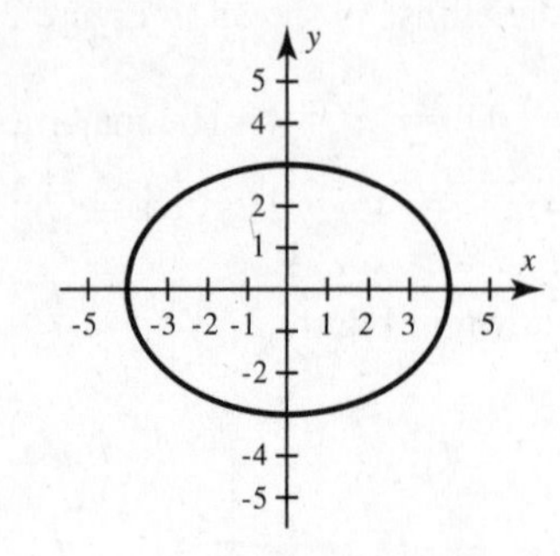

Figure 25

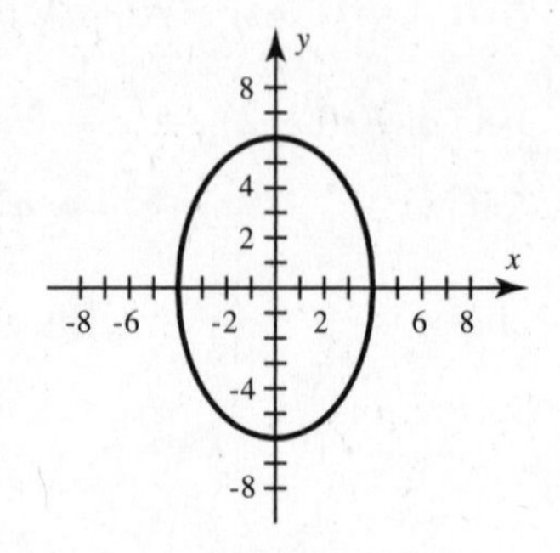

Figure 26

26. Vertical major axis of length $12 \Rightarrow a = 6$. Minor axis of length $8 \Rightarrow b = 4$. The major axis lies on the $y$-axis. The equation of the ellipse is $\frac{x^2}{16} + \frac{y^2}{36} = 1$. Its graph is shown in Figure 26.

27. $e = \frac{c}{a} = \frac{2}{3} \Rightarrow 3c = 2a \Rightarrow c = \frac{2}{3}a$. Since the major axis is length $6 \Rightarrow a = 3$. Thus, $c = \frac{2}{3}(3) = 2$. Then the value of $b$ is given by the following: $a^2 - b^2 = c^2 \Rightarrow a^2 - c^2 = b^2 \Rightarrow 3^2 - 2^2 = b^2 \Rightarrow b^2 = 5 \Rightarrow b = \sqrt{5}$. The equation of the ellipse is $\frac{x^2}{9} + \frac{y^2}{5} = 1$. Its graph is shown in Figure 27.

28. $e = \frac{c}{a} = \frac{3}{4} \Rightarrow 4c = 3a \Rightarrow c = \frac{3}{4}a$. Since the vertices are $V(0, \pm 8) \Rightarrow a = 8$. Thus, $c = \frac{3}{4}(8) = 6$. Then the value of $b$ is given by the following: $a^2 - b^2 = c^2 \Rightarrow a^2 - c^2 = b^2 \Rightarrow 8^2 - 6^2 = b^2 \Rightarrow b^2 = 28 \Rightarrow b = \sqrt{28}$. Since the major axis is located on the $y$-axis, the equation of the ellipse is $\frac{x^2}{28} + \frac{y^2}{64} = 1$. Its graph is shown in Figure 28.

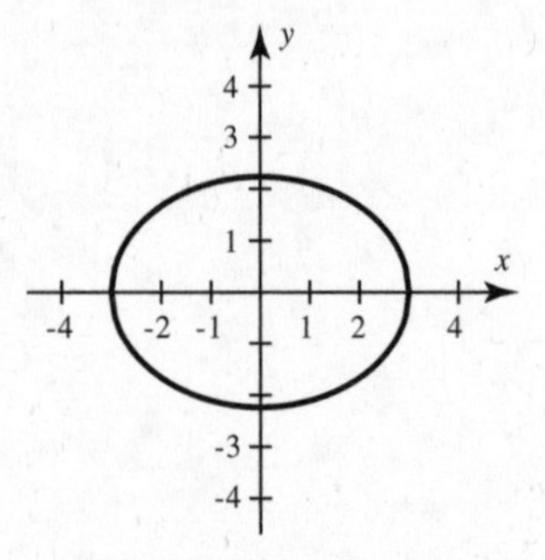

Figure 27

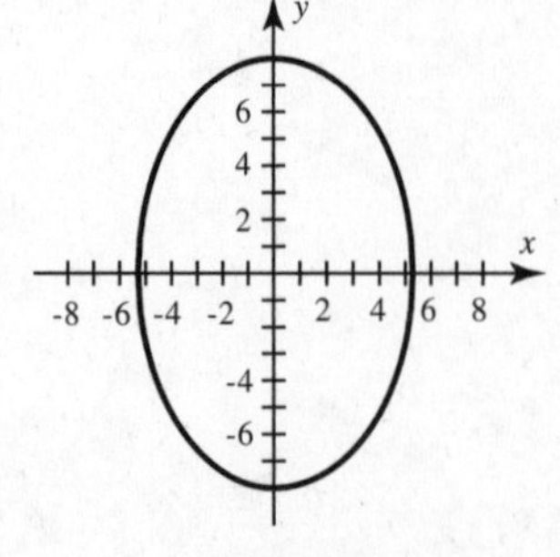

Figure 28

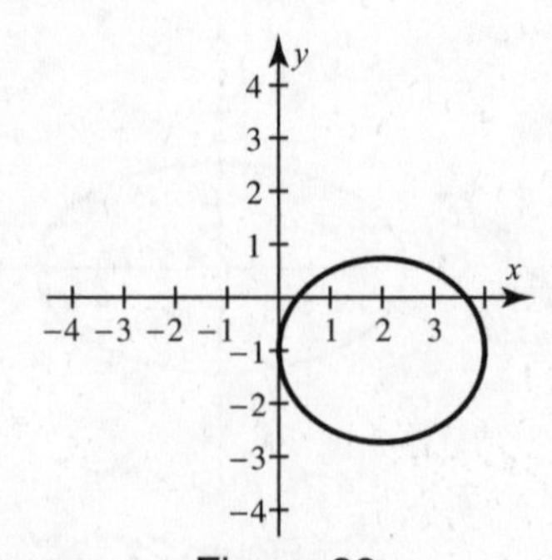

Figure 29

29. To translate the center from $(0, 0)$ to $(2, -1)$ replace $x$ with $(x - 2)$ and $y$ with $(y + 1)$. This new equation is $\dfrac{(x-2)^2}{4} + \dfrac{(y+1)^2}{3} = 1$. See Figure 29.

30. To translate the center from $(0, 0)$ to $(-3, 7)$ replace $x$ with $(x + 3)$ and $y$ with $(y - 7)$. This new equation is $\dfrac{(x+3)^2}{9} + \dfrac{(y-7)^2}{2} = 1$. See Figure 30.

31. To translate the center from $(0, 0)$ to $(-3, -4)$ replace $x$ with $(x + 3)$ and $y$ with $(y + 4)$. This new equation is $\dfrac{(x+3)^2}{2} + \dfrac{(y+4)^2}{9} = 1$. See Figure 31.

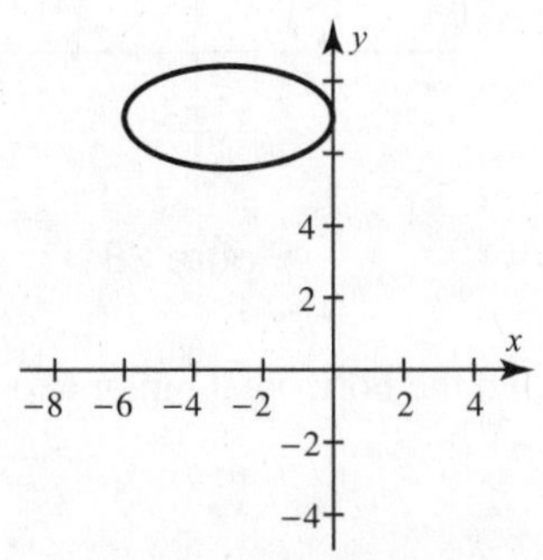

Figure 30

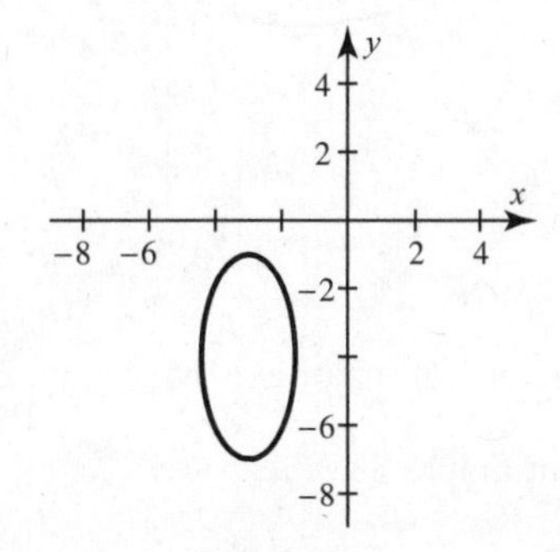

Figure 31

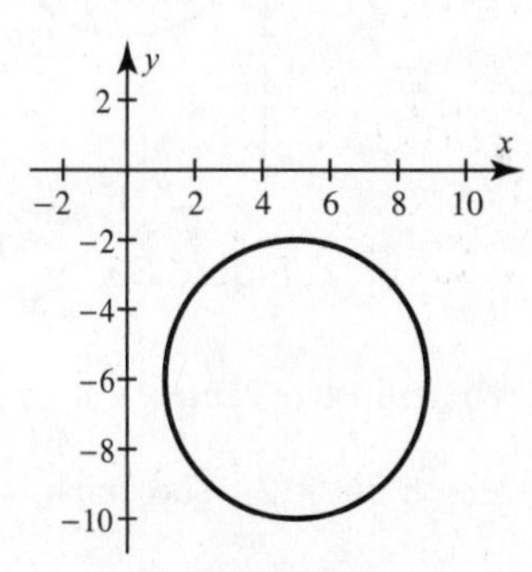

Figure 32

32. To translate the center from $(0, 0)$ to $(5, -6)$ replace $x$ with $(x - 5)$ and $y$ with $(y + 6)$. This new equation is $\dfrac{(x-5)^2}{15} + \dfrac{(y+6)^2}{16} = 1$. See Figure 32.

33. The ellipse is centered at $(2, 1)$. The major axis has length $2a = 6$ and the length of the minor axis is $2b = 4$. The major axis is parallel to the $y$-axis. The graph is shown in Figure 33.

34. The ellipse is centered at $(-1, -3)$. The major axis has length $2a = 8$ and the length of the minor axis is $2b = 6$. The major axis is parallel to the $x$-axis. The graph is shown in Figure 34.

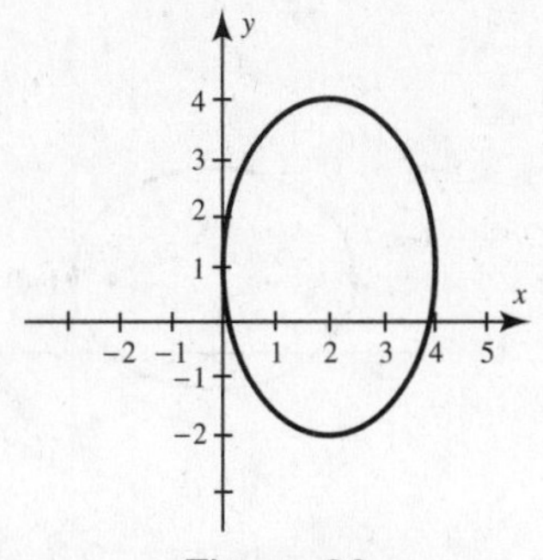

Figure 33

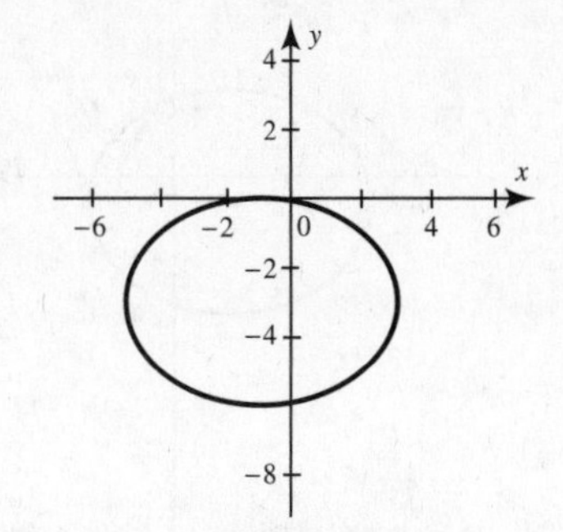

Figure 34

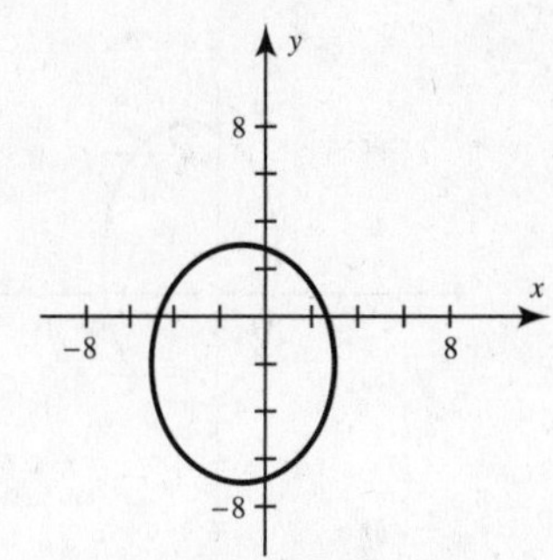

Figure 35

35. The ellipse is centered at $(-1, -2)$. The major axis has length $2a = 10$ and the length of the minor axis is $2b = 8$. The major axis is parallel to the $y$-axis. The graph is shown in Figure 35.

36. The ellipse is centered at $(4, 0)$. The horizontal major axis has length $2a = 6$ and the vertical minor axis has length $2b = 4$. The graph is shown in Figure 36.

37. The ellipse is centered at $(-2, 0)$. The horizontal major axis has length $2a = 4$ and the vertical minor axis has length $2b = 2$. The graph is shown in Figure 37.

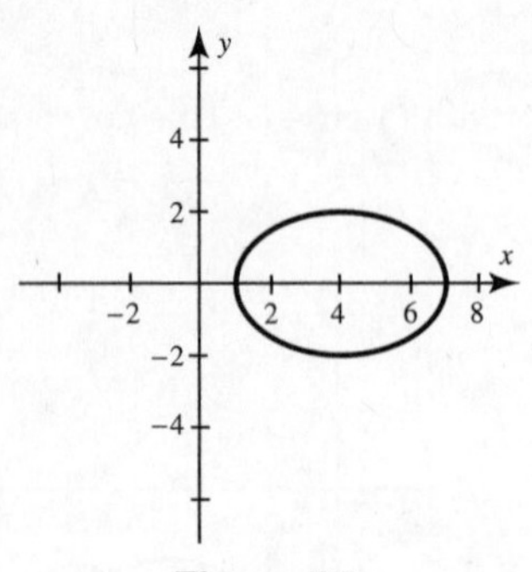

Figure 36

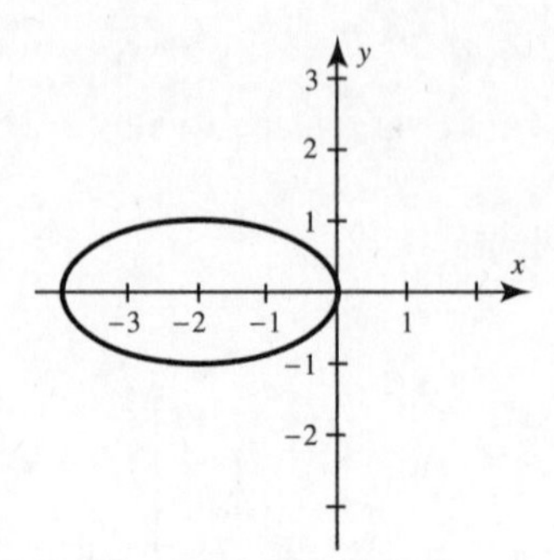

Figure 37

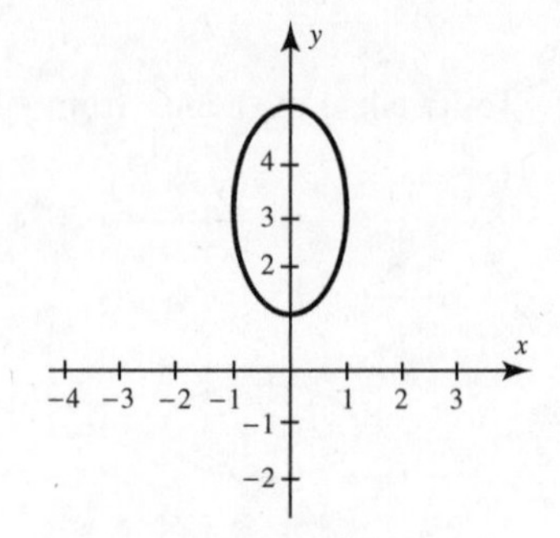

Figure 38

38. The ellipse is centered at $(0, 3)$. The vertical major axis has length $2a = 4$ and the horizontal minor axis has length $2b = 2$. The graph is shown in Figure 38.

39. Center at $(2, -4)$; d

40. Center at $(-1, 0)$; a

41. Center at $(-1, 1)$; c

42. Center at $(0, -1)$; b

43. Center at $(1, 1)$, $a = 5$, $b = 3$, major axis vertical. $c^2 = a^2 - b^2 = 25 - 9 = 16 \Rightarrow c = 4$.

Foci: $(1, 1 \pm 4)$; veritices: $(1, 1 \pm 5)$; the graph is shown in Figure 43.

44. Center at $(-2, -1)$, $a = 5$, $b = 4$, major axis horizontal. $c^2 = a^2 - b^2 = 25 - 16 = 9 \Rightarrow c = 3$.

Foci: $(-2 \pm 3, -1)$; veritices: $(-2 \pm 5, -1)$; the graph is shown in Figure 44.

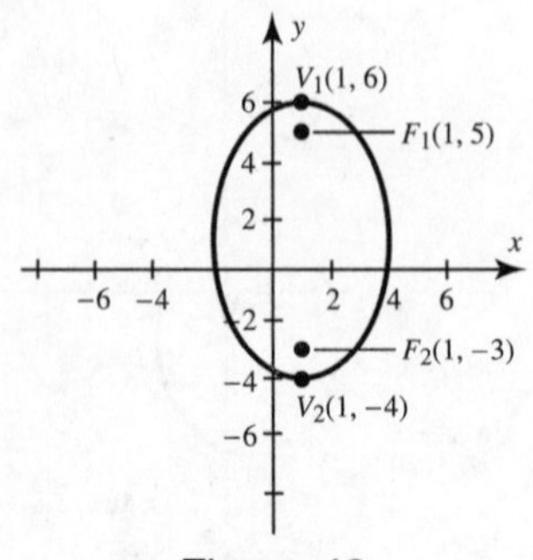

Figure 43

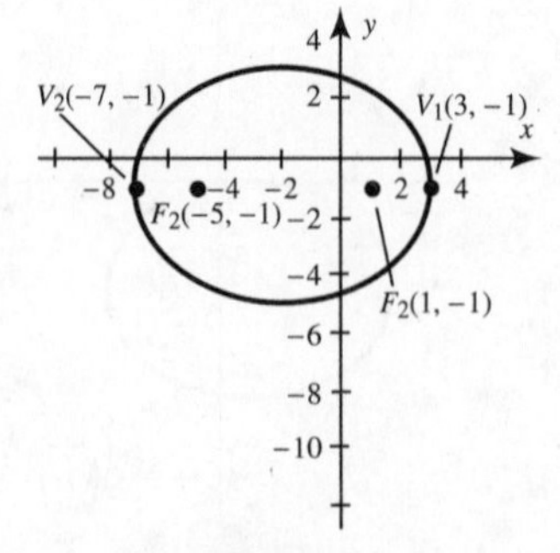

Figure 44

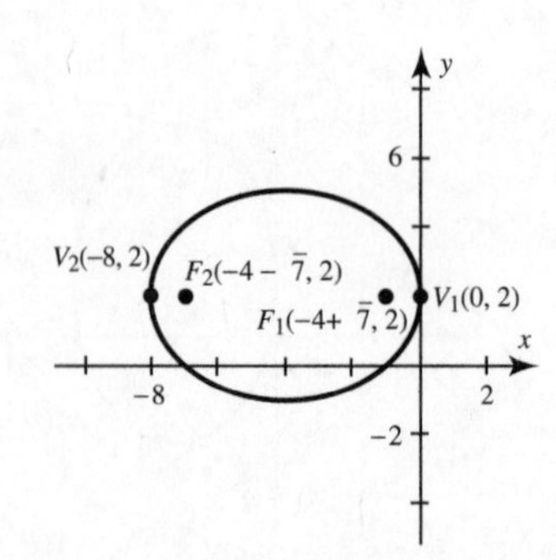

Figure 45

45. Center at $(-4, 2)$, $a = 4$, $b = 3$, major axis horizontal. $c^2 = a^2 - b^2 = 16 - 9 = 7 \Rightarrow c = \sqrt{7}$.

Foci: $(-4 \pm \sqrt{7}, 2)$; veritices: $(-4 \pm 4, 2)$; the graph is shown in Figure 45.

46. Center at $(0, 1)$, $a = 3$, $b = 2$, major axis vertical. $c^2 = a^2 - b^2 = 9 - 4 = 5 \Rightarrow c = \sqrt{5}$.

Foci: $(0, 1 \pm \sqrt{5})$; veritices: $(0, 1 \pm 3)$; the graph is shown in Figure 46.

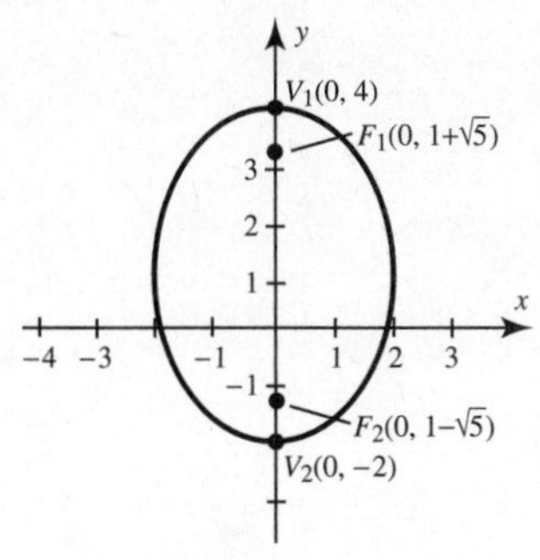


Figure 46

47. Since the center is $(2, 1)$ and a focus is $(2, 3)$, $c = 2$. Since the vertex is $(2, 4)$, $a = 3$;

$b^2 = a^2 - c^2 = 9 - 4 = 5$; the major axis is vertical. The equation is $\dfrac{(x-2)^2}{5} + \dfrac{(y-1)^2}{9} = 1$.

48. Since the center is $(-3, -2)$ and a focus is $(-1, -2)$, $c = 2$. Since the vertex is $(1, -2)$, $a = 4$;

$b^2 = a^2 - c^2 = 16 - 4 = 12$; the major axis is horizontal. The equation is $\dfrac{(x+3)^2}{16} + \dfrac{(y+2)^2}{12} = 1$.

49. The center is halfway between the vertices at $(0, 2)$; $a = 3$ and $c = 2$; $b^2 = a^2 - c^2 = 9 - 4 = 5$; the major axis is horizontal. The equation is $\dfrac{x^2}{9} + \dfrac{(y-2)^2}{5} = 1$.

50. The center is halfway between the vertices at $(-1, 0)$; $a = 3$ and $c = 1$; $b^2 = a^2 - c^2 = 9 - 1 = 8$; the major axis is vertical. The equation is $\dfrac{(x+1)^2}{8} + \dfrac{y^2}{9} = 1$.

51. Center at $(2, 4)$, $a = 4$ and $b = 2$, major axis parallel to the $x$-axis; the equation is

$\dfrac{(x-2)^2}{16} + \dfrac{(y-4)^2}{4} = 1$.

52. Center at $(-2, 1)$, $a = 2$ and $b = 1$, major axis parallel to the $y$-axis; the equation is

$\dfrac{(x+2)^2}{1} + \dfrac{(y-1)^2}{4} = 1$.

53. $9x^2 + 18x + 4y^2 - 8y - 23 = 0 \Rightarrow 9(x^2 + 2x) + 4(y^2 - 2y) = 23 \Rightarrow$

$9(x^2 + 2x + 1) + 4(y^2 - 2y + 1) = 23 + 9 + 4 \Rightarrow 9(x+1)^2 + 4(y-1)^2 = 36 \Rightarrow$

$\dfrac{(x+1)^2}{4} + \dfrac{(y-1)^2}{9} = 1$; The center is $(-1, 1)$. The vertices are

$(-1, 1 - 3), (-1, 1 + 3)$ or $(-1, -2), (-1, 4)$.

54. $9x^2 - 36x + 16y^2 - 64y - 44 = 0 \Rightarrow 9(x^2 - 4x) + 16(y^2 - 4y) = 44 \Rightarrow$

$9(x^2 - 4x + 4) + 16(y^2 - 4y + 4) = 44 + 36 + 64 \Rightarrow 9(x-2)^2 + 16(y-2)^2 = 144 \Rightarrow$

$\dfrac{(x-2)^2}{16} + \dfrac{(y-2)^2}{9} = 1$; The center is $(2, 2)$. The vertices are $(2 - 4, 2), (2 + 4, 2)$ or $(-2, 2), (6, 2)$.

55. $4x^2 + 8x + y^2 + 2y + 1 = 0 \Rightarrow 4(x^2 + 2x) + (y^2 + 2y) = -1 \Rightarrow$

$4(x^2 + 2x + 1) + (y^2 + 2y + 1) = -1 + 4 + 1 \Rightarrow 4(x + 1)^2 + (y + 1)^2 = 4 \Rightarrow$

$\dfrac{(x + 1)^2}{1} + \dfrac{(y + 1)^2}{4} = 1$; The center is $(-1, -1)$. The vertices are

$(-1, -1 - 2), (-1, -1 + 2)$ or $(-1, -3), (-1, 1)$.

56. $x^2 - 6x + 9y^2 = 0 \Rightarrow (x^2 - 6x) + 9y^2 = 0 \Rightarrow (x^2 - 6x + 9) + 9y^2 = 0 + 9 \Rightarrow$

$(x - 3)^2 + 9(y - 0)^2 = 9 \Rightarrow \dfrac{(x - 3)^2}{9} + \dfrac{(y - 0)^2}{1} = 1$

The center is $(3, 0)$. The vertices are $(3 - 3, 0), (3 + 3, 0)$ or $(0, 0), (6, 0)$.

57. $4x^2 + 16x + 5y^2 - 10y + 1 = 0 \Rightarrow 4(x^2 + 4x) + 5(y^2 - 2y) = -1 \Rightarrow$

$4(x^2 + 4x + 4) + 5(y^2 - 2y + 1) = -1 + 16 + 5 \Rightarrow 4(x + 2)^2 + 5(y - 1)^2 = 20 \Rightarrow$

$\dfrac{(x + 2)^2}{5} + \dfrac{(y - 1)^2}{4} = 1$; The center is $(-2, 1)$. The vertices are $(-2 - \sqrt{5}, 1), (-2 + \sqrt{5}, 1)$.

58. $2x^2 + 4x + 3y^2 - 18y + 23 = 0 \Rightarrow 2(x^2 + 2x) + 3(y^2 - 6y) = -23 \Rightarrow$

$2(x^2 + 2x + 1) + 3(y^2 - 6y + 9) = -23 + 2 + 27 \Rightarrow 2(x + 1)^2 + 3(y - 3)^2 = 6 \Rightarrow$

$\dfrac{(x + 1)^2}{3} + \dfrac{(y - 3)^2}{2} = 1$; The center is $(-1, 3)$. The vertices are $(-1 - \sqrt{3}, 3), (-1 + \sqrt{3}, 3)$.

59. $16x^2 - 16x + 4y^2 + 12y = 51 \Rightarrow 16(x^2 - x) + 4(y^2 + 3y) = 51 \Rightarrow$

$16\left(x^2 - x + \dfrac{1}{4}\right) + 4\left(y^2 + 3y + \dfrac{9}{4}\right) = 51 + 4 + 9 \Rightarrow 16\left(x - \dfrac{1}{2}\right)^2 + 4\left(y + \dfrac{3}{2}\right)^2 = 64 \Rightarrow$

$\dfrac{(x - \frac{1}{2})^2}{4} + \dfrac{(y + \frac{3}{2})^2}{16} = 1$

The center is $\left(\dfrac{1}{2}, -\dfrac{3}{2}\right)$. The vertices are $\left(\dfrac{1}{2}, -\dfrac{3}{2} - 4\right), \left(\dfrac{1}{2}, -\dfrac{3}{2} + 4\right)$ or $\left(\dfrac{1}{2}, -\dfrac{11}{2}\right), \left(\dfrac{1}{2}, \dfrac{5}{2}\right)$.

60. $16x^2 + 48x + 4y^2 - 20y + 57 = 0 \Rightarrow 16(x^2 + 3x) + 4(y^2 - 5y) = -57 \Rightarrow$

$16\left(x^2 + 3x + \dfrac{9}{4}\right) + 4\left(y^2 - 5y + \dfrac{25}{4}\right) = -57 + 36 + 25 \Rightarrow 16\left(x + \dfrac{3}{2}\right)^2 + 4\left(y - \dfrac{5}{2}\right)^2 = 4 \Rightarrow$

$\dfrac{(x + \frac{3}{2})^2}{\frac{1}{4}} + \dfrac{(y - \frac{5}{2})^2}{1} = 1$

The center is $\left(-\dfrac{3}{2}, \dfrac{5}{2}\right)$. The vertices are $\left(-\dfrac{3}{2}, \dfrac{5}{2} - 1\right), \left(-\dfrac{3}{2}, \dfrac{5}{2} + 1\right)$ or $\left(-\dfrac{3}{2}, \dfrac{3}{2}\right), \left(-\dfrac{3}{2}, \dfrac{7}{2}\right)$.

61. $y = \pm\sqrt{10\left(1 - \dfrac{x^2}{15}\right)}$; See Figure 61.

62. $y = \pm\sqrt{3.5\left(1 - \dfrac{(x - 1.2)^2}{7.1}\right)}$; See Figure 62.

63. $y = \pm\sqrt{\dfrac{25 - 4.1x^2}{6.3}}$; See Figure 63.

64. $y = \pm\sqrt{\dfrac{1}{2}(1 - 3x^2)}$; See Figure 64.

[−6, 6, 1] by [−4, 4, 1]

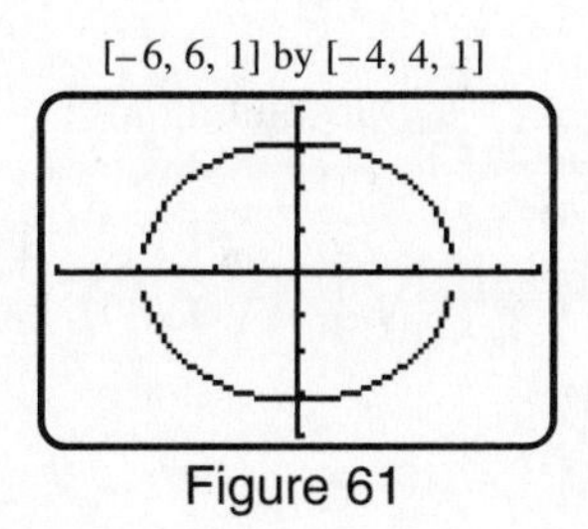

Figure 61

[−2, 6, 1] by [−4, 4, 1]

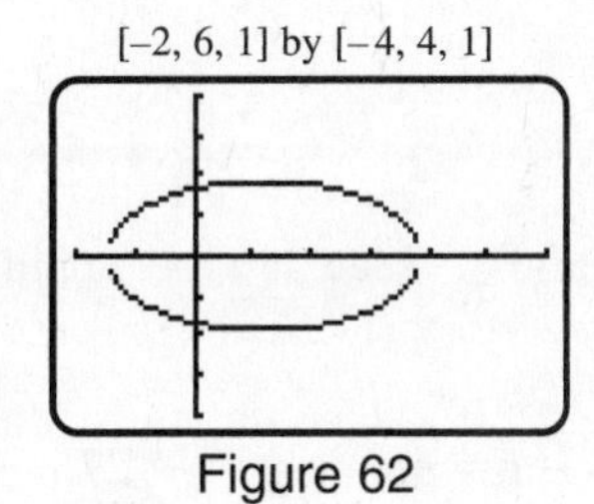

Figure 62

[−4.7, 4.7, 1] by [−3.1, 3.1, 1]

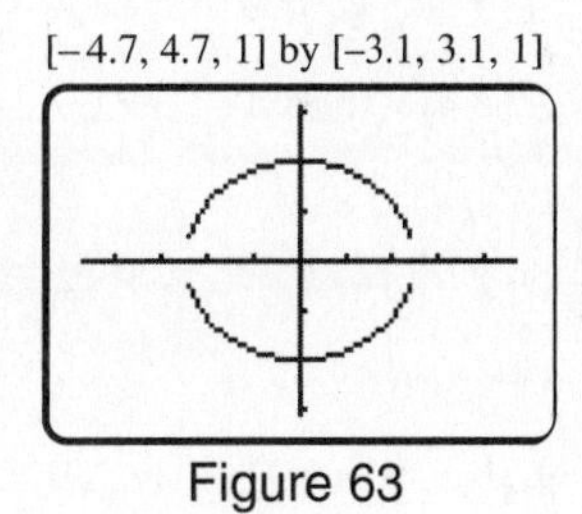

Figure 63

[−1, 1, 0.1] by [−1, 1, 0.1]

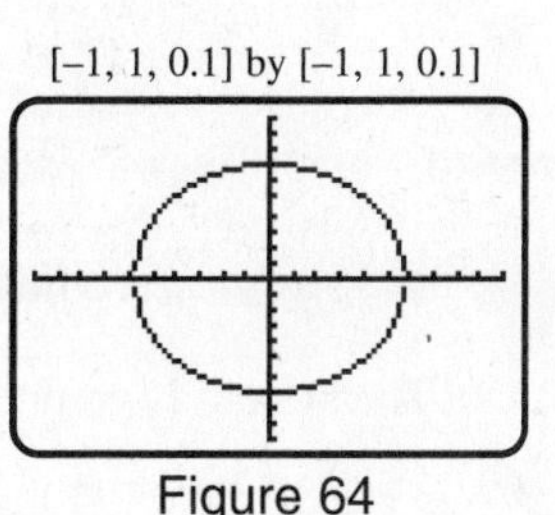

Figure 64

65. $\frac{x^2}{4} + \frac{y^2}{9} = 1 \Rightarrow 9x^2 + 4y^2 = 36 \Rightarrow 9x^2 + 4(3 - x)^2 = 36 \Rightarrow 9x^2 + 4(9 - 6x + x^2) = 36 \Rightarrow$

$13x^2 - 24x = 0$. Then $x(13x - 24) = 0 \Rightarrow x = 0$ or $x = \frac{24}{13}$. Since $y = 3 - x$, the corresponding $y$ values

are $3 - 0 = 3$ and $3 - \frac{24}{13} = \frac{15}{13}$. The solutions are $(0, 3)$ and $\left(\frac{24}{13}, \frac{15}{13}\right)$. The system is graphed in Figure 65.

66. $\frac{x^2}{16} + \frac{y^2}{25} = 1 \Rightarrow 25x^2 + 16y^2 = 400 \Rightarrow 25x^2 + 16(5 + 2x)^2 = 400 \Rightarrow$

$25x^2 + 16(25 + 20x + 4x^2) = 400 \Rightarrow 89x^2 + 320x = 0$. Then

$x(89x + 320) = 0 \Rightarrow x = 0$ or $x = -\frac{320}{89}$.

Since $y = 5 + 2x$, the corresponding $y$ values are $5 + 2 \cdot 0 = 5$ and $5 - \frac{640}{89} = -\frac{195}{89}$. The solutions are

$(0, 5)$ and $\left(-\frac{320}{89}, -\frac{195}{89}\right)$. The system is graphed in Figure 66.

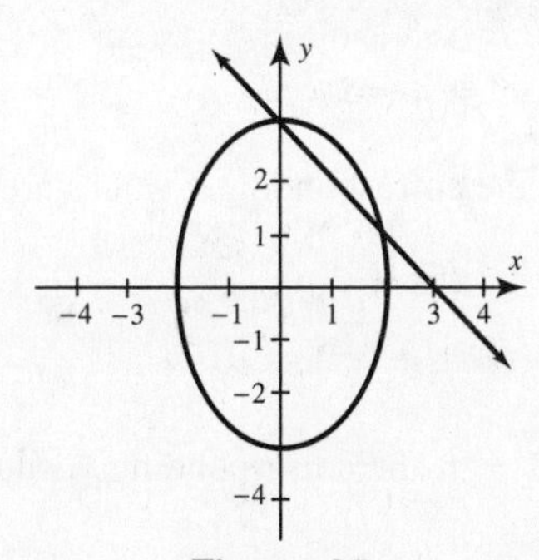



Figure 65

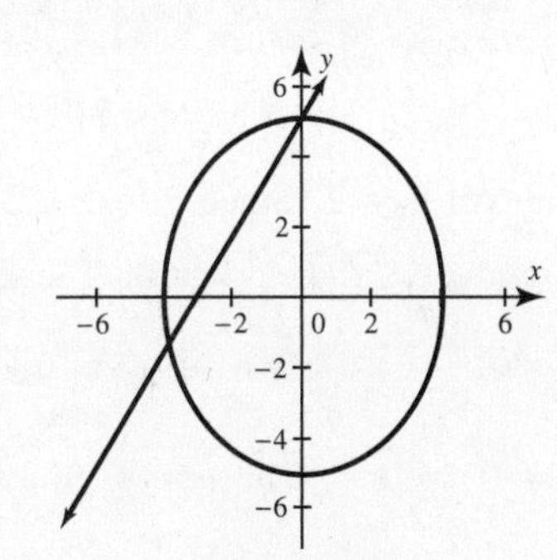



Figure 66

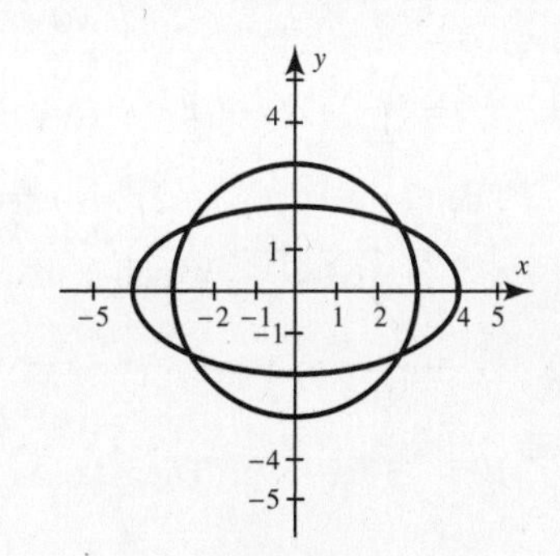



Figure 67

67. $x^2 + y^2 = 9 \Rightarrow x^2 = 9 - y^2$; then $4(9 - y^2) + 16y^2 = 64 \Rightarrow 36 - 4y^2 + 16y^2 = 64 \Rightarrow$

$y^2 = \frac{7}{3} \Rightarrow y = \pm\sqrt{\frac{7}{3}}$. Substituting in

$x^2 + y^2 = 9$ we find $x^2 + \frac{7}{3} = 9$, $x^2 = \frac{27}{3} - \frac{7}{3} = \frac{20}{3}$, so $x = \pm\sqrt{\frac{20}{3}}$.

There are four solutions: $\left(\pm\sqrt{\frac{20}{3}}, \pm\sqrt{\frac{7}{3}}\right)$. The system is graphed in Figure 67.

68. $x^2 + y^2 = 2 \Rightarrow y^2 = 2 - x^2$; then $4x^2 + 2 - x^2 = 4 \Rightarrow 3x^2 = 2 \Rightarrow x = \pm\sqrt{\frac{2}{3}}$. Substituting in $x^2 + y^2 = 2$ we find $\frac{2}{3} + y^2 = 2, y^2 = \frac{4}{3}$, so $y = \pm\sqrt{\frac{4}{3}}$. There are four solutions: $\left(\pm\sqrt{\frac{2}{3}}, \pm\sqrt{\frac{4}{3}}\right)$. The system is graphed in Figure 68.

69. $x^2 + y^2 = 9 \Rightarrow y^2 = 9 - x^2$; then $2x^2 + 3(9 - x^2) = 18 \Rightarrow 2x^2 + 27 - 3x^2 = 18 \Rightarrow x^2 = 9 \Rightarrow x = \pm 3$;
Substituting in $x^2 + y^2 = 9$ we find $9 + y^2 = 9$, so $y = 0$. There are two solutions: $(\pm 3, 0)$. The system is graphed in Figure 69.

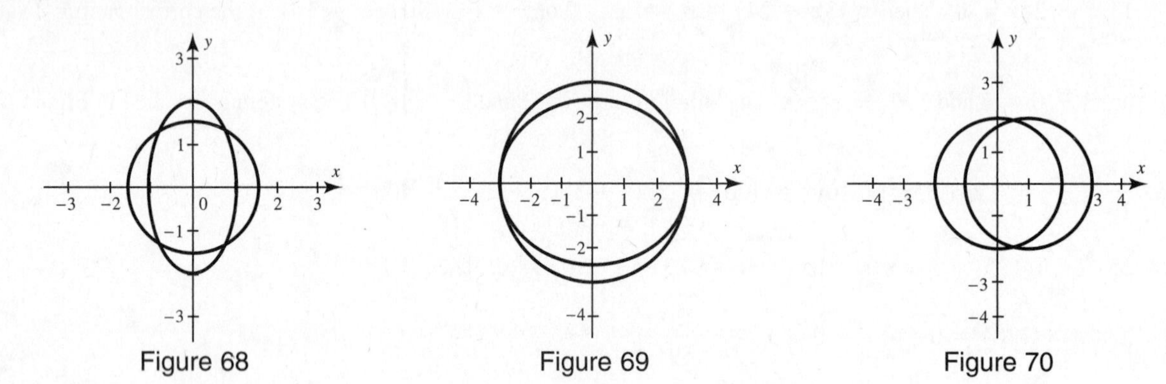

Figure 68 Figure 69 Figure 70

70. $x^2 + y^2 = 4 \Rightarrow y^2 = 4 - x^2$; then $(x - 1)^2 + 4 - x^2 = 4 \Rightarrow x^2 - 2x + 1 + 4 - x^2 = 4 \Rightarrow 2x = 1 \Rightarrow x = \frac{1}{2}$; Substituting in $x^2 + y^2 = 4$ we find $\frac{1}{4} + y^2 = 4, y^2 = \frac{15}{4}$, so $y = \pm\frac{\sqrt{15}}{2}$. There are two solutions: $\left(\frac{1}{2}, \pm\frac{\sqrt{15}}{2}\right)$. The system is graphed in Figure 70.

71. $\frac{x^2}{2} + \frac{y^2}{4} = 1 \Rightarrow 2x^2 + y^2 = 4 \Rightarrow 2(2y - 4) + y^2 = 4 \Rightarrow 4y - 8 + y^2 = 4 \Rightarrow y^2 + 4y - 12 = 0$
Then $(y + 6)(y - 2) = 0 \Rightarrow y = -6$ or $y = 2$. Since $x = \pm\sqrt{2y - 4}$, the corresponding $x$ values are $\pm\sqrt{2(-6) - 4}$, which is undefined, and $\pm\sqrt{2(2) - 4} = 0$. The solution is $(0, 2)$.

72. $x^2 + \frac{1}{9}y^2 = 1 \Rightarrow 9x^2 + y^2 = 9 \Rightarrow 9x^2 + (3 - x)^2 = 9 \Rightarrow 9x^2 + (9 - 6x + x^2) = 9 \Rightarrow 10x^2 - 6x = 0$. Then $2x(5x - 3) = 0 \Rightarrow x = 0$ or $x = \frac{3}{5}$. Since $y = 3 - x$, the corresponding $y$ values are $3 - 0 = 3$ and $3 - \frac{3}{5} = \frac{12}{5}$. The solutions are $(0, 3)$ and $\left(\frac{3}{5}, \frac{12}{5}\right)$.

73. From the first equation $\frac{x^2}{2} + \frac{y^2}{4} = 1 \Rightarrow 2x^2 + y^2 = 4 \Rightarrow y^2 = 4 - 2x^2$.
From the second equation $\frac{x^2}{4} + \frac{y^2}{2} = 1 \Rightarrow x^2 + 2y^2 = 4 \Rightarrow y^2 = 2 - \frac{1}{2}x^2$. That is $4 - 2x^2 = 2 - \frac{1}{2}x^2$.
$4 - 2x^2 = 2 - \frac{1}{2}x^2 \Rightarrow \frac{3}{2}x^2 = 2 \Rightarrow x^2 = \frac{4}{3} \Rightarrow x = \pm\frac{2}{\sqrt{3}} = \pm\frac{2\sqrt{3}}{3}$
Since $y = \pm\sqrt{4 - 2x^2}$, the $y$ values are $\pm\sqrt{4 - 2\left(\frac{2}{\sqrt{3}}\right)^2} = \pm\sqrt{4 - \frac{8}{3}} = \pm\sqrt{\frac{4}{3}}$.
There are four solutions: $\left(\pm\sqrt{\frac{4}{3}}, \pm\sqrt{\frac{4}{3}}\right)$.

74. From the first equation $\frac{x^2}{5} + \frac{y^2}{10} = 1 \Rightarrow 2x^2 + y^2 = 10 \Rightarrow y^2 = 10 - 2x^2$.

From the second equation $\frac{x^2}{10} + \frac{y^2}{5} = 1 \Rightarrow x^2 + 2y^2 = 10 \Rightarrow y^2 = 5 - \frac{1}{2}x^2$. That is $10 - 2x^2 = 5 - \frac{1}{2}x^2$.

$10 - 2x^2 = 5 - \frac{1}{2}x^2 \Rightarrow \frac{3}{2}x^2 = 5 \Rightarrow x^2 = \frac{10}{3} \Rightarrow x = \pm\frac{\sqrt{10}}{\sqrt{3}} = \pm\sqrt{\frac{10}{3}}$

Since $y = \pm\sqrt{10 - 2x^2}$, the $y$ values are $\pm\sqrt{10 - 2\left(\sqrt{\frac{10}{3}}\right)^2} = \pm\sqrt{10 - \frac{20}{3}} = \pm\sqrt{\frac{10}{3}}$.

There are four solutions: $\left(\pm\sqrt{\frac{10}{3}}, \pm\sqrt{\frac{10}{3}}\right)$.

75. Subtracting the second equation from the first equation yields $(x - 2)^2 - x^2 = 0$.

$(x - 2)^2 - x^2 = 0 \Rightarrow x^2 - 4x + 4 - x^2 = 0 \Rightarrow -4x + 4 = 0 \Rightarrow -4x = -4 \Rightarrow x = 1$

Since $y = \pm\sqrt{9 - x^2}$, the $y$ values are $\pm\sqrt{9 - (1)^2} = \pm\sqrt{8}$.

The solutions are $(1, -\sqrt{8}), (1, \sqrt{8})$.

76. The first equation can be written $x - y^2 = 2$. From the second equation $\frac{x^2}{4} + \frac{y^2}{9} = 1 \Rightarrow 9x^2 + 4y^2 = 36$.

Multiplying the first equation by 4 and adding the second equation yields $9x^2 + 4x = 44$.

$9x^2 + 4x = 44 \Rightarrow 9x^2 + 4x - 44 = 0 \Rightarrow (x - 2)(9x + 22) = 0 \Rightarrow x = 2$ or $x = -\frac{22}{9}$

Since $y = \pm\sqrt{x - 2}$, the $y$ values are $\pm\sqrt{(2) - 2} = 0$ and $\pm\sqrt{\left(-\frac{22}{9}\right) - 2}$, which is undefined.

The solution is $(2, 0)$.

77. The system is $(x - 1)^2 + (y + 1)^2 < 4$ and $(x + 1)^2 + y^2 > 1$. See Figure 77.

78. The system is $\frac{x^2}{16} + \frac{y^2}{25} < 1$ and $\frac{x^2}{4} + \frac{y^2}{9} > 1$. See Figure 78.

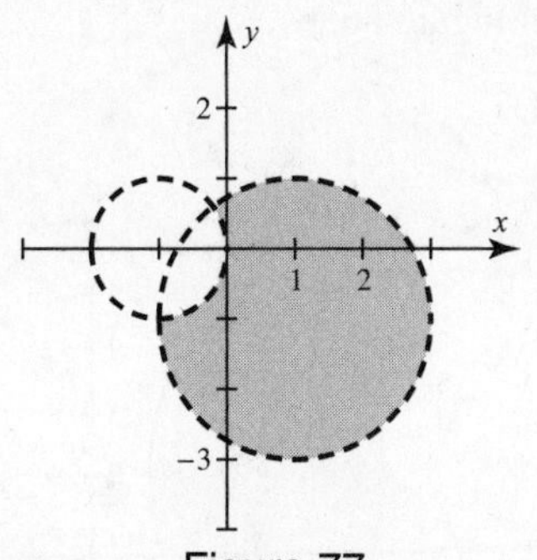

Figure 77

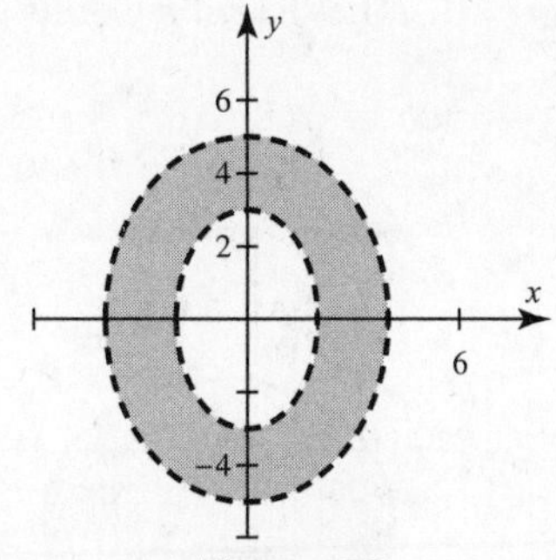

Figure 78

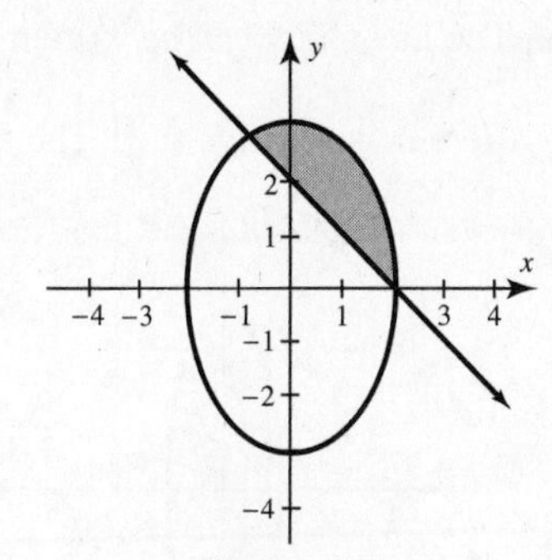

Figure 79

79. The system is $\frac{x^2}{4} + \frac{y^2}{9} \leq 1$ and $x + y \geq 2$. See Figure 79.

80. The system is $\dfrac{x^2}{16} + \dfrac{y^2}{25} \le 1$ and $-x + y \le 4$. See Figure 80.

81. The system is $x^2 + y^2 \le 4$ and $x^2 + (y - 2)^2 \le 4$. See Figure 81.

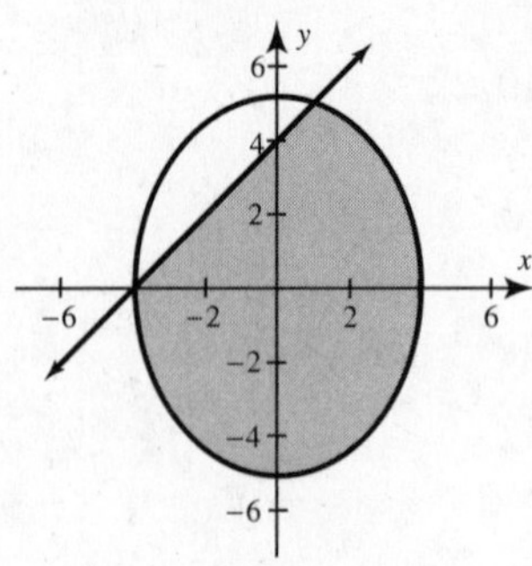

Figure 80

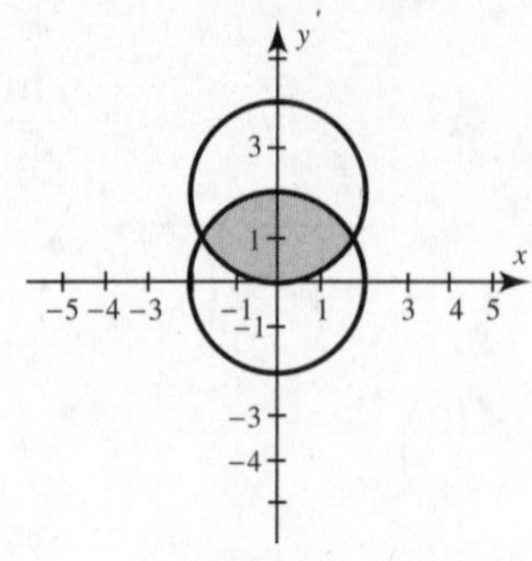

Figure 81

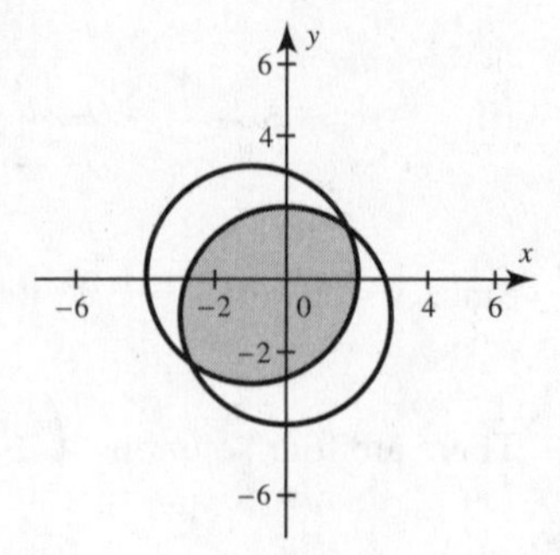

Figure 82

82. The system is $x^2 + (y + 1)^2 \le 9$ and $(x + 1)^2 + y^2 \le 9$. See Figure 82.

83. The system is $x^2 + y^2 \le 4$ and $(x + 1)^2 - y \le 0$. See Figure 83.

84. The system is $4x^2 + 9y^2 \le 36$ and $x - (y - 2)^2 \ge 0$. See Figure 84.

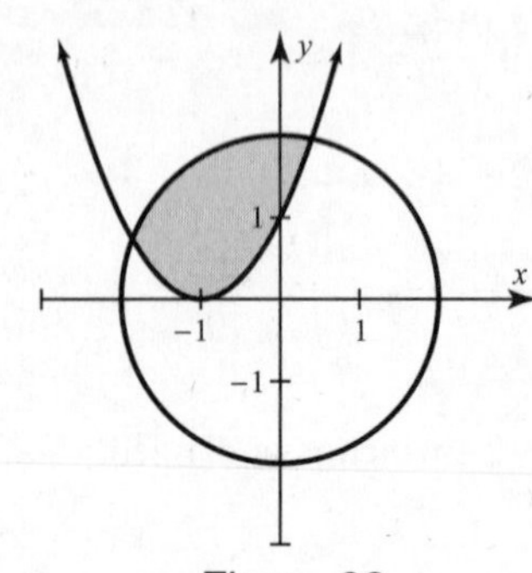

Figure 83

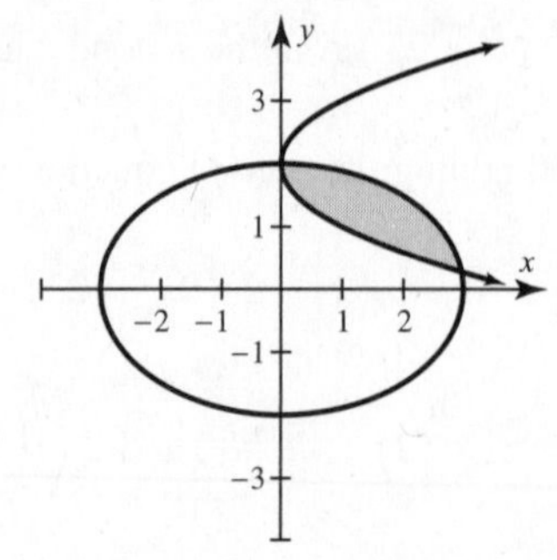

Figure 84

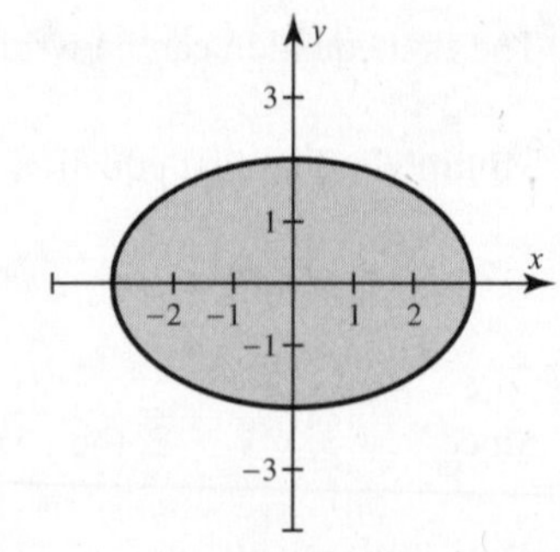

Figure 85

85. The inequality can be written $\dfrac{x^2}{9} + \dfrac{y^2}{4} \le 1$. The shaded region is shown in Figure 85.

Here $a = 3$ and $b = 2$. The area is $A = \pi ab = \pi(3)(2) = 6\pi \approx 18.85 \text{ ft}^2$.

86. The inequality can be written $\dfrac{x^2}{1} + \dfrac{y^2}{9} \le 1$. The shaded region is shown in Figure 86.

Here $a = 1$ and $b = 3$. The area is $A = \pi ab = \pi(1)(3) = 3\pi \approx 9.42 \text{ ft}^2$.

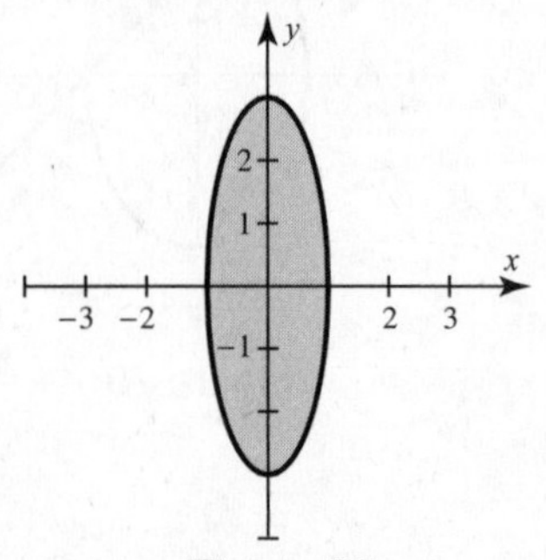

Figure 86

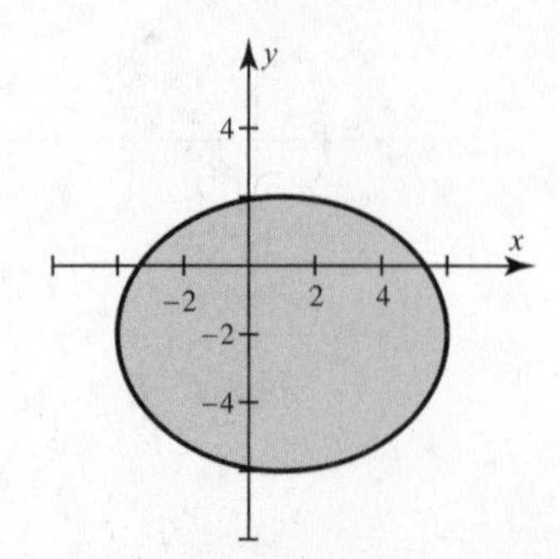

Figure 87

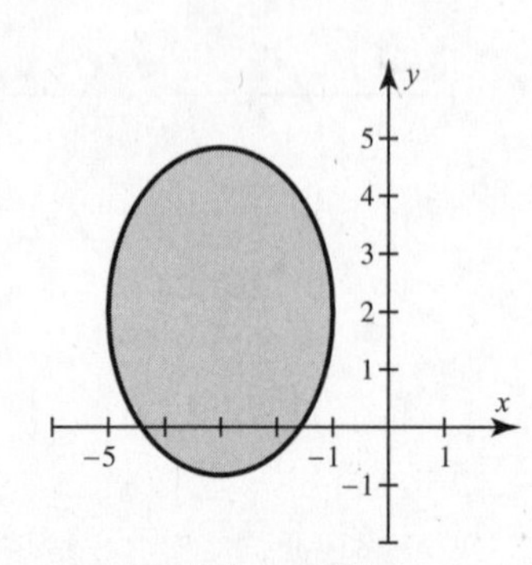

Figure 88

87. The shaded region is shown in Figure 87.

Here $a = 5$ and $b = 4$. The area is $A = \pi ab = \pi(5)(4) = 20\pi \approx 62.83 \text{ ft}^2$.

88. The shaded region is shown in Figure 88.

Here $a = 2$ and $b = \sqrt{8} = 2\sqrt{2}$. The area is $A = \pi ab = \pi(2)(2\sqrt{2}\,) = 4\pi\sqrt{2} \approx 17.77 \text{ ft}^2$.

89. $e = \dfrac{c}{a} = 0.206 \Rightarrow c = 0.206a$. Since $a = 0.387$, it follows that $c = 0.206(0.387) \approx 0.0797$. Then, the value of $b$ is given by the following: $a^2 - b^2 = c^2 \Rightarrow a^2 - c^2 = b^2 \Rightarrow 0.387^2 - 0.0797^2 = b^2 \Rightarrow$ $b^2 \approx 0.1434 \Rightarrow b \approx 0.379$. The major axis could be located on either the $x$- or $y$-axis. We will choose the $x$-axis. Thus, the equation of the orbit is $\dfrac{x^2}{0.387^2} + \dfrac{y^2}{0.379^2} = 1$. The sun can be located on either of the foci. We will locate the sun at (0.0797, 0). To graph the orbit with a graphing calculator, solve the equation for the ellipse for the variable $y$: $\dfrac{x^2}{0.387^2} + \dfrac{y^2}{0.379^2} = 1 \Rightarrow y = \pm 0.379\sqrt{1 - \dfrac{x^2}{0.387^2}}$. Graph each of the equations and plot the sun at (0.0797, 0). $Y_1 = 0.379\sqrt{}((1 - X\text{^}2)/0.387\text{^}2)$, $Y_2 = -Y_1$. See Figure 89.

[−0.6, 0.6, 0.1] by [−0.4, 0.4, 0.1] [−1.6, 1.6, 0.4] by [−2.4, 2.4, 0.4]

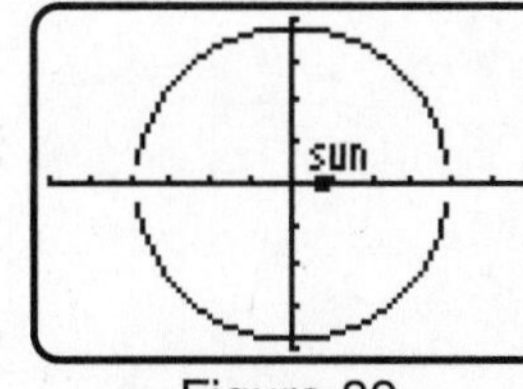


Figure 89

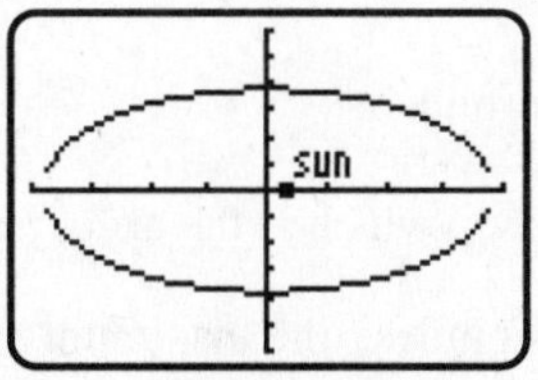

Figure 90

90. $e = \dfrac{c}{a} = 0.093 \Rightarrow c = 0.093a$. Since $a = 1.524$, it follows that $c = 0.093(1.524) \approx 0.142$. Then, the value of $b$ is given by the following: $a^2 - b^2 = c^2 \Rightarrow a^2 - c^2 = b^2 \Rightarrow 1.524^2 - 0.142^2 \approx b^2 \Rightarrow b \approx 1.517$. The major axis could be located on either the $x$- or $y$-axis. We will choose the $x$-axis. Thus, the equation of the orbit is $\dfrac{x^2}{1.524^2} + \dfrac{y^2}{1.517^2} = 1$. The sun can be located on either of the foci. We will locate the sun at (0.142, 0). To graph the orbit with a graphing calculator, solve the equation for the ellipse for the variable $y$: $\dfrac{x^2}{1.524^2} + \dfrac{y^2}{1.517^2} = 1 \Rightarrow y = \pm 1.517\sqrt{1 - \dfrac{x^2}{1.524^2}}$. Graph each of the equations and plot the sun at (0.142, 0). $Y_1 = 1.517\sqrt{}((1 - X\text{^}2)/1.524\text{^}2)$, $Y_2 = -Y_1$. See Figure 90.

91. The source and the stone are at the two foci of the ellipse, so the distance between them is $2c$.

$c^2 = a^2 - b^2 = 4^2 - (2.5)^2 = 16 - 6.25 = 9.75 \Rightarrow c = \sqrt{9.75}$. Thus, $2c = 2\sqrt{9.75} \approx 6.245$. The stone should be 6.245 inches from the source.

92. The source and the stone are at the two foci of the ellipse, so the distance between them is $2c = 12 \Rightarrow c = 6$.

$c^2 = a^2 - b^2 \Rightarrow 36 = a^2 - 64 \Rightarrow a^2 = 100$. Thus, the equation is $\dfrac{x^2}{100} + \dfrac{y^2}{64} = 1$.

93. $c = 50$ and $b = 40$ for the elliptical floor. $a = \sqrt{50^2 + 40^2} = 10 \cdot \sqrt{41} \approx 64.03$. The area of the ellipse is $\pi ab$, so the area of the floor is $\pi(64.03)(40) \approx 8046.25$ square feet.

94. (a) $\dfrac{x^2}{17.95^2} + \dfrac{y^2}{4.44^2} = 1$

(b) $c = \sqrt{17.95^2 - 4.44^2} \approx 17.39$, so the sun is at $(17.39, 0)$.

(c) The minimum distance is $a - c = 17.95 - 17.39 = 0.56$, or 0.56 units, which is about 52 million miles.

The maximum distance is $a + c = 17.95 + 17.39 = 35.34$, or 35.34 units, which is about 3.3 billion miles.

95. The ellipse with a mjor axis of 620 feet and minor axis of 513 feet inplies vertices of $(\pm 310, 0)$ and $(0, \pm 256.5)$. $c^2 = a^2 - b^2 \Rightarrow c^2 = (310)^2 - (256.5)^2 \Rightarrow c \approx 174.1$. The distance between the foci is given as $2c = 2(174.1) = 348.2$ feet.

96. $c = ea = 0.0167(93) \approx 1.6$. The minimum distance is $a - c \approx 91.4$ million miles; the maximum distance is $a + c = 94.6$ million miles.

97. The equation of the ellipse is $\dfrac{x^2}{30^2} + \dfrac{y^2}{25^2} = 1$. Solving for $y$ we get $y = 25\sqrt{1 - \dfrac{x^2}{900}}$. When $x = 15$,

$y = 25\sqrt{1 - \dfrac{225}{900}} \approx 21.65$ feet.

98. (a) $2\pi\sqrt{\dfrac{36.0^2 + 35.2^2}{2}} \approx 223.7$ million miles.

(b) Yes. If the orbit is circular, $a = b = r$. So the formula is

$P = 2\pi\sqrt{\dfrac{r^2 + r^2}{2}} = 2\pi\sqrt{\dfrac{2r^2}{2}} = 2\pi\sqrt{r^2} = 2\pi r$; which is the exact perimeter.

99. The minimum height is $4464 - (3960 + 164) = 340$ miles; the maximum height is $4464 - (3960 - 164) = 668$ miles.

100. (a) $v_{max} = \dfrac{2\pi a}{P}\sqrt{\dfrac{1 + e}{1 - e}} = \dfrac{2\pi \times 5.913 \times 10^9}{2.86 \times 10^{12}} \times \sqrt{\dfrac{1 + 0.249}{1 - 0.249}} \approx 0.0168$ km/second.

$v_{min} = \dfrac{2\pi a}{P}\sqrt{\dfrac{1 - e}{1 + e}} = \dfrac{2\pi \times 5.913 \times 10^9}{2.86 \times 10^{12}} \times \sqrt{\dfrac{1 - 0.249}{1 + 0.249}} \approx 0.01007$ km/second.

(b) For a circle $e = 1$, so $v_{max} = v_{min} = \dfrac{2\pi}{P}$. The minimum and maximum velocities are equal.

Therefore, the planet's velocity is constant.

## Extended and Discovery Exercises for Section 7.2

1. The slope of the line through $(-2, 6)$ and $(4, -3)$ is $-\dfrac{3}{2}$ and has equation $y - 6 = -\dfrac{3}{2}(x + 2)$.

$0 - 6 = -\dfrac{3}{2}(x + 2) \Rightarrow x = 2$, $x$-intercept is $(2, 0)$. $y - 6 = -\dfrac{3}{2}(0 + 2) \Rightarrow y = 3$, $y$-intercept is $(0, 3)$.

The equation of the line in intercept form is $\dfrac{x}{2} + \dfrac{y}{3} = 1$.

2. The slope of the line through $(-6, -4)$ and $(3, 8)$ is $\dfrac{4}{3}$ and has equation $y - 8 = \dfrac{4}{3}(x - 3)$.

$0 - 8 = \dfrac{4}{3}(x - 3) \Rightarrow x = -3$, $x$-intercept is $(-3, 0)$. $y - 8 = \dfrac{4}{3}(0 - 3) \Rightarrow y = 4$, $y$-intercept is $(0, 4)$.

The equation of the line in intercept form is $\dfrac{x}{-3} + \dfrac{y}{4} = 1$.

3. The equation of the line through $(3, -1)$ with slope of $-2$ is $y + 1 = -2(x - 3)$.
$0 + 1 = -2(x - 3) \Rightarrow x = 2.5$, $x$-intercept is $(2.5, 0)$. $y + 1 = -2(0 - 3) \Rightarrow y = 5$, $y$-intercept is $(0, 5)$.
The equation of the line in intercept form is $\frac{x}{2.5} + \frac{y}{5} = 1$.

4. The equation of the line through $(-2, 1)$ with slope of 4 is $y - 1 = 4(x + 2)$.
$0 - 1 = 4(x + 2) \Rightarrow x = -2.25$, $x$-intercept is $(-2.25, 0)$. $y - 1 = 4(0 + 2) \Rightarrow y = 9$,
$y$-intercept is $(0, 9)$. The equation of the line in intercept form is $\frac{x}{-2.25} + \frac{y}{9} = 1$.

5. The ellipse $\frac{x^2}{25} + \frac{y^2}{9} = 1 \Rightarrow a = 5$ and $b = 3$. Therefore, the $x$-intercept is $(\pm 5, 0)$ and $y$-intercept is $(0, \pm 3)$.

6. The ellipse with vertices $(0, \pm 13)$ and foci $(0, \pm 12)$ implies vertical major axis with $a = 3$ and $c = 12$.
$c^2 = a^2 - b^2 \Rightarrow 12^2 = 13^2 - b^2 \Rightarrow b^2 = 25$. The equation on the ellipse is $\frac{x^2}{25} + \frac{y^2}{169} = 1$.
The $x$-intercept is $(\pm 5, 0)$ and the $y$-intercept is $(0, \pm 13)$.

## Checking Basic Concepts for Sections 7.1 and 7.2

1. The equation $x = \frac{1}{2}y^2$ can be written as $y^2 = 2x$, which is in the form $y^2 = 4px$. The vertex is $V(0, 0)$. Thus, $2 = 4p$ or $p = \frac{1}{2}$. The focus is $F\left(\frac{1}{2}, 0\right)$, the equation of the directrix is $x = -\frac{1}{2}$, and the parabola opens to the right. The graph of $x = \frac{1}{2}y^2$ is shown in Figure 1.

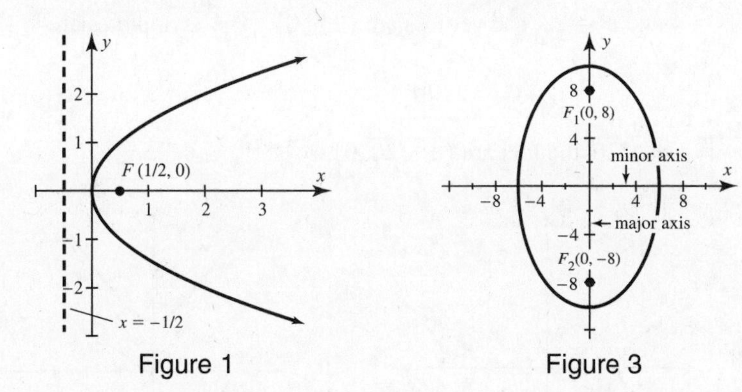


Figure 1

Figure 3

2. The vertex is halfway between the focus and the directrix, at $\left(-1, \frac{3}{2}\right)$, and $p = -\frac{3}{2}$. Since the parabola opens downward, the equation has the form $(x - h)^2 = 4p(y - k)$. The equation is $(x + 1)^2 = -6\left(y - \frac{3}{2}\right)$.

3. $\frac{x^2}{36} + \frac{y^2}{100} = 1 \Rightarrow a = 10$ and $b = 6$. $a^2 - b^2 = 10^2 - 6^2 = 64 = c^2 \Rightarrow c = 8$. The foci are $(0, \pm 8)$, the endpoints of the major axis (vertical) are $(0, \pm 10)$, while the endpoints of the minor axis are $(\pm 6, 0)$. The ellipse is graphed in Figure 3.

4. The equation is $\dfrac{(x-3)^2}{4} + \dfrac{(y+2)^2}{9} = 1$; $c = \sqrt{9-4} = \sqrt{5}$. Since the major axis is vertical, the foci are at $(3, -2 \pm \sqrt{5})$.

5. For a parabola with vertex at the origin and passing through (2, 1), the equation $x^2 = 4py$ becomes $4 = 4p$, so $p = 1$. The filament should be located 1 foot from the vertex of the reflector.

6. $x^2 + y^2 = 10 \Rightarrow x^2 = 10 - y^2$; then $2(10 - y^2) + 3y^2 = 29 \Rightarrow 20 - 2y^2 + 3y^2 = 29 \Rightarrow y^2 = 9$, so $y = \pm 3$. Substituting in $x^2 + y^2 = 10$ we find $x^2 + 9 = 10$, $x^2 = 1$, so $x = \pm 1$. There are four solutions $(\pm 1, \pm 3)$.

7. $x^2 - 4x + 4y^2 + 8y - 8 = 0 \Rightarrow (x^2 - 4x) + 4(y^2 + 2y) = 8 \Rightarrow$
$(x^2 - 4x + 4) + 4(y^2 + 2y + 1) = 8 + 4 + 4 \Rightarrow (x-2)^2 + 4(y+1)^2 = 16 \Rightarrow$
$\dfrac{(x-2)^2}{16} + \dfrac{(y+1)^2}{4} = 1$; The center is $(2, -1)$. The vertices are
$(2-4, -1), (2+4, -1)$ or $(-2, -1), (6, -1)$.

## Section 7.3: Hyperbolas

1. The transverse axis is horizontal with $a = 3$ and $b = 7$. The vertices are $(\pm 3, 0)$. The asymptotes are $y = \pm \frac{7}{3}x$. See Figure 1.

   Since $c^2 = a^2 + b^2 \Rightarrow c = \pm\sqrt{9 + 49} \Rightarrow \sqrt{58}$, the foci are $(\pm\sqrt{58}, 0)$.

2. The transverse axis is horizontal with $a = 4$ and $b = 2$. The vertices are $(\pm 4, 0)$. The asymptotes are $y = \pm \frac{1}{2}x$. See Figure 2.

   Since $c^2 = a^2 + b^2 \Rightarrow c = \pm\sqrt{16 + 4} \Rightarrow \sqrt{20}$, the foci are $(\pm\sqrt{20}, 0)$.

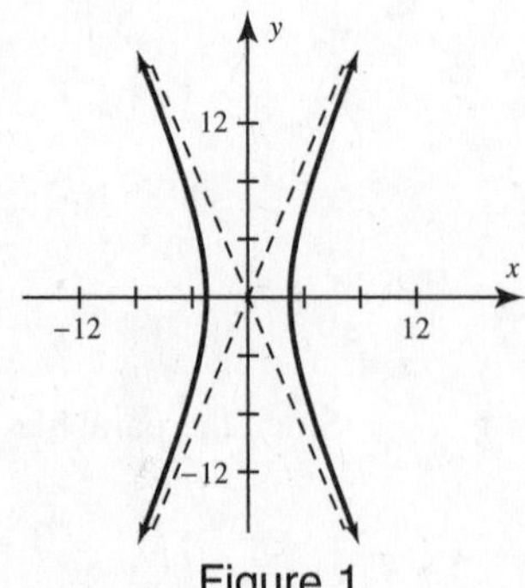

Figure 1

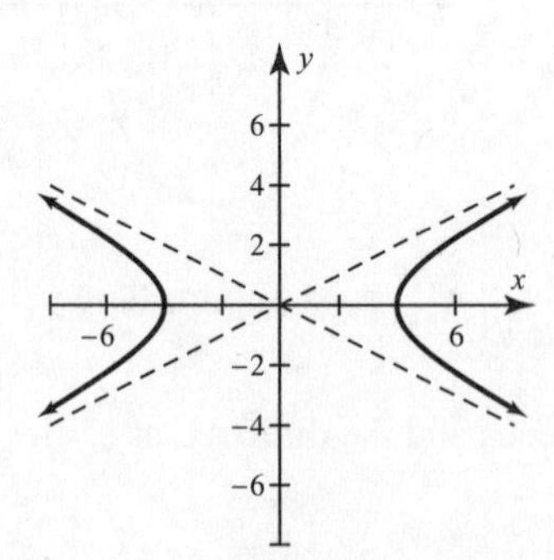

Figure 2

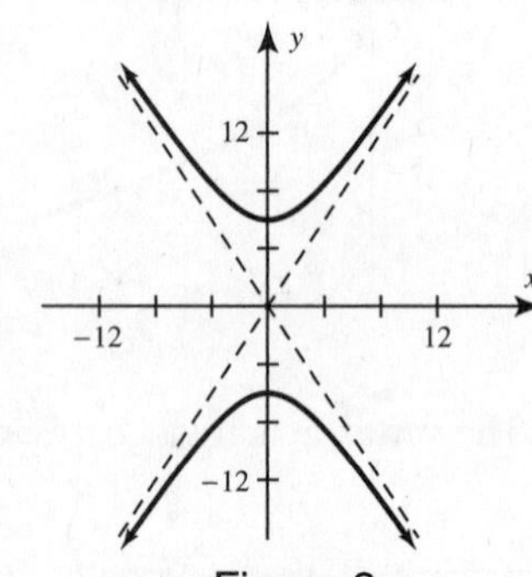

Figure 3

3. The transverse axis is vertical with $a = 6$ and $b = 4$. The vertices are $(0, \pm 6)$. The asymptotes are $y = \pm \frac{3}{2}x$. See Figure 3.

   Since $c^2 = a^2 + b^2 \Rightarrow c = \pm\sqrt{36 + 16} \Rightarrow \sqrt{52}$, the foci are $(0, \pm\sqrt{52})$.

4. The transverse axis is vertical with $a = 2$ and $b = 2$. The vertices are $(0, \pm 2)$. The asymptotes are $y = \pm x$. See Figure 4. Since $c^2 = a^2 + b^2 \Rightarrow c = \pm\sqrt{4 + 4} \Rightarrow \sqrt{8}$, the foci are $(0, \pm\sqrt{8})$.

5. $x^2 - y^2 = 9 \Rightarrow \dfrac{x^2}{9} - \dfrac{y^2}{9} = 1$. The transverse axis is horizontal with $a = 3$ and $b = 3$. The vertices are $(\pm 3, 0)$. The asymptotes are $y = \pm x$. See Figure 5.
Since $c^2 = a^2 + b^2 \Rightarrow c = \pm\sqrt{9 + 9} \Rightarrow \sqrt{18}$, the foci are $(\pm\sqrt{18}, 0)$.

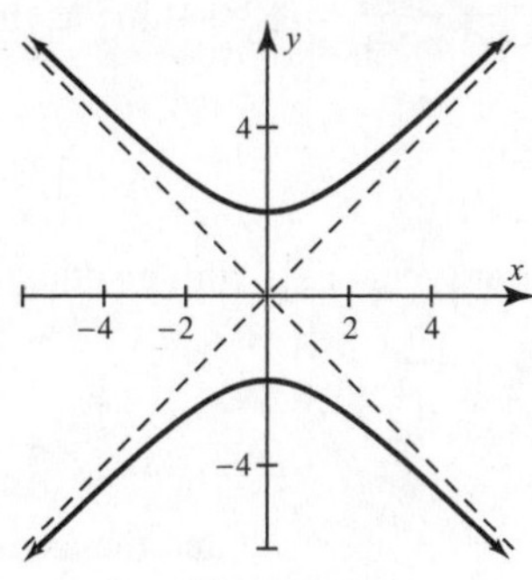

Figure 4

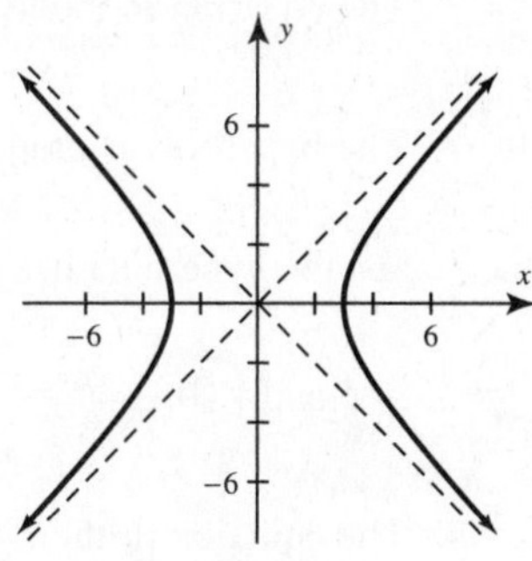

Figure 5

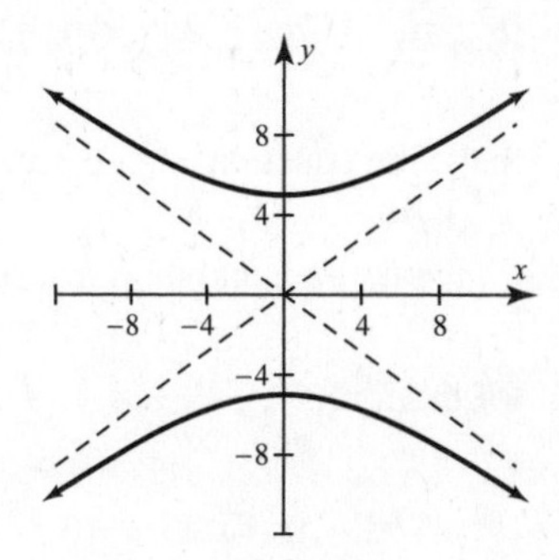

Figure 6

6. $49y^2 - 25x^2 = 1225 \Rightarrow \dfrac{y^2}{25} - \dfrac{x^2}{49} = 1$. The transverse axis is vertical with $a = 5$ and $b = 7$. The vertices are $(0, \pm 5)$. The asymptotes are $y = \pm\dfrac{5}{7}x$. See Figure 6.
Since $c^2 = a^2 + b^2 \Rightarrow c = \pm\sqrt{25 + 49} \Rightarrow \sqrt{74}$, the foci are $(0, \pm\sqrt{74})$.

7. $9y^2 - 16x^2 = 144 \Rightarrow \dfrac{y^2}{16} - \dfrac{x^2}{9} = 1$. The transverse axis is vertical with $a = 4$ and $b = 3$. The vertices are $(0, \pm 4)$. The asymptotes are $y = \pm\dfrac{4}{3}x$. See Figure 7.
Since $c^2 = a^2 + b^2 \Rightarrow c = \pm\sqrt{16 + 9} \Rightarrow \pm 5$, the foci are $(0, \pm 5)$.

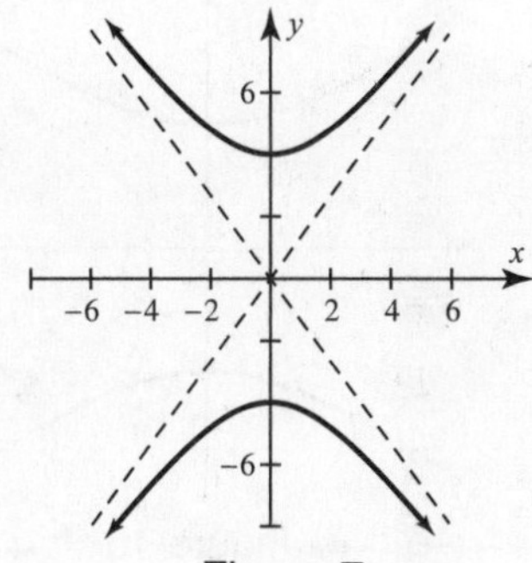

Figure 7

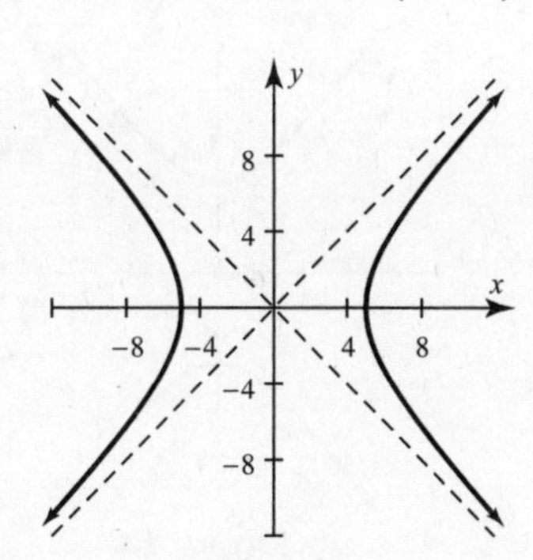

Figure 8

8. $4x^2 - 4y^2 = 100 \Rightarrow \dfrac{x^2}{25} - \dfrac{y^2}{25} = 1$. The transverse axis is horizontal with $a = 5$ and $b = 5$. The vertices are $(\pm 5, 0)$. The asymptotes are $y = \pm x$. See Figure 8.
Since $c^2 = a^2 + b^2 \Rightarrow c = \pm\sqrt{25 + 25} \Rightarrow 5\sqrt{2}$, the foci are $(\pm\sqrt{50}, 0)$.

9. Horizontal transverse axis, vertices $(\pm 2, 0)$; d

10. Horizontal transverse axis, vertices $(\pm 3, 0)$; b

11. Vertical transverse axis, vertices $(0, \pm 3)$; a

12. Vertical transverse axis, vertices $(0, \pm 2)$; c

13. Since the foci and the vertices lie on the $x$-axis, the hyperbola has a horizontal transverse axis with an equation of the form $\frac{x^2}{a^2} - \frac{y^2}{b^2} = 1$. $F(\pm 5, 0) \Rightarrow c = 5$ and $V(\pm 4, 0) \Rightarrow a = 4$. $c^2 = a^2 + b^2 \Rightarrow$ $b^2 = c^2 - a^2 = 25 - 16 = 9 \Rightarrow b = 3$. The equation of the hyperbola is $\frac{x^2}{16} - \frac{y^2}{9} = 1$, and the asymptotes have the equation $y = \pm\frac{b}{a}x$ or $y = \pm\frac{3}{4}x$. The hyperbola is graphed in Figure 13.

14. Since the foci and the vertices lie on the $y$-axis, the hyperbola has a vertical transverse axis with an equation of the form $\frac{y^2}{a^2} - \frac{x^2}{b^2} = 1$. $F(0, \pm 5) \Rightarrow c = 5$ and $V(0, \pm 4) \Rightarrow a = 4$. $c^2 = a^2 + b^2 \Rightarrow$ $b^2 = c^2 - a^2 = 25 - 16 = 9 \Rightarrow b = 3$. The equation of the hyperbola is $\frac{y^2}{16} - \frac{x^2}{9} = 1$, and the asymptotes have the equation $y = \pm\frac{a}{b}x$ or $y = \pm\frac{4}{3}x$. The hyperbola is graphed in Figure 14.

15. Since the foci and the vertices lie on the $y$-axis, the hyperbola has a vertical transverse axis with an equation of the form $\frac{y^2}{a^2} - \frac{x^2}{b^2} = 1$. $F(0, \pm 10) \Rightarrow c = 10$ and $V(0, \pm 6) \Rightarrow a = 6$. $c^2 = a^2 + b^2 \Rightarrow$ $b^2 = c^2 - a^2 = 100 - 36 = 64 \Rightarrow b = 8$. The equation of the hyperbola is $\frac{y^2}{36} - \frac{x^2}{64} = 1$, and the asymptotes have the equation $y = \pm\frac{a}{b}x$ or $y = \pm\frac{3}{4}x$. The hyperbola is graphed in Figure 15.

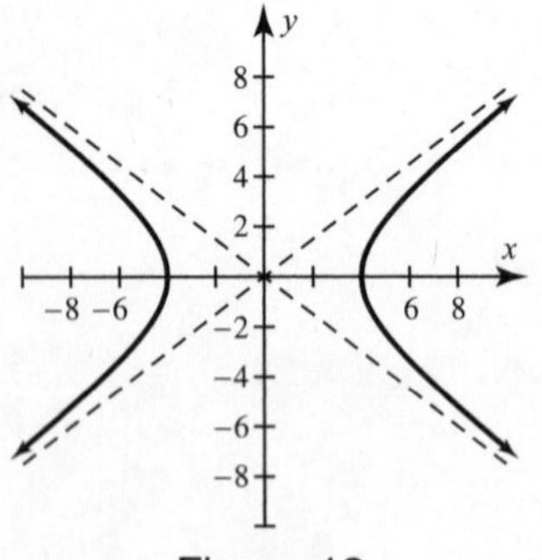

Figure 13

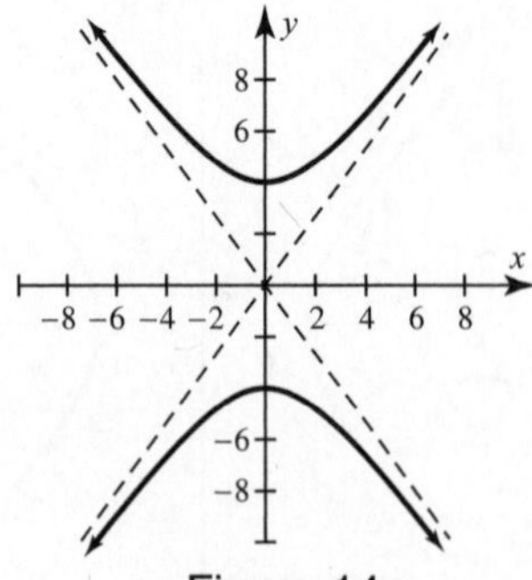

Figure 14

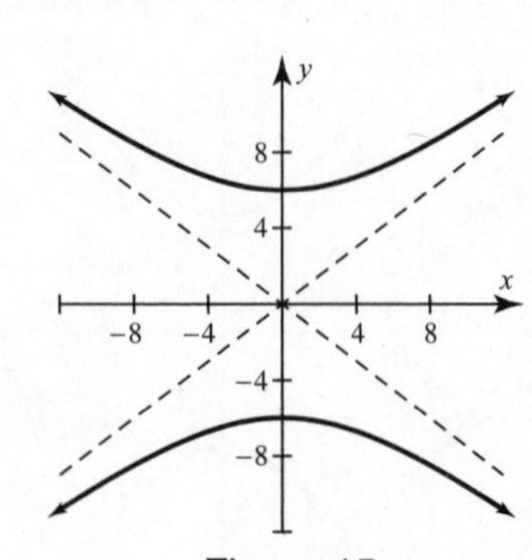

Figure 15

16. Since the foci and the vertices lie on the $x$-axis, the hyperbola has a horizontal transverse axis with an equation of the form $\frac{x^2}{a^2} - \frac{y^2}{b^2} = 1$. $F(\pm 4, 0) \Rightarrow c = 4$ and $V(\pm 3, 0) \Rightarrow a = 3$. $c^2 = a^2 + b^2 \Rightarrow$ $b^2 = c^2 - a^2 = 16 - 9 = 7 \Rightarrow b = \sqrt{7}$. The equation of the hyperbola is $\frac{x^2}{9} - \frac{y^2}{7} = 1$, and the asymptotes have the equation $y = \pm\frac{b}{a}x$ or $y = \pm\frac{\sqrt{7}}{3}x$. The hyperbola is graphed in Figure 16.

17. Since the foci and the vertices lie on the $y$-axis, the hyperbola has a vertical transverse axis with an equation of the form $\frac{y^2}{a^2} - \frac{x^2}{b^2} = 1$. $F(0, \pm 13) \Rightarrow c = 13$ and $V(0, \pm 12) \Rightarrow a = 12$. $c^2 = a^2 + b^2 \Rightarrow$ $b^2 = c^2 - a^2 = 169 - 144 = 25 \Rightarrow b = 5$. The equation of the hyperbola is $\frac{y^2}{144} - \frac{x^2}{25} = 1$, and the asymptotes have the equation $y = \pm\frac{a}{b}x$ or $y = \pm\frac{12}{5}x$. The hyperbola is graphed in Figure 17.

18. Since the foci and the vertices lie on the $x$-axis, the hyperbola has a horizontal transverse axis with an equation of the form $\frac{x^2}{a^2} - \frac{y^2}{b^2} = 1$. $F(\pm 13, 0) \Rightarrow c = 13$ and $V(\pm 5, 0) \Rightarrow a = 5$. $c^2 = a^2 + b^2 \Rightarrow$ $b^2 = c^2 - a^2 = 169 - 25 = 144 \Rightarrow b = 12$. The equation of the hyperbola is $\frac{x^2}{25} - \frac{y^2}{144} = 1$, and the asymptotes have the equation $y = \pm\frac{b}{a}x$ or $y = \pm\frac{12}{5}x$. The hyperbola is graphed in Figure 18.

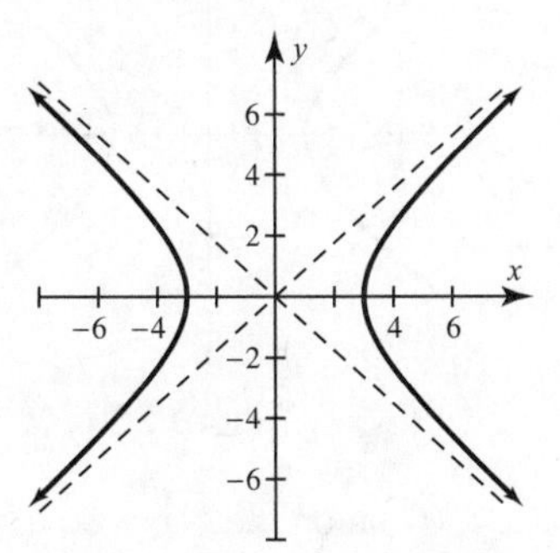

Figure 16

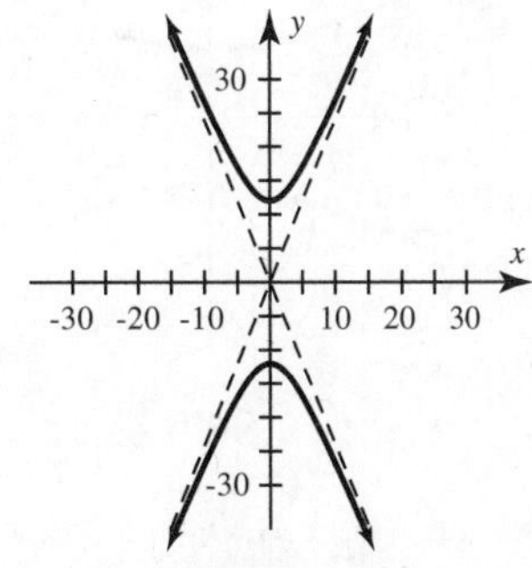

Figure 17

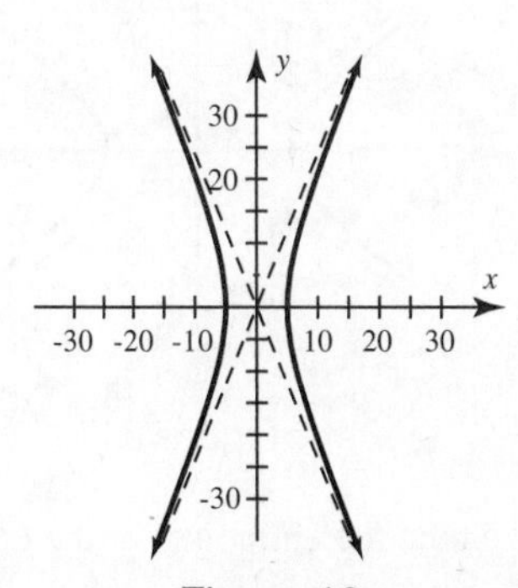

Figure 18

19. Since the foci are $(0, \pm 5)$, $c = 5$. Since the transverse axis is vertical of length 4, $a = 2$. The equation has the form $\frac{y^2}{a^2} - \frac{x^2}{b^2} = 1$. $c^2 = a^2 + b^2 \Rightarrow b^2 = c^2 - a^2 = 25 - 4 = 21 \Rightarrow b = \sqrt{21} \approx 4.58$. The equation of the hyperbola is $\frac{y^2}{4} - \frac{x^2}{21} = 1$, and the asymptotes have the equation $y = \pm\frac{a}{b}x$ or $y = \pm\frac{2}{\sqrt{21}}x$. The hyperbola is graphed in Figure 19.

20. Since the foci are $(\pm 10, 0)$, $c = 10$. Since the transverse axis is horizontal of length $2a = 12$, $a = 6$. The equation has the form $\frac{x^2}{a^2} - \frac{y^2}{b^2} = 1$. $c^2 = a^2 + b^2 \Rightarrow b^2 = c^2 - a^2 = 100 - 36 = 64 \Rightarrow b = 8$. The equation of the hyperbola is $\frac{x^2}{36} - \frac{y^2}{64} = 1$, and the asymptotes have the equation $y = \pm\frac{b}{a}x$ or $y = \pm\frac{4}{3}x$. The hyperbola is graphed in Figure 20.

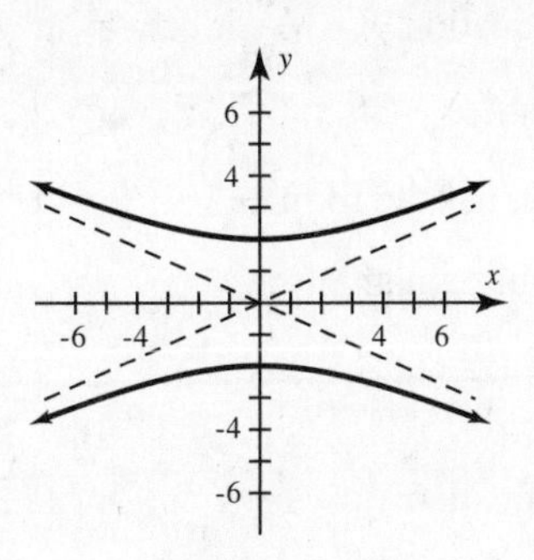

Figure 19

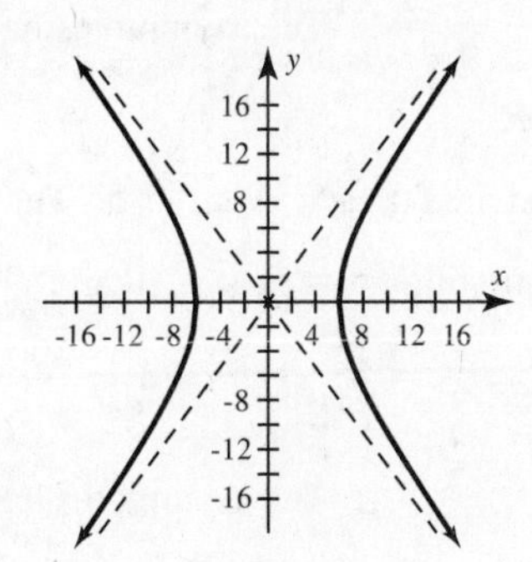

Figure 20

21. Since the vertices lie on the $x$-axis and are $(\pm 3, 0)$, $a = 3$. The equation has the form $\frac{x^2}{a^2} - \frac{y^2}{b^2} = 1$. Since $y = \pm\frac{b}{a}x = \pm\frac{2}{3}x$ and $a = 3$, it follows that $b = 2$. The equation of the hyperbola is $\frac{x^2}{9} - \frac{y^2}{4} = 1$. The hyperbola is graphed in Figure 21.

22. Since the vertices lie on the $y$-axis and are $(0, \pm 4)$, $a = 4$. The equation has the form $\frac{y^2}{a^2} - \frac{x^2}{b^2} = 1$. Since $y = \pm\frac{a}{b}x = \pm\frac{1}{2}x$ and $a = 4$, it follows that $b = 8$. The equation of the hyperbola is $\frac{y^2}{16} - \frac{x^2}{64} = 1$. The hyperbola is graphed in Figure 22.

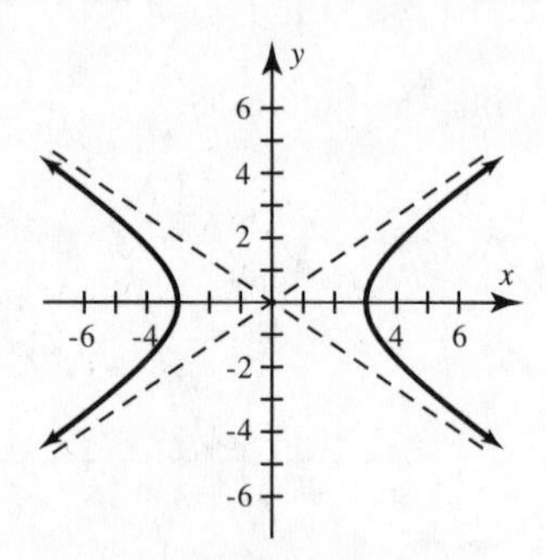

Figure 21

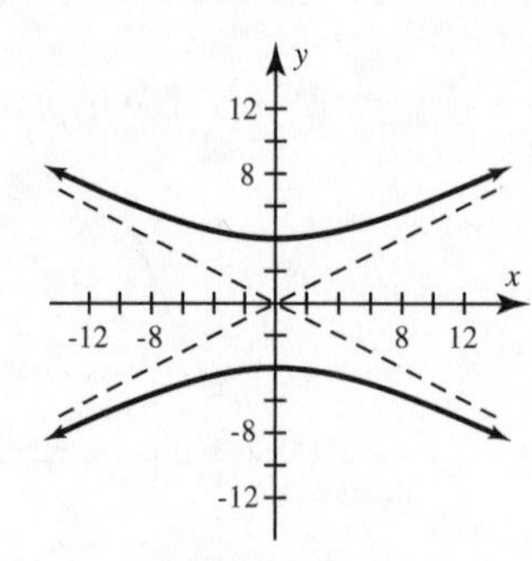

Figure 22

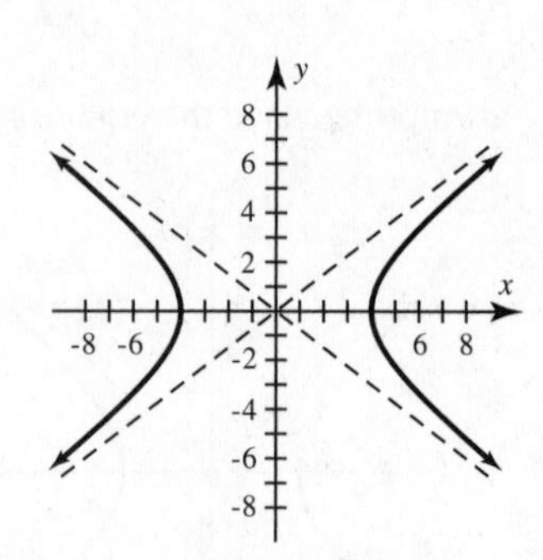

Figure 23

23. Since the endpoints of the conjugate axis are $(0, \pm 3)$, $b = 3$. The vertices $(\pm 4, 0)$ lie on the $x$-axis so $a = 4$ and the equation of the hyperbola is $\frac{x^2}{a^2} - \frac{y^2}{b^2} = 1$ or $\frac{x^2}{16} - \frac{y^2}{9} = 1$. The asymptotes have the equation $y = \pm\frac{b}{a}x$ or $y = \pm\frac{3}{4}x$. The hyperbola is graphed in Figure 23.

24. Since the endpoints of the conjugate axis are $(\pm 4, 0)$, $b = 4$. The vertices $(0, \pm 2)$ lie on the $y$-axis so $a = 2$ and the equation of the hyperbola is $\frac{y^2}{a^2} - \frac{x^2}{b^2} = 1$ or $\frac{y^2}{4} - \frac{x^2}{16} = 1$. The asymptotes have the equation $y = \pm\frac{a}{b}x$ or $y = \pm\frac{1}{2}x$. The hyperbola is graphed in Figure 24.

25. Since the vertices lie on the $x$-axis and are $(\pm\sqrt{10}, 0)$, $a^2 = 10$. The equation has the form $\frac{x^2}{a^2} - \frac{y^2}{b^2} = 1$. The value of $b^2$ can be found by substituting $a^2 = 10$, $x = 10$, and $y = 9$ in this equation.
$\frac{(10)^2}{10} - \frac{(9)^2}{b^2} = 1 \Rightarrow \frac{100}{10} - \frac{81}{b^2} = 1 \Rightarrow 10 - \frac{81}{b^2} = 1 \Rightarrow 9 = \frac{81}{b^2} \Rightarrow b^2 = \frac{81}{9} \Rightarrow b^2 = 9$
The equation of the hyperbola is $\frac{x^2}{10} - \frac{y^2}{9} = 1$. The asymptotes have the equation $y = \pm\frac{b}{a}x$ or $y = \pm\frac{3}{\sqrt{10}}x$.
The hyperbola is graphed in Figure 25.

26. Since the vertices lie on the $y$-axis and are $(0, \pm\sqrt{5})$, $a^2 = 5$. The equation has the form $\frac{y^2}{a^2} - \frac{x^2}{b^2} = 1$. The value of $b^2$ can be found by substituting $a^2 = 5$, $x = 4$, and $y = 5$ in this equation.
$\frac{(5)^2}{5} - \frac{(4)^2}{b^2} = 1 \Rightarrow \frac{25}{5} - \frac{16}{b^2} = 1 \Rightarrow 5 - \frac{16}{b^2} = 1 \Rightarrow 4 = \frac{16}{b^2} \Rightarrow b^2 = \frac{16}{4} \Rightarrow b^2 = 4$
The equation of the hyperbola is $\frac{y^2}{5} - \frac{x^2}{4} = 1$. The asymptotes have the equation $y = \pm\frac{a}{b}x$ or $y = \pm\frac{\sqrt{5}}{2}x$.
The hyperbola is graphed in Figure 26.

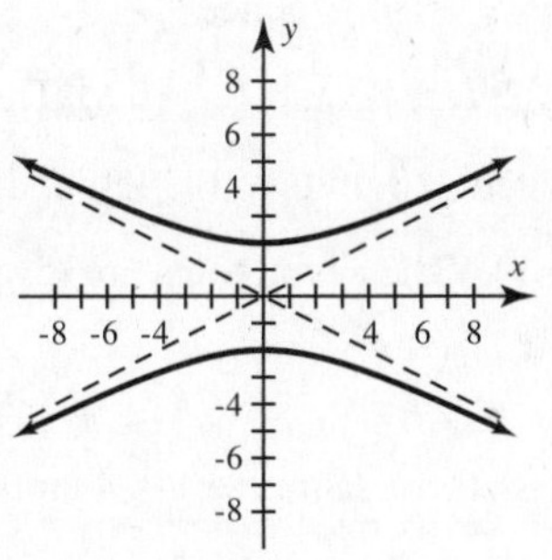

Figure 24

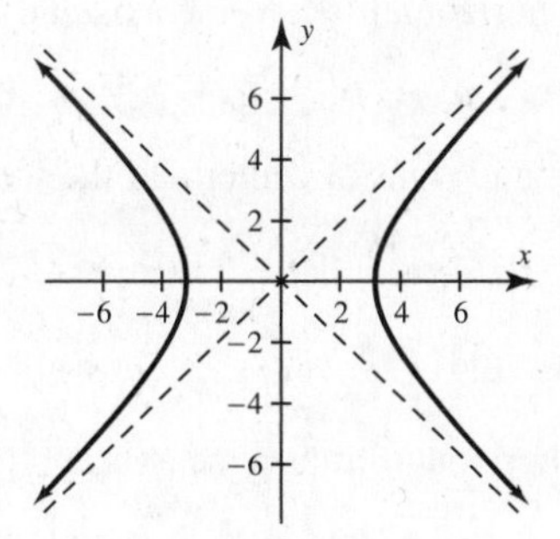

Figure 25

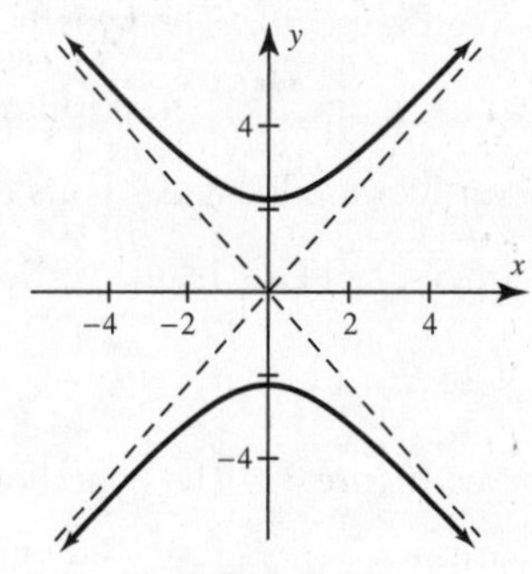

Figure 26

27. See Figure 27. The hyperbola has a horizontal transverse axis and its center is $(1, 2)$. Since $a^2 = 16$ and $b^2 = 4$, it follows that $c^2 = a^2 + b^2 = 16 + 4 = 20$. Thus, $a = 4$, $b = 2$, and $c = \sqrt{20}$. The vertices are located 4 units to the left and right of center and the foci are located $\sqrt{20}$ units to the left and right of center. That is, the vertices are $(1 \pm 4, 2)$ and the foci are $(1 \pm \sqrt{20}, 2)$. The asymptotes are given by $y = \pm\frac{b}{a}(x - h) + k \Rightarrow y = \pm\frac{1}{2}(x - 1) + 2$.

28. See Figure 28. The hyperbola has a vertical transverse axis and its center is $(-3, -1)$. Since $a^2 = 16$ and $b^2 = 9$, it follows that $c^2 = a^2 + b^2 = 16 + 9 = 25$. Thus, $a = 4$, $b = 3$, and $c = 5$. The vertices are located 4 units above and below center and the foci are located 5 units above and below center. That is, the vertices are $(-3, -1 \pm 4)$ and the foci are $(-3, -1 \pm 5)$. The asymptotes are given by $y = \pm\frac{b}{a}(x - h) + k \Rightarrow y = \pm\frac{4}{3}(x + 3) - 1$.

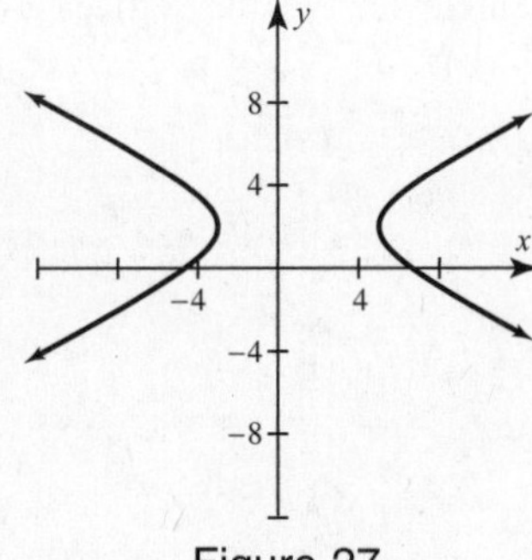

Figure 27

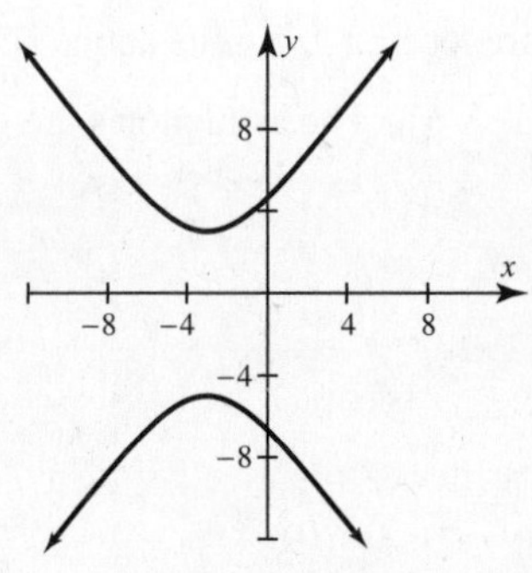

Figure 28

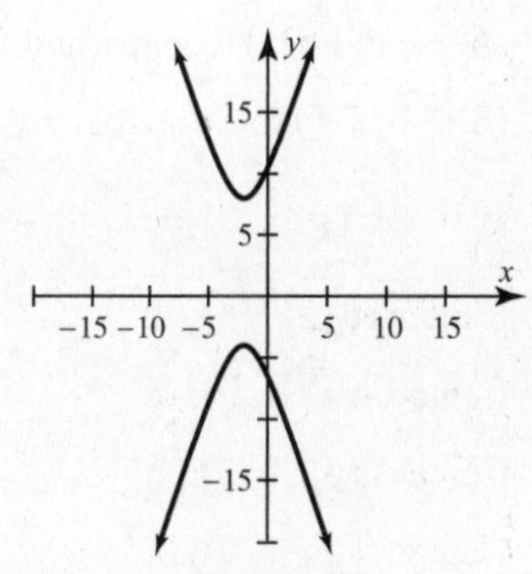

Figure 29

29. See Figure 29. The hyperbola has a vertical transverse axis and its center is $(-2, 2)$. Since $a^2 = 36$ and $b^2 = 4$, it follows that $c^2 = a^2 + b^2 = 36 + 4 = 40$. Thus, $a = 6$, $b = 2$, and $c = \sqrt{40}$. The vertices are located 6 units above and below center and the foci are located $\sqrt{40}$ units above and below center. That is, the vertices are $(-2, 2 \pm 6)$ and the foci are $(-2, 2 \pm \sqrt{40})$. The asymptotes are given by $y = \pm\frac{b}{a}(x - h) + k \Rightarrow y = \pm 3(x + 2) + 2$.

30. See Figure 30. The hyperbola has a horizontal transverse axis and its center is $(-1, 1)$. Since $a^2 = 4$ and $b^2 = 4$, it follows that $c^2 = a^2 + b^2 = 4 + 4 = 8$. Thus, $a = 2, b = 2$, and $c = \sqrt{8}$. The vertices are located 2 units to the left and right of center and the foci are located $\sqrt{8}$ units to the left and right of center. That is, the vertices are $(-1 \pm 2, 1)$ and the foci are $(-1 \pm \sqrt{8}, 1)$. The asymptotes are given by $y = \pm\frac{b}{a}(x - h) + k \Rightarrow y = \pm(x + 1) + 1$.

31. See Figure 31. The hyperbola has a horizontal transverse axis and its center is $(0, 1)$. Since $a^2 = 4$ and $b^2 = 1$, it follows that $c^2 = a^2 + b^2 = 4 + 1 = 5$. Thus, $a = 2, b = 1$, and $c = \sqrt{5}$. The vertices are located 2 units to the left and right of center and the foci are located $\sqrt{5}$ units to the left and right of center. That is, the vertices are $(\pm 2, 1)$ and the foci are $(\pm\sqrt{5}, 1)$. The asymptotes are given by $y = \pm\frac{b}{a}(x - h) + k \Rightarrow y = \pm\frac{1}{2}x + 1$.

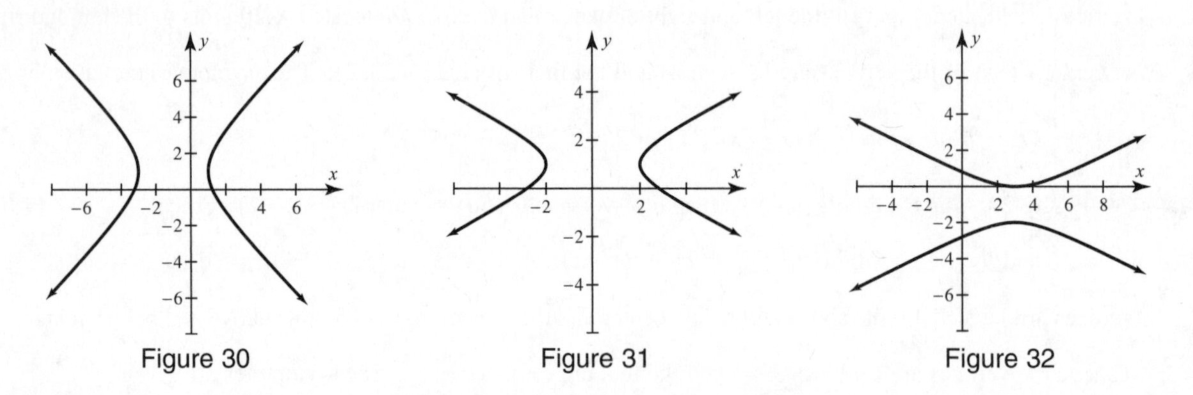

Figure 30 Figure 31 Figure 32

32. See Figure 32. The hyperbola has a vertical transverse axis and its center is $(3, -1)$. Since $a^2 = 1$ and $b^2 = 4$, it follows that $c^2 = a^2 + b^2 = 1 + 4 = 5$. Thus, $a = 1, b = 2$, and $c = \sqrt{5}$. The vertices are located 1 unit above and below center and the foci are located $\sqrt{5}$ units above and below center. That is, the vertices are $(3, -1 \pm 1)$ and the foci are $(3, -1 \pm \sqrt{5})$. The asymptotes are given by $y = \pm\frac{b}{a}(x - h) + k \Rightarrow y = \pm\frac{1}{2}(x - 3) - 1$.

33. Center at $(2, -4)$; b

34. Center at $(-1, 0)$; d

35. Center at $(2, -1)$; c

36. Center at $(-1, 0)$; a

37. The hyperbola is centered at $(4, -4)$. The vertical transverse axis has length 8 so $a = 4$. The conjugate axis has length 4, so $b = 2$. Its equation is $\frac{(y + 4)^2}{16} - \frac{(x - 4)^2}{4} = 1$ with vertices $(4, -4 \pm 4)$, foci $(4, -4 \pm \sqrt{20})$. The asymptotes are given by $y = \pm\frac{b}{a}(x - h) + k \Rightarrow y = \pm 2(x - 4) - 4$.

38. The hyperbola is centered at $(0, 2)$. The horizontal transverse axis has length 2 so $a = 1$. The conjugate axis has length 2, so $b = 1$. Its equation is $x^2 - (y - 2)^2 = 1$ with vertices $(\pm 1, 2)$, foci $(\pm\sqrt{2}, 2)$. The asymptotes are given by $y = \pm\frac{b}{a}(x - h) + k \Rightarrow y = \pm x + 2$.

39. The hyperbola has a horizontal transverse axis, and its center is (1, 1). Since $a^2 = 4, b^2 = 4$, and $c^2 = a^2 + b^2 = 8, a = 2, b = 2$, and $c = \sqrt{8}$. Thus, the vertices are $(1 \pm 2, 1)$ and the foci are $(1 \pm \sqrt{8}, 1)$. The asymptotes are the lines $y = \pm(x - 1) + 1$. See Figure 39.

40. The hyperbola has a horizontal transverse axis, and its center is (–2, –1). Since $a^2 = 4, b^2 = 16$, and $c^2 = a^2 + b^2 = 20, a = 2, b = 4$, and $c = \sqrt{20}$. Thus, the vertices are $(-2 \pm 2, -1)$ and the foci are $(-2 - \sqrt{20}, -1)$. The asymptotes are the lines $y = \pm 2(x + 2) - 1$. See Figure 40.

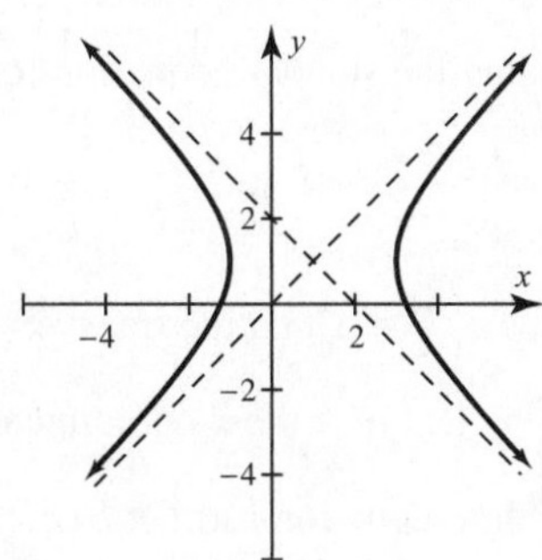

Figure 39

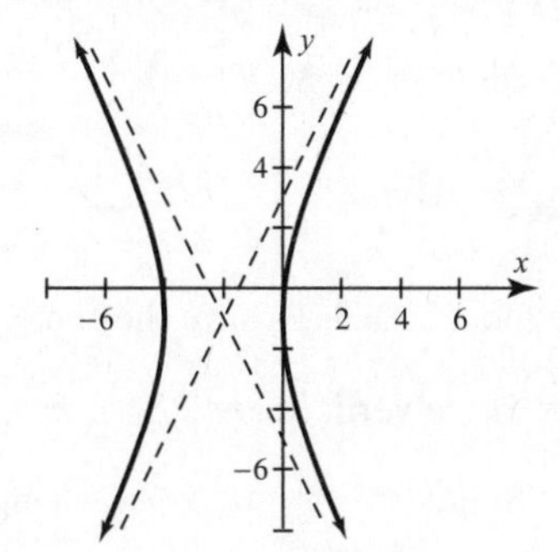

Figure 40

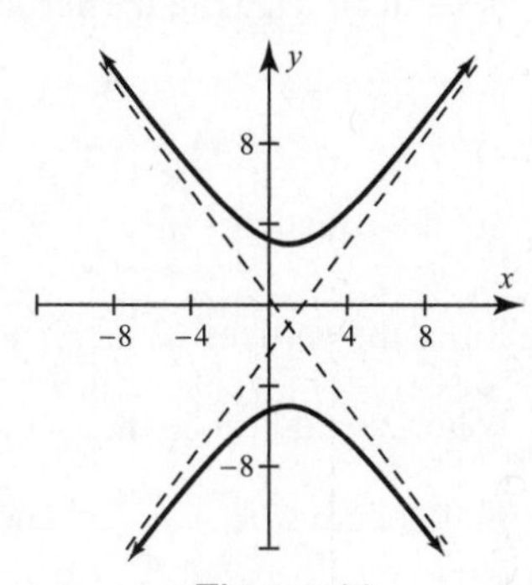

Figure 41

41. The hyperbola has a vertical transverse axis, and its center is (1, –1). Since $a^2 = 16, b^2 = 9$, and $c^2 = a^2 + b^2 = 25, a = 4, b = 3$, and $c = 5$. Thus, the vertices are $(1, -1 \pm 4)$ and the foci are $(1, -1 \pm 5)$. The asymptotes are the lines $y = \pm\frac{4}{3}(x - 1) - 1$. See Figure 41.

42. The hyperbola has a vertical transverse axis, and its center is (2, 0). Since $a^2 = 1, b^2 = 4$, and $c^2 = a^2 + b^2 = 5, a = 1, b = 2$, and $c = \sqrt{5}$. Thus, the vertices are $(2, \pm 1)$ and the foci are $(2, \pm\sqrt{5})$. The asymptotes are the lines $y = \pm\frac{1}{2}(x - 2)$. See Figure 42.

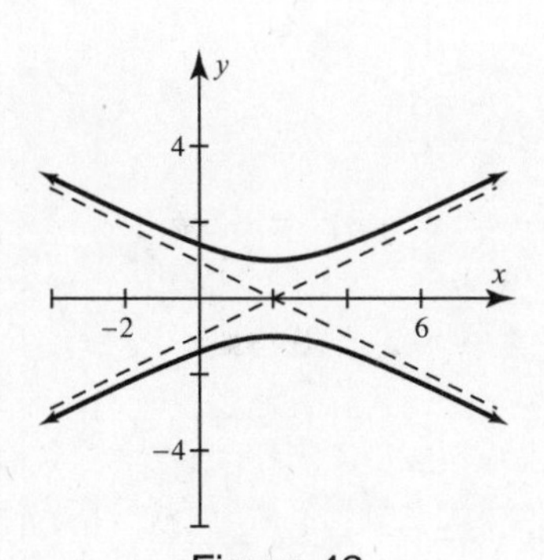

Figure 42

43. Center $(2, -2) \Rightarrow h = 2$ and $k = -2$. Rewrite the coordinates for the given vertex: $(3, -2) \Rightarrow (1 + 2, -2)$. Rewrite the coordinates for the given focus: $(4, -2) \Rightarrow (2 + 2, -2)$. Thus, the transverse axis is horizontal with $a = 1$ and $c = 2$. $b^2 = c^2 - a^2 = 3$. Using the standard equation form, we get the equation: $\frac{(x - h)^2}{a^2} - \frac{(y - k)^2}{b^2} = 1 \Rightarrow (x - 2)^2 - \frac{(y + 2)^2}{3} = 1$.

44. Center $(-1, 1) \Rightarrow h = -1$ and $k = 1$. Rewrite the coordinates for the given vertex: $(-1, 3) \Rightarrow (-1, 2 + 1)$. Rewrite the coordinates for the given focus: $(-1, 4) \Rightarrow (-1, 3 + 1)$. Thus, the transverse axis is vertical with $a = 2$ and $c = 3$. $b^2 = c^2 - a^2 = 5$. Using the standard equation form, we get the equation:
$\frac{(y-k)^2}{a^2} - \frac{(x-h)^2}{b^2} = 1 \Rightarrow \frac{(y-1)^2}{4} - \frac{(x+1)^2}{5} = 1.$

45. Since the vertices $(-1, \pm 1)$ and the foci $(-1, \pm 3)$ have the same $x$-coordinate, $h = -1$ and the transverse axis is vertical. Rewrite the vertices: $(-1, \pm 1) \Rightarrow (-1, 0 \pm 1)$, so $k = 0$ and $a = 1 \Rightarrow a^2 = 1$. Rewrite the foci: $(-1, \pm 3) \Rightarrow (-1, 0 \pm 3)$, so $k = 0$ and $c = 3$. So, $b^2 = c^2 - a^2 = 8$. Using the standard equation form, we get the equation: $\frac{(y-k)^2}{a^2} - \frac{(x-h)^2}{b^2} = 1 \Rightarrow y^2 - \frac{(x+1)^2}{8} = 1.$

46. Since the vertices $(2 \pm 1, 1)$ and the foci $(2 \pm 3, 1)$ have the same $y$-coordinate, $k = 1$ and the transverse axis is horizontal. Since the $x$-coordinates of the vertices are $2 \pm 1$, $h = 2$ and $a = 1$. Since the $x$-coordinates of the foci are $2 \pm 3$, $h = 2$ and $c = 3$. So, $b^2 = c^2 - a^2 = 8$. Using the standard equation form, we get the equation: $\frac{(x-h)^2}{a^2} - \frac{(y-k)^2}{b^2} = 1 \Rightarrow (x-2)^2 - \frac{(y-1)^2}{8} = 1.$

47. $x^2 - 2x - y^2 + 2y = 4 \Rightarrow (x^2 - 2x + 1) - (y^2 - 2y + 1) = 4 + 1 - 1 \Rightarrow$
$(x-1)^2 - (y-1)^2 = 4 \Rightarrow \frac{(x-1)^2}{4} - \frac{(y-1)^2}{4} = 1$. The center is $(1, 1)$. The vertices are $(1 - 2, 1), (1 + 2, 1)$ or $(-1, 1), (3, 1)$.

48. $y^2 + 4y - x^2 + 2x = 6 \Rightarrow (y^2 + 4y + 4) - (x^2 - 2x + 1) = 6 + 4 - 1 \Rightarrow$
$(y+2)^2 - (x-1)^2 = 9 \Rightarrow \frac{(y+2)^2}{9} - \frac{(x-1)^2}{9} = 1$. The center is $(1, -2)$. The vertices are $(1, -2 - 3), (1, -2 + 3)$ or $(1, -5), (1, 1)$.

49. $3y^2 + 24y - 2x^2 + 12x + 24 = 0 \Rightarrow 3(y^2 + 8y) - 2(x^2 - 6x) = -24 \Rightarrow$
$3(y^2 + 8y + 16) - 2(x^2 - 6x + 9) = -24 + 48 - 18 \Rightarrow 3(y+4)^2 - 2(x-3)^2 = 6 \Rightarrow$
$\frac{(y+4)^2}{2} - \frac{(x-3)^2}{3} = 1$. The center is $(3, -4)$. The vertices are $(3, -4 - \sqrt{2}), (3, -4 + \sqrt{2})$.

50. $4x^2 + 16x - 9y^2 + 18y = 29 \Rightarrow 4(x^2 + 4x) - 9(y^2 - 2y) = 29 \Rightarrow$
$4(x^2 + 4x + 4) - 9(y^2 - 2y + 1) = 29 + 16 - 9 \Rightarrow 4(x+2)^2 - 9(y-1)^2 = 36 \Rightarrow$
$\frac{(x+2)^2}{9} - \frac{(y-1)^2}{4} = 1$. The center is $(-2, 1)$. The vertices are
$(-2 - 3, 1), (-2 + 3, 1)$ or $(-5, 1), (1, 1)$.

51. $x^2 - 6x - 2y^2 + 7 = 0 \Rightarrow (x^2 - 6x + 9) - 2y^2 = -7 + 9 \Rightarrow (x-3)^2 - 2(y-0)^2 = 2 \Rightarrow$
$\frac{(x-3)^2}{2} - \frac{(y-0)^2}{1} = 1$. The center is $(3, 0)$. The vertices are $(3 - \sqrt{2}, 0), (3 + \sqrt{2}, 0)$.

52. $y^2 + 8y - 3x^2 + 13 = 0 \Rightarrow (y^2 + 8y + 16) - 3x^2 = -13 + 16 \Rightarrow (y + 4)^2 - 3(x - 0)^2 = 3 \Rightarrow$

$\frac{(y + 4)^2}{3} - \frac{(x - 0)^2}{1} = 1$. The center is $(0, -4)$. The vertices are $(0, -4 - \sqrt{3}), (0, -4 + \sqrt{3})$.

53. $4y^2 + 32y - 5x^2 - 10x + 39 = 0 \Rightarrow 4(y^2 + 8y) - 5(x^2 + 2x) = -39 \Rightarrow$

$4(y^2 + 8y + 16) - 5(x^2 + 2x + 1) = -39 + 64 - 5 \Rightarrow 4(y + 4)^2 - 5(x + 1)^2 = 20 \Rightarrow$

$\frac{(y + 4)^2}{5} - \frac{(x + 1)^2}{4} = 1$. The center is $(-1, -4)$. The vertices are $(-1, -4 - \sqrt{5}), (-1, -4 + \sqrt{5})$.

54. $5x^2 + 10x - 7y^2 + 28y = 58 \Rightarrow 5(x^2 + 2x) - 7(y^2 - 4y) = 58 \Rightarrow$

$5(x^2 + 2x + 1) - 7(y^2 - 4y + 4) = 58 + 5 - 28 \Rightarrow 5(x + 1)^2 - 7(y - 2)^2 = 35 \Rightarrow$

$\frac{(x + 1)^2}{7} - \frac{(y - 2)^2}{5} = 1$. The center is $(-1, 2)$. The vertices are $(-1 - \sqrt{7}, 2), (-1 + \sqrt{7}, 2)$.

55. Solve for $y$: $\frac{(y - 1)^2}{11} - \frac{x^2}{5.9} = 1 \Rightarrow \frac{(y - 1)^2}{11} = 1 + \frac{x^2}{5.9} \Rightarrow (y - 1)^2 = 11\left(1 + \frac{x^2}{5.9}\right) \Rightarrow$

$y - 1 = \pm\sqrt{11\left(1 + \frac{x^2}{5.9}\right)} \Rightarrow y = 1 \pm \sqrt{11\left(1 + \frac{x^2}{5.9}\right)}$. Graph $Y_1 = 1 + \sqrt{}(11 \cdot (1 + (X\text{^}2/5.9)))$ and

$Y_2 = 1 - \sqrt{}(11 \cdot (1 + (X\text{^}2/5.9)))$. See Figure 55.

56. Solve for $y$: $\frac{x^2}{5.3} - \frac{y^2}{6.7} = 1 \Rightarrow \frac{y^2}{6.7} = \frac{x^2}{5.3} - 1 \Rightarrow y^2 = 6.7\left(\frac{x^2}{5.3} - 1\right) \Rightarrow y = \pm\sqrt{6.7\left(\frac{x^2}{5.3} - 1\right)}$.

Graph $Y_1 = \sqrt{}(6.7 \cdot (X\text{^}2/5.3 - 1))$ and $Y_2 = -\sqrt{}(6.7 \cdot (X\text{^}2/5.3 - 1))$. See Figure 56.

[−15, 15, 5] by [−10, 10, 5]

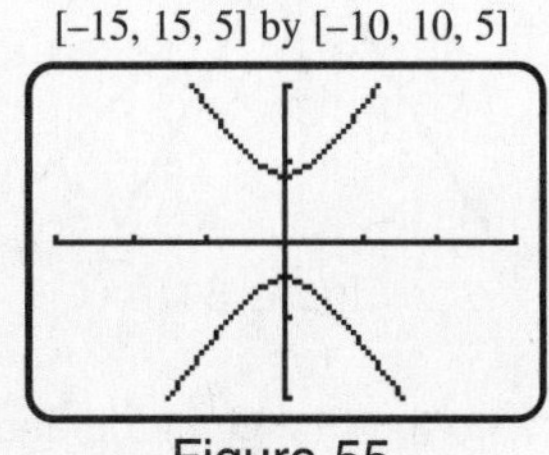

Figure 55

[−10, 10, 1] by [−10, 10, 1]

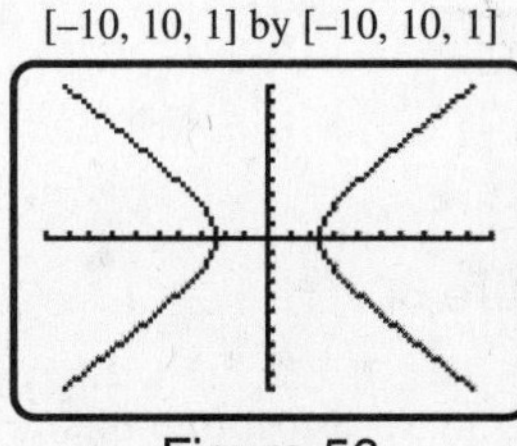

Figure 56

[−9, 9, 1] by [−6, 6, 1]

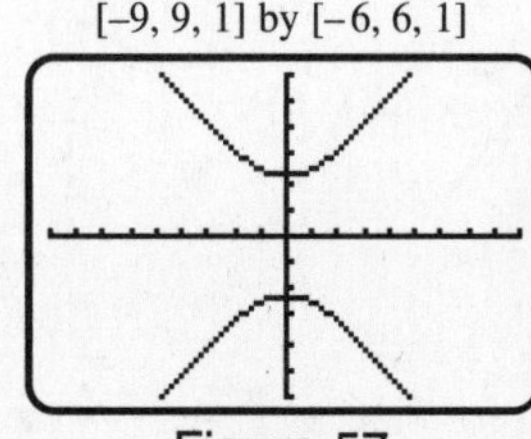

Figure 57

[−8, 8, 1] by [−6, 6, 1]

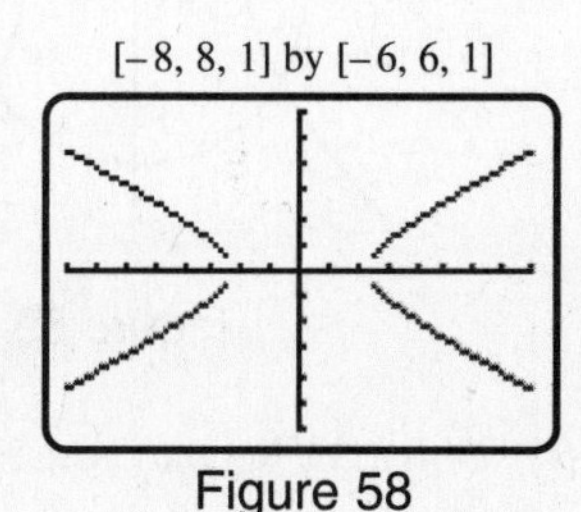

Figure 58

57. Solve for $y$: $3y^2 - 4x^2 = 15 \Rightarrow 3y^2 = 4x^2 + 15 \Rightarrow y^2 = \frac{4x^2 + 15}{3} \Rightarrow y = \pm\sqrt{\frac{4x^2 + 15}{3}}$.

Graph $Y_1 = \sqrt{}((4X\text{^}2 + 15)/3)$ and $Y_2 = -\sqrt{}((4X\text{^}2 + 15)/3)$. See Figure 57.

58. Solve for $y$: $2.1x^2 - 6y^2 = 12 \Rightarrow 6y^2 = 2.1x^2 - 12 \Rightarrow y^2 = \frac{2.1x^2 - 12}{6} \Rightarrow y = \pm\sqrt{\frac{2.1x^2 - 12}{6}}$.

Graph $Y_1 = \sqrt{}((2.1X\text{^}2 - 12)/6)$ and $Y_2 = -\sqrt{}((2.1X\text{^}2 - 12)/6)$. See Figure 58.

59. Add both equations together to eliminate the $y^2$-term:

$$\begin{aligned} x^2 - y^2 &= 4 \\ x^2 + y^2 &= 9 \\ \hline 2x^2 \quad &= 13 \Rightarrow x^2 = \frac{13}{2} \Rightarrow x = \pm\sqrt{\frac{13}{2}} \end{aligned}$$

Substitute $x^2 = \frac{13}{2}$ into the first equation and solve for $y$: $x^2 - y^2 = 4 \Rightarrow \frac{13}{2} - y^2 = 4 \Rightarrow y^2 = \frac{5}{2} \Rightarrow$

$y = \pm\sqrt{\frac{5}{2}}$ There are four solutions to the system:

$\left(\sqrt{\frac{13}{2}}, \sqrt{\frac{5}{2}}\right), \left(-\sqrt{\frac{13}{2}}, \sqrt{\frac{5}{2}}\right), \left(\sqrt{\frac{13}{2}}, -\sqrt{\frac{5}{2}}\right)$, and $\left(-\sqrt{\frac{13}{2}}, -\sqrt{\frac{5}{2}}\right)$. See Figure 59.

60. Add both equations together to eliminate the $y^2$-term:

$$\begin{aligned} x^2 - 4y^2 &= 16 \\ x^2 + 4y^2 &= 16 \\ \hline 2x^2 \quad &= 32 \Rightarrow x^2 = 16 \Rightarrow x = \pm 4 \end{aligned}$$

Substitute $x^2 = 16$ into the first equation and solve for $y$:

$x^2 - 4y^2 = 16 \Rightarrow 16 - 4y^2 = 16 \Rightarrow 4y^2 = 0 \Rightarrow y^2 = 0 \Rightarrow y = 0$. There are two solutions to the system: $(4, 0)$ and $(-4, 0)$. See Figure 60.

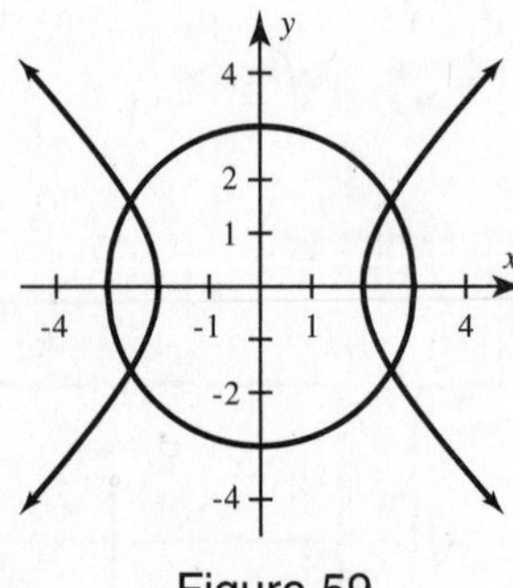

Figure 59

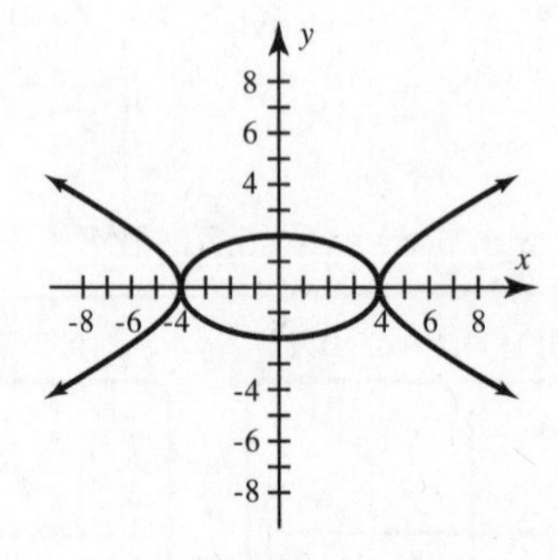

Figure 60

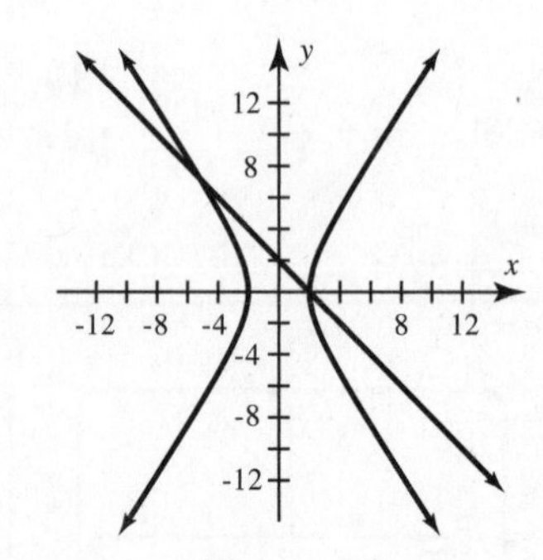

Figure 61

61. Solve the second equation for $y$: $x + y = 2 \Rightarrow y = 2 - x$. Substitute this result into the first equation and solve for $x$: $\frac{x^2}{4} - \frac{y^2}{9} = 1 \Rightarrow \frac{x^2}{4} - \frac{(2 - x)^2}{9} = 1 \Rightarrow 9x^2 - 4(4 - 4x + x^2) = 36 \Rightarrow$

$9x^2 - 16 + 16x - 4x^2 = 36 \Rightarrow 5x^2 + 16x - 52 = 0 \Rightarrow (5x + 26)(x - 2) = 0 \Rightarrow$

$x = -\frac{26}{5} = -5.2$ or $x = 2$. Substitute for $x$ to find $y$: $y = 2 - x \Rightarrow y = 2 - (-5.2) = 7.2$ and

$y = 2 - x \Rightarrow y = 2 - 2 = 0$. There are two solutions to the system: $(2, 0)$ and $(-5.2, 7.2)$. See Figure 61.

62. Solve the second equation for $y$: $x + y = 2 \Rightarrow y = 2 - x$. Substitute this result into the first equation and solve for $x$: $x^2 - y^2 = 4 \Rightarrow x^2 - (2 - x)^2 = 4 \Rightarrow x^2 - 4 + 4x - x^2 = 4 \Rightarrow 4x = 8 \Rightarrow x = 2$.

Substitute for $x$ to find $y$: $y = 2 - x \Rightarrow y = 2 - 2 = 0$. There is one solution to the system: $(2, 0)$. See Figure 62.

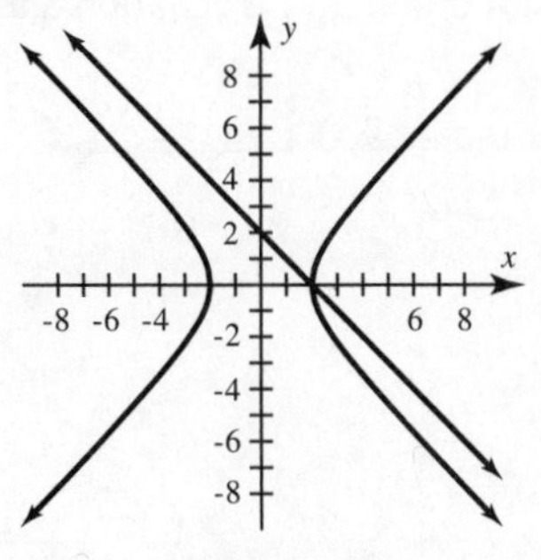

Figure 62

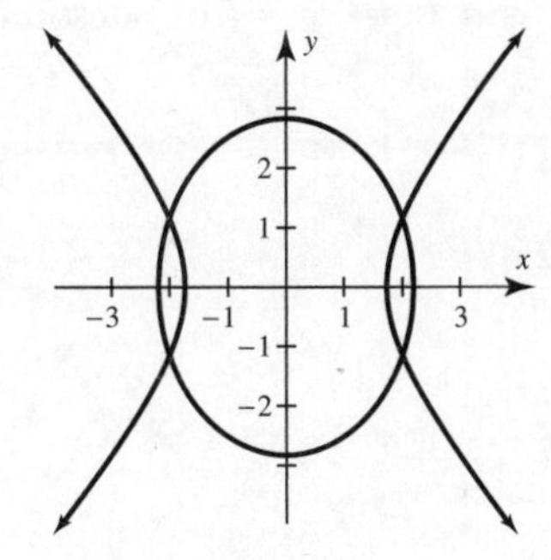

Figure 63

63. Multiply the second equation by 2 and add the equations to eliminate the $y^2$-term:

$$\begin{aligned} 8x^2 - 6y^2 &= 24 \\ 10x^2 + 6y^2 &= 48 \\ \hline 18x^2 \qquad &= 72 \Rightarrow x^2 = 4 \Rightarrow x = \pm 2 \end{aligned}$$

Substitute $x^2 = 4$ into the first equation and solve for $y$:

$$8x^2 - 6y^2 = 24 \Rightarrow 8(4) - 6y^2 = 24 \Rightarrow 6y^2 = 8 \Rightarrow y^2 = \frac{4}{3} \Rightarrow y = \pm\sqrt{\frac{4}{3}} \Rightarrow y = \pm\frac{2}{\sqrt{3}}.$$

There are four solutions to the system: $\left(-2, -\frac{2}{\sqrt{3}}\right), \left(-2, \frac{2}{\sqrt{3}}\right), \left(2, -\frac{2}{\sqrt{3}}\right), \left(2, \frac{2}{\sqrt{3}}\right)$. See Figure 63.

64. Multiply the second equation by 2 and add the equations to eliminate the $x^2$-term:

$$\begin{aligned} 3y^2 - 4x^2 &= 12 \\ 2y^2 + 4x^2 &= 68 \\ \hline 5y^2 \qquad &= 80 \Rightarrow y^2 = 16 \Rightarrow y = \pm 4 \end{aligned}$$

Substitute $y^2 = 16$ into the second equation and solve for $x$:

$$y^2 + 2x^2 = 34 \Rightarrow 16 + 2x^2 = 34 \Rightarrow 2x^2 = 18 \Rightarrow x^2 = 9 \Rightarrow x = \pm 3.$$

There are four solutions to the system: $(-3, -4), (-3, 4), (3, -4), (3, 4)$. See Figure 64.

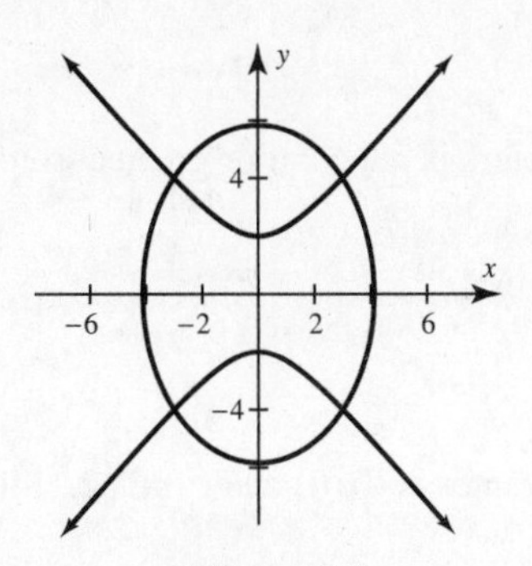

Figure 64

65. Solve the second equation for $y$: $3x - y = 0 \Rightarrow y = 3x$. Substitute this result into the first equation and solve for $x$: $\frac{y^2}{3} - \frac{x^2}{4} = 1 \Rightarrow \frac{(3x)^2}{3} - \frac{x^2}{4} = 1 \Rightarrow \frac{9x^2}{3} - \frac{x^2}{4} = 1 \Rightarrow 3x^2 - \frac{x^2}{4} = 1 \Rightarrow 12x^2 - x^2 = 4 \Rightarrow$ $11x^2 = 4 \Rightarrow x^2 = \frac{4}{11} \Rightarrow x = \pm\frac{2}{\sqrt{11}}$.

Substitute for $x$ to find $y$: When $x = \frac{2}{\sqrt{11}}$, $y = 3x \Rightarrow y = 3\left(\frac{2}{\sqrt{11}}\right) \Rightarrow y = \frac{6}{\sqrt{11}}$.

When $-\frac{2}{\sqrt{11}}$, $y = 3x \Rightarrow y = 3\left(-\frac{2}{\sqrt{11}}\right) \Rightarrow y = -\frac{6}{\sqrt{11}}$.

The two solutions are: $\left(\frac{2}{\sqrt{11}}, \frac{6}{\sqrt{11}}\right), \left(-\frac{2}{\sqrt{11}}, -\frac{6}{\sqrt{11}}\right)$. See Figure 65.

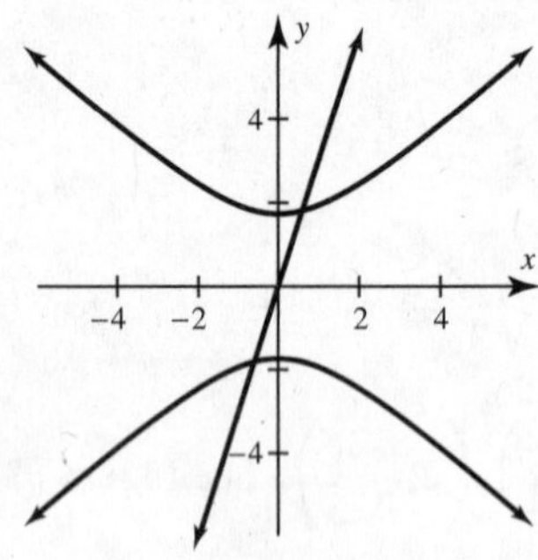

Figure 65

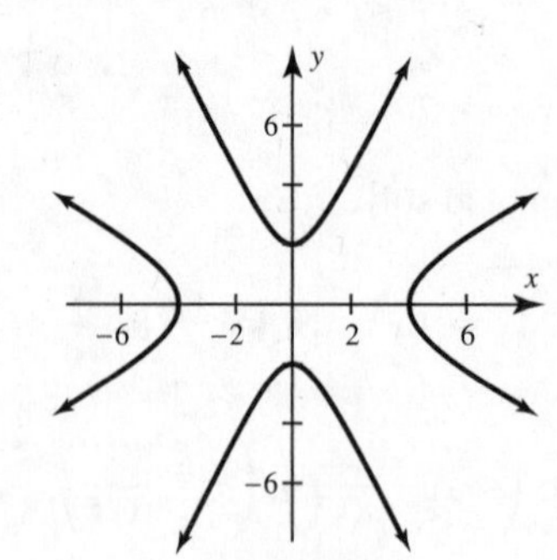

Figure 66

66. Rewrite the second equation, multiply it by 4 and add the equations to eliminate the $y^2$-term:

$$\begin{array}{rl} x^2 - 4y^2 &= 16 \\ -16x^2 + 4y^2 &= 16 \\ \hline -15x^2 \quad\quad &= 32 \end{array} \Rightarrow x^2 = -\frac{32}{15} \Rightarrow$$ There are no real solutions. See Figure 66.

67. (a) $k = 2.82 \times 10^7$ and $D = 42.5 \times 10^6 \Rightarrow \frac{k}{\sqrt{D}} = \frac{2.82 \times 10^7}{\sqrt{42.5 \times 10^6}} \Rightarrow \frac{k}{\sqrt{D}} \approx 4325.68$. Since $V = 2090$ and $V < \frac{k}{\sqrt{D}}$, the trajectory is elliptic.

(b) For $V > \frac{k}{\sqrt{D}}$, $V > 4326$. the speed of Explorer IV should be 4326 meters per second or greater so its trajectory is hyperbolic.

(c) If $D$ is larger, then $\frac{k}{\sqrt{D}}$ is smaller, so smaller values for $V$ satisfy $V > \frac{k}{\sqrt{D}}$.

68. Since $F_1 = (0, 5.2)$ and $F_2 = (0, -5.2)$, the transverse axis is vertical, the center is $(0, 0)$ and $c = 5.2$. Since $V = (0, 4.1)$, $a = 4.1$. So $b^2 = c^2 - a^2 = 5.2^2 - 4.1^2 = 10.23$ and $b \approx 3.2$. Using the standard equation form, we get the equation: $\frac{y^2}{a^2} - \frac{x^2}{b^2} = 1 \Rightarrow \frac{y^2}{16.81} - \frac{x^2}{10.23} = 1$.

## Extended and Discovery Exercises for Section 7.3

1. (a) Find $a$ and $b$ in the equation $\frac{x^2}{a^2} - \frac{y^2}{b^2} = 1$. Because the equations of the asymptotes of a hyperbola with horizontal transverse axis are $y = \pm\frac{b}{a}x$, and the given asymptotes are $y = \pm x$, it follows that $\frac{b}{a} = 1$ or $a = b$. Since the line $y = x$ intersects the $x$-axis at a 45° angle, the triangle shown in the third quadrant is a 45°-45°-90° right triangle and both legs must have length $d$. Then by the Pythagorean theorem, $c^2 = d^2 + d^2 = 2d^2$. That is $c = d\sqrt{2}$. Also, for a hyperbola $c^2 = a^2 + b^2$, and since $a = b$, $c^2 = a^2 + a^2 = 2a^2$. That is $c = a\sqrt{2}$. From these two equations, $a\sqrt{2} = d\sqrt{2}$ and so $a = d$. That is, $a = b = d = 5 \times 10^{-14}$. Thus the equation of the trajectory of $A$, where $x > 0$, is given by

$\frac{x^2}{(5 \times 10^{-14})^2} - \frac{y^2}{(5 \times 10^{-14})^2} = 1$. Solving for $x$ yields

$x^2 - y^2 = (5 \times 10^{-14})^2 \Rightarrow x^2 = y^2 + 2.5 \times 10^{-27} \Rightarrow x = \sqrt{y^2 + 2.5 \times 10^{-27}}$. This equation represents the right half of the hyperbola, as shown in the textbook.

(b) Since $a = 5 \times 10^{-14}$, the distance from the origin to the vertex is $5 \times 10^{-14}$. The distance from $N$ to the origin can be found using the Pythagorean theorem. Let $h$ represent this distance, then $h^2 = d^2 + d^2$. That is, $h^2 = (5 \times 10^{-14})^2 + (5 \times 10^{-14})^2 \Rightarrow h^2 = 5 \times 10^{-27} \Rightarrow h \approx 7 \times 10^{-14}$. The minimum distance between the centers of the alpha partical and the gold nucleus is

$5 \times 10^{-14} + 7 \times 10^{-14} \approx 1.2 \times 10^{-13}$ m.

2. Use the formula $t = \frac{d}{r}$ and the distance formula to set up an equation that shows the difference in the times that it takes the sound to reach each microphone. This equation is $\frac{\sqrt{(x + c)^2 + y^2}}{330} - \frac{\sqrt{(x - c)^2 + y^2}}{330} = t$.

$\sqrt{(x + c)^2 + y^2} - \sqrt{(x - c)^2 + y^2} = 330t$ Multiply each side by 330.

$\sqrt{(x + c)^2 + y^2} = 330t + \sqrt{(x - c)^2 + y^2}$ Add $\sqrt{(x - c)^2 + y^2}$ to each side.

$(x + c)^2 + y^2 = 330^2t^2 + 2 \cdot 330t\sqrt{(x - c)^2 + y^2} + (x - c)^2 + y^2$ Square each side.

$4cx - 330^2t^2 = 2 \cdot 330t\sqrt{(x - c)^2 + y^2}$ Expand the binomials and simplify.

$16c^2x^2 - 8cx \cdot 330^2t^2 + 330^4t^4 = 4 \cdot 330^2t^2[(x - c)^2 + y^2]$ Square each side.

$16c^2x^2 + 330^4t^4 = 4 \cdot 330^2t^2x^2 + 4 \cdot 330^2c^2t^2 + 4 \cdot 330^2t^2y^2$ Expand the right side and simplify.

$16c^2x^2 - 4 \cdot 330^2t^2x^2 - 4 \cdot 330^2t^2y^2 = 4 \cdot 330^2c^2t^2 - 330^4t^4$ Rewrite equation.

$4x^2(4c^2 - 330^2t^2) - 4 \cdot 330^2t^2y^2 = 330^2t^2(4c^2 - 330^2t^2)$ Factor.

$\frac{x^2}{330^2t^2} - \frac{y^2}{4c^2 - 330^2t^2} = \frac{1}{4}$ Divide by $4 \cdot 330^2t^2(4c^2 - 330^2t^2)$.

## Checking Basic Concepts for Section 7.3

1. The center is (0, 0). Since the vertices lie on the $x$-axis and are $(\pm 4, 0)$, $a = 4$. The equation of one asymptote is $y = \frac{3}{4}x$ because the line goes through the points (0, 0) and (8, 6). Thus, $a = 4$ and $b = 3$. Using the standard equation form, we get the equation: $\frac{x^2}{a^2} - \frac{y^2}{b^2} = 1 \Rightarrow \frac{x^2}{16} - \frac{y^2}{9} = 1$.

2. For $\frac{x^2}{9} - \frac{y^2}{16} = 1$, the transverse axis is horizontal, $a^2 = 9$ and $b^2 = 16$. So $c^2 = a^2 + b^2 = 25 \Rightarrow c = 5$. Thus, the foci are $(\pm 5, 0)$, and the asymptotes are the line $y = \pm\frac{4}{3}x$. Finally, the vertices are $(\pm 3, 0)$. See Figure 2.

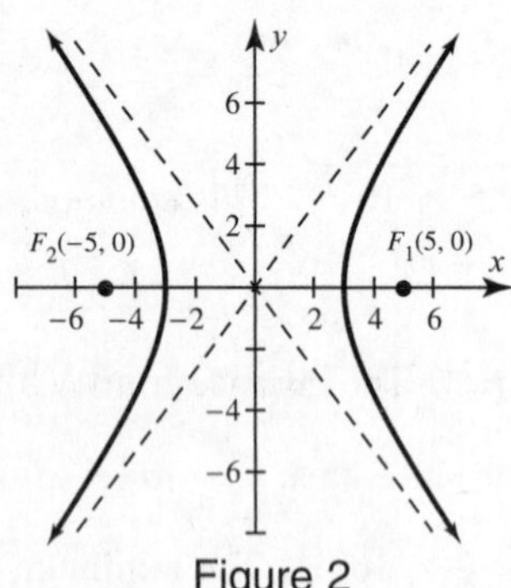

Figure 2

3. $h = 1$ and $k = 3$. Since the horizontal transverse axis has length 6, $2a = 6 \Rightarrow a = 3$. Since the conjugate axis has length 4, $2b = 4 \Rightarrow b = 2$. $c^2 = a^2 + b^2 = 9 + 4 = 13 \Rightarrow c = \sqrt{13}$. Thus the foci are $(1 \pm \sqrt{13}, 3)$. Using the standard equation form, we get the equation:
$\frac{(x - h)^2}{a^2} - \frac{(y - k)^2}{b^2} = 1 \Rightarrow \frac{(x - 1)^2}{9} - \frac{(y - 3)^2}{4} = 1$.

4. $9y^2 - 54y - 16x^2 - 32x = 79 \Rightarrow 9(y^2 - 6y + 9) - 16(x^2 + 2x + 1) = 79 + 81 - 16 \Rightarrow$
$9(y - 3)^2 - 16(x + 1)^2 = 144 \Rightarrow \frac{(y - 3)^2}{16} - \frac{(x + 1)^2}{9} = 1$.
The center is $(-1, 3)$. The vertices are $(-1, 3 - 4), (-1, 3 + 4)$ or $(-1, -1), (-1, 7)$.

## Chapter 7 Review Exercises

1. The equation is $-x^2 = y$. See Figure 1.

2. The equation is $y^2 = 2x$. See Figure 2.

3. The equation is $\frac{x^2}{25} + \frac{y^2}{49} = 1$. See Figure 3.

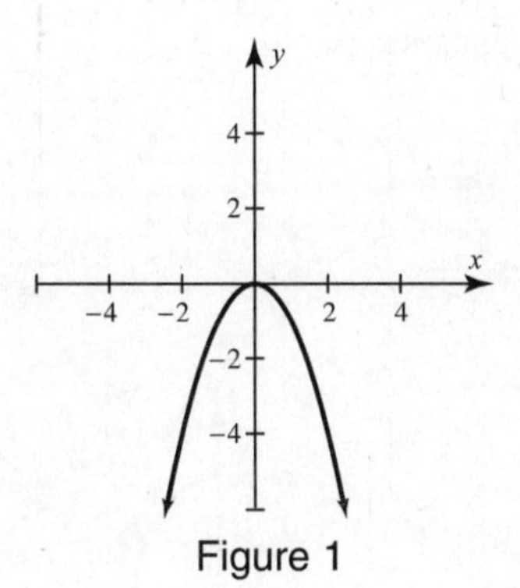

Figure 1

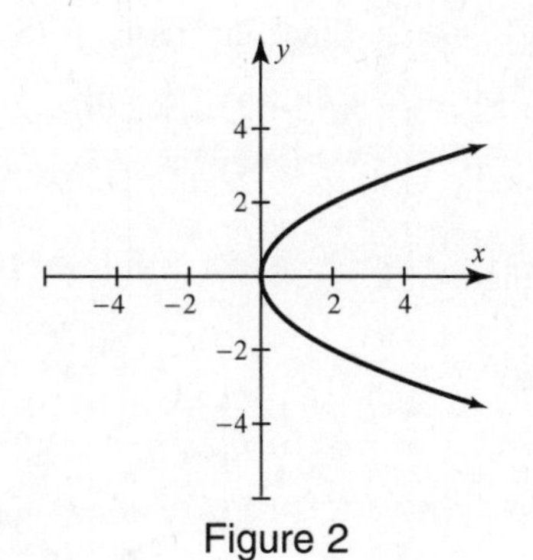

Figure 2

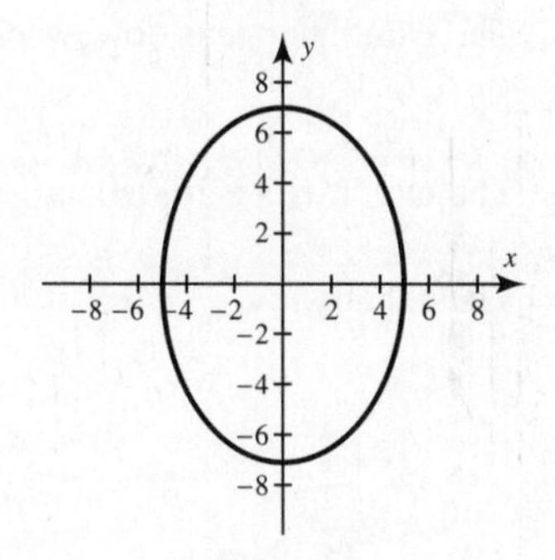

Figure 3

4. The equation is $\dfrac{y^2}{4} + \dfrac{x^2}{2} = 1$. See Figure 4.

5. The equation is $\dfrac{y^2}{4} - \dfrac{x^2}{9} = 1$. See Figure 5.

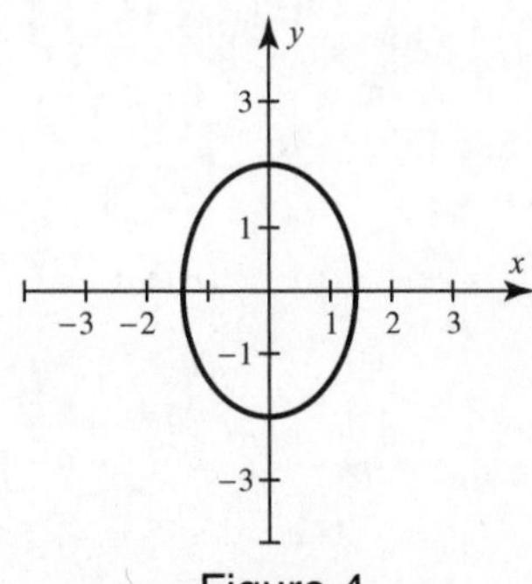

Figure 4

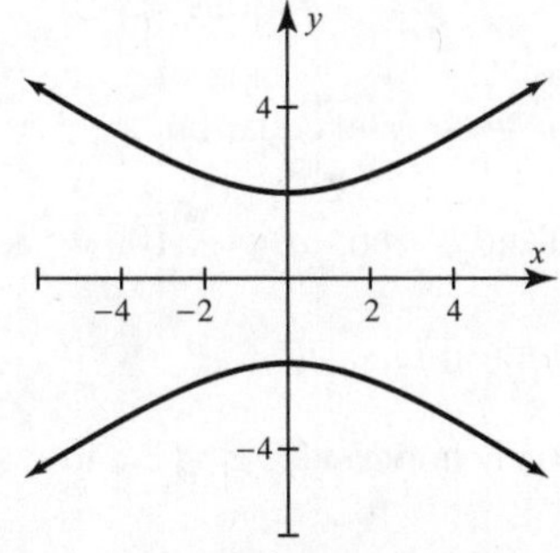

Figure 5

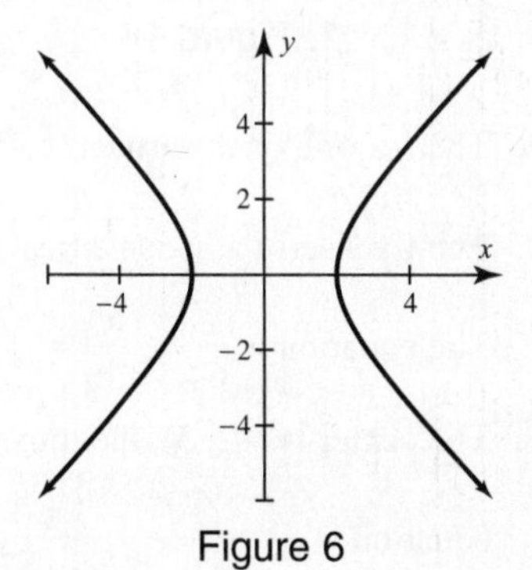

Figure 6

6. The equation is $x^2 - y^2 = 4$. See Figure 6.
7. A parabola opening upwards; d
8. A parabola opening to the left; f
9. A circle; a
10. An ellipse with vertical major axis; c
11. A hyperbola with horizontal transverse axis; e
12. A hyperbola with vertical transverse axis; b
13. The parabola opens to the right and $p = 2$. $y^2 = 4px$, so $y^2 = 8x$. See Figure 13.

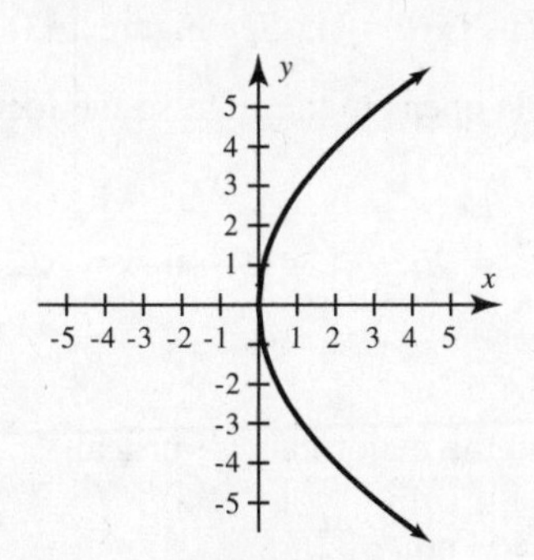

Figure 13

14. The parabola opens downward, with $p = -2$. Since the vertex is (5, 2) the equation is $(x - 5)^2 = 4(-2)(y - 2)$ or $(x - 5)^2 = -8(y - 2)$. See Figure 14.

15. The major axis is horizontal, $a = 5$ and $c = 4$; $b = \sqrt{a^2 - c^2} = \sqrt{25 - 16} = 3$.

    The equation is $\dfrac{x^2}{25} + \dfrac{y^2}{9} = 1$. See Figure 15.

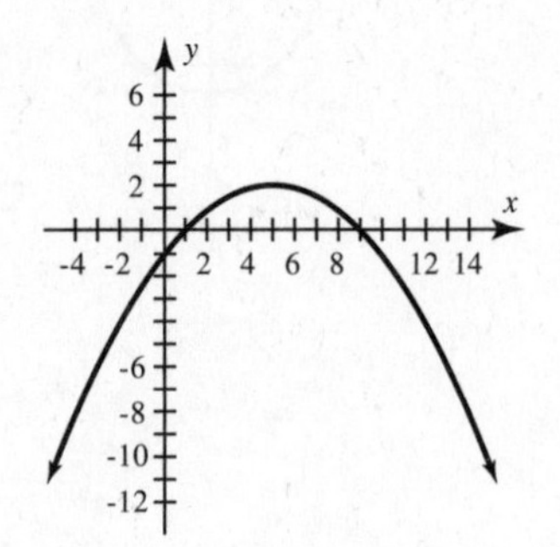

Figure 14

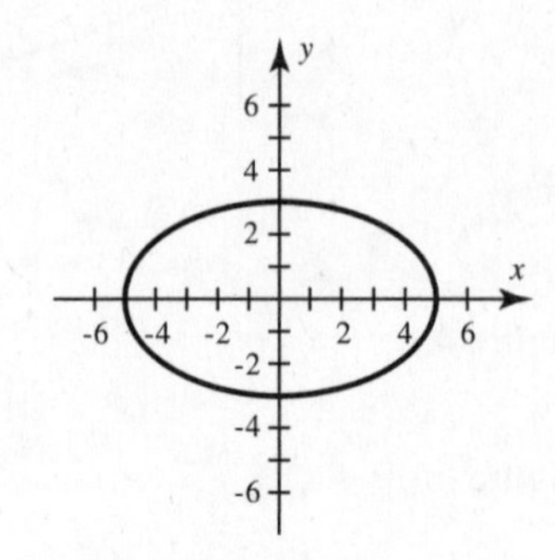

Figure 15

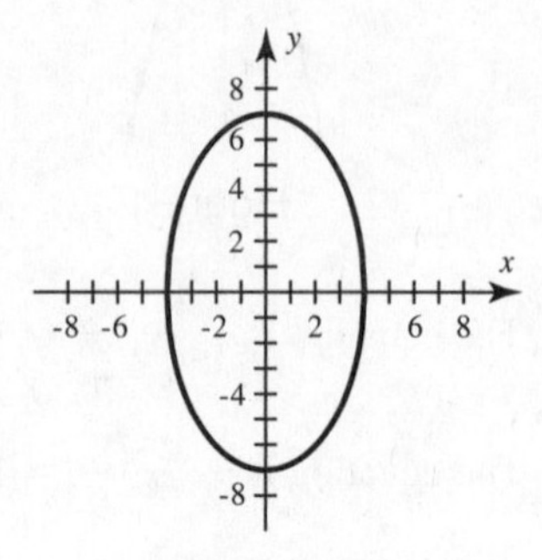

Figure 16

16. The major axis is vertical, $a = 7$ and $b = 4$. The equation is $\dfrac{x^2}{16} + \dfrac{y^2}{49} = 1$. See Figure 16.

17. The transverse axis is vertical, $c = 10$ and $b = 6$; $a = \sqrt{100 - 36} = 8$.

    The equation is $\dfrac{y^2}{64} - \dfrac{x^2}{36} = 1$. See Figure 17.

18. The center is (–2, 3), the transverse axis is horizontal, $a = 3$ and $c = 4$; $b^2 = c^2 - a^2 = 16 - 9 = 7$. The equation is $\dfrac{(x + 2)^2}{9} - \dfrac{(y - 3)^2}{7} = 1$. See Figure 18.

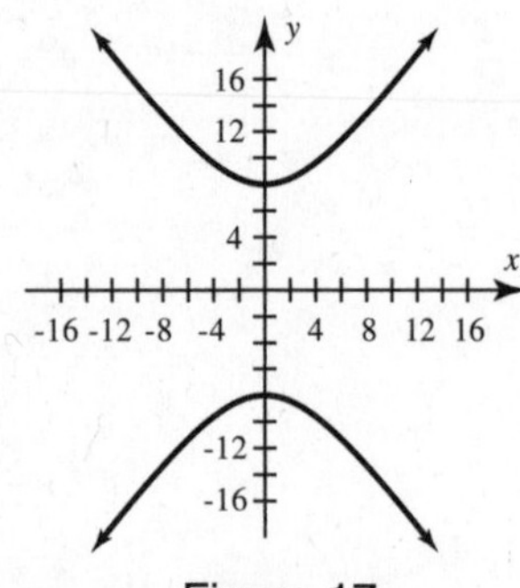

Figure 17

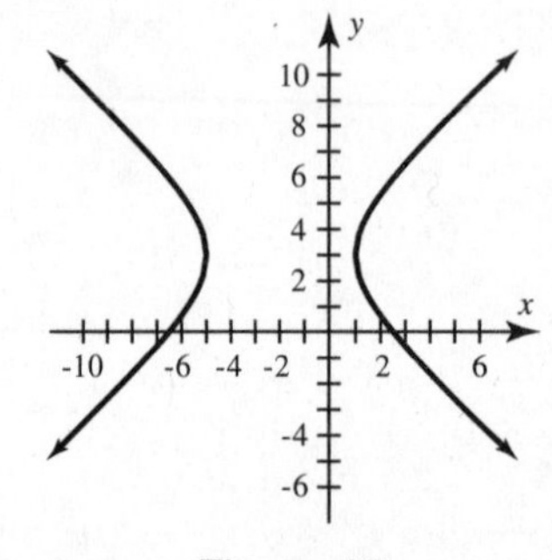

Figure 18

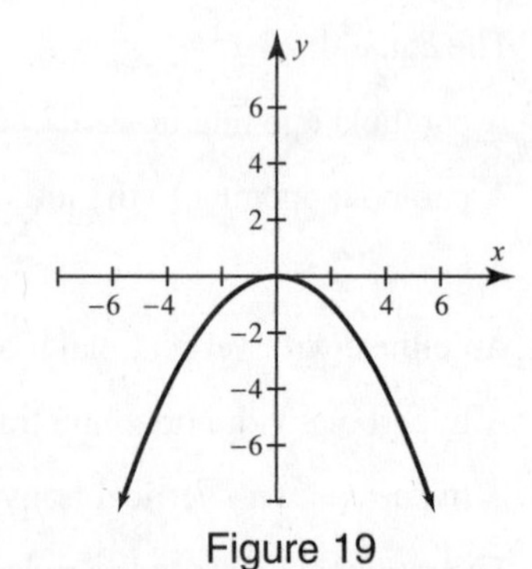

Figure 19

19. $x^2 = 4py \Rightarrow 4p = -4$, so $p = -1$. The vertex is at the origin and the focus is (0, –1). See Figure 19.

20. $y^2 = 4px \Rightarrow 4p = 8$, so $p = 2$. The vertex is at the origin and the parabola opens to the right so the focus is (2, 0). See Figure 20.

21. The major axis is horizontal, the center is at the origin, $a = 5$ and $b = 2$. $c^2 = 25 - 4 = 21$, so $c = \sqrt{21}$; the foci are $(\pm\sqrt{21}, 0)$. See Figure 21.

22. The equation can be written as $\dfrac{x^2}{36} + \dfrac{y^2}{49} = 1$. The center is at the origin and the major axis is vertical.

    $c^2 = a^2 - b^2 = 49 - 36 = 13$, so $c = \sqrt{13}$. The foci are $(0, \pm\sqrt{13})$. See Figure 22.

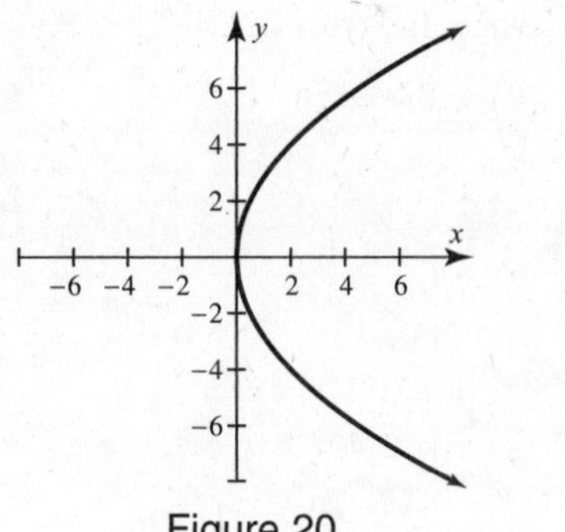


Figure 20

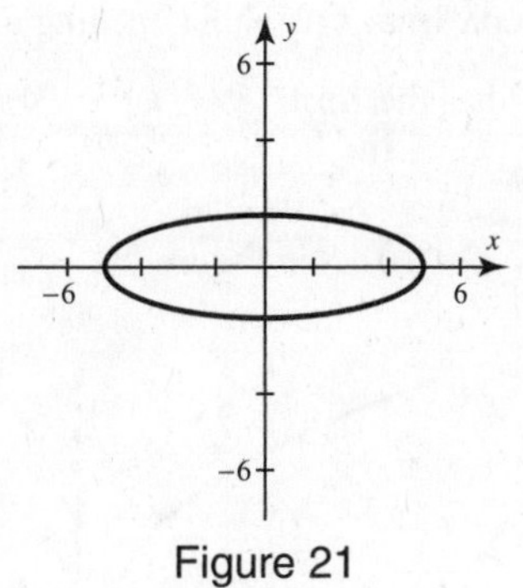


Figure 21

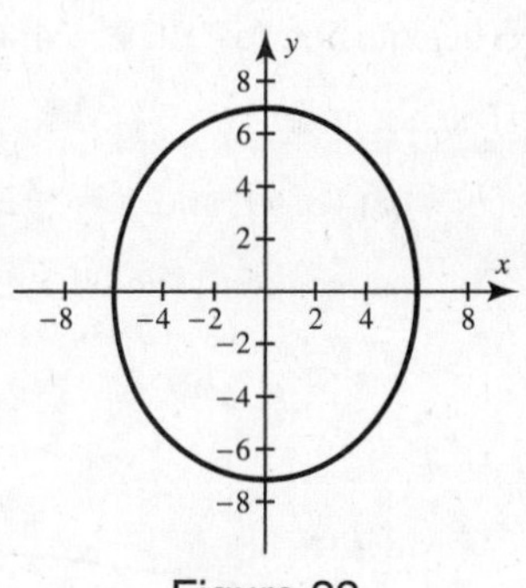


Figure 22

23. The center is the origin and the transverse axis is horizontal. $c^2 = a^2 + b^2 = 16 + 9 = 25$, so $c = 5$. The foci are $(\pm 5, 0)$. See Figure 23.

24. The center is the origin and the transverse axis is vertical. $c^2 = a^2 + b^2 = 4 + 1 = 5$, so $c = \sqrt{5}$. The foci are $(0, \pm\sqrt{5})$. See Figure 24.

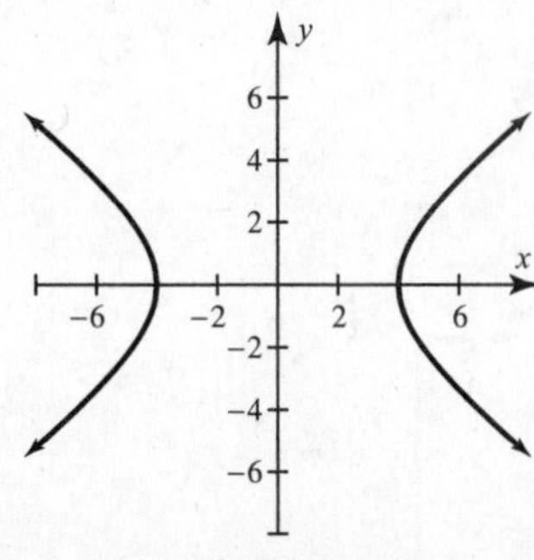


Figure 23

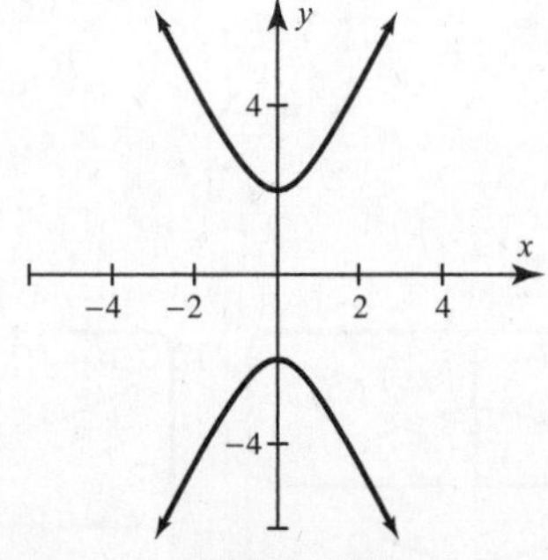


Figure 24

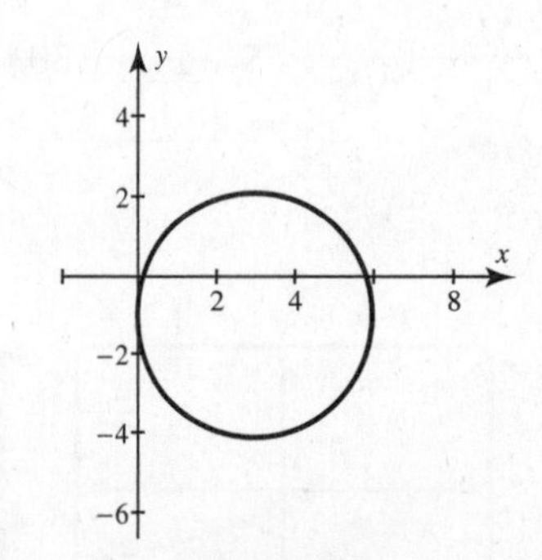


Figure 25

25. The equation represents a circle of radius 3, centered at (3, –1). If we think of the circle as an ellipse, both foci are at (3, –1). See Figure 25.

26. The equation $\dfrac{(y-2)^2}{4} + \dfrac{(x+1)^2}{16} = 1$ represents an ellipse with horizontal major axis and center (–1, 2). See Figure 26.

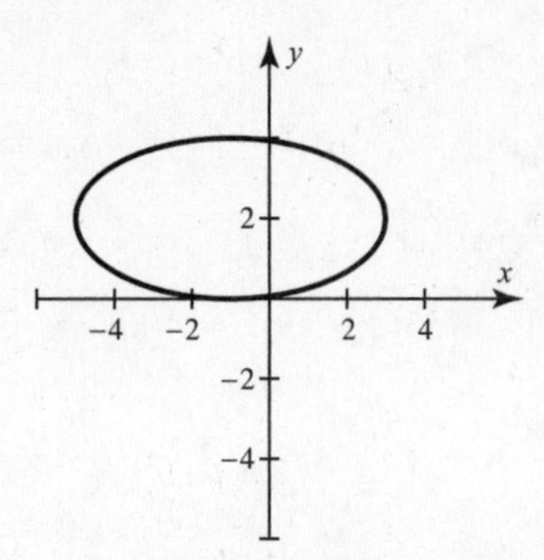


Figure 26

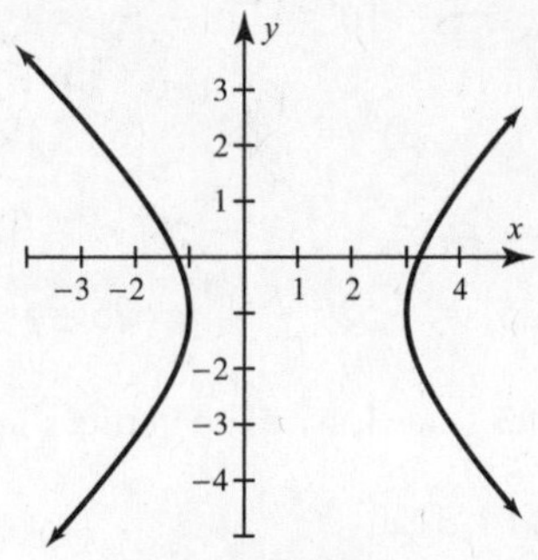


Figure 27

27. The equation $\dfrac{(x-1)^2}{4} - \dfrac{(y+1)^2}{4} = 1$ represents a hyperbola with horizontal transverse axis and center (1, –1). See Figure 27.

28. The equation $(x + 2) = 4(y - 1)^2$ represents a parabola opening to the right with vertex (–2, 1). See Figure 28.
29. The equation $(y - 4)^2 = -8(x - 8)$ has the form $(y - k)^2 = 4p(x - h)$ with vertex $(h, k)$ at $(8, 4)$, and $p = -2$.

    The focus is (6, 4) and the directrix is $x = 10$. See Figure 29.

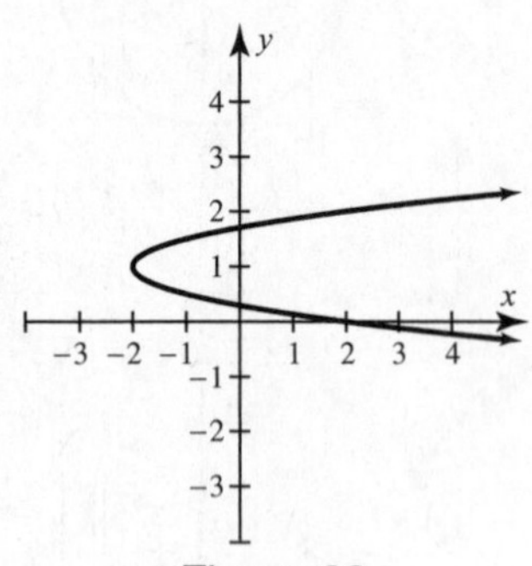

Figure 28

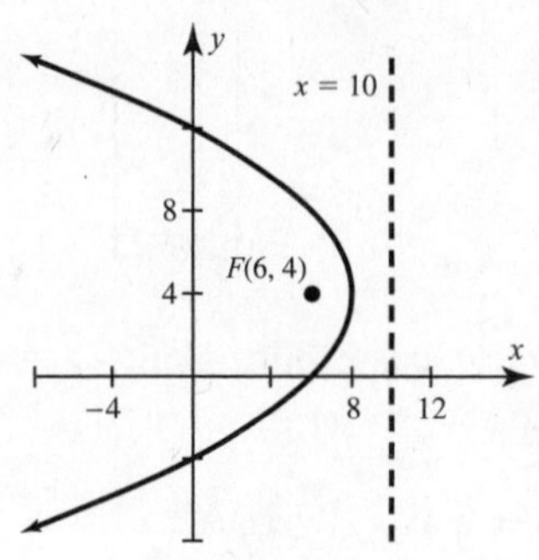

Figure 29

30. $y = \pm\sqrt{\dfrac{3}{4}x}$; See Figure 30.
31. $y = \pm\sqrt{\dfrac{1}{8.2}(60 - 7.1x^2)}$; See Figure 31.

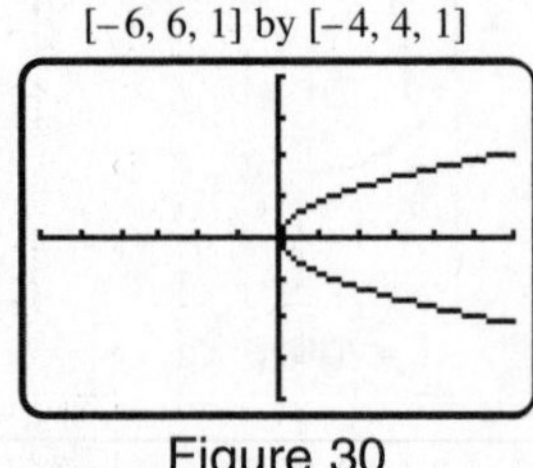

Figure 30

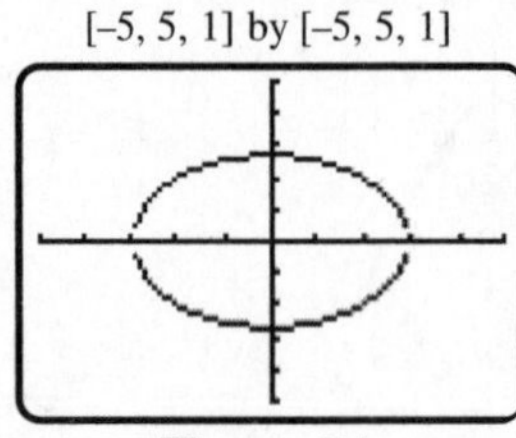

Figure 31

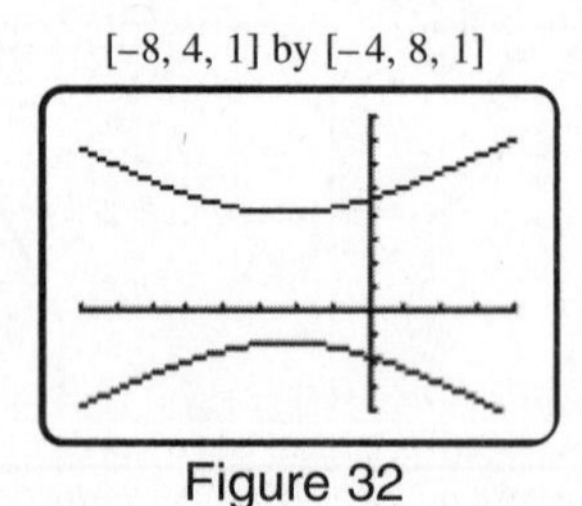

Figure 32

32. $y = 1.4 \pm \sqrt{7\left(1 + \dfrac{(x + 2.3)^2}{11}\right)}$; See Figure 32.
33. $-2x = y^2 + 8x + 14 \Rightarrow y^2 = -10x - 14 \Rightarrow (y - 0)^2 = -10\left(x + \dfrac{7}{5}\right)$
34. $2y^2 - 12y + 16 = x \Rightarrow 2y^2 - 12y = x - 16 \Rightarrow y^2 - 6y = \dfrac{1}{2}(x - 16) \Rightarrow$

    $y^2 - 6y + 9 = \dfrac{1}{2}(x - 16) + 9 \Rightarrow (y - 3)^2 = \dfrac{1}{2}(x - 16 + 18) \Rightarrow (y - 3)^2 = \dfrac{1}{2}(x + 2)$
35. $4x^2 + 8x + 25y^2 - 250y = -529 \Rightarrow 4(x^2 + 2x) + 25(y^2 - 10y) = -529 \Rightarrow$

    $4(x^2 + 2x + 1) + 25(y^2 - 10y + 25) = -529 + 4 + 625 \Rightarrow 4(x + 1)^2 + 25(y - 5)^2 = 100 \Rightarrow$

    $\dfrac{(x + 1)^2}{25} + \dfrac{(y - 5)^2}{4} = 1$; The center is $(-1, 5)$. The vertices are

    $(-1 - 5, 5), (-1 + 5, 5)$ or $(-6, 5), (4, 5)$.
36. $5x^2 + 20x + 2y^2 - 8y = -18 \Rightarrow 5(x^2 + 4x) + 2(y^2 - 4y) = -18 \Rightarrow$

    $5(x^2 + 4x + 4) + 2(y^2 - 4y + 4) = -18 + 20 + 8 \Rightarrow 5(x + 2)^2 + 2(y - 2)^2 = 10 \Rightarrow$

    $\dfrac{(x + 2)^2}{2} + \dfrac{(y - 2)^2}{5} = 1$; The center is $(-2, 2)$. The vertices are $(-2, 2 - \sqrt{5}), (-2, 2 + \sqrt{5})$.

37. $x^2 + 4x - 4y^2 + 24y = 36 \Rightarrow (x^2 + 4x + 4) - 4(y^2 - 6y + 9) = 36 + 4 - 36 \Rightarrow$

$(x + 2)^2 - 4(y - 3)^2 = 4 \Rightarrow \dfrac{(x + 2)^2}{4} - \dfrac{(y - 3)^2}{1} = 1.$

The center is $(-2, 3)$. The vertices are $(-2 - 2, 3), (-2 + 2, 3)$ or $(-4, 3), (0, 3)$.

38. $4y^2 + 8y - 3x^2 + 6x = 11 \Rightarrow 4(y^2 + 2y + 1) - 3(x^2 - 2x + 1) = 11 + 4 - 3 \Rightarrow$

$4(y + 1)^2 - 3(x - 1)^2 = 12 \Rightarrow \dfrac{(y + 1)^2}{3} - \dfrac{(x - 1)^2}{4} = 1.$

The center is $(1, -1)$. The vertices are $(1, -1 - \sqrt{3}\,), (1, -1 + \sqrt{3}\,)$.

39. Clear fractions: $x^2 + y^2 = 4 \Rightarrow y^2 = 4 - x^2$. Substituting in $x^2 + 4y^2 = 8$ gives $x^2 + 4(4 - x^2) = 8$ or $3x^2 = 8$, so $x = \pm\sqrt{\dfrac{8}{3}}$. Substituting in $x^2 + y^2 = 4$ we find $y^2 = 4 - \dfrac{8}{3} = \dfrac{4}{3}$, so $y = \pm\sqrt{\dfrac{4}{3}}$. There are four solutions: $\left(\pm\sqrt{\dfrac{8}{3}}, \pm\sqrt{\dfrac{4}{3}}\right)$.

40. $x + y = 2 \Rightarrow y = 2 - x$, so $x^2 - (2 - x)^2 = 1$. Then, $x^2 - 4 + 4x - x^2 = 1 \Rightarrow 4x = 5$ or $x = \dfrac{5}{4}$.

Then, $y = 2 - x = 2 - \dfrac{5}{4} = \dfrac{3}{4}$. The solution is $\left(\dfrac{5}{4}, \dfrac{3}{4}\right)$.

41. The system is $\dfrac{x^2}{9} + \dfrac{y^2}{4} \le 1$ and $x + y \le 3$. See Figure 41.

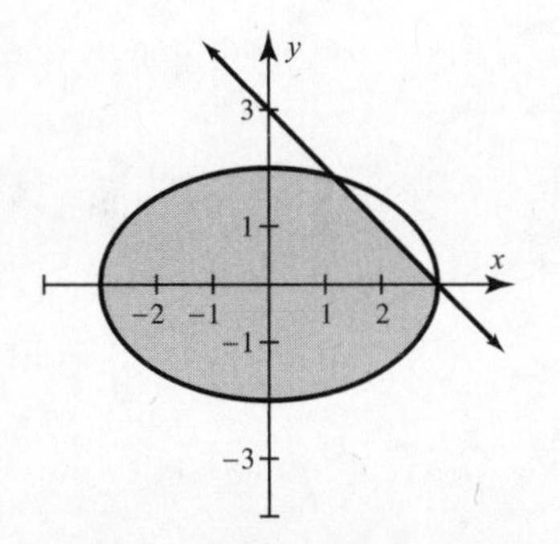

Figure 41

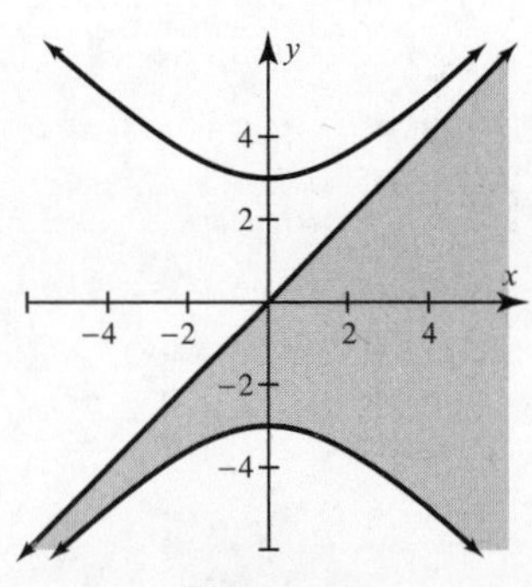

Figure 42

42. The system is $y^2 - x^2 \le 9$ and $y - x \le 0$. See Figure 42.

43. (a) $c = \sqrt{500^2 - 70^2} \approx 495.08$, and $a = 500$. The minimum distance is $a - c \approx 4.92$ million miles. The maximum distance is $a + c \approx 995.08$ million miles.

(b) $2\pi\sqrt{\dfrac{500^2 + 70^2}{2}} \approx 2243$ million miles or 2.243 billion miles.

44. Substituting the point (10, 7) in $x^2 = 4py$ we find $100 = 28p$ or $p = \dfrac{100}{28} \approx 3.57$. The bulb should be 3.57 inches from the vertex.

45. The equation of the ellipse is $\dfrac{x^2}{40^2} + \dfrac{y^2}{30^2} = 1$. Solving for $y$ gives $y = 30\sqrt{1 - \dfrac{x^2}{40^2}}$. When $x = 10$,

$y = 30\sqrt{1 - \left(\dfrac{10}{40}\right)^2} \approx 29.05$ feet.

## Extended and Discovery Exercises for Chapter 7

1. Neptune: $(0.009)(30.10) \approx 0.271$; Pluto: $(0.249)(39.44) \approx 9.82$

2. Neptune: $(0.271, 0)$; Pluto: $(9.82, 0)$

3. For the nearly circular orbit of Neptune, $a$ and $b$ are both approximately 30.10, so the equation is $\dfrac{(x-0.271)^2}{30.10^2}+\dfrac{y^2}{30.10^2}=1$. For Pluto, $b^2=a^2-c^2=39.44^2-9.82^2\approx 1459.08$, so $b\approx 38.20$. The equation is $\dfrac{(x-9.82)^2}{39.44^2}+\dfrac{y^2}{38.20^2}=1$.

4. The graph is shown in Figure 4.

[−50, 50, 10] by [−50, 50, 10]

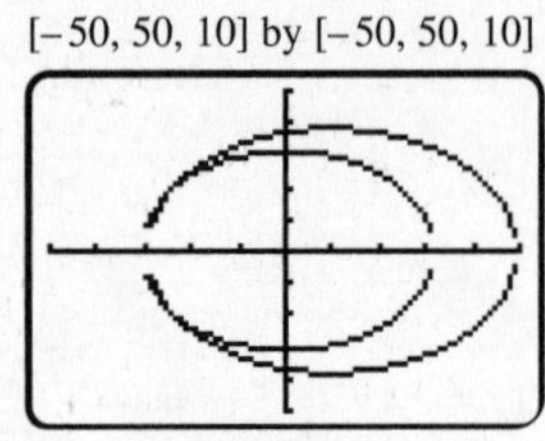

Figure 4

5. No. Because Pluto's orbit is so eccentric, there is a period of time when Pluto is not the farthest from the sun. However, its average distance $a$ from the sun is greater than any of the other planets.

# Chapter 8: Further Topics in Algebra

## 8.1: Sequences

1. $a_1 = 2(1) + 1 = 3$; $a_2 = 2(2) + 1 = 5$; $a_3 = 2(3) + 1 = 7$; $a_4 = 2(4) + 1 = 9$.

   The first four terms are 3, 5, 7, and 9.

2. $a_1 = 3(1 - 1) + 5 = 5$; $a_2 = 3(2 - 1) + 5 = 8$; $a_3 = 3(3 - 1) + 5 = 11$; $a_4 = 3(4 - 1) + 5 = 14$.

   The first four terms are 5, 8, 11, and 14.

3. $a_1 = 4(-2)^{1-1} = 4$; $a_2 = 4(-2)^{2-1} = -8$; $a_3 = 4(-2)^{3-1} = 16$; $a_4 = 4(-2)^{4-1} = -32$.

   The first four terms are 4, –8, 16, and –32.

4. $a_1 = 2(3)^1 = 6$; $a_2 = 2(3)^2 = 18$; $a_3 = 2(3)^3 = 54$; $a_4 = 2(3)^4 = 162$.

   The first four terms are 6, 18, 54, and 162.

5. $a_1 = \frac{1}{1^2 + 1} = \frac{1}{2}$; $a_2 = \frac{2}{2^2 + 1} = \frac{2}{5}$; $a_3 = \frac{3}{3^2 + 1} = \frac{3}{10}$; $a_4 = \frac{4}{4^2 + 1} = \frac{4}{17}$.

   The first four terms are $\frac{1}{2}, \frac{2}{5}, \frac{3}{10}$, and $\frac{4}{17}$.

6. $a_1 = 5 - \frac{1}{1^2} = 4$; $a_2 = 5 - \frac{1}{2^2} = \frac{19}{4}$; $a_3 = 5 - \frac{1}{3^2} = \frac{44}{9}$; $a_4 = 5 - \frac{1}{4^2} = \frac{79}{16}$.

   The first four terms are $4, \frac{19}{4}, \frac{44}{9}$, and $\frac{79}{16}$.

7. $a_1 = (-1)^1\left(\frac{1}{2}\right)^1 = -\frac{1}{2}$; $a_2 = (-1)^2\left(\frac{1}{2}\right)^2 = \frac{1}{4}$; $a_3 = (-1)^3\left(\frac{1}{2}\right)^3 = -\frac{1}{8}$; $a_4 = (-1)^4\left(\frac{1}{2}\right)^4 = \frac{1}{16}$.

   The first four terms are $-\frac{1}{2}, \frac{1}{4}, -\frac{1}{8}$, and $\frac{1}{16}$.

8. $a_1 = (-1)^1\left(\frac{1}{1}\right) = -1$; $a_2 = (-1)^2\left(\frac{1}{2}\right) = \frac{1}{2}$; $a_3 = (-1)^3\left(\frac{1}{3}\right) = -\frac{1}{3}$; $a_4 = (-1)^4\left(\frac{1}{4}\right) = \frac{1}{4}$.

   The first four terms are $-1, \frac{1}{2}, -\frac{1}{3}$, and $\frac{1}{4}$.

9. $a_1 = (-1)^0\left(\frac{2}{1 + 2}\right) = \frac{2}{3}$; $a_2 = (-1)^1\left(\frac{4}{1 + 4}\right) = -\frac{4}{5}$; $a_3 = (-1)^2\left(\frac{8}{1 + 8}\right) = \frac{8}{9}$;

   $a_4 = (-1)^3\left(\frac{16}{1 + 16}\right) = -\frac{16}{17}$. The first four terms are $\frac{2}{3}, -\frac{4}{5}, \frac{8}{9}$, and $-\frac{16}{17}$.

10. $a_1 = (-1)^0\left(\frac{1}{3}\right) = \frac{1}{3}$; $a_2 = (-1)^1\left(\frac{1}{9}\right) = -\frac{1}{9}$; $a_3 = (-1)^2\left(\frac{1}{27}\right) = \frac{1}{27}$; $a_4 = (-1)^3\left(\frac{1}{81}\right) = -\frac{1}{81}$.

    The first four terms are $\frac{1}{3}, -\frac{1}{9}, \frac{1}{27}$, and $-\frac{1}{81}$.

11. $a_1 = 2 + 1^2 = 3$; $a_2 = 4 + 2^2 = 8$; $a_3 = 8 + 3^2 = 17$; $a_4 = 16 + 4^2 = 32$.

    The first four terms are 3, 8, 17, and 32.

12. $a_1 = \frac{1}{1} + \frac{1}{3} = \frac{4}{3}$; $a_2 = \frac{1}{2} + \frac{1}{6} = \frac{2}{3}$; $a_3 = \frac{1}{3} + \frac{1}{9} = \frac{4}{9}$; $a_4 = \frac{1}{4} + \frac{1}{12} = \frac{1}{3}$.

    The first four terms are $\frac{4}{3}, \frac{2}{3}, \frac{4}{9}$, and $\frac{1}{3}$.

13. The points (1, 2), (2, 4), (3, 3), (4, 5), (5, 3), (6, 6), (7, 4) lie on the graph. Therefore, the terms of the sequence are 2, 4, 3, 5, 3, 6, 4.

14. The points (1, 1), (2, 5), (3, 3), (4, 2), (5, 5) are points on the graph. Therefore, the terms of the sequence are 1, 5, 3, 2, 5.

15. (a) $a_1 = 1$; $a_2 = 2a_1 = 2(1) = 2$; $a_3 = 2a_2 = 2(2) = 4$; $a_4 = 2a_3 = 2(4) = 8$.

    The first four terms are 1, 2, 4, and 8.

    (b) The graph of the points (1, 1), (2, 2), (3, 4), and (4, 8) is shown in Figure 15.

16. (a) $a_1 = -4$; $a_2 = a_1 + 5 = -4 + 5 = 1$; $a_3 = a_2 + 5 = 1 + 5 = 6$; $a_4 = a_3 + 5 = 6 + 5 = 11$.

    The first four terms are $-4$, 1, 6, and 11.

    (b) The graph of the points (1, –4), (2, 1), (3, 6), and (4, 1) is shown in Figure 16.

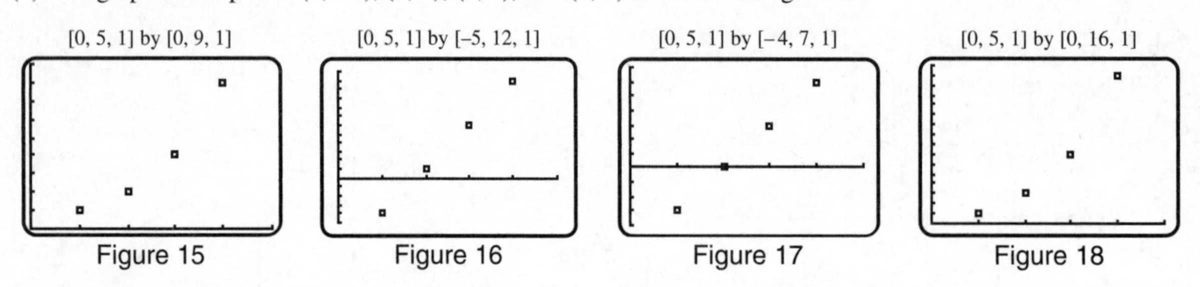


Figure 15 Figure 16 Figure 17 Figure 18

17. (a) $a_1 = -3$; $a_2 = a_1 + 3 = -3 + 3 = 0$; $a_3 = a_2 + 3 = 0 + 3 = 3$; $a_4 = a_3 + 3 = 3 + 3 = 6$.

    The first four terms are $-3$, 0, 3, and 6.

    (b) See Figure 17.

18. (a) $a_1 = 1$; $a_2 = 2a_1 + 1 = 2(1) + 1 = 3$; $a_3 = 2a_2 + 1 = 2(3) + 1 = 7$;

    $a_4 = 2a_3 + 1 = 2(7) + 1 = 15$. The first four terms are 1, 3, 7, and 15.

    (b) See Figure 18.

19. (a) $a_1 = 2$; $a_2 = 3a_1 - 1 = 3(2) - 1 = 5$; $a_3 = 3a_2 - 1 = 3(5) - 1 = 14$;

    $a_4 = 3a_3 - 1 = 3(14) - 1 = 41$. The first four terms are 2, 5, 14, and 41.

    (b) See Figure 19.

20. (a) $a_1 = 16$; $a_2 = \frac{1}{2}(a_1) = \frac{1}{2}(16) = 8$; $a_3 = \frac{1}{2}(a_2) = \frac{1}{2}(8) = 4$; $a_4 = \frac{1}{2}(a_3) = \frac{1}{2}(4) = 2$.

    The first four terms are 16, 8, 4, and 2.

    (b) See Figure 20.

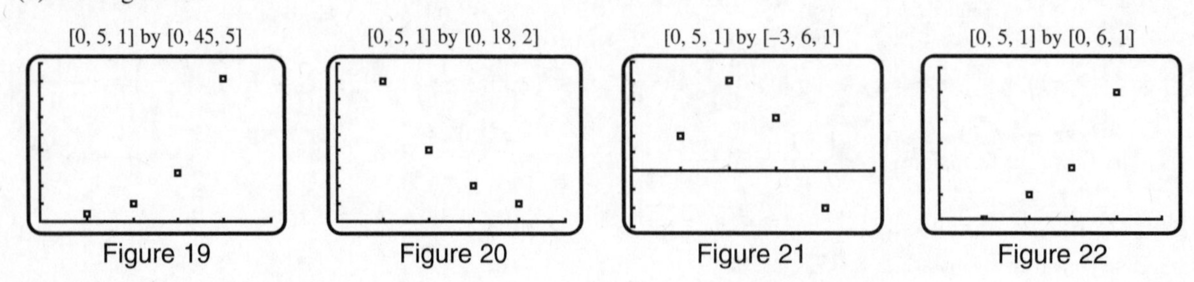


Figure 19 Figure 20 Figure 21 Figure 22

21. (a) $a_1 = 2$; $a_2 = 5$; $a_3 = a_2 - a_1 = 5 - 2 = 3$; $a_4 = a_3 - a_2 = 3 - 5 = -2$.

    The first four terms are 2, 5, 3, and –2.

    (b) The graph of the points (1, 2), (2, 5), (3, 3), and (4, –2) is shown in Figure 21.

22. (a) $a_1 = 0$; $a_2 = 1$; $a_3 = 2a_2 + a_1 = 2(1) + 0 = 2$; $a_4 = 2a_3 + a_2 = 2(2) + 1 = 5$.

The first four terms are 0, 1, 2, and 5.

(b) The graph of the points (1, 0), (2, 1), (3, 2), and (4, 5) is shown in Figure 22.

23. (a) $a_1 = 2$; $a_2 = a_1^2 = 2^2 = 4$; $a_3 = a_2^2 = 4^2 = 16$; $a_4 = a_3^2 = 16^2 = 256$.

The first four terms are 2, 4, 16, and 256.

(b) The graph of the points (1, 2), (2, 4), (3, 16), and (4, 256) is shown in Figure 23.

24. (a) $a_1 = 0$; $a_2 = \frac{1}{2}a_1^3 + 1 = \frac{1}{2}(0)^3 + 1 = 1$; $a_3 = \frac{1}{2}a_2^3 + 1 = \frac{1}{2}(1)^3 + 1 = \frac{3}{2}$;

$a_4 = \frac{1}{2}a_3^3 + 1 = \frac{1}{2}\left(\frac{3}{2}\right)^3 + 1 = \frac{43}{16}$. The first four terms are 0, 1, $\frac{3}{2}$, and $\frac{43}{16}$.

(b) The graph of the points (1, 0), (2, 1), $\left(3, \frac{3}{2}\right)$, and $\left(4, \frac{43}{16}\right)$ is shown in Figure 24.

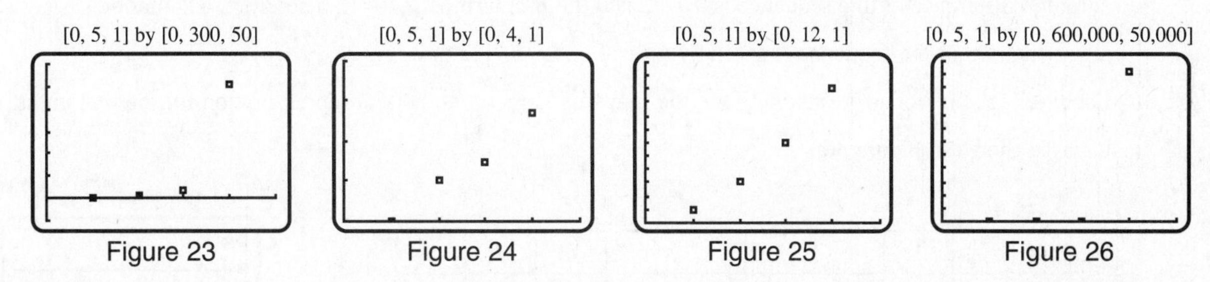

Figure 23 Figure 24 Figure 25 Figure 26

25. (a) $a_1 = 1$; $a_2 = a_1 + 2 = 1 + 2 = 3$; $a_3 = a_2 + 3 = 3 + 3 = 6$; $a_4 = a_3 + 4 = 6 + 4 = 10$.

The first four terms are 1, 3, 6, and 10.

(b) The graph of the points (1, 1), (2, 3), (3, 6), and (4, 10) is shown in Figure 25.

26. (a) $a_1 = 2$; $a_2 = 3(2^2) = 12$; $a_3 = 3(12^2) = 432$; $a_4 = 3(432^2) = 559{,}872$.

The first four terms are 2, 12, 432, and 559,872.

(b) The graph of the points (1, 2), (2, 12), (3, 432), and (4, 559,872) is shown in Figure 26.

27. (a) $a_1 = 2$; $a_2 = 3$; $a_3 = a_2 \cdot a_1 = 2 \cdot 3 = 6$; $a_4 = a_3 \cdot a_2 = 6 \cdot 3 = 18$

The first four terms are 2, 3, 6, and 18.

(b) The graph of the points (1, 2), (2, 3), (3, 6), and (4, 18) is shown in Figure 27.

28. (a) $a_1 = 2$; $a_2 = 1$; $a_3 = 2a_2^2 + a_1 = 2(1)^2 + 2 = 4$; $a_4 = 2(a_3^2) + a_2 = 2(4)^2 + 1 = 33$.

The first four terms are 2, 1, 4, and 33.

(b) The graph of the points (1, 2), (2, 1), (3, 4), and (4, 33) is shown in Figure 28.

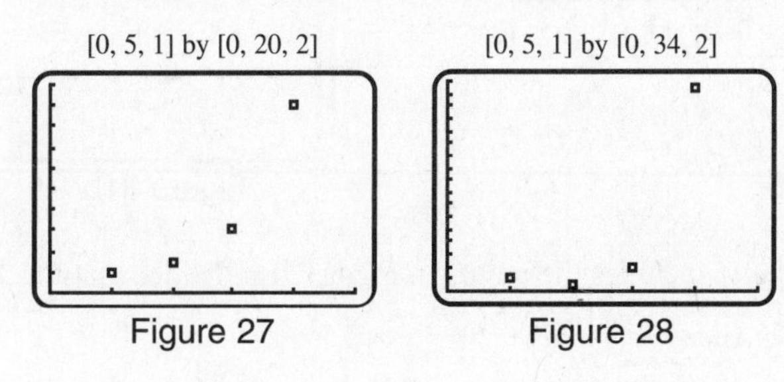

Figure 27 Figure 28

29. (a) Each term can be found by adding 2 to the previous term. A numerical representation for the first eight terms is shown in Figure 29a.

| $n$ | 1 | 2 | 3 | 4 | 5 | 6 | 7 | 8 |
|---|---|---|---|---|---|---|---|---|
| $a_n$ | 1 | 3 | 5 | 7 | 9 | 11 | 13 | 15 |

Figure 29a

[0, 10, 1] by [0, 16, 1]

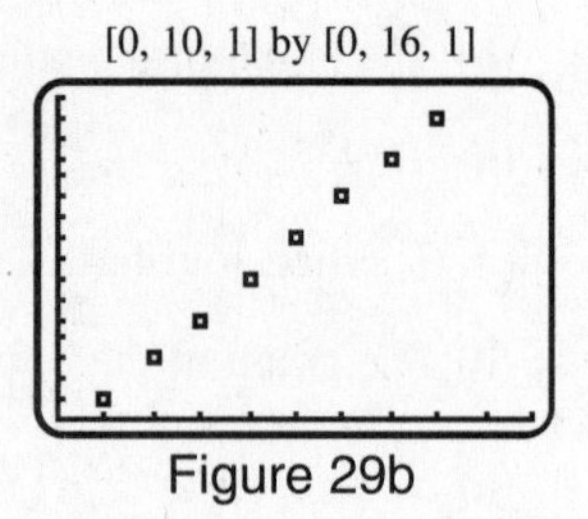

Figure 29b

(b) A graphical representation is shown in Figure 29b and includes the points in Figure 29a. Notice that the points lie on a line with slope 2 because the sequence is arithmetic.

(c) To find the symbolic representation, we will use the formula $a_n = a_1 + (n - 1)d$, where $a_n = f(n)$. The common difference of this sequence is $d = 2$ and the first term is $a_1 = 1$. Therefore, a symbolic representation of the sequence is given by $a_n = 1 + (n - 1)2$ or $a_n = 2n - 1$.

30. (a) Each term can be found by adding –3 to the previous term. A numerical representation for the first eight terms is shown in Figure 30a.

| $n$ | 1 | 2 | 3 | 4 | 5 | 6 | 7 | 8 |
|---|---|---|---|---|---|---|---|---|
| $a_n$ | 4 | 1 | −2 | −5 | −8 | −11 | −14 | −17 |

Figure 30a

[0, 10, 1] by [–18, 6, 2]

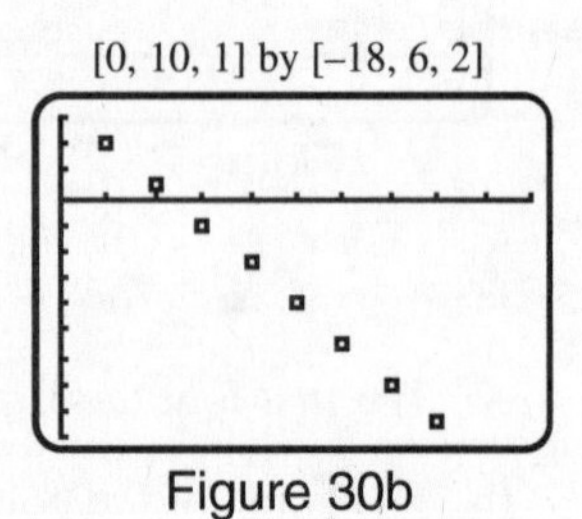

Figure 30b

(b) A graphical representation is shown in Figure 30b and includes the points in Figure 30a. Notice that the points lie on a line with slope –3 because the sequence is arithmetic.

(c) To find the symbolic representation, we will use the formula $a_n = a_1 + (n - 1)d$, where $a_n = f(n)$. The common difference of this sequence is $d = -3$ and the first term is $a_1 = 4$. Therefore, a symbolic representation of the sequence is given by $a_n = 4 + (n - 1)(-3)$ or $a_n = -3n + 7$.

31. (a) Each term can be found by subtracting 1.5 to the previous term. A numerical representation for the first eight terms is shown in Figure 31a.

| $n$ | 1 | 2 | 3 | 4 | 5 | 6 | 7 | 8 |
|---|---|---|---|---|---|---|---|---|
| $a_n$ | 7.5 | 6 | 4.5 | 3 | 1.5 | 0 | −1.5 | −3 |

Figure 31a

[0, 12, 1] by [–4, 8, 1]

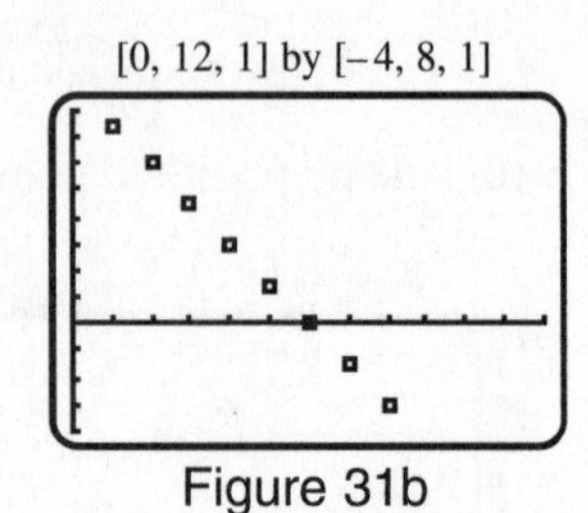

Figure 31b

(b) A graphical representation is shown in Figure 31b and includes the points in Figure 31a. Notice that the points lie on a line with slope –1.5 because the sequence is arithmetic.

(c) To find the symbolic representation, we will use the formula $a_n = a_1 + (n - 1)d$, where $a_n = f(n)$. The common difference of this sequence is $d = -1.5$ and the first term is $a_1 = 7.5$. Therefore, a symbolic representation of the sequence is given by $a_n = 7.5 + (n - 1)(-1.5)$ or $a_n = -1.5n + 9$.

32. (a) Each term can be found by adding 0.4 to the previous term. A numerical representation for the first eight terms is shown in Figure 32a.

| $n$ | 1 | 2 | 3 | 4 | 5 | 6 | 7 | 8 |
|---|---|---|---|---|---|---|---|---|
| $a_n$ | 5.1 | 5.5 | 5.9 | 6.3 | 6.7 | 7.1 | 7.5 | 7.9 |

Figure 32a

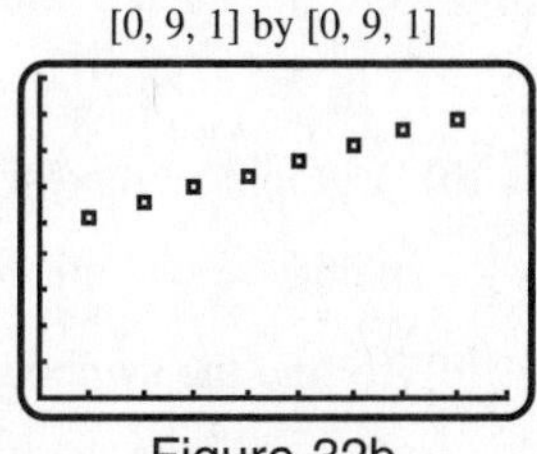

Figure 32b

(b) A graphical representation is shown in Figure 32b and includes the points in Figure 32a. Notice that the points lie on a line with slope 0.4 because the sequence is arithmetic.

(c) To find the symbolic representation, we will use the formula $a_n = a_1 + (n - 1)d$, where $a_n = f(n)$. The common difference of this sequence is $d = 0.4$ and the first term is $a_1 = 5.1$. Therefore, a symbolic representation of the sequence is given by $a_n = 5.1 + (n - 1)(0.4)$ or $a_n = 0.4n + 4.7$.

33. (a) Each term can be found by adding $\frac{3}{2}$ to the previous term. A numerical representation for the first eight terms is shown in Figure 33a.

| $n$ | 1 | 2 | 3 | 4 | 5 | 6 | 7 | 8 |
|---|---|---|---|---|---|---|---|---|
| $a_n$ | $\frac{1}{2}$ | 2 | $\frac{7}{2}$ | 5 | $\frac{13}{2}$ | 8 | $\frac{19}{2}$ | 11 |

Figure 33a

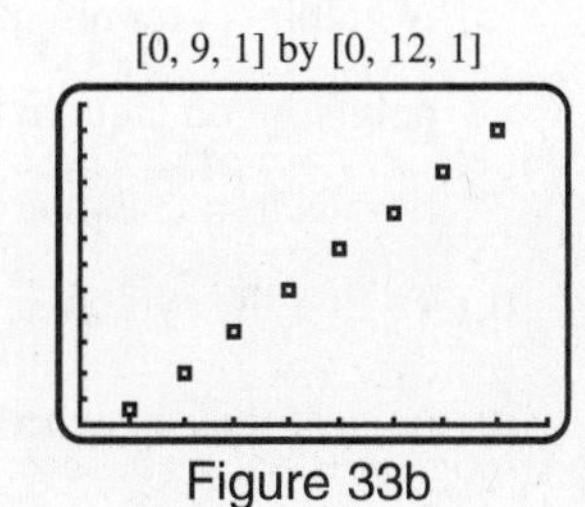

Figure 33b

(b) A graphical representation is shown in Figure 33b and includes the points in Figure 33a. Notice that the points lie on a line with slope $\frac{3}{2}$ because the sequence is arithmetic.

(c) To find the symbolic representation, we will use the formula $a_n = a_1 + (n - 1)d$, where $a_n = f(n)$. The common difference of this sequence is $d = \frac{3}{2}$ and the first term is $a_1 = \frac{1}{2}$. Therefore, a symbolic representation of the sequence is given by $a_n = \frac{1}{2} + (n - 1)\left(\frac{3}{2}\right)$ or $a_n = \frac{3}{2}n - 1$.

34. (a) Each term can be found by adding 2 to the previous term. A numerical representation for the first eight terms is shown in Figure 34a.

| $n$ | 1 | 2 | 3 | 4 | 5 | 6 | 7 | 8 |
|---|---|---|---|---|---|---|---|---|
| $a_n$ | 2 | 4 | 6 | 8 | 10 | 12 | 14 | 16 |

Figure 34a

[0, 9, 1] by [0, 18, 2]

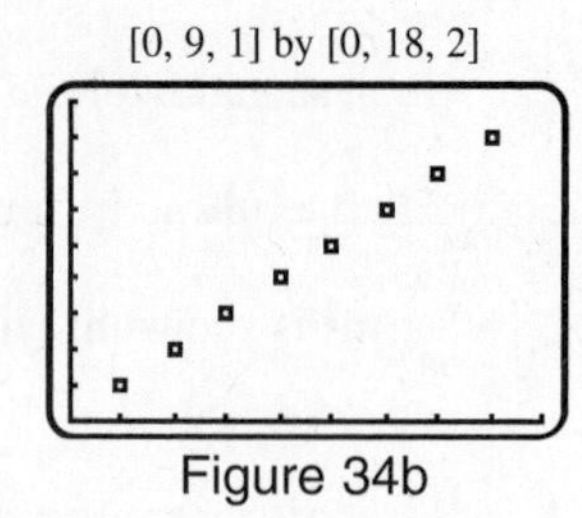

Figure 34b

(b) A graphical representation is shown in Figure 34b and includes the points in Figure 34a. Notice that the points lie on a line with slope 2 because the sequence is arithmetic.

(c) To find the symbolic representation, we will use the formula $a_n = a_1 + (n - 1)d$, where $a_n = f(n)$. The common difference of this sequence is $d = 2$ and the first term is $a_1 = 2$. Therefore, a symbolic representation of the sequence is given by $a_n = 2 + (n - 1)(2)$ or $a_n = 2n$.

35. (a) Each term can be found by multiplying the previous term by $\frac{1}{2}$. A numerical representation for the first eight terms is shown in Figure 35a.

| $n$ | 1 | 2 | 3 | 4 | 5 | 6 | 7 | 8 |
|---|---|---|---|---|---|---|---|---|
| $a_n$ | 8 | 4 | 2 | 1 | $\frac{1}{2}$ | $\frac{1}{4}$ | $\frac{1}{8}$ | $\frac{1}{16}$ |

Figure 35a

[0, 10, 1] by [–1, 9, 1]

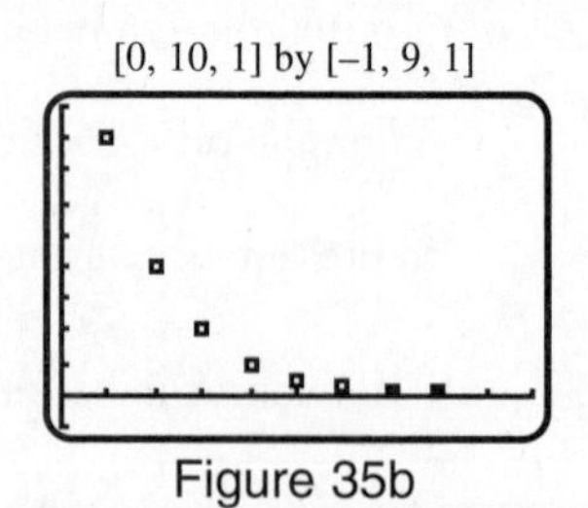

Figure 35b

(b) A graphical representation is shown in Figure 35b and includes the points in Figure 35a. Notice that the points lie on a curve that is decaying exponentially, because the sequence is geometric and the common ratio is less than one in absolute value.

(c) To find the symbolic representation, we will use the formula $a_n = a_1r^{n-1}$, where $a_n = f(n)$. The common ratio of this sequence is $r = \frac{1}{2}$ and the first term is $a_1 = 8$. Therefore, a symbolic representation of the sequence is given by $a_n = 8\left(\frac{1}{2}\right)^{n-1}$.

36. (a) Each term can be found by multiplying the previous term by $-\frac{1}{4}$. A numerical representation for the first eight terms is shown in Figure 36a.

| $n$ | 1 | 2 | 3 | 4 | 5 | 6 | 7 | 8 |
|---|---|---|---|---|---|---|---|---|
| $a_n$ | 32 | $-8$ | 2 | $-\frac{1}{2}$ | $\frac{1}{8}$ | $-\frac{1}{32}$ | $\frac{1}{128}$ | $-\frac{1}{512}$ |

Figure 36a

[0, 10, 1] by [–12, 36, 4]

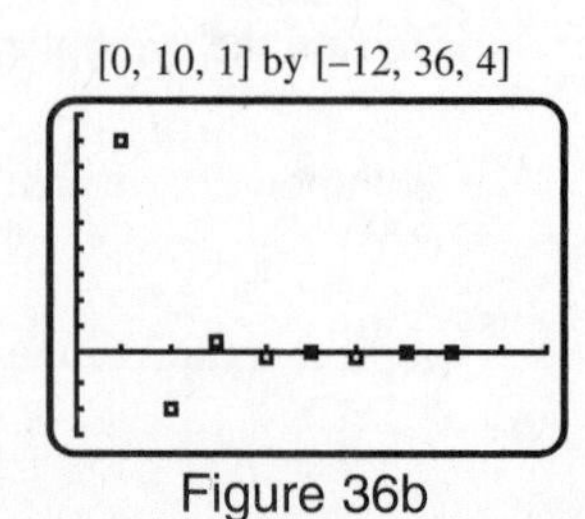

Figure 36b

(b) A graphical representation is shown in Figure 36b and includes the points in Figure 36a. Notice that the points oscillate about the $x$-axis, and come closer and closer to this axis. This is because the sequence is geometric and the common ratio is negative with an absolute value less than one.

(c) To find the symbolic representation, we will use the formula $a_n = a_1r^{n-1}$, where $a_n = f(n)$. The common ratio of this sequence is $r = -\frac{1}{4}$ and the first term is $a_1 = 32$. Therefore, a symbolic representation of the sequence is given by $a_n = 32\left(-\frac{1}{4}\right)^{n-1}$.

37. (a) Each term can be found by multiplying the previous term by 2. A numerical representation for the first eight terms is shown in Figure 37a.

| $n$ | 1 | 2 | 3 | 4 | 5 | 6 | 7 | 8 |
|---|---|---|---|---|---|---|---|---|
| $a_n$ | $\frac{3}{4}$ | $\frac{3}{2}$ | 3 | 6 | 12 | 24 | 48 | 96 |

Figure 37a

[0, 10, 1] by [–10, 110, 10]

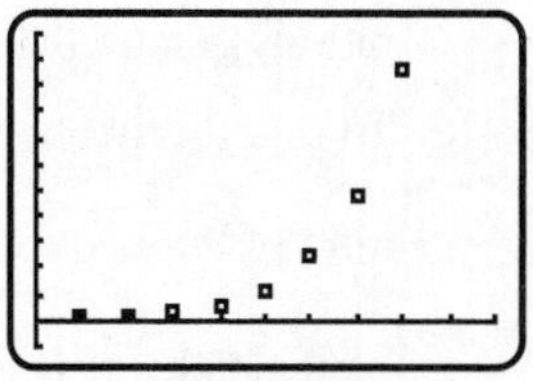

Figure 37b

(b) A graphical representation is shown in Figure 37b and includes the points in Figure 37a. Notice that the points lie on a curve that is increasing exponentially, because the sequence is geometric and the common ratio is greater than one in absolute value.

(c) To find the symbolic representation, we will use the formula $a_n = a_1r^{n-1}$, where $a_n = f(n)$. The common ratio of this sequence is $r = 2$ and the first term is $a_1 = \frac{3}{4}$. Therefore, a symbolic representation of the sequence is given by $a_n = \frac{3}{4}(2)^{n-1}$.

38. (a) Each term can be found by multiplying the previous term by 3. A numerical representation for the first eight terms is shown in Figure 38a.

| $n$ | 1 | 2 | 3 | 4 | 5 | 6 | 7 | 8 |
|---|---|---|---|---|---|---|---|---|
| $a_n$ | $\frac{1}{27}$ | $\frac{1}{9}$ | $\frac{1}{3}$ | 1 | 3 | 9 | 27 | 81 |

Figure 38a

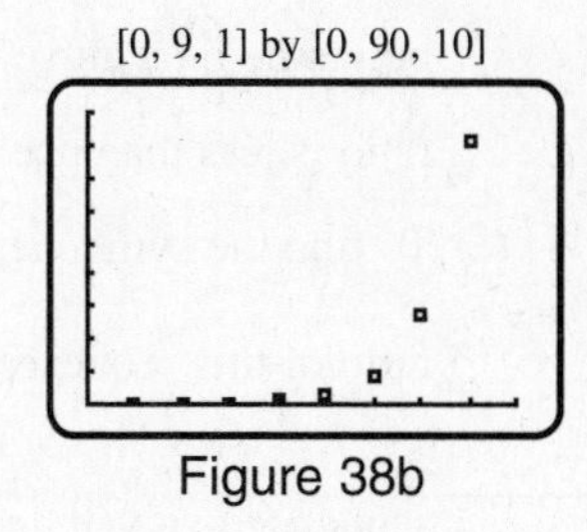


Figure 38b

(b) A graphical representation is shown in Figure 38b and includes the points in Figure 38a. Notice that the points lie on a curve that is increasing exponentially, because the sequence is geometric and the common ratio is greater than one in absolute value.

(c) To find the symbolic representation, we will use the formula $a_n = a_1r^{n-1}$, where $a_n = f(n)$. The common ratio of this sequence is $r = 3$ and the first term is $a_1 = \frac{1}{27}$. Therefore, a symbolic representation of the sequence is given by $a_n = \frac{1}{27}(3)^{n-1}$.

39. (a) Each term can be found by multiplying the previous term by 2. A numerical representation for the first eight terms is shown in Figure 39a.

| $n$ | 1 | 2 | 3 | 4 | 5 | 6 | 7 | 8 |
|---|---|---|---|---|---|---|---|---|
| $a_n$ | $-\frac{1}{4}$ | $-\frac{1}{2}$ | $-1$ | $-2$ | $-4$ | $-8$ | $-16$ | $-32$ |

Figure 39a

[0, 9, 1] by [–36, 4, 4]

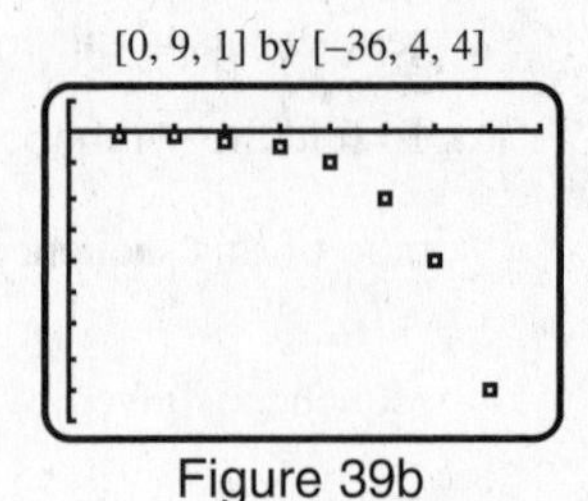

Figure 39b

(b) A graphical representation is shown in Figure 39b and includes the points in Figure 39a. Notice that the points lie on a curve that is increasing exponentially, because the sequence is geometric and the common ratio is greater than one in absolute value.

(c) To find the symbolic representation, we will use the formula $a_n = a_1 r^{n-1}$, where $a_n = f(n)$. The common ratio of this sequence is $r = 2$ and the first term is $a_1 = -\frac{1}{4}$. Therefore, a symbolic representation of the sequence is given by $a_n = -\frac{1}{4}(2)^{n-1}$.

40. (a) Each term can be found by multiplying the previous term by $\frac{2}{3}$. A numerical representation for the first eight terms is shown in Figure 40a.

| $n$ | 1 | 2 | 3 | 4 | 5 | 6 | 7 | 8 |
|---|---|---|---|---|---|---|---|---|
| $a_n$ | 9 | 6 | 4 | $\frac{8}{3}$ | $\frac{16}{9}$ | $\frac{32}{27}$ | $\frac{64}{81}$ | $\frac{128}{243}$ |

Figure 40a

[0, 9, 1] by [0, 10, 1]

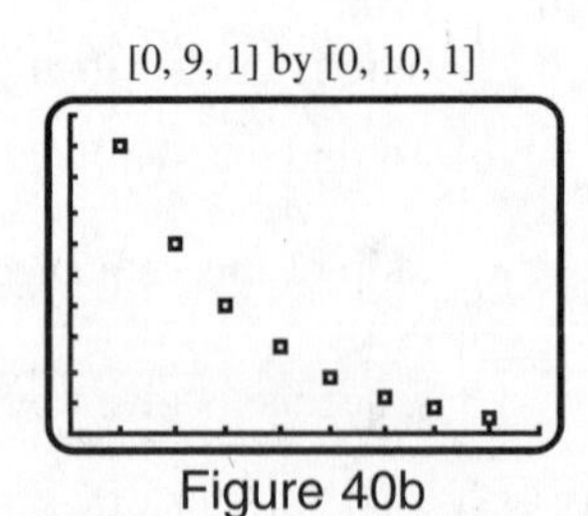

Figure 40b

(b) A graphical representation is shown in Figure 40b and includes the points in Figure 40a. Notice that the points lie on a curve that is decaying exponentially, because the sequence is geometric and the common ratio is less than one in absolute value.

(c) To find the symbolic representation, we will use the formula $a_n = a_1 r^{n-1}$, where $a_n = f(n)$. The common ratio of this sequence is $r = \frac{2}{3}$ and the first term is $a_1 = 9$. Therefore, a symbolic representation of the sequence is given by $a_n = 9\left(\frac{2}{3}\right)^{n-1}$.

41. Let $a_n = f(n)$, where $f(n) = dn + c$. Then, $f(n) = -2n + c$. Since $f(1) = -2(1) + c = 5 \Rightarrow c = 7$. Thus, $a_n = f(n) = -2n + 7$. An alternate solution is to use the formula:
$a_n = a_1 + (n-1)d = 5 + (n-1)(-2) \Rightarrow a_n = -2n + 7$.

42. Let $a_n = f(n)$, where $f(n) = dn + c$. Then, $f(n) = 5n + c$. Since $f(1) = 5(1) + c = -3 \Rightarrow c = -8$. Thus, $a_n = f(n) = 5n - 8$. An alternate solution is to use the formula:
$a_n = a_1 + (n-1)d = -3 + (n-1)(5) \Rightarrow a_n = 5n - 8$.

43. Let $a_n = f(n)$, where $f(n) = dn + c$. Then, $f(n) = 3n + c$. Since $f(3) = 3(3) + c = 1 \Rightarrow c = -8$.
Thus, $a_n = f(n) = 3n - 8$.

44. Let $a_n = f(n)$, where $f(n) = dn + c$. Then, $f(n) = -10n + c$. Since $f(4) = -10(4) + c = 12 \Rightarrow$
$c = 52$. Thus, $a_n = f(n) = -10n + 52$.

45. Let $a_n = f(n)$, where $f(n) = dn + c$. $a_2 = 5 \Rightarrow f(2) = 5$ and $a_6 = 13 \Rightarrow f(6) = 13$.
Thus, $d = \dfrac{f(6) - f(2)}{6 - 2} = \dfrac{13 - 5}{4} = 2$. Then, $f(n) = 2n + c$. $f(2) = 2(2) + c = 5 \Rightarrow c = 1$.
Thus, $a_n = f(n) = 2n + 1$.

46. Let $a_n = f(n)$, where $f(n) = dn + c$. $a_3 = 2 \Rightarrow f(3) = 22$ and $a_{17} = -20 \Rightarrow f(17) = -20$.
Thus, $d = \dfrac{f(17) - f(3)}{17 - 3} = \dfrac{-20 - 22}{14} = -3$.
Then, $f(n) = -3n + c$. $f(3) = -3(3) + c = 22 \Rightarrow c = 31$. Thus, $a_n = f(n) = -3n + 31$.

47. Let $a_n = f(n)$, where $f(n) = dn + c$. $a_1 = 8 \Rightarrow f(1) = 8$ and $a_4 = 17 \Rightarrow f(4) = 17$.
Thus, $d = \dfrac{f(4) - f(1)}{4 - 1} = \dfrac{17 - 8}{3} = 3$. Then, $f(n) = 3n + c$. $f(1) = 3(1) + c = 8 \Rightarrow c = 5$.
Thus, $a_n = f(n) = 3n + 5$.

48. Let $a_n = f(n)$, where $f(n) = dn + c$. $a_1 = -2 \Rightarrow f(1) = -2$ and $a_5 = 8 \Rightarrow f(5) = 8$.
Thus, $d = \dfrac{f(5) - f(1)}{5 - 1} = \dfrac{8 - (-2)}{4} = 2.5$.
Then, $f(n) = 2.5n + c$. $f(1) = 2.5(1) + c = -2 \Rightarrow c = -4.5$. Thus, $a_n = f(n) = 2.5n - 4.5$.

49. Let $a_n = f(n)$, where $f(n) = dn + c$. $a_5 = -4 \Rightarrow f(5) = -4$ and $a_8 = -2.5 \Rightarrow f(8) = -2.5$.
Thus, $d = \dfrac{f(8) - f(5)}{8 - 5} = \dfrac{-2.5 - (-4)}{3} = 0.5$.
Then, $f(n) = 0.5n + c$. $f(5) = 0.5(5) + c = -4 \Rightarrow c = -6.5$. Thus, $a_n = f(n) = 0.5n - 6.5$.

50. Let $a_n = f(n)$, where $f(n) = dn + c$. $a_3 = 10 \Rightarrow f(3) = 10$ and $a_7 = -4 \Rightarrow f(7) = -4$.
Thus, $d = \dfrac{f(7) - f(3)}{7 - 3} = \dfrac{-4 - 10}{4} = -3.5$.
Then, $f(n) = -3.5n + c$. $f(3) = -3.5(3) + c = 10 \Rightarrow c = 20.5$. Thus, $a_n = f(n) = -3.5n + 20.5$.

51. Let $a_n = f(n)$, where $f(n) = a_1 r^{n-1}$. Then, $a_n = f(n) = 2\left(\dfrac{1}{2}\right)^{n-1}$.

52. Let $a_n = f(n)$, where $f(n) = a_1 r^{n-1}$. Then, $a_n = f(n) = 0.8(-3)^{n-1}$.

53. Let $a_n = f(n)$, where $f(n) = a_1 r^{n-1}$. Then, $a_n = f(n) = a_1\left(-\dfrac{1}{4}\right)^{n-1}$.
Since $f(3) = a_1\left(-\dfrac{1}{4}\right)^{3-1} = \dfrac{1}{32} \Rightarrow a_1 = \dfrac{16}{32} = \dfrac{1}{2}$. Thus, $a_n = f(n) = \dfrac{1}{2}\left(-\dfrac{1}{4}\right)^{n-1}$.

54. Let $a_n = f(n)$, where $f(n) = a_1 r^{n-1}$. Then, $a_n = f(n) = a_1(3)^{n-1}$.
Since $f(4) = a_1(3)^{4-1} = 3 \Rightarrow a_1 = \dfrac{3}{27} = \dfrac{1}{9}$. Thus, $a_n = f(n) = \dfrac{1}{9}(3)^{n-1}$.

55. Let $a_n = f(n)$, where $f(n) = a_1r^{n-1}$. $a_3 = 2$ and $a_6 = \frac{1}{4} \Rightarrow \frac{1}{8} = \frac{\frac{1}{4}}{2} = \frac{a_6}{a_3} = \frac{a_1r^{6-1}}{a_1r^{3-1}} = \frac{r^5}{r^2} = r^3 \Rightarrow$
$r = \frac{1}{2}$. Then, $f(n) = a_1\left(\frac{1}{2}\right)^{n-1}$. $f(3) = a_1\left(\frac{1}{2}\right)^{3-1} = 2 \Rightarrow a_1 = 8$. Thus, $a_n = f(n) = 8\left(\frac{1}{2}\right)^{n-1}$.

56. Let $a_n = f(n)$, where $f(n) = a_1r^{n-1}$. $a_2 = 6$ and $a_4 = 24 \Rightarrow 4 = \frac{24}{6} = \frac{a_4}{a_2} = \frac{a_1r^{4-1}}{a_1r^{2-1}} = \frac{r^3}{r^1} = r^2 \Rightarrow$
$r = 2$. Then, $f(n) = a_1(2)^{n-1}$. $f(2) = a_1(2)^{2-1} = 6 \Rightarrow a_1 = 3$. Thus, $a_n = f(n) = 3(2)^{n-1}$.

57. Let $a_n = f(n)$, where $f(n) = a_1r^{n-1}$. $a_1 = -5$ and $a_3 = -125 \Rightarrow$
$25 = \frac{-125}{-5} = \frac{a_3}{a_1} = \frac{a_1r^{3-1}}{a_1r^{1-1}} = \frac{r^2}{r^0} = r^2 \Rightarrow r = -5$. Thus, $a_n = f(n) = -5(-5)^{n-1}$.

58. Let $a_n = f(n)$, where $f(n) = a_1r^{n-1}$. $a_1 = 10$ and $a_2 = 2 \Rightarrow \frac{1}{5} = \frac{2}{10} = \frac{a_2}{a_1} = \frac{a_1r^{2-1}}{a_1r^{1-1}} = \frac{r^1}{r^0} = r^1 \Rightarrow$
$r = \frac{1}{5}$. Thus, $a_n = f(n) = 10\left(\frac{1}{5}\right)^{n-1}$.

59. Let $a_n = f(n)$, where $f(n) = a_1r^{n-1}$. $a_2 = -1$ and $a_7 = -32 \Rightarrow$
$32 = \frac{-32}{-1} = \frac{a_7}{a_2} = \frac{a_1r^{7-1}}{a_1r^{2-1}} = \frac{r^6}{r^1} = r^5 \Rightarrow r = 2$.
Then, $f(n) = a_1(2)^{n-1}$. $f(2) = a_1(2)^{2-1} = -1 \Rightarrow a_1 = -\frac{1}{2}$. Thus, $a_n = f(n) = -\frac{1}{2}(2)^{n-1}$.

60. Let $a_n = f(n)$, where $f(n) = a_1r^{n-1}$. $a_2 = \frac{9}{4}$ and $a_4 = \frac{81}{4} \Rightarrow$
$9 = \frac{\frac{81}{4}}{\frac{9}{4}} = \frac{a_4}{a_2} = \frac{a_1r^{4-1}}{a_1r^{2-1}} = \frac{r^3}{r^1} = r^2 \Rightarrow r = -3$.
Then, $f(n) = a_1(-3)^{n-1}$. $f(2) = a_1(-3)^{2-1} = \frac{9}{4} \Rightarrow a_1 = -\frac{3}{4}$. Thus, $a_n = f(n) = -\frac{3}{4}(-3)^{n-1}$.

61. Since $f(n) = 4 - 3n^3$ is not a linear function, it does not represent an arithmetic sequence.

62. Since $f(n) = 2(n - 1) = 2n - 2$ is a linear function, it represents an arithmetic sequence.

63. Since $f(n) = 4n - (3 - n) = 5n - 3$ is a linear function, it represents an arithmetic sequence.

64. Since $f(n) = n^2 - n + 2$ is not a linear function, it does not represent an arithmetic sequence.

65. Since the plotted points appear to be collinear, the graph represents an arithmetic sequence.

66. Since the plotted points do not appear to be collinear, the graph does not represent an arithmetic sequence.

67. Since the common difference is $-2$, the table represents an arithmetic sequence.

68. Since there is no common difference, the table does not represent an arithmetic sequence.

69. Since $f(n) = 4(2)^{n-1}$ is written in the form $f(n) = cr^{n-1}$, it represents a geometric sequence.

70. Since $f(n) = -3(0.25)^n$ can written in the form $f(n) = -0.75(0.25)^{n-1}$, it represents a geometric sequence.

71. Since $f(n) = -3(n)^2$ cannot be written in the form $f(n) = cr^{n-1}$, it does not represents a geometric sequence.

72. Since $f(n) = 2(n - 1)^n$ cannot be written in the form $f(n) = cr^{n-1}$, it does not represents a geometric sequence.

73. Since the plotted points appear to be collinear, the graph does not represent a geometric sequence.

74. Since the plotted points have the shape of an exponential curve, the graph represents a geometric sequence.

75. Since there is no common ratio, the table does not represent a geometric sequence.

76. Since the common ratio is $\frac{1}{3}$, the table represents a geometric sequence.

77. These terms represent an arithmetic sequence. Each term can be obtained by adding 7 to the previous term.

78. These terms represent neither an arithmetic nor a geometric sequence. There is no common ratio or difference.

79. These terms represent a geometric sequence. Each term can be obtained by multiplying the previous term by 4.

80. These terms represent an arithmetic sequence. Each term can be obtained by adding $-0.25$ to the previous term.

81. These terms represent neither an arithmetic nor a geometric sequence. There is no common ratio or difference.

82. These terms represent a geometric sequence. Each term can be obtained by multiplying the previous term by 0.3.

83. This sequence is arithmetic since the points lie on a line (and are evenly spaced). Since the sequence is decreasing the common difference must be negative. The slope of the line passing through these points is $-1$, so the common difference is $d = -1$.

84. The sequence is assumed to be either geometric or arithmetic. This sequence must be geometric, since it is not arithmetic. The terms of the sequence do not alternate sign, so $r$ is positive. Since the terms sequence is increasing, $|\, r \,| > 1$.

85. The sequence is either geometric or arithmetic. This sequence must be geometric, since the points do not lie on a line. Since the terms alternate sign, the common ratio $r$ is negative. The absolute value of the terms are dampening to a value of 0. Therefore, $|\, r \,| < 1$.

86. This sequence is arithmetic since the points lie on a line (and are evenly spaced). Since the sequence is increasing the common difference must be positive. The slope of the line passing through these points is 2, so the common difference is 2.

87. The insect population increases rapidly and then levels off at 5000 per acre.

88. The insect population decreases significantly from the first year to the second year. Then it increases, after which the population starts to oscillate around 7000 insects per acre.

89. (a) The initial density is 500. The population density each successive year is 0.8 of the previous year. Therefore $a_1 = 500$ and $a_n = 0.8a_{n-1}$.

(b) $a_1 = 500$, $a_2 = 0.8(500) = 400$, $a_3 = 0.8(400) = 320$, $a_4 = 0.8(320) = 256$, $a_5 = 0.8(256) = 204.8$ and $a_6 = 0.8(204.8) = 163.84$. The population density is decreasing each year by 20%

(c) The terms of the sequence 500, 400, 320, 256, ... are a geometric sequence with $a_1 = 500$ and $r = 0.8$. Therefore, the $n$th term is given by $a_n = 500(0.8)^{n-1}$.

90. (a) The recursive sequence can be written as: $a_1 = 300$, $a_n = 2a_{n-1}$, $n > 1$.

The first five terms are $a_1 = 300$, $a_2 = 600$, $a_3 = 1200$, $a_4 = 2400$, $a_5 = 4800$.

(b) Ten hours represent 600 minutes, or fifteen 40 minute intervals, so we must find $a_{16}$. Since 300 must be doubled 15 times, the result is $a_{16} = (300)2^{15} = 9{,}830{,}400$ bacteria per milliliter.

(c) The sequence is geometric, because the terms are found by multiplying the previous term by 2.

91. (a) $a_1 = 8,\ a_2 = 2.9a_1 - 0.2a_1^2 = 2.9(8) - 0.2(8)^2 = 10.4,$

$a_3 = 2.9a_2 - 0.2a_2^2 = 2.9(10.4) - 0.2(10.4)^2 = 8.528.$

(b) Figures 91a & 91b show how to enter the sequence and a graph of the first twenty terms. The population density oscillates above and below 9.5 (approximately).

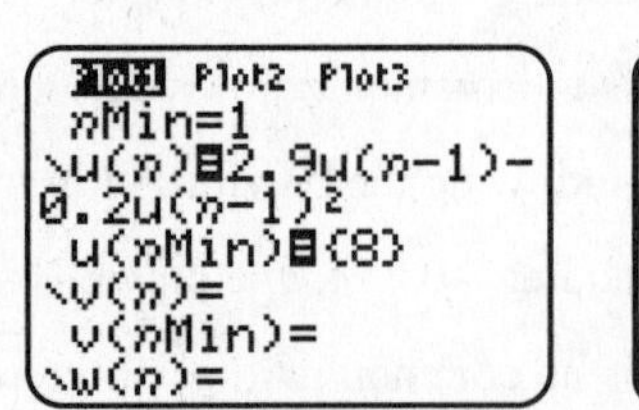

Figure 91a

[0, 21, 1] by [0, 14, 1]

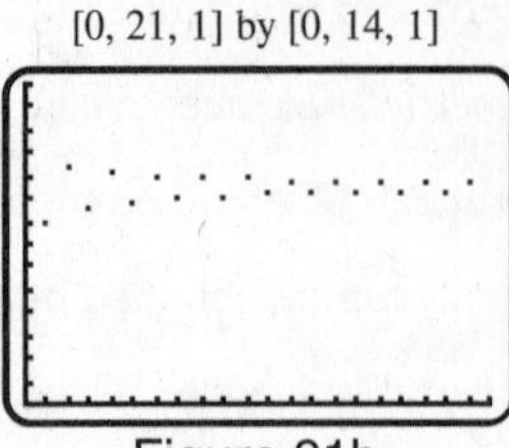
Figure 91b

Figure 92a

[0, 25, 5] by [0, 12,000, 1000]

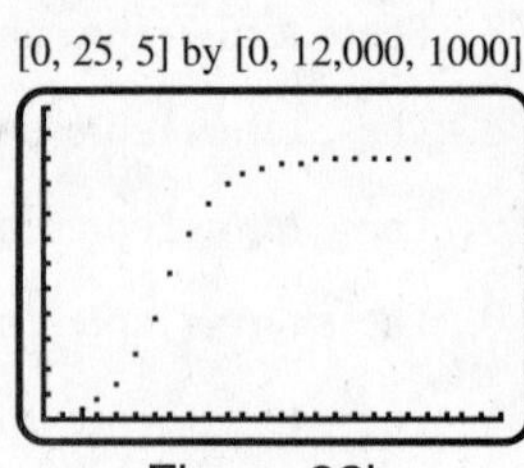
Figure 92b

92. (a) The sequence is entered in Figure 92a, and the graph is shown in Figure 92b.

(b) The number of bacteria increases quickly and then levels off at 10,000 since there are limited nutrients.

(c) Since the number of bacteria levels off at 10,000, which is equal to $K$, it is reasonable to conjecture that the carrying capacity of the medium is $K$. That is, $K$ gives the maximum number of bacteria that can be supported on the given medium. When $a_n \approx K$, the medium becomes saturated. Changing $K$ in the formula demonstrates that this conjecture is correct.

93. (a) The terms in this sequence can be found by adding the previous two terms. $a_1 = 1,\ a_2 = 1,\ a_3 = 2,$ $a_4 = 3,\ a_5 = 5,\ a_6 = 8,\ a_7 = 13,\ a_8 = 21,\ a_9 = 34,\ a_{10} = 55,\ a_{11} = 89$, and $a_{12} = 144$.

(b) $\frac{a_2}{a_1} = \frac{1}{1} = 1,\ \frac{a_3}{a_2} = \frac{2}{1} = 2,\ \frac{a_4}{a_3} = \frac{3}{2} = 1.5,\ \frac{a_5}{a_4} = \frac{5}{3} \approx 1.6667,\ \frac{a_6}{a_5} = \frac{8}{5} = 1.6,\ \frac{a_7}{a_6} = \frac{13}{8} = 1.625,$

$\frac{a_8}{a_7} = \frac{21}{13} \approx 1.6154,\ \frac{a_9}{a_8} = \frac{34}{21} = 1.6190,\ \frac{a_{10}}{a_9} = \frac{55}{34} \approx 1.6176,\ \frac{a_{11}}{a_{10}} = \frac{89}{55} = 1.6182$, and

$\frac{a_{12}}{a_{11}} = \frac{144}{89} \approx 1.6180$. These ratios seem to be approaching a number near 1.618. This number is called the golden ratio.

(c) $n = 2\colon\ a_1 \cdot a_3 - a_2^2 = (1)(2) - (1)^2 = 1 = (-1)^2;$

$n = 3\colon\ a_2 \cdot a_4 - a_3^2 = (1)(3) - (2)^2 = -1 = (-1)^3;$

$n = 4\colon\ a_3 \cdot a_5 - a_4^2 = (2)(5) - (3)^2 = 1 = (-1)^4$

94. (a) The initial height is 5 feet. On the first rebound it reaches 80% or 4 feet. On the second rebound it attains a height 80% of 4 or 3.2 feet. Each term in this sequence is found by multiplying the previous term by 0.8. Thus, the first five terms are 5, 4, 3.2, 2.56, and 2.048. This is a geometric sequence.

(b) Plot the points (1, 5), (2, 4), (3, 3.2), (4, 2.56), and (5, 2.048) as shown in Figure 94.

(c) The first term is 5 and the common ratio is 0.8. Thus, $a_n = 5(0.8)^{n-1}$.

[0, 6, 1] by [0, 6, 1]

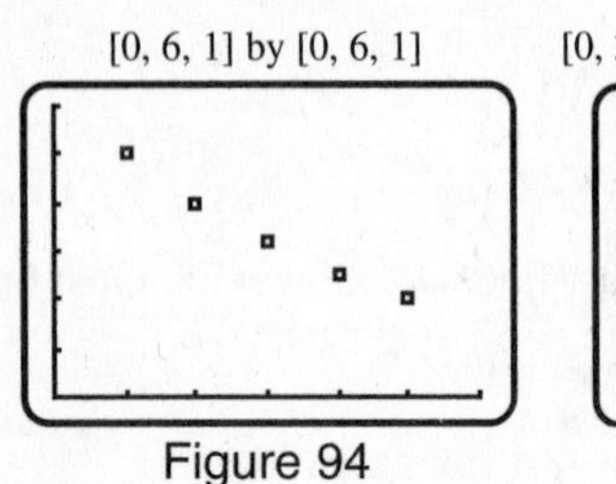
Figure 94

[0, 30, 10] by [0, 150,000, 50,000]

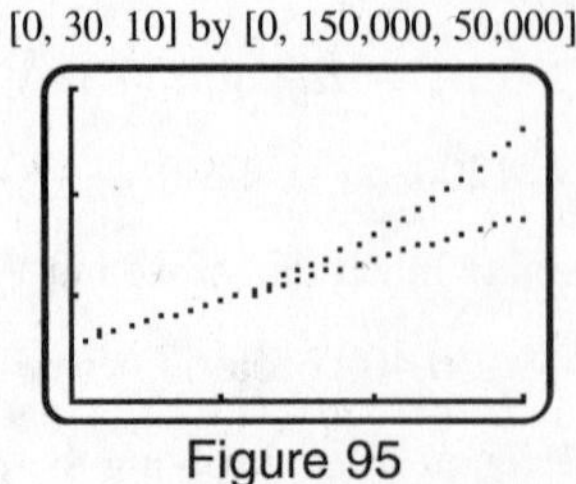
Figure 95

95. (a) The salary of the first employee at the beginning of the $n$th year is given by:

$a_n = 30{,}000 + (n - 1)(2000) = 2000n + 28{,}000.$

This is a arithmetic sequence with $a_1 = 30{,}000$ and $d = 2000$.

(b) The salary of the second employee at the beginning of the $n$th year is given by: $b_n = 30{,}000(1.05)^{n-1}$.

This is a geometric sequence with $b_1 = 30{,}000$ and $d = 1.05$.

(c) At the beginning of the 10th year each salary is:

$a_{10} = 2000(10) + 28{,}000 = \$48{,}000,\ b_{10} = 30{,}000(1.05)^{10-1} \approx \$46{,}540.$

At the beginning of the 20th year each salary is:

$a_{20} = 2000(20) + 28{,}000 = \$68{,}000,\ b_{20} = 30{,}000(1.05)^{20-1} \approx \$75{,}809.$

(d) The graph of each sequence is shown in Figure 95. With time the geometric sequence overtakes the arithmetic sequence since $r > 1$.

96. The area of each successive smaller square is $\frac{1}{2}$ the area of the previous (larger) square. Since the area of the larger square is 1 unit, the area of successive squares is given by the terms of the sequence $1, \frac{1}{2}, \frac{1}{4}, \frac{1}{8}, \frac{1}{16}, \ldots$.

This is a geometric sequence with $a_1 = 1$ and $r = \frac{1}{2}$. The area of the $n$th square is given by $a_n = \left(\frac{1}{2}\right)^{n-1}$.

97. Let $a_1 = 2$. Then, $a_2 = \frac{1}{2}\left(a_1 + \frac{k}{a_1}\right) = \frac{1}{2}\left(2 + \frac{2}{2}\right) = 1.5,\ a_3 = \frac{1}{2}\left(a_2 + \frac{k}{a_2}\right) = \frac{1}{2}\left(1.5 + \frac{2}{1.5}\right) = 1.41\overline{6}$

In a similar manner, $a_4 \approx 1.414215686$, $a_5 \approx 1.414213562$, and $a_6 \approx 1.414213562$. Since $\sqrt{2} \approx 1.414213562$ this is a very accurate approximation.

98. Let $a_1 = 11$. Then, $a_2 = \frac{1}{2}\left(a_1 + \frac{k}{a_1}\right) = \frac{1}{2}\left(11 + \frac{11}{11}\right) = 6,\ a_3 = \frac{1}{2}\left(a_2 + \frac{k}{a_2}\right) = \frac{1}{2}\left(6 + \frac{11}{6}\right) = 3.91\overline{6}$

In a similar manner, $a_4 \approx 3.362588652$, $a_5 \approx 3.316938935$, and $a_6 \approx 3.316624805$. Since $\sqrt{11} \approx 3.31662479$ this is an accurate approximation.

99. Let $a_1 = 21$. Then, $a_2 = \frac{1}{2}\left(a_1 + \frac{k}{a_1}\right) = \frac{1}{2}\left(21 + \frac{21}{21}\right) = 11,\ a_3 = \frac{1}{2}\left(a_2 + \frac{k}{a_2}\right) = \frac{1}{2}\left(11 + \frac{21}{11}\right) = 6.\overline{45}$

In a similar manner, $a_4 \approx 4.854033291$, $a_5 \approx 4.59016621$, and $a_6 \approx 4.582581971$. Since $\sqrt{21} \approx 4.582575695$ this is an accurate approximation.

100. Let $a_1 = 41$. Then, $a_2 = \frac{1}{2}\left(a_1 + \frac{k}{a_1}\right) = \frac{1}{2}\left(41 + \frac{41}{41}\right) = 21,$

$a_3 = \frac{1}{2}\left(a_2 + \frac{k}{a_2}\right) = \frac{1}{2}\left(21 + \frac{41}{21}\right) \approx 11.47619048$

In a similar manner, $a_4 \approx 7.524402292$, $a_5 \approx 6.486670041$, and $a_6 \approx 6.403662256$. Since $\sqrt{41} \approx 6.403124237$ this is an accurate approximation.

101. By definition $a_n = a_1 + (n - 1)d_1$ and $b_n = b_1 + (n - 1)d_2$. Then

$c_n = a_n + b_n = [a_1 + (n - 1)d_1] + [b_1 + (n - 1)d_2] = (a_1 + b_1) + [(n - 1)d_1 + (n - 1)d_2] =$

$(a_1 + b_1) + (n - 1)(d_1 + d_2) = c_1 + (n - 1)d$ where $c_1 = a_1 + b_1$ and $d = d_1 + d_2$.

102. By the power rule for logarithms $a_1 = \log 2$, $a_2 = \log 4 = \log 2^2 = 2\log 2$, $a_3 = \log 8 = \log 2^3 = 3\log 2$, $a_4 = \log 16 = \log 2^4 = 4\log 2$, and so on. The common difference is $a_2 - a_1 = 2\log 2 - \log 2 = \log 2$. The sequence is $a_n = \log 2 + (n-1)\log 2$.

## 8.2: Series

1. The first six positive even integers are 2, 4, 6, 8, 10, 12.
2. The first seven positive odd integers are 1, 3, 5, 7, 9, 11, 13.
3. The sum of the first six positive even integers is shown by $2 + 4 + 6 + 8 + 10 + 12$. The sum is 42.
4. The sum of the first seven positive odd integers is shown by $1 + 3 + 5 + 7 + 9 + 11 + 13$. The sum is 49.
5. Since $A_n$ represents the number of AIDS deaths after 2000, the sum from 2005 to 2009 is given by $A_5 + A_6 + A_7 + A_8 + A_9$.
6. $S_6$ represents the cumulative number od AIDS deaths from 2001 to 2006.
7. $S_5 = 3(1) + 3(2) + 3(3) + 3(4) + 3(5) = 3 + 6 + 9 + 12 + 15 = 45$
8. $S_5 = (1+4) + (2+4) + (3+4) + (4+4) + (5+4) = 5 + 6 + 7 + 8 + 9 = 35$
9. $S_5 = (2(1)-1) + (2(2)-1) + (2(3)-1) + (2(4)-1) + (2(5)-1) = 1 + 3 + 5 + 7 + 9 = 25$
10. $S_5 = (4(1)+1) + (4(2)+1) + (4(3)+1) + (4(4)+1) + (4(5)+1) =$ $5 + 9 + 13 + 17 + 21 = 65$
11. $S_5 = (1^2+1) + (2^2+1) + (3^2+1) + (4^2+1) + (5^2+1) = 2 + 5 + 10 + 17 + 26 = 60$
12. $S_5 = 2(1)^2 + 2(2)^2 + 2(3)^2 + 2(4)^2 + 2(5)^2 = 2 + 8 + 18 + 32 + 50 = 110$
13. $S_5 = \frac{1}{1+1} + \frac{2}{2+1} + \frac{3}{3+1} + \frac{4}{4+1} + \frac{5}{5+1} = \frac{1}{2} + \frac{2}{3} + \frac{3}{4} + \frac{4}{5} + \frac{5}{6} = \frac{71}{20}$
14. $S_5 = \frac{1}{2(1)} + \frac{1}{2(2)} + \frac{1}{2(3)} + \frac{1}{2(4)} + \frac{1}{2(5)} = \frac{1}{2} + \frac{1}{4} + \frac{1}{6} + \frac{1}{8} + \frac{1}{10} = \frac{137}{120}$
15. The first term is $a_1 = 3$ and the last term is $a_8 = 17$. To find the sum use:
    $S_n = n\left(\frac{a_1 + a_n}{2}\right) \Rightarrow S_8 = 8\left(\frac{3 + 17}{2}\right) = 80$. The sum is 80.
16. The first term is $a_1 = 7.5$ and the last term is $a_7 = -1.5$. To find the sum use:
    $S_n = n\left(\frac{a_1 + a_n}{2}\right) \Rightarrow S_7 = 7\left(\frac{7.5 + (-1.5)}{2}\right) = 21$. The sum is 21.
17. The first term is $a_1 = 1$ and the last term is $a_{50} = 50$. To find the sum use:
    $S_n = n\left(\frac{a_1 + a_n}{2}\right) \Rightarrow S_{50} = 50\left(\frac{1 + 50}{2}\right) = 1275$. The sum is 1275.
18. The first term is $a_1 = 1$ and $d = 2$. The last term is 97, but we must determine $n$. The term of 97 is $\frac{97 - 1}{2} = 48$ terms after $a_1$. thus, the last term is $a_{49} = 97$. To find the sum use the following:
    $S_n = n\left(\frac{a_1 + a_n}{2}\right) \Rightarrow S_{49} = 49\left(\frac{1 + 97}{2}\right) = 2401$. The sum is 2401.

19. The first term is $a_1 = -7$ and $d = 3$. The last term is 101, but we must determine $n$. The term of 101 is $\frac{101 - (-7)}{3} = 36$ terms after $a_1$. Thus, the last term is $a_{37} = 101$. To find the sum use the following: $S_n = n\left(\frac{a_1 + a_n}{2}\right) \Rightarrow S_{37} = 37\left(\frac{-7 + 101}{2}\right) = 1739$. The sum is 1739.

20. The first term is $a_1 = 89$ and $d = -5$. The last term is 4, but we must determine $n$. The term of 4 is $\frac{4 - 89}{-5} = 17$ terms after $a_1$. Thus, the last term is $a_{18} = 4$. To find the sum use the following: $S_n = n\left(\frac{a_1 + a_n}{2}\right) \Rightarrow S_{18} = 18\left(\frac{89 + 4}{2}\right) = 837$. The sum is 837.

21. The number of terms to be added is 40, so $n = 40$. The first term is $a_1 = 5(1) = 5$. The last term is $a_{40} = 5(40) = 200$. $S_n = n\left(\frac{a_1 + a_n}{2}\right) \Rightarrow S_{40} = 40\left(\frac{5 + 200}{2}\right) = 4100$. The sum is 4100.

22. The number of terms to be added is 50, so $n = 50$. The first term is $a_1 = 1 - 3(1) = -2$. The last term is $a_{50} = 1 - 3(50) = -149$. $S_n = n\left(\frac{a_1 + a_n}{2}\right) \Rightarrow S_{50} = 50\left(\frac{-2 + (-149)}{2}\right) = -3775$. The sum is $-3775$.

23. $S_{15} = 15\left(\frac{a_1 + a_{15}}{2}\right) \Rightarrow 255 = 15\left(\frac{3 + a_{15}}{2}\right) \Rightarrow 17 = \frac{3 + a_{15}}{2} \Rightarrow 34 = 3 + a_{15} \Rightarrow a_{15} = 31$

24. $S_{20} = 20\left(\frac{a_1 + a_{20}}{2}\right) \Rightarrow 610 = 20\left(\frac{a_1 + 59}{2}\right) \Rightarrow 30.5 = \frac{a_1 + 59}{2} \Rightarrow 61 = a_1 + 59 \Rightarrow a_1 = 2$

25. Since $a_1 = 4$ and $d = 2$, use the formula $S_n = \frac{n}{2}(2a_1 + (n - 1)d)$.

$$S_{20} = \frac{20}{2}(2(4) + (20 - 1)2) = 10(8 + 19(2)) = 10(8 + 38) = 10(46) = 460$$

26. Since $a_1 = -3$ and $d = \frac{2}{3}$, use the formula $S_n = \frac{n}{2}(2a_1 + (n - 1)d)$.

$$S_{20} = \frac{20}{2}\left(2(-3) + (20 - 1)\frac{2}{3}\right) = 10\left(-6 + 19\left(\frac{2}{3}\right)\right) = 10\left(-6 + \frac{38}{3}\right) = 10\left(\frac{20}{3}\right) = \frac{200}{3} = 66.\overline{6}$$

27. Since $a_1 = 10$ and $d = -\frac{1}{2}$, use the formula $S_n = \frac{n}{2}(2a_1 + (n - 1)d)$.

$$S_{20} = \frac{20}{2}\left(2(10) + (20 - 1)\left(-\frac{1}{2}\right)\right) = 10\left(20 + 19\left(-\frac{1}{2}\right)\right) = 10\left(20 - \frac{19}{2}\right) = 10\left(\frac{21}{2}\right) = 105$$

28. Since $a_1 = 0$ and $d = -4$, use the formula $S_n = \frac{n}{2}(2a_1 + (n - 1)d)$.

$$S_{20} = \frac{20}{2}(2(0) + (20 - 1)(-4)) = 10(0 + 19(-4)) = 10(-76) = -760$$

29. Since $a_1 = 4$ and $a_{20} = 190.2$, use the formula $S_n = n\left(\frac{a_1 + a_n}{2}\right)$.

$$S_{20} = 20\left(\frac{4 + 190.2}{2}\right) = 20\left(\frac{194.2}{2}\right) = 20(97.1) = 1942$$

30. Since $a_1 = -4$ and $a_{20} = 15$, use the formula $S_n = n\left(\frac{a_1 + a_n}{2}\right)$.

$$S_{20} = 20\left(\frac{-4 + 15}{2}\right) = 20\left(\frac{11}{2}\right) = 20(5.5) = 110$$

31. Since $a_1 = -2$ and $a_{11} = 50$, the common difference is $d = \dfrac{50 - (-2)}{11 - 1} = \dfrac{52}{10} = 5.2$.

Use the formula $S_n = \dfrac{n}{2}(2a_1 + (n - 1)d)$.

$$S_{20} = \frac{20}{2}(2(-2) + (20 - 1)5.2) = 10(-4 + 19(5.2)) = 10(-4 + 98.8) = 10(94.8) = 948$$

32. Since $a_1 = 6$ and $a_5 = -30$, the common difference is $d = \dfrac{-30 - 6}{5 - 1} = \dfrac{-36}{4} = -9$.

Use the formula $S_n = \dfrac{n}{2}(2a_1 + (n - 1)d)$.

$$S_{20} = \frac{20}{2}(2(6) + (20 - 1)(-9)) = 10(12 + 19(-9)) = 10(12 - 171) = 10(-159) = -1590$$

33. Since $a_2 = 6$ and $a_{12} = 31$, the common difference is $d = \dfrac{31 - 6}{12 - 2} = \dfrac{25}{10} = 2.5$ and so $a_1 = 6 - 2.5 = 3.5$.

Use the formula $S_n = \dfrac{n}{2}(2a_1 + (n - 1)d)$.

$$S_{20} = \frac{20}{2}(2(3.5) + (20 - 1)2.5) = 10(7 + 19(2.5)) = 10(7 + 47.5) = 10(54.5) = 545$$

34. Since $a_8 = 4$ and $a_{10} = 14$, the common difference is $d = \dfrac{14 - 4}{10 - 8} = \dfrac{10}{2} = 5$ and so $a_1 = 4 - 7(5) = -31$.

Use the formula $S_n = \dfrac{n}{2}(2a_1 + (n - 1)d)$.

$$S_{20} = \frac{20}{2}(2(-31) + (20 - 1)5) = 10(-62 + 19(5)) = 10(-62 + 95) = 10(33) = 330$$

35. The first term is $a_1 = 1$ and the common ratio is $r = 2$. Since there are 8 terms, the sum is

$$S_n = a_1\left(\frac{1 - r^n}{1 - r}\right) \Rightarrow S_8 = 1\left(\frac{1 - 2^8}{1 - 2}\right) = 255.$$

This sum can be verified by adding $1 + 2 + 4 + 8 + 16 + 32 + 64 + 128 = 255$.

36. The first term is $a_1 = 2$ and the common ratio is $r = \dfrac{1}{4}$. Since there are 6 terms, the sum is

$$S_n = a_1\left(\frac{1 - r^n}{1 - r}\right) \Rightarrow S_6 = 2\left(\frac{1 - (\frac{1}{4})^6}{1 - \frac{1}{4}}\right) = 2.666015625.$$

This sum can be verified by adding $2 + \dfrac{1}{2} + \dfrac{1}{8} + \dfrac{1}{32} + \dfrac{1}{128} + \dfrac{1}{512} = 2.666015625$.

37. The first term is $a_1 = 0.5$ and the common ratio is $r = 3$. Since there are 7 terms, the sum is

$$S_n = a_1\left(\frac{1 - r^n}{1 - r}\right) \Rightarrow S_7 = 0.5\left(\frac{1 - (3)^7}{1 - 3}\right) = 546.5.$$

This sum can be verified by adding $0.5 + 1.5 + 4.5 + 13.5 + 40.5 + 121.5 + 364.5 = 546.5$.

38 The first term is $a_1 = 0.6$ and the common ratio is $r = \dfrac{1}{2} = 0.5$. Since there are 5 terms, the sum is

$$S_n = a_1\left(\frac{1 - r^n}{1 - r}\right) \Rightarrow S_5 = 0.6\left(\frac{1 - (0.5)^5}{1 - 0.5}\right) = 1.1625.$$

This sum can be verified by adding $0.6 + 0.3 + 0.15 + 0.075 + 0.0375 = 1.1625$.

39. The first term is $a_1 = 3(2)^0 = 3$ and the common ratio is $r = 2$. Since there are 20 terms, the sum is

$$S_n = a_1\left(\frac{1 - r^n}{1 - r}\right) \Rightarrow S_{20} = 3\left(\frac{1 - 2^{20}}{1 - 2}\right) = 3{,}145{,}725.$$

40. The first term is $a_1 = 2\left(\frac{1}{3}\right)^1 = \frac{2}{3}$ and the common ratio is $r = \frac{1}{3}$. Since there are 15 terms, the sum is

$$S_n = a_1\left(\frac{1 - r^n}{1 - r}\right) \Rightarrow S_{15} = \frac{2}{3}\left(\frac{1 - \left(\frac{1}{3}\right)^{15}}{1 - \frac{1}{3}}\right) = 0.99999993 \approx 1.0.$$

41. Using the formula $S_n = a_1\left(\frac{1 - r^n}{1 - r}\right)$ with $a_1 = 1$ and $r = -\frac{1}{2}$,

$$S_4 = 1\left(\frac{1 - \left(-\frac{1}{2}\right)^4}{1 - \left(-\frac{1}{2}\right)}\right) = 0.625;\ S_7 = 1\left(\frac{1 - \left(-\frac{1}{2}\right)^7}{1 - \left(-\frac{1}{2}\right)}\right) = 0.671875;\ S_{10} = 1\left(\frac{1 - \left(-\frac{1}{2}\right)^{10}}{1 - \left(-\frac{1}{2}\right)}\right) = 0.666015625$$

42. Using the formula $S_n = a_1\left(\frac{1 - r^n}{1 - r}\right)$ with $a_1 = 3$ and $r = -\frac{1}{3}$,

$$S_4 = 3\left(\frac{1 - \left(-\frac{1}{3}\right)^4}{1 - \left(-\frac{1}{3}\right)}\right) = 2.\overline{2};\ S_7 = 3\left(\frac{1 - \left(-\frac{1}{3}\right)^7}{1 - \left(-\frac{1}{3}\right)}\right) \approx 2.251028807;\ S_{10} = 3\left(\frac{1 - \left(-\frac{1}{3}\right)^{10}}{1 - \left(-\frac{1}{3}\right)}\right) \approx 2.249961896$$

43. Using the formula $S_n = a_1\left(\frac{1 - r^n}{1 - r}\right)$ with $a_1 = \frac{1}{3}$ and $r = 2$,

$$S_4 = \frac{1}{3}\left(\frac{1 - 2^4}{1 - 2}\right) = 5;\ S_7 = \frac{1}{3}\left(\frac{1 - 2^7}{1 - 2}\right) = 42.\overline{3};\ S_{10} = \frac{1}{3}\left(\frac{1 - 2^{10}}{1 - 2}\right) = 341$$

44. Using the formula $S_n = a_1\left(\frac{1 - r^n}{1 - r}\right)$ with $a_1 = 4$ and $r = \frac{2}{3}$,

$$S_4 = 4\left(\frac{1 - \left(\frac{2}{3}\right)^4}{1 - \left(\frac{2}{3}\right)}\right) = 9.\overline{629};\ S_7 = 4\left(\frac{1 - \left(\frac{2}{3}\right)^7}{1 - \left(\frac{2}{3}\right)}\right) \approx 11.29766804;\ S_{10} = 4\left(\frac{1 - \left(\frac{2}{3}\right)^{10}}{1 - \left(\frac{2}{3}\right)}\right) = 11.79190164$$

45. The first term is $a_1 = 1$ and the common ratio is $r = \frac{1}{3}$. The sum is $S = a_1\left(\frac{1}{1 - r}\right) \Rightarrow S = 1\left(\frac{1}{1 - \frac{1}{3}}\right) = \frac{3}{2}$.

46. The first term is $a_1 = 5$ and the common ratio is $r = \frac{1}{2}$ or 0.5. The sum is

$$S = a_1\left(\frac{1}{1 - r}\right) \Rightarrow S = 5\left(\frac{1}{1 - 0.5}\right) = 10.$$

47. The first term is $a_1 = 6$ and the common ratio is $r = -\frac{2}{3}$. The sum is

$$S = a_1\left(\frac{1}{1 - r}\right) \Rightarrow S = 6\left(\frac{1}{1 - \left(-\frac{2}{3}\right)}\right) = \frac{18}{5}.$$

48. The first term is $a_1 = -2$ and the common ratio is $r = -\frac{1}{4}$ or $-0.25$. The sum is

$$S = a_1\left(\frac{1}{1 - r}\right) \Rightarrow S = -2\left(\frac{1}{1 - (-0.25)}\right) = -\frac{8}{5}.$$

49. The first term is $a_1 = 1$ and the common ratio is $r = -\frac{1}{10}$ or $-0.1$. The sum is

$$S = a_1\left(\frac{1}{1 - r}\right) \Rightarrow S = 1\left(\frac{1}{1 - (-0.1)}\right) = \frac{1}{1.1} = \frac{10}{11}.$$

50. The first term is $a_1 = 25$ and the common ratio is $r = -\frac{1}{5}$ or $-0.2$. The sum is

$$S = a_1\left(\frac{1}{1 - r}\right) \Rightarrow S = 25\left(\frac{1}{1 - (-0.2)}\right) = \frac{25}{1.2} = \frac{125}{6}.$$

51. $\frac{2}{3} = 0.6666666\ldots = 0.6 + 0.06 + 0.006 + 0.0006 + 0.00006 + \cdots$

52. $\frac{1}{9} = 0.1111111\ldots = 0.1 + 0.01 + 0.001 + 0.0001 + 0.00001 + \cdots$

53. $\frac{9}{11} = 0.81818181\ldots = 0.81 + 0.0081 + 0.000081 + 0.00000081 + \cdots$

54. $\frac{14}{33} = 0.42424242\ldots = 0.42 + 0.0042 + 0.000042 + 0.00000042 + \cdots$

55. $\frac{1}{7} = 0.142857142857\ldots = 0.142857 + 0.000000142857 + 0.000000000000142857 + \cdots$

56. $\frac{23}{99} = 0.23232323\ldots = 0.23 + 0.0023 + 0.000023 + 0.00000023 + \cdots$

57. The series $0.8 + 0.08 + 0.008 + 0.0008 + \cdots$ is an infinite geometric series with $a_1 = 0.8$ and $r = 0.1$.
$S = \frac{a_1}{1 - r} = \frac{0.8}{1 - 0.1} = \frac{8}{9}$.

58. The series $0.9 + 0.09 + 0.009 + 0.0009 + \cdots$ is an infinite geometric series with $a_1 = 0.9$ and $r = 0.1$.
$S = \frac{a_1}{1 - r} = \frac{0.9}{1 - 0.1} = \frac{9}{9} = 1$.

59. The series $0.45 + 0.0045 + 0.000045 + \cdots$ is an infinite geometric series with $a_1 = 0.45$ and $r = 0.01$.
$S = \frac{a_1}{1 - r} = \frac{0.45}{1 - 0.01} = \frac{45}{99} = \frac{5}{11}$.

60. The series $0.36 + 0.0036 + 0.000036 + \cdots$ is an infinite geometric series with $a_1 = 0.36$ and $r = 0.01$.
$S = \frac{a_1}{1 - r} = \frac{0.36}{1 - 0.01} = \frac{36}{99} = \frac{4}{11}$.

61. $\sum_{k=1}^{4}(k + 1) = (1 + 1) + (2 + 1) + (3 + 1) + (4 + 1) = 2 + 3 + 4 + 5 = 14$

62. $\sum_{k=1}^{6}(3k - 1) = 2 + 5 + 8 + 11 + 14 + 17 = 57$

63. $\sum_{k=1}^{8}4 = 4 + 4 + 4 + 4 + 4 + 4 + 4 + 4 = 32$

64. $\sum_{k=2}^{6}(5 - 2k) = 1 + (-1) + (-3) + (-5) + (-7) = -15$

65. $\sum_{k=1}^{7}k^3 = 1^3 + 2^3 + 3^3 + 4^3 + 5^3 + 6^3 + 7^3 = 1 + 8 + 27 + 64 + 125 + 216 + 343 = 784$

66. $\sum_{k=1}^{4}5(2)^{k-1} = 5 + 10 + 20 + 40 = 75$

67. $\sum_{k=4}^{5}(k^2 - k) = (4^2 - 4) + (5^2 - 5) = 12 + 20 = 32$

68. $\sum_{k=1}^{5}\log k = \log 1 + \log 2 + \log 3 + \log 4 + \log 5 = \log 120 \approx 2.08$

69. $1^4 + 2^4 + 3^4 + 4^4 + 5^4 + 6^4 = \sum_{k=1}^{6}k^4$

70. $1 + \frac{1}{5} + \frac{1}{25} + \frac{1}{125} + \frac{1}{625} = \sum_{k=1}^{5} \left(\frac{1}{5}\right)^{k-1}$

71. $1 + \frac{4}{3} + \frac{6}{4} + \frac{8}{5} + \frac{10}{6} + \frac{12}{7} + \frac{14}{8} = \sum_{k=1}^{7} \left(\frac{2k}{k+1}\right)$

72. $2 + \frac{5}{8} + \frac{10}{27} + \frac{17}{64} + \frac{26}{125} + \frac{37}{216} = \sum_{k=1}^{6} \left(\frac{k^2+1}{k^3}\right)$

73. $1 + \frac{1}{2^2} + \frac{1}{3^2} + \frac{1}{4^2} + \frac{1}{5^2} + \cdots = \sum_{k=1}^{\infty} \left(\frac{1}{k^2}\right)$

74. $1 + \frac{1}{10} + \frac{1}{100} + \frac{1}{1000} + \frac{1}{10{,}000} + \cdots = \sum_{k=1}^{\infty} \left(\frac{1}{10}\right)^{k-1}$

75. Because $\sum_{k=6}^{9} k^3 = 6^3 + 7^3 + 8^3 + 9^3$, the summation has 4 terms. We will write $k = 6, 7, 8, 9$ as $n = 1, 2, 3, 4$. It follows that $n + 5 = k$, and $\sum_{n=1}^{4} (n+5)^3$.

76. Because $\sum_{k=5}^{10} (k^2 - 2) = (5^2 - 2) + (6^2 - 2) + (7^2 - 2) + \cdots + (10^2 - 2)$, the summation has 6 terms. We will write $k = 5, 6, 7, 8, 9, 10$ as $n = 1, 2, 3, 4, 5, 6$. It follows that $n + 4 = k$, and

$$\sum_{n=1}^{6} ((n+4)^2 - 2) \Rightarrow \sum_{n=1}^{6} (n^2 + 8n + 16 - 2) \Rightarrow \sum_{n=1}^{6} (n^2 + 8n + 14).$$

77. Because $\sum_{k=9}^{32} (3k - 2) = (3(9) - 2) + (3(10) - 2) + \cdots + (3(32) - 2)$, the summation has 24 terms. We will write $k = 9, 10, 11, \ldots 32$ as $n = 1, 2, 3, 4, \ldots 24$. It follows that $n + 8 = k$, and

$$\sum_{n=1}^{24} (3(n+8) - 2) \Rightarrow \sum_{n=1}^{24} (3n + 24 - 2) \Rightarrow \sum_{n=1}^{24} (3n + 22).$$

78. Because $\sum_{k=8}^{21} (4k + 1) = (4(8) + 1) + (4(9) + 1) + \cdots + (4(21) + 1)$, the summation has 14 terms. We will write $k = 8, 9, 10, 11, \ldots 21$ as $n = 1, 2, 3, \ldots 14$. It follows that $n + 7 = k$, and

$$\sum_{n=1}^{14} (4(n+7) + 1) \Rightarrow \sum_{n=1}^{14} (4n + 28 + 1) \Rightarrow \sum_{n=1}^{14} (4n + 29).$$

79. Because $\sum_{k=16}^{52} (k^2 - 3k) = (16^2 - 3(16)) + (17^2 - 3(17)) + \cdots + (52^2 - 3(52))$, the summation has 37 terms. We will write $k = 16, 17, 18, \ldots 52$ as $n = 1, 2, 3, \ldots 37$. It follows that $n + 15 = k$, and

$$\sum_{n=1}^{37} ((n+15)^2 - 3(n+15)) \Rightarrow \sum_{n=1}^{37} (n^2 + 30n + 225 - 3n - 45) \Rightarrow \sum_{n=1}^{37} (n^2 + 27n + 180).$$

80. Because $\sum_{k=25}^{59} (k^2 + 4k) = (25^2 + 4(25)) + (26^2 + 4(26)) + \cdots + (59^2 + 4(59))$, the summation has 35 terms. We will write $k = 25, 26, 27, \ldots 59$ as $n = 1, 2, 3, \ldots 35$. It follows that $n + 24 = k$, and

$$\sum_{n=1}^{35} ((n+24)^2 + 4(n+24)) \Rightarrow \sum_{n=1}^{35} (n^2 + 48n + 576 + 4n + 96) \Rightarrow \sum_{n=1}^{35} (n^2 + 52n + 672).$$

81. $\sum_{k=1}^{60} 9 = 60(9) = 540$

82. $\sum_{k=1}^{43} -4 = 43(-4) = -172$

83. $\sum_{k=1}^{15} 5k = 5\sum_{k=1}^{15} k = 5\left[\frac{15(16)}{2}\right] = 600$

84. $\sum_{k=1}^{22} -2k = -2\sum_{k=1}^{22} k = -2\left[\frac{22(23)}{2}\right] = -506$

85. $\sum_{k=1}^{31} (3k - 3) = 3\sum_{k=1}^{31} k - \sum_{k=1}^{31} 3 = 3\left[\frac{31(32)}{2}\right] - 31(3) = 1488 - 93 = 1395$

86. $\sum_{k=1}^{17} (1 - 4k) = \sum_{k=1}^{17} 1 - 4\sum_{k=1}^{17} k = 17(1) - 4\left[\frac{17(18)}{2}\right] = 17 - 612 = -595$

87. $\sum_{k=1}^{25} k^2 = \frac{(25)(26)(51)}{6} = 5525$

88. $\sum_{k=1}^{12} 3k^2 = 3\sum_{k=1}^{12} k^2 = 3\left[\frac{(12)(13)(25)}{6}\right] = 1950$

89. $\sum_{k=1}^{16} (k^2 - k) = \sum_{k=1}^{16} k^2 - \sum_{k=1}^{16} k = \frac{(16)(17)(33)}{6} - \frac{(16)(17)}{2} = 1496 - 136 = 1360$

90. $\sum_{k=1}^{18} (k^2 - 4k + 3) = \sum_{k=1}^{18} k^2 - 4\sum_{k=1}^{18} k + \sum_{k=1}^{18} 3 = \frac{(18)(19)(37)}{6} - \frac{4(18)(19)}{2} + 18(3) =$
$2109 - 684 + 54 = 1479$

91. $\sum_{k=5}^{24} k = \sum_{k=1}^{24} k - \sum_{k=1}^{4} k = \frac{(24)(25)}{2} - \frac{(4)(5)}{2} = 300 - 10 = 290$

92. $\sum_{k=7}^{19} (k^2 + 1) = \sum_{k=1}^{19} (k^2 + 1) - \sum_{k=1}^{6} (k^2 + 1) = \sum_{k=1}^{19} k^2 + \sum_{k=1}^{19} 1 - \sum_{k=1}^{6} k^2 - \sum_{k=1}^{6} 1 =$
$\frac{(19)(20)(39)}{6} + 19 - \frac{(6)(7)(13)}{6} - 6 = 2470 + 19 - 91 - 6 = 2392$

93. $\sum_{k=1}^{n} k = 1 + 2 + 3 + 4 + \cdots + n$. This is an arithmetic series with $a_1 = 1$ and $a_n = n$. The sum is given by
$S_n = n\left(\frac{a_1 + a_n}{2}\right) = n\left(\frac{1 + n}{2}\right) = \frac{n(n + 1)}{2}$.

94. $\sum_{k=1}^{200} k = \frac{200(201)}{2} = 20{,}100$

95. (a) The arithmetic sequence describing the salary during year $n$ is computed by $a_n = 42{,}000 + 1800(n - 1)$.
The 1st and 15th years salaries are: $a_1 = 42{,}000 + 1800(1 - 1) = 42{,}000$ and
$a_{15} = 42{,}000 + 1800(15 - 1) = 67{,}200$. The total amount earned during the 15 year period is
$S_{15} = \frac{15(42{,}000 + 67{,}200)}{2} = 819{,}000$.

(b) Verify with a calculator, compute the sum $a_1 + a_2 + a_3 + \cdots + a_{15}$, where
$a_n = 42{,}000 + 1800(n - 1)$. See Figure 95.

Figure 95

Figure 96

96. (a) The arithmetic sequence describing the salary during year $n$ is computed by $a_n = 35{,}000 + 2500(n - 1)$.

The 1st and 15th years salaries are: $a_1 = 35{,}000 + 2500(1 - 1) = 35{,}000$ and

$a_{15} = 35{,}000 + 2500(15 - 1) = 70{,}000$. The total amount earned during the 15 year period is

$$S_{15} = \frac{15(35{,}000 + 70{,}000)}{2} = 787{,}500.$$

(b) Verify with a calculator, compute the sum $a_1 + a_2 + a_3 + \cdots + a_{15}$, where

$a_n = 35{,}000 + 2500(n - 1)$. See Figure 96.

97. Future value is given by $S_n = A_0\left(\frac{(1 + i)^n - 1}{i}\right)$, where $A_0 = a_1$.

$S_{20} = 2000\left(\frac{(1 + 0.08)^{20} - 1}{0.08}\right) \approx 91{,}523.93$. If \$2000 is deposited in an account at the end of each year for 20 years and the account pays 8% interest, the future value of this annuity will be \$91,523.93.

98. Future value is given by $S_n = A_0\left(\frac{(1 + i)^n - 1}{i}\right)$, where $A_0 = a_1$.

$S_{10} = 500\left(\frac{(1 + 0.15)^{10} - 1}{0.15}\right) \approx 10{,}151.86$. If \$500 is deposited in an account at the end of each year for 10 years and the account pays 15% interest, the future value of this annuity will be \$10,151.86.

99. Future value is given by $S_n = A_0\left(\frac{(1 + i)^n - 1}{i}\right)$, where $A_0 = a_1$.

$S_5 = 10{,}000\left(\frac{(1 + 0.11)^5 - 1}{0.11}\right) \approx 62{,}278.01$. If \$10,000 is deposited in an account at the end of each year for 5 years and the account pays 11% interest, the future value of this annuity will be \$62,278.01.

100. Future value is given by $S_n = A_0\left(\frac{(1 + i)^n - 1}{i}\right)$, where $A_0 = a_1$.

$S_{45} = 3000\left(\frac{(1 + 0.19)^{45} - 1}{0.19}\right) \approx 39{,}610{,}272.68$. If \$3000 is deposited in an account at the end of each year for 45 years and the account pays 19% interest, the future value of this annuity will be \$39,610,272.68.

101. The number of logs in the stack is given by $7 + 8 + 9 + 10 + 11 + 12 + 13 + 14 + 15$. This series is arithmetic with first term $a_1 = 7$ and the last term $a_9 = 15$ so its sum is given by $S_9 = 9\left(\frac{7 + 15}{2}\right) = 99$. So, there are 99 logs in the stack.

102. The number of logs in the stack is given by an arithmetic series with first term $a_1 = 13$, $d = 1$, and $n = 7$. The number of logs is given by $13 + 14 + 15 + 16 + 17 + 18 + 19 = 7\left(\frac{13 + 19}{2}\right) = 112$. So, there are 112 logs in the stack.

103. (a) Since each filter lets half of the impurities through, the series is can be written as $0.5(1) + 0.5(0.5) + 0.5(0.25) + \cdots = \sum_{k=1}^{n} 0.5(0.5)^{k-1}$.

(b) The series sums to 1 only if an infinite number of filters are used.

104. $1 + \frac{1}{3} + \frac{1}{9} + \ldots = \left(\frac{1}{3}\right)^0 + \left(\frac{1}{3}\right)^1 + \left(\frac{1}{3}\right)^2 + \cdots = \sum_{k=1}^{\infty}\left(\frac{1}{3}\right)^{k-1} = 1\left(\frac{1}{1 - \frac{1}{3}}\right) = \frac{3}{2} = 1.5$ mi.

105. The area of the largest square is 1, the area of the next largest square is $\frac{1}{2}$, and each successive square has an area that is $\frac{1}{2}$ the area of the previous square. If there are an infinite number of squares, then the area is represented by the geometric series $1 + \frac{1}{2} + \frac{1}{4} + \frac{1}{8} + \frac{1}{16} + \cdots$. This is an infinite geometric series with $a_1 = 1$ and $r = \frac{1}{2}$, whose sum is $S = \frac{1}{1 - r} = \frac{1}{1 - \frac{1}{2}} = 2$. The area is 2.

106. The perimeter of the largest square is 4 since the area is 1, the area of the next largest square is $\frac{1}{2}$ so its dimensions are $\frac{1}{\sqrt{2}}$ by $\frac{1}{\sqrt{2}}$. The perimeter of the second square is $4 \cdot \frac{1}{\sqrt{2}} = \frac{4}{\sqrt{2}}$. The perimeter of the second square is reduced by a factor of $\frac{1}{\sqrt{2}}$. The third square has an area of $\frac{1}{4}$ so each side is $\frac{1}{2}$. Its perimeter is $4 \cdot \frac{1}{2} = 2$, or equivalently, the perimeter is equal to the perimeter of the second square multiplied times $\frac{1}{\sqrt{2}}$, since $\frac{4}{\sqrt{2}} \cdot \frac{1}{\sqrt{2}} = \frac{4}{2} = 2$. If the area of a square is reduced by half, its perimeter is reduced by a factor of $\frac{1}{\sqrt{2}}$. The perimeters of the squares can be represented by the geometric series $4 + \frac{4}{\sqrt{2}} + \frac{4}{(\sqrt{2})^2} + \frac{4}{(\sqrt{2})^3} + \frac{4}{(\sqrt{2})^4} + \cdots$. This is an infinite geometric series with $a_1 = 4$ and $r = \frac{1}{\sqrt{2}}$, whose sum is $S = \frac{a_1}{1 - r} = \frac{4}{1 - (1/\sqrt{2})} = 4(\sqrt{2} + 2) \approx 13.65685$. The sum of the perimeters is approximately 13.65685.

107. The value of $e^a$ is approximated by $e^a = 1 + a + \frac{a^2}{2!} + \frac{a^3}{3!} + \cdots + \frac{a^n}{n!}$. Apply the series by letting $a = 1$, since $e^1 = e$. The first 8 terms sum to $e^1 \approx 1 + 1 + \frac{1}{2!} + \frac{1}{3!} + \frac{1}{4!} + \frac{1}{5!} + \frac{1}{6!} + \frac{1}{7!} =$ $1 + 1 + \frac{1}{2} + \frac{1}{6} + \frac{1}{24} + \frac{1}{120} + \frac{1}{720} + \frac{1}{5040} \approx 2.718254$. The actual value is $e \approx 2.718282$, so only 8 terms of the series provides an approximation for $e$ that is accurate to 4 decimal places.

108. Apply the series by letting $a = -1$. The first 8 terms sum to

$$e^{-1} \approx 1 + (-1) + \frac{(-1)^2}{2!} + \frac{(-1)^3}{3!} + \frac{(-1)^4}{4!} + \frac{(-1)^5}{5!} + \frac{(-1)^6}{6!} + \frac{(-1)^7}{7!} =$$

$1 - 1 + \frac{1}{2} - \frac{1}{6} + \frac{1}{24} - \frac{1}{120} + \frac{1}{720} - \frac{1}{5040} \approx 0.367857$. The actual value is $e^{-1} \approx 0.367879$, so only 8 terms of this series provide an approximation for $e^{-1}$ that is accurate to 4 decimal places.

109. One can either add the terms directly or apply the formula $S_n = a_1\left(\frac{1 - r^n}{1 - r}\right)$. We will apply the formula. In this sequence $a_1 = 1$ and $r = \frac{1}{3}$. $S_2 = 1\left(\frac{1 - (\frac{1}{3})^2}{1 - (\frac{1}{3})}\right) = \frac{4}{3} \approx 1.3333$; $S_4 = 1\left(\frac{1 - (\frac{1}{3})^4}{1 - (\frac{1}{3})}\right) = \frac{40}{27} \approx 1.4815$;

$S_8 = 1\left(\frac{1 - (\frac{1}{3})^8}{1 - (\frac{1}{3})}\right) \approx 1.49977$; $S_{16} = 1\left(\frac{1 - (\frac{1}{3})^{16}}{1 - (\frac{1}{3})}\right) \approx 1.49999997$. The sum of the infinite series

$\sum_{k=1}^{\infty}\left(\frac{1}{3}\right)^{k-1}$ is given by $S = \frac{a_1}{1 - r} = \frac{1}{1 - \frac{1}{3}} = \frac{3}{2} = 1.5$. As $n$ increases, the partial sums $S_2, S_4, S_8$, and $S_{16}$ become closer and closer to the value of 1.5.

110. One can either add the terms directly or apply the formula $S_n = a_1\left(\frac{1 - r^n}{1 - r}\right)$. We will apply the formula. In this sequence $a_1 = 3$ and $r = \frac{1}{2}$. $S_5 = 3\left(\frac{1 - (\frac{1}{2})^5}{1 - (\frac{1}{2})}\right) = 5.8125$; $S_{10} = 3\left(\frac{1 - (\frac{1}{2})^{10}}{1 - (\frac{1}{2})}\right) \approx 5.99414$;

$S_{15} = 3\left(\frac{1 - (\frac{1}{2})^{15}}{1 - (\frac{1}{2})}\right) \approx 5.999817$; $S_{20} = 3\left(\frac{1 - (\frac{1}{2})^{20}}{1 - (\frac{1}{2})}\right) \approx 5.9999943$. The sum of the infinite series

$\sum_{k=1}^{\infty}3\left(\frac{1}{2}\right)^{k-1}$ is given by $S = \frac{a_1}{1 - r} = \frac{3}{1 - \frac{1}{2}} = 6$. As $n$ increases, the partial sums $S_5, S_{10}, S_{15}$, and $S_{20}$ become closer and closer to the value of 6.

111. One can either add the terms directly or apply the formula $S_n = a_1\left(\frac{1 - r^n}{1 - r}\right)$. We will apply the formula. In this sequence $a_1 = 4$ and $r = -\frac{1}{10}$. $S_1 = 4\left(\frac{1 - (-\frac{1}{10})^1}{1 - (-\frac{1}{10})}\right) = 4$; $S_2 = 4\left(\frac{1 - (-\frac{1}{10})^2}{1 - (-\frac{1}{10})}\right) = 3.6$;

$S_3 = 4\left(\frac{1 - (-\frac{1}{10})^3}{1 - (-\frac{1}{10})}\right) = 3.64$; $S_4 = 4\left(\frac{1 - (-\frac{1}{10})^4}{1 - (-\frac{1}{10})}\right) = 3.636$; $S_5 = 4\left(\frac{1 - (-\frac{1}{10})^5}{1 - (-\frac{1}{10})}\right) = 3.6364$;

$S_6 = 4\left(\frac{1 - (-\frac{1}{10})^6}{1 - (-\frac{1}{10})}\right) = 3.63636$; The sum of the infinite series $\sum_{k=1}^{\infty}4\left(-\frac{1}{10}\right)^{k-1}$ is given by

$S = \frac{a_1}{1 - r} = \frac{4}{1 - (-0.1)} = \frac{40}{11} = 3.\overline{63}$. As $n$ increases, the partial sums become closer and closer to the value of $3.\overline{63}$.

112. In this sequence $a_1 = 2$ and $r = -0.02$. $S_1 = 2\left(\frac{1-(-0.02)^1}{1-(-0.02)}\right) = 2$; $S_2 = 2\left(\frac{1-(-0.02)^2}{1-(-0.02)}\right) = 1.96$;

$S_3 = 2\left(\frac{1-(-0.02)^3}{1-(-0.02)}\right) = 1.9608$; $S_4 = 2\left(\frac{1-(-0.02)^4}{1-(-0.02)}\right) = 1.960784$;

$S_5 = 2\left(\frac{1-(-0.02)^5}{1-(-0.02)}\right) = 1.96078432$; $S_6 = 2\left(\frac{1-(-0.02)^6}{1-(-0.02)}\right) = 1.960784314$. The sum of the infinite series $\sum_{k=1}^{\infty} 2(-0.02)^{k-1}$ is given by $S = \frac{a_1}{1-r} = \frac{2}{1-(-0.02)} = \frac{100}{51} \approx 1.960784314$. As $n$ increases, the partial sums become closer and closer to the value of $\frac{100}{51}$.

## Checking Basic Concepts for Sections 8.1 & 8.2

1. A graphical representation of $a_n = -2n + 3$ is shown in Figure 1a. A numerical representation is shown in Figure 1b. The first six terms are 1, –1, –3, –5, –7, –9.

[0, 7, 1] by [–10, 2, 1]

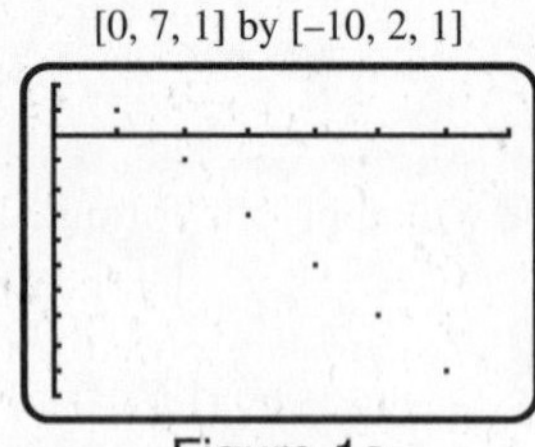

Figure 1a

| $n$ | u(n) |
|---|---|
| 1 | 1 |
| 2 | -1 |
| 3 | -3 |
| 4 | -5 |
| 5 | -7 |
| 6 | -9 |
| 7 | -11 |

u(n)=-2n+3

Figure 1b

2. (a) The sequence is geometric since each term is obtained by multiplying the previous term by –2. The common ratio is –2.

   (b) The sequence is arithmetic since each term is obtained by adding 3 to the previous term. The common difference is 3.

   (c) The sequence is geometric since each term is obtained by multiplying the previous term by $\frac{1}{2}$. The common ratio is $\frac{1}{2}$.

3. (a) The series is arithmetic since the common difference between the terms is 4. The sum of the first 10 terms shown is $10\left(\frac{1+37}{2}\right) = 190$.

   (b) The series is geometric since the common ratio is $\frac{1}{3}$. The sum of the first 6 terms shown is

   $$3\left(\frac{1-\left(\frac{1}{3}\right)^6}{1-\left(\frac{1}{3}\right)}\right) = 3\left(\frac{1-\left(\frac{1}{729}\right)}{1-\left(\frac{1}{3}\right)}\right) = 3\left(\frac{\frac{728}{729}}{\frac{2}{3}}\right) = 3\left(\frac{364}{243}\right) = \frac{364}{81} \approx 4.494.$$

   (c) The series is an infinite geometric series with a common ratio of $\frac{1}{4}$.

   The sum of the series is $\frac{2}{1-\frac{1}{4}} = \frac{2}{0.75} = \frac{8}{3} \approx 2.667$.

   (d) The series is an infinite geometric series with a common ratio of 0.1.

   The sum of the series is $\frac{0.9}{1-0.1} = \frac{0.9}{0.9} = 1$.

4. (a) The terms of the series can be written as $4k - 3$ for $k = 1, 2, 3, \ldots, 10$.

Thus, $1 + 5 + 9 + 13 + \cdots + 37 = \sum_{k=1}^{10}(4k - 3)$.

(b) The terms of the series can be written as $3\left(\frac{1}{3}\right)^{k-1}$ for $k = 1, 2, 3, \ldots, 6$.

Thus, $3 + 1 + \frac{1}{3} + \frac{1}{9} + \frac{1}{27} + \frac{1}{81} = \sum_{k=1}^{6} 3\left(\frac{1}{3}\right)^{k-1}$.

(c) The terms of the series can be written as $2\left(\frac{1}{4}\right)^{k-1}$ for $k = 1, 2, 3, \ldots$.

Thus, $2 + \frac{1}{2} + \frac{1}{8} + \frac{1}{32} + \cdots = \sum_{k=1}^{\infty} 2\left(\frac{1}{4}\right)^{k-1}$.

(d) The terms of the series can be written as $0.9(0.1)^{k-1}$ for $k = 1, 2, 3, \ldots$.

Thus, $0.9 + 0.09 + 0.009 + 0.0009 + \cdots = \sum_{k=1}^{\infty} 0.9(0.1)^{k-1}$.

5. (a) $\sum_{k=1}^{15}(k + 2) = \sum_{k=1}^{15} k + \sum_{k=1}^{15} 2 = \frac{15(16)}{2} + 15(2) = 150$

(b) $\sum_{k=1}^{21} 2k^2 = 2\sum_{k=1}^{21} k^2 = 2\left[\frac{21(22)(43)}{6}\right] = 6622$

6. If the height attained by the ball is doubled for each bounce, the series sums to

$$2\cdot 6\left(\frac{2}{3}\right)^0 + 2\cdot 6\left(\frac{2}{3}\right) + 2\cdot 6\left(\frac{2}{3}\right)^2 + 2\cdot 6\left(\frac{2}{3}\right)^3 + \cdots = 12\left[\left(\frac{2}{3}\right)^0 + \left(\frac{2}{3}\right)^1 + \left(\frac{2}{3}\right)^2 + \left(\frac{2}{3}\right)^3 + \cdots\right] =$$

$12\sum_{k=1}^{\infty}\left(\frac{2}{3}\right)^{k-1} = 12\left(\frac{1}{1 - \frac{2}{3}}\right) = 12(3) = 36$. Since the ball was dropped from a height of 6 feet, it did not travel upward for the first "bounce", so 6 must be subtracted. The total distance travelled is $36 - 6 = 30$ feet.

## 8.3: Counting

1. There are $2\cdot 2\cdot 2\cdot 2\cdot 2\cdot 2\cdot 2\cdot 2\cdot 2\cdot 2 = 2^{10} = 1024$ different ways to answer the exam.
2. There are $5\cdot 5\cdot 5\cdot 5\cdot 5\cdot 5\cdot 5\cdot 5\cdot 5\cdot 5 = 5^{10} = 9{,}765{,}625$ different ways to answer the exam.
3. There are $2\cdot 2\cdot 2\cdot 2\cdot 2\cdot 4\cdot 4\cdot 4\cdot 4\cdot 4\cdot 4\cdot 4\cdot 4\cdot 4\cdot 4 = 2^5\cdot 4^{10} = 33{,}554{,}432$ different ways.
4. There are $10\cdot 9\cdot 8\cdot 7\cdot 6\cdot 5\cdot 4\cdot 3\cdot 2\cdot 1 = 10! = 3{,}628{,}800$ different ways to answer this question.
5. There are 10 digits and 26 letters. There are $10\cdot 10\cdot 10\cdot 26\cdot 26\cdot 26 = 17{,}576{,}000$ different license plates.
6. There are 10 digits and 26 letters. There are $26\cdot 26\cdot 10\cdot 10\cdot 10\cdot 10 = 6{,}760{,}000$ different license plates.
7. There are 36 digits and letters. There are $26\cdot 26\cdot 26\cdot 36\cdot 36\cdot 36 = 820{,}025{,}856$ different license plates.
8. $26\cdot 26\cdot 10\cdot 10\cdot 10 + 26\cdot 26\cdot 10\cdot 10\cdot 10\cdot 10 = 7{,}436{,}000$
9. There are 3 choices for each of the 5 letters. There are $3\cdot 3\cdot 3\cdot 3\cdot 3 = 3^5 = 243$ different strings.
10. There are 4 choices for each of the 5 letters. There are $4\cdot 4\cdot 4\cdot 4\cdot 4 = 4^5 = 1024$ different strings.
11. There are 5 choices for each of the 5 letters. There are $5\cdot 5\cdot 5\cdot 5\cdot 5 = 5^5 = 3125$ different strings.

12. There are 2 choices for each of the 5 letters. There are $2 \cdot 2 \cdot 2 \cdot 2 \cdot 2 = 2^5 = 32$ different strings.
13. Since there are 2 letters that can only be used once, each string must be 2 letters long. For the first position there are 2 choices and for the second position there is only 1 choice. There are $2 \cdot 1 = 2$ possible strings.
14. Since there are 3 letters that can only be used once, each string must be 3 letters long. For the first position there are 3 choices and for the second position there are 2 choices and for the third position there is only 1 choice. There are $3 \cdot 2 \cdot 1 = 6$ possible strings.
15. There are $4 \cdot 3 \cdot 2 \cdot 1 = 24$ possible strings.
16. There are $5 \cdot 4 \cdot 3 \cdot 2 \cdot 1 = 120$ possible strings.
17. Each combination can vary between 000 and 999. Thus, there are 1000 possibilities for each lock. That is, there are $1000 \cdot 1000 = 1{,}000{,}000$ different combinations in all.
18. There are 40 different choices for each number in the combination. Thus, there are $40 \cdot 40 \cdot 40 = 64{,}000$ different combinations possible.
19. There are 2 settings (on or off) for each of the 12 switches.
    There are $2 \cdot 2 \cdot 2 \cdot 2 \cdot 2 \cdot 2 \cdot 2 \cdot 2 \cdot 2 \cdot 2 \cdot 2 \cdot 2 = 2^{12} = 4096$ different codes for the garage door opener.
20. There is a possibility of 10 different choices for each of the 3 numbers. Thus, there are $10 \cdot 10 \cdot 10 = 1000$ different ways to play the game. Looking at it a different way, one can pick any number from 000 to 999, so there are 1000 possibilities.
21. For the first letter there are 2 possibilities, whereas there are 26 possibilities for each of the last 3 positions. There are $2 \cdot 26 \cdot 26 \cdot 26 = 35{,}152$ different call letters possible. There is no shortage of call letters.
22. An access code can vary between 0000 and 9999, which is 10,000 different access codes. An alternate solution uses the following method. There are 10 digits that can be placed in each of 4 positions, so there are $10 \cdot 10 \cdot 10 \cdot 10 = 10{,}000$ different codes.
23. There are $2 \cdot 3 \cdot 4 = 24$ different packages that can be purchased.
24. There are 3 even numbers on each die. Therefore, there are $3 \cdot 3 = 9$ different possibilities.
25. There are $8 \cdot 10 \cdot 10 \cdot 10 \cdot 10 \cdot 10 \cdot 10 = 8{,}000{,}000$ such phone numbers.
26. There are $5 \cdot 10 \cdot 4 = 200$ different ways to order a salad, an entrée and a dessert.
27. $6! = 6 \cdot 5 \cdot 4 \cdot 3 \cdot 2 \cdot 1 = 720$
28. By definition, $0! = 1$.
29. $10! = 10 \cdot 9 \cdot 8 \cdot 7 \cdot 6 \cdot 5 \cdot 4 \cdot 3 \cdot 2 \cdot 1 = 3{,}628{,}800$
30. $7! = 7 \cdot 6 \cdot 5 \cdot 4 \cdot 3 \cdot 2 \cdot 1 = 5040$
31. $P(n, r) = \dfrac{n!}{(n - r)!} \Rightarrow P(5, 3) = \dfrac{5!}{(5 - 3)!} = \dfrac{5!}{2!} = \dfrac{120}{2} = 60$
32. $P(n, r) = \dfrac{n!}{(n - r)!} \Rightarrow P(10, 2) = \dfrac{10!}{(10 - 2)!} = \dfrac{10!}{8!} = \dfrac{10 \cdot 9 \cdot 8!}{8!} = 10 \cdot 9 = 90$
33. $P(n, r) = \dfrac{n!}{(n - r)!} \Rightarrow P(8, 1) = \dfrac{8!}{(8 - 1)!} = \dfrac{8!}{7!} = \dfrac{8 \cdot 7!}{7!} = 8$

34. $P(n, r) = \frac{n!}{(n-r)!} \Rightarrow P(6, 6) = \frac{6!}{(6-6)!} = \frac{6!}{0!} = 6! = 720$

35. $P(n, r) = \frac{n!}{(n-r)!} \Rightarrow P(7, 3) = \frac{7!}{(7-3)!} = \frac{7!}{4!} = \frac{7 \cdot 6 \cdot 5 \cdot 4!}{4!} = 7 \cdot 6 \cdot 5 = 210$

36. $P(n, r) = \frac{n!}{(n-r)!} \Rightarrow P(12, 3) = \frac{12!}{(12-3)!} = \frac{12!}{9!} = \frac{12 \cdot 11 \cdot 10 \cdot 9!}{9!} = 12 \cdot 11 \cdot 10 = 1320$

37. $P(n, r) = \frac{n!}{(n-r)!} \Rightarrow P(25, 2) = \frac{25!}{(25-2)!} = \frac{25!}{23!} = \frac{25 \cdot 24 \cdot 23!}{23!} = 25 \cdot 24 = 600$

38. $P(n, r) = \frac{n!}{(n-r)!} \Rightarrow P(20, 1) = \frac{20!}{(20-1)!} = \frac{20!}{19!} = \frac{20 \cdot 19!}{19!} = 20$

39. $P(n, r) = \frac{n!}{(n-r)!} \Rightarrow P(10, 4) = \frac{10!}{(10-4)!} = \frac{10!}{6!} = \frac{10 \cdot 9 \cdot 8 \cdot 7 \cdot 6!}{6!} = 10 \cdot 9 \cdot 8 \cdot 7 = 5040$

40. $P(n, r) = \frac{n!}{(n-r)!} \Rightarrow P(34, 2) = \frac{34!}{(34-2)!} = \frac{34!}{32!} = \frac{34 \cdot 33 \cdot 32!}{32!} = 34 \cdot 33 = 1122$

41. $P(4, 4) = \frac{4!}{(4-4)!} = \frac{4!}{0!} = 4! = 24$

42. There are $6 \cdot 5 \cdot 4 \cdot 3 \cdot 2 \cdot 1 = 720$ or $P(6, 6) = 6! = 720$ different arrangements.

43. There are $15 \cdot 14 \cdot 13 = 2730$ different arrangements of 3 students from a class of 15.

44. There are $5 \cdot 4 \cdot 3 \cdot 2 \cdot 1 = 120$ or $P(5, 5) = 5! = 120$ different orderings of the players.

45. There are $7 \cdot 6 \cdot 5 = 210$ different routes.

46. The total number of routes the salesperson can take is $3! = 6$. ABCDA: $50 + 103 + 67 + 88 = 308$ miles, ABDCA: $50 + 72 + 67 + 147 = 336$ miles, ACBDA: $147 + 103 + 72 + 88 = 410$ miles, ACDBA: $147 + 67 + 72 + 50 = 336$ miles, ADBCA: $88 + 72 + 103 + 147 = 410$ miles, and ADCBA: $88 + 67 + 103 + 50 = 308$ miles. Either route ABCDA or ADCBA will be the route with the least miles.

47. The remaining 4 digits for the 7 digit number are independent events. Since the last 4 digits can be any number from 0 to 9. The total is given by $10 \cdot 10 \cdot 10 \cdot 10 = 10{,}000$. The first 3 numbers are restricted to 3 different possibilities and there will be $(3) \cdot (10{,}000)$ or 30,000 phone numbers.

48. Initially any key can be put on the ring. Then the remaining 3 keys can be put on in $3! = 6$ different ways. If the keys are numbered 1 to 4, it is important to remember it is not possible to distinguish between the arrangements 1234, 2341, 3412, and 4123 on the key ring. There are only 6 ways to arrange the keys.

49. Initially any person can sit at the table. Then the remaining 6 people can sit in $6! = 720$ different ways. Since there is no difference between the people sitting clockwise or counterclockwise around the table, we must divide this result by 2 for the final answer. There are 360 different ways to seat the 7 people.

50. There are $10! = 3{,}628{,}800$ different batting orders with 10 players.

51. $P(9, 9) = \frac{9!}{(9-9)!} = \frac{9!}{0!} = 9! = 362{,}880$

52. Any of the 7 children can sit in one of the chairs. After this child sits down, there are 6 children left who could sit to the right of the first child, 5 children who could sit to the right of the second child, and so on. That is, there are $7 \cdot 6 \cdot 5 \cdot 4 \cdot 3 \cdot 2 = 5040$ ways for the children to sit. Now, since the the first child could sit in any one of 6 positions without creating a new distinguishable arrangement, we must divide by 6. Finally, clockwise and counterclockwise seatings are indistinguishable, we must also divide by 2. There are 420 different ways.

53. Counting February 29th, $P(366, 5) = \dfrac{366!}{(366-5)!} = \dfrac{366!}{361!} = \dfrac{366 \cdot 365 \cdot 364 \cdot 363 \cdot 362 \cdot 361!}{361!} \approx 6.39 \times 10^{12}$.

54. $P(5, 5) = \dfrac{5!}{(5-5)!} = \dfrac{5!}{0!} = 5! = 120$

55. There are 8 choices for the first and fourth digits and 10 choices for each of the other digits.
$8 \cdot 10 \cdot 10 \cdot 8 \cdot 10 \cdot 10 \cdot 10 \cdot 10 \cdot 10 \cdot 10 = 6{,}400{,}000{,}000$

56. $10 \cdot 5 = 50$

57. $C(n, r) = \dfrac{n!}{(n-r)!\, r!} \Rightarrow C(3, 1) = \dfrac{3!}{(3-1)!\, 1!} = \dfrac{3!}{2!\, 1!} = \dfrac{6}{2} = 3$

58. $C(n, r) = \dfrac{n!}{(n-r)!\, r!} \Rightarrow C(4, 3) = \dfrac{4!}{(4-3)!\, 3!} = \dfrac{4!}{1!\, 3!} = \dfrac{4!}{3!} = \dfrac{4 \cdot 3!}{3!} = 4$

59. $C(n, r) = \dfrac{n!}{(n-r)!\, r!} \Rightarrow C(6, 3) = \dfrac{6!}{(6-3)!\, 3!} = \dfrac{6!}{3!\, 3!} = \dfrac{720}{36} = 20$

60. $C(n, r) = \dfrac{n!}{(n-r)!\, r!} \Rightarrow C(7, 5) = \dfrac{7!}{(7-5)!\, 5!} = \dfrac{7!}{2!\, 5!} = \dfrac{7 \cdot 6 \cdot 5!}{2!\, 5!} = \dfrac{42}{2} = 21$

61. $C(n, r) = \dfrac{n!}{(n-r)!\, r!} \Rightarrow C(5, 0) = \dfrac{5!}{(5-0)!\, 0!} = \dfrac{5!}{5!\, 0!} = \dfrac{5!}{5!} = 1$

62. $C(n, r) = \dfrac{n!}{(n-r)!\, r!} \Rightarrow C(10, 2) = \dfrac{10!}{(10-2)!\, 2!} = \dfrac{10!}{8!\, 2!} = \dfrac{10 \cdot 9 \cdot 8!}{8!\, 2!} = \dfrac{90}{2} = 45$

63. $\dbinom{n}{r} = \dfrac{n!}{(n-r)!\, r!} \Rightarrow \dbinom{8}{2} = \dfrac{8!}{(8-2)!\, 2!} = \dfrac{8!}{6!\, 2!} = \dfrac{8 \cdot 7 \cdot 6!}{6!\, 2!} = \dfrac{56}{2} = 28$

64. $\dbinom{n}{r} = \dfrac{n!}{(n-r)!\, r!} \Rightarrow \dbinom{9}{4} = \dfrac{9!}{(9-4)!\, 4!} = \dfrac{9!}{5!\, 4!} = \dfrac{9 \cdot 8 \cdot 7 \cdot 6 \cdot 5!}{5!\, 4!} = \dfrac{9 \cdot 8 \cdot 7 \cdot 6}{4 \cdot 3 \cdot 2 \cdot 1} = 126$

65. $\dbinom{n}{r} = \dfrac{n!}{(n-r)!\, r!} \Rightarrow \dbinom{20}{18} = \dfrac{20!}{(20-18)!\, 18!} = \dfrac{20!}{2!\, 18!} = \dfrac{20 \cdot 19 \cdot 18!}{2!\, 18!} = \dfrac{20 \cdot 19}{2} = 190$

66. $\dbinom{n}{r} = \dfrac{n!}{(n-r)!\, r!} \Rightarrow \dbinom{100}{2} = \dfrac{100!}{(100-2)!\, 2!} = \dfrac{100!}{98!\, 2!} = \dfrac{100 \cdot 99 \cdot 98!}{98!\, 2!} = \dfrac{100 \cdot 99}{2} = 4950$

67. From 39 numbers a player picks 5 numbers. Since order is unimportant, there are $C(39, 5) = 575{,}757$ different ways of doing this.

68. From a group of 8 people, we must select a set of 5 people. This can be done $C(8, 5) = 56$ different ways.

69. Two women can be selected from 5 women in $C(5, 2)$ different ways. Two men can be selected from 3 men in $C(3, 2)$ different ways. The total number of committees is $C(5, 2) \cdot C(3, 2) = 10 \cdot 3 = 30$.

70. They can be selected in $C(6, 4) = 15$ different ways.

71. Three questions can be selected from 5 questions in $C(5, 3)$ different ways. Four questions can be selected from 5 questions in $C(5, 4)$ different ways. The total number of possibilities is $C(5, 3) \cdot C(5, 4) = 10 \cdot 5 = 50$.

72. There are $C(52, 5) = 2{,}598{,}960$ different ways to draw a 5-card hand from a 52-card deck.

73. Three red marbles can be drawn from 10 red marbles in $C(10, 3)$ different ways. Two blue marbles can be drawn from 12 blue marbles in $C(12, 2)$ different ways. There are $C(10, 3) \cdot C(12, 2) = 120 \cdot 66 = 7920$ ways.

74. Since there are 7 positions to fill on the shelf, there are $C(7, 4) = 35$ different ways to place the calculus books. Once these books are placed, the algebra books can be placed randomly in the remaining positions. Note that at this point, all remaining arrangements of the algebra books are indistinguishable. The answer is 35.

75. Since order is not important, there are $C(24, 3) = 2024$ ways to do this.

76. The person can choose a red rose in 3 ways, then a yellow rose in 4 ways, and finally a white rose in 5 ways. There are a total of $3 \cdot 4 \cdot 5 = 60$ ways to choose the flowers.

77. $P(n, n-1) = \dfrac{n!}{(n-(n-1))!} = \dfrac{n!}{1} = n!$ and $P(n, n) = \dfrac{n!}{(n-n)!} = \dfrac{n!}{0!} = \dfrac{n!}{1} = n!$

For example $P(7, 6) = 5040 = P(7, 7)$.

78. $\dbinom{n}{n-r} = \dfrac{n!}{(n-(n-r))!(n-r)!} = \dfrac{n!}{r!(n-r!)} = \dfrac{n!}{(n-r)!r!} = \dbinom{n}{r}$

For example $\dbinom{8}{3} = 56 = \dbinom{8}{5}$.

## 8.4: The Binomial Theorem

1. $\dbinom{5}{4} = \dfrac{5!}{1!\ 4!} = \dfrac{5 \cdot 4!}{1 \cdot 4!} = 5$

2. $\dbinom{6}{2} = \dfrac{6!}{4!\ 2!} = \dfrac{6 \cdot 5 \cdot 4!}{4! \cdot 2} = \dfrac{30}{2} = 15$

3. $\dbinom{4}{0} = \dfrac{4!}{4!\ 0!} = \dfrac{4!}{4! \cdot 1} = 1$

4. $\dbinom{4}{2} = \dfrac{4!}{2!\ 2!} = \dfrac{4 \cdot 3 \cdot 2!}{2! \cdot 2} = \dfrac{12}{2} = 6$

5. $\dbinom{6}{5} = \dfrac{6!}{1!\ 5!} = \dfrac{6 \cdot 5!}{1 \cdot 5!} = \dfrac{6}{1} = 6$

6. $\dbinom{6}{3} = \dfrac{6!}{3!\ 3!} = \dfrac{6 \cdot 5 \cdot 4 \cdot 3!}{3 \cdot 2 \cdot 1 \cdot 3!} = \dfrac{120}{6} = 20$

7. $\dbinom{3}{3} = \dfrac{3!}{0!\ 3!} = \dfrac{3!}{1 \cdot 3!} = 1$

8. $\dbinom{5}{2} = \dfrac{5!}{3!\ 2!} = \dfrac{5 \cdot 4 \cdot 3!}{3! \cdot 2} = \dfrac{20}{2} = 10$

9. Three $a$'s, two $b$'s $\Rightarrow C(5, 2) = 10$ different strings.

10. Five $a$'s, three $b$'s $\Rightarrow C(8, 3) = 56$ different strings.

11. Four $a$'s, four $b$'s $\Rightarrow C(8, 4) = 70$ different strings.

12. One $a$, five $b$'s $\Rightarrow C(6, 5) = 6$ different strings.

13. Five $a$'s, zero $b$'s $\Rightarrow C(5, 0) = 1$ string.

14. Zero $a$'s, three $b$'s $\Rightarrow C(3, 3) = 1$ string.

15. Four $a$'s, one $b$ $\Rightarrow C(5, 1) = 5$ different strings.

16. Four $a$'s, two $b$'s $\Rightarrow C(6, 2) = 15$ different strings.

17. $(x + y)^2 = \binom{2}{0}x^2y^0 + \binom{2}{1}x^1y^1 + \binom{2}{2}x^0y^2 = x^2 + 2xy + y^2$

18. $(x + y)^4 = \binom{4}{0}x^4y^0 + \binom{4}{1}x^3y^1 + \binom{4}{2}x^2y^2 + \binom{4}{3}x^1y^3 + \binom{4}{4}x^0y^4 = x^4 + 4x^3y + 6x^2y^2 + 4xy^3 + y^4$

19. $(m + 2)^3 = \binom{3}{0}m^3(2)^0 + \binom{3}{1}m^2(2)^1 + \binom{3}{2}m^1(2)^2 + \binom{3}{3}m^0(2)^3 = m^3 + 6m^2 + 12m + 8$

20. $(m + 2n)^5 = \binom{5}{0}m^5(2n)^0 + \binom{5}{1}m^4(2n)^1 + \binom{5}{2}m^3(2n)^2 + \binom{5}{3}m^2(2n)^3 + \binom{5}{4}m^1(2n)^4 + \binom{5}{5}m^0(2n)^5$
$= m^5 + 10m^4n + 40m^3n^2 + 80m^2n^3 + 80mn^4 + 32n^5$

21. $(2x - 3)^3 = \binom{3}{0}(2x)^3(-3)^0 + \binom{3}{1}(2x)^2(-3)^1 + \binom{3}{2}(2x)^1(-3)^2 + \binom{3}{3}(2x)^0(-3)^3 =$
$8x^3 - 36x^2 + 54x - 27$

22. $(x + y^2)^3 = \binom{3}{0}x^3(y^2)^0 + \binom{3}{1}x^2(y^2)^1 + \binom{3}{2}x^1(y^2)^2 + \binom{3}{3}x^0(y^2)^3 = x^3 + 3x^2y^2 + 3xy^4 + y^6$

23. $(p - q)^6 = \binom{6}{0}p^6(-q)^0 + \binom{6}{1}p^5(-q)^1 + \binom{6}{2}p^4(-q)^2 + \binom{6}{3}p^3(-q)^3 + \binom{6}{4}p^2(-q)^4 +$
$\binom{6}{5}p^1(-q)^5 + \binom{6}{6}p^0(-q)^6 = p^6 - 6p^5q + 15p^4q^2 - 20p^3q^3 + 15p^2q^4 - 6pq^5 + q^6$

24. $(p^2 - 3)^4 = \binom{4}{0}(p^2)^4(-3)^0 + \binom{4}{1}(p^2)^3(-3)^1 + \binom{4}{2}(p^2)^2(-3)^2 + \binom{4}{3}(p^2)^1(-3)^3 + \binom{4}{4}(p^2)^0(-3)^4$
$= p^8 - 12p^6 + 54p^4 - 108p^2 + 81$

25. $(2m + 3n)^3 = \binom{3}{0}(2m)^3(3n)^0 + \binom{3}{1}(2m)^2(3n)^1 + \binom{3}{2}(2m)^1(3n)^2 + \binom{3}{3}(2m)^0(3n)^3 =$
$8m^3 + 36m^2n + 54mn^2 + 27n^3$

26. $(3a - 2b)^5 = \binom{5}{0}(3a)^5(-2b)^0 + \binom{5}{1}(3a)^4(-2b)^1 + \binom{5}{2}(3a)^3(-2b)^2 + \binom{5}{3}(3a)^2(-2b)^3 +$
$\binom{5}{4}(3a)^1(-2b)^4 + \binom{5}{5}(3a)^0(-2b)^5 = 243a^5 - 810a^4b + 1080a^3b^2 - 720a^2b^3 + 240ab^4 - 32b^5$

27. $(1 - x^2)^4 = \binom{4}{0}(1)^4(-x^2)^0 + \binom{4}{1}(1)^3(-x^2)^1 + \binom{4}{2}(1)^2(-x^2)^2 + \binom{4}{3}(1)^1(-x^2)^3 + \binom{4}{4}(1)^0(-x^2)^4$
$= 1 - 4x^2 + 6x^4 - 4x^6 + x^8$

28. $(2 + 3x^2)^3 = \binom{3}{0}(2)^3(3x^2)^0 + \binom{3}{1}(2)^2(3x^2)^1 + \binom{3}{2}(2)^1(3x^2)^2 + \binom{3}{3}(2)^0(3x^2)^3 =$
$8 + 36x^2 + 54x^4 + 27x^6$

29. $(2p^3 - 3)^3 = \binom{3}{0}(2p^3)^3(-3)^0 + \binom{3}{1}(2p^3)^2(-3)^1 + \binom{3}{2}(2p^3)^1(-3)^2 + \binom{3}{3}(2p^3)^0(-3)^3 =$

$8p^9 - 36p^6 + 54p^3 - 27$

30. $(2r + 3t)^4 = \binom{4}{0}(2r)^4(3t)^0 + \binom{4}{1}(2r)^3(3t)^1 + \binom{4}{2}(2r)^2(3t)^2 + \binom{4}{3}(2r)^1(3t)^3 + \binom{4}{4}(2r)^0(3t)^4 =$

$16r^4 + 96r^3t + 216r^2t^2 + 216rt^3 + 81t^4$

31. Using Pascal's triangle, the coefficients are 1, 2, and 1.

$(x + y)^2 = 1x^2y^0 + 2x^1y^1 + 1x^0y^2 = x^2 + 2xy + y^2$

32. Using Pascal's triangle, the coefficients are 1, 3, 3, and 1.

$(m + n)^3 = 1m^3n^0 + 3m^2n^1 + 3m^1n^2 + 1m^0n^3 = m^3 + 3m^2n + 3mn^2 + n^3$

33. Using Pascal's triangle, the coefficients are 1, 4, 6, 4, and 1.

$(3x + 1)^4 = 1(3x)^4(1)^0 + 4(3x)^3(1)^1 + 6(3x)^2(1)^2 + 4(3x)^1(1)^3 + 1(3x)^0(1)^4 =$

$81x^4 + 108x^3 + 54x^2 + 12x + 1$

34. Using Pascal's triangle, the coefficients are 1, 4, 6, 4, and 1.

$(2x - 1)^4 = 1(2x)^4(-1)^0 + 4(2x)^3(-1)^1 + 6(2x)^2(-1)^2 + 4(2x)^1(-1)^3 + 1(2x)^0(-1)^4 =$

$16x^4 - 32x^3 + 24x^2 - 8x + 1$

35. Using Pascal's triangle, the coefficients are 1, 5, 10, 10, 5, and 1.

$(2 - x)^5 = 1(2)^5(-x)^0 + 5(2)^4(-x)^1 + 10(2)^3(-x)^2 + 10(2)^2(-x)^3 + 5(2)^1(-x)^4 + 1(2)^0(-x)^5 =$

$32 - 80x + 80x^2 - 40x^3 + 10x^4 - x^5$

36. Using Pascal's triangle, the coefficients are 1, 3, 3, and 1.

$(2a + 3b)^3 = 1(2a)^3(3b)^0 + 3(2a)^2(3b)^1 + 3(2a)^1(3b)^2 + 1(2a)^0(3b)^3 =$

$8a^3 + 36a^2b + 54ab^2 + 27b^3$

37. Using Pascal's triangle, the coefficients are 1, 4, 6, 4, and 1.

$(x^2 + 2)^4 = 1(x^2)^4(2)^0 + 4(x^2)^3(2)^1 + 6(x^2)^2(2)^2 + 4(x^2)^1(2)^3 + 1(x^2)^0(2)^4 =$

$x^8 + 8x^6 + 24x^4 + 32x^2 + 16$

38. Using Pascal's triangle, the coefficients are 1, 3, 3, and 1.

$(5 - x^2)^3 = 1(5)^3(-x^2)^0 + 3(5)^2(-x^2)^1 + 3(5)^1(-x^2)^2 + 1(5)^0(-x^2)^3 = 125 - 75x^2 + 15x^4 - x^6$

39. Using Pascal's triangle, the coefficients are 1, 4, 6, 4, and 1.

$(4x - 3y)^4 = 1(4x)^4(-3y)^0 + 4(4x)^3(-3y)^1 + 6(4x)^2(-3y)^2 + 4(4x)^1(-3y)^3 + 1(4x)^0(-3y)^4 =$

$256x^4 - 768x^3y + 864x^2y^2 - 432xy^3 + 81y^4$

40. Using Pascal's triangle, the coefficients are 1, 5, 10, 10, 5, and 1.

$(3 - 2x)^5 = 1(3)^5(-2x)^0 + 5(3)^4(-2x)^1 + 10(3)^3(-2x)^2 + 10(3)^2(-2x)^3 + 5(3)^1(-2x)^4 +$

$1(3)^0(-2x)^5 = 243 - 810x + 1080x^2 - 720x^3 + 240x^4 - 32x^5$

41. Using Pascal's triangle, the coefficients are 1, 6, 15, 20, 15, 6, and 1.

$(m + n)^6 = m^6 + 6m^5n + 15m^4n^2 + 20m^3n^3 + 15m^2n^4 + 6mn^5 + n^6$

42. Using Pascal's triangle, the coefficients are 1, 4, 6, 4, and 1.

$(2m - n)^4 = 1(2m)^4(-n)^0 + 4(2m)^3(-n)^1 + 6(2m)^2(-n)^2 + 4(2m)^1(-n)^3 + 1(2m)^0(-n)^4 =$

$16m^4 - 32m^3n + 24m^2n^2 - 8mn^3 + n^4$

43. Using Pascal's triangle, the coefficients are 1, 3, 3, and 1.

$(2x^3 - y^2)^3 = 1(2x^3)^3(-y^2)^0 + 3(2x^3)^2(-y^2)^1 + 3(2x^3)^1(-y^2)^2 + 1(2x^3)^0(-y^2)^3 =$

$8x^9 - 12x^6y^2 + 6x^3y^4 - y^6$

44. Using Pascal's triangle, the coefficients are 1, 4, 6, 4, and 1.

$(3x^2 + y^3)^4 = 1(3x^2)^4(y^3)^0 + 4(3x^2)^3(y^3)^1 + 6(3x^2)^2(y^3)^2 + 4(3x^2)^1(y^3)^3 + 1(3x^2)^0(y^3)^4 =$

$81x^8 + 108x^6y^3 + 54x^4y^6 + 12x^2y^9 + y^{12}$

45. The fourth term of $(a + b)^9$ is $\binom{9}{6}a^{9-3}b^3 = \binom{9}{6}a^6b^3 = 84a^6b^3$.

46. The second term of $(m - n)^9$ is $\binom{9}{8}m^{9-1}(-n)^1 = \binom{9}{8}m^8(-n)^1 = -9m^8n$.

47. The fifth term of $(x + y)^8$ is $\binom{8}{4}x^{8-4}y^4 = \binom{8}{4}x^4y^4 = 70x^4y^4$.

48. The third term of $(a + b)^7$ is $\binom{7}{5}a^{7-2}b^2 = \binom{7}{5}a^5b^2 = 21a^5b^2$.

49. The fourth term of $(2x + y)^5$ is $\binom{5}{2}(2x)^{5-3}y^3 = \binom{5}{2}(2x)^2y^3 = 40x^2y^3$.

50. The eighth term of $(2a - b)^9$ is $\binom{9}{2}(2a)^{9-7}(-b)^7 = \binom{9}{2}(2a)^2(-b)^7 = -144a^2b^7$.

51. The sixth term of $(3x - 2y)^6$ is $\binom{6}{1}(3x)^{6-5}(-2y)^5 = \binom{6}{1}(3x)(-2y)^5 = -576xy^5$.

52. The seventh term of $(2a + b)^9$ is $\binom{9}{3}(2a)^{9-6}(b)^6 = \binom{9}{3}(2a)^3(b)^6 = 672a^3b^6$.

## Checking Basic Concepts for Sections 8.3 and 8.4

1. There are $2 \cdot 2 \cdot 2 \cdot 2 \cdot 2 \cdot 2 \cdot 2 \cdot 2 = 2^8 = 256$ different ways to answer the quiz.
2. There are $C(52, 5) = 2{,}598{,}960$ different poker hands.
3. There are $26 \cdot 36 \cdot 36 \cdot 36 \cdot 36 \cdot 36 = 26 \cdot 36^5 = 1{,}572{,}120{,}576$ different license plates of this kind.
4. (a) Using Pascal's triangle, the coefficients are 1, 4, 6, 4, and 1.

   $(2x + 1)^4 = 1(2x)^4(1)^0 + 4(2x)^3(1)^1 + 6(2x)^2(1)^2 + 4(2x)^1(1)^3 + 1(2x)^0(1)^4 =$

   $16x^4 + 32x^3 + 24x^2 + 8x + 1$

   (b) Using Pascal's triangle, the coefficients are 1, 3, 3, and 1.

   $(4 - 3x)^3 = 1(4)^3(-3x)^0 + 3(4)^2(-3x)^1 + 3(4)^1(-3x)^2 + 1(4)^0(-3x)^3 =$

   $64 - 144x + 108x^2 - 27x^3$

# 8.5: Mathematical Induction

1. $3 + 6 + 9 + \cdots + 3n = \dfrac{3n(n+1)}{2}$

(i) Show that the statement is true for $n = 1$: $3(1) = \dfrac{3(1)(2)}{2} \Rightarrow 3 = 3$

(ii) Assume that $S_k$ is true: $3 + 6 + 9 + \cdots + 3k = \dfrac{3k(k+1)}{2}$

Show that $S_{k+1}$ is true: $3 + 6 + \cdots + 3(k+1) = \dfrac{3(k+1)(k+2)}{2}$

Add $3(k+1)$ to each side of $S_k$: $3 + 6 + 9 + \cdots + 3k + 3(k+1) = \dfrac{3k(k+1)}{2} + 3(k+1) =$

$\dfrac{3k(k+1) + 6(k+1)}{2} = \dfrac{(k+1)(3k+6)}{2} = \dfrac{3(k+1)(k+2)}{2}$

Since $S_k$ implies $S_{k+1}$, the statement is true for every positive integer $n$.

2. $1 + 3 + 5 + \cdots + (2n-1) = n^2$

(i) Show that the statement is true for $n = 1$: $2(1) - 1 = 1^2 \Rightarrow 1 = 1$

(ii) Assume that $S_k$ is true: $1 + 3 + 5 + \cdots + (2k-1) = k^2$

Show that $S_{k+1}$ is true: $1 + 3 + \cdots + (2(k+1) - 1) = (k+1)^2$

Add $2k + 1$ to each side of $S_k$: $1 + 3 + 5 + \cdots + (2k-1) + (2k+1) = k^2 + 2k + 1 = (k+1)^2$

Since $S_k$ implies $S_{k+1}$, the statement is true for every positive integer $n$.

3. $5 + 10 + 15 + \cdots + 5n = \dfrac{5n(n+1)}{2}$

(i) Show that the statement is true for $n = 1$: $5(1) = \dfrac{5(1)(2)}{2} \Rightarrow 5 = 5$

(ii) Assume that $S_k$ is true: $5 + 10 + 15 + \cdots + 5k = \dfrac{5k(k+1)}{2}$

Show that $S_{k+1}$ is true: $5 + 10 + \cdots + 5(k+1) = \dfrac{5(k+1)(k+2)}{2}$

Add $5(k+1)$ to each side of $S_k$: $5 + 10 + 15 + \cdots + 5k + 5(k+1) = \dfrac{5k(k+1)}{2} + 5(k+1) =$

$\dfrac{5k(k+1) + 10(k+1)}{2} = \dfrac{(k+1)(5k+10)}{2} = \dfrac{5(k+1)(k+2)}{2}$

Since $S_k$ implies $S_{k+1}$, the statement is true for every positive integer $n$.

4. $4 + 7 + 10 + \cdots + (3n + 1) = \dfrac{n(3n + 5)}{2}$

(i) Show that the statement is true for $n = 1$: $3(1) + 1 = \dfrac{1(3(1) + 5)}{2} \Rightarrow 4 = 4$

(ii) Assume that $S_k$ is true: $4 + 7 + 10 + \cdots + (3k + 1) = \dfrac{k(3k + 5)}{2}$

Show that $S_{k+1}$ is true: $4 + 7 + 10 + \cdots + (3(k + 1) + 1) = \dfrac{(k + 1)(3(k + 1) + 5)}{2}$

Add $3(k + 1) + 1$ to each side of $S_k$: $4 + 7 + \cdots + (3k + 1) + 3(k + 1) + 1 =$

$$\frac{k(3k + 5)}{2} + 3(k + 1) + 1 = \frac{3k^2 + 5k}{2} + 3k + 4 = \frac{3k^2 + 5k + 6k + 8}{2} = \frac{3k^2 + 11k + 8}{2} =$$

$$\frac{(k + 1)(3k + 8)}{2} = \frac{(k + 1)(3k + 3 + 5)}{2} = \frac{(k + 1)(3(k + 1) + 5)}{2}$$

Since $S_k$ implies $S_{k+1}$, the statement is true for every positive integer $n$.

5. $3 + 3^2 + 3^3 + \cdots + 3^n = \dfrac{3(3^n - 1)}{2}$

(i) Show that the statement is true for $n = 1$: $3^1 = \dfrac{3(3^1 - 1)}{2} \Rightarrow 3 = 3$

(ii) Assume that $S_k$ is true: $3 + 3^2 + 3^3 + \cdots + 3^k = \dfrac{3(3^k - 1)}{2}$

Show that $S_{k+1}$ is true: $3 + 3^2 + 3^3 + \cdots + 3^{k+1} = \dfrac{3(3^{k+1} - 1)}{2}$

Add $3^{k+1}$ to each side of $S_k$: $3 + 3^2 + 3^3 + \cdots + 3^k + 3^{k+1} = \dfrac{3(3^k - 1)}{2} + 3^{k+1} =$

$$\frac{3(3^k - 1) + 2(3^{k+1})}{2} = \frac{3^{k+1} - 3 + 2(3^{k+1})}{2} = \frac{3(3^{k+1}) - 3}{2} = \frac{3(3^{k+1} - 1)}{2}$$

Since $S_k$ implies $S_{k+1}$, the statement is true for every positive integer $n$.

6. $1^2 + 2^2 + 3^2 + \cdots + n^2 = \dfrac{n(n + 1)(2n + 1)}{6}$

(i) Show that the statement is true for $n = 1$: $1^2 = \dfrac{1(1 + 1)(2(1) + 1)}{6} \Rightarrow 1 = 1$

(ii) Assume that $S_k$ is true: $1^2 + 2^2 + 3^2 + \cdots + k^2 = \dfrac{k(k + 1)(2k + 1)}{6}$

Show that $S_{k+1}$ is true: $1^2 + 2^2 + 3^2 + \cdots + k^2 + (k + 1)^2 = \dfrac{(k + 1)(k + 2)(2(k + 1) + 1)}{6}$

Add $(k + 1)^2$ to each side of $S_k$: $1^2 + 2^2 + 3^2 + \cdots + k^2 + (k + 1)^2 =$

$$\frac{k(k + 1)(2k + 1)}{6} + (k + 1)^2 = \frac{k(k + 1)(2k + 1) + 6(k + 1)^2}{6} =$$

$$\frac{(k + 1)[k(2k + 1) + 6(k + 1)]}{6} = \frac{(k + 1)(2k^2 + 7k + 6)}{6} = \frac{(k + 1)(k + 2)(2k + 3)}{6} =$$

$$\frac{(k + 1)(k + 2)(2k + 2 + 1)}{6} = \frac{(k + 1)(k + 2)(2(k + 1) + 1)}{6}$$

Since $S_k$ implies $S_{k+1}$, the statement is true for every positive integer $n$.

7. $1^3 + 2^3 + 3^3 + \cdots + n^3 = \dfrac{n^2(n+1)^2}{4}$

(i) Show that the statement is true for $n = 1$: $1^3 = \dfrac{1^2(1+1)^2}{4} \Rightarrow 1 = 1$

(ii) Assume that $S_k$ is true: $1^3 + 2^3 + 3^3 + \cdots + k^3 = \dfrac{k^2(k+1)^2}{4}$

Show that $S_{k+1}$ is true: $1^3 + 2^3 + \cdots + (k+1)^3 = \dfrac{(k+1)^2(k+2)^2}{4}$

Add $(k+1)^3$ to each side of $S_k$: $1^3 + 2^3 + 3^3 + \cdots + k^3 + (k+1)^3 = \dfrac{k^2(k+1)^2}{4} + (k+1)^3 =$

$\dfrac{k^2(k+1)^2 + 4(k+1)^3}{4} = \dfrac{(k+1)^2(k^2+4k+4)}{4} = \dfrac{(k+1)^2(k+2)^2}{4}$

Since $S_k$ implies $S_{k+1}$, the statement is true for every positive integer $n$.

8. $5 \cdot 6 + 5 \cdot 6^2 + \cdots + 5 \cdot 6^n = 6(6^n - 1)$

(i) Show that the statement is true for $n = 1$: $5 \cdot 6^1 = 6(6^1 - 1) \Rightarrow 30 = 30$

(ii) Assume that $S_k$ is true: $5 \cdot 6 + 5 \cdot 6^2 + \cdots + 5 \cdot 6^k = 6(6^k - 1)$

Show that $S_{k+1}$ is true: $5 \cdot 6 + 5 \cdot 6^2 + \cdots + 5 \cdot 6^{k+1} = 6(6^{k+1} - 1)$

Add $5 \cdot 6^{k+1}$ to each side of $S_k$: $5 \cdot 6 + 5 \cdot 6^2 + \cdots + 5 \cdot 6^k + 5 \cdot 6^{k+1} = 6(6^k - 1) + 5 \cdot 6^{k+1}$

$= 6^{k+1} - 6 + 5 \cdot 6^{k+1} = 6 \cdot 6^{k+1} - 6 = 6(6^{k+1} - 1)$

Since $S_k$ implies $S_{k+1}$, the statement is true for every positive integer $n$.

9. $\dfrac{1}{1 \cdot 2} + \dfrac{1}{2 \cdot 3} + \cdots + \dfrac{1}{n(n+1)} = \dfrac{n}{n+1}$

(i) Show that the statement is true for $n = 1$: $\dfrac{1}{1(1+1)} = \dfrac{1}{1+1} \Rightarrow \dfrac{1}{2} = \dfrac{1}{2}$

(ii) Assume that $S_k$ is true: $\dfrac{1}{1 \cdot 2} + \dfrac{1}{2 \cdot 3} + \cdots + \dfrac{1}{k(k+1)} = \dfrac{k}{k+1}$

Show that $S_{k+1}$ is true: $\dfrac{1}{1 \cdot 2} + \dfrac{1}{2 \cdot 3} + \cdots + \dfrac{1}{(k+1)(k+2)} = \dfrac{k+1}{k+2}$

Add $\dfrac{1}{(k+1)(k+2)}$ to each side of $S_k$: $\dfrac{1}{1 \cdot 2} + \dfrac{1}{2 \cdot 3} + \cdots + \dfrac{1}{(k+1)(k+2)} =$

$\dfrac{k}{k+1} + \dfrac{1}{(k+1)(k+2)} = \dfrac{k(k+2)+1}{(k+1)(k+2)} = \dfrac{k^2+2k+1}{(k+1)(k+2)} = \dfrac{(k+1)(k+1)}{(k+1)(k+2)} = \dfrac{k+1}{k+2}$

Since $S_k$ implies $S_{k+1}$, the statement is true for every positive integer $n$.

10. $7 \cdot 8 + 7 \cdot 8^2 + \cdots + 7 \cdot 8^n = 8(8^n - 1)$

(i) Show that the statement is true for $n = 1$: $7 \cdot 8^1 = 8(8^1 - 1) \Rightarrow 56 = 56$

(ii) Assume that $S_k$ is true: $7 \cdot 8 + 7 \cdot 8^2 + \cdots + 7 \cdot 8^k = 8(8^k - 1)$

Show that $S_{k+1}$ is true: $7 \cdot 8 + 7 \cdot 8^2 + \cdots + 7 \cdot 8^{k+1} = 8(8^{k+1} - 1)$

Add $7 \cdot 8^{k+1}$ to each side of $S_k$: $7 \cdot 8 + 7 \cdot 8^2 + \cdots + 7 \cdot 8^k + 7 \cdot 8^{k+1} = 8(8^k - 1) + 7 \cdot 8^{k+1}$

$= 8^{k+1} - 8 + 7 \cdot 8^{k+1} = 8 \cdot 8^{k+1} - 8 = 8(8^{k+1} - 1)$

Since $S_k$ implies $S_{k+1}$, the statement is true for every positive integer $n$.

11. $\frac{4}{5} + \frac{4}{5^2} + \frac{4}{5^3} + \cdots + \frac{4}{5^n} = 1 - \frac{1}{5^n}$

(i) Show that the statement is true for $n = 1$: $\frac{4}{5^1} = 1 - \frac{1}{5^1} \Rightarrow \frac{4}{5} = \frac{4}{5}$

(ii) Assume that $S_k$ is true: $\frac{4}{5} + \frac{4}{5^2} + \frac{4}{5^3} + \cdots + \frac{4}{5^k} = 1 - \frac{1}{5^k}$

Show that $S_{k+1}$ is true: $\frac{4}{5} + \frac{4}{5^2} + \cdots + \frac{4}{5^{k+1}} = 1 - \frac{1}{5^{k+1}}$

Add $\frac{4}{5^{k+1}}$ to each side of $S_k$: $\frac{4}{5} + \frac{4}{5^2} + \frac{4}{5^3} + \cdots + \frac{4}{5^k} + \frac{4}{5^{k+1}} = 1 - \frac{1}{5^k} + \frac{4}{5^{k+1}} =$

$1 - \frac{1}{5^k} \cdot \frac{5}{5} + \frac{4}{5^{k+1}} = 1 - \frac{5}{5^{k+1}} + \frac{4}{5^{k+1}} = 1 - \frac{1}{5^{k+1}}$

Since $S_k$ implies $S_{k+1}$, the statement is true for every positive integer $n$.

12. $\frac{1}{2} + \frac{1}{2^2} + \frac{1}{2^3} + \cdots + \frac{1}{2^n} = 1 - \frac{1}{2^n}$

(i) Show that the statement is true for $n = 1$: $\frac{1}{2^1} = 1 - \frac{1}{2^1} \Rightarrow \frac{1}{2} = \frac{1}{2}$

(ii) Assume that $S_k$ is true: $\frac{1}{2} + \frac{1}{2^2} + \frac{1}{2^3} + \cdots + \frac{1}{2^k} = 1 - \frac{1}{2^k}$

Show that $S_{k+1}$ is true: $\frac{1}{2} + \frac{1}{2^2} + \cdots + \frac{1}{2^{k+1}} = 1 - \frac{1}{2^{k+1}}$

Add $\frac{1}{2^{k+1}}$ to each side of $S_k$: $\frac{1}{2} + \frac{1}{2^2} + \frac{1}{2^3} + \cdots + \frac{1}{2^k} + \frac{1}{2^{k+1}} = 1 - \frac{1}{2^k} + \frac{1}{2^{k+1}} =$

$1 - \frac{1}{2^k} \cdot \frac{2}{2} + \frac{1}{2^{k+1}} = 1 - \frac{2}{2^{k+1}} + \frac{1}{2^{k+1}} = 1 - \frac{1}{2^{k+1}}$

Since $S_k$ implies $S_{k+1}$, the statement is true for every positive integer $n$.

13. $\frac{1}{1 \cdot 4} + \frac{1}{4 \cdot 7} + \cdots + \frac{1}{(3n - 2)(3n + 1)} = \frac{n}{3n + 1}$

(i) Show that the statement is true for $n = 1$: $\frac{1}{1 \cdot 4} = \frac{1}{3(1) + 1} \Rightarrow \frac{1}{4} = \frac{1}{4}$

(ii) Assume that $S_k$ is true: $\frac{1}{1 \cdot 4} + \cdots + \frac{1}{(3k - 2)(3k + 1)} = \frac{k}{3k + 1}$

Show that $S_{k+1}$ is true: $\frac{1}{1 \cdot 4} + \cdots + \frac{1}{[3(k + 1) - 2][3(k + 1) + 1]} = \frac{k + 1}{3(k + 1) + 1}$

Add $\frac{1}{[3(k + 1) - 2][3(k + 1) + 1]}$ to each side of $S_k$: $\frac{1}{1 \cdot 4} + \cdots + \frac{1}{[3(k + 1) - 2][3(k + 1) + 1]}$

$= \frac{k}{3k + 1} + \frac{1}{[3(k + 1) - 2][3(k + 1) + 1]} = \frac{k}{3k + 1} + \frac{1}{(3k + 1)(3k + 4)} = \frac{k(3k + 4) + 1}{(3k + 1)(3k + 4)} =$

$\frac{3k^2 + 4k + 1}{(3k + 1)(3k + 4)} = \frac{(3k + 1)(k + 1)}{(3k + 1)(3k + 4)} = \frac{k + 1}{3k + 4} = \frac{k + 1}{3(k + 1) + 1}$

Since $S_k$ implies $S_{k+1}$, the statement is true for every positive integer $n$.

14. $x^{2n} + x^{2n-1}y + \cdots + xy^{2n-1} + y^{2n} = \dfrac{x^{2n+1} - y^{2n+1}}{x - y}$

(i) Show that the statement is true for $n = 1$: $x^2 + xy + y^2 = \dfrac{x^3 - y^3}{x - y} \Rightarrow$

$x^2 + xy + y^2 = \dfrac{(x - y)(x^2 + xy + y^2)}{x - y} \Rightarrow x^2 + xy + y^2 = x^2 + xy + y^2$

(ii) Assume that $S_k$ is true: $x^{2k} + x^{2k-1}y + \cdots + xy^{2k-1} + y^{2k} = \dfrac{x^{2k+1} - y^{2k+1}}{x - y}$

Show that $S_{k+1}$ is true: $x^{2(k+1)} + x^{2(k+1)-1}y + \cdots + xy^{2(k+1)-1} + y^{2(k+1)} = \dfrac{x^{2(k+1)+1} - y^{2(k+1)+1}}{x - y}$

Multiply each side of $S_k$ by $x^2$ and then add $xy^{2k+1} + y^{2k+2}$ to each side.

The left side is $x^2(x^{2k} + x^{2k-1}y + \cdots + xy^{2k-1} + y^{2k}) + xy^{2k+1} + y^{2k+2} =$

$x^{2k+2} + x^{2k+1}y + \cdots + x^3y^{2k-1} + x^2y^{2k} + xy^{2k+1} + y^{2k+2} =$

$x^{2(k+1)} + x^{2(k+1)-1}y + \cdots + xy^{2(k+1)-1} + y^{2(k+1)} = S_{k+1}$. The right side is

$x^2 \cdot \dfrac{x^{2k+1} - y^{2k+1}}{x - y} + xy^{2k+1} + y^{2k+2}$.

Multiply, write the expression using the LCD, and then simplify to obtain

$\dfrac{x^{2k+3} - y^{2k+3}}{x - y} = \dfrac{x^{2(k+1)+1} - y^{2(k+1)+1}}{x - y}$.

Since $S_k$ implies $S_{k+1}$, the statement is true for every positive integer $n$.

15. When $n = 1, 3^1 < 6(1) \Rightarrow 3 < 6$. When $n = 2, 3^2 < 6(2) \Rightarrow 9 < 12$.

When $n = 3, 3^3 > 6(3) \Rightarrow 27 > 18$. For all $n \geq 3, 3^n > 6n$. The only values are 1 and 2.

16. When $n = 1, 3^1 = 2(1) + 1 \Rightarrow 3 = 3$. When $n = 2, 3^2 > 2(2) + 1 \Rightarrow 9 > 5$.

When $n = 3, 3^3 > 2(3) + 1 \Rightarrow 27 > 7$. For all $n \geq 2, 3^n > 2n + 1$. The only value is 1.

17. When $n = 1, 2^1 > 1^2 \Rightarrow 2 > 1$. When $n = 2, 2^2 = 2^2 \Rightarrow 4 = 4$. When $n = 3, 2^3 < 3^2 \Rightarrow 8 < 9$.

When $n = 4, 2^4 = 4^2 \Rightarrow 16 = 16$. For all $n \geq 5, 2^n > n^2$. The only values are 2, 3, and 4.

18. When $n = 1, 1! < 2(1) \Rightarrow 1 < 2$. When $n = 2, 2! < 2(2) \Rightarrow 2 < 4$. When $n = 3, 3! = 2(3) \Rightarrow 6 = 6$.

When $n = 4, 4! > 2(4) \Rightarrow 24 > 8$. For all $n \geq 4, n! > 2n$. The only values are 1, 2, and 3.

19. $(a^m)^n = a^{mn}$

(i) Show that the statement is true for $n = 1$: $(a^m)^1 = a^{m \cdot 1} \Rightarrow a^m = a^m$

(ii) Assume that $S_k$ is true: $(a^m)^k = a^{mk}$

Show that $S_{k+1}$ is true: $(a^m)^{k+1} = a^{m(k+1)}$

Multiply each side of $S_k$ by $a^m$: $(a^m)^k \cdot (a^m)^1 = a^{mk} \cdot a^m \Rightarrow (a^m)^{k+1} = a^{mk+m} \Rightarrow (a^m)^{k+1} = a^{m(k+1)}$

Since $S_k$ implies $S_{k+1}$, the statement is true for every positive integer $n$.

20. $(ab)^n = a^n b^n$

(i) Show that the statement is true for $n = 1$: $(ab)^1 = a^1 b^1 \Rightarrow ab = ab$

(ii) Assume that $S_k$ is true: $(ab)^k = a^k b^k$

Show that $S_{k+1}$ is true: $(ab)^{k+1} = a^{k+1} b^{k+1}$

Multiply each side of $S_k$ by $ab$: $(ab)^k \cdot (ab)^1 = a^k b^k \cdot a^1 b^1 \Rightarrow (ab)^{k+1} = (a^k \cdot a^1)(b^k \cdot b^1) \Rightarrow$

$(ab)^{k+1} = a^{k+1} b^{k+1}$

Since $S_k$ implies $S_{k+1}$, the statement is true for every positive integer $n$.

21. $2^n > 2n$, if $n \geq 3$

(i) Show that the statement is true for $n = 3$: $2^3 > 2(3) \Rightarrow 8 > 6$

(ii) Assume that $S_k$ is true: $2^k > 2k$

Show that $S_{k+1}$ is true: $2^{k+1} > 2(k + 1)$

Multiply each side of $S_k$ by 2: $2^k \cdot 2 > 2k \cdot 2 \Rightarrow 2^{k+1} > 2(k + 1)$

Since $S_k$ implies $S_{k+1}$, the statement is true for every positive integer $n \geq 3$.

22. $3^n > 2n + 1$, if $n \geq 2$

(i) Show that the statement is true for $n = 2$: $3^2 > 2(2) + 1 \Rightarrow 9 > 5$

(ii) Assume that $S_k$ is true: $3^k > 2k + 1$

Show that $S_{k+1}$ is true: $3^{k+1} > 2(k + 1) + 1$

Multiply each side of $S_k$ by 3: $3^k \cdot 3 > (2k + 1) \cdot 3 \Rightarrow 3^{k+1} > 6k + 3 \Rightarrow 3^{k+1} > 6k + 2 + 1 \Rightarrow$

$3^{k+1} > 2(3k + 1) + 1$

Because $3k + 1 > k + 1$ for all $k \geq 2$, we may substitute $k + 1$ for $3k + 1$ in the expression.

That is $3^{k+1} > 2(k + 1) + 1$.

Since $S_k$ implies $S_{k+1}$, the statement is true for every positive integer $n \geq 2$.

23. $a^n > 1$, if $a > 1$

(i) Show that the statement is true for $n = 1$: $a^1 > 1 \Rightarrow a > 1$, which is true by the given restriction.

(ii) Assume that $S_k$ is true: $a^k > 1$

Show that $S_{k+1}$ is true: $a^{k+1} > 1$

Multiply each side of $S_k$ by $a$: $a^k \cdot a > 1 \cdot a \Rightarrow a^{k+1} > a$

Because $a > 1$, we may substitute 1 for $a$ in the expression. That is $a^{k+1} > 1$

Since $S_k$ implies $S_{k+1}$, the statement is true for every positive integer $n$.

24. $a^n > a^{n-1}$, if $a > 1$

(i) Show that the statement is true for $n = 1$: $a^1 > a^0 \Rightarrow a > 1$, which is true by the given restriction.

(ii) Assume that $S_k$ is true: $a^k > a^{k-1}$

Show that $S_{k+1}$ is true: $a^{k+1} > a^k$

Multiply each side of $S_k$ by $a$: $a^k \cdot a > a^{k-1} \cdot a \Rightarrow a^{k+1} > a^k$

Since $S_k$ implies $S_{k+1}$, the statement is true for every positive integer $n$.

25. $a^n < a^{n-1}$, if $0 < a < 1$

(i) Show that the statement is true for $n = 1$: $a^1 < a^0 \Rightarrow a < 1$, which is true by the given restriction.

(ii) Assume that $S_k$ is true: $a^k < a^{k-1}$

Show that $S_{k+1}$ is true: $a^{k+1} < a^k$

Multiply each side of $S_k$ by $a$: $a^k \cdot a < a^{k-1} \cdot a \Rightarrow a^{k+1} < a^k$

Since $S_k$ implies $S_{k+1}$, the statement is true for every positive integer $n$.

26. $2^n > n^2$, if $n > 4$

(i) Show that the statement is true for $n = 5$: $2^5 > 5^2 \Rightarrow 32 > 25$

(ii) Assume that $S_k$ is true: $2^k > k^2$

Show that $S_{k+1}$ is true: $2^{k+1} > (k + 1)^2$

Multiply each side of $S_k$ by 2: $2^k \cdot 2 > k^2 \cdot 2 \Rightarrow 2^{k+1} > 2k^2$

Because $2k^2 > (k + 1)^2$ for all $k \geq 5$, we may substitute $(k + 1)^2$ for $2k^2$ in the expression.

That is $2^{k+1} > (k + 1)^2$.

Since $S_k$ implies $S_{k+1}$, the statement is true for every positive integer $n > 4$.

27. $n! > 2^n$, if $n \geq 4$

(i) Show that the statement is true for $n = 4$: $4! > 2^4 \Rightarrow 24 > 16$

(ii) Assume that $S_k$ is true: $k! > 2^k$

Show that $S_{k+1}$ is true: $(k + 1)! > 2^{k+1}$

Multiply each side of $S_k$ by $k + 1$: $(k + 1)k! > 2^k(k + 1) \Rightarrow (k + 1)! > 2^k(k + 1)$

Because $(k + 1) > 2$ for all $k \geq 4$, we may substitute 2 for $(k + 1)$ in the expression.

That is $(k + 1)! > 2^k(2)$ or $(k + 1)! > 2^{k+1}$.

Since $S_k$ implies $S_{k+1}$, the statement is true for every positive integer $n \geq 4$.

28. $4^n > n^4$, if $n \geq 5$

(i) Show that the statement is true for $n = 5$: $4^5 > 5^4 \Rightarrow 1024 > 625$

(ii) Assume that $S_k$ is true: $4^k > k^4$

Show that $S_{k+1}$ is true: $4^{k+1} > (k + 1)^4$

Multiply each side of $S_k$ by 4: $4^k \cdot 4 > k^4 \cdot 4 \Rightarrow 4^{k+1} > 4k^4$

Because $4k^4 > (k + 1)^4$ for all $k \geq 5$, we may substitute $(k + 1)^4$ for $4k^4$ in the expression.

That is $4^{k+1} > (k + 1)^4$.

Since $S_k$ implies $S_{k+1}$, the statement is true for every positive integer $n \geq 5$.

29. The number of handshakes is $\frac{n^2 - n}{2}$ if $n \geq 2$.

(i) Show that the statement is true for $n = 2$: The number of handshakes for 2 people is $\frac{2^2 - 2}{2} = \frac{2}{2} = 1$, which is true.

(ii) Assume that $S_k$ is true: The number of handshakes for $k$ people is $\frac{k^2 - k}{2}$.

Show that $S_{k+1}$ is true: The number of handshakes for $k + 1$ people is

$$\frac{(k + 1)^2 - (k + 1)}{2} = \frac{k^2 + 2k + 1 - k - 1}{2} = \frac{k^2 + k}{2}.$$

When a person joins a group of $k$ people, each person must shake hands with the new person.

Since there are a total of $k$ people that will shake hands with the new person, the total number of handshakes for $k + 1$ people is $\frac{k^2 - k}{2} + k = \frac{k^2 - k + 2k}{2} = \frac{k^2 + k}{2}$.

Since $S_k$ implies $S_{k+1}$, the statement is true for every positive integer $n \geq 2$.

30. The number of sides is $3(4)^{n-1}$.

(i) Show that the statement is true for $n = 1$: The number of sides in the first figure is

$3(4)^{1-1} = 3(4)^0 = 3(1) = 3$, which is true.

(ii) Assume that $S_k$ is true: The number of sides in figure $k$ is $3(4)^{k-1}$.

Show that $S_{k+1}$ is true: The number sides in figure $k + 1$ is $3(4)^k$.

When a new figure is made, each side of the previous figure was broken into 4 smaller sides.

That is, the total number of sides in figure $k + 1$ is 4 times the number of sides in figure $k$.

This is given by $4 \cdot 3(4)^{k-1} = 3(4)^k$.

Since $S_k$ implies $S_{k+1}$, the statement is true for every positive integer $n$.

31. The first figure has perimeter $P = 3$. When a new figure is generated, each side if the previous figure increases in length by a factor of $\frac{4}{3}$. Thus, the second figure has perimeter $P = 3\left(\frac{4}{3}\right)$, the third figure has perimeter $P = 3\left(\frac{4}{3}\right)^2$, and so on. In general, the $n$th figure has perimeter $P = 3\left(\frac{4}{3}\right)^{n-1}$.

32. The area of an equilateral triangle is $A = \frac{\sqrt{3}}{4}s^2$. In the first figure, $s = 1$ so $A_1 = \frac{\sqrt{3}}{4} \cdot 1^2 = \frac{\sqrt{3}}{4}$.

The second figure has three smaller equilateral triangles with $s = \frac{1}{3}$. Each of these triangles has area $A = \frac{\sqrt{3}}{4} \cdot \left(\frac{1}{3}\right)^2 = \frac{\sqrt{3}}{36}$ and $3A = \frac{\sqrt{3}}{12}$. The total area of the second figure is $A_1 + 3A$. The third figure has twelve smaller equilateral triangles with $s = \frac{1}{9}$. Each of these triangles has area $A = \frac{\sqrt{3}}{4} \cdot \left(\frac{1}{9}\right)^2 = \frac{\sqrt{3}}{324}$ and $12A = \frac{\sqrt{3}}{27}$. The total area of the third figure is $A_2 + 12A$. Likewise the fourth figure has an additional area of $\frac{4\sqrt{3}}{243}$. The sequence of *additional* areas is given by $\frac{\sqrt{3}}{4}, \frac{\sqrt{3}}{12}, \frac{\sqrt{3}}{27}, \frac{4\sqrt{3}}{243}, \ldots$.

The sum of the first $n$ numbers in this sequence gives the area of the $n$th figure. Starting with the second number listed, the sequence is geometric with $a_1 = \frac{\sqrt{3}}{12}$ and $r = \frac{4}{9}$.

$$A = \frac{a_1(1 - r^{n-1})}{1 - r} + \frac{\sqrt{3}}{4} = \frac{\frac{\sqrt{3}}{12}(1 - (\frac{4}{9})^{n-1})}{1 - \frac{4}{9}} + \frac{\sqrt{3}}{4} = \frac{\frac{\sqrt{3}}{12}(1 - (\frac{4}{9})^{n-1})}{\frac{5}{9}} \cdot \frac{9}{9} + \frac{\sqrt{3}}{4} =$$

$$\frac{\frac{3\sqrt{3}}{4}(1 - (\frac{4}{9})^{n-1})}{5} + \frac{\sqrt{3}}{4} = \frac{3\sqrt{3}(1 - (\frac{4}{9})^{n-1}) + 5\sqrt{3}}{20} = \frac{3\sqrt{3} - 3\sqrt{3}(\frac{4}{9})^{n-1} + 5\sqrt{3}}{20} =$$

$$\frac{8\sqrt{3} - 3\sqrt{3}(\frac{4}{9})^{n-1}}{20} = \sqrt{3}\left[\frac{8 - 3(\frac{4}{9})^{n-1}}{20}\right] = \sqrt{3}\left[\frac{2}{5} - \frac{3}{20}\left(\frac{4}{9}\right)^{n-1}\right]$$

33. With 1 ring, 1 move is required. With 2 rings, 3 moves are required. Note that $3 = 2 + 1$. With 3 rings, 7 moves are required. Note that $7 = 2^2 + 2 + 1$.

With $n$ rings $2^{n-1} + 2^{n-2} + \cdots + 2^1 + 1 = 2^n - 1$ moves are required.

(i) Show that the statement is true for $n = 1$: The number of moves for 1 ring is $2^1 - 1 = 1$, which is true.

(ii) Assume that $S_k$ is true: The number of moves for $k$ rings is $2^k - 1$.

Show that $S_{k+1}$ is true: The number of moves for $k + 1$ rings is $2^{k+1} - 1$.

Assume $k + 1$ rings are on the first peg. Since $S_k$ is true, the top $k$ rings can be moved to the second peg in $2^k - 1$ moves. Now move the bottom ring to the third peg. Since $S_k$ is true, move the $k$ rings from the second peg on top of the ring on the third peg in $2^k - 1$ moves. The total number of moves is

$(2^k - 1) + 1 + (2^k - 1) = 2 \cdot 2^k - 1 = 2^{k+1} - 1$

Since $S_k$ implies $S_{k+1}$, the statement is true for every positive integer $n$.

## 8.6: Probability

1. Yes. The number is between 0 and 1.
2. Yes. The number is between 0 and 1.
3. No. The number is greater 1.
4. Yes. The number is between 0 and 1, inclusive.
5. Yes. The number is between 0 and 1, inclusive.
6. No. 110% = 1.1 which is greater than 1.
7. No. This number is less than 0.
8. No. This number is greater than 1.
9. A head when tossing a fair coin $\Rightarrow \frac{1}{2}$.
10. A tail when tossing a fair coin $\Rightarrow \frac{1}{2}$.
11. Rolling a 2 with a fair die $\Rightarrow \frac{1}{6}$.
12. Rolling a 5 or 6 with a fair die $\Rightarrow \frac{2}{6} = \frac{1}{3}$.
13. Guessing the correct answer for a true-false question $\Rightarrow \frac{1}{2}$.
14. Guessing the correct answer for a multiple-choice question with five choices $\Rightarrow \frac{1}{5}$.
15. Drawing a king from a standard deck of 52 cards $\Rightarrow \frac{4}{52} = \frac{1}{13}$.
16. Drawing a club from a standard deck of 52 cards $\Rightarrow \frac{13}{52} = \frac{1}{4}$.
17. The access code can vary between 0000 and 9999. This is 10,000 possibilities, so the probability of guessing the ATM code at random is $\frac{1}{10{,}000}$.

18. Randomly picking the winning team at a baseball game $\Rightarrow \frac{1}{2}$.

19. (a) The probability that their favorite is pepperoni is 0.43, so the probability it is not pepperoni is

    $1 - 0.43 = 0.57$ or 57%.

    (b) 19% + 14% = 33% or 0.33

20. (a) $\frac{2103}{98{,}941} \approx 0.021$ or 2.1%

    (b) $\frac{2608 + 16{,}287}{98{,}941} \approx 0.19$ or 19%

21. The probability of one tail is $\frac{1}{2}$. The events of tossing a coin are independent so the probability of tossing two tails is $\frac{1}{2} \cdot \frac{1}{2} = \frac{1}{4}$.

22. The probability of one head is $\frac{1}{2}$. The events of tossing a coin are independent so the probability of tossing three heads is $\frac{1}{2} \cdot \frac{1}{2} \cdot \frac{1}{2} = \frac{1}{8}$.

23. The probability of rolling either a 5 or a 6 is $\frac{2}{6} = \frac{1}{3}$. The probability of obtaining a 5 or 6 on three consecutive roles is $\frac{1}{3} \cdot \frac{1}{3} \cdot \frac{1}{3} = \frac{1}{27}$.

24. Refer to Table 8.9 in this section. There are 6 outcomes from a sample space of 36 outcomes that result in the event of the sum being 7. They are (1, 6), (2, 5), (3, 4), (4, 3), (5, 2), and (6, 1). Thus, the probability of rolling a sum of 7 is $\frac{6}{36} = \frac{1}{6}$.

25. To obtain a sum of 2, both die must show a 1. The probability of rolling a 1 with one die is $\frac{1}{6}$. Since the events are independent, the probability of obtaining a 1 on two dice is $\frac{1}{6} \cdot \frac{1}{6} = \frac{1}{36}$.

26. This is the complement of the solution to exercise 24. The probability of not rolling a sum of 7 is $1 - \frac{1}{6} = \frac{5}{6}$.

27. The probability of rolling a die and not obtaining a 6 is $\frac{5}{6}$. The probability of rolling a die four times and not obtaining a 6 is $\frac{5}{6} \cdot \frac{5}{6} \cdot \frac{5}{6} \cdot \frac{5}{6} = \frac{625}{1296} \approx 0.482$.

28. This is the complement of the solution to the previous exercise. The probability of rolling at least one 6 is $1 - \frac{625}{1296} = \frac{671}{1296} \approx 0.518$.

29. The probability of drawing the first ace is $\frac{4}{52}$, the second ace $\frac{3}{51}$, the third ace $\frac{2}{50}$, and the fourth ace $\frac{1}{49}$. The probability of drawing four aces is $\frac{4}{52} \cdot \frac{3}{51} \cdot \frac{2}{50} \cdot \frac{1}{49} = \frac{24}{6{,}497{,}400} = \frac{1}{270{,}725}$.

30. The first card can be any card in the deck. The second card must match the first card. There are 3 cards in the remaining 51 cards that satisfy this condition. The probability of the second card matching the first card is $\frac{3}{51} = \frac{1}{17}$.

31. There are $\binom{13}{3}$ ways to draw 3 hearts, and there are $\binom{13}{2}$ ways to draw 2 diamonds. there are $\binom{52}{5}$ different poker hands. Thus, the probability of drawing 3 hearts and 2 diamonds is

$$P(E) = \frac{n(E)}{n(S)} = \frac{\binom{13}{3} \cdot \binom{13}{2}}{\binom{52}{5}} = \frac{286 \cdot 78}{2{,}598{,}960} = 0.0086, \text{ or a } 0.86\% \text{ chance.}$$

32. There are $\binom{4}{3}$ ways to draw 3 kings, and there are $\binom{4}{2}$ ways to draw 2 queens. There are $\binom{52}{5}$ different poker hands. Thus, the probability of drawing 3 kings and 2 queens is

$$P(E) = \frac{n(E)}{n(S)} = \frac{\binom{4}{3} \cdot \binom{4}{2}}{\binom{52}{5}} = \frac{4 \cdot 6}{2{,}598{,}960} = 0.00000923, \text{ or a } 0.0009\% \text{ chance.}$$

33. There are 4 strings out of 20 that are defective. Therefore, there is a $\frac{4}{20} = 0.2$ probability or 20% chance of drawing a defective string and rejecting the box.

34. There are $C(20, 3)$ different ways to select 3 strings of lights from a box of 20. In order to not test a defective string, we must pick 3 strings from the 16 good strings. This can be done $C(16, 3)$ different ways. The probability that the box is not rejected is given by $\frac{C(16, 3)}{C(20, 3)} \approx 0.491$. the probability of rejecting the box is approximately $1 - 0.491 = 0.509$.

35. (a) Figure 35 shows a Venn diagram of the data.

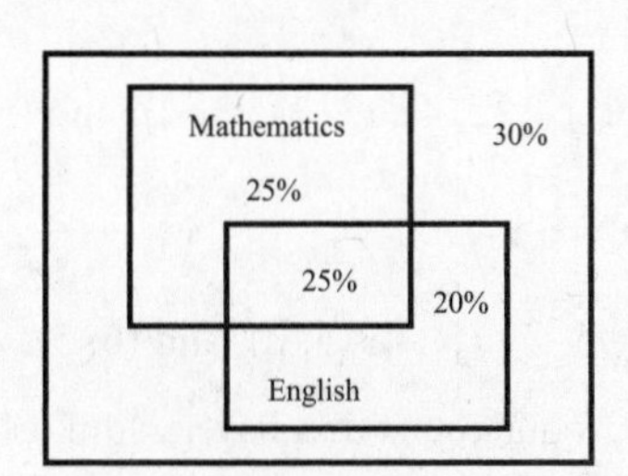


Figure 35

(b) The percentage of students needing help with mathematics, English, or both is $25 + 25 + 20 = 70\%$. The probability of needing help in mathematics, English, or both is 0.7.

(c) If $M$ represents the event of a student needing help with mathematics, and $E$ represents the event that a student needs help with English, then

$$P(M \text{ or } E) = P(M \cup E) = P(M) + P(E) - P(M \cap E) = 0.5 + 0.45 - 0.25 = 0.7.$$

36. Let $E$ represent the event of a student being enrolled in an English class, and $B$ the event that a student is enrolled in a business class, then

$$P(E \text{ or } B) = P(E \cup B) = P(E) + P(B) - P(E \cap B) = \frac{950}{5500} + \frac{1220}{5500} - \frac{350}{5500} = \frac{1820}{5500} = \frac{182}{550} \approx 0.331.$$

37. (a) There were $4481 + 1614 = 6095$ books published in the areas of art and music out of a possible 119,923. The probability of a new book or edition being in the area of art or music is $\frac{6095}{119{,}923} \approx 0.051$.

(b) The number of books published in science or religion was $7032 + 6659 = 13{,}691$. The probability of a new book or edition not being published in the areas of science or religion is $1 - \frac{13{,}691}{119{,}923} = \frac{106{,}232}{119{,}923} \approx 0.886$.

38. The probability is $\frac{817}{100{,}000} \approx 0.00817$.

39. The probability is $\frac{94}{100{,}000} \approx 0.00094$.

40. The probability of tossing a coin $n$ times and obtaining $n$ heads is $\left(\frac{1}{2}\right)^n$. As $n$ increases the probability decreases. This agrees with intuition. The probability of tossing a long string of consecutive heads is small. The longer the string of heads, the less chance there is of it happening.

41. (a) The probability is $\frac{158{,}502}{984{,}155} \approx 0.161$.

(b) This is the complement of the event in part (a), which is $1 - \frac{158{,}502}{984{,}155} = \frac{825{,}653}{984{,}155} \approx 0.839$.

(c) The probability is $\frac{49{,}913 + 29{,}092}{984{,}155} \approx 0.080$.

42. The probability of obtaining a 5 or 6 is $\frac{1}{6}$, and the probability of obtaining a 1, 2, 3, or 4 on one roll is $\frac{4}{6}$. The probability of obtaining two 6's, one 5, and then two shakes with a 4 or less is $\frac{1}{6} \cdot \frac{1}{6} \cdot \frac{1}{6} \cdot \frac{4}{6} \cdot \frac{4}{6} = \frac{16}{7776} = \frac{1}{486} \approx 0.002$.

43. The possible outcomes for a sum of 5 or 6 are (1, 4), (2, 3), (3, 2), (4, 1), (1, 5), (2, 4), (3, 3), (4, 2), and (5, 1). This is a total of 9 outcomes out of 36 possible outcomes. The probability is $\frac{9}{36} = \frac{1}{4}$.

44. The possible outcomes for a sum of 7 or 11 are (1, 6), (2, 5), (3, 4), (4, 3), (5, 2), (6, 1), (5, 6), and (6, 5). This is a total of 8 outcomes out of 36 possible outcomes. Then there are 28 outcomes that have a sum other than 7 or 11. The probability is $\frac{28}{36} = \frac{7}{9}$.

45. There are four 2's, four 3's and four 4's in a standard deck. The probability is $\frac{12}{52} = \frac{3}{13}$.

46. The first card drawn must be one of the 44 cards (out of 52) that are neither an ace nor a queen. When the second card is drawn, it must be one of the 43 remaining cards (out of 51) that are neither an ace nor a queen. The probability is $\frac{44}{52} \cdot \frac{43}{51} = \frac{473}{663} \approx 0.7134$

47. (a) Since the events of rolling a 4, 5, or 6 are mutually exclusive, the probability of either a 4, 5, or 6 is $0.2 + 0.2 + 0.3 = 0.7$.

(b) The events of rolling a 6 followed by a second 6 are independent events. The probability of two consecutive 6's is $(0.3)(0.3) = 0.09$.

48. (a) The probability of HT is $\frac{3}{4}\cdot\frac{1}{4} = \frac{3}{16}$.

(b) The probability of HH is $\frac{3}{4}\cdot\frac{3}{4} = \frac{9}{16}$.

(c) The probability of HHT is $\frac{3}{4}\cdot\frac{3}{4}\cdot\frac{1}{4} = \frac{9}{64}$.

(d) The probability of THT is $\frac{1}{4}\cdot\frac{3}{4}\cdot\frac{1}{4} = \frac{3}{64}$.

49. (a) The only way to obtain a sum of 12 is for both dice to show a 6. Since these events are independent, the probability of two 6's is $(0.3)(0.3) = 0.09$ or 9%.

(b) There are two ways to obtain a sum of 11. The red die shows a 5 and the blue die a 6, or vice versa. The roll of the two dice are independent. The probability of the red die showing a 5 is 0.2 and the probability of the blue die showing a 6 is 0.3. The probability of a sum of 11 is $(0.2)(0.3) = 0.06$. Similarly, the probability of the red die showing a 6 and the blue die showing a 5 is 0.06. Since these events are mutually exclusive, the probability of a sum of 11 is $0.06 + 0.06 = 0.12$ or 12%.

50. There are two ways of setting the first switch, two ways for the second switch, and so on. By the fundamental counting principle the switches can be set $2\cdot2\cdot2\cdot2\cdot2\cdot2\cdot2\cdot2\cdot2\cdot2\cdot2\cdot2 = 2^{12} = 4096$ different ways. There is a probability of $\frac{1}{4096}$ at selecting the correct code at random.

51. There are ten possibilities for each of the three digits. By the fundamental counting principle, there are $10\cdot10\cdot10 = 10^3 = 1000$ different ways to pick these numbers. There is only one winning number so the probability is $\frac{1}{1000}$.

52. There are $C(55, 5)$ different ways to select 5 numbers from 55. There are 42 different ways to select the powerball. The total number of ways of playing the game are $C(55, 5)\cdot 42 = 146{,}107{,}962$. Since there is only one way to win the jackpot, the probability of winning the jackpot is $\frac{1}{146{,}107{,}962}$.

53. (a) There are a total of $22 + 18 + 10 = 50$ marbles in the jar. Since 22 of them are red, there is a probability of $\frac{22}{50} = 0.44$ of drawing a red ball.

(b) Since there is a 0.44 probability of drawing a red ball, there is a $1 - 0.44 = 0.56$ probability of not drawing a red ball.

(c) Drawing a blue or green ball is equivalent to not drawing a red ball. The probability is the same as in part (b), which was 0.56.

54. (a) There are 100 balls in the jar. The probability of drawing the first blue ball is $\frac{45}{100}$. The probability of drawing a second blue ball, given the first ball is blue, is $\frac{44}{99}$. The probability of drawing two balls that are blue is $\frac{45}{100} \cdot \frac{44}{99} = \frac{1}{5}$.

(b) The probability that neither are blue is equal to the probability that both are red: $\frac{55}{100} \cdot \frac{54}{99} = \frac{3}{10}$.

(c) The probability that the first ball is red is $\frac{55}{100}$ and the probability that the second ball is blue, given the first ball is red, is $\frac{45}{99}$. The probability that the first ball is red an the second ball is blue is given by $\frac{55}{100} \cdot \frac{45}{99} = \frac{1}{4}$.

55. Since one card, a queen, has been drawn, there are 3 queens left in the set of 51 cards. So the probability of drawing a queen is $\frac{3}{51}$.

56. Since two cards, both kings, have been drawn, there are 2 kings left in the set of 50 cards. So the probability of drawing a queen is $\frac{2}{50} = \frac{1}{25}$.

57. Since there are 4 kings in a total of 12 face cards, the probability of drawing a king is $\frac{4}{12} = \frac{1}{3}$.

58. Since there is no replacement on each draw, the probability of drawing first an ace, then a king, and then a queen is $\frac{4}{52} \cdot \frac{4}{51} \cdot \frac{4}{50} = \frac{8}{16{,}575}$.

59. Since 2 red out of 10 red marbles and 4 blue out of 23 blue marbles have already been drawn, 6 marbles out of 33 marbles have been removed from the jar. There are $23 - 4 = 19$ blue marbles left out of $33 - 6 = 27$ marbles in the jar. The probability of drawing a blue marble next is $\frac{19}{27}$.

60. Let $E_1$ denote the event that the first serve is out of bounds and $E_2$ denote the event that the second serve is in bounds. $P(E_1 \text{ and } E_2) = P(E_1 \cap E_2) = P(E_1) \cdot P(E_2\text{, given that } E_1 \text{ has occured}) = 0.3 \cdot 0.8 = 0.24$.

61. Let $E_1$ denote the event that it is cloudy and $E_2$ denote the event that it is windy. $P(E_1) = 0.30$ and $P(E_1 \text{ and } E_2) = P(E_1 \cap E_2) = 0.12$. $P(E_1 \cap E_2) = P(E_1) \cdot P(E_2\text{, given that } E_1 \text{ has occured}) \Rightarrow$ $0.12 = 0.30 \cdot P(E_2\text{, given that } E_1 \text{ has occured}) \Rightarrow 0.4 = P(E_2\text{, given that } E_1 \text{ has occured})$. The probability that it will be windy given that the day is cloudy is 40%.

62. Let $E_1$ denote the event that it is rainy and $E_2$ denote the event that it is windy. $P(E_1) = 0.80$ and $P(E_1 \text{ and } E_2) = P(E_1 \cap E_2) = 0.72$. $P(E_1 \cap E_2) = P(E_1) \cdot P(E_2\text{, given that } E_1 \text{ has occured}) \Rightarrow$ $0.72 = 0.80 \cdot P(E_2\text{, given that } E_1 \text{ has occured}) \Rightarrow 0.9 = P(E_2\text{, given that } E_1 \text{ has occured})$. The probability that it will be windy given that the day is rainy is 90%.

63. The possibilities for the result that the first die is a 2 and the sum of the two dice is 7 or more, can be represented by {(2, 5), (2, 6)}. The sample space can be represented by {(2, 1), (2, 2), (2, 3), (2, 4), (2, 5), and (2, 6)}. Out of a total of 6, 2 outcomes satisfy the conditions, so the probability is $\frac{2}{6} = \frac{1}{3}$.

64. The possibilities for the result that the first die is a 4 and the sum of the three dice is less than 12, can be represented by {(4, 1, 1), (4, 1, 2), (4, 1, 3), (4, 1, 4), (4, 1, 5), (4, 1, 6), (4, 2, 1), (4, 2, 2), (4, 2, 3), (4, 2, 4), (4, 2, 5), (4, 3, 1), (4, 3, 2), (4, 3, 3), (4, 3, 4), (4, 4, 1), (4, 4, 2), (4, 4, 3), (4, 5, 1), (4, 5, 2), (4, 6, 1)}. The total number of outcomes in the sample space is $1 \cdot 6 \cdot 6 = 36$. Thus, out of a total of 36, 21 outcomes satisfy the conditions, so the probability is $\frac{21}{36} = \frac{7}{12}$.

65. (a) Let $D$ represent the event that part is defective. Since 18 of the 235 parts are defective, $P(D) = \frac{18}{235}$.

(b) Let $A$ represent the event that part is type $A$. Since 7 of the 18 parts are type A, $P(A, \text{given } D) = \frac{7}{18}$.

(c) $P(D \text{ and } A) = P(D \cap A) = P(D) \cdot P(A, \text{given } D) = \frac{18}{235} \cdot \frac{7}{18} = \frac{7}{235}$.

66. Let $F$ represent the event that the person is female and $B$ represent the event that the person has disease B.

$P(F \text{ and } B) = P(F \cap B) = P(F) \cdot P(B, \text{given } F) = \frac{996}{1607} \cdot \frac{851}{996} = \frac{851}{1607}$.

67. (a) Let $O$ represent the event that the number is odd. Since 8 of the 15 numbers are odd, $P(O) = \frac{8}{15}$.

(b) Let $E$ represent the event that the number is even. Since 7 of the 15 numbers are even, $P(E) = \frac{7}{15}$.

(c) Let $M$ represent the event that the number is prime. Since 6 of the 15 numbers are prime,

$P(M) = \frac{6}{15} = \frac{2}{5}$.

(d) Since 5 of the 6 prime numbers are odd, $P(M \cap O) = \frac{5}{15} = \frac{1}{3}$.

(e) Since 1 of the 6 prime numbers is even, $P(M \cap E) = \frac{1}{15}$.

68. (a) Let $M$ represent the event that the student is male. Since 65 of the 110 students are male,

$P(M) = \frac{65}{110} = \frac{13}{22}$.

(b) Let $F$ represent the event that the student takes French. Since 25 of the 65 males are taking French,

$P(F, \text{given } M) = \frac{25}{65} = \frac{5}{13}$.

(c) $P(M \text{ and } F) = P(M \cap F) = P(M) \cdot P(F, \text{given } M) = \frac{13}{22} \cdot \frac{5}{13} = \frac{5}{22}$. The table shows that 25 of the 110 students are male and taking French. The $P(M \text{ and } F) = \frac{25}{110} = \frac{5}{22}$, which agrees with the previous calculations.

## Checking Basic Concepts for Sections 8.5 and 8.6

1. $4 + 8 + 12 + \cdots + 4n = 2n(n + 1)$

   (i) Show that the statement is true for $n = 1$: $4(1) = 2(1)(1 + 1) \Rightarrow 4 = 4$

   (ii) Assume that $S_k$ is true: $4 + 8 + 12 + \cdots + 4k = 2k(k + 1)$

   Show that $S_{k+1}$ is true: $4 + 8 + \cdots + 4(k + 1) = 2(k + 1)(k + 2)$

   Add $4(k + 1)$ to each side of $S_k$: $4 + 8 + 12 + \cdots + 4k + 4(k + 1) = 2k(k + 1) + 4(k + 1) =$
   $2k^2 + 6k + 4 = 2(k + 1)(k + 2)$

   Since $S_k$ implies $S_{k+1}$, the statement is true for every positive integer $n$.

2. $n^2 \leq 2^n$, if $n \geq 4$

   (i) Show that the statement is true for $n = 4$: $4^2 \leq 2^4 \Rightarrow 16 \leq 16$

   (ii) Assume that $S_k$ is true: $k^2 \leq 2^k$

   Show that $S_{k+1}$ is true: $(k + 1)^2 \leq 2^{k+1}$

   Multiply each side of $S_k$ by 2: $k^2 \cdot 2 \leq 2^k \cdot 2 \Rightarrow 2k^2 \leq 2^{k+1}$

   Because $(k + 1)^2 < 2k^2$ for all $k \geq 4$, we may substitute $(k + 1)^2$ for $2k^2$ in the expression.

   That is $(k + 1)^2 \leq 2^{k+1}$.

   Since $S_k$ implies $S_{k+1}$, the statement is true for every positive integer $n \geq 4$.

3. The probability of one head is $\frac{1}{2}$. The events of tossing a coin are independent so the probability of tossing four heads is $\frac{1}{2} \cdot \frac{1}{2} \cdot \frac{1}{2} \cdot \frac{1}{2} = \frac{1}{16}$.

4. Rolling a sum of 11 with two dice can be represented by $\{(5, 6), (6, 5)\}$. The total number of outcomes in the sample space is $6 \cdot 6 = 36$. Thus, the probability of rolling a sum of 11 with two dice is $\frac{2}{36} = \frac{1}{18}$.

5. There are $\binom{4}{4}$ different ways to draw four aces and $\binom{4}{1}$ different ways to draw a queen. There are a total of $\binom{52}{5}$ different 5-card hands in a set of 52 cards. Thus, the probability of drawing four aces and a queen is

$$\frac{\binom{4}{4} \cdot \binom{4}{1}}{\binom{52}{5}} = \frac{1 \cdot 4}{2{,}598{,}960} = 0.0000015.$$

6. There are 2.7 million high school graduates of which 1.3 million were male. This means that $2{,}700{,}000 - 1{,}300{,}000 = 1{,}400{,}000$ were female. The probability of randomly selecting a female graduate is $\frac{1{,}400{,}000}{2{,}700{,}000} = \frac{14}{27}$.

## Chapter 8 Review Exercises

1. $a_1 = -3(1) + 2 = -1$; $a_2 = -3(2) + 2 = -4$; $a_3 = -3(3) + 2 = -7$; $a_4 = -3(4) + 2 = -10$

   The first four terms are –1, –4, –7, and –10.

2. $a_1 = 1^2 + 1 = 2; a_2 = 2^2 + 2 = 6; a_3 = 3^2 + 3 = 12; a_4 = 4^2 + 4 = 20$

The first four terms are 2, 6, 12, and 20.

3. $a_1 = 0; a_2 = 2a_1 + 1 = 2(0) + 1 = 1; a_3 = 2a_2 + 1 = 2(1) + 1 = 3; a_4 = 2a_3 + 1 = 2(3) + 1 = 7$

The first four terms are 0, 1, 3, and 7.

4. $a_1 = 1; a_2 = 4; a_3 = a_2 + 2a_1 = 4 + 2(1) = 6; a_4 = a_3 + 2a_2 = 6 + 2(4) = 14$

The first four terms are 1, 4, 6, and 14.

5. The points (1, 5), (2, 3), (3, 1), (4, 2), (5, 4), and (6, 6) lie on the graph. Therefore, the terms of this sequence are 5, 3, 1, 2, 4, 6.

6. The points (1, 1), (2, 2), (3, 3), (4, 2), and (5, 1) lie on the graph. Therefore, the terms of this sequence are 1, 2, 3, 2, 1.

7. (a) Each term can be found by adding –2 to the previous term, beginning with 3. It is an arithmetic sequence. A numerical representation for the first eight terms is shown in Figure 7a.

| $n$ | 1 | 2 | 3 | 4 | 5 | 6 | 7 | 8 |
|---|---|---|---|---|---|---|---|---|
| $a_n$ | 3 | 1 | $-1$ | $-3$ | $-5$ | $-7$ | $-9$ | $-11$ |

Figure 7a

[0, 10, 1] by [–12, 4, 1]

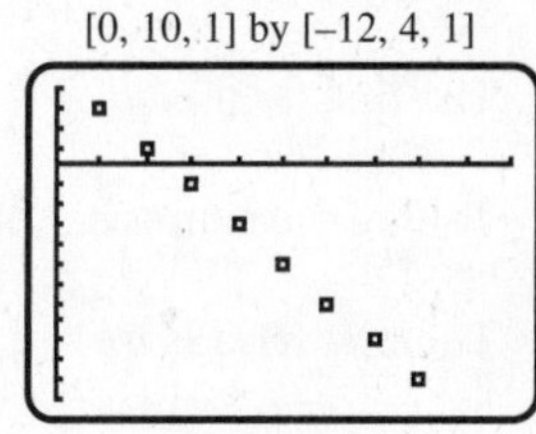

Figure 7b

(b) A graphical representation for the first eight terms is shown in Figure 7b. Notice that the points lie on a line with slope –2 because the sequence is arithmetic with $d = -2$.

(c) To find the symbolic representation, we will use the formula $a_n = a_1 + (n - 1)d$, where $a_n = f(n)$. The common difference of the sequence is $d = -2$ and the first term is $a_1 = 3$. Therefore a symbolic representation is given by $a_n = 3 + (n - 1)(-2)$ or $a_n = -2n + 5$.

8. (a) Each term can be found by multiplying the previous term by –2, beginning with 1.5. It is a geometric sequence. A numerical representation for the first eight terms is shown in Figure 8a.

| $n$ | 1 | 2 | 3 | 4 | 5 | 6 | 7 | 8 |
|---|---|---|---|---|---|---|---|---|
| $a_n$ | 1.5 | $-3$ | 6 | $-12$ | 24 | $-48$ | 96 | $-192$ |

Figure 8a

[0, 10, 1] by [–200, 200, 20]

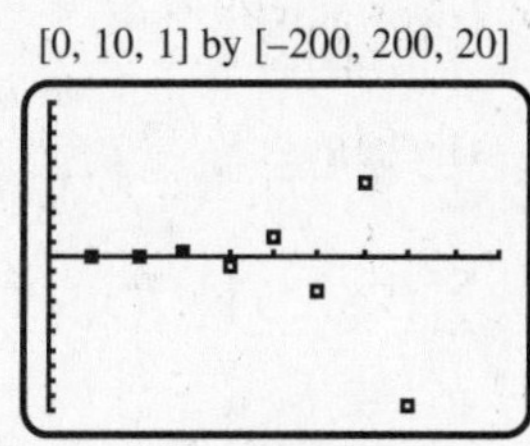

Figure 8b

(b) A graphical representation for the first eight terms is shown in Figure 8b. Notice that the points oscillate about the $x$-axis and become farther and farther from the $x$-axis. This is because the common ratio is negative with an absolute value greater than 1.

(c) To find the symbolic representation, we will use the formula $a_n = a_1r^{n-1}$, where $a_n = f(n)$. The common ratio of this sequence is $r = -2$ and the first term is $a_1 = 1.5$. Therefore a symbolic representation is given by $a_n = 1.5(-2)^{n-1}$.

9. Let $a_n = f(n)$, where $f(n) = dn + c$. Then, $f(n) = 4n + c$. Since $f(3) = 4(3) + c = -3 \Rightarrow$ . $c = -15$. Thus $a_n = f(n) = 4n - 15$.

10. Let $a_n = a_1 r^{n-1}$. Then, $\frac{-80}{2.5} = \frac{a_6}{a_1} = \frac{a_1 r^5}{a_1} = r^5 \Rightarrow r^5 = -32 \Rightarrow r = -2$. Thus, $a_n = 2.5(-2)^{n-1}$.

11. Since $f$ is a linear function, the sequence is arithmetic.

12. Since $f$ is neither a linear function nor can it be written in the form $f(n) = cr^{n-1}$, the sequence is neither.

13. Since $f$ can be written in the form $f(n) = cr^{n-1}$, the sequence is geometric.

14. Since $f$ is neither a linear function nor can it be written in the form $f(n) = cr^{n-1}$, the sequence is neither.

15. $S_5 = (4(1) + 1) + (4(2) + 1) + (4(3) + 1) + (4(4) + 1) + (4(5) + 1) =$
$5 + 9 + 13 + 17 + 21 = 65$

16. $S_5 = 3(4)^0 + 3(4)^1 + 3(4)^2 + 3(4)^3 + 3(4)^4 = 3 + 12 + 48 + 192 + 768 = 1023$

17. The first term is $a_1 = -2$ and the last term is $a_9 = 22$.
To find the sum use $S_n = n\left(\frac{a_1 + a_n}{2}\right) \Rightarrow S_9 = 9\left(\frac{-2 + 22}{2}\right) = 90$. The sum is 90.

18. The first term is $a_1 = 2$ and the last term is $a_{50} = 100$.
To find the sum use $S_n = n\left(\frac{a_1 + a_n}{2}\right) \Rightarrow S_{50} = 50\left(\frac{2 + 100}{2}\right) = 2550$. The sum is 2550.

19. The first term is $a_1 = 1$ and the common ratio is $r = 3$. Since there are 8 terms, the sum is
$S_n = a_1\left(\frac{1 - r^n}{1 - r}\right) \Rightarrow S_8 = 1\left(\frac{1 - 3^8}{1 - 3}\right) = 3280$.

20. The first term is $a_1 = 64$ and the common ratio is $r = \frac{1}{4}$. Since there are 6 terms, the sum is
$S_n = a_1\left(\frac{1 - r^n}{1 - r}\right) \Rightarrow S_6 = 64\left(\frac{1 - (\frac{1}{4})^6}{1 - \frac{1}{4}}\right) = \frac{1365}{16} = 85.3125$.

21. The first term is $a_1 = 4$ and the common ratio is $r = -\frac{1}{3}$. The sum is
$S_n = a_1\left(\frac{1}{1 - r}\right) \Rightarrow S = 4\left(\frac{1}{1 + \frac{1}{3}}\right) = 3$.

22. The first term is $a_1 = 0.2$ and the common ratio is $r = \frac{1}{10}$.
The sum is $S_n = a_1\left(\frac{1}{1 - r}\right) \Rightarrow S = 0.2\left(\frac{1}{1 - \frac{1}{10}}\right) = \frac{2}{10} \cdot \frac{10}{9} = \frac{2}{9}$.

23. $\sum_{k=1}^{5}(5k + 1) = (5 + 1) + (10 + 1) + (15 + 1) + (20 + 1) + (25 + 1) = 6 + 11 + 16 + 21 + 26$

24. $\sum_{k=1}^{4}(2 - k^2) = (2 - 1^2) + (2 - 2^2) + (2 - 3^2) + (2 - 4^2) = 1 + (-2) + (-7) + (-14)$

25. $1^3 + 2^3 + 3^3 + 4^3 + 5^3 + 6^3 = \sum_{k=1}^{6} k^3$

26. $1 + \frac{1}{10} + \frac{1}{100} + \frac{1}{1000} + \frac{1}{10{,}000} = \sum_{k=1}^{5}\left(\frac{1}{10}\right)^{k-1}$

27. Since $a_1 = 5$ and $d = -3$, use the formula $S_n = \frac{n}{2}(2a_1 + (n - 1)d)$.
$S_{30} = \frac{30}{2}(2(5) + (30 - 1)(-3)) = 15(10 + 29(-3)) = 15(-77) = -1155$

28. Since $a_1 = -2$ and $a_{10} = 16$, the common difference is $d = \frac{16-(-2)}{10-1} = \frac{18}{9} = 2$.

Use the formula $S_n = \frac{n}{2}(2a_1 + (n-1)d)$.

$S_{30} = \frac{30}{2}(2(-2) + (30-1)2) = 15(-4 + 29(2)) = 15(-4 + 58) = 15(54) = 810$

29. $\frac{2}{11} = 0.18181818\ldots = 0.18 + 0.0018 + 0.000018 + 0.00000018 + \cdots$

30. The series $0.23 + 0.0023 + 0.000023 + \cdots$ is an infinite geometric series with $a_1 = 0.23$ and $r = 0.01$.

$S = \frac{a_1}{1-r} = \frac{0.23}{1-0.01} = \frac{23}{99}$.

31. $P(n, r) = \frac{n!}{(n-r)!} \Rightarrow P(6, 3) = \frac{6!}{(6-3)!} = \frac{6!}{3!} = \frac{6\cdot 5\cdot 4\cdot 3!}{3!} = 6\cdot 5\cdot 4 = 120$

32. $C(n, r) = \frac{n!}{(n-r)!\,r!} \Rightarrow C(7, 4) = \frac{7!}{(7-4)!\,4!} = \frac{7!}{3!\,4!} = \frac{7\cdot 6\cdot 5\cdot 4!}{3!\,4!} = \frac{7\cdot 6\cdot 5}{3\cdot 2\cdot 1} = 35$

33. $1 + 3 + 5 + \cdots + (2n-1) = n^2$

(i) Show that the statement is true for $n = 1$: $2(1) - 1 = 1^2 \Rightarrow 1 = 1$

(ii) Assume that $S_k$ is true: $1 + 3 + 5 + \cdots + (2k-1) = k^2$

Show that $S_{k+1}$ is true: $1 + 3 + \cdots + (2(k+1)-1) = (k+1)^2$

Add $2k+1$ to each side of $S_k$: $1 + 3 + 5 + \cdots + (2k-1) + (2k+1) = k^2 + 2k + 1 = (k+1)^2$

Since $S_k$ implies $S_{k+1}$, the statement is true for every positive integer $n$.

34. $2 + 2^2 + 2^3 + \cdots + 2^n = 2(2^n - 1)$

(i) Show that the statement is true for $n = 1$: $2^1 = 2(2^1 - 1) \Rightarrow 2 = 2$

(ii) Assume that $S_k$ is true: $2 + 2^2 + 2^3 + \cdots + 2^k = 2(2^k - 1)$

Show that $S_{k+1}$ is true: $2 + 2^2 + 2^3 + \cdots + 2^{k+1} = 2(2^{k+1} - 1)$

Add $2^{k+1}$ to each side of $S_k$: $2 + 2^2 + 2^3 + \cdots + 2^k + 2^{k+1} = 2(2^k - 1) + 2^{k+1} =$

$2^{k+1} - 2 + 2^{k+1} = 2(2^{k+1} - 1)$

Since $S_k$ implies $S_{k+1}$, the statement is true for every positive integer $n$.

35. Since 1, 2, or 3 are three outcomes out of six possible outcomes, the probability is $\frac{3}{6} = \frac{1}{2}$.

36. The events are independent, each having a probability of $\frac{1}{2}$. The probability of three heads is $\frac{1}{2}\cdot\frac{1}{2}\cdot\frac{1}{2} = \frac{1}{8}$.

37. There are $P(5, 5) = 5! = 120$ different arrangements.

38. There are $P(15, 4) = 15\cdot 14\cdot 13\cdot 12 = 32{,}760$ different arrangements.

39. There are $4^{20} \approx 1.1 \times 10^{12}$ different ways to answer the exam.

40. There are 10 digits and 26 letters. Thus, there are $10\cdot 10\cdot 10\cdot 10\cdot 26\cdot 26 = 6{,}760{,}000$ different license plates.

41. There are 50 choices for each number in the combination. So there are $50^4 = 6{,}250{,}000$ possible combinations.

42. Let the ordered pair $(x, y)$ denote a roll of the dice, where $x$ represents the red die and $y$ represents the blue die.

Then there are 3 possible ways to obtain a sum of 4. They are (1, 3), (2, 2), and (3, 1).

43. (a) The initial height is 4 feet. On the first rebound it reaches 90% of 4 or 3.6 feet. On the second rebound it attains a height of 90% of 3.6 or 3.24 feet. Each term in this sequence is found by multiplying the previous term by 0.9. Thus, the first five terms are 4, 3.6, 3.24, 2.916, 2.6244. This is a geometric sequence.
(b) Plot the points (1, 4), (2, 3.6), (3, 3.24), (4, 2.916), and (5, 2.6244) as shown in Figure 43.
(c) The first term is 4 and the common ratio is 0.9. Thus, $a_n = 4(0.9)^{n-1}$.

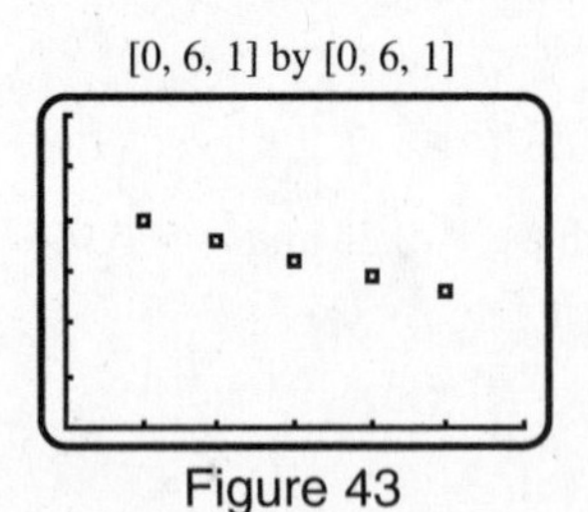

Figure 43

44. (a) The first four terms of the sequence are 16, 48, 80, 112. Each successive term is 32 more than the previous term. Therefore, the sequence is arithmetic with $a_1 = 16$ and $d = 32$.
(b) The distances are 16, 48, 80, 112, 144, and 176, respectively. The object falls 176 feet during the sixth second.
(c) The $n$th term is given by $a_n = a_1 + (n-1)d = 16 + (n-1)(32) \Rightarrow a_n = 32n - 16$.

45. From a group of 6 people, we must select a set of 3 people. This can be done $C(6, 3) = 20$ different ways.

46. Three women can be selected from seven women in $C(7, 3)$ different ways. Three men can be selected from five men in $C(5, 3)$ different ways. The total number of committees is $C(7, 3) \cdot C(5, 3) = 35 \cdot 10 = 350$.

47. They can be selected in $C(10, 6) = 210$ different ways.

48. Using Pascal's triangle, the coefficients are 1, 4, 6, 4, and 1.
$(2x - y)^4 = 1(2x)^4(-y)^0 + 4(2x)^3(-y)^1 + 6(2x)^2(-y)^2 + 4(2x)^1(-y)^3 + 1(2x)^0(-y)^4 =$
$16x^4 - 32x^3y + 24x^2y^2 - 8xy^3 + y^4$

49. There are $C(16, 2)$ different ways to select 2 batteries from a pack of 16. In order to avoid testing a defective battery, we must pick 2 batteries from the 14 good ones. This can be done in $C(14, 2)$ different ways. The probability that the box is not rejected is $\dfrac{C(14, 2)}{C(16, 2)} = \dfrac{91}{120} \approx 0.758$.

50. (a) A Venn diagram for this data is shown in Figure 50.
(b) The number of students taking art, music, or both is $9 + 10 + 12 = 31$. The probability of a student taking one or both of the classes is $\dfrac{31}{82} \approx 0.378$.
(c) If $A$ represents the event "a student takes art" and $M$ represents the event "a student takes music", then
$P(A \text{ or } M) = P(A \cup M) = P(A) + P(M) - P(A \cap M) = \dfrac{22}{82} + \dfrac{19}{82} - \dfrac{10}{82} = \dfrac{31}{82} \approx 0.378$
This agrees with the answer found in part (b).

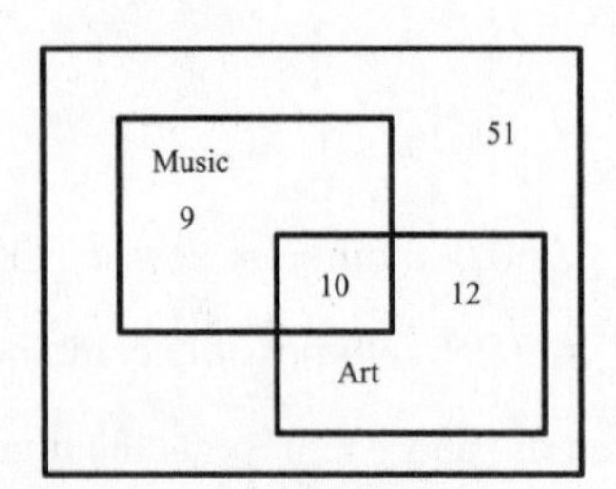

Figure 50

51. (a) The total number of marbles in the jar is $13 + 27 + 20 = 60$. Since 27 of the marbles are blue, there is a probability of $\frac{27}{60} = 0.45$ of drawing a blue marble.

(b) Since there is a 0.45 probability of drawing a blue marble, there is a $1 - 0.45 = 0.55$ probability of drawing a marble that is not blue.

(c) There is a $\frac{13}{60} \approx 0.217$ probability of drawing a red marble.

52. The probability of drawing the first diamond is $\frac{13}{52}$, while the probability of drawing the second diamond is $\frac{12}{51}$. The probability of drawing both diamonds is $\frac{13}{52} \cdot \frac{12}{51} = \frac{1}{17}$.

53. The sequence is graphed in Figure 53. Initially, the population density grows slowly, then it increases rapidly. After some time, it levels off near 4000 thousand (4,000,000) per acre.

[0, 16, 1] by [0, 5000, 1000]

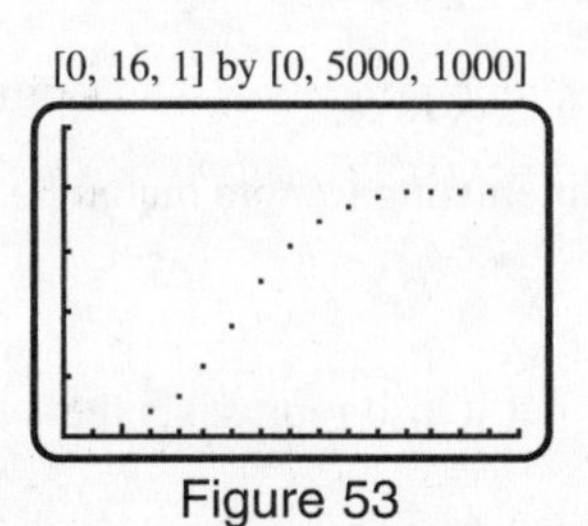

Figure 53

## Extended and Discovery Exercises for Chapter 8

1. (a) $P_{kj} = \dfrac{\binom{2k}{j}\binom{4-2k}{2-j}}{\binom{4}{2}} \Rightarrow P_{00} = \dfrac{\binom{0}{0}\binom{4}{2}}{\binom{4}{2}} = 1;\ P_{01} = \dfrac{\binom{0}{1}\binom{4}{1}}{\binom{4}{2}} = 0;\ P_{02} = \dfrac{\binom{0}{2}\binom{4}{0}}{\binom{4}{2}} = 0;$

$P_{10} = \dfrac{\binom{2}{0}\binom{2}{2}}{\binom{4}{2}} = \dfrac{1}{6};\ P_{11} = \dfrac{\binom{2}{1}\binom{2}{1}}{\binom{4}{2}} = \dfrac{2}{3};\ P_{12} = \dfrac{\binom{2}{2}\binom{2}{0}}{\binom{4}{2}} = \dfrac{1}{6};\ P_{20} = \dfrac{\binom{4}{0}\binom{0}{2}}{\binom{4}{2}} = 0;$

$P_{21} = \dfrac{\binom{4}{1}\binom{0}{1}}{\binom{4}{2}} = 0;\ P_{22} = \dfrac{\binom{4}{2}\binom{0}{0}}{\binom{4}{2}} = 1.$ Thus, $P = \begin{bmatrix} P_{00} & P_{01} & P_{02} \\ P_{10} & P_{11} & P_{12} \\ P_{20} & P_{21} & P_{22} \end{bmatrix} = \begin{bmatrix} 1 & 0 & 0 \\ \frac{1}{6} & \frac{2}{3} & \frac{1}{6} \\ 0 & 0 & 1 \end{bmatrix}.$

(b) The sum of the probabilities in each row is 1. The greatest probabilities lie along the diagonal. A mother cell is most likely to produce a daughter cell like itself. *Answers may vary.*

2. (a) It is reasonable to conjecture that since all bacteria are resistant to both antibiotics, future generations will continue to be resistant to both antibiotics as well. Another conjecture is that there will be $\frac{1}{3}$ of the cells in each of the three possible categories, that is $A_n = \left[\frac{1}{3}, \frac{1}{3}, \frac{1}{3}\right]$.

(b) $A_n = A_{n-1}P = [a_1, a_2, a_3]\begin{bmatrix} P_{00} & P_{01} & P_{02} \\ P_{10} & P_{11} & P_{12} \\ P_{20} & P_{21} & P_{22} \end{bmatrix}$

$$A_2 = A_1P = [0, 1, 0]\begin{bmatrix} 1 & 0 & 0 \\ \frac{1}{6} & \frac{2}{3} & \frac{1}{6} \\ 0 & 0 & 1 \end{bmatrix} = \left[\frac{1}{6}, \frac{2}{3}, \frac{1}{6}\right]; \; A_3 = A_2P = \left[\frac{1}{6}, \frac{2}{3}, \frac{1}{6}\right]\begin{bmatrix} 1 & 0 & 0 \\ \frac{1}{6} & \frac{2}{3} & \frac{1}{6} \\ 0 & 0 & 1 \end{bmatrix} = \left[\frac{5}{18}, \frac{4}{9}, \frac{5}{18}\right];$$

Similarly $A_4 = \left[\frac{19}{54}, \frac{8}{27}, \frac{19}{54}\right]$; $A_5 = \left[\frac{65}{162}, \frac{16}{81}, \frac{65}{162}\right]$; $A_6 = \left[\frac{211}{486}, \frac{32}{243}, \frac{211}{486}\right]$;

$A_7 \approx [0.456, 0.0878, 0.456]$; $A_8 \approx [0.47, 0.06, 0.47]$; $A_9 \approx [0.48, 0.04, 0.48]$;

$A_{10} \approx [0.487, 0.026, 0.487]$; $A_{11} \approx [0.491, 0.017, 0.491]$; $A_{12} \approx [0.494, 0.012, 0.494]$.

The elements of $A_n$ appear to be approaching [0.5, 0, 0.5]. This means that as time progresses, half of the bacteria are resistant to ampicillin and half are resistant to tetracycline. It is interesting to note that *none* of the bacteria are resistant to both antibiotics!

3. The quantity $\frac{a_1 + a_n}{2}$ represents not only the average of the two terms $a_1$ and $a_n$, but it also represents the average of all of the terms $a_1, a_2, a_3, \ldots, a_n$ in the series. This is true whether $n$ is odd or even. The total sum is equal to $n$ times the average of the terms.

## Chapters 1-8 Cumulative Review Exercises

1. $34{,}500 = 3.45 \times 10^4$; $1.52 \times 10^{-4} = 0.000152$

2. $\dfrac{5 - \sqrt[3]{4}}{\pi^2 - (\sqrt{3} + 1)} \approx 0.48$

3. $d\sqrt{(1 - (-4))^2 + (-2 - 2)^2} = \sqrt{5^2 + (-4)^2} = \sqrt{25 + 16} = \sqrt{41}$

4. For the graphs of parts (a) – (h), see Figures 4a – 4h.

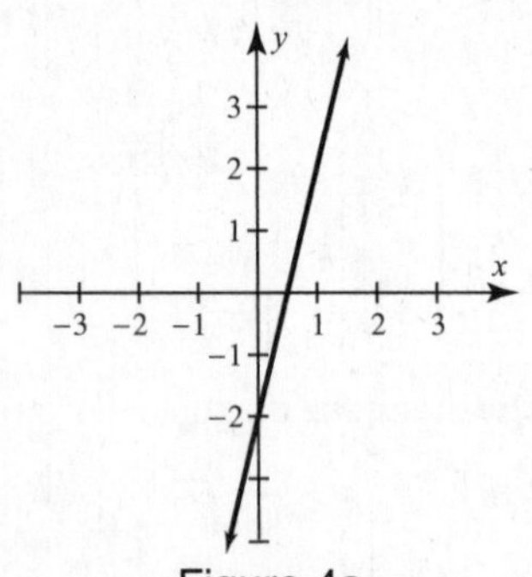

Figure 4a

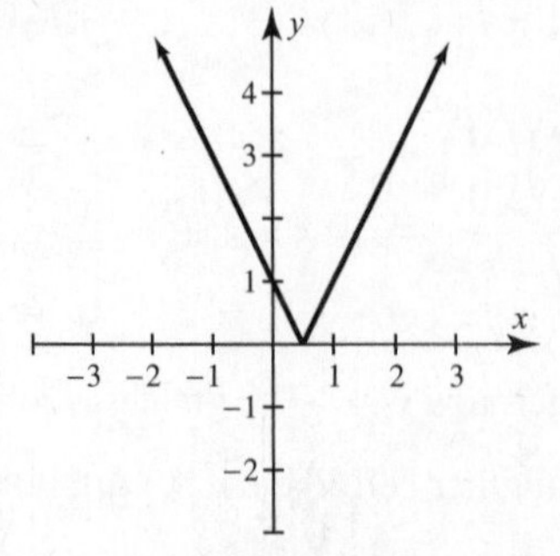

Figure 4b

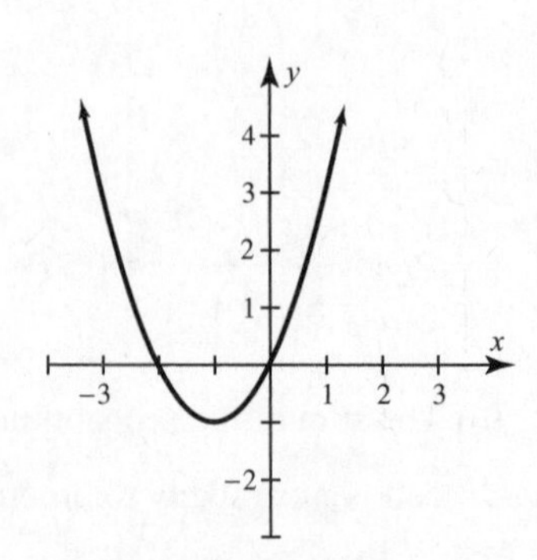

Figure 4c

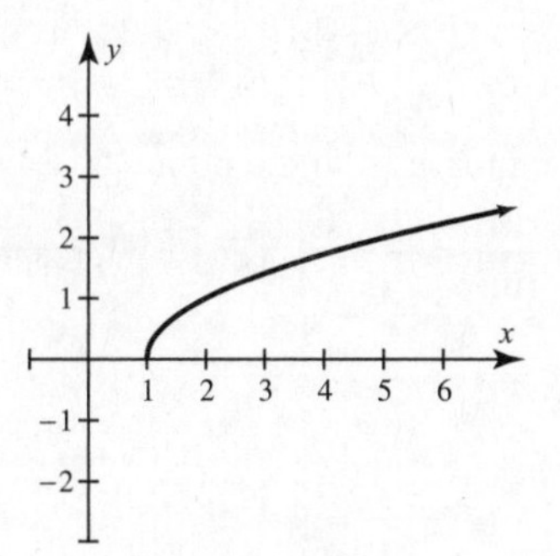

Figure 4d

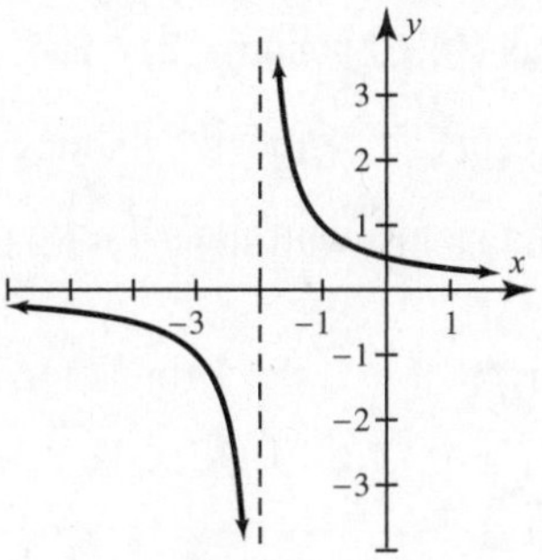

Figure 4e

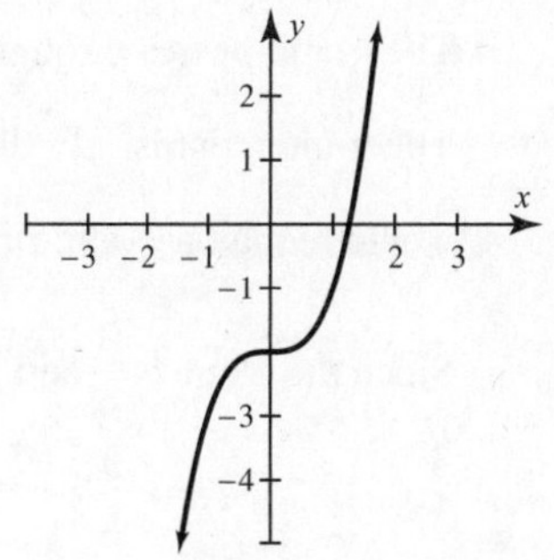

Figure 4f

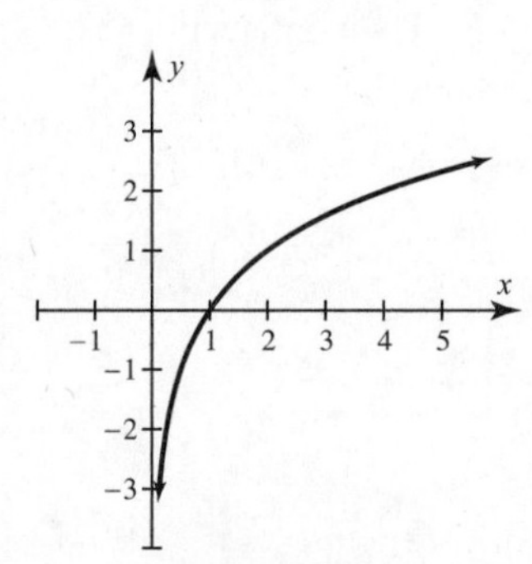

Figure 4g

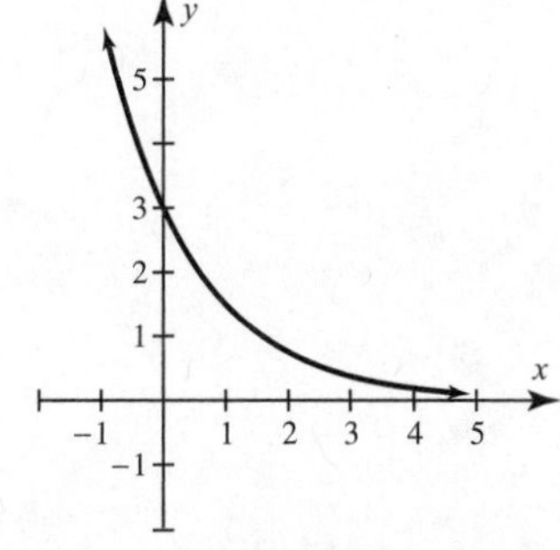

Figure 4h

5. (a) $f(-3) = \sqrt{1 - (-3)} = \sqrt{4} = 2$; $f(a + 1) = \sqrt{1 - (a + 1)} = \sqrt{-a}$

(b) For $f$ to be defined, $1 - x \geq 0$. Thus, the domain is $D = \{x \mid x \leq 1\}$.

6. (a) $f(-3) = \dfrac{1}{(-3)^2 - 4} = \dfrac{1}{9 - 4} = \dfrac{1}{5}$; $f(a + 1) = \dfrac{1}{(a + 1)^2 - 4} = \dfrac{1}{a^2 + 2a + 1 - 4} = \dfrac{1}{a^2 + 2a - 3}$

(b) For $f$ to be defined, $x^2 - 4 \neq 0$. Thus, the domain is $D = \{x \mid x \neq -2, x \neq 2\}$.

7. $\dfrac{f(-1) - f(-2)}{-1 - (-2)} = \dfrac{((-1)^3 - 4) - ((-2)^3 - 4)}{1} = -5 - (-12) = 7$

8. $\dfrac{f(x + h) - f(x)}{h} = \dfrac{(x + h)^2 - 3(x + h) - (x^2 - 3x)}{h} = \dfrac{x^2 + 2xh + h^2 - 3x - 3h - x^2 + 3x}{h} =$

$\dfrac{2xh + h^2 - 3h}{h} = \dfrac{h(2x + h - 3)}{h} = 2x + h - 3$

9. A line passing through the points $(2, -4)$ and $(-3, 2)$ has slope $m = \dfrac{2 - (-4)}{-3 - 2} = \dfrac{6}{-5} = -\dfrac{6}{5}$.

Using the point $(2, -4)$, the equation is $y = -\dfrac{6}{5}(x - 2) - 4 \Rightarrow y = -\dfrac{6}{5}x - \dfrac{8}{5}$.

10. A that is perpendicular to the line $y = -\dfrac{3}{4}x + 1$ has slope $m = \dfrac{4}{3}$, the negative reciprocal of $-\dfrac{3}{4}$.

Using the point $(-1, 3)$, the equation is $y = \dfrac{4}{3}(x + 1) + 3 \Rightarrow y = \dfrac{4}{3}x + \dfrac{13}{3}$.

11. (a) The graph passes through the points $(0, -1)$ and $(4, 2)$. The slope is $m = \dfrac{2 - (-1)}{4 - 0} = \dfrac{3}{4}$.

The $y$-intercept is $-1$. The $x$-intercept can be found by noting that a 1-unit rise from the point $(0, -1)$ would require a $\frac{4}{3}$-unit run to return to a line with slope $\frac{3}{4}$. That is, $m = \dfrac{\text{rise}}{\text{run}} = \dfrac{1}{\frac{4}{3}} = \dfrac{3}{4}$. The $x$-intercept is $\frac{4}{3}$.

(b) Since the slope is $\frac{3}{4}$ and the $y$-intercept is $-1$, the formula for $f$ is $f(x) = \frac{3}{4}x - 1$.

(c) $\frac{3}{4}x - 1 = 0 \Rightarrow \frac{3}{4}x = 1 \Rightarrow x = \frac{4}{3}$

12. To find the $x$-intercept, let $y = 0$ in the equation: $-3x + 4(0) = 12 \Rightarrow x = -4$. The $x$-intercept is $-4$.

To find the $y$-intercept, let $x = 0$ in the equation: $-3(0) + 4y = 12 \Rightarrow y = 3$. The $y$-intercept is 3.

The graph is shown in figure 12.

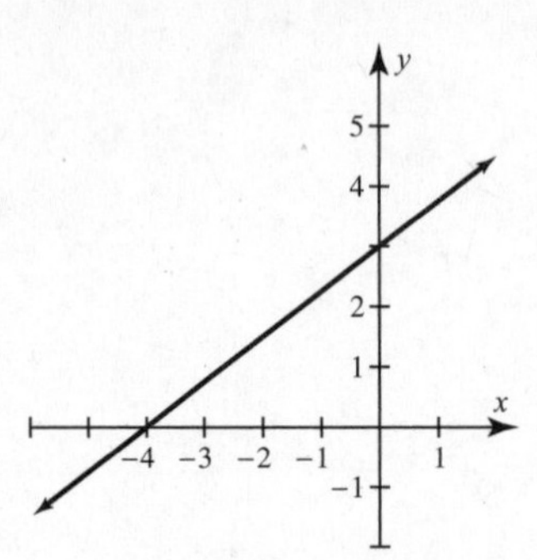


Figure 12

13. (a) $4(x - 2) + 1 = 3 - \frac{1}{2}(2x + 3) \Rightarrow 4x - 8 + 1 = 3 - x - \frac{3}{2} \Rightarrow 5x = \frac{17}{2} \Rightarrow x = \frac{17}{10}$

(b) $6x^2 = 13x + 5 \Rightarrow 6x^2 - 13x - 5 = 0 \Rightarrow (3x + 1)(2x - 5) = 0 \Rightarrow x = -\frac{1}{3}$ or $x = \frac{5}{2}$

(c) By the quadratic formula, $x = \dfrac{-b \pm \sqrt{b^2 - 4ac}}{2a} \Rightarrow x = \dfrac{-(-1) \pm \sqrt{(-1)^2 - 4(1)(-3)}}{2(1)} = \dfrac{1 \pm \sqrt{13}}{2}$

(d) $x^3 + x^2 = 4x + 4 \Rightarrow x^3 + x^2 - 4x - 4 = 0 \Rightarrow x^2(x + 1) - 4(x + 1) = 0 \Rightarrow$

$(x^2 - 4)(x + 1) = 0 \Rightarrow (x + 2)(x - 2)(x + 1) = 0 \Rightarrow x = -2, -1,$ or $2$

(e) $x^4 - 4x^2 + 3 = 0 \Rightarrow (x^2 - 3)(x^2 - 1) = 0 \Rightarrow x^2 = 3$ or $x^2 = 1 \Rightarrow x = \pm\sqrt{3}$ or $\pm 1$

(f) $\dfrac{1}{x - 3} = \dfrac{4}{x + 5} \Rightarrow (x - 3)(x + 5) \cdot \dfrac{1}{x - 3} = \dfrac{4}{x + 5} \cdot (x - 3)(x + 5) \Rightarrow x + 5 = 4(x - 3) \Rightarrow$

$x + 5 = 4x - 12 \Rightarrow -3x = -17 \Rightarrow x = \frac{17}{3}$

(g) $3e^{2x} - 5 = 23 \Rightarrow 3e^{2x} = 28 \Rightarrow e^{2x} = \frac{28}{3} \Rightarrow \ln e^{2x} = \ln \frac{28}{3} \Rightarrow 2x = \ln \frac{28}{3} \Rightarrow x = \dfrac{\ln\left(\frac{28}{3}\right)}{2} \approx 1.117$

(h) $2 \log(x + 1) - 1 = 2 \Rightarrow 2 \log(x + 1) = 3 \Rightarrow \log(x + 1) = \frac{3}{2} \Rightarrow 10^{\log(x+1)} = 10^{3/2} \Rightarrow$

$x + 1 = 10^{3/2} \Rightarrow x = 10^{3/2} - 1 \approx 30.623$

(i) $\sqrt{x + 3} + 4 = x + 1 \Rightarrow \sqrt{x + 3} = x - 3 \Rightarrow (\sqrt{x + 3})^2 = (x - 3)^2 \Rightarrow$

$x + 3 = x^2 - 6x + 9 \Rightarrow x^2 - 7x + 6 = 0 \Rightarrow (x - 1)(x - 6) = 0 \Rightarrow x = 1$ or $x = 6$. Note, 1 is extraneous. The only solution is 6.

(j) $|3x - 1| = 5 \Rightarrow 3x - 1 = -5$ or $3x - 1 = 5 \Rightarrow 3x = -4$ or $3x = 6 \Rightarrow x = -\frac{4}{3}$ or $2$

14. (a) $3x - 5 < x + 1 \Rightarrow 2x < 6 \Rightarrow x < 3 \Rightarrow (-\infty, 3)$ or $\{x | x < 3\}$.

(b) To solve $x^2 - 4x - 5 \le 0$, start by solving $x^2 - 4x - 5 = 0 \Rightarrow (x + 1)(x - 5) = 0 \Rightarrow x = -1$, or 5. The left side of the inequality is a parabola that opens upward with $x$-intercepts $-1$ and 5. This parabola is below or touches the $x$-axis for values of $x$ between $-1$ and 5. The solution interval is $[-1, 5]$ or $\{x | -1 \le x \le 5\}$.

(c) Start by solving $(x + 1)(x - 2)(x - 3) = 0 \Rightarrow x = -1, 2$, or 3.
The left side of the inequality is a cubic graph with $x$-intercepts $-1$, 2 and 3. This graph is above the $x$-axis for values of $x$ between $-1$ and 2 or values larger than 3. The solution interval is $(-1, 2) \cup (3, \infty)$ or $\{x | -1 < x < 2 \text{ or } x > 3\}$.

(d) Start by solving $\dfrac{2}{x - 1} = 0$ (which has no solution) or finding any values of $x$ for which $\dfrac{2}{x - 1}$ is undefined. The only such value is 1. The left side of the inequality is a graph with a vertical asymptote at $x = 1$. The graph is below the $x$-axis for values of $x$ smaller than 1. The solution interval is $(-\infty, 1)$ or $\{x | x < 1\}$.

(e) The solutions to $|3x - 5| \le 4$ satisfy $s_1 \le x \le s_2$ where $s_1$ and $s_2$ are the solutions to $|3x - 5| = 4$. $|3x - 5| = 4$ is equivalent to $3x - 5 = -4 \Rightarrow x = \dfrac{1}{3}$ and $3x - 5 = 4 \Rightarrow x = 3$. The interval is $\left[\dfrac{1}{3}, 3\right]$ or $\left\{x \middle| \dfrac{1}{3} \le x \le 3\right\}$.

(f) The solutions to $|4 - x| > 0$ satisfy $x < s_1$ or $x > s_2$ where $s_1$ and $s_2$ are the solutions to $|4 - x| = 0$. $|4 - x| = 0$ is equivalent to $4 - x = 0 \Rightarrow x = 4$. The interval is $(-\infty, 4) \cup (4, \infty)$ or $\{x | x < 4 \text{ or } x > 4\}$.

(g) Multiplying by 12. $\dfrac{3}{4} \le \dfrac{1 - 2x}{3} < \dfrac{5}{2} \Rightarrow 9 \le 4 - 8x < 30 \Rightarrow 5 \le -8x < 26 \Rightarrow$
$-\dfrac{5}{8} \ge x > -\dfrac{13}{4} \Rightarrow -\dfrac{13}{4} < x \le -\dfrac{5}{8}$. The interval is $\left(-\dfrac{13}{4}, -\dfrac{5}{8}\right]$ or $\left\{x \middle| -\dfrac{13}{4} < x \le -\dfrac{5}{8}\right\}$.

15. $f$ is continuous. See Figure 15.

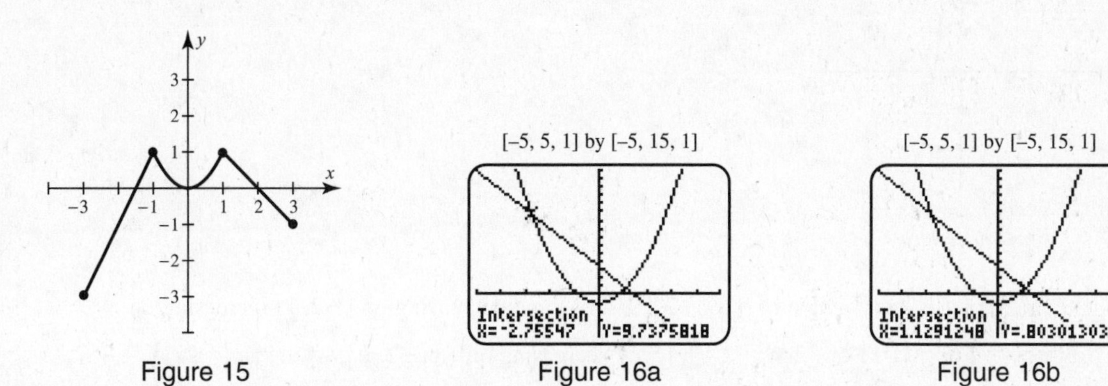


Figure 15 Figure 16a Figure 16b

16. Graph $Y_1 = -2.3X + 3.4$ and $Y_2 = \sqrt{(2)}X^2 - 1$ and find the intersection points as shown in Figure 16a and Figure 16b. The solutions to the equation are the $x$-coordinates of the intersection points, $-2.8$ and 1.1.

17. (a) The solution to $f(x) = 0$ is the $x$-intercepts. The solutions are $-2, -1, 1,$ and $2$.

    (b) The graph of $f$ is above the $x$-axis on the interval $(-\infty, -2)\cup(-1, 1)\cup(2, \infty)$ or $\{x \mid x < -2 \text{ or } -1 < x < 1 \text{ or } x > 2\}$.

    (c) The graph of $f$ is on or below the $x$-axis on the interval $[-2, -1]\cup[1, 2]$ or $\{x \mid -2 \le x \le -1 \text{ or } 1 \le x \le 2\}$.

18. $f(x) = 3x^2 + 24x + 43 \Rightarrow f(x) = 3(x^2 + 8x) + 43 \Rightarrow f(x) = 3(x^2 + 8x + 16) + 43 - 48 \Rightarrow$ $f(x) = 3(x + 4)^2 - 5$

19. The $x$-coordinate of the vertex is $x = -\dfrac{b}{2a} = -\dfrac{9}{2(-3)} = \dfrac{3}{2}$. The $y$-coordinate of the vertex is $f\left(\dfrac{3}{2}\right)$.

$$y = f\left(\frac{3}{2}\right) = -3\left(\frac{3}{2}\right)^2 + 9\left(\frac{3}{2}\right) + 1 = -\frac{27}{4} + \frac{27}{2} + 1 = -\frac{27}{4} + \frac{54}{4} + \frac{4}{4} = \frac{31}{4}.$$ The vertex is $\left(\dfrac{3}{2}, \dfrac{31}{4}\right)$.

20. (a) The graph should be shifted 1 unit to the right and 2 units upward. See Figure 20a.

    (b) The graph should be vertically compressed. See Figure 20b.

    (c) The graph should be reflected across the $x$-axis. See Figure 20c.

    (d) The graph should be horizontally compressed. See Figure 20d.

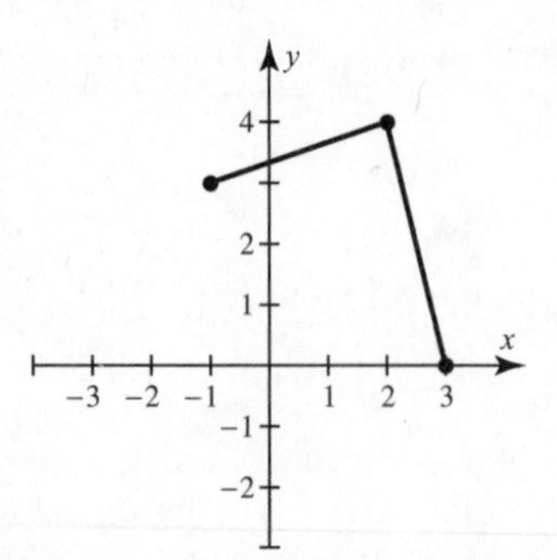

Figure 20a

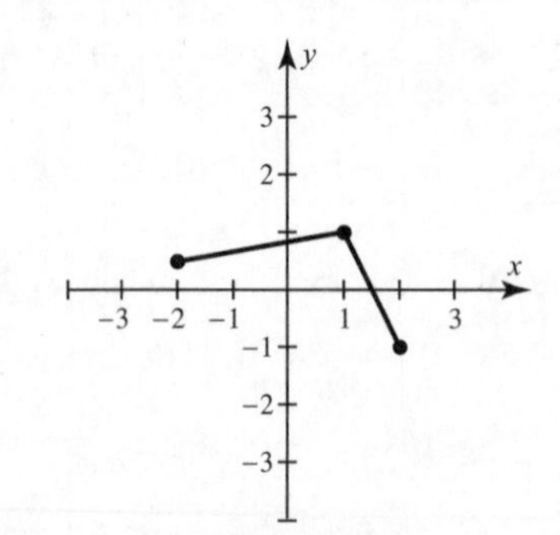

Figure 20b

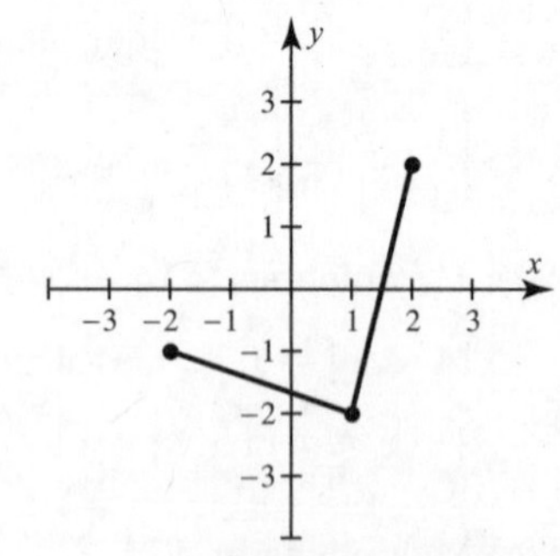

Figure 20c

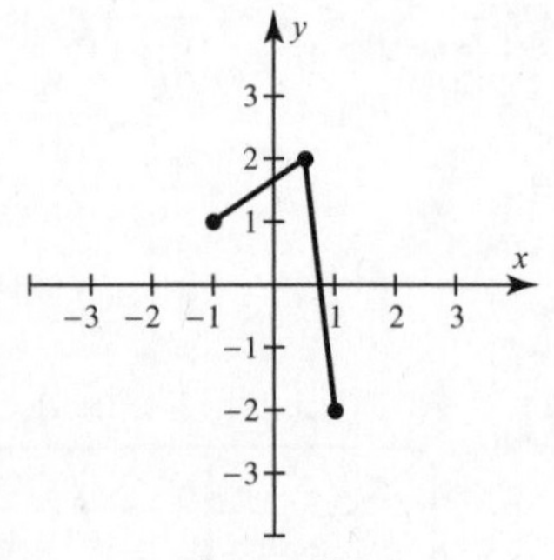

Figure 20d

21. (a) The graph of $f$ is increasing on $(-\infty, -2]\cup[1, \infty)$ and decreasing on $[-2, 1]$ increasing on $\{x \mid x \le -2 \text{ or } x \ge 1\}$ or $(-\infty, -2]\cup[1, \infty)$ decreasing on $\{x \mid -2 \le x \le 1\}$ or $[-2, 1]$.

    (b) The zeros of $f$ are the $x$-intercepts which are approximately $-3.3$, $0$, and $1.8$.

    (c) The turning points are approximately $(-2, 2)$ and $(1, -0.7)$.

    (d) There is a local minimum of $-0.7$ and a local maximum of $2$.

22. The function is odd since it is a polynomial function with only odd powers of the variable.

23. (a) $\dfrac{6x^4 - 2x^2 + 1}{2x^2} = \dfrac{6x^4}{2x^2} - \dfrac{2x^2}{2x^2} + \dfrac{1}{2x^2} = 3x^2 - 1 + \dfrac{1}{2x^2}$

(b)
$$\begin{array}{r} 2x^3 - 5x^2 + 5x - 6 \\ x + 1\,\overline{)\,2x^4 - 3x^3 + 0x^2 - x + 2} \\ \underline{2x^4 + 2x^3} \qquad\qquad\qquad \\ -5x^3 + 0x^2 - x + 2 \\ \underline{-5x^3 - 5x^2} \qquad\qquad \\ 5x^2 - x + 2 \\ \underline{5x^2 + 5x} \qquad \\ -6x + 2 \\ \underline{-6x - 6} \\ 8 \end{array}$$

The solution is: $2x^3 - 5x^2 + 5x - 6 + \dfrac{8}{x + 1}$

24. $f(x) = 6(x - (-2))(x - (-1))(x - 1)(x - 2)$ or $f(x) = 6(x + 2)(x + 1)(x - 1)(x - 2)$

25. Since $3i$ is a zero its conjugate, $-3i$, is also a zero.

The complete factored form is

$f(x) = 3(x - (-1))(x - (-3i))(x - 3i)$ or $f(x) = 3(x + 1)(x + 3i)(x - 3i)$.

To find the expanded form, first multiply $(x + 3i)(x - 3i) = x^2 + 9$. Continuing to multiply out gives

$f(x) = 3(x + 1)(x^2 + 9) = 3(x^3 + x^2 + 9x + 9)$ or $f(x) = 3x^3 + 3x^2 + 27x + 27$.

26. $(2 - i)(2 + 3i) = 4 + 6i - 2i - 3i^2 = 4 + 4i - 3(-1) = 4 + 4i + 3 = 7 + 4i$

27. $x = \dfrac{-b \pm \sqrt{b^2 - 4ac}}{2a} \Rightarrow x = \dfrac{-2 \pm \sqrt{2^2 - 4(1)(5)}}{2(1)} = \dfrac{-2 \pm \sqrt{-16}}{2} = \dfrac{-2 \pm 4i}{2} = -1 \pm 2i$

28. The function is defined when $x + 5 \neq 0$ or $x \neq -5$. The domain is $\{x \mid x \neq -5\}$. A vertical asymptote exists where the function is undefined, or at $x = -5$. multiplying both the numerator and denominator by $\dfrac{1}{x}$ yields $\dfrac{2 - \frac{5}{x}}{1 + \frac{5}{x}}$. As $|x|$ increases without bound, this expression evaluates to 2. The horizontal asymptote is $y = 2$.

29. $\sqrt[5]{(x + 1)^3} = (x + 1)^{3/5}$. When $x = 31$, $(x + 1)^{3/5} = (31 + 1)^{3/5} = 32^{3/5} = (\sqrt[5]{32})^3 = 2^3 = 8$

30. (a) $(f - g)(1) = f(1) - g(1) = 2 - 3 = -1$

(b) $(f/g)(2) = \dfrac{f(2)}{g(2)} = \dfrac{4}{2} = 2$

(c) $(g \circ f)(3) = g(f(3)) = g(5)$ which is not defined. It is not possible to evaluate this expression.

(d) Note, for $f^{-1}(5)$, read the table backward. $(g \circ f^{-1})(5) = g(f^{-1}(5)) = g(3) = 1$

31. (a) $(f + g)(2) = f(2) + g(2) = 3 + 0 = 3$

(b) $(fg)(0) = f(0) \cdot g(0) = -1(1) = -1$

(c) $(g \circ f)(1) = g(f(1)) = g(0) = 1$

(d) Note, for $g^{-1}(3)$, read the graph backward. $(g^{-1} \circ f)(-2) = g^{-1}(f(-2)) = g^{-1}(3) = -4$

32. (a) $(f - g)(0) = f(0) - g(0) = \frac{1}{0 + 2} - (0^2 + 0 - 4) = \frac{1}{2} + 4 = \frac{9}{2}$

(b) $(g \circ f)(-1) = g(f(-1)) = g\left(\frac{1}{-1 + 2}\right) = g(1) = 1^2 + 1 - 4 = -2$

(c) $(fg)(x) = f(x) \cdot g(x) = \frac{1}{x + 2} \cdot (x^2 + x - 4) = \frac{x^2 + x - 4}{x + 2}$

(d) $(g \circ f)(x) = g(f(x)) = g\left(\frac{1}{x + 2}\right) = \left(\frac{1}{x + 2}\right)^2 + \left(\frac{1}{x + 2}\right) - 4$

33. Let $y = f(x)$: $y = \frac{x}{x + 1}$. Interchange $x$ and $y$: $x = \frac{y}{y + 1}$. Then solve for $y$.

$$x = \frac{y}{y + 1} \Rightarrow x(y + 1) = y \Rightarrow xy + x = y \Rightarrow x = y - xy \Rightarrow x = y(1 - x) \Rightarrow \frac{x}{1 - x} = y$$

The inverse function is $f^{-1}(x) = \frac{x}{1 - x}$ or $f^{-1}(x) = -\frac{x}{x - 1}$.

34. The graph of $f$ and its inverse are reflection across the line $y = x$. See Figure 34.

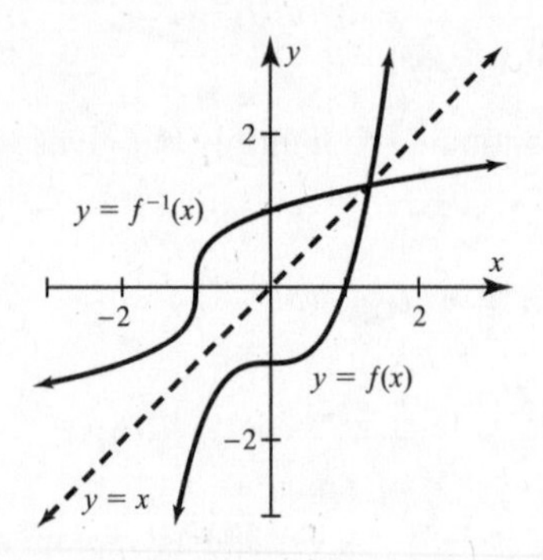


Figure 34

35. Since each unit increase in $x$ results in $f(x)$ increasing by a factor of 3, the function is exponential with base 3.

Since $f(0) = 2$, the initial value is 2 and the function is $f(x) = 2(3^x)$.

36. (a) Because the initial number of bacteria is 1000, $C = 1000$. To find the value of $a$, note that the population doubles every 2 hours. That is, after 2 hours $1000a^2 = 2000 \Rightarrow a^2 = 2 \Rightarrow a = \sqrt{2}$.

(b) $1000(\sqrt{2})^{5.2} \approx 6063$ bacteria

(c) Graph $Y_1 = 1000(\sqrt{}(2))$^X and $Y_2 = 9000$. The solution is about 6.3 hours as shown in Figure 36.

[0, 8, 1] by [0, 10,000, 1000]

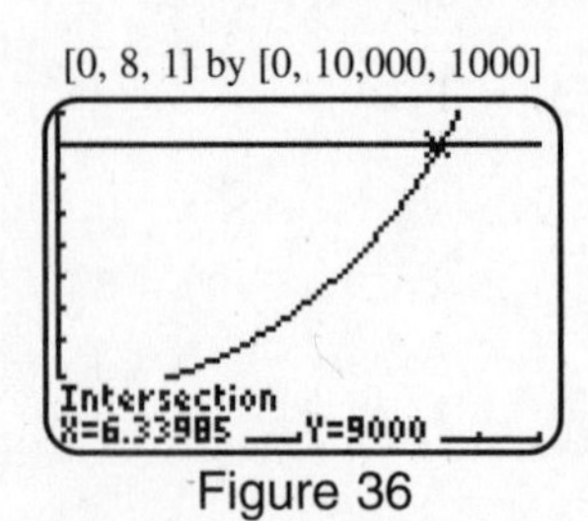


Figure 36

37. $A = 500\left(1 + \frac{0.06}{4}\right)^{15 \cdot 4} \approx \$1221.61$

38. (a) $\log_2 \frac{1}{16} = \log_2 \frac{1}{2^4} = \log_2 2^{-4} = -4$

(b) $\log \sqrt{10} = \log 10^{1/2} = \frac{1}{2}$

(c) $\ln e^4 = 4$

(d) $\log_4 2 + \log_4 32 = \log_4 (2 \cdot 32) = \log_4 64 = \log_4 4^3 = 3$

39. (a) A quadratic function is defined for all real inputs. The domain is $D = (-\infty, \infty)$ or $\{x \mid -\infty < x < \infty\}$.

The graph of $f$ is a parabola opening upward with vertex $(1, 0)$. The range is $R = [0, \infty)$ or $\{x \mid x \geq 0\}$.

(b) An exponential function is defined for all real inputs. The domain is $D = (-\infty, \infty)$ or

$\{x \mid -\infty < x < \infty\}$.

The function $f(x) = 10^x$ has only positive outputs. The range is $R = (0, \infty)$ or $\{x \mid x > 0\}$.

(c) The natural logarithm function is defined for only positive real inputs. The domain is $D = (0, \infty)$ or

$\{x \mid x > 0\}$.

The natural logarithm function can output any real value. The range is $R = (-\infty, \infty)$ or

$\{x \mid -\infty < x < \infty\}$.

(d) The reciprocal function is defined for all real inputs except 0. The domain is $D = (-\infty, 0) \cup (0, \infty)$ or

$\{x \mid x \neq 0\}$.

The reciprocal function can output any real value except 0. The range is $R = (-\infty, 0) \cup (0, \infty)$ or

$\{x \mid x \neq 0\}$.

40. $\log \sqrt{\frac{x+1}{yz}} = \log \left(\frac{x+1}{yz}\right)^{1/2} = \frac{1}{2} \log \left(\frac{x+1}{yz}\right) = \frac{1}{2} [\log (x+1) - \log yz] =$

$\frac{1}{2} [\log (x+1) - (\log y + \log z)] = \frac{1}{2} [\log (x+1) - \log y - \log z] =$

$\frac{1}{2} \log (x+1) - \frac{1}{2} \log y - \frac{1}{2} \log z$

41. $2 \log x + 3 \log y - \frac{1}{3} \log z = \log x^2 + \log y^3 - \log z^{1/3} = \log \frac{x^2 y^3}{z^{1/3}} = \log \frac{x^2 y^3}{\sqrt[3]{z}}$

42. $\log_4 52 = \frac{\ln 52}{\ln 4} \approx 2.850$

43. (a) Multiplying the first equation by $-1$ and adding the two equations will eliminate the variable $x$.

$$\begin{array}{r} -2x - 3y = -4 \\ 2x - 5y = -12 \\ \hline -8y = -16 \end{array}$$

Thus, $y = 2$. And so $2x + 3(2) = 4 \Rightarrow x = -1$. The solution is $(-1, 2)$.

(b) Multiplying the first equation by 2 and adding the two equations will eliminate both variables.

$$\begin{array}{r} -4x + y = 2 \\ 4x - y = -2 \\ \hline 0 = 0 \end{array}$$

This is an identity. The system is dependent with solutions $\{(x, y) \mid 4x - y = -2\}$.

(c) Adding the two equations will eliminate the variable $y$.

$$\begin{array}{r} x^2 + y^2 = 16 \\ 2x^2 - y^2 = 11 \\ \hline 3x^2 = 27 \end{array}$$

Thus, $x = \pm 3$. And so $(\pm 3)^2 + y^2 = 16 \Rightarrow y^2 = 7 \Rightarrow y = \pm\sqrt{7}$.

There are four solutions, $(\pm 3, \pm\sqrt{7})$.

(d) Multiply the first equation by 2 and subtract the second equations to eliminate the variable $x$.

$$\begin{array}{r} 2x + 2y - 4z = -12 \\ 2x - y - 3z = -18 \\ \hline 3y - z = 6 \end{array}$$

Subtract the third equation from this *new* equation to eliminate both $y$ and $z$.

$$\begin{array}{r} 3y - z = 6 \\ 3y - z = 6 \\ \hline 0 = 0 \end{array}$$

This is an identity which means there are an infinite number of solutions to the system.

Solving the third equation for $y$ yields $3y - z = 6 \Rightarrow 3y = z + 6 \Rightarrow y = \frac{z + 6}{3}$. Substituting this result for $y$ in the first equation yields $x + \frac{z + 6}{3} - 2z = -6 \Rightarrow x = 2z - \frac{z + 6}{3} - 6 \Rightarrow$

$x + \frac{z + 6}{3} - 2z = -6 \Rightarrow x = 2z - \frac{z + 6}{3} - 6 \Rightarrow x = \frac{5z - 24}{3}$.

The solutions set is $\left\{(x, y, z) \mid x = \frac{5z - 24}{3}, y = \frac{z + 6}{3}, \text{ and } z = z\right\}$.

44. $z = \frac{k}{x^2} \Rightarrow$ When $x = 50$, $z = 8$, so $8 = \frac{k}{50^2} \Rightarrow k = 20{,}000$. Now when $x = 36$, $z = \frac{20{,}000}{36^2} = \frac{1250}{81}$

45. For the graphs of parts (a) and (b), see Figures 45a and 45b.

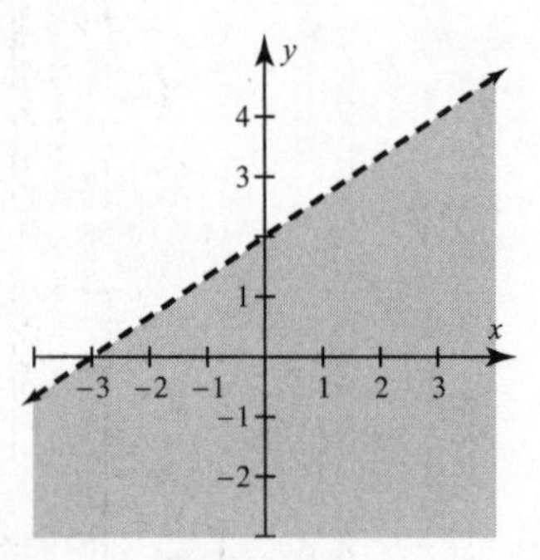

Figure 45a

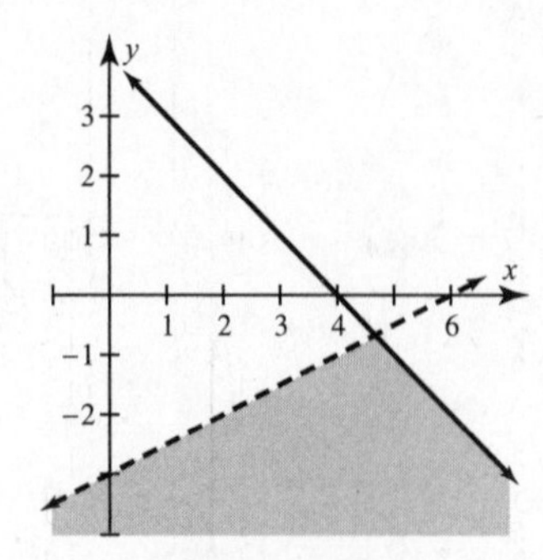

Figure 45b

46. $2A + B = 2\begin{bmatrix} -1 & 0 & 2 \\ 1 & -3 & 1 \\ 0 & -3 & 4 \end{bmatrix} + \begin{bmatrix} 1 & 5 & 1 \\ -2 & 2 & 1 \\ 0 & 1 & -2 \end{bmatrix} = \begin{bmatrix} -1 & 5 & 5 \\ 0 & -4 & 3 \\ 0 & -5 & 6 \end{bmatrix}$

$$AB = \begin{bmatrix} -1 & 0 & 2 \\ 1 & -3 & 1 \\ 0 & -3 & 4 \end{bmatrix}\begin{bmatrix} 1 & 5 & 1 \\ -2 & 2 & 1 \\ 0 & 1 & -2 \end{bmatrix} = \begin{bmatrix} -1+0+0 & -5+0+2 & -1+0+(-4) \\ 1+6+0 & 5+(-6)+1 & 1+(-3)+(-2) \\ 0+6+0 & 0+(-6)+4 & 0+(-3)+(-8) \end{bmatrix} =$$

$$\begin{bmatrix} -1 & -3 & -5 \\ 7 & 0 & -4 \\ 6 & -2 & -11 \end{bmatrix}$$

47. $\left[\begin{array}{cc|cc} 1 & -2 & 1 & 0 \\ -3 & 4 & 0 & 1 \end{array}\right] R_2 + 3R_1 \rightarrow \left[\begin{array}{cc|cc} 1 & -2 & 1 & 0 \\ 0 & -2 & 3 & 1 \end{array}\right] R_1 - R_2 \rightarrow \left[\begin{array}{cc|cc} 1 & 0 & -2 & -1 \\ 0 & -2 & 3 & 1 \end{array}\right] -\tfrac{1}{2}R_2 \rightarrow \left[\begin{array}{cc|cc} 1 & 0 & -2 & -1 \\ 0 & 1 & -\frac{3}{2} & -\frac{1}{2} \end{array}\right]$

That is $A^{-1} = \begin{bmatrix} -2 & -1 \\ -1.5 & -0.5 \end{bmatrix}$.

48. The system can be written $\begin{bmatrix} 1 & -1 & -2 \\ -1 & 2 & 3 \\ 0 & 2 & 1 \end{bmatrix}\begin{bmatrix} x \\ y \\ z \end{bmatrix} = \begin{bmatrix} 5 \\ -7 \\ -2 \end{bmatrix}$. Using a graphing calculator,

$$A^{-1} = \begin{bmatrix} 4 & 3 & -1 \\ -1 & -1 & 1 \\ 2 & 2 & -1 \end{bmatrix}.$$

$X = A^{-1}B = \begin{bmatrix} 4 & 3 & -1 \\ -1 & -1 & 1 \\ 2 & 2 & -1 \end{bmatrix}\begin{bmatrix} 5 \\ -7 \\ -2 \end{bmatrix} = \begin{bmatrix} 1 \\ 0 \\ -2 \end{bmatrix}$. The solution is $(1, 0, -2)$.

49. $\det\left(\begin{bmatrix} -1 & 4 \\ 2 & 3 \end{bmatrix}\right) = -1(3) - 2(4) = -11$

$$\det\left(\begin{bmatrix} 2 & 3 & -1 \\ 3 & -1 & 5 \\ 0 & 0 & -2 \end{bmatrix}\right) = 0(3(5) - (-1)(-1)) - 0(2(5) - 3(-1)) + -2(2(-1) - 3(3)) =$$

$-2(-11) = 22$

50. For the graphs of parts (a) – (d), see Figures 50a – 50d.

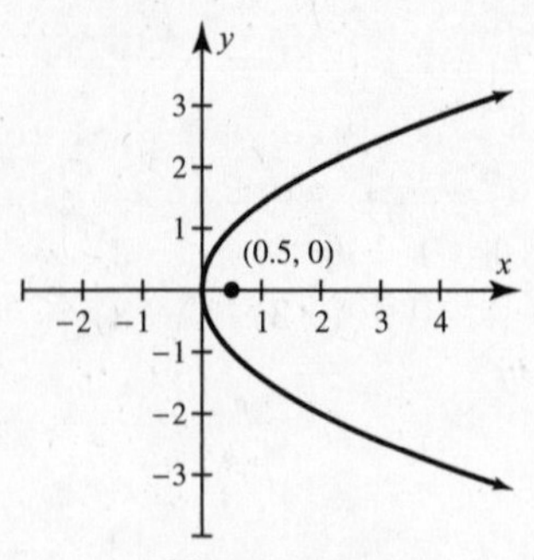

Figure 50a

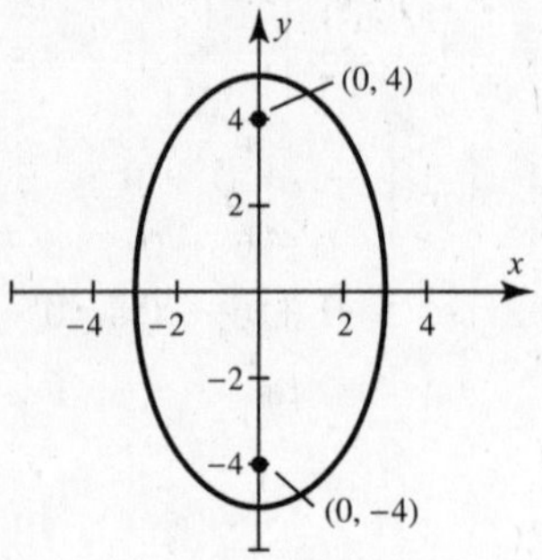

Figure 50b

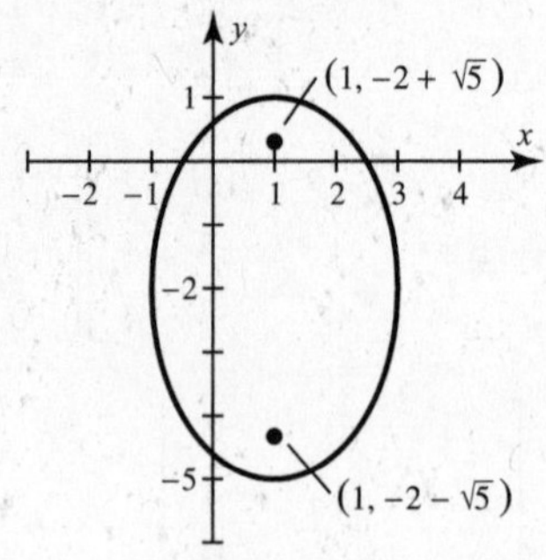

Figure 50c

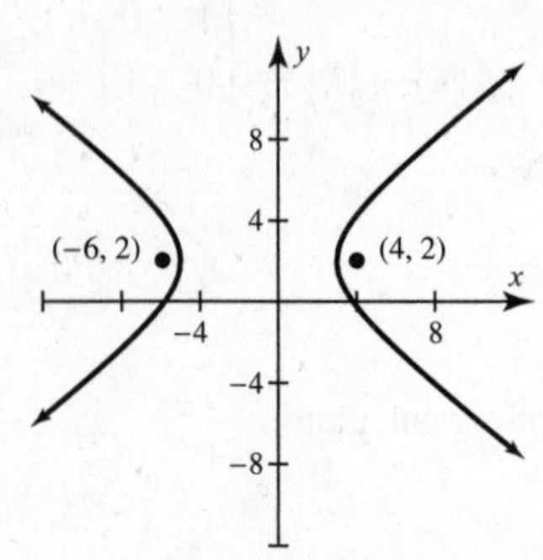

Figure 50d

51. If the focus is at $\left(\frac{3}{4}, 0\right)$ and the vertex at $(0, 0)$, the parabola opens to the right and $p = \frac{3}{4}$. Substituting in $(y - h)^2 = 4p(x - k)$, we get $(y - 0)^2 = 4\left(\frac{3}{4}\right)(x - 0)$ or $y^2 = 3x$.

52. The center is halfway between the vertices at $(0, 1)$; $a = 3$ and $c = 2$; $b^2 = a^2 - c^2 = 9 - 4 = 5$; the major axis is horizontal. The equation is $\frac{x^2}{9} + \frac{(y - 1)^2}{5} = 1$.

53. Since the foci and the vertices lie on the $y$-axis, the hyperbola has a vertical transverse axis with an equation of the form $\frac{y^2}{a^2} - \frac{x^2}{b^2} = 1$. $F(0, \pm 13) \Rightarrow c = 13$ and $V(0, \pm 5) \Rightarrow a = 5$. $c^2 = a^2 + b^2 \Rightarrow$ $b^2 = c^2 - a^2 = 169 - 25 = 144 \Rightarrow b = 12$. The equation of the hyperbola is $\frac{y^2}{25} - \frac{x^2}{144} = 1$.

54. (a) $a_1 = (-1)^0(3) = 3$; $a_2 = (-1)^1(3^2) = -9$; $a_3 = (-1)^2(3^3) = 27$; $a_4 = (-1)^3(3^4) = -81$.

The first four terms are $3, -9, 27$, and $-81$.

(b) $a_1 = 2$; $a_2 = 3$; $a_3 = 3(2) = 6$; $a_4 = 6(3) = 18$. The first four terms are 2, 3, 6, and 18.

55. Let $a_n = f(n)$, where $f(n) = dn + c$. $a_1 = 4 \Rightarrow f(1) = 4$ and $a_3 = 12 \Rightarrow f(3) = 12$.

Thus, $d = \frac{f(3) - f(1)}{3 - 1} = \frac{12 - 4}{2} = 4$. Then, $f(n) = 4n + c$. $f(1) = 4(1) + c = 4 \Rightarrow c = 0$.

Thus, $a_n = f(n) = 4n$.

56. Let $a_n = f(n)$, where $f(n) = a_1 r^{n-1}$. Then, $a_n = f(n) = a_1\left(\frac{1}{2}\right)^{n-1}$.

Since $f(2) = a_1\left(\frac{1}{2}\right)^{2-1} = 6 \Rightarrow a_1 = 6(2) = 12$. Thus, $a_n = f(n) = 12\left(\frac{1}{2}\right)^{n-1}$.

57. (a) The first term is $a_1 = 2$ and the last term is $a_{25} = 74$. There are 25 terms. To find the sum use:

$$S_n = n\left(\frac{a_1 + a_n}{2}\right) \Rightarrow S_{25} = 25\left(\frac{2 + 74}{2}\right) = 950.$$ The sum is 950.

(b) The first term is $a_1 = 0.2$ and the common ratio is $r = \frac{1}{10}$ or 0.1. The sum is

$$S = a_1\left(\frac{1}{1 - r}\right) \Rightarrow S = 0.2\left(\frac{1}{1 - (0.1)}\right) = \frac{0.2}{0.9} = \frac{2}{9}.$$

58. $\sum_{k=1}^{7}(k^2 + k) = (1^2 + 1) + (2^2 + 2) + (3^2 + 3) + (4^2 + 4) + (5^2 + 5) + (6^2 + 6) + (7^2 + 7) = 168$

59. There are $26 \cdot 26 \cdot 26 \cdot 10 \cdot 10 \cdot 10 \cdot 10 = 175{,}760{,}000$ such license plates.

60. $P(n, r) = \frac{n!}{(n - r)!} \Rightarrow P(4, 2) = \frac{4!}{(4 - 2)!} = \frac{4!}{2!} = \frac{24}{2} = 12;$

$$\binom{n}{r} = \frac{n!}{(n - r)!\, r!} \Rightarrow \binom{6}{3} = \frac{6!}{(6 - 3)!\, 3!} = \frac{6!}{3!\, 3!} = \frac{6 \cdot 5 \cdot 4 \cdot 3!}{3!\, 3!} = \frac{120}{6} = 20$$

61. $(2x - 1)^4 = \binom{4}{0}(2x)^4(-1)^0 + \binom{4}{1}(2x)^3(-1)^1 + \binom{4}{2}(2x)^2(-1)^2 + \binom{4}{3}(2x)^1(-1)^3 + \binom{4}{4}(2x)^0(-1)^4$

$= 16x^4 - 32x^3 + 24x^2 - 8x + 1$

62. $5 + 7 + 9 + \cdots + (2n + 3) = n(n + 4)$

(i) Show that the statement is true for $n = 1$: $2(1) + 3 = 1(1 + 4) \Rightarrow 5 = 5$

(ii) Assume that $S_k$ is true: $5 + 7 + 9 + \cdots + (2k + 3) = k(k + 4)$

Show that $S_{k+1}$ is true: $5 + 7 + 9 + \cdots + 2(k + 1) + 3 = (k + 1)(k + 5)$

Add $2(k + 1) + 3 = 2k + 5$ to each side of $S_k$:

$5 + 7 + 9 + \cdots + (2k + 3) + (2k + 5) = k(k + 4) + 2k + 5 = k^2 + 6x + 5 = (k + 1)(k + 5)$

Since $S_k$ implies $S_{k+1}$, the statement is true for every positive integer $n$.

63. The card must be one of the 16 cards (out of 52) that is either a heart or an ace. The probability is $\frac{16}{52} = \frac{4}{13}$.

64. The possible outcomes that sum to seven are (1, 6), (2, 5), (3, 4), (4, 3), (5, 2), and (6, 1). There are 6 ways to roll a sum of seven from a possible 36 outcomes in the sample space. The probability is $\frac{6}{36} = \frac{1}{6}$.

65. There are 8 primes from 1 to 20 (2, 3, 5, 7, 11, 13, 17, 19). The probability is $\frac{8}{20} = \frac{2}{5}$.

66. Let $E_1$ denote the event that it is cloudy and $E_2$ denote the event that it is windy. $P(E_1) = 0.40$ and $P(E_1 \text{ and } E_2) = P(E_1 \cap E_2) = 0.15$. $P(E_1 \cap E_2) = P(E_1) \cdot P(E_2$, given that $E_1$ has occured$) \Rightarrow$ $0.15 = 0.40 \cdot P(E_2$, given that $E_1$ has occured$) \Rightarrow 0.375 = P(E_2$, given that $E_1$ has occured$)$. The probability that it will be windy given that the day is cloudy is 37.5%.

67. From noon to 1:45 PM car A travelled $1.75(50) = 87.5$ miles and thus would be located $87.5 + 30 = 117.5$ miles north of the original location of car B. From noon to 1:45 PM car B travelled $1.75(50) = 87.5$ miles and thus would be located 87.5 miles east of its original location. The paths of the two cars form a right triangle with legs of length 117.5 and 87.5. The length of the hypotenuse is equal to the distance between the cars. $c^2 = 117.5^2 + 87.5^2 \Rightarrow c^2 = 21{,}462.5 \Rightarrow c \approx 146.5$ miles

68. (a) The rate of change is $-60$ because the car is moving toward home at 60 miles per hour. The initial position of the car is 240 miles from home. Thus the formula is $D(x) = -60x + 240$.

(b) Since $D(4) = 0$, the car is home after 4 hours. An appropriate domain is $D = \{x \mid 0 \le x \le 4\}$.

(c) See Figure 68.

(d) The $x$-intercept is 4 since the car is home after 4 hours. The $y$-intercept is 240 since the car is initially 240 miles from home.

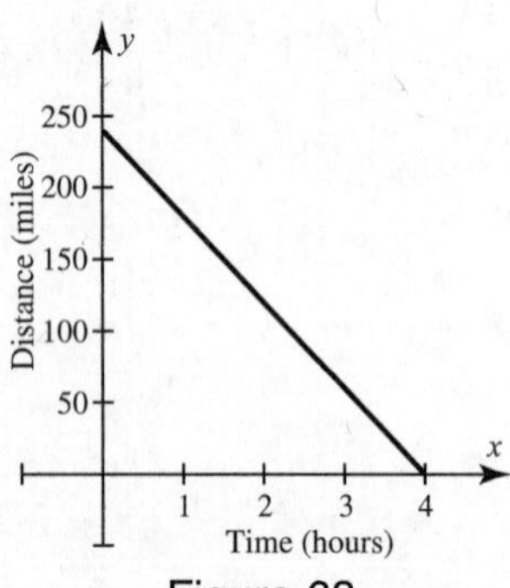


Figure 68

69. Let $x$ represent the time spent jogging at 7 miles per hour and let $y$ represent the time spent jogging at 9 miles per hour. Then the system of equations to be solved is $x + y = 1.3$ and $7x + 9y = 10.5$. Solving the first equation for $y$ gives $y = 1.3 - x$. Substituting this expression in the second equation and solving for $x$ yields $7x + 9(1.3 - x) = 10.5 \Rightarrow -2x + 11.7 = 10.5 \Rightarrow -2x = -1.2 \Rightarrow x = 0.6$. From the first equation $0.6 + y = 1.3 \Rightarrow y = 0.7$. The jogger ran for 0.6 hours at 7 mph and 0.7 hours at 9 mph.

70. (a) $\dfrac{D(1) - D(0)}{1 - 0} = \dfrac{3(1^2) - 3(0^2)}{1 - 0} = \dfrac{3}{1} = 3$ ft/sec; $\dfrac{D(4) - D(3)}{4 - 3} = \dfrac{3(4^2) - 3(3^2)}{4 - 3} = \dfrac{21}{1} = 21$ ft/sec

(b) From 0 to 1 second, the average speed of the horse is 3 ft/sec. From 3 to 4 seconds, the average speed of the horse is 21 ft/sec.

71. Let $x$ represent the number of hours they work together. The the first person mows $\frac{x}{5}$ of the lawn in $x$ hours and the second person mows $\frac{x}{4}$ of the lawn in $x$ hours. Together they mow $\frac{x}{5} + \frac{x}{4}$ of the lawn in $x$ hours. The job is complete when the fraction of the lawn mowed is 1. That is, we must solve $\frac{x}{5} + \frac{x}{4} = 1$.

The LCD is 20. The first step is to multiply each side of the equation by the LCD.

$20 \cdot \left(\frac{x}{5} + \frac{x}{4}\right) = 1 \cdot 20 \Rightarrow 4x + 5x = 20 \Rightarrow 9x = 20 \Rightarrow x = \frac{20}{9} \approx 2.22$ hours.

72. The maximum height occurs at the vertex. $t = -\frac{b}{2a} = -\frac{96}{2(-16)} = 3$. The $y$-value of the vertex is the maximum height. $y = f(3) = -16(3)^2 + 96(3) + 4 = 148$ feet

73. (a) The cost of 1 ticket is $1(405 - 1(5)) = 400$. The cost for 2 tickets is $2(405 - 2(5)) = \$790$. The cost for 3 tickets is $3(405 - 3(5)) = \$1170$. Following this pattern, the cost for $x$ tickets is $C(x) = x(405 - 5x)$.

(b) $x(405 - 5x) = 7000 \Rightarrow 405x - 5x^2 = 7000 \Rightarrow 5x^2 - 405x + 7000 = 0 \Rightarrow$ $x^2 - 81x + 1400 = 0 \Rightarrow (x - 25)(x - 56) = 0 \Rightarrow x = 25$ or $x = 56$. It costs \$7000 to buy either 25 or 56 tickets.

(c) The maximum for the function occurs at the vertex of its graph - a parabola. For $C(x) = -5x^2 + 405x$, $x = -\frac{b}{2a} = -\frac{405}{2(-5)} = 40.5$. Since the number of tickets must be an integer, the maximum occurs at either 40 or 41 tickets being purchased. In either case, the maximum expenditure is $40(405 - 5(40)) = \$8200$.

74. Let $l$ represent the length of the rectangle and let $w$ represent the width. Since the perimeter of a rectangle is given by $P = 2l + 2w$, and the given perimeter is 48, $2l + 2w = 48 \Rightarrow w = 24 - l$. Since the area of a rectangle is given by $A = lw$, and the given area is 143, $lw = 143 \Rightarrow l(24 - l) = 143 \Rightarrow$ $24l - l^2 = 143 \Rightarrow l^2 - 24l + 143 = 0 \Rightarrow (l - 13)(l - 11) = 0 \Rightarrow l = 13$ or $l = 11$. The length is the larger of these two values, so $l = 13$ and $w = 24 - 13 = 11$. The dimensions are 13 by 11 inches.

75. Substitute the point (1.5, 0.5) into $x^2 = 4py$ and solve for $p$; $1.5^2 = 4p(0.5) \Rightarrow 2.25 = 2p \Rightarrow p = 1.125$. The receiver should be 1.125 feet from the vertex.

76. If the height attained by the ball is doubled for each bounce, the series sums to

$$2\cdot 4\left(\frac{3}{4}\right)^0 + 2\cdot 4\left(\frac{3}{4}\right) + 2\cdot 4\left(\frac{3}{4}\right)^2 + 2\cdot 4\left(\frac{3}{4}\right)^3 + \cdots = 8\left[\left(\frac{3}{4}\right)^0 + \left(\frac{3}{4}\right)^1 + \left(\frac{3}{4}\right)^2 + \left(\frac{3}{4}\right)^3 + \cdots\right] =$$

$8\sum_{k=1}^{\infty}\left(\frac{3}{4}\right)^{k-1} = 8\left(\frac{1}{1-\frac{3}{4}}\right) = 8(4) = 32$. Since the ball was dropped from a height of 4 feet, it did not travel upward for the first "bounce", so 4 must be subtracted. The total distance travelled is $32 - 4 = 28$ feet.

77. There are 49 marbles that are not blue and there are a total of 77 marbles. The probability of drawing a marble that is not blue is $\frac{49}{77} = \frac{7}{11}$.

# Chapter R: Basic Concepts from Algebra and Geometry

## R.1: Formulas from Geometry

1. $A = LW = (15)(7) = 105 \text{ ft}^2$; $P = 2L + 2W = 2(15) + 2(7) = 30 + 14 = 44 \text{ ft}$
2. $A = LW = (16)(10) = 160 \text{ in.}^2$; $P = 2L + 2W = 2(16) + 2(10) = 32 + 20 = 52 \text{ in.}$
3. $A = LW = (100)(35) = 3500 \text{ m}^2$; $P = 2L + 2W = 2(100) + 2(35) = 200 + 70 = 270 \text{ m}$
4. $A = LW = (80)(13) = 1040 \text{ yd}^2$; $P = 2L + 2W = 2(80) + 2(13) = 160 + 26 = 186 \text{ yd}$
5. $A = LW = (3x)(y) = 3xy$ square units; $P = 2L + 2W = 2(3x) + 2(y) = 6x + 2y$ units
6. $A = LW = (a + 5)(a) = a(a + 5)$ square units; $P = 2L + 2W = 2(a + 5) + 2(a) = 4a + 10$ units
7. Since the width is half of the length, $L = 2W$.

   $A = LW = (2W)(W) = 2W^2$ square units; $P = 2L + 2W = 2(2W) + 2(W) = 6W$ units
8. Since the length is triple the width minus 3, $L = 3W - 3$.

   $A = LW = (3W - 3)(W) = W(3W - 3)$ square units;

   $P = 2L + 2W = 2(3W - 3) + 2(W) = 8W - 6$ units
9. Since the length equals the width plus 5, $L = W + 5$.

   $A = LW = (W + 5)(W) = W(W + 5)$ square units; $P = 2L + 2W = 2(W + 5) + 2(W) = 4W + 10$ units
10. Since the length is 2 less than twice the width, $L = 2W - 2$.

    $A = LW = (2W - 2)(W) = W(2W - 2)$ square units;

    $P = 2L + 2W = 2(2W - 2) + 2(W) = 6W - 4$ units
11. $A = \frac{1}{2}bh = \left(\frac{1}{2}\right)(8)(5) = 20 \text{ cm}^2$
12. $A = \frac{1}{2}bh = \left(\frac{1}{2}\right)(8)(6) = 24 \text{ ft}^2$
13. $A = \frac{1}{2}bh = \left(\frac{1}{2}\right)(5)(8) = 20 \text{ in.}^2$
14. Since 24 inches is 2 feet, $A = \frac{1}{2}bh = \left(\frac{1}{2}\right)(2)(9) = 9 \text{ ft}^2$.
15. $A = \frac{1}{2}bh = \left(\frac{1}{2}\right)(10.1)(730) = 3686.5 \text{ m}^2$
16. Since 102 feet is 34 yards, $A = \frac{1}{2}bh = \left(\frac{1}{2}\right)(52)(34) = 884 \text{ yd}^2$.
17. $A = \frac{1}{2}bh = \left(\frac{1}{2}\right)(2x)(6x) = 6x^2$ square units
18. $A = \frac{1}{2}bh = \left(\frac{1}{2}\right)(x)(x + 4) = \frac{1}{2}x^2 + 2x$ square units
19. $A = \frac{1}{2}bh = \left(\frac{1}{2}\right)(z)(5z) = \frac{5}{2}z^2$ square units

20. $A = \frac{1}{2}bh = \left(\frac{1}{2}\right)(y + 1)(2y) = y^2 + y$ square units

21. $C = 2\pi r = 2\pi(4) = 8\pi \approx 25.1$ m; $A = \pi r^2 = \pi(4)^2 = 16\pi \approx 50.3\text{ m}^2$

22. $C = 2\pi r = 2\pi(1.5) = 3\pi \approx 9.4$ ft; $A = \pi r^2 = \pi(1.5)^2 = 2.25\pi \approx 7.1\text{ ft}^2$

23. $C = 2\pi r = 2\pi(19) = 38\pi \approx 119.4$ in.; $A = \pi r^2 = \pi(19)^2 = 361\pi \approx 1134.1\text{ in.}^2$

24. $C = 2\pi r = 2\pi(22) = 44\pi \approx 138.2$ mi; $A = \pi r^2 = \pi(22)^2 = 484\pi \approx 1520.5\text{ m}^2$

25. $C = 2\pi r = 2\pi(2x) = 4\pi x$ units; $A = \pi r^2 = \pi(2x)^2 = 4\pi x^2$ square units

26. $C = 2\pi r = 2\pi(5z) = 10\pi z$ units; $A = \pi r^2 = \pi(5z)^2 = 25\pi z^2$ square units

27. $c^2 = a^2 + b^2 \Rightarrow c^2 = (60)^2 + (11)^2 \Rightarrow c^2 = 3721 \Rightarrow c = \sqrt{3721} \Rightarrow c = 61$ ft

$P = 60 + 11 + 61 = 132$ ft

28. Since 21 feet is 7 yards, $c^2 = a^2 + b^2 \Rightarrow c^2 = (7)^2 + (11)^2 \Rightarrow c^2 = 170 \Rightarrow c = \sqrt{170} \Rightarrow c \approx 13.0$ yd

$P \approx 7 + 11 + 13.0 \approx 31.0$ yd

29. $c^2 = a^2 + b^2 \Rightarrow b^2 = c^2 - a^2 \Rightarrow b^2 = (13)^2 - (5)^2 \Rightarrow b^2 = 144 \Rightarrow b = \sqrt{144} \Rightarrow b = 12$ cm

$P = 5 + 12 + 13 = 30$ cm

30. $c^2 = a^2 + b^2 \Rightarrow b^2 = c^2 - a^2 \Rightarrow b^2 = (15)^2 - (6)^2 \Rightarrow b^2 = 189 \Rightarrow b = \sqrt{189} \Rightarrow b \approx 13.7$ m

$P \approx 6 + 13.7 + 15 \approx 34.7$ m

31. $c^2 = a^2 + b^2 \Rightarrow a^2 = c^2 - b^2 \Rightarrow a^2 = (10)^2 - (7)^2 \Rightarrow a^2 = 51 \Rightarrow a = \sqrt{51} \Rightarrow a \approx 7.1$ mm

$P \approx 7.1 + 7 + 10 = 24.1$ mm

32. $c^2 = a^2 + b^2 \Rightarrow a^2 = c^2 - b^2 \Rightarrow a^2 = (2)^2 - (1.2)^2 \Rightarrow a^2 = 2.56 \Rightarrow a = \sqrt{2.56} \Rightarrow a = 1.6$ mi

$P = 1.6 + 1.2 + 2 = 4.8$ mi

33. $A = \frac{1}{2}bh = \left(\frac{1}{2}\right)(6)(3) = 9\text{ ft}^2$

34. $c^2 = a^2 + b^2 \Rightarrow b^2 = c^2 - a^2 \Rightarrow b^2 = (10)^2 - (6)^2 \Rightarrow b^2 = 64 \Rightarrow b = \sqrt{64} \Rightarrow b = 8$ in.

$A = \frac{1}{2}bh = \left(\frac{1}{2}\right)(6)(8) = 24\text{ in.}^2$

35. $c^2 = a^2 + b^2 \Rightarrow b^2 = c^2 - a^2 \Rightarrow b^2 = (15)^2 - (11)^2 \Rightarrow b^2 = 104 \Rightarrow b = \sqrt{104} \Rightarrow b \approx 10.2$ in.

$A = \frac{1}{2}bh = \left(\frac{1}{2}\right)(11)(\sqrt{104}) \approx 56.1\text{ in.}^2$

36. $c^2 = a^2 + b^2 \Rightarrow b^2 = c^2 - a^2 \Rightarrow b^2 = (80)^2 - (40)^2 \Rightarrow b^2 = 4800 \Rightarrow b = \sqrt{4800} \Rightarrow b \approx 69.3$ cm

$A = \frac{1}{2}bh = \left(\frac{1}{2}\right)(40)(\sqrt{4800}) \approx 1385.6\text{ cm}^2$

37. $V = LWH = (4)(3)(2) = 24\text{ ft}^3$; $S = 2LW + 2WH + 2LH = 2(4)(3) + 2(3)(2) + 2(4)(2) = 52\text{ ft}^2$

38. $V = LWH = (6)(4)(1.5) = 36\text{ m}^3$;

$S = 2LW + 2WH + 2LH = 2(6)(4) + 2(4)(1.5) + 2(6)(1.5) = 78\text{ m}^2$

39. Since 1 foot is 12 inches, $V = LWH = (4.5)(4)(12) = 216\text{ in.}^3$

$S = 2LW + 2WH + 2LH = 2(4.5)(4) + 2(4)(12) + 2(4.5)(12) = 240\text{ in.}^2$

40. Since 6 feet is 2 yards, $V = LWH = (9.1)(8)(2) = 145.6 \text{ yd}^3$

$S = 2LW + 2WH + 2LH = 2(9.1)(8) + 2(8)(2) + 2(9.1)(2) = 214 \text{ yd}^2$

41. $V = LWH = (3x)(2x)(x) = 6x^3$ cubic units

$S = 2LW + 2WH + 2LH = 2(3x)(2x) + 2(2x)(x) + 2(3x)(x) = 22x^2$ square units

42. $V = LWH = (6z)(5z)(7z) = 210z^3$ cubic units

$S = 2LW + 2WH + 2LH = 2(6z)(5z) + 2(5z)(7z) + 2(6z)(7z) = 214z^2$ square units

43. $V = LWH = (x)(2y)(3z) = 6xyz$ cubic units

$S = 2LW + 2WH + 2LH = 2(x)(2y) + 2(2y)(3z) + 2(x)(3z) = 4xy + 12yz + 6xz$ square units

44. $V = LWH = (8x)(y)(z) = 8xyz$ cubic units

$S = 2LW + 2WH + 2LH = 2(8x)(y) + 2(y)(z) + 2(8x)(z) = 16xy + 2yz + 16xz$ square units

45. Since the length is twice $W$ and the height is half $W$, $L = 2W$ and $H = 0.5W$

$V = LWH = (2W)(W)(0.5W) = W^3$

46. Since $W$ is three times the height and one-third the length, $L = 3W$ and $H = \frac{1}{3}W$

$V = LWH = (3W)(W)\left(\frac{1}{3}W\right) = W^3$

47. $V = \frac{4}{3}\pi r^3 \Rightarrow V = \frac{4}{3}\pi(3)^3 = 36\pi \approx 113.1 \text{ ft}^3$; $S = 4\pi r^2 \Rightarrow S = 4\pi(3)^2 = 36\pi \approx 113.1 \text{ ft}^2$

48. $V = \frac{4}{3}\pi r^3 \Rightarrow V = \frac{4}{3}\pi(4.1)^3 \approx 91.9\pi \approx 288.7 \text{ in.}^3$; $S = 4\pi r^2 \Rightarrow S = 4\pi(4.1)^2 \approx 67.2\pi \approx 211.1 \text{ in.}^2$

49. $V = \frac{4}{3}\pi r^3 \Rightarrow V = \frac{4}{3}\pi(3.2)^3 \approx 43.7\pi \approx 137.3 \text{ m}^3$; $S = 4\pi r^2 \Rightarrow S = 4\pi(3.2)^2 \approx 41.0\pi \approx 128.8 \text{ m}^2$

50. $V = \frac{4}{3}\pi r^3 \Rightarrow V = \frac{4}{3}\pi(8)^3 \approx 682.7\pi \approx 2144.7 \text{ ft}^3$; $S = 4\pi r^2 \Rightarrow S = 4\pi(8)^2 = 256\pi \approx 804.2 \text{ ft}^2$

51. $V = \pi r^2 h \Rightarrow V = \pi(0.5)^2(2) = 0.5\pi \approx 1.6 \text{ ft}^3$; $S_{side} = 2\pi rh \Rightarrow S_{side} = 2\pi(0.5)(2) = 2\pi \approx 6.3 \text{ ft}^2$

$S_{total} = 2\pi rh + 2\pi r^2 \Rightarrow S_{total} = 2\pi(0.5)(2) + 2\pi(0.5)^2 = 2.5\pi \approx 7.9 \text{ ft}^2$

52. Since one-third yard is one foot, $V = \pi r^2 h \Rightarrow V = \pi(1)^2(2) = 2\pi \approx 6.3 \text{ ft}^3$

$S_{side} = 2\pi rh \Rightarrow S_{side} = 2\pi(1)(2) = 4\pi \approx 12.6 \text{ ft}^2$

$S_{total} = 2\pi rh + 2\pi r^2 \Rightarrow S_{total} = 2\pi(1)(2) + 2\pi(1)^2 \approx 6\pi \approx 18.8 \text{ ft}^2$

53. Since $h$ is twice $r$, $h = 2(12) = 24$, thus $V = \pi r^2 h \Rightarrow V = \pi(12)^2(24) = 3456\pi \approx 10{,}857.3 \text{ mm}^3$

$S_{side} = 2\pi rh \Rightarrow S_{side} = 2\pi(12)(24) = 576\pi \approx 1809.6 \text{ mm}^2$

$S_{total} = 2\pi rh + 2\pi r^2 \Rightarrow S_{total} = 2\pi(12)(24) + 2\pi(12)^2 = 864\pi \approx 2714.3 \text{ mm}^2$

54. Since $r$ is one-fourth of $h$, $r = 0.25(2.1) = 0.525$, thus $V = \pi r^2 h \Rightarrow V = \pi(0.525)^2(2.1) \approx 0.6\pi \approx 1.9 \text{ ft}^3$

$S_{side} = 2\pi rh \Rightarrow S_{side} = 2\pi(0.525)(2.1) \approx 2.2\pi \approx 6.9 \text{ ft}^2$

$S_{total} = 2\pi rh + 2\pi r^2 \Rightarrow S_{total} = 2\pi(0.525)(2.1) + 2\pi(0.525)^2 \approx 2.8\pi \approx 8.8 \text{ ft}^2$

55. $V = \frac{1}{3}\pi r^2 h \Rightarrow V = \frac{1}{3}\pi(5)^2(6) \approx 157.1 \text{ cm}^3$;

$S = \pi r\sqrt{r^2 + h^2} \Rightarrow S = \pi(5)\sqrt{(5)^2 + (6)^2} \approx 122.7 \text{ cm}^2$

56. $V = \frac{1}{3}\pi r^2 h \Rightarrow V = \frac{1}{3}\pi(8)^2(30) \approx 2010.6$ in.$^3$;

$S = \pi r\sqrt{r^2 + h^2} \Rightarrow S = \pi(8)\sqrt{(8)^2 + (30)^2} \approx 780.3$ in.$^2$

57. Since 24 inches is 2 feet,

$V = \frac{1}{3}\pi r^2 h \Rightarrow V = \frac{1}{3}\pi(2)^2(3) \approx 12.6$ ft$^3$; $S = \pi r\sqrt{r^2 + h^2} \Rightarrow S = \pi(2)\sqrt{(2)^2 + (3)^2} \approx 22.7$ ft$^2$

58. Since 100 centimeters is 1 meter,

$V = \frac{1}{3}\pi r^2 h \Rightarrow V = \frac{1}{3}\pi(1)^2(1.3) \approx 1.4$ m$^3$; $S = \pi r\sqrt{r^2 + h^2} \Rightarrow S = \pi(1)\sqrt{(1)^2 + (1.3)^2} \approx 5.2$ m$^2$

59. Since $h$ is three times $r$, $h = 3(2.4) = 7.2$.

$V = \frac{1}{3}\pi r^2 h \Rightarrow V = \frac{1}{3}\pi(2.4)^2(7.2) \approx 43.4$ ft$^3$;

$S = \pi r\sqrt{r^2 + h^2} \Rightarrow S = \pi(2.4)\sqrt{(2.4)^2 + (7.2)^2} \approx 57.2$ ft$^2$

60. Since $r$ is equal to twice $h$, $r = 2(3) = 6$.

$V = \frac{1}{3}\pi r^2 h \Rightarrow V = \frac{1}{3}\pi(6)^2(3) \approx 113.1$ cm$^3$; $S = \pi r\sqrt{r^2 + h^2} \Rightarrow S = \pi(6)\sqrt{(6)^2 + (3)^2} \approx 126.4$ cm$^2$

61. $\frac{x}{4} = \frac{5}{3} \Rightarrow 3x = 20 \Rightarrow x = \frac{20}{3} \approx 6.7$

62. $\frac{x}{6} = \frac{7}{4} \Rightarrow 4x = 42 \Rightarrow x = \frac{42}{4} = \frac{21}{2} = 10.5$

63. $\frac{x}{7} = \frac{9}{6} \Rightarrow 6x = 63 \Rightarrow x = \frac{63}{6} = \frac{21}{2} = 10.5$

64. $\frac{x}{5} = \frac{4}{8} \Rightarrow 8x = 20 \Rightarrow x = \frac{20}{8} = \frac{5}{2} = 2.5$

## R.2: Integer Exponents

1. No. $2^3 = 8$ and $3^2 = 9$
2. No. $-4^2 = -16$ and $(-4)^2 = 16$
3. $\frac{1}{7^n}$
4. $6^{m+n}$
5. $5^{m-n}$
6. $3^k x^k$
7. $2^{mk}$
8. $\frac{x^m}{y^m}$
9. 5000
10. 0.005
11. $2^3$
12. $10^3$
13. $4^4$

14. $4^{-3}$

15. $3^0$

16. $7^{-2}$

17. $5^3 = 125$

18. $5^{-3} = \frac{1}{5^3} = \frac{1}{125}$

19. $-2^4 = -16$

20. $(-2)^4 = 16$

21. $5^0 = 1$

22. $\left(-\frac{2}{3}\right)^{-3} = \left(-\frac{3}{2}\right)^3 = \left(-\frac{3}{2}\right)\cdot\left(-\frac{3}{2}\right)\cdot\left(-\frac{3}{2}\right) = -\frac{27}{8}$

23. $\left(\frac{2}{3}\right)^3 = \frac{2^3}{3^3} = \frac{2\cdot 2\cdot 2}{3\cdot 3\cdot 3} = \frac{8}{27}$

24. $\frac{1}{4^{-2}} = 4^2 = 16$

25. $\left(-\frac{1}{2}\right)^4 = \left(-\frac{1}{2}\right)\cdot\left(-\frac{1}{2}\right)\cdot\left(-\frac{1}{2}\right)\cdot\left(-\frac{1}{2}\right) = \frac{1}{16}$

26. $\left(-\frac{3}{4}\right)^3 = \left(-\frac{3}{4}\right)\cdot\left(-\frac{3}{4}\right)\cdot\left(-\frac{3}{4}\right) = -\frac{27}{64}$

27. $4^{-3} = \frac{1}{4^3} = \frac{1}{64}$

28. $10^{-4} = \frac{1}{10^4} = \frac{1}{10{,}000}$

29. $\frac{1}{2^{-4}} = 2^4 = 16$

30. $\frac{1}{3^{-2}} = 3^2 = 9$

31. $\left(\frac{3}{4}\right)^{-3} = \left(\frac{4}{3}\right)^3 = \left(\frac{4}{3}\right)\cdot\left(\frac{4}{3}\right)\cdot\left(\frac{4}{3}\right) = \frac{64}{27}$

32. $\left(\frac{1}{2}\right)^0 = 1$

33. $\frac{3^{-2}}{2^{-3}} = \frac{2^3}{3^2} = \frac{8}{9}$

34. $\frac{10^{-4}}{4^{-3}} = \frac{4^3}{10^4} = \frac{64}{10{,}000} = \frac{4}{625}$

35. $6^3\cdot 6^{-4} = 6^{3+(-4)} = 6^{-1} = \frac{1}{6}$

36. $10^2\cdot 10^5\cdot 10^{-3} = 10^{2+5+(-3)} = 10^4 = 10{,}000$

37. $2x^2\cdot 3x^{-3}\cdot x^4 = 6x^{2+(-3)+4} = 6x^3$

38. $3y^4\cdot 6y^{-4}\cdot y = 18y^{4+(-4)+1} = 18y$

39. $10^0\cdot 10^6\cdot 10^2 = 10^{0+6+2} = 10^8 = 100{,}000{,}000$

40. $y^3 \cdot y^{-5} \cdot y^4 = y^{3+(-5)+4} = y^2$

41. $5^{-2} \cdot 5^3 \cdot 2^{-4} \cdot 2^3 = 5^{-2+3} \cdot 2^{-4+3} = 5^1 \cdot 2^{-1} = 5 \cdot \frac{1}{2} = \frac{5}{2}$

42. $2^{-3} \cdot 3^4 \cdot 3^{-2} \cdot 2^5 = 2^{-3+5} \cdot 3^{4+(-2)} = 2^2 \cdot 3^2 = 4 \cdot 9 = 36$

43. $2a^3 \cdot b^2 \cdot a^{-4} \cdot 4b^{-5} = 2a^{3+(-4)} \cdot 4b^{2+(-5)} = 8a^{-1}b^{-3} = \frac{8}{ab^3}$

44. $3x^{-4} \cdot 2x^2 \cdot 5y^4 \cdot y^{-3} = 6x^{-4+2} \cdot 5y^{4+(-3)} = 30x^{-2}y^1 = \frac{30y}{x^2}$

45. $\frac{5^4}{5^2} = 5^{4-2} = 5^2 = 25$

46. $\frac{6^2}{6^{-7}} = 6^{2-(-7)} = 6^9 = 10{,}077{,}696$

47. $\frac{a^{-3}}{a^2 \cdot a} = a^{-3-(2+1)} = a^{-6} = \frac{1}{a^6}$

48. $\frac{y^0 \cdot y \cdot y^5}{y^{-2} \cdot y^{-3}} = y^{0+1+5-(-2+(-3))} = y^{11}$

49. $\frac{24x^3}{6x} = \frac{24}{6}x^{3-1} = 4x^2$

50. $\frac{10x^5}{5x^{-3}} = \frac{10}{5}x^{5-(-3)} = 2x^8$

51. $\frac{12a^2b^3}{18a^4b^2} = \frac{12}{18}\, a^{2-4} \cdot b^{3-2} = \frac{2}{3}\, a^{-2}b^1 = \frac{2b}{3a^2}$

52. $\frac{-6x^7y^3}{3x^2y^{-5}} = -\frac{6}{3}\, x^{7-2} \cdot y^{3-(-5)} = -2x^5y^8$

53. $\frac{21x^{-3}y^4}{7x^4y^{-2}} = \frac{21}{7}\, x^{-3-4} \cdot y^{4-(-2)} = 3x^{-7}y^6 = \frac{3y^6}{x^7}$

54. $\frac{32x^3y}{-24x^5y^{-3}} = -\frac{32}{24}x^{3-5} \cdot y^{1-(-3)} = -\frac{4}{3}x^{-2}y^4 = -\frac{4y^4}{3x^2}$

55. $(5^{-1})^3 = 5^{-1(3)} = 5^{-3} = \frac{1}{5^3} = \frac{1}{125}$

56. $(-4^2)^3 = -4^{2(3)} = -4^6 = -4096$

57. $(y^4)^{-2} = y^{4(-2)} = y^{-8} = \frac{1}{y^8}$

58. $(x^2)^4 = x^{2 \cdot 4} = x^8$

59. $(4y^2)^3 = 4^3 \cdot y^{2 \cdot 3} = 64y^6$

60. $(-2xy^3)^{-4} = \frac{1}{(2xy^3)^4} = \frac{1}{2^4 \cdot x^4 \cdot y^{3 \cdot 4}} = \frac{1}{16x^4y^{12}}$

61. $\left(\frac{4}{x}\right)^3 = \frac{4^3}{x^3} = \frac{64}{x^3}$

62. $\left(\frac{-3}{x^3}\right)^2 = \frac{(-3)^2}{(x^3)^2} = \frac{9}{x^{3 \cdot 2}} = \frac{9}{x^6}$

63. $\left(\frac{2x}{z^4}\right)^{-5} = \left(\frac{z^4}{2x}\right)^5 = \frac{(z^4)^5}{(2x)^5} = \frac{z^{4 \cdot 5}}{2^5 \cdot x^5} = \frac{z^{20}}{32x^5}$

64. $\left(\frac{2xy}{3z^5}\right)^{-1} = \left(\frac{3z^5}{2xy}\right)^1 = \frac{3z^5}{2xy}$

65. $\frac{2}{(ab)^{-1}} = 2(ab)^1 = 2ab$

66. $\frac{5a^2}{(xy)^{-1}} = 5a^2(xy)^1 = 5a^2xy$

67. $\frac{2^{-3}}{2t^{-2}} = \frac{t^2}{2(2^3)} = \frac{t^2}{16}$

68. $\frac{t^{-3}}{2t^{-1}} = \frac{1}{2} \cdot t^{-3-(-1)} = \frac{1}{2} \cdot t^{-2} = \frac{1}{2t^2}$

69. $\frac{6a^2b^{-3}}{4ab^{-2}} = \frac{6}{4} \cdot a^{2-1}b^{-3-(-2)} = \frac{3}{2} \cdot ab^{-1} = \frac{3a}{2b}$

70. $\frac{20a^{-2}b}{4a^{-2}b^{-1}} = \frac{20}{4} \cdot a^{-2-(-2)}b^{1-(-1)} = 5a^0b^2 = 5b^2$

71. $\frac{5r^2st^{-3}}{25rs^{-2}t^2} = \frac{5}{25} \cdot r^{2-1}s^{1-(-2)}t^{-3-2} = \frac{1}{5} \cdot rs^3t^{-5} = \frac{rs^3}{5t^5}$

72. $\frac{36r^{-1}(st)^2}{9(rs)^2t^{-1}} = \frac{36r^{-1}s^2t^2}{9r^2s^2t^{-1}} = \frac{36}{9} \cdot r^{-1-2}s^{2-2}t^{2-(-1)} = 4r^{-3}s^0t^3 = \frac{4t^3}{r^3}$

73. $(3x^2y^{-3})^{-2} = \frac{1}{(3x^2y^{-3})^2} = \frac{1}{3^2(x^2)^2(y^{-3})^2} = \frac{1}{9x^{2\cdot 2}y^{-3\cdot 2}} = \frac{1}{9x^4y^{-6}} = \frac{y^6}{9x^4}$

74. $(-2x^{-3}y^{-2})^3 = (-2)^3(x^{-3})^3(y^{-2})^3 = -8x^{-3\cdot 3}y^{-2\cdot 3} = -8x^{-9}y^{-6} = -\frac{8}{x^9y^6}$

75. $\frac{(d^3)^{-2}}{(d^{-2})^3} = \frac{d^{3\cdot(-2)}}{d^{-2\cdot 3}} = \frac{d^{-6}}{d^{-6}} = d^{-6-(-6)} = d^0 = 1$

76. $\frac{(b^2)^{-1}}{(b^{-4})^3} = \frac{b^{2\cdot(-1)}}{b^{-4\cdot 3}} = \frac{b^{-2}}{b^{-12}} = b^{-2-(-12)} = b^{10}$

77. $\left(\frac{3t^2}{2t^{-1}}\right)^3 = \frac{(3t^2)^3}{(2t^{-1})^3} = \frac{3^3(t^2)^3}{2^3(t^{-1})^3} = \frac{27t^{2\cdot 3}}{8t^{-1\cdot 3}} = \frac{27t^6}{8t^{-3}} = \frac{27}{8} \cdot t^{6-(-3)} = \frac{27}{8} \cdot t^9 = \frac{27t^9}{8}$

78. $\left(\frac{-2t}{4t^{-2}}\right)^{-1} = \left(\frac{4t^{-2}}{-2t}\right)^1 = \frac{4}{-2} \cdot t^{-2-1} = -2t^{-3} = -\frac{2}{t^3}$

79. $\frac{(-m^2n^{-1})^{-2}}{(mn)^{-1}} = \frac{(mn)^1}{(-m^2n^{-1})^2} = \frac{mn}{(-m^2)^2(n^{-1})^2} = \frac{mn}{m^{2\cdot 2}n^{-1\cdot 2}} = \frac{mn}{m^4n^{-2}} = m^{1-4}n^{1-(-2)} = m^{-3}n^3 = \frac{n^3}{m^3}$

80. $\frac{(-mn^4)^{-1}}{(m^2n)^{-3}} = \frac{(m^2n)^3}{(-mn^4)^1} = \frac{(m^2)^3n^3}{-mn^4} = \frac{m^{2\cdot 3}n^3}{-mn^4} = \frac{m^6n^3}{-mn^4} = -m^{6-1}n^{3-4} = -m^5n^{-1} = -\frac{m^5}{n}$

81. $\left(\frac{2a^3}{6b}\right)^4 = \left(\frac{a^3}{3b}\right)^4 = \frac{(a^3)^4}{3^4b^4} = \frac{a^{3\cdot 4}}{81b^4} = \frac{a^{12}}{81b^4}$

82. $\left(\frac{-3a^2}{9b^3}\right)^4 = \left(\frac{-a^2}{3b^3}\right)^4 = \frac{(-a^2)^4}{3^4(b^3)^4} = \frac{a^{2\cdot 4}}{81b^{3\cdot 4}} = \frac{a^8}{81b^{12}}$

83. $\frac{8x^{-3}y^{-2}}{4x^{-2}y^{-4}} = \frac{8}{4}\, x^{-3-(-2)}y^{-2-(-4)} = 2x^{-1}y^2 = \frac{2y^2}{x}$

84. $\dfrac{6x^{-1}y^{-1}}{9x^{-2}y^{3}} = \dfrac{6}{9}x^{-1-(-2)}y^{-1-3} = \dfrac{2}{3}x^{1}y^{-4} = \dfrac{2x}{3y^{4}}$

85. $\dfrac{(r^2t^2)^{-2}}{(r^3t)^{-1}} = \dfrac{r^3t}{(r^2t^2)^2} = \dfrac{r^3t}{(r^2)^2(t^2)^2} = \dfrac{r^3t}{r^{2\cdot2}t^{2\cdot2}} = \dfrac{r^3t}{r^4t^4} = r^{3-4}t^{1-4} = r^{-1}t^{-3} = \dfrac{1}{rt^3}$

86. $\dfrac{(2rt)^2}{(rt^4)^{-2}} = \dfrac{2^2r^2t^2}{r^{-2}(t^4)^{-2}} = \dfrac{4r^2t^2}{r^{-2}t^{4\cdot(-2)}} = \dfrac{4r^2t^2}{r^{-2}t^{-8}} = 4r^{2-(-2)}t^{2-(-8)} = 4r^4t^{10}$

87. $\dfrac{4x^{-2}y^3}{(2x^{-1}y)^2} = \dfrac{4x^{-2}y^3}{2^2(x^{-1})^2y^2} = \dfrac{4x^{-2}y^3}{4x^{-1\cdot2}y^2} = \dfrac{4x^{-2}y^3}{4x^{-2}y^2} = \left(\dfrac{4x^{-2}}{4x^{-2}}\right)y^{3-2} = 1y = y$

88. $\dfrac{(ab)^3}{a^4b^{-4}} = \dfrac{a^3b^3}{a^4b^{-4}} = a^{3-4}b^{3-(-4)} = a^{-1}b^7 = \dfrac{b^7}{a}$

89. $\left(\dfrac{15r^2t}{3r^{-3}t^4}\right)^3 = \left(\dfrac{15}{3}r^{2-(-3)}t^{1-4}\right)^3 = (5r^5t^{-3})^3 = 5^3(r^5)^3(t^{-3})^3 = 125r^{5\cdot3}t^{-3\cdot3} = 125r^{15}t^{-9} = \dfrac{125r^{15}}{t^9}$

90. $\left(\dfrac{4(xy)^2}{(2xy^{-2})^3}\right)^{-2} = \left(\dfrac{(2xy^{-2})^3}{4(xy)^2}\right)^2 = \left(\dfrac{2^3x^3(y^{-2})^3}{4x^2y^2}\right)^2 = \left(\dfrac{8}{4}x^{3-2}y^{-6-2}\right)^2 = (2xy^{-8})^2 = 2^2x^2(y^{-8})^2 = \dfrac{4x^2}{y^{16}}$

## R.3: Polynomial Expressions

1. $3x^3 + 5x^3 = 8x^3$
2. $-9z + 6z = -3z$
3. $5y^7 - 8y^7 = -3y^7$
4. $9x - 7x = 2x$
5. $5x^2 + 8x + x^2 = 6x^2 + 8x$
6. $5x + 2x + 10x = 17x$
7. $9x^2 - x + 4x - 6x^2 = 3x^2 + 3x$
8. $-y^2 - \frac{1}{2}y^2 = -\frac{3}{2}y^2$
9. $x^2 + 9x - 2 + 4x^2 + 4x = 5x^2 + 13x - 2$
10. $6y + 4y^2 - 6y + y^2 = 5y^2$
11. $7y + 9x^2y - 5y + x^2y = 2y + 10x^2y = 10x^2y + 2y$
12. $5ab - b^2 + 7ab + 6b^2 = 12ab + 5b^2$
13. The degree is 2. The leading coefficient is 5.
14. The degree is 4. The leading coefficient is –9.
15. The degree is 3. The leading coefficient is $-\frac{2}{5}$.
16. The degree is 4. The leading coefficient is 4.
17. The degree is 5. The leading coefficient is 1.
18. The degree is 4. The leading coefficient is 7.
19. $(5x + 6) + (-2x + 6) = 3x + 12$
20. $(5y^2 + y^3) + (12y^2 - 5y^3) = -4y^3 + 17y^2$

21. $(2x^2 - x + 7) + (-2x^2 + 4x - 9) = 3x - 2$

22. $(x^3 - 5x^2 + 6) + (5x^2 + 3x + 1) = x^3 + 3x + 7$

23. $(4x) + (1 - 4.5x) = -0.5x + 1$

24. $(y^5 + y) + \left(5 - y + \frac{1}{3}y^2\right) = y^5 + \frac{1}{3}y^2 + 5$

25. $(x^4 - 3x^2 - 4) + \left(-8x^4 + x^2 - \frac{1}{2}\right) = -7x^4 - 2x^2 - \frac{9}{2}$

26. $(3z + z^4 + 2) + (-3z^4 - 5 + z^2) = -2z^4 + z^2 + 3z - 3$

27. $(2z^3 + 5z - 6) + (z^2 - 3z + 2) = 2z^3 + z^2 + 2z - 4$

28. $(z^4 - 6z^2 + 3) + (5z^3 + 3z^2 - 3) = z^4 + 5z^3 - 3z^2$

29. $-(7x^3) = -7x^3$

30. $-(-3z^8) = 3z^8$

31. $-(19z^5 - 5z^2 + 3z) = -19z^5 + 5z^2 - 3z$

32. $-(-x^2 - x + 6) = x^2 + x - 6$

33. $-(z^4 - z^2 - 9) = -z^4 + z^2 + 9$

34. $-\left(1 - 8x + 6x^2 - \frac{1}{6}x^3\right) = \frac{1}{6}x^3 - 6x^2 + 8x - 1$

35. $(5x - 3) - (2x + 4) = 5x - 3 - 2x - 4 = 3x - 7$

36. $(10x + 5) - (-6x - 4) = 10x + 5 + 6x + 4 = 16x + 9$

37. $(x^2 - 3x + 1) - (-5x^2 + 2x - 4) = x^2 - 3x + 1 + 5x^2 - 2x + 4 = 6x^2 - 5x + 5$

38. $(-x^2 + x - 5) - (x^2 - x + 5) = -x^2 + x - 5 - x^2 + x - 5 = -2x^2 + 2x - 10$

39. $(4x^4 + 2x^2 - 9) - (x^4 - 2x^2 - 5) = 4x^4 + 2x^2 - 9 - x^4 + 2x^2 + 5 = 3x^4 + 4x^2 - 4$

40. $(8x^3 + 5x^2 - 3x + 1) - (-5x^3 + 6x - 11) = 8x^3 + 5x^2 - 3x + 1 + 5x^3 - 6x + 11 =$
$13x^3 + 5x^2 - 9x + 12$

41. $(x^4 - 1) - (4x^4 + 3x + 7) = x^4 - 1 - 4x^4 - 3x - 7 = -3x^4 - 3x - 8$

42. $(5x^4 - 6x^3 + x^2 + 5) - (x^3 + 11x^2 + 9x - 3) = 5x^4 - 6x^3 + x^2 + 5 - x^3 - 11x^2 - 9x + 3 =$
$5x^4 - 7x^3 - 10x^2 - 9x + 8$

43. $5x(x - 5) = 5x^2 - 25x$

44. $3x^2(-2x + 2) = -6x^3 + 6x^2$

45. $-5(3x + 1) = -15x - 5$

46. $-(-3x + 1) = 3x - 1$

47. $5(y + 2) = 5y + 10$

48. $4(x - 7) = 4x - 28$

49. $-2(5x + 9) = -10x - 18$

50. $-3x(5 + x) = -15x - 3x^2 = -3x^2 - 15x$

51. $(y - 3)6y = 6y^2 - 18y$

52. $(2x - 5)8x^3 = 16x^4 - 40x^3$

53. $-4(5x - y) = -20x + 4y$

54. $-6(3y - 2x) = -18y + 12x$

55. $(y + 5)(y - 7) = y^2 - 7y + 5y - 35 = y^2 - 2y - 35$

56. $(3x + 1)(2x + 1) = 6x^2 + 3x + 2x + 1 = 6x^2 + 5x + 1$

57. $(3 - 2x)(3 + x) = 9 + 3x - 6x - 2x^2 = -2x^2 - 3x + 9$

58. $(7x - 3)(4 - 7x) = 28x - 49x^2 - 12 + 21x = -49x^2 + 49x - 12$

59. $(-2x + 3)(x - 2) = -2x^2 + 4x + 3x - 6 = -2x^2 + 7x - 6$

60. $(z - 2)(4z + 3) = 4z^2 + 3z - 8z - 6 = 4z^2 - 5z - 6$

61. $\left(x - \frac{1}{2}\right)\left(x + \frac{1}{4}\right) = x^2 + \frac{1}{4}x - \frac{1}{2}x - \frac{1}{8} = x^2 - \frac{1}{4}x - \frac{1}{8}$

62. $\left(z - \frac{1}{3}\right)\left(z - \frac{1}{6}\right) = z^2 - \frac{1}{6}z - \frac{1}{3}z + \frac{1}{18} = z^2 - \frac{1}{2}z + \frac{1}{18}$

63. $(x^2 + 1)(2x^2 - 1) = 2x^4 - x^2 + 2x^2 - 1 = 2x^4 + x^2 - 1$

64. $(x^2 - 2)(x^2 + 4) = x^4 + 4x^2 - 2x^2 - 8 = x^4 + 2x^2 - 8$

65. $(x + y)(x - 2y) = x^2 - 2xy + xy - 2y^2 = x^2 - xy - 2y^2$

66. $(x^2 + y^2)(x - y) = x^3 - x^2y + xy^2 - y^3$

67. $3x(2x^2 - x - 1) = 6x^3 - 3x^2 - 3x$

68. $-2x(3 - 2x + 5x^2) = -6x + 4x^2 - 10x^3 = -10x^3 + 4x^2 - 6x$

69. $-x(2x^4 - x^2 + 10) = -2x^5 + x^3 - 10x$

70. $-2x^2(5x^3 + x^2 - 2) = -10x^5 - 2x^4 + 4x^2$

71. $(2x^2 - 4x + 1)(3x^2) = 6x^4 - 12x^3 + 3x^2$

72. $(x - y + 5)(xy) = x^2y - xy^2 + 5xy$

73. $(x + 1)(x^2 + 2x - 3) = x^3 + 2x^2 - 3x + x^2 + 2x - 3 = x^3 + 3x^2 - x - 3$

74. $(2x - 1)(3x^2 - x + 6) = 6x^3 - 2x^2 + 12x - 3x^2 + x - 6 = 6x^3 - 5x^2 + 13x - 6$

75. $(2 - 3x)(5 - 2x)(x^2 - 1) \Rightarrow [(2 - 3x)(5 - 2x)](x^2 - 1) = (10 - 19x + 6x^2)(x^2 - 1) =$
$10x^2 - 19x^3 + 6x^4 - 10 + 19x - 6x^2 = 6x^4 - 19x^3 + 4x^2 + 19x - 10$

76. $(3 + z)(6 - 4z)(4 + 2z^2) \Rightarrow [(3 + z)(6 - 4z)](4 + 2z^2) = (18 - 6z - 4z^2)(4 + 2z^2) =$
$72 - 24z - 16z^2 + 36z^2 - 12z^3 - 8z^4 = -8z^4 - 12z^3 + 20z^2 - 24z + 72$

77. $(x^2 + 2)(3x - 2) = 3x^3 - 2x^2 + 6x - 4$

78. $(4 + x)(2x^2 - 3) = 8x^2 - 12 + 2x^3 - 3x = 2x^3 + 8x^2 - 3x - 12$

79. $(x - 7)(x + 7) = x^2 - 7^2 = x^2 - 49$

80. $(x + 9)(x - 9) = x^2 - 9^2 = x^2 - 81$

81. $(3x + 4)(3x - 4) = (3x)^2 - 4^2 = 9x^2 - 16$

82. $(9x - 4)(9x + 4) = (9x)^2 - 4^4 = 81x^2 - 16$

83. $(2x - 3y)(2x + 3y) = (2x)^2 - (3y)^2 = 4x^2 - 9y^2$

84. $(x + 2y)(x - 2y) = x^2 - (2y)^2 = x^2 - 4y^2$

85. $(x + 4)^2 = x^2 + 2(4)x + 4^2 = x^2 + 8x + 16$

86. $(z + 9)^2 = z^2 + 2(9)z + 9^2 = z^2 + 18z + 81$

87. $(2x + 1)^2 = 4x^2 + 2(2x) + 1 = 4x^2 + 4x + 1$

88. $(3x + 5)^2 = 9x^2 + 2(15x) + 25 = 9x^2 + 30x + 25$

89. $(x - 1)^2 = x^2 - 2(x) + 1 = x^2 - 2x + 1$

90. $(x - 7)^2 = x^2 - 2(7x) + 49 = x^2 - 14x + 49$

91. $(2 - 3x)^2 = 4 - 2(6x) + 9x^2 = 4 - 12x + 9x^2$

92. $(5 - 6x)^2 = 25 - 2(30x) + 36x^2 = 25 - 60x + 36x^2$

93. $3x(x + 1)(x - 1) = 3x(x^2 - 1) = 3x^3 - 3x$

94. $-4x(3x - 5)^2 = -4x(9x^2 - 30x + 25) = -36x^3 + 120x^2 - 100x$

95. $(2 - 5x^2)(2 + 5x^2) = 2^2 - (5x^2)^2 = 4 - 25x^4$

96. $(6y - x^2)(6y + x^2) = (6y)^2 - (x^2)^2 = 36y^2 - x^4$

## R.4: Factoring Polynomials

1. $10x - 15 = 5(2x - 3)$
2. $32 - 16x = 16(2 - x)$
3. $2x^3 - 5x = x(2x^2 - 5)$
4. $3y - 9y^2 = 3y(1 - 3y)$
5. $8x^3 - 4x^2 + 16x = 4x(2x^2 - x + 4)$
6. $-5x^3 + x^2 - 4x = x(-5x^2 + x - 4)$
7. $5x^4 - 15x^3 + 15x^2 = 5x^2(x^2 - 3x + 3)$
8. $28y + 14y^3 - 7y^5 = 7y(4 + 2y^2 - y^4)$
9. $15x^3 + 10x^2 - 30x = 5x(3x^2 + 2x - 6)$
10. $14a^4 - 21a^2 + 35a = 7a(2a^3 - 3a + 5)$
11. $6r^5 - 8r^4 + 12r^3 = 2r^3(3r^2 - 4r + 6)$
12. $15r^6 + 20r^4 - 10r^3 = 5r^3(3r^3 + 4r - 2)$
13. $8x^2y^2 - 24x^2y^3 = 8x^2y^2(1 - 3y)$
14. $36xy - 24x^3y^3 = 12xy(3 - 2x^2y^2)$
15. $18mn^2 - 12m^2n^3 = 6mn^2(3 - 2mn)$
16. $24m^2n^3 + 12m^3n^2 = 12m^2n^2(2n + m)$
17. $-4a^2 - 2ab + 6ab^2 = -2a(2a + b - 3b^2)$
18. $28y + 14y^3 - 14y^3 - 7y^5 = 7y(4 + 2y^2 - y^4)$
19. $x^3 + 3x^2 + 2x + 6 = x^2(x + 3) + 2(x + 3) = (x + 3)(x^2 + 2)$
20. $4x^3 + 3x^2 + 8x + 6 = x^2(4x + 3) + 2(4x + 3) = (4x + 3)(x^2 + 2)$
21. $6x^3 - 4x^2 + 9x - 6 = 2x^2(3x - 2) + 3(3x - 2) = (3x - 2)(2x^2 + 3)$

22. $x^3 - 3x^2 - 5x + 15 = x^2(x - 3) - 5(x - 3) = (x - 3)(x^2 - 5)$

23. $z^3 - 5z^2 + z - 5 = z^2(z - 5) + 1(z - 5) = (z - 5)(z^2 + 1)$

24. $y^3 - 7y^2 + 8y - 56 = y^2(y - 7) + 8(y - 7) = (y - 7)(y^2 + 8)$

25. $y^4 + 2y^3 - 5y^2 - 10y = y(y^3 + 2y^2 - 5y - 10) = y[y^2(y + 2) - 5(y + 2)] = y(y + 2)(y^2 - 5)$

26. $4z^4 + 4z^3 + z^2 + z = z(4z^3 + 4z^2 + z + 1) = z[4z^2(z + 1) + 1(z + 1)] = z(z + 1)(4z^2 + 1)$

27. $2x^3 - 3x^2 + 2x - 3 = x^2(2x - 3) + 1(2x - 3) = (x^2 + 1)(2x - 3)$

28. $15x^3 + 10x^2 - 30x = 5x(3x^2 + 2x - 6)$

29. $2x^4 - x^3 + 4x - 2 = x^3(2x - 1) + 2(2x - 1) = (x^3 + 2)(2x - 1)$

30. $2x^4 - 5x^3 + 10x - 25 = x^3(2x - 5) + 5(2x - 5) = (x^3 + 5)(2x - 5)$

31. $ab - 3a + 2b - 6 = a(b - 3) + 2(b - 3) = (a + 2)(b - 3)$

32. $2ax - 6bx - ay + 3by = 2x(a - 3b) - y(a - 3b) = (2x - y)(a - 3b)$

33. $x^2 + 7x + 10 = (x + 2)(x + 5)$

34. $x^2 + 3x - 10 = (x + 5)(x - 2)$

35. $x^2 + 8x + 12 = (x + 2)(x + 6)$

36. $x^2 - 8x + 12 = (x - 6)(x - 2)$

37. $z^2 + z - 42 = (z - 6)(z + 7)$

38. $z^2 - 9z + 20 = (z - 5)(z - 4)$

39. $z^2 + 11z + 24 = (z + 3)(z + 8)$

40. $z^2 + 15z + 54 = (z + 9)(z + 6)$

41. $24x^2 + 14x - 3 = (4x + 3)(6x - 1)$

42. $25x^2 - 5x - 6 = (5x + 2)(5x - 3)$

43. $6x^2 - x - 2 = (2x + 1)(3x - 2)$

44. $10x^2 + 3x - 1 = (2x + 1)(5x - 1)$

45. $1 + x - 2x^2 = (1 - x)(1 + 2x)$

46. $3 - 5x - 2x^2 = (3 + x)(1 - 2x)$

47. $20 + 7x - 6x^2 = (5 - 2x)(4 + 3x)$

48. $4 + 13x - 12x^2 = (4 - 3x)(1 + 4x)$

49. $5x^3 + x^2 - 6x = x(5x^2 + x - 6) = x(x - 1)(5x + 6)$

50. $2x^3 + 8x^2 - 24x = 2x(x^2 + 4x - 12) = 2x(x - 2)(x + 6)$

51. $3x^3 + 12x^2 + 9x = 3x(x^2 + 4x + 3) = 3x(x + 3)(x + 1)$

52. $12x^3 - 8x^2 - 20x = 4x(3x^2 - 2x - 5) = 4x(x + 1)(3x - 5)$

53. $2x^2 - 14x + 20 = 2(x^2 - 7x + 10) = 2(x - 5)(x - 2)$

54. $7x^2 + 35x + 42 = 7(x^2 + 5x + 6) = 7(x + 2)(x + 3)$

55. $60t^4 + 230t^3 - 40t^2 = 10t^2(6t^2 + 23t - 4) = 10t^2(t + 4)(6t - 1)$

56. $24r^4 + 8r^3 - 80r^2 = 8r^2(3r^2 + r - 10) = 8r^2(r + 2)(3r - 5)$

57. $4m^3 + 10m^2 - 6m = 2m(2m^2 + 5m - 3) = 2m(m + 3)(2m - 1)$

58. $30m^4 + 3m^3 - 9m^2 = 3m^2(10m^2 + m - 3) = 3m^2(2m - 1)(5m + 3)$

59. $x^2 - 25 = (x - 5)(x + 5)$

60. $z^2 - 169 = (z + 13)(z - 13)$

61. $4x^2 - 25 = (2x - 5)(2x + 5)$

62. $36 - y^2 = (6 - y)(6 + y)$

63. $36x^2 - 100 = 4(9x^2 - 25) = 4(3x - 5)(3x + 5)$

64. $9x^2 - 4y^2 = (3x - 2y)(3x + 2y)$

65. $64z^2 - 25z^4 = z^2(64 - 25z^2) = z^2(8 - 5z)(8 + 5z)$

66. $100x^3 - x = x(100x^2 - 1) = x(10x - 1)(10x + 1)$

67. $16x^4 - y^4 = (4x^2 - y^2)(4x^2 + y^2) = (2x - y)(2x + y)(4x^2 + y^2)$

68. $x^4 - 9y^2 = (x^2 - 3y)(x^2 + 3y)$

69. The sum of two squares does not factor using real numbers.

70. The sum of two squares does not factor using real numbers.

71. $4 - r^2t^2 = (2 - rt)(2 + rt)$

72. $25 - x^4y^2 = (5 - x^2y)(5 + x^2y)$

73. $(x - 1)^2 - 16 = ((x - 1) - 4)((x - 1) + 4) = (x - 5)(x + 3)$

74. $(y + 2)^2 - 1 = ((y + 2) - 1)((y + 2) + 1) = (y + 1)(y + 3)$

75. $4 - (z + 3)^2 = (2 - (z + 3))(2 + (z + 3)) = (-1 - z)(5 + z) = -(z + 1)(z + 5)$

76. $64 - (t - 3)^2 = (8 - (t - 3))(8 + (t - 3)) = (11 - t)(5 + t) = -(t - 11)(t + 5)$

77. $x^2 + 2x + 1 = (x + 1)^2$

78. $x^2 - 6x + 9 = (x - 3)^2$

79. $4x^2 + 20x + 25 = (2x + 5)^2$

80. $x^2 + 10x + 25 = (x + 5)^2$

81. $x^2 - 12x + 36 = (x - 6)^2$

82. $16z^4 - 24z^3 + 9z^2 = z^2(16z^2 - 24z + 9) = z^2(4z - 3)^2$

83. $9z^3 - 6z^2 + z = z(9z^2 - 6z + 1) = z(3z - 1)^2$

84. $49y^2 + 42y + 9 = (7y + 3)^2$

85. $9y^3 + 30y^2 + 25y = y(9y^2 + 30y + 25) = y(3y + 5)^2$

86. $25y^3 - 20y^2 + 4y = y(25y^2 - 20y + 4) = y(5y - 2)^2$

87. $4x^2 - 12xy + 9y^2 = (2x - 3y)^2$

88. $25a^2 + 60ab + 36b^2 = (5a + 6b)^2$

89. $9a^3b - 12a^2b + 4ab = ab(9a^2 - 12a + 4) = ab(3a - 2)^2$

90. $16a^3 + 8a^2b + ab^2 = a(16a^2 + 8ab + b^2) = a(4a + b)^2$

91. $x^3 - 1 = (x - 1)(x^2 + 1x + 1^2) = (x - 1)(x^2 + x + 1)$

92. $x^3 + 1 = (x + 1)(x^2 - 1x + 1^2) = (x + 1)(x^2 - x + 1)$

93. $y^3 + z^3 = (y + z)(y^2 - yz + z^2)$

94. $y^3 - z^3 = (y - z)(y^2 + yz + z^2)$

95. $8x^3 - 27 = (2x)^3 - 3^3 = (2x - 3)((2x)^2 + 2x(3) + 3^2) = (2x - 3)(4x^2 + 6x + 9)$

96. $(8 - z^3) = (2^3 - z^3) = (2 - z)(2^2 + 2z + z^2) = (2 - z)(4 + 2z + z^2)$

97. $x^4 + 125x = x(x^3 + 5^3) = x(x + 5)(x^2 - 5x + 5^2) = x(x + 5)(x^2 - 5x + 25)$

98. $3x^4 - 81x = 3x(x^3 - 3^3) = 3x(x - 3)(x^2 + 3x + 3^2) = 3x(x - 3)(x^2 + 3x + 9)$

99. $8r^6 - t^3 = (2r^2 - t)((2r^2)^2 + 2r^2t + t^2) = (2r^2 - t)(4r^4 + 2r^2t + t^2)$

100. $125r^6 + 64t^3 = (5r^2 + 4t)((5r^2)^2 - 20r^2t + (4t)^2) = (5r^2 + 4t)(25r^4 - 20r^2t + 16t^2)$

101. $10m^9 - 270n^6 = 10(m^9 - 27n^6) = 10(m^3 - 3n^2)((m^3)^2 + 3m^3n^2 + (3n^2)^2) =$
$10(m^3 - 3n^2)(m^6 + 3m^3n^2 + 9n^4)$

102. $5t^6 + 40r^3 = 5(t^6 + 8r^3) = 5(t^2 + 2r)((t^2)^2 - 2t^2r + (2r)^2) = 5(t^2 + 2r)(t^4 - 2t^2r + 4r^2)$

103. $16x^2 - 25 = (4x)^2 - 5^2 = (4x - 5)(4x + 5)$

104. $25x^2 - 30x + 9 = (5x - 3)(5x - 3) = (5x - 3)^2$

105. $x^3 - 64 = x^3 - 4^3 = (x - 4)(x^2 + 4x + 4^2) = (x - 4)(x^2 + 4x + 16)$

106. $1 + 8y^3 = 1^3 + (2y)^3 = (1 + 2y)(1^2 - 1(2y) + (2y)^2) = (1 + 2y)(1 - 2y + 4y^2)$

107. $x^2 + 16x + 64 = (x + 8)(x + 8) = (x + 8)^2$

108. $12x^2 + x - 6 = (3x - 2)(4x + 3)$

109. $5x^2 - 38x - 16 = (x - 8)(5x + 2)$

110. $125x^3 - 1 = (5x - 1)(25x^2 + 5x + 1)$

111. $x^4 + 8x = x(x^3 + 8) = x(x + 2)(x^2 - 2x + 4)$

112. $2x^3 - 12x^2 + 18x = 2x(x^2 - 6x + 9) = 2x(x - 3)^2$

113. $64x^3 + 8y^3 = 8(8x^3 + y^3) = 8(2x + y)(4x^2 - 2xy + y^2)$

114. $54 - 16x^3 = 2(27 - 8x^3) = 2(3 - 2x)(9 + 6x + 4x^2)$

115. $3x^2 - 5x - 8 = (x + 1)(3x - 8)$

116. $15x^2 - 11x + 2 = (3x - 1)(5x - 2)$

117. $7a^3 + 20a^2 - 3a = a(7a^2 + 20a - 3) = a(a + 3)(7a - 1)$

118. $b^3 - b^2 - 2b = b(b^2 - b - 2) = b(b - 2)(b + 1)$

119. $2x^3 - x^2 + 6x - 3 = x^2(2x - 1) + 3(2x - 1) = (x^2 + 3)(2x - 1)$

120. $3x^3 - 5x^2 + 3x - 5 = x^2(3x - 5) + 1(3x - 5) = (x^2 + 1)(3x - 5)$

121. $2x^4 - 5x^3 - 25x^2 = x^2(2x^2 - 5x - 25) = x^2(2x + 5)(x - 5)$

122. $10x^3 + 28x^2 - 6x = 2x(5x^2 + 14x - 3) = 2x(5x - 1)(x + 3)$

123. $2x^4 + 5x^2 + 3 = (2x^2 + 3)(x^2 + 1)$

124. $2x^4 + 2x^2 - 4 = 2(x^4 + x^2 - 2) = 2(x^2 + 2)(x^2 - 1) = 2(x^2 + 2)(x + 1)(x - 1)$

125. $x^3 + 3x^2 + x + 3 = x^2(x + 3) + (x + 3) = (x + 3)(x^2 + 1)$

126. $x^3 + 5x^2 + 4x + 20 = x^2(x + 5) + 4(x + 5) = (x + 5)(x^2 + 4)$

127. $5x^3 - 5x^2 + 10x - 10 = 5x^2(x - 1) + 10(x - 1) = (x - 1)(5x^2 + 10) = 5(x^2 + 2)(x - 1)$

128. $5x^4 - 20x^3 + 10x - 40 = 5(x^4 - 4x^3 + 2x - 8) = 5[x^3(x - 4) + 2(x - 4)] = 5(x - 4)(x^3 + 2)$

129. $ax + bx - ay - by = x(a + b) - y(a + b) = (a + b)(x - y)$

130. $ax - bx - ay + by = x(a - b) - y(a - b) = (a - b)(x - y)$

131. $18x^2 + 12x + 2 = 2(9x^2 + 6x + 1) = 2(3x + 1)^2$

132. $-3x^2 + 30x - 75 = -3(x^2 - 10x + 25) = -3(x - 5)^2$

133. $-4x^3 + 24x^2 - 36x = -4x(x^2 - 6x + 9) = -4x(x - 3)^2$

134. $18x^3 - 60x^2 + 50x = 2x(9x^2 - 30x + 25) = 2x(3x - 5)^2$

135. $27x^3 - 8 = (3x - 2)(9x^2 + 6x + 4)$

136. $27x^3 + 8 = (3x + 2)(9x^2 - 6x + 4)$

137. $-x^4 - 8x = -x(x^3 + 8) = -x(x + 2)(x^2 - 2x + 4)$

138. $x^5 - 27x^2 = x^2(x^3 - 27) = x^2(x - 3)(x^2 + 3x + 9)$

139. $x^4 - 2x^3 - x + 2 = x^3(x - 2) - 1(x - 2) = (x - 2)(x^3 - 1) = (x - 2)(x - 1)(x^2 + x + 1)$

140. $x^4 + 3x^3 + x + 3 = x^3(x + 3) + (x + 3) = (x + 3)(x^3 + 1) = (x + 3)(x + 1)(x^2 - x + 1)$

141. $r^4 - 16 = (r^2 - 4)(r^2 + 4) = (r + 2)(r - 2)(r^2 + 4)$

142. $r^4 - 81 = (r^2 - 9)(r^2 + 9) = (r + 3)(r - 3)(r^2 + 9)$

143. $25x^2 - 4a^2 = (5x - 2a)(5x + 2a)$

144. $9y^2 - 16z^2 = (3y - 4z)(3y + 4z)$

145. $(2x^4 - 2y^4) = 2(x^4 - y^4) = 2(x^2 - y^2)(x^2 + y^2) = 2(x - y)(x + y)(x^2 + y^2)$

146. $a^4 - b^4 = (a^2 - b^2)(a^2 + b^2) = (a - b)(a + b)(a^2 + b^2)$

147. $9x^3 + 6x^2 - 3x = 3x(3x^2 + 2x - 1) = 3x(3x - 1)(x + 1)$

148. $8x^3 + 28x^2 - 16x = 4x(2x^2 + 7x - 4) = 4x(2x - 1)(x + 4)$

149. $(z - 2)^2 - 9 = (z - 2 - 3)(z - 2 + 3) = (z - 5)(z + 1)$

150. $(y + 2)^2 - 4 = (y + 2 - 2)(y + 2 + 2) = y(y + 4)$

151. $3x^5 - 27x^3 + 3x^2 - 27 = 3(x^5 - 9x^3 + x^2 - 9) = 3[x^3(x^2 - 9) + (x^2 - 9)] =$
$3(x^2 - 9)(x^3 + 1) = 3(x + 3)(x - 3)(x + 1)(x^2 - x + 1)$

152. $2x^5 - 8x^3 - 16x^2 + 64 = 2(x^5 - 4x^3 - 8x^2 + 32) = 2[x^3(x^2 - 4) - 8(x^2 - 4)] =$
$2(x^2 - 4)(x^3 - 8) = 2(x + 2)(x - 2)^2(x^2 + 2x + 4)$

153. $(x + 2)^2(x + 4)^4 + (x + 2)^3(x + 4)^3 = (x + 2)^2(x + 4)^3[x + 4 + x + 2] =$
$(x + 2)^2(x + 4)^3(2x + 6) = 2(x + 2)^2(x + 4)^3(x + 3)$

154. $(x - 3)(2x + 1)^3 + (x - 3)^2(2x + 1)^2 = (x - 3)(2x + 1)^2[2x + 1 + x - 3] =$
$(x - 3)(2x + 1)^2(3x - 2)$

155. $(6x + 1)(8x - 3)^4 - (6x + 1)^2(8x - 3)^3 = (6x + 1)(8x - 3)^3[8x - 3 - (6x + 1)] =$
$(6x + 1)(8x - 3)^2(2x - 4) = 2(6x + 1)(8x - 3)^3(x - 2)$

156. $(2x + 3)^4(x + 1)^4 - (2x + 3)^3(x + 1)^5 = (x + 1)^4(2x + 3)^3[2x + 3 - (x + 1)] =$
$(x + 1)^4(2x + 3)^3(x + 2)$

157. $4x^2(5x - 1)^5 + 2x(5x - 1)^6 = 2x(5x - 1)^5[2x + 5x - 1] = 2x(5x - 1)^5(7x - 1)$

158. $x^4(7x + 3)^3 + x^5(7x + 3)^2 = x^4(7x + 2)^2[7x + 3 + x] = x^4(7x + 2)^2(8x + 3)$

## R.5: Rational Expressions

1. $\dfrac{10x^3}{5x^2} = 2x$

2. $\dfrac{24t^3}{6t^2} = 4t$

3. $\dfrac{(x - 5)(x + 5)}{x - 5} = x + 5$

4. $-\dfrac{5 - a}{a - 5} = \dfrac{-(5 - a)}{a - 5} = \dfrac{a - 5}{a - 5} = 1$

5. $\dfrac{x^2 - 16}{x - 4} = \dfrac{(x - 4)(x + 4)}{x - 4} = x + 4$

6. $\dfrac{(x + 5)(x - 4)}{(x + 7)(x + 5)} = \dfrac{x - 4}{x + 7}$

7. $\dfrac{x + 3}{2x^2 + 5x - 3} = \dfrac{x + 3}{(2x - 1)(x + 3)} = \dfrac{1}{2x - 1}$

8. $\dfrac{2x^2 - 9x + 4}{6x^2 + 7x - 5} = \dfrac{(2x - 1)(x - 4)}{(2x - 1)(3x + 5)} = \dfrac{x - 4}{3x + 5}$

9. $-\dfrac{z + 2}{4z + 8} = -\dfrac{z + 2}{4(z + 2)} = -\dfrac{1}{4}$

10. $\dfrac{x^2 - 25}{x^2 + 10x + 25} = \dfrac{(x - 5)(x + 5)}{(x + 5)(x + 5)} = \dfrac{x - 5}{x + 5}$

11. $\dfrac{x^2 + 2x}{x^2 + 3x + 2} = \dfrac{x(x + 2)}{(x + 1)(x + 2)} = \dfrac{x}{x + 1}$

12. $\dfrac{x^2 - 3x - 10}{x^2 - 6x + 5} = \dfrac{(x - 5)(x + 2)}{(x - 5)(x - 1)} = \dfrac{x + 2}{x - 1}$

13. $\dfrac{a^3 + b^3}{a + b} = \dfrac{(a + b)(a^2 - ab + b^2)}{a + b} = a^2 - ab + b^2$

14. $\dfrac{a^3 - b^3}{a - b} = \dfrac{(a - b)(a^2 + ab + b^2)}{a - b} = a^2 + ab + b^2$

15. $\dfrac{5}{8} \cdot \dfrac{4}{15} = \dfrac{1}{6}$

16. $\dfrac{7}{2} \cdot \dfrac{4}{21} = \dfrac{2}{3}$

17. $\dfrac{5}{6} \cdot \dfrac{3}{10} \cdot \dfrac{8}{3} = \dfrac{2}{3}$

18. $\frac{9}{5}\cdot\frac{10}{3}\cdot\frac{1}{27} = \frac{2}{9}$

19. $\frac{4}{7} \div \frac{8}{7} = \frac{4}{7}\cdot\frac{7}{8} = \frac{1}{2}$

20. $\frac{5}{12} \div \frac{10}{9} = \frac{5}{12}\cdot\frac{9}{10} = \frac{3}{8}$

21. $\frac{1}{2} \div \frac{3}{4} \div \frac{5}{6} = \left(\frac{1}{2}\cdot\frac{4}{3}\right) \div \frac{5}{6} = \frac{2}{3}\cdot\frac{6}{5} = \frac{4}{5}$

22. $\frac{3}{4} \div \frac{7}{8} \div \frac{5}{14} = \left(\frac{3}{4}\cdot\frac{8}{7}\right) \div \frac{5}{14} = \frac{6}{7}\cdot\frac{14}{5} = \frac{12}{5}$

23. $\frac{3}{8} + \frac{5}{8} = \frac{8}{8} = 1$

24. $\frac{5}{9} + \frac{2}{9} = \frac{7}{9}$

25. $\frac{3}{7} - \frac{4}{7} = -\frac{1}{7}$

26. $\frac{8}{11} - \frac{9}{11} = -\frac{1}{11}$

27. $\frac{2}{3} + \frac{5}{11} = \frac{22}{33} + \frac{15}{33} = \frac{37}{33}$

28. $\frac{9}{13} + \frac{3}{2} = \frac{18}{26} + \frac{39}{26} = \frac{57}{26}$

29. $\frac{4}{5} - \frac{1}{10} = \frac{8}{10} - \frac{1}{10} = \frac{7}{10}$

30. $\frac{3}{4} - \frac{7}{12} = \frac{9}{12} - \frac{7}{12} = \frac{2}{12} = \frac{1}{6}$

31. $\frac{1}{3} + \frac{3}{4} - \frac{3}{7} = \frac{28}{84} + \frac{63}{84} - \frac{36}{84} = \frac{55}{84}$

32. $\frac{6}{11} - \frac{1}{2} + \frac{3}{8} = \frac{48}{88} - \frac{44}{88} + \frac{33}{88} = \frac{37}{88}$

33. $\frac{1}{x^2}\cdot\frac{3x}{2} = \frac{3}{2x}$

34. $\frac{6a}{5}\cdot\frac{5}{12a^2} = \frac{1}{2a}$

35. $\frac{5x}{3} \div \frac{10x}{6} = \frac{5x}{3}\cdot\frac{6}{10x} = \frac{2}{2} = 1$

36. $\frac{2x^2 + x}{3x + 9} \div \frac{x}{x + 3} = \frac{x(2x + 1)}{3(x + 3)}\cdot\frac{x + 3}{x} = \frac{2x + 1}{3}$

37. $\frac{x + 1}{2x - 5}\cdot\frac{x}{x + 1} = \frac{x}{2x - 5}$

38. $\frac{4x + 8}{2x}\cdot\frac{x^2}{x + 2} = \frac{4(x + 2)}{2x}\cdot\frac{x^2}{x + 2} = 2x$

39. $\frac{(x - 5)(x + 3)}{3x - 1}\cdot\frac{x(3x - 1)}{(x - 5)} = \frac{x + 3}{1}\cdot\frac{x}{1} = x(x + 3)$

40. $\frac{b^2+1}{b^2-1}\cdot\frac{b-1}{b+1}=\frac{b^2+1}{(b-1)(b+1)}\cdot\frac{b-1}{b+1}=\frac{b^2+1}{b+1}\cdot\frac{1}{b+1}=\frac{b^2+1}{(b+1)^2}$

41. $\frac{x^2-2x-35}{2x^3-3x^2}\cdot\frac{x^3-x^2}{2x-14}=\frac{(x-7)(x+5)}{x^2(2x-3)}\cdot\frac{x^2(x-1)}{2(x-7)}=\frac{x+5}{2x-3}\cdot\frac{x-1}{2}=\frac{(x-1)(x+5)}{2(2x-3)}$

42. $\frac{2x+4}{x+1}\cdot\frac{x^2+3x+2}{4x+2}=\frac{2(x+2)}{x+1}\cdot\frac{(x+1)(x+2)}{2(2x+1)}=\frac{x+2}{1}\cdot\frac{x+2}{2x+1}=\frac{(x+2)^2}{2x+1}$

43. $\frac{6b}{b+2}\div\frac{3b^4}{2b+4}=\frac{6b}{b+2}\cdot\frac{2(b+2)}{3b^4}=\frac{2}{1}\cdot\frac{2}{b^3}=\frac{4}{b^3}$

44. $\frac{5x^5}{x-2}\div\frac{10x^3}{5x-10}=\frac{5x^5}{x-2}\cdot\frac{5(x-2)}{10x^3}=\frac{5x^2}{1}\cdot\frac{1}{2}=\frac{5x^2}{2}$

45. $\frac{3a+1}{a^7}\div\frac{a+1}{3a^8}=\frac{3a+1}{a^7}\cdot\frac{3a^8}{a+1}=\frac{3a+1}{1}\cdot\frac{3a}{a+1}=\frac{3a(3a+1)}{a+1}$

46. $\frac{x^2-16}{x+3}\div\frac{x+4}{x^2-9}=\frac{(x-4)(x+4)}{x+3}\cdot\frac{(x-3)(x+3)}{x+4}=\frac{x-4}{1}\cdot\frac{x-3}{1}=(x-4)(x-3)$

47. $\frac{x+5}{x^3-x}\div\frac{x^2-25}{x^3}=\frac{x+5}{x(x^2-1)}\cdot\frac{x^3}{(x-5)(x+5)}=\frac{1}{x^2-1}\cdot\frac{x^2}{x-5}=\frac{x^2}{(x-5)(x^2-1)}$

48. $\frac{x^2+x-12}{2x^2-9x-5}\div\frac{x^2+7x+12}{2x^2-7x-4}=\frac{(x+4)(x-3)}{(2x+1)(x-5)}\cdot\frac{(2x+1)(x-4)}{(x+4)(x+3)}=\frac{x-3}{x-5}\cdot\frac{x-4}{x+3}=$
$\frac{(x-4)(x-3)}{(x-5)(x+3)}$

49. $\frac{x-2}{x^3-x}\div\frac{x^2-2x}{x^2-1}=\frac{x-2}{x(x+1)(x-1)}\cdot\frac{(x+1)(x-1)}{x(x-2)}=\frac{1}{x^2}$

50. $\frac{x^2+3x+2}{2x^2+7x+3}\div\frac{x^2-4}{2x^2-x-1}=\frac{(x+1)(x+2)}{(2x+1)(x+3)}\cdot\frac{(2x+1)(x-1)}{(x+2)(x-2)}=\frac{(x-1)(x+1)}{(x-2)(x+3)}$

51. $\frac{x^2-3x+2}{x^2+5x+6}\div\frac{x^2+x-2}{x^2+2x-3}=\frac{(x-2)(x-1)}{(x+3)(x+2)}\cdot\frac{(x+3)(x-1)}{(x+2)(x-1)}=\frac{(x-2)(x-1)}{(x+2)^2}$

52. $\frac{2x^2+x-1}{6x^2+x-2}\div\frac{2x^2+5x+3}{6x^2+13x+6}=\frac{(2x-1)(x+1)}{(3x+2)(2x-1)}\cdot\frac{(3x+2)(2x+3)}{(2x+3)(x+1)}=1$

53. $\frac{x^2-4}{x^2+x-2}\div\frac{x-1}{x-2}=\frac{(x+2)(x-2)}{(x+2)(x-1)}\cdot\frac{x-1}{x-2}=1$

54. $\frac{x^2+2x+1}{x-2}\div\frac{x+1}{2x-4}=\frac{(x+1)(x+1)}{x-2}\cdot\frac{2(x-2)}{x+1}=2(x+1)$

55. $\frac{3y}{x^2}\div\frac{y^2}{x}\div\frac{y}{5x}=\left(\frac{3y}{x^2}\cdot\frac{x}{y^2}\right)\div\frac{y}{5x}=\frac{3}{xy}\cdot\frac{5x}{y}=\frac{15}{y^2}$

56. $\frac{x+1}{y-2}\div\frac{2x+2}{y-2}\div\frac{x}{y}=\left(\frac{x+1}{y-2}\cdot\frac{y-2}{2(x+1)}\right)\div\frac{x}{y}=\frac{1}{2}\cdot\frac{y}{x}=\frac{y}{2x}$

57. $\frac{x-3}{x-1}\div\frac{x^2}{x-1}\div\frac{x-3}{x}=\left(\frac{x-3}{x-1}\cdot\frac{x-1}{x^2}\right)\div\frac{x-3}{x}=\frac{x-3}{x^2}\cdot\frac{x}{x-3}=\frac{1}{x}$

58. $\frac{2x}{x-2}\div\frac{x+2}{x}\div\frac{7x}{x^2-4}=\left(\frac{2x}{x-2}\cdot\frac{x}{(x+2)}\right)\div\frac{7x}{x^2-4}=\frac{2x^2}{(x-2)(x+2)}\cdot\frac{(x+2)(x-2)}{7x}=\frac{2x}{7}$

59. Since $12=2\cdot2\cdot3$ and $18=2\cdot3\cdot3$, the LCM is $2\cdot2\cdot3\cdot3=36$.

60. Since $9=3\cdot3$ and $15=3\cdot5$, the LCM is $3\cdot3\cdot5=45$.

61. Since $5a^3 = 5 \cdot a \cdot a \cdot a$ and $10a = 2 \cdot 5 \cdot a$, the LCM is $2 \cdot 5 \cdot a \cdot a \cdot a = 10a^3$.

62. Since $6a^2 = 2 \cdot 3 \cdot a \cdot a$ and $9a^5 = 3 \cdot 3 \cdot a \cdot a \cdot a \cdot a \cdot a$, the LCM is $2 \cdot 3 \cdot 3 \cdot a \cdot a \cdot a \cdot a \cdot a = 18a^5$.

63. Since $z^2 - 4z = z(z - 4)$ and $(z - 4)^2 = (z - 4)(z - 4)$, the LCM is $z(z - 4)(z - 4) = z(z - 4)^2$.

64. Since $z^2 - 1 = (z - 1)(z + 1)$ and $z^2 + 2z + 1 = (z + 1)(z + 1)$, the LCM is $(z - 1)(z + 1)(z + 1) = (z - 1)(z + 1)^2$.

65. Since $x^2 - 6x + 9 = (x - 3)(x - 3)$ and $x^2 - 5x + 6 = (x - 2)(x - 3)$, the LCM is $(x - 2)(x - 3)(x - 3) = (x - 2)(x - 3)^2$.

66. Since $x^2 - 4 = (x - 2)(x + 2)$ and $x^2 - 4x + 4 = (x - 2)(x - 2)$, the LCM is $(x + 2)(x - 2)(x - 2) = (x + 2)(x - 2)^2$.

67. The factored denominators are $x + 1$ and 7. The LCD is $7(x + 1)$.

68. The factored denominators are $2x - 1$ and $x + 1$. The LCD is $(x + 1)(2x - 1)$.

69. The factored denominators are $x + 4$ and $(x + 4)(x - 4)$. The LCD is $(x + 4)(x - 4)$.

70. The factored denominators are $2x^2$ and $2(x + 1)$. The LCD is $2x^2(x + 1)$.

71. The factored denominators are 2 and $2x + 1$ and $2(x - 2)$. The LCD is $2(2x + 1)(x - 2)$.

72. The factored denominators are $x$ and $x(x - 4)$ and $2x$. The LCD is $2x(x - 4)$.

73. $\frac{4}{x + 1} + \frac{3}{x + 1} = \frac{7}{x + 1}$

74. $\frac{2}{x^2} + \frac{5}{x^2} = \frac{7}{x^2}$

75. $\frac{2}{x^2 - 1} - \frac{x + 1}{x^2 - 1} = \frac{2 - (x + 1)}{x^2 - 1} = \frac{2 - x - 1}{x^2 - 1} = \frac{-x + 1}{(x - 1)(x + 1)} = \frac{-(x - 1)}{(x + 1)(x - 1)} = -\frac{1}{x + 1}$

76. $\frac{2x}{x^2 + x} - \frac{2x}{x + 1} = \frac{2x}{x(x + 1)} - \frac{2x}{x + 1} = \frac{2}{x + 1} - \frac{2x}{x + 1} = \frac{2 - 2x}{x + 1} = \frac{-2(x - 1)}{x + 1}$

77. $\frac{x}{x + 4} - \frac{x + 1}{x(x + 4)} = \frac{x^2}{x(x + 4)} - \frac{x + 1}{x(x + 4)} = \frac{x^2 - (x + 1)}{x(x + 4)} = \frac{x^2 - x - 1}{x(x + 4)}$

78. $\frac{4x}{x + 2} + \frac{x - 5}{x - 2} = \frac{4x(x - 2)}{(x + 2)(x - 2)} + \frac{(x + 2)(x - 5)}{(x + 2)(x - 2)} = \frac{4x^2 - 8x + x^2 - 3x - 10}{(x + 2)(x - 2)} = \frac{5x^2 - 11x - 10}{(x + 2)(x - 2)}$

79. $\frac{2}{x^2} - \frac{4x - 1}{x} = \frac{2}{x^2} - \frac{x(4x - 1)}{x^2} = \frac{2 - (4x^2 - x)}{x^2} = \frac{-4x^2 + x + 2}{x^2}$

80. $\frac{2x}{x - 5} - \frac{x}{x + 5} = \frac{2x(x + 5)}{(x - 5)(x + 5)} - \frac{x(x - 5)}{(x - 5)(x + 5)} = \frac{2x^2 + 10x - (x^2 - 5x)}{(x - 5)(x + 5)} = \frac{x(x + 15)}{(x - 5)(x + 5)}$

81. $\frac{x + 3}{x - 5} + \frac{5}{x - 3} = \frac{(x + 3)(x - 3)}{(x - 5)(x - 3)} + \frac{5(x - 5)}{(x - 5)(x - 3)} = \frac{x^2 - 9 + 5x - 25}{(x - 5)(x - 3)} = \frac{x^2 + 5x - 34}{(x - 5)(x - 3)}$

82. $\frac{x}{2x - 1} + \frac{1 - x}{3x} = \frac{3x^2}{3x(2x - 1)} + \frac{(1 - x)(2x - 1)}{3x(2x - 1)} = \frac{3x^2 - 2x^2 + 3x - 1}{3x(2x - 1)} = \frac{x^2 + 3x - 1}{3x(2x - 1)}$

83. $\frac{3}{x - 5} - \frac{1}{x - 3} - \frac{2x}{x - 5} = \frac{3(x - 3)}{(x - 5)(x - 3)} - \frac{x - 5}{(x - 5)(x - 3)} - \frac{2x(x - 3)}{(x - 5)(x - 3)} = \frac{-2(x^2 - 4x + 2)}{(x - 5)(x - 3)}$

84. $\dfrac{2x+1}{x-1}-\dfrac{3}{x+1}+\dfrac{x}{x-1}=\dfrac{(2x+1)(x+1)}{(x-1)(x+1)}-\dfrac{3(x-1)}{(x-1)(x+1)}+\dfrac{x(x+1)}{(x-1)(x+1)}=\dfrac{3x^2+x+4}{(x-1)(x+1)}$

85. $\dfrac{x}{x^2-9}+\dfrac{5x}{x-3}=\dfrac{x}{(x-3)(x+3)}+\dfrac{5x(x+3)}{(x-3)(x+3)}=\dfrac{x+5x^2+15x}{(x-3)(x+3)}=\dfrac{x(5x+16)}{(x-3)(x+3)}$

86. $\dfrac{a^2+1}{a^2-1}+\dfrac{a}{1-a^2}=\dfrac{a^2+1}{a^2-1}-\dfrac{a}{a^2-1}=\dfrac{a^2+1-a}{a^2-1}=\dfrac{a^2-a+1}{(a-1)(a+1)}$

87. $\dfrac{b}{2b-4}-\dfrac{b-1}{b-2}=\dfrac{b}{2(b-2)}-\dfrac{2(b-1)}{2(b-2)}=\dfrac{b-(2b-2)}{2(b-2)}=\dfrac{-(b-2)}{2(b-2)}=-\dfrac{1}{2}$

88. $\dfrac{y^2}{2-y}-\dfrac{y}{y^2-4}=\dfrac{-y^2(y+2)}{(y-2)(y+2)}-\dfrac{y}{(y-2)(y+2)}=\dfrac{-y^3-2y^2-y}{(y-2)(y+2)}=\dfrac{-y(y+1)^2}{(y-2)(y+2)}$

89. $\dfrac{2x}{x-5}+\dfrac{2x-1}{3x^2-16x+5}=\dfrac{2x(3x-1)}{(x-5)(3x-1)}+\dfrac{2x-1}{(x-5)(3x-1)}=\dfrac{6x^2-2x+2x-1}{(x-5)(3x-1)}=$
$\dfrac{6x^2-1}{(x-5)(3x-1)}$

90. $\dfrac{x+3}{2x-1}+\dfrac{3}{10x^2-5x}=\dfrac{5x(x+3)}{5x(2x-1)}+\dfrac{3}{5x(2x-1)}=\dfrac{5x^2+15x+3}{5x(2x-1)}$

91. $\dfrac{x}{(x-1)^2}-\dfrac{1}{(x-1)(x+3)}=\dfrac{x(x+3)}{(x-1)^2(x+3)}-\dfrac{x-1}{(x-1)^2(x+3)}=\dfrac{x^2+3x-x+1}{(x-1)^2(x+3)}=$
$\dfrac{x^2+2x+1}{(x-1)^2(x+3)}=\dfrac{(x+1)^2}{(x-1)^2(x+3)}$

92. $\dfrac{3}{x^2-x-6}-\dfrac{2}{x^2+5x+6}=\dfrac{3}{(x-3)(x+2)}-\dfrac{2}{(x+3)(x+2)}=$
$\dfrac{3(x+3)}{(x-3)(x+3)(x+2)}-\dfrac{2(x-3)}{(x-3)(x+3)(x+2)}=\dfrac{3x+9-2x+6}{(x-3)(x+3)(x+2)}=$
$\dfrac{x+15}{(x-3)(x+3)(x+2)}$

93. $\dfrac{x}{x^2-5x+4}+\dfrac{2}{x^2-2x-8}=\dfrac{x}{(x-4)(x-1)}+\dfrac{2}{(x-4)(x+2)}=$
$\dfrac{x(x+2)}{(x-4)(x+2)(x-1)}+\dfrac{2(x-1)}{(x-4)(x+2)(x-1)}=\dfrac{x^2+2x+2x-2}{(x-4)(x+2)(x-1)}=$
$\dfrac{x^2+4x-2}{(x-4)(x+2)(x-1)}$

94. $\dfrac{3}{x^2-2x+1}+\dfrac{1}{x^2-3x+2}=\dfrac{3}{(x-1)(x-1)}+\dfrac{1}{(x-2)(x-1)}=$
$\dfrac{3(x-2)}{(x-1)^2(x-2)}+\dfrac{x-1}{(x-1)^2(x-2)}=\dfrac{3x-6+x-1}{(x-1)^2(x-2)}=\dfrac{4x-7}{(x-1)^2(x-2)}$

95. $\dfrac{x}{x^2-4}-\dfrac{1}{x^2+4x+4}=\dfrac{x}{(x-2)(x+2)}-\dfrac{1}{(x+2)(x+2)}=$
$\dfrac{x(x+2)}{(x+2)^2(x-2)}-\dfrac{x-2}{(x+2)^2(x-2)}=\dfrac{x^2+2x-x+2}{(x+2)^2(x-2)}=\dfrac{x^2+x+2}{(x+2)^2(x-2)}$

96. $\dfrac{3x}{x^2+2x-3}+\dfrac{1}{x^2-2x+1}=\dfrac{3x}{(x+3)(x-1)}+\dfrac{1}{(x-1)(x-1)}=$

$\dfrac{3x(x-1)}{(x+3)(x-1)^2}+\dfrac{x+3}{(x+3)(x-1)^2}=\dfrac{3x^2-3x+x+3}{(x+3)(x-1)^2}=\dfrac{3x^2-2x+3}{(x+3)(x-1)^2}$

97. $\dfrac{3x}{x-y}-\dfrac{3y}{x^2-2xy+y^2}=\dfrac{3x}{x-y}-\dfrac{3y}{(x-y)(x-y)}=$

$\dfrac{3x(x-y)}{(x-y)^2}-\dfrac{3y}{(x-y)^2}=\dfrac{3x^2-3xy-3y}{(x-y)^2}=\dfrac{3(x^2-xy-y)}{(x-y)^2}$

98. $\dfrac{4c}{ab}+\dfrac{3b}{ac}-\dfrac{2a}{bc}=\dfrac{4c^2}{abc}+\dfrac{3b^2}{abc}-\dfrac{2a^2}{abc}=\dfrac{4c^2+3b^2-2a^2}{abc}$

99. $x+\dfrac{1}{x-1}-\dfrac{1}{x+1}=\dfrac{x(x-1)(x+1)}{(x-1)(x+1)}+\dfrac{x+1}{(x-1)(x+1)}-\dfrac{x-1}{(x-1)(x+1)}=$

$\dfrac{x^3-x+x+1-x+1}{(x-1)(x+1)}=\dfrac{x^3-x+2}{(x-1)(x+1)}$

100. $5-\dfrac{6}{n^2-36}+\dfrac{3}{n-6}=\dfrac{5(n-6)(n+6)}{(n-6)(n+6)}-\dfrac{6}{(n-6)(n+6)}+\dfrac{3(n+6)}{(n-6)(n+6)}=$

$\dfrac{5n^2-180-6+3n+18}{(n-6)(n+6)}=\dfrac{5n^2+3n-168}{(n-6)(n+6)}$

101. $\dfrac{6}{t-1}+\dfrac{2}{t-2}+\dfrac{1}{t}=\dfrac{6t(t-2)}{t(t-1)(t-2)}+\dfrac{2t(t-1)}{t(t-1)(t-2)}+\dfrac{(t-1)(t-2)}{t(t-1)(t-2)}=$

$\dfrac{6t^2-12t+2t^2-2t+t^2-3t+2}{t(t-1)(t-2)}=\dfrac{9t^2-17t+2}{t(t-1)(t-2)}$

102. $\dfrac{3}{x-5}-\dfrac{1}{x-3}-\dfrac{2x}{x-5}=\dfrac{3(x-3)}{(x-5)(x+3)}-\dfrac{x-5}{(x-5)(x-3)}-\dfrac{2x(x-3)}{(x-5)(x-3)}=$

$\dfrac{3x-9-x+5-2x^2+6x}{(x-5)(x-3)}=\dfrac{-2x^2+8x-4}{(x-5)(x-3)}=\dfrac{-2(x^2-4x+2)}{(x-5)x-3)}$

103. The factored denominators are $x$ and $x^2$. The LCD is $x^2$.

$\dfrac{1}{x}+\dfrac{3}{x^2}=0\Rightarrow\dfrac{1(x^2)}{x}+\dfrac{3(x^2)}{x^2}=0(x^2)\Rightarrow x+3=0\Rightarrow x=-3$

104. The factored denominators are $x-2$ and $x+1$. The LCD is $(x-2)(x+1)$.

$\dfrac{1}{x-2}+\dfrac{3}{x+1}=0\Rightarrow\dfrac{1(x-2)(x+1)}{x-2}+\dfrac{3(x-2)(x+1)}{x+1}=0(x-2)(x+1)\Rightarrow$

$1(x+1)+3(x-2)=0\Rightarrow x+1+3x-6=0\Rightarrow 4x-5=0\Rightarrow x=\dfrac{5}{4}$

105. The factored denominators are $x$ and $2x-1$. The LCD is $x(2x-1)$.

$\dfrac{1}{x}+\dfrac{3x}{2x-1}=0\Rightarrow\dfrac{1(x)(2x-1)}{x}+\dfrac{3x(x)(2x-1)}{2x-1}=0(x)(2x-1)\Rightarrow 2x-1+3x^2=0\Rightarrow$

$3x^2+2x-1=0\Rightarrow(3x-1)(x+1)=0\Rightarrow x=\dfrac{1}{3}\text{ or }x=-1$

106. The factored denominators are $2x - 5$ and $x$. The LCD is $x(2x - 5)$.

$$\frac{x}{2x-5} + \frac{4}{x} = 0 \Rightarrow \frac{x(x)(2x-5)}{2x-5} + \frac{4(x)(2x-5)}{x} = 0(x)(2x-5) \Rightarrow x^2 + 4(2x-5) = 0 \Rightarrow$$

$$x^2 + 8x - 20 = 0 \Rightarrow (x+10)(x-2) = 0 \Rightarrow x = -10 \text{ or } x = 2$$

107. The factored denominators are $(3 - x)(3 + x)$ and $3 - x$. The LCD is $(3 - x)(3 + x)$.

$$\frac{2x}{9-x^2} + \frac{1}{3-x} = 0 \Rightarrow \frac{2x(3-x)(3+x)}{9-x^2} + \frac{1(3-x)(3+x)}{3-x} = 0(3-x)(3+x) \Rightarrow$$

$$2x + 3 + x = 0 \Rightarrow 3x + 3 = 0 \Rightarrow x = -1$$

108. The factored denominators are $(1 - x)(1 + x)$ and $1 + x$. The LCD is $(1 - x)(1 + x)$.

$$\frac{1}{1-x^2} + \frac{1}{1+x} = 0 \Rightarrow \frac{1(1-x)(1+x)}{1-x^2} + \frac{1(1-x)(1+x)}{1+x} = 0(1-x)(1+x) \Rightarrow$$

$$1 + 1 - x = 0 \Rightarrow 2 - x = 0 \Rightarrow x = 2$$

109. The factored denominators are $2x$, $2x^2$ and $x^3$. The LCD is $2x^3$.

$$\frac{1}{2x} + \frac{1}{2x^2} - \frac{1}{x^3} = 0 \Rightarrow \frac{1(2x^3)}{2x} + \frac{1(2x^3)}{2x^2} - \frac{1(2x^3)}{x^3} = 0(2x^3) \Rightarrow x^2 + x - 2 = 0 \Rightarrow$$

$$(x+2)(x-1) = 0 \Rightarrow x = -2 \text{ or } x = 1$$

110. The factored denominators are $(x + 4)(x - 4)$, $x + 4$ and $x - 4$. The LCD is $(x + 4)(x - 4)$.

$$\frac{1}{x^2-16} + \frac{4}{x+4} - \frac{5}{x-4} = 0 \Rightarrow$$

$$\frac{1(x+4)(x-4)}{x^2-16} + \frac{4(x+4)(x-4)}{x+4} - \frac{5(x+4)(x-4)}{x-4} = 0(x+4)(x-4) \Rightarrow$$

$$1 + 4(x-4) - 5(x+4) = 0 \Rightarrow 1 + 4x - 16 - 5x - 20 = 0 \Rightarrow -x - 35 = 0 \Rightarrow x = -35$$

111. The factored denominators are $x$, $x + 5$ and $x - 5$. The LCD is $x(x + 5)(x - 5)$.

$$\frac{1}{x} - \frac{2}{x+5} + \frac{1}{x-5} = 0 \Rightarrow$$

$$\frac{1(x)(x+5)(x-5)}{x} - \frac{2(x)(x+5)(x-5)}{x+5} + \frac{1(x)(x+5)(x-5)}{x-5} = 0(x)(x+5)(x-5) \Rightarrow$$

$$(x+5)(x-5) - 2x(x-5) + x(x+5) = 0 \Rightarrow x^2 - 25 - 2x^2 + 10x + x^2 + 5x = 0 \Rightarrow$$

$$15x - 25 = 0 \Rightarrow x = \frac{25}{15} = \frac{5}{3}$$

112. The factored denominators are $x - 2$, $x - 3$ and $x$. The LCD is $x(x - 2)(x - 3)$.

$$\frac{1}{x-2} + \frac{1}{x-3} - \frac{2}{x} = 0 \Rightarrow$$

$$\frac{1(x)(x-2)(x-3)}{x-2} + \frac{1(x)(x-2)(x-3)}{x-3} - \frac{2(x)(x-2)(x-3)}{x} = 0(x)(x-2)(x-3) \Rightarrow$$

$$x(x-3) + x(x-2) - 2(x-2)(x-3) = 0 \Rightarrow x^2 - 3x + x^2 - 2x - 2x^2 + 10x - 12 = 0 \Rightarrow$$

$$5x - 12 = 0 \Rightarrow x = \frac{12}{5}$$

113. $$\frac{1+\frac{1}{x}}{1-\frac{1}{x}}=\frac{1+\frac{1}{x}}{1-\frac{1}{x}}\cdot\frac{x}{x}=\frac{x+1}{x-1}$$

114. $$\frac{\frac{1}{2}-x}{\frac{1}{x}-2}=\frac{\frac{1}{2}-x}{\frac{1}{x}-2}\cdot\frac{2x}{2x}=\frac{x-2x^2}{2-4x}=\frac{x(1-2x)}{2(1-2x)}=\frac{x}{2}$$

115. $$\frac{\frac{1}{x-5}}{\frac{4}{x}-\frac{1}{x-5}}=\frac{\frac{1}{x-5}}{\frac{4}{x}-\frac{1}{x-5}}\cdot\frac{x(x-5)}{x(x-5)}=\frac{x}{4(x-5)-x}=\frac{x}{4x-20-x}=\frac{x}{3x-20}$$

116. $$\frac{1+\frac{1}{x-3}}{\frac{1}{x-3}-1}=\frac{1+\frac{1}{x-3}}{\frac{1}{x-3}-1}\cdot\frac{x-3}{x-3}=\frac{x-3+1}{1-(x-3)}=\frac{x-2}{4-x}$$

117. $$\frac{\frac{1}{x}+\frac{2-x}{x^2}}{\frac{3}{x^2}-\frac{1}{x}}=\frac{\frac{1}{x}+\frac{2-x}{x^2}}{\frac{3}{x^2}-\frac{1}{x}}\cdot\frac{x^2}{x^2}=\frac{x+2-x}{3-x}=\frac{2}{3-x}$$

118. $$\frac{\frac{1}{x-1}+\frac{2}{x}}{2-\frac{1}{x}}=\frac{\frac{1}{x-1}+\frac{2}{x}}{2-\frac{1}{x}}\cdot\frac{x(x-1)}{x(x-1)}=\frac{x+2(x-1)}{2x(x-1)-(x-1)}=\frac{x+2x-2}{2x^2-2x-x+1}=\frac{3x-2}{(x-1)(2x-1)}$$

119. $$\frac{\frac{1}{x+3}+\frac{2}{x-3}}{2-\frac{1}{x-3}}=\frac{\frac{1}{x+3}+\frac{2}{x-3}}{2-\frac{1}{x-3}}\cdot\frac{(x-3)(x+3)}{(x-3)(x+3)}=\frac{x-3+2(x+3)}{2(x-3)(x+3)-(x+3)}=\frac{3(x+1)}{(x+3)(2x-7)}$$

120. $$\frac{\frac{1}{x}+\frac{2}{x}}{\frac{1}{x-1}+\frac{x}{2}}=\frac{\frac{1}{x}+\frac{2}{x}}{\frac{1}{x-1}+\frac{x}{2}}\cdot\frac{2x(x-1)}{2x(x-1)}=\frac{2(x-1)+4(x-1)}{2x+x^2(x-1)}=\frac{2x-2+4x-4}{2x+x^3-x^2}=\frac{6(x-1)}{x(x^2-x+2)}$$

121. $$\frac{\frac{4}{x-5}}{\frac{1}{x+5}+\frac{1}{x}}=\frac{\frac{4}{x-5}}{\frac{1}{x+5}+\frac{1}{x}}\cdot\frac{x(x-5)(x+5)}{x(x-5)(x+5)}=\frac{4x(x+5)}{x(x-5)+(x-5)(x+5)}=\frac{4x(x+5)}{(x-5)(2x+5)}$$

122. $$\frac{\frac{2}{x-4}}{1-\frac{1}{x+4}}=\frac{\frac{2}{x-4}}{1-\frac{1}{x+4}}\cdot\frac{(x-4)(x+4)}{(x-4)(x+4)}=\frac{2(x+4)}{(x-4)(x+4)-(x-4)}=\frac{2(x+4)}{(x-4)(x+3)}$$

123. $$\frac{\frac{1}{2a}-\frac{1}{2b}}{\frac{1}{a^2}-\frac{1}{b^2}}=\frac{\frac{1}{2a}-\frac{1}{2b}}{\frac{1}{a^2}-\frac{1}{b^2}}\cdot\frac{2a^2b^2}{2a^2b^2}=\frac{ab^2-a^2b}{2b^2-2a^2}=\frac{ab(b-a)}{2(b+a)(b-a)}=\frac{ab}{2(a+b)}$$

124. $\dfrac{\dfrac{1}{2x^2}-\dfrac{1}{2y^2}}{\dfrac{1}{3y^2}+\dfrac{1}{3x^2}}=\dfrac{\dfrac{1}{2x^2}-\dfrac{1}{2y^2}}{\dfrac{1}{3y^2}+\dfrac{1}{3x^2}}\cdot\dfrac{6x^2y^2}{6x^2y^2}=\dfrac{3y^2-3x^2}{2x^2+2y^2}=\dfrac{-3(x^2-y^2)}{2(x^2+y^2)}=-\dfrac{3(x^2-y^2)}{2(x^2+y^2)}$

## R.6: Radical Notation and Rational Exponents

1. $-\sqrt{25}=-\sqrt{5^2}=-5$ and $\sqrt{25}=\sqrt{5^2}=5$
2. $-\sqrt{49}=-\sqrt{7^2}=-7$ and $\sqrt{49}=\sqrt{7^2}=7$
3. $-\sqrt{\dfrac{16}{25}}=-\sqrt{\left(\dfrac{4}{5}\right)^2}=-\dfrac{4}{5}$ and $\sqrt{\dfrac{16}{25}}=\sqrt{\left(\dfrac{4}{5}\right)^2}=\dfrac{4}{5}$
4. $-\sqrt{\dfrac{64}{81}}=-\sqrt{\left(\dfrac{8}{9}\right)^2}=-\dfrac{8}{9}$ and $\sqrt{\dfrac{64}{81}}=\sqrt{\left(\dfrac{8}{9}\right)^2}=\dfrac{8}{9}$
5. $-\sqrt{11}\approx-3.32$ and $\sqrt{11}\approx 3.32$
6. $-\sqrt{17}\approx-4.12$ and $\sqrt{17}\approx 4.12$
7. $\sqrt{144}=\sqrt{12^2}=12$
8. $\sqrt{100}=\sqrt{10^2}=10$
9. $\sqrt{23}\approx 4.80$
10. $\sqrt{45}\approx 6.71$
11. $\sqrt{\dfrac{4}{49}}=\sqrt{\left(\dfrac{2}{7}\right)^2}=\dfrac{2}{7}$
12. $\sqrt{\dfrac{16}{121}}=\sqrt{\left(\dfrac{4}{11}\right)^2}=\dfrac{4}{11}$
13. Since $b<0$, $\sqrt{b^2}=-b$.
14. Since $xy>0$, $\sqrt{(xy)^2}=xy$.
15. $\sqrt[3]{27}=\sqrt[3]{3^3}=3$
16. $\sqrt[3]{64}=\sqrt[3]{4^3}=4$
17. $\sqrt[3]{-8}=\sqrt[3]{(-2)^3}=-2$
18. $\sqrt[3]{-125}=\sqrt[3]{(-5)^3}=-5$
19. $\sqrt[3]{\dfrac{1}{27}}=\sqrt[3]{\left(\dfrac{1}{3}\right)^3}=\dfrac{1}{3}$
20. $\sqrt[3]{-\dfrac{1}{64}}=\sqrt[3]{\left(-\dfrac{1}{4}\right)^3}=-\dfrac{1}{4}$
21. $\sqrt[3]{b^9}=\sqrt[3]{(b^3)^3}=b^3$
22. $\sqrt[3]{8x^6}=\sqrt[3]{(2x^2)^3}=2x^2$
23. $\sqrt{9}=3$
24. $\sqrt{121}=11$

25. $-\sqrt{5} \approx -2.24$

26. $\sqrt{11} \approx 3.32$

27. $\sqrt[3]{27} = 3$

28. $\sqrt[3]{64} = 4$

29. $\sqrt[3]{-64} = -4$

30. $-\sqrt[3]{-1} = -(-1) = 1$

31. $\sqrt[3]{5} \approx 1.71$

32. $\sqrt[3]{-13} \approx -2.35$

33. $-\sqrt[3]{x^9} = -\sqrt[3]{(x^3)^3} = -x^3$

34. $\sqrt[3]{(x+1)^6} = \sqrt[3]{((x+1)^2)^3} = (x+1)^2$

35. $\sqrt[3]{(2x)^6} = \sqrt[3]{((2x)^2)^3} = (2x)^2 = 4x^2$

36. $\sqrt[3]{9x^3} \approx 2.08x$

37. $\sqrt[4]{81} = 3$

38. $\sqrt[5]{-1} = -1$

39. $\sqrt[5]{-7} \approx -1.48$

40. $\sqrt[4]{6} \approx 1.57$

41. $6^{1/2} = \sqrt{6}$

42. $7^{1/3} = \sqrt[3]{7}$

43. $(xy)^{1/2} = \sqrt{xy}$

44. $x^{2/3}y^{1/5} = \sqrt[3]{x^2} \cdot \sqrt[5]{y}$

45. $y^{-1/5} = \dfrac{1}{\sqrt[5]{y}}$

46. $\left(\dfrac{x}{y}\right)^{-2/7} = \left(\dfrac{y}{x}\right)^{2/7} = \sqrt[7]{\left(\dfrac{y}{x}\right)^2} = \sqrt[7]{\dfrac{y^2}{x^2}}$

47. The expression can be written $27^{2/3} = \sqrt[3]{27^2}$ or $(\sqrt[3]{27})^2$ and evaluated as $(\sqrt[3]{27})^2 = 3^2 = 9$.

48. The expression can be written $8^{4/3} = \sqrt[3]{8^4}$ or $(\sqrt[3]{8})^4$ and evaluated as $(\sqrt[3]{8})^4 = 2^4 = 16$.

49. The expression can be written $(-1)^{4/3} = \sqrt[3]{(-1)^4}$ or $(\sqrt[3]{-1})^4$ and evaluated as $(\sqrt[3]{-1})^4 = (-1)^4 = 1$.

50. The expression can be written $81^{3/4} = \sqrt[4]{81^3}$ or $(\sqrt[4]{81})^3$ and evaluated as $(\sqrt[4]{81})^3 = 3^3 = 27$.

51. The expression can be written $8^{-1/3} = \dfrac{1}{8^{1/3}} = \dfrac{1}{\sqrt[3]{8}}$ and evaluated as $\dfrac{1}{\sqrt[3]{8}} = \dfrac{1}{2}$.

52. The expression can be written $16^{-3/4} = \dfrac{1}{16^{3/4}} = \dfrac{1}{\sqrt[4]{16^3}}$ or $\dfrac{1}{(\sqrt[4]{16})^3}$ and evaluated as $\dfrac{1}{(\sqrt[4]{16})^3} = \dfrac{1}{2^3} = \dfrac{1}{8}$.

53. The expression can be written $13^{-3/5} = \dfrac{1}{13^{3/5}} = \dfrac{1}{\sqrt[5]{13^3}}$ or $\dfrac{1}{(\sqrt[5]{13})^3}$. The result is not an integer.

54. The expression can be written $23^{-1/2} = \dfrac{1}{23^{1/2}} = \dfrac{1}{\sqrt{23}}$. The result is not an integer.

55. $16^{1/2} = \sqrt{16} = 4$

56. $8^{1/3} = \sqrt[3]{8} = 2$

57. $256^{1/4} = \sqrt[4]{256} = 4$

58. $4^{3/2} = (\sqrt{4})^3 = 2^3 = 8$

59. $32^{1/5} = \sqrt[5]{32} = 2$

60. $(-32)^{1/5} = \sqrt[5]{-32} = -2$

61. $(-8)^{4/3} = (\sqrt[3]{-8})^4 = (-2)^4 = 16$

62. $(-1)^{3/5} = (\sqrt[5]{-1})^3 = (-1)^3 = -1$

63. $2^{1/2} \cdot 2^{2/3} = 2^{1/2+2/3} = 2^{7/6} \approx 2.24$

64. $5^{3/5} \cdot 5^{1/10} = 5^{3/5+1/10} = 5^{7/10} \approx 3.09$

65. $\left(\frac{4}{9}\right)^{1/2} = \frac{4^{1/2}}{9^{1/2}} = \frac{\sqrt{4}}{\sqrt{9}} = \frac{2}{3}$

66. $\left(\frac{27}{64}\right)^{1/3} = \frac{27^{1/3}}{64^{1/3}} = \frac{\sqrt[3]{27}}{\sqrt[3]{64}} = \frac{3}{4}$

67. $\frac{4^{2/3}}{4^{1/2}} = 4^{2/3-1/2} = 4^{1/6} \approx 1.26$

68. $\frac{6^{1/5} \cdot 6^{3/5}}{6^{2/5}} = \frac{6^{1/5+3/5}}{6^{2/5}} = \frac{6^{4/5}}{6^{2/5}} = 6^{4/5-2/5} = 6^{2/5} \approx 2.05$

69. $4^{-1/2} = \frac{1}{4^{1/2}} = \frac{1}{\sqrt{4}} = \frac{1}{2}$

70. $9^{-3/2} = \frac{1}{9^{3/2}} = \frac{1}{(\sqrt{9})^3} = \frac{1}{3^3} = \frac{1}{27}$

71. $(-8)^{-1/3} = \frac{1}{(-8)^{1/3}} = \frac{1}{\sqrt[3]{-8}} = \frac{1}{-2} = -\frac{1}{2}$

72. $(49)^{-1/2} = \frac{1}{49^{1/2}} = \frac{1}{\sqrt{49}} = \frac{1}{7}$

73. $\left(\frac{1}{16}\right)^{-1/4} = 16^{1/4} = \sqrt[4]{16} = 2$

74. $\left(\frac{16}{25}\right)^{-3/2} = \left(\frac{25}{16}\right)^{3/2} = \frac{25^{3/2}}{16^{3/2}} = \frac{(\sqrt{25})^3}{(\sqrt{16})^3} = \frac{5^3}{4^3} = \frac{125}{64}$

75. $(2^{1/2})^3 = 2^{1/2 \cdot 3} = 2^{3/2} \approx 2.83$

76. $(5^{6/5})^{-1/2} = 5^{6/5 \cdot (-1/2)} = 5^{-3/5} = \frac{1}{5^{3/5}} \approx 0.38$

77. $(x^2)^{3/2} = x^{2 \cdot 3/2} = x^3$

78. $(y^4)^{1/2} = y^{4 \cdot 1/2} = y^2$

79. $(x^2y^8)^{1/2} = x^{2 \cdot 1/2} \cdot y^{8 \cdot 1/2} = xy^4$

80. $(y^{10}z^4)^{1/4} = y^{10 \cdot 1/4} \cdot z^{4 \cdot 1/4} = y^{5/2}z$

81. $\sqrt[3]{x^3y^6} = (x^3y^6)^{1/3} = x^{3 \cdot 1/3} \cdot y^{6 \cdot 1/3} = xy^2$

82. $\sqrt{16x^4} = (16x^4)^{1/2} = 16^{1/2} \cdot x^{4 \cdot 1/2} = \sqrt{16} \cdot x^2 = 4x^2$

83. $\sqrt{\frac{y^4}{x^2}} = \left(\frac{y^4}{x^2}\right)^{1/2} = \frac{y^{4\cdot 1/2}}{x^{2\cdot 1/2}} = \frac{y^2}{x}$

84. $\sqrt[3]{\frac{x^{12}}{z^6}} = \left(\frac{x^{12}}{z^6}\right)^{1/3} = \frac{x^{12\cdot 1/3}}{z^{6\cdot 1/3}} = \frac{x^4}{z^2}$

85. $\sqrt{y^3}\cdot\sqrt[3]{y^2} = (y^3)^{1/2}\cdot(y^2)^{1/3} = y^{3\cdot 1/2}\cdot y^{2\cdot 1/3} = y^{3/2}\cdot y^{2/3} = y^{3/2+2/3} = y^{13/6}$

86. $\left(\frac{x^6}{81}\right)^{1/4} = \frac{x^{6\cdot 1/4}}{81^{1/4}} = \frac{x^{3/2}}{\sqrt[4]{81}} = \frac{x^{3/2}}{3}$

87. $\left(\frac{x^6}{27}\right)^{2/3} = \frac{x^{6\cdot 2/3}}{27^{2/3}} = \frac{x^4}{(\sqrt[3]{27})^2} = \frac{x^4}{3^2} = \frac{x^4}{9}$

88. $\left(\frac{1}{x^8}\right)^{-1/4} = (x^8)^{1/4} = x^{8\cdot 1/4} = x^2$

89. $\left(\frac{x^2}{y^6}\right)^{-1/2} = \left(\frac{y^6}{x^2}\right)^{1/2} = \frac{y^{6\cdot 1/2}}{x^{2\cdot 1/2}} = \frac{y^3}{x}$

90. $\frac{\sqrt{x}}{\sqrt[3]{27x^6}} = \frac{x^{1/2}}{(27x^6)^{1/3}} = \frac{x^{1/2}}{\sqrt[3]{27}\cdot x^{6\cdot 1/3}} = \frac{x^{1/2}}{3x^2} = \frac{x^{1/2-2}}{3} = \frac{x^{-3/2}}{3} = \frac{1}{3x^{3/2}}$

91. $\sqrt{\sqrt{y}} = (y^{1/2})^{1/2} = y^{1/2\cdot 1/2} = y^{1/4}$

92. $\sqrt{\sqrt[3]{(3x)^2}} = ((3x)^{2/3})^{1/2} = (3x)^{1/3}$

93. $(a^{-1/2})^{4/3} = a^{-1/2\cdot 4/3} = a^{-2/3} = \frac{1}{a^{2/3}}$

94. $(x^{-3/2})^{2/3} = x^{-3/2\cdot 2/3} = x^{-1} = \frac{1}{x}$

95. $(a^3b^6)^{1/3} = a^{3\cdot 1/3}\cdot b^{6\cdot 1/3} = ab^2$

96. $(64x^3y^{18})^{1/6} = 64^{1/6}\cdot x^{3\cdot 1/6}\cdot y^{18\cdot 1/6} = \sqrt[6]{64}\cdot x^{1/2}\cdot y^3 = 2x^{1/2}y^3$

97. $\frac{(k^{1/2})^{-3}}{(k^2)^{1/4}} = \frac{k^{-3/2}}{k^{1/2}} = k^{-3/2-1/2} = k^{-4/2} = k^{-2} = \frac{1}{k^2}$

98. $\frac{(b^{3/4})^4}{(b^{4/5})^{-5}} = \frac{b^3}{b^{-4}} = b^{3-(-4)} = b^7$

99. $\sqrt{b}\cdot\sqrt[4]{b} = b^{1/2}\cdot b^{1/4} = b^{1/2+1/4} = b^{3/4}$

100. $\sqrt[3]{t}\cdot\sqrt[5]{t} = t^{1/3}\cdot t^{1/5} = t^{1/3+1/5} = t^{8/15}$

101. $\sqrt{z}\cdot\sqrt[3]{z^2}\cdot\sqrt[4]{z^3} = z^{1/2}\cdot z^{2/3}\cdot z^{3/4} = z^{1/2+2/3+3/4} = z^{23/12}$

102. $\sqrt{b}\cdot\sqrt[3]{b}\cdot\sqrt[5]{b} = b^{1/2}\cdot b^{1/3}\cdot b^{1/5} = b^{1/2+1/3+1/5} = b^{31/30}$

103. $p^{1/2}(p^{3/2} + p^{1/2}) = p^{1/2+3/2} + p^{1/2+1/2} = p^2 + p$

104. $d^{3/4}(d^{1/4} - d^{-1/4}) = d^{3/4+1/4} - d^{3/4+(-1/4)} = d - d^{1/2}$

105. $\sqrt[3]{x}(\sqrt{x} - \sqrt[3]{x^2}) = x^{1/3}(x^{1/2} - x^{2/3}) = x^{1/3+1/2} - x^{1/3+2/3} = x^{5/6} - x$

106. $\frac{1}{2}\sqrt{x}(\sqrt{x} + \sqrt[4]{x^2}) = \frac{1}{2}x^{1/2}(x^{1/2} + x^{2/4}) = \frac{1}{2}x^{1/2}(2x^{1/2}) = \frac{1}{2}\cdot 2\cdot x^{1/2+1/2} = x$

## R.7: Radical Expressions

1. $\sqrt{3} \cdot \sqrt{3} = \sqrt{3 \cdot 3} = \sqrt{9} = 3$

2. $\sqrt{2} \cdot \sqrt{18} = \sqrt{2 \cdot 18} = \sqrt{36} = 6$

3. $\sqrt{2} \cdot \sqrt{50} = \sqrt{2 \cdot 50} = \sqrt{100} = 10$

4. $\sqrt[3]{-2} \cdot \sqrt[3]{-4} = \sqrt[3]{(-2)(-4)} = \sqrt[3]{8} = 2$

5. $\sqrt[3]{4} \cdot \sqrt[3]{16} = \sqrt[3]{4 \cdot 16} = \sqrt[3]{64} = 4$

6. $\sqrt[3]{x} \cdot \sqrt[3]{x^2} = \sqrt[3]{x \cdot x^2} = \sqrt[3]{x^3} = x$

7. $\sqrt{\frac{9}{25}} = \frac{\sqrt{9}}{\sqrt{25}} = \frac{3}{5}$

8. $\sqrt[3]{\frac{x}{8}} = \frac{\sqrt[3]{x}}{\sqrt[3]{8}} = \frac{\sqrt[3]{x}}{2}$

9. $\sqrt{\frac{1}{2}} \cdot \sqrt{\frac{1}{8}} = \sqrt{\frac{1 \cdot 1}{2 \cdot 8}} = \sqrt{\frac{1}{16}} = \frac{\sqrt{1}}{\sqrt{16}} = \frac{1}{4}$

10. $\sqrt{\frac{5}{3}} \cdot \sqrt{\frac{1}{3}} = \sqrt{\frac{5 \cdot 1}{3 \cdot 3}} = \sqrt{\frac{5}{9}} = \frac{\sqrt{5}}{\sqrt{9}} = \frac{\sqrt{5}}{3}$

11. $\sqrt{\frac{x}{2}} \cdot \sqrt{\frac{x}{8}} = \sqrt{\frac{x \cdot x}{2 \cdot 8}} = \sqrt{\frac{x^2}{16}} = \frac{\sqrt{x^2}}{\sqrt{16}} = \frac{x}{4}$

12. $\sqrt{\frac{4}{y}} \cdot \sqrt{\frac{y}{5}} = \sqrt{\frac{4 \cdot y}{y \cdot 5}} = \sqrt{\frac{4y}{5y}} = \sqrt{\frac{4}{5}} = \frac{\sqrt{4}}{\sqrt{5}} = \frac{2}{\sqrt{5}}$ or $\frac{2\sqrt{5}}{5}$

13. $\frac{\sqrt{45}}{\sqrt{5}} = \sqrt{\frac{45}{5}} = \sqrt{9} = 3$

14. $\frac{\sqrt{7}}{\sqrt{28}} = \sqrt{\frac{7}{28}} = \sqrt{\frac{1}{4}} = \frac{\sqrt{1}}{\sqrt{4}} = \frac{1}{2}$

15. $\sqrt[4]{9} \cdot \sqrt[4]{9} = \sqrt[4]{9 \cdot 9} = \sqrt[4]{81} = 3$

16. $\sqrt[5]{16} \cdot \sqrt[5]{-2} = \sqrt[5]{16 \cdot (-2)} = \sqrt[5]{-32} = -2$

17. $\frac{\sqrt[5]{64}}{\sqrt[5]{-2}} = \sqrt[5]{\frac{64}{-2}} = \sqrt[5]{-32} = -2$

18. $\frac{\sqrt[4]{324}}{\sqrt[4]{4}} = \sqrt[4]{\frac{324}{4}} = \sqrt[4]{81} = 3$

19. $\frac{\sqrt{a^2 b}}{\sqrt{b}} = \sqrt{\frac{a^2 b}{b}} = \sqrt{a^2} = a$

20. $\frac{\sqrt{4xy^2}}{\sqrt{x}} = \sqrt{\frac{4xy^2}{x}} = \sqrt{4y^2} = \sqrt{4} \cdot \sqrt{y^2} = 2y$

21. $\sqrt[3]{\frac{x^3}{8}} = \frac{\sqrt[3]{x^3}}{\sqrt[3]{8}} = \frac{x}{2}$

22. $\sqrt{\frac{36}{z^4}} = \frac{\sqrt{36}}{\sqrt{z^4}} = \frac{6}{z^2}$

23. $\sqrt{4x^4} = \sqrt{4}\cdot\sqrt{(x^2)^2} = 2x^2$

24. $\sqrt[3]{-8y^3} = \sqrt[3]{-8}\cdot\sqrt[3]{y^3} = -2y$

25. $\sqrt[4]{16x^4y} = \sqrt[4]{16}\cdot\sqrt[4]{x^4}\cdot\sqrt[4]{y} = 2x\sqrt[4]{y}$

26. $\sqrt[3]{8xy^3} = \sqrt[3]{8}\cdot\sqrt[3]{x}\cdot\sqrt[3]{y^3} = 2\sqrt[3]{x}\cdot y = 2y\sqrt[3]{x}$

27. $\sqrt{3x}\cdot\sqrt{12x} = \sqrt{3\cdot 12\cdot x\cdot x} = \sqrt{36x^2} = \sqrt{36}\cdot\sqrt{x^2} = 6x$

28. $\sqrt{6x^5}\cdot\sqrt{6x} = \sqrt{6\cdot 6\cdot x^5\cdot x} = \sqrt{36x^6} = \sqrt{36}\cdot\sqrt{(x^3)^2} = 6x^3$

29. $\sqrt[3]{8x^6y^3z^9} = \sqrt[3]{8}\cdot\sqrt[3]{(x^2)^3}\cdot\sqrt[3]{y^3}\cdot\sqrt[3]{(z^3)^3} = 2x^2yz^3$

30. $\sqrt{16x^4y^6} = \sqrt{16}\cdot\sqrt{(x^2)^2}\cdot\sqrt{(y^3)^2} = 4x^2y^3$

31. $\sqrt[4]{\frac{3}{4}}\cdot\sqrt[4]{\frac{27}{4}} = \sqrt[4]{\frac{3}{4}\cdot\frac{27}{4}} = \sqrt[4]{\frac{81}{16}} = \frac{\sqrt[4]{81}}{\sqrt[4]{16}} = \frac{3}{2}$

32. $\sqrt[5]{\frac{4}{-9}}\cdot\sqrt[5]{\frac{8}{-27}} = \sqrt[5]{\frac{4}{-9}\cdot\frac{8}{-27}} = \sqrt[5]{\frac{32}{243}} = \frac{2}{3}$

33. $\sqrt[4]{25z}\cdot\sqrt[4]{25z} = \sqrt[4]{625z^2} = \sqrt[4]{625}\cdot\sqrt[4]{z^2} = 5\sqrt{z}$

34. $\sqrt[5]{3z^2}\cdot\sqrt[5]{7z} = \sqrt[5]{21z^3}$

35. $\sqrt[5]{\frac{7a}{b^2}}\cdot\sqrt[5]{\frac{b^2}{7a^6}} = \sqrt[5]{\frac{7ab^2}{7a^6b^2}}\sqrt[5]{\frac{1}{a^5}} = \frac{1}{a}$

36. $\sqrt[3]{\frac{8m}{n}}\cdot\sqrt[3]{\frac{n^4}{m^2}} = \sqrt[3]{\frac{8mn^4}{nm^2}} = \sqrt[3]{\frac{8n^3}{m}} = \frac{\sqrt[3]{8n^3}}{\sqrt[3]{m}} = \frac{2n}{\sqrt[3]{m}}$

37. $\sqrt{200} = \sqrt{100\cdot 2} = \sqrt{100}\cdot\sqrt{2} = 10\sqrt{2}$

38. $\sqrt{72} = \sqrt{36\cdot 2} = \sqrt{36}\cdot\sqrt{2} = 6\sqrt{2}$

39. $\sqrt[3]{81} = \sqrt[3]{27\cdot 3} = \sqrt[3]{27}\cdot\sqrt[3]{3} = 3\sqrt[3]{3}$

40. $\sqrt[3]{256} = \sqrt[3]{64\cdot 4} = \sqrt[3]{64}\cdot\sqrt[3]{4} = 4\sqrt[3]{4}$

41. $\sqrt[4]{64} = \sqrt[4]{16\cdot 4} = \sqrt[4]{16}\cdot\sqrt[4]{4} = 2\sqrt[4]{4} = 2\sqrt[4]{2^2} = 2\sqrt{2}$

42. $\sqrt[5]{27\cdot 81} = \sqrt[5]{3^3\cdot 3^4} = \sqrt[5]{3^7} = \sqrt[5]{3^5\cdot 3^2} = \sqrt[5]{3^5}\cdot\sqrt[5]{3^2} = 3\sqrt[5]{9}$

43. $\sqrt[5]{-64} = \sqrt[5]{-2^6} = \sqrt[5]{-2^5\cdot 2} = \sqrt[5]{-2^5}\cdot\sqrt[5]{2} = -2\sqrt[5]{2}$

44. $\sqrt[3]{-81} = \sqrt[3]{-3^4} = \sqrt[3]{-3^3\cdot 3} = \sqrt[3]{-3^3}\cdot\sqrt[3]{3} = -3\sqrt[3]{3}$

45. $\sqrt{8n^3} = \sqrt{(2n^2\cdot 2n)} = \sqrt{(2n)^2}\cdot\sqrt{2n} = 2n\sqrt{2n}$

46. $\sqrt{32a^2} = \sqrt{(4a)^2\cdot 2} = \sqrt{(4a)^2}\cdot\sqrt{2} = 4a\sqrt{2}$

47. $\sqrt{12a^2b^5} = \sqrt{(2ab^2)^2\cdot 3b} = \sqrt{(2ab^2)^2}\cdot\sqrt{3b} = 2ab^2\sqrt{3b}$

48. $\sqrt{20a^3b^2} = \sqrt{(2ab)^2\cdot 5a} = \sqrt{(2ab)^2}\cdot\sqrt{5a} = 2ab\sqrt{5a}$

49. $\sqrt[3]{-125x^4y^5} = \sqrt[3]{(-5xy)^3\cdot xy^2} = \sqrt[3]{(-5xy)^3}\cdot\sqrt[3]{xy^2} = -5xy\sqrt[3]{xy^2}$

50. $\sqrt[3]{-81a^5b^2} = \sqrt[3]{(-3a)^3\cdot 3a^2b^2} = \sqrt[3]{(-3a)^3}\cdot\sqrt[3]{3a^2b^2} = -3a\sqrt[3]{3a^2b^2}$

51. $\sqrt[3]{5t}\cdot\sqrt[3]{125t} = \sqrt[3]{625t^2} = \sqrt[3]{5^4t^2} = \sqrt[3]{5^3\cdot 5t^2} = \sqrt[3]{5^3}\cdot\sqrt[3]{5t^2} = 5\sqrt[3]{5t^2}$

52. $\sqrt[4]{4bc^3}\cdot\sqrt[4]{64ab^3c^2} = \sqrt[4]{256ab^4c^5} = \sqrt[4]{4^4ab^4c^5} = \sqrt[4]{(4bc)^4\cdot ac} = \sqrt[4]{(4bc)^4}\cdot\sqrt[4]{ac} = 4bc\sqrt[4]{ac}$

53. $\sqrt[4]{\dfrac{9t^5}{r^8}}\cdot\sqrt[4]{\dfrac{9r}{5t}} = \sqrt[4]{\dfrac{81rt^5}{5r^8t}} = \sqrt[4]{\dfrac{81t^4}{5r^7}} = \dfrac{\sqrt[4]{(3t)^4}}{\sqrt[4]{r^4\cdot 5r^3}} = \dfrac{3t}{r\sqrt[4]{5r^3}}$

54. $\sqrt[5]{\dfrac{4t^6}{r}}\cdot\sqrt[5]{\dfrac{8t}{r^6}} = \sqrt[5]{\dfrac{32t^7}{r^7}} = \dfrac{\sqrt[5]{(2t)^5\cdot t^2}}{\sqrt[5]{r^5\cdot r^2}} = \dfrac{2t\sqrt[5]{t^2}}{r\sqrt[5]{r^2}} = \dfrac{2t}{r}\sqrt[5]{\dfrac{t^2}{r^2}}$

55. $\sqrt{3}\cdot\sqrt[3]{3} = 3^{1/2}\cdot 3^{1/3} = 3^{1/2+1/3} = 3^{5/6} = \sqrt[6]{3^5}$

56. $\sqrt{5}\cdot\sqrt[3]{5} = 5^{1/2}\cdot 5^{1/3} = 5^{1/2+1/3} = 5^{5/6} = \sqrt[6]{5^5}$

57. $\sqrt[4]{8}\cdot\sqrt[3]{4} = \sqrt[4]{2^3}\cdot\sqrt[3]{2^2} = 2^{3/4}\cdot 2^{2/3} = 2^{3/4+2/3} = 2^{17/12} = 2^{12/12+5/12} = 2\cdot 2^{5/12} = 2\sqrt[12]{2^5}$

58. $\sqrt[5]{16}\cdot\sqrt{2} = \sqrt[5]{2^4}\cdot\sqrt{2} = 2^{4/5}\cdot 2^{1/2} = 2^{4/5+1/2} = 2^{13/10} = 2^{10/10}\cdot 2^{3/10} = 2\sqrt[10]{2^3}$

59. $\sqrt[4]{x^3}\cdot\sqrt[3]{x} = x^{3/4}\cdot x^{1/3} = x^{3/4+1/3} = x^{13/12} = x^{12/12}\cdot x^{1/12} = x\sqrt[12]{x}$

60. $\sqrt[4]{x^3}\cdot\sqrt{x} = x^{3/4}\cdot x^{1/2} = x^{3/4+1/2} = x^{5/4} = x^{4/4}\cdot x^{1/4} = x\cdot x^{1/4} = x\sqrt[4]{x}$

61. $\sqrt[4]{rt}\cdot\sqrt[3]{r^2t} = (rt)^{1/4}\cdot(r^2t)^{1/3} = r^{1/4}t^{1/4}\cdot r^{2/3}t^{1/3} = r^{1/4+2/3}t^{1/4+1/3} = r^{11/12}t^{7/12} = \sqrt[12]{r^{11}t^7}$

62. $\sqrt[3]{a^3b^2}\cdot\sqrt{a^2b} = (a^3b^2)^{1/3}\cdot(a^2b)^{1/2} = ab^{2/3}\cdot ab^{1/2} = a^{1+1}b^{2/3+1/2} = a^2b^{7/6} = a^2b^{6/6}\cdot b^{1/6} = a^2b\sqrt[6]{b}$

63. $2\sqrt{3} + 7\sqrt{3} = 9\sqrt{3}$

64. $8\sqrt{7} + 2\sqrt{7} = 10\sqrt{7}$

65. $\sqrt{x} + \sqrt{x} - \sqrt{y} = 2\sqrt{x} - \sqrt{y}$

66. $\sqrt{xy^2} - \sqrt{x} = \sqrt{x}\cdot\sqrt{y^2} - \sqrt{x} = y\sqrt{x} - \sqrt{x} = (y-1)\sqrt{x}$

67. $2\sqrt[3]{6} - 7\sqrt[3]{6} = -5\sqrt[3]{6}$

68. $18\sqrt[3]{3} + 3\sqrt[3]{3} = 21\sqrt[3]{3}$

69. $3\sqrt{28} + 3\sqrt{7} = 3\sqrt{4\cdot 7} + 3\sqrt{7} = 3\cdot 2\sqrt{7} + 3\sqrt{7} = 9\sqrt{7}$

70. $9\sqrt{18} - 2\sqrt{8} = 9\sqrt{9\cdot 2} - 2\sqrt{4\cdot 2} = 9\cdot 3\sqrt{2} - 2\cdot 2\sqrt{2} = 23\sqrt{2}$

71. $\sqrt{44} - 4\sqrt{11} = \sqrt{4\cdot 11} - 4\sqrt{11} = 2\sqrt{11} - 4\sqrt{11} = -2\sqrt{11}$

72. $\sqrt[4]{5} + 2\sqrt[4]{5} = 3\sqrt[4]{5}$

73. $2\sqrt[3]{16} + \sqrt[3]{2} - \sqrt{2} = 2\sqrt[3]{8\cdot 2} + \sqrt[3]{2} - \sqrt{2} = 2\cdot 2\sqrt[3]{2} + \sqrt[3]{2} - \sqrt{2} = 5\sqrt[3]{2} - \sqrt{2}$

74. $5\sqrt[3]{x} - 3\sqrt[3]{x} = 2\sqrt[3]{x}$

75. $\sqrt[3]{xy} - 2\sqrt[3]{xy} = -\sqrt[3]{xy}$

76. $3\sqrt{x^3} - \sqrt{x} = 3\sqrt{x^2\cdot x} - \sqrt{x} = 3\sqrt{x^2}\cdot\sqrt{x} - \sqrt{x} = 3x\sqrt{x} - \sqrt{x} = (3x-1)\sqrt{x}$

77. $\sqrt{4x+8} + \sqrt{x+2} = \sqrt{4(x+2)} + \sqrt{x+2} = 2\sqrt{x+2} + \sqrt{x+2} = 3\sqrt{x+2}$

78. $\sqrt{2a+1} + \sqrt{8a+4} = \sqrt{2a+1} + \sqrt{4(2a+1)} = \sqrt{2a+1} + 2\sqrt{2a+1} = 3\sqrt{2a+1}$

79. $\dfrac{15\sqrt{8}}{4} - \dfrac{2\sqrt{2}}{5} = \dfrac{15\cdot 2\sqrt{2}}{4}\cdot\dfrac{5}{5} - \dfrac{2\sqrt{2}}{5}\cdot\dfrac{4}{4} = \dfrac{150\sqrt{2}}{20} - \dfrac{8\sqrt{2}}{20} = \dfrac{150\sqrt{2} - 8\sqrt{2}}{20} = \dfrac{142\sqrt{2}}{20} = \dfrac{71\sqrt{2}}{10}$

80. $\dfrac{23\sqrt{11}}{2} - \dfrac{\sqrt{44}}{8} = \dfrac{23\sqrt{11}}{2}\cdot\dfrac{4}{4} - \dfrac{2\sqrt{11}}{8} = \dfrac{92\sqrt{11}}{8} - \dfrac{2\sqrt{11}}{8} = \dfrac{92\sqrt{11} - 2\sqrt{11}}{8} = \dfrac{90\sqrt{11}}{8} = \dfrac{45\sqrt{11}}{4}$

81. $2\sqrt[4]{64} - \sqrt[4]{324} + \sqrt[4]{4} = 2\sqrt[4]{16 \cdot 4} - \sqrt[4]{81 \cdot 4} + \sqrt[4]{4} = 4\sqrt[4]{4} - 3\sqrt[4]{4} + \sqrt[4]{4} = 2\sqrt[4]{4} = 2\sqrt{2}$

82. $20\sqrt[3]{b^4} - 4\sqrt[3]{b} = 20\sqrt[3]{b^3 \cdot b} - 4\sqrt[3]{b} = 20b\sqrt[3]{b} - 4\sqrt[3]{b} = 4\sqrt[3]{b}(5b - 1)$

83. $2\sqrt{3z} + 3\sqrt{12z} + 3\sqrt{48z} = 2\sqrt{3z} + 3\sqrt{4 \cdot 3z} + 3\sqrt{16 \cdot 3z} = 2\sqrt{3z} + 6\sqrt{3z} + 12\sqrt{3z} = 20\sqrt{3z}$

84. $\sqrt{64x^3} - \sqrt{x} + 3\sqrt{x} = \sqrt{(8x)^2 \cdot x} - \sqrt{x} + 3\sqrt{x} = 8x\sqrt{x} - \sqrt{x} + 3\sqrt{x} = 2\sqrt{x}(4x + 1)$

85. $\sqrt[4]{81a^5b^5} - \sqrt[4]{ab} = \sqrt[4]{(3ab)^4 \cdot ab} - \sqrt[4]{ab} = 3ab\sqrt[4]{ab} - \sqrt[4]{ab} = (3ab - 1)\sqrt[4]{ab}$

86. $\sqrt[4]{xy^5} + \sqrt[4]{x^5y} = \sqrt[4]{y^4 \cdot xy} + \sqrt[4]{x^4 \cdot xy} = y\sqrt[4]{xy} + x\sqrt[4]{xy} = (y + x)\sqrt[4]{xy}$

87. $5\sqrt[3]{\frac{n^4}{125}} - 2\sqrt[3]{n} = 5\sqrt[3]{\frac{n^3}{125} \cdot n} - 2\sqrt[3]{n} = 5 \cdot \frac{n}{5}\sqrt[3]{n} - 2\sqrt[3]{n} = n\sqrt[3]{n} - 2\sqrt[3]{n} = (n - 2)\sqrt[3]{n}$

88. $\sqrt[3]{\frac{8x}{27}} - \frac{2\sqrt[3]{x}}{3} = \frac{\sqrt[3]{8x}}{\sqrt[3]{27}} - \frac{2\sqrt[3]{x}}{3} = \frac{2\sqrt[3]{x}}{3} - \frac{2\sqrt[3]{x}}{3} = 0$

89. $(3 + \sqrt{7})(3 - \sqrt{7}) = 3^2 - (\sqrt{7})^2 = 9 - 7 = 2$

90. $(5 - \sqrt{5})(5 + \sqrt{5}) = 5^2 - (\sqrt{5})^2 = 25 - 5 = 20$

91. $(\sqrt{x} + 8)(\sqrt{x} - 8) = (\sqrt{x})^2 - 8^2 = x - 64$

92. $(\sqrt{ab} - 3)(\sqrt{ab} + 3) = (\sqrt{ab})^2 - 3^2 = ab - 9$

93. $(\sqrt{ab} - \sqrt{c})(\sqrt{ab} + \sqrt{c}) = (\sqrt{ab})^2 - (\sqrt{c})^2 = ab - c$

94. $(\sqrt{2x} + \sqrt{3y})(\sqrt{2x} - \sqrt{3y}) = (\sqrt{2x})^2 - (\sqrt{3y})^2 = 2x - 3y$

95. $(\sqrt{x} - 7)(\sqrt{x} + 8) = (\sqrt{x})^2 + 8\sqrt{x} - 7\sqrt{x} - 56 = x + \sqrt{x} - 56$

96. $(\sqrt{ab} - 1)(\sqrt{ab} - 2) = (\sqrt{ab})^2 - 2\sqrt{ab} - \sqrt{ab} + 2 = ab - 3\sqrt{ab} + 2$

97. $\frac{4}{\sqrt{3}} = \frac{4}{\sqrt{3}} \cdot \frac{\sqrt{3}}{\sqrt{3}} = \frac{4\sqrt{3}}{3}$

98. $\frac{8}{\sqrt{2}} = \frac{8}{\sqrt{2}} \cdot \frac{\sqrt{2}}{\sqrt{2}} = \frac{8\sqrt{2}}{2} = 4\sqrt{2}$

99. $\frac{5}{3\sqrt{5}} = \frac{5}{3\sqrt{5}} \cdot \frac{\sqrt{5}}{\sqrt{5}} = \frac{5\sqrt{5}}{3 \cdot 5} = \frac{5\sqrt{5}}{15} = \frac{\sqrt{5}}{3}$

100. $\frac{6}{11\sqrt{3}} = \frac{6}{11\sqrt{3}} \cdot \frac{\sqrt{3}}{\sqrt{3}} = \frac{6\sqrt{3}}{11 \cdot 3} = \frac{2\sqrt{3}}{11}$

101. $\sqrt{\frac{b}{12}} = \frac{\sqrt{b}}{\sqrt{12}} = \frac{\sqrt{b}}{\sqrt{12}} \cdot \frac{\sqrt{12}}{\sqrt{12}} = \frac{\sqrt{12b}}{12} = \frac{\sqrt{4 \cdot 3b}}{12} = \frac{2\sqrt{3b}}{12} = \frac{\sqrt{3b}}{6}$

102. $\sqrt{\frac{5b}{72}} = \frac{\sqrt{5b}}{6\sqrt{2}} = \frac{\sqrt{5b}}{6\sqrt{2}} \cdot \frac{\sqrt{2}}{\sqrt{2}} = \frac{\sqrt{10b}}{6 \cdot 2} = \frac{\sqrt{10b}}{12}$

103. $\frac{1}{3 - \sqrt{2}} = \frac{1}{3 - \sqrt{2}} \cdot \frac{3 + \sqrt{2}}{3 + \sqrt{2}} = \frac{3 + \sqrt{2}}{9 - 2} = \frac{3 + \sqrt{2}}{7}$

104. $\frac{1}{\sqrt{3} - 2} = \frac{1}{\sqrt{3} - 2} \cdot \frac{\sqrt{3} + 2}{\sqrt{3} + 2} = \frac{\sqrt{3} + 2}{3 - 4} = \frac{\sqrt{3} + 2}{-1} = -\sqrt{3} - 2$

105. $\dfrac{\sqrt{2}}{\sqrt{5}+2} = \dfrac{\sqrt{2}}{\sqrt{5}+2} \cdot \dfrac{\sqrt{5}-2}{\sqrt{5}-2} = \dfrac{\sqrt{10}-2\sqrt{2}}{5-4} = \dfrac{\sqrt{10}-2\sqrt{2}}{1} = \sqrt{10}-2\sqrt{2}$

106. $\dfrac{\sqrt{3}-1}{\sqrt{3}+1} = \dfrac{\sqrt{3}-1}{\sqrt{3}+1} \cdot \dfrac{\sqrt{3}-1}{\sqrt{3}-1} = \dfrac{3-2\sqrt{3}+1}{3-1} = \dfrac{4-2\sqrt{3}}{2} = 2-\sqrt{3}$

107. $\dfrac{1}{\sqrt{7}-\sqrt{6}} = \dfrac{1}{\sqrt{7}-\sqrt{6}} \cdot \dfrac{\sqrt{7}+\sqrt{6}}{\sqrt{7}+\sqrt{6}} = \dfrac{\sqrt{7}+\sqrt{6}}{7-6} = \dfrac{\sqrt{7}+\sqrt{6}}{1} = \sqrt{7}+\sqrt{6}$

108. $\dfrac{1}{\sqrt{8}-\sqrt{7}} = \dfrac{1}{\sqrt{8}-\sqrt{7}} \cdot \dfrac{\sqrt{8}+\sqrt{7}}{\sqrt{8}+\sqrt{7}} = \dfrac{\sqrt{8}+\sqrt{7}}{8-7} = \dfrac{\sqrt{8}+\sqrt{7}}{1} = \sqrt{8}+\sqrt{7}$

109. $\dfrac{\sqrt{z}}{\sqrt{z}-3} = \dfrac{\sqrt{z}}{\sqrt{z}-3} \cdot \dfrac{\sqrt{z}+3}{\sqrt{z}+3} = \dfrac{z+3\sqrt{z}}{z-9}$

110. $\dfrac{2\sqrt{z}}{2-\sqrt{z}} = \dfrac{2\sqrt{z}}{2-\sqrt{z}} \cdot \dfrac{2+\sqrt{z}}{2+\sqrt{z}} = \dfrac{4\sqrt{z}+2z}{4-z}$

111. $\dfrac{\sqrt{a}+\sqrt{b}}{\sqrt{a}-\sqrt{b}} = \dfrac{\sqrt{a}+\sqrt{b}}{\sqrt{a}-\sqrt{b}} \cdot \dfrac{\sqrt{a}+\sqrt{b}}{\sqrt{a}+\sqrt{b}} = \dfrac{a+2\sqrt{ab}+b}{a-b}$

112. $\dfrac{1}{\sqrt{a+1}+\sqrt{a}} = \dfrac{1}{\sqrt{a+1}+\sqrt{a}} \cdot \dfrac{\sqrt{a+1}-\sqrt{a}}{\sqrt{a+1}-\sqrt{a}} = \dfrac{\sqrt{a+1}-\sqrt{a}}{a+1-a} = \dfrac{\sqrt{a+1}-\sqrt{a}}{1} =$
$\sqrt{a+1}-\sqrt{a}$

# Appendix C: Partial Fractions

1. Multiply $\dfrac{5}{3x(2x+1)} = \dfrac{A}{3x} + \dfrac{B}{2x+1}$ by $3x(2x+1) \Rightarrow 5 = A(2x+1) + B(3x)$.

   Let $x = 0 \Rightarrow 5 = A(1) \Rightarrow A = 5$. Let $x = -\dfrac{1}{2} \Rightarrow 5 = B\left(-\dfrac{3}{2}\right) \Rightarrow B = -\dfrac{10}{3}$.

   The expression can be written $\dfrac{5}{3x} + \dfrac{-10}{3(2x+1)}$.

2. Multiply $\dfrac{3x-1}{x(x+1)} = \dfrac{A}{x} + \dfrac{B}{x+1}$ by $x(x+1) \Rightarrow 3x - 1 = A(x+1) + B(x)$.

   Let $x = 0 \Rightarrow -1 = A(1) \Rightarrow A = -1$. Let $x = -1 \Rightarrow -4 = B(-1) \Rightarrow B = 4$.

   The expression can be written $\dfrac{-1}{x} + \dfrac{4}{x+1}$.

3. Multiply $\dfrac{4x+2}{(x+2)(2x-1)} = \dfrac{A}{x+2} + \dfrac{B}{2x-1}$ by $(x+2)(2x-1) \Rightarrow 4x + 2 = A(2x-1) + B(x+2)$.

   Let $x = -2 \Rightarrow -6 = A(-5) \Rightarrow A = \dfrac{6}{5}$. Let $x = \dfrac{1}{2} \Rightarrow 4 = B\left(\dfrac{5}{2}\right) \Rightarrow B = \dfrac{8}{5}$.

   The expression can be written $\dfrac{6}{5(x+2)} + \dfrac{8}{5(2x-1)}$.

4. Multiply $\dfrac{x+2}{(x+1)(x-1)} = \dfrac{A}{x+1} + \dfrac{B}{x-1}$ by $(x+1)(x-1) \Rightarrow x + 2 = A(x-1) + B(x+1)$.

   Let $x = -1 \Rightarrow 1 = A(-2) \Rightarrow A = -\dfrac{1}{2}$. Let $x = 1 \Rightarrow 3 = B(2) \Rightarrow B = \dfrac{3}{2}$.

   The expression can be written $\dfrac{-1}{2(x+1)} + \dfrac{3}{2(x-1)}$.

5. Factoring $\dfrac{x}{x^2 + 4x - 5}$ results in $\dfrac{x}{(x+5)(x-1)}$.

   Multiply $\dfrac{x}{(x+5)(x-1)} = \dfrac{A}{x+5} + \dfrac{B}{x-1}$ by $(x+5)(x-1) \Rightarrow x = A(x-1) + B(x+5)$.

   Let $x = -5 \Rightarrow -5 = A(-6) \Rightarrow A = \dfrac{5}{6}$. Let $x = 1 \Rightarrow 1 = B(6) \Rightarrow B = \dfrac{1}{6}$.

   The expression can be written $\dfrac{5}{6(x+5)} + \dfrac{1}{6(x-1)}$.

6. Multiply $\dfrac{5x-3}{(x+1)(x-3)} = \dfrac{A}{x+1} + \dfrac{B}{x-3}$ by $(x+1)(x-3) \Rightarrow 5x - 3 = A(x-3) + B(x+1)$.

   Let $x = -1 \Rightarrow -8 = A(-4) \Rightarrow A = 2$. Let $x = 3 \Rightarrow 12 = B(4) \Rightarrow B = 3$.

   The expression can be written $\dfrac{2}{x+1} + \dfrac{3}{x-3}$.

7. Multiply $\dfrac{2x}{(x+1)(x+2)^2} = \dfrac{A}{x+1} + \dfrac{B}{x+2} + \dfrac{C}{(x+2)^2}$ by $(x+1)(x+2)^2 \Rightarrow$

   $2x = A(x+2)^2 + B(x+1)(x+2) + C(x+1)$. Let $x = -1 \Rightarrow -2 = A(1) \Rightarrow A = -2$.

   Let $x = -2 \Rightarrow -4 = C(-1) \Rightarrow C = 4$. Let $x = 0$ with $A = -2$ and $C = 4 \Rightarrow$

   $0 = -2(4) + B(2) + 4(1) \Rightarrow 4 = 2B \Rightarrow B = 2$. The expression can be written $\dfrac{-2}{x+1} + \dfrac{2}{x+2} + \dfrac{4}{(x+2)^2}$.

8. Multiply $\dfrac{2}{x^2(x+3)} = \dfrac{A}{x} + \dfrac{B}{x^2} + \dfrac{C}{x+3}$ by $x^2(x+3) \Rightarrow 2 = Ax(x+3) + B(x+3) + Cx^2$.

   Let $x = 0 \Rightarrow 2 = B(3) \Rightarrow B = \dfrac{2}{3}$. Let $x = -3 \Rightarrow 2 = C(9) \Rightarrow C = \dfrac{2}{9}$.

   Let $x = 1$ with $B = \dfrac{2}{3}$ and $C = \dfrac{2}{9} \Rightarrow 2 = A(4) + \dfrac{2}{3}(4) + \dfrac{2}{9}(1) \Rightarrow 18 = 36A + 24 + 2 \Rightarrow$

   $-8 = 36A \Rightarrow A = -\dfrac{2}{9}$. The expression can be written $\dfrac{-2}{9x} + \dfrac{2}{3x^2} + \dfrac{2}{9(x+3)}$.

9. Multiply $\dfrac{4}{x(1-x)} = \dfrac{A}{x} + \dfrac{B}{1-x}$ by $x(1-x) \Rightarrow 4 = A(1-x) + B(x)$.

   Let $x = 0 \Rightarrow 4 = A(1) \Rightarrow A = 4$. Let $x = 1 \Rightarrow 4 = B(1) \Rightarrow B = 4$.

   The expression can be written $\dfrac{4}{x} + \dfrac{4}{1-x}$.

10. $\dfrac{4x^2 - 4x^3}{x^2(1-x)} = \dfrac{4x^2(1-x)}{x^2(1-x)} = 4$

11. Multiply $\dfrac{4x^2 - x - 15}{x(x+1)(x-1)} = \dfrac{A}{x} + \dfrac{B}{x+1} + \dfrac{C}{x-1}$ by $x(x+1)(x-1) \Rightarrow$

    $4x^2 - x - 15 = A(x-1)(x+1) + B(x)(x-1) + C(x)(x+1)$. Let $x = 0 \Rightarrow -15 = A(-1) \Rightarrow$

    $A = 15$. Let $x = 1 \Rightarrow -12 = C(1)(2) \Rightarrow C = -6$. Let $x = -1 \Rightarrow -10 = B(-1)(-2) \Rightarrow B = -5$.

    The expression can be written $\dfrac{15}{x} + \dfrac{-5}{x+1} + \dfrac{-6}{x-1}$.

12. Multiply $\dfrac{2x+1}{(x+2)^3} = \dfrac{A}{x+2} + \dfrac{B}{(x+2)^2} + \dfrac{C}{(x+2)^3}$ by $(x+2)^3 \Rightarrow 2x + 1 = A(x+2)^2 + B(x+2) + C$.

    Let $x = -2 \Rightarrow -3 = C$. Multiplying out with $C = -3$ gives $2x + 1 = Ax^2 + 4Ax + 4A + Bx + 2B - 3$.

    Equate coefficients. For $x^2$: $0 = Ax^2 \Rightarrow A = 0$. For $x$: $2x = (4A + B)x \Rightarrow B = 2$.

    The expression can be written $\dfrac{2}{(x+2)^2} + \dfrac{-3}{(x+2)^3}$.

13. By long division $\dfrac{x^2}{x^2 + 2x + 1} = 1 + \dfrac{-2x - 1}{(x+1)^2}$.

    Multiply $\dfrac{-2x-1}{(x+1)^2} = \dfrac{A}{x+1} + \dfrac{B}{(x+1)^2}$ by $(x+1)^2 \Rightarrow -2x - 1 = A(x+1) + B$.

    Let $x = -1 \Rightarrow 1 = B$. Let $x = 0$ with $B = 1 \Rightarrow -1 = A + 1 \Rightarrow A = -2$.

    The expression can be written $1 + \dfrac{-2}{x+1} + \dfrac{1}{(x+1)^2}$.

14. Factoring $\dfrac{3}{x^2 + 4x + 3}$ results in $\dfrac{3}{(x+3)(x+1)}$.

    Multiply $\dfrac{3}{(x+3)(x+1)} = \dfrac{A}{x+3} + \dfrac{B}{x+1}$ by $(x+3)(x+1) \Rightarrow 3 = A(x+1) + B(x+3)$.

    Let $x = -1 \Rightarrow 3 = B(2) \Rightarrow B = \dfrac{3}{2}$. Let $x = -3 \Rightarrow 3 = A(-2) \Rightarrow A = -\dfrac{3}{2}$.

    The expression can be written $\dfrac{-3}{2(x+3)} + \dfrac{3}{2(x+1)}$.

15. By long division $\dfrac{2x^5 + 3x^4 - 3x^3 - 2x^2 + x}{2x^2 + 5x + 2} = x^3 - x^2 + \dfrac{x}{2x^2 + 5x + 2} = x^3 - x^2 + \dfrac{x}{(2x+1)(x+2)}$.

Multiply $\dfrac{x}{(2x+1)(x+2)} = \dfrac{A}{2x+1} + \dfrac{B}{x+2}$ by $(2x+1)(x+2) \Rightarrow x = A(x+2) + B(2x+1)$.

Let $x = -\dfrac{1}{2} \Rightarrow -\dfrac{1}{2} = A\left(\dfrac{3}{2}\right) \Rightarrow A = -\dfrac{1}{3}$. Let $x = -2 \Rightarrow -2 = B(-3) \Rightarrow B = \dfrac{2}{3}$.

The expression can be written $x^3 - x^2 + \dfrac{-1}{3(2x+1)} + \dfrac{2}{3(x+2)}$.

16. By long division $\dfrac{6x^5 + 7x^4 - x^2 + 2x}{3x^2 + 2x - 1} = 2x^3 + x^2 + \dfrac{2x}{3x^2 + 2x - 1} = 2x^3 + x^2 + \dfrac{2x}{(3x-1)(x+1)}$.

Multiply $\dfrac{2x}{(3x-1)(x+1)} = \dfrac{A}{3x-1} + \dfrac{B}{x+1}$ by $(3x-1)(x+1) \Rightarrow 2x = A(x+1) + B(3x-1)$.

Let $x = \dfrac{1}{3} \Rightarrow \dfrac{2}{3} = A\left(\dfrac{4}{3}\right) \Rightarrow A = \dfrac{1}{2}$. Let $x = -1 \Rightarrow -2 = B(-4) \Rightarrow B = \dfrac{1}{2}$.

The expression can be written $2x^3 + x^2 + \dfrac{1}{2(3x-1)} + \dfrac{1}{2(x+1)}$.

17. By long division $\dfrac{x^3 + 4}{9x^3 - 4x} = \dfrac{1}{9} + \dfrac{\frac{4}{9}x + 4}{9x^3 - 4x} = \dfrac{1}{9} + \dfrac{\frac{4}{9}x + 4}{x(3x+2)(3x-2)}$.

Multiply $\dfrac{\frac{4}{9}x + 4}{x(3x+2)(3x-2)} = \dfrac{A}{x} + \dfrac{B}{3x+2} + \dfrac{C}{3x-2}$ by $x(3x+2)(3x-2) \Rightarrow$

$\dfrac{4}{9}x + 4 = A(3x+2)(3x-2) + B(x)(3x-2) + C(x)(3x+2)$. Let $x = 0 \Rightarrow 4 = A(-4) \Rightarrow A = -1$.

Let $x = -\dfrac{2}{3} \Rightarrow -\dfrac{8}{27} + 4 = B\left(-\dfrac{2}{3}\right)(-4) \Rightarrow \dfrac{100}{27} = \dfrac{8}{3}B \Rightarrow B = \dfrac{25}{18}$.

Let $x = \dfrac{2}{3} \Rightarrow \dfrac{8}{27} + 4 = C\left(\dfrac{2}{3}\right)(4) \Rightarrow \dfrac{116}{27} = \dfrac{8}{3}C \Rightarrow C = \dfrac{29}{18}$.

The expression can be written $\dfrac{1}{9} + \dfrac{-1}{x} + \dfrac{25}{18(3x+2)} + \dfrac{29}{18(3x-2)}$.

18. By long division $\dfrac{x^3 + 2}{x^3 - 3x^2 + 2x} = 1 + \dfrac{3x^2 - 2x + 2}{x^3 - 3x^2 + 2x} = 1 + \dfrac{3x^2 - 2x + 2}{x(x-2)(x-1)}$.

Multiply $\dfrac{3x^2 - 2x + 2}{x(x-2)(x-1)} = \dfrac{A}{x} + \dfrac{B}{x-2} + \dfrac{C}{x-1}$ by $x(x-2)(x-1) \Rightarrow$

$3x^2 - 2x + 2 = A(x-2)(x-1) + B(x)(x-1) + C(x)(x-2) \Rightarrow$

$3x^2 - 2x + 2 = Ax^2 - 3Ax + 2A + Bx^2 - Bx + Cx^2 - 2Cx$. Equate coefficients.

For $x^2$: $3 = A + B + C$. For $x$: $-2 = -3A - B - 2C$. For the constants: $2 = 2A \Rightarrow A = 1$.

Simultaneously solve the first two equations with $A = 1$.

$$\begin{array}{r} B + C = 2 \\ -B - 2C = 1 \\ \hline -C = 3 \end{array} \Rightarrow C = -3, \text{ then } B + C = 2 \Rightarrow B = 5$$

The expression can be written $1 + \dfrac{1}{x} + \dfrac{5}{x-2} + \dfrac{-3}{x-1}$.

19. Multiply $\dfrac{-3}{x^2(x^2+5)} = \dfrac{A}{x} + \dfrac{B}{x^2} + \dfrac{Cx+D}{x^2+5}$ by $x^2(x^2+5) \Rightarrow$

$-3 = A(x)(x^2+5) + B(x^2+5) + (Cx+D)(x^2) \Rightarrow -3 = Ax^3 + 5Ax + Bx^2 + 5B + Cx^3 + Dx^2.$

Equate coefficients. For $x^3$: $0 = A + C$.

For $x^2$: $0 = B + D$. For $x$: $0 = 5A \Rightarrow A = 0$. For the constants: $-3 = 5B \Rightarrow B = -\dfrac{3}{5}$.

Substitute $A = 0$ in the first equation. $C = 0$. Substitute $B = -\dfrac{3}{5}$ in the second equation. $D = \dfrac{3}{5}$.

The expression can be written $\dfrac{-3}{5x^2} + \dfrac{3}{5(x^2+5)}$.

20. Multiply $\dfrac{2x+1}{(x+1)(x^2+2)} = \dfrac{A}{x+1} + \dfrac{Bx+C}{x^2+2}$ by $(x+1)(x^2+2) \Rightarrow$

$2x+1 = A(x^2+2) + (Bx+C)(x+1) \Rightarrow 2x+1 = Ax^2 + 2A + Bx^2 + Bx + Cx + C.$

Let $x = -1 \Rightarrow -1 = 3A \Rightarrow A = -\dfrac{1}{3}$. Equate coefficients.

For $x^2$: $0 = A + B \Rightarrow 0 = -\dfrac{1}{3} + B \Rightarrow B = \dfrac{1}{3}$. For $x$: $2 = B + C \Rightarrow 2 = \dfrac{1}{3} + C \Rightarrow C = \dfrac{5}{3}$.

The expression can be written $\dfrac{-1}{3(x+1)} + \dfrac{x+5}{3(x^2+2)}$.

21. Multiply $\dfrac{3x-2}{(x+4)(3x^2+1)} = \dfrac{A}{x+4} + \dfrac{Bx+C}{3x^2+1}$ by $(x+4)(3x^2+1) \Rightarrow$

$3x-2 = A(3x^2+1) + (Bx+C)(x+4) \Rightarrow 3x-2 = 3Ax^2 + A + Bx^2 + 4Bx + Cx + 4C.$

Let $x = -4 \Rightarrow -14 = 49A \Rightarrow A = -\dfrac{2}{7}$. Equate coefficients.

For $x^2$: $0 = 3A + B \Rightarrow 0 = -\dfrac{6}{7} + B \Rightarrow B = \dfrac{6}{7}$. For $x$: $3 = 4B + C \Rightarrow 3 = \dfrac{24}{7} + C \Rightarrow C = -\dfrac{3}{7}$.

The expression can be written $\dfrac{-2}{7(x+4)} + \dfrac{6x-3}{7(3x^2+1)}$.

22. Multiply $\dfrac{3}{x(x+1)(x^2+1)} = \dfrac{A}{x} + \dfrac{B}{x+1} + \dfrac{Cx+D}{x^2+1}$ by $x(x+1)(x^2+1) \Rightarrow$

$3 = A(x+1)(x^2+1) + B(x)(x^2+1) + (Cx+D)(x)(x+1).$

Let $x = 0 \Rightarrow 3 = A(1) \Rightarrow A = 3$. Let $x = -1 \Rightarrow 3 = B(-1)(2) \Rightarrow B = -\dfrac{3}{2}$.

Multiply the right side out. $3 = A(x^3 + x^2 + x + 1) + Bx^3 + Bx + Cx^3 + Cx^2 + Dx^2 + Dx \Rightarrow$

$3 = Ax^3 + Ax^2 + Ax + A + Bx^3 + Bx + Cx^3 + Cx^2 + Dx^2 + Dx.$

Equate coefficients. For $x^3$: $0 = A + B + C \Rightarrow 0 = 3 - \dfrac{3}{2} + C \Rightarrow C = -\dfrac{3}{2}$.

For $x^2$: $0 = A + C + D \Rightarrow 0 = 3 - \dfrac{3}{2} + D \Rightarrow D = -\dfrac{3}{2}$.

The expression can be written $\dfrac{3}{x} + \dfrac{-3}{2(x+1)} + \dfrac{-3(x+1)}{2(x^2+1)}$.

23. Multiply $\dfrac{1}{x(2x+1)(3x^2+4)} = \dfrac{A}{x} + \dfrac{B}{2x+1} + \dfrac{Cx+D}{3x^2+4}$ by $x(2x+1)(3x^2+4) \Rightarrow$

$1 = A(2x+1)(3x^2+4) + B(x)(3x^2+4) + (Cx+D)(x)(2x+1)$.

Let $x = 0 \Rightarrow 1 = A(1)(4) \Rightarrow A = \dfrac{1}{4}$. Let $x = -\dfrac{1}{2} \Rightarrow 1 = B\left(-\dfrac{1}{2}\right)\left(\dfrac{19}{4}\right) \Rightarrow B = -\dfrac{8}{19}$.

Multiply the right side out. $1 = A(6x^3 + 3x^2 + 8x + 4) + 3Bx^3 + 4Bx + 2Cx^3 + Cx^2 + 2Dx^2 + Dx \Rightarrow$

$1 = 6Ax^3 + 3Ax^2 + 8Ax + 4A + 3Bx^3 + 4Bx + 2Cx^3 + Cx^2 + 2Dx^2 + Dx$. Equate coefficients.

For $x^3$: $0 = 6A + 3B + 2C \Rightarrow 0 = 6\left(\dfrac{1}{4}\right) + 3\left(-\dfrac{8}{19}\right) + 2C \Rightarrow 0 = \dfrac{9}{38} + 2C \Rightarrow C = -\dfrac{9}{76}$.

For $x^2$: $0 = 3A + C + 2D \Rightarrow 0 = \dfrac{3}{4} - \dfrac{9}{76} + 2D \Rightarrow 0 = \dfrac{48}{76} + 2D \Rightarrow D = -\dfrac{24}{76}$.

The expression can be written $\dfrac{1}{4x} + \dfrac{-8}{19(2x+1)} + \dfrac{-9x-24}{76(3x^2+4)}$.

24. Multiply $\dfrac{x^4+1}{x(x^2+1)^2} = \dfrac{A}{x} + \dfrac{Bx+C}{x^2+1} + \dfrac{Dx+E}{(x^2+1)^2}$ by $x(x^2+1)^2 \Rightarrow$

$x^4 + 1 = A(x^2+1)^2 + (Bx+C)(x)(x^2+1) + (Dx+E)(x)$.

Let $x = 0 \Rightarrow 1 = A(1) \Rightarrow A = 1$. Multiply the right side out.

$x^4 + 1 = A(x^4 + 2x^2 + 1) + Bx^4 + Cx^3 + Bx^2 + Cx + Dx^2 + Ex \Rightarrow$

$x^4 + 1 = Ax^4 + 2Ax^2 + A + Bx^4 + Cx^3 + Bx^2 + Cx + Dx^2 + Ex$.

Equate coefficients. For $x^4$: $1 = A + B \Rightarrow 1 = 1 + B \Rightarrow B = 0$. For $x^3$: $0 = C$.

For $x^2$: $0 = 2A + B + D \Rightarrow 0 = 2 + 0 + D \Rightarrow D = -2$. For $x$: $0 = C + E \Rightarrow 0 = 0 + E \Rightarrow$

$E = 0$. The expression can be written $\dfrac{1}{x} + \dfrac{-2x}{(x^2+1)^2}$.

25. Multiply $\dfrac{3x-1}{x(2x^2+1)^2} = \dfrac{A}{x} + \dfrac{Bx+C}{2x^2+1} + \dfrac{Dx+E}{(2x^2+1)^2}$ by $x(2x^2+1)^2 \Rightarrow$

$3x - 1 = A(2x^2+1)^2 + (Bx+C)(x)(2x^2+1) + (Dx+E)(x)$.

Let $x = 0 \Rightarrow -1 = A(1) \Rightarrow A = -1$. Multiply the right side out.

$3x - 1 = A(4x^4 + 4x^2 + 1) + 2Bx^4 + Bx^2 + Cx + 2Cx^3 + Dx^2 + Ex \Rightarrow$

$3x - 1 = 4Ax^4 + 4Ax^2 + A + 2Bx^4 + Bx^2 + Cx + 2Cx^3 + Dx^2 + Ex$.

Equate coefficients. For $x^4$: $0 = 4A + 2B \Rightarrow 0 = -4 + 2B \Rightarrow B = 2$. For $x^3$: $0 = 2C \Rightarrow C = 0$.

For $x^2$: $0 = 4A + B + D \Rightarrow 0 = -4 + 2 + D \Rightarrow D = 2$. For $x$: $3 = C + E \Rightarrow 3 = 0 + E \Rightarrow$

$E = 3$. The expression can be written $\dfrac{-1}{x} + \dfrac{2x}{2x^2+1} + \dfrac{2x+3}{(2x^2+1)^2}$.

26. Multiply $\dfrac{3x^4 + x^3 + 5x^2 - x + 4}{(x-1)(x^2+1)^2} = \dfrac{A}{x-1} + \dfrac{Bx+C}{x^2+1} + \dfrac{Dx+E}{(x^2+1)^2}$ by $(x-1)(x^2+1)^2 \Rightarrow$

$3x^4 + x^3 + 5x^2 - x + 4 = A(x^2+1)^2 + (Bx+C)(x-1)(x^2+1) + (Dx+E)(x-1).$

Let $x = 1 \Rightarrow 12 = A(4) \Rightarrow A = 3$. Multiply the right side out.

$3x^4 + x^3 + 5x^2 - x + 4 =$

$Ax^4 + 2Ax^2 + A + Bx^4 - Bx^3 + Bx^2 - Bx + Cx^3 - Cx^2 + Cx - C + Dx^2 - Dx + Ex - E.$

Equate coefficients.

For $x^4$: $3 = A + B \Rightarrow 3 = 3 + B \Rightarrow B = 0$. For $x^3$: $1 = -B + C \Rightarrow 1 = 0 + C \Rightarrow C = 1$.

For $x^2$: $5 = 2A + B - C + D \Rightarrow 5 = 6 + 0 - 1 + D \Rightarrow D = 0$.

For $x$: $-1 = -B + C - D + E \Rightarrow -1 = 0 + 1 - 0 + E \Rightarrow E = -2$.

The expression can be written $\dfrac{3}{x-1} + \dfrac{1}{x^2+1} + \dfrac{-2}{(x^2+1)^2}$.

27. Multiply $\dfrac{-x^4 - 8x^2 + 3x - 10}{(x+2)(x^2+4)^2} = \dfrac{A}{x+2} + \dfrac{Bx+C}{x^2+4} + \dfrac{Dx+E}{(x^2+4)^2}$ by $(x+2)(x^2+4)^2 \Rightarrow$

$-x^4 - 8x^2 + 3x - 10 = A(x^2+4)^2 + (Bx+C)(x+2)(x^2+4) + (Dx+E)(x+2).$

Let $x = -2 \Rightarrow -64 = A(64) \Rightarrow A = -1$. Multiply the right side out.

$-x^4 - 8x^2 + 3x - 10 = Ax^4 + 8Ax^2 + 16A + Bx^4 + 2Bx^3 + 4Bx^2 + 8Bx + Cx^3 + 2Cx^2 +$ .

$4Cx + 8C + Dx^2 + 2Dx + Ex + 2E.$

Equate coefficients.

For $x^4$: $-1 = A + B \Rightarrow -1 = -1 + B \Rightarrow B = 0$. For $x^3$: $0 = 2B + C \Rightarrow 0 = 0 + C \Rightarrow C = 0$.

For $x^2$: $-8 = 8A + 4B + 2C + D \Rightarrow -8 = -8 + 0 + 0 + D \Rightarrow D = 0$.

For $x$: $3 = 8B + 4C + 2D + E \Rightarrow 3 = 0 + 0 + 0 + E \Rightarrow E = 3$.

The expression can be written $\dfrac{-1}{x+2} + \dfrac{3}{(x^2+4)^2}$.

28. Factoring $\dfrac{x^2}{x^4-1}$ results in $\dfrac{x^2}{(x+1)(x-1)(x^2+1)}$.

Multiply $\dfrac{x^2}{(x+1)(x-1)(x^2+1)} = \dfrac{A}{x+1} + \dfrac{B}{x-1} + \dfrac{Cx+D}{x^2+1}$ by $(x+1)(x-1)(x^2+1) \Rightarrow$

$x^2 = A(x-1)(x^2+1) + B(x+1)(x^2+1) + (Cx+D)(x-1)(x+1)$

Let $x = -1 \Rightarrow 1 = A(-2)(2) \Rightarrow A = -\dfrac{1}{4}$. Let $x = 1 \Rightarrow 1 = B(2)(2) \Rightarrow B = \dfrac{1}{4}$. Multiply the right side out. $x^2 = Ax^3 - Ax^2 + Ax - A + Bx^3 + Bx^2 + Bx + B + Cx^3 - Cx + Dx^2 - D$

Equate coefficients. For $x^3$: $0 = A + B + C \Rightarrow 0 = -\dfrac{1}{4} + \dfrac{1}{4} + C \Rightarrow C = 0$.

For $x^2$: $1 = -A + B + D \Rightarrow 1 = \dfrac{1}{4} + \dfrac{1}{4} + D \Rightarrow D = \dfrac{1}{2}$.

The expression can be written $\dfrac{-1}{4(x+1)} + \dfrac{1}{4(x-1)} + \dfrac{1}{2(x^2+1)}$.

29. By long division $\frac{5x^5 + 10x^4 - 15x^3 + 4x^2 + 13x - 9}{x^3 + 2x^2 - 3x} = 5x^2 + \frac{4x^2 + 13x - 9}{x^3 + 2x^2 - 3x} = 5x^2 + \frac{4x^2 + 13x - 9}{x(x + 3)(x - 1)}$.

Multiply $\frac{4x^2 + 13x - 9}{x(x + 3)(x - 1)} = \frac{A}{x} + \frac{B}{x + 3} + \frac{C}{x - 1}$ by $x(x + 3)(x - 1) \Rightarrow$

$4x^2 + 13x - 9 = A(x + 3)(x - 1) + B(x)(x - 1) + C(x)(x + 3)$ Let $x = 0 \Rightarrow -9 = A(-3) \Rightarrow$

$A = 3$. Let $x = -3 \Rightarrow -12 = B(-3)(-4) \Rightarrow B = -1$. Let $x = 1 \Rightarrow 8 = C(4) \Rightarrow C = 2$.

The expression can be written $5x^2 + \frac{3}{x} + \frac{-1}{x + 3} + \frac{2}{x - 1}$.

30. By long division $\frac{3x^6 + 3x^4 + 3x}{x^4 + x^2} = 3x^2 + \frac{3x}{x^4 + x^2} = 3x^2 + \frac{3x}{x^2(x^2 + 1)}$.

Multiply $\frac{3x}{x^2(x^2 + 1)} = \frac{A}{x} + \frac{B}{x^2} + \frac{Cx + D}{x^2 + 1}$ by $x^2(x^2 + 1) \Rightarrow$

$3x = A(x)(x^2 + 1) + B(x^2 + 1) + (Cx + D)(x^2) \Rightarrow 3x = Ax^3 + Ax + Bx^2 + B + Cx^3 + Dx^2$

Let $x = 0 \Rightarrow 0 = B$. Equate coefficients. For $x$: $3 = A$. For $x^3$: $0 = A + C \Rightarrow 0 = 3 + C \Rightarrow C = -3$.

For $x^2$: $0 = B + D \Rightarrow 0 = 0 + D \Rightarrow D = 0$.

The expression can be written $3x^2 + \frac{3}{x} + \frac{-3x}{x^2 + 1}$.